Encyclopedia of
Endangered Species

Other Titles in Gale's Environmental Library

Encyclopedia of Environmental Information Sources

Environmental Encyclopedia

Environmental Industries Marketplace

Environmental Statistics Handbook: Europe

Environmental Viewpoints

Gale Environmental Almanac

Gale Environmental Sourcebook

Hazardous Substances Resource Guide

Nuclear Power Plants Worldwide

Recycling Sourcebook

Statistical Record of the Environment

GALE
ENVIRONMENTAL
LIBRARY

Encyclopedia of Endangered Species

Edited by Mary Emanoil
In Association with IUCN-The World Conservation Union

The World Conservation Union

SPECIES SURVIVAL COMMISSION

 **Gale Research Inc.**

DETROIT • WASHINGTON, D. C. • LONDON

Mary Emanoil, *Editor*

Gale Research Inc. Staff

Christine B. Jeryan and Kyung-Sun Lim, *Project Coordinators*

James A. Edwards, Denise Kasinec, Paul Lewon, Jacqueline Longe, Kimberley A. McGrath,
Zoran Minderović, Jeffrey Muhr, Neil Schlager, Bridget Travers, Sheila Walencewicz, Robyn V. Young,
Assisting Editors

Jeanne A. Gough, *Permissions & Production Manager*

Margaret A. Chamberlain, *Permissions Supervisor (Pictures)*
Keith Reed, *Permissions Associate*
Susan Brohman, *Permissions Assistant*

Mary Beth Trimper, *Production Director*
Shanna Heilveil, *Production Assistant*

Cynthia Baldwin, *Art Director*
Mary Krzewinski, *Graphic Designer*
C. J. Jonik, *Keyliner*

ISBN 0-8103-8857-X
ISSN 1077-1352

3833   Printed in the United States of America
Published simultaneously in the United Kingdom
by Gale Research International Limited
(An affiliated company of Gale Research Inc.)
10 9 8 7 6 5 4 3 2 1

The trademark **ITP** is used under license.

Table of Contents

A Word about Gale and the Environment

We at Gale would like to take this opportunity to publicly affirm our commitment to preserving the environment. Our commitment encompasses not only a zeal to publish information helpful to a variety of people pursuing environmental goals, but also a rededication to creating a safe and healthy workplace for our employees.

In our effort to make responsible use of natural resources, we are publishing all books in the Gale Environmental Library on recycled paper. Our Production Department is continually researching ways to use new environmentally safe inks and manufacturing technologies for all Gale Books.

In our quest to become better environmental citizens, we've organized a task force representing all operating functions within Gale. With the complete backing of Gale senior management, the task force reviews our current practices and, using the Valdez Principles* as a starting point, makes recommendations that will help us to: reduce waste, make wise use of energy and sustainable use of natural resources, reduce health and safety risks to our employees, and finally, should we cause any damage or injury, take full responsibility.

We look forward to becoming the best environmental citizens we can be and hope that you, too, have joined in the cause of caring for our fragile planet.

The Employees of Gale Research, Inc.

---

*The Valdez Principles were set forth in 1989 by the Coalition for Environmentally Responsible Economics (CERES). The Principles serve as guidelines for companies concerned with improving their environmental behavior. For a copy of the Valdez Principles, write to CERES at 711 Atlantic Avenue, 5th Floor, Boston, MA 02111.

Acknowledgments

Photographs and illustrations appearing in *Encyclopedia of Endangered Species* **were received from the following sources:**

© 1989 John Cancalosi: **pp. xix, 236;** © Tom McHugh, The National Audubon Society Collection/Photo Researchers: **pp. 1, 10, 143, 187, 311, 408, 423, 499, 594, 781, 789;** © 1987 John Cancalosi: **p. 3;** © 1986 John Cancalosi: **p. 5;** Australian Information Service, The National Audubon Society Collection/Photo Researchers: **p. 8;** Ford Kristo/Planet Earth Pictures: **p. 21;** © John Cancalosi: **pp. 26, 141, 799;** © Tom McHugh 1972, The National Audubon Society Collection/Photo Researchers: **p. 29;** © N. Smythe, The National Audubon Society Collection/Photo Researchers: **p. 37;** Paul Crum, The National Audubon Society Collection/Photo Researchers: **p. 39;** Ken Lucas/Planet Earth Pictures: **pp. 43, 164, 293, 297, 299, 303, 362, 367, 379, 448, 489, 805, 816, 882, 900, 986;** © J. A. Hancock, The National Audubon Society Collection/Photo Researchers: **p. 44;** H. Uible, The National Audubon Society Collection/Photo Researchers: **p. 50;** Merlin D. Tuttle, Bat Conservation International: **pp. 65, 76, 79, 81, 84, 87;** © 1981 Jack Fields, The National Audubon Society Collection/Photo Researchers: **p. 72;** © Alvin Staffan, The National Audubon Society Collection/Photo Researchers: **p. 85;** © 1979 Kenneth W. Fink, The National Audubon Society Collection/Photo Researchers: **p. 94;** © A. W. Ambler, The National Audubon Society Collection/Photo Researchers: **pp. 96, 678;** Nick Garbutt/Planet Earth Pictures: **pp. 100, 103, 108, 494, 562, 720, 748;** Pieter Folkens/Planet Earth Pictures: **p. 102;** Will McIntyre, The National Audubon Society Collection/Photo Researchers: **p. 110;** Peter Gasson/Planet Earth Pictures: **p. 116;** Chris Howes/Planet Earth Pictures: **p. 120;** © Andrew L. Young, The National Audubon Society Collection/Photo Researchers: **p. 123;** © Gregory G. Dimijian, The National Audubon Society Collection/Photo Researchers: **p. 128;** © Arthur W. Ambler, The National Audubon Society Collection/Photo Researchers: **pp. 129, 369;** © Mark D. Phillips, The National Audubon Society Collection/Photo Researchers: **p. 146;** © R. Van Nostrand, The National Audubon Society Collection/Photo Researchers: **pp. 149, 156;** © Mark Newman/Phototake NYC: **pp. 167, 242;** © The Stock Market/Eddie Adams: **p. 170;** K & K Ammann/Planet Earth Pictures: **p. 173;** U.S. Fish and Wildlife Service photo by Curtis Carley: **p. 176;** Keith Scholey/Planet Earth Pictures: **p. 178;** R. L. Matthews/Planet Earth Pictures: **p. 179;** © Anup and Mahuj Shah/Planet Earth Pictures: **p. 181;** Jen and Des Bartlett, The National Audubon Society Collection/Photo Researchers: **pp. 186, 729, 833;** © Camerpix, The National Audubon Society Collection/Photo Researchers: **p. 192;** Carol Farneti/Planet Earth Pictures: **pp. 199, 295;** Anup Shah/Planet Earth Pictures: **pp. 203, 309, 360, 517, 665, 720, 795;** © Ron Austing, The National Audubon Society Collection/Photo Researchers: **p. 206;** Jonathon Scott/Planet Earth Pictures: **pp. 201, 305;** Nick Greaves/Planet Earth Pictures: **p. 209;** Norbert Wu 1991/Planet Earth Pictures: **p. 213;** Franz Camenzind/Planet Earth Pictures: **p. 219;** © André Bärtschi/Planet Earth Pictures: **p. 222, 778, 785, 791;** C. Allan Morgan: **pp. 225, 334;** George Holton, The National Audubon Society Collection/Photo Researchers: **p. 228;** © George Laycock, The National Audubon Society Collection/Photo Researchers: **p. 230;** Mary Clay/Planet Earth Pictures: **p. 233;** © E. Hanumantha Rao, The National Audubon Society Collection/Photo Researchers: **pp. 237, 383;** © Doug Wechsler: **pp. 240, 807;** © Tom McHugh 1977, The National Audubon Society Collection/Photo Researchers: **pp. 243, 744, 863;** © Richard Ellis, The National Audubon Society Collection/Photo Researchers: **pp. 252, 259, 265, 269;** Marty Snyderman/Planet Earth Pictures: **p. 254;** © Painted by Richard Ellis, The National Audubon Society Collection/Photo Researchers: **p. 257;** © R. Ellis 1975, The National Audubon Society Collection/Photo Researchers: **p. 261;** U.S. Fish and Wildlife Service Photo by Robin Hunter: **p. 263;** © Varin-Visage/Jacana, The National Audubon Society Collection/Photo Researchers: **p. 271;** Gary Bell/Planet Earth Pictures: **p. 275;** U.S. Fish and Wildlife Service Photo: **pp. 277, 473, 514;** © Mark N. Boulton, The National Audubon Society Collection/Photo Researchers: **p. 281;** U.S. Fish and Wildlife Service Photo

How to Use This Book

This encyclopedia describes over 700 animals and plants worldwide that are currently threatened with extinction. Divided into eight sections, it covers mammals, birds, reptiles, amphibians, fish, molluscs, invertebrates (arachnids, crustaceans, and insects), and plants. Within each section, the species are arranged taxonomically by family and genus. This arrangement places closely related organisms together in the volume; for users unfamiliar with taxonomic relationships, an index to the common and scientific name of each species is provided.

Most entries begin with the **common name** of the species, followed by its **scientific name**. In some cases, an alternate scientific name is given in parentheses. The shaded box contains **phylum**, **class**, **order**, and **family** information. The **status** line describes the status of the species in the wild according to IUCN-The World Conservation Union, the U.S. Fish and Wildlife Service (USFWS), and the Convention on International Trade in Endangered Species of Wild Fauna and Flora (CITES). Some species are considered threatened by one organization and not by another, depending on the criteria used. The **range** section lists regions or countries where the species is currently found.

Description and Biology provides a general description of the plant or animal, including physical dimensions, reproductive information, and social organization or behavior.

Habitat and Current Distribution describes the preferred habitat of the species, where the species is found, and recent estimates of population size, if available.

History and Conservation Measures describes the history of the species and highlights factors currently threatening the species. When available, it also describes conservation efforts and the survival outlook for the species.

Inclusion Criteria

The animals and plants included in this book have been selected from lists of endangered and threatened species compiled by the U.S. Fish and Wildlife Service (USFWS) under the provisions of the U.S. Endangered Species Act, by the Convention on International Trade in Endangered Species of Wild Fauna and Flora (CITES), and by the Species Survival Commission of IUCN-The World Conservation Union. IUCN provided invaluable guidance in this selection process. A serious effort was made to include a wide range of animals and plants from all parts of the world. The species selected are subject to a variety of threats and benefit from many kinds of conservation initiatives.

The U.S. Endangered Species Act of 1973 is designed to protect all endangered species through the use of "all methods and procedures necessary to bring any endangered or threatened species to a point at which the measures provided pursuant to [the] Act are no longer necessary." The law, administered primarily by the U.S. Fish and Wildlife Service, created two levels of concern: endangered and threatened. An endangered species is "in danger of extinction throughout all or a significant portion of its range." A threatened species is "likely to become an endangered species in the foreseeable future throughout all or a significant portion of its range." As of 1990, more than 1,100 species throughout the world were listed as endangered or threatened under this Act.

CITES, an international treaty which currently has more than 100 participating countries, came into force in 1975. Its aim is to prevent international trade of endangered or threatened animal and plant species and products made from them. CITES recognizes three categories: Appendix I, Appendix II, and Appendix III. Appendix I lists those species that are threatened with extinction, and commercial trade in these species is generally prohibited. Over 600 species are currently listed in Appendix I. Appendix II applies to "all species which although not necessarily now threatened with extinction may become so unless trade in specimens of such species is subject to strict regulation." Currently, over 2,300 animals and 24,000 plants (mainly orchids) are listed in Appendix II. Appendix III is designed to help individual nations control the trade of any species, and any species may be listed in Appendix III by any country. Once listed, any export of this species from the listing country requires an export permit. Usually a species listed in Appendix III is protected within that nation's borders.

IUCN-The World Conservation Union is a unique partnership of some 770 States, government agencies, and non-governmental organizations encompassing over 123 countries. The IUCN's mission is "to provide leadership and promote a common approach for the world conservation movement in order to safeguard the integrity and diversity of the natural world, and to ensure that human use of natural resources is appropriate, sustainable, and equitable." The Species Survival Commission, the largest and most active of IUCN's commissions, is charged with conserving biological diversity by developing and executing programs to study, save, restore, and manage species and their habitats. As part of this mission, SSC produces the IUCN Red List for each triennial meeting of the IUCN General Assembly. IUCN classifies threatened species in the following six categories:

(Ex) Extinct
The species has not been located in the wild during the past 50 years (criterion as used by CITES). On a few occasions, the category "Ex?" is used to denote the very probable extinction of the species in the wild.

(E) Endangered
The species is in danger of extinction, and its survival is unlikely if the causal factors continue operating. Included in this category are those species whose numbers have been reduced to a critical level or whose habitats have been so drastically reduced that they are deemed to be in immediate danger of extinction.

(V) Vulnerable
The species is believed likely to move into the "Endangered" category in the near future if the causal factors continue operating. Included in this category are those species whose populations are decreasing because of over-exploitation, extensive destruction of habitat, or other environmental disturbance; species whose populations have been seriously depleted and whose ultimate security has not yet been assured; and species with populations that are still abundant but are under threat from severe adverse factors throughout their range.

(R) Rare
The species has a small world population, but it is not at present "Endangered" or "Vulnerable," but at risk. These species are usually localized within restricted geographical areas or habitats or are thinly scattered over a more extensive range.

(I) Indeterminate
The species is known to be "Endangered," "Vulnerable," or "Rare," but there is not enough information to say which of the three categories is appropriate.

(K) Insufficiently Known
Information on the species is insufficient to make a determination.

The *1994 IUCN Red List of Threatened Animals* lists 741 mammals, 970 birds, 316 reptiles, 169 amphibians, 979 fish, and 2,754 invertebrates, a total of nearly 6,000 species.

Appendices and Indexes

This encyclopedia also includes a **species watch** summary, a list of **wildlife and conservation organizations**, and a bibliography of sources for further reading. The **geographic index** is preceded by 10 maps to help the user find unfamiliar countries or locations. The **species index** provides access via both common and scientific name to all species appearing in the book.

Contributors

The following IUCN staff and consultants contributed in a major way to the compilation and production of this encyclopedia: Simon Stuart, David Stone, The Nature Conservation Bureau, Sandra Hails, and Wendy Strahm. We would also like to acknowledge the considerable assistance provided by many members of the IUCN Species Survival Commission who willingly gave their time and expertise to this project.

The following is a list of the many contributors who reviewed the species accounts featured in this encyclopedia, helping to ensure that the information provided is as up-to-date as possible. Of these, we are especially grateful to Nigel Collar and Roland Wirth who frequently had to contend with a large number of requests at short notice. Other SSC members who generously assisted with this review and production are as follows:

Agosti, Donat
Alonso, María Rosario
Amman, Klaus
Amaral, Michael
Amori, Giovanni
Anderson, E. F.
Archibald, George
Ashton, Liz

Babu, C. R.
Barash, David P.
Belk, Denton
Bloxam, Quentin
Bouchet, Philippe
Bowman, Thomas E.
Bramwell, D.
Braun, Janet K.
Brooks, Martin
Brouwer, Koen
Bruton, M. N.
Burbidge, Andrew A.

Cheek, Martin
Coggar, Hal
Collar, Nigel
Contréras, Luis C.
Coulter, Malcolm C.
Cox, C. R.
Cree, Alison
Crivelli, Alain J.
Cronk, Quentin

Dawson, S. M.
Dodd, C. Kenneth, Jr.
Dublin, Holly
Duffy, D. C.
Duncan, Patrick
Duvall, David

East, Rod
Ecroyd, Chris
Eltringham, S. R.
Estes, R.
Eudey, Ardith

Farjon, Aljos
Feistner, Anna T. C.
Fitzpatrick, Joseph
Fleming, T. H.
Forero, Enrique
Foster-Turley, Pat
Fowler, Sarah

Gadsby, Elizabeth
Garson, Peter
Gartlan, Steve
Giddy, Cynthia
Gillespie, Rosemary G.
Gillett, J. B.
Ginsberg, Joshua R.
Given, David
Goodyear, Numi C.
Goriup, Paul

Gradstein, S. Rob
Green, Andy J.
Grimmett, Richard
Groombridge, Brian
Groves, Madeleine

Hails, A. J.
Hall, A. V.
Hall, Joseph G.
Hall, Leslie
Hallingback, Tomas
Henderson, Robert W.
Hickman, Graham
Hilton-Taylor, Craig
Hodgetts, Nick
Holsinger, John R.
Howarth, Francis G.
Huber, Otto

Jackson, Peter
Jenkins, Hank
Jermy, Clive
Johnsingh, A. J. T.
Johnson, Dennis V.
Jones, Carl

Kuwabara, Kazushi
Kirkland, Gordon L., Jr.
Klemens, Mike
Klocek, Roger
Knisley, C. Barry

Knowles, John
Kunz, Thomas

Laessoe, Thomas
Lane, Robert S.
Lanfranco, Edwin
Laurie, Andrew
Leatherwood, Stephen
Lee, Julian C.
Lesouëf, J. Y.
Lewinsky, Jette
Lloyd, Brian
Lockwood, Jeffrey A.
Lorence, David H.
Lovari, Sandro

Mares, Michael
Marsh, Helene
Martin, Esmond B.
Martin, Joel W.
Matola, Sharon
Matthews, Brian
Maunder, Michael
McCullock, Neil
McNeely, Jeffrey
Meads, M. J.
Mech, L. David
Meyburg, Bernd-U
Mickleburgh, Simon
Miller, Tony
Mills, Gus
Mittermeier, Russel
Mohlenbrock, Robert H.
Moore, Norman
Morris, M. G.
Moyle, Peter B.
Murphy, Dennis

Németh, Ferenc
New, Tim R.

Newman, Donald G.
Nicoll, Martin

O'Shea, Tom
Oates, John F.
Oldfield, Sara
Oliver, E. G. H.
Oliver, William L. R.
Opler, Paul A.
Ortiz von Halle, Bernardo

Patton, James
Pearce-Kelly, Paul
Phillipson, Peter
Pierson, Elizabeth
Platts, Elizabeth
Polhemus, Dan
Prakash, Ishwar
Pritchard, Peter
Pucek, Zdzislaw

Quin, Darren

Racey, Paul A.
Rathbun, Galen
Redford, Kent
Reijnders, Peter
Reza, Fernando A. Cervantes
Ross, James Perran

Santiapillai, Charles
Schenck, Christof
Seddon, Mary B.
Sérgio, Cecilia
Servheen, Christopher
Shackleton, David
Simpson, Rosemary
Slooten, E.
Smith, Andrew P.
Smith, Andrew T.

Staib, Elke
Stanford, Ruth
Stevenson, Dennis
Stone, David R.
Strahm, Wendy
Stuart, Simon
Sullivan, Tim

Taber, Andrew
Tan, Benito
Taylor, Nigel
Teleki, Geza
Thompson-Handler,
  Nancy
Tolson, Peter J.
Towns, David

van Strien, N. J.
van Zyll De Jong, C. G.
Vána, Jirí
Villamil, Carlos B.

Wakefield, Simon
Walter, Kerry
Wang, Xianpu
Wells, Sue
Whitaker, Romulus
White, Lee
Wirth, Roland
Wise, Amanda

Zhao, Ermi

Introduction

The rate at which species are becoming extinct around the world is increasing rapidly. It is very hard to put a figure on the actual rate of extinctions, and scientists are still debating this point. However, all agree that, whatever the actual rate, it is getting worse, and quickly so. One reason why it is almost impossible to assess the number of species going extinct is that, incredibly in our modern electronic age, only a small percentage of the world's species has actually been described and named by scientists. About 1.4 million species have been described so far, out of an estimated 10 million or so. Obviously, it is very hard to make an assessment of the extinction rate among unknown species. But even among those that are known, we understand so little about them, and carry out such a small amount of fieldwork, that it is quite possible for most species to be extinct many years before we know anything about them. Our comprehension of the world's living natural resources is still primitive.

Lack of knowledge of species is one thing. Another problem has been the lack of a clear definition of what constitutes a threatened species. In the past, most assessments of threatened species have been carried out in a very vague manner. The fundamental problem is that there is no hard and fast dividing line between those species that are threatened and those that are not. There is now a major focus by scientists and conservation managers within IUCN's Species Survival Commission (SSC) to come up with some clear definitions of threatened species. This will result in a new system of IUCN Red List Categories being adopted towards the end of 1994, and they will be used publicly for the first time in the 1996 edition of the IUCN Red List of Threatened Animals.

What is IUCN and its Species Survival Commission? IUCN-The World Conservation Union is a global alliance of governments, government agencies and non-governmental organizations committed to the conservation of nature. The mission of IUCN is to influence, encourage and assist societies throughout the world to conserve the integrity and diversity of nature and to ensure that any use of natural resources is equitable and ecologically sustainable. As of May 1994, IUCN's members comprised 69 state governments, 101 government agencies, and over 600 non-governmental organizations. The hybrid governmental/non-governmental status of IUCN conferred by its membership assures IUCN formal access to governmental and intergovernmental arenas, while still allowing it to operate with the flexibility and independence of a non-governmental organization. One of the most important services that IUCN provides to its member governments and organizations is expertise and guidance on a wide range of conservation-oriented issues. To a large extent, this advice is provided through the voluntary networks that comprise the IUCN commissions. The SSC is the largest and most active of the commissions. The mission of the SSC is to conserve biological diversity by developing and executing programs to study, save, restore and manage species and their habitats. Since its small beginnings in 1949, the SSC has grown into a network of some 5,000 members in 170 countries—professionals in the field of taxonomy, conservation biology, wildlife management and other fields relevant to species conservation.

The SSC works by: (1) assessing the conservation status of and threats to species worldwide so as to generate recommendations and strategies necessary for the conservation of biological diversity; 2) identifying conservation priorities for species and their habitats; 3) promoting the implementation of actions needed for the survival of species; 4) developing and promoting policies for the conservation of species and their habitats; 5) enhancing the efforts of individuals working on biodiversity conservation by linking them and providing access to an international forum; and 6) raising conservation awareness and promoting an understanding of the importance of species to people.

One of the many activities of the members of the SSC, who work mainly in a voluntary capacity, is the production of the IUCN Red List. This is normally produced for each meeting of the IUCN General Assembly, which is the gathering of IUCN's members every three years. The Red List has provided the background document for this *Encyclopedia of Endangered Species*. The Red List is still very far from complete, and mammals and birds remain the best studied species in terms of their threats. Accordingly, this encyclopedia contains a preponderance of mammals and birds, though a good number of lesser-known species, such as reptiles, amphibians, fish, invertebrates and plants are also included. It must be emphasized that this is in no way an exhaustive list, but instead aims to be a representative cross-section, showing a wide range of examples of the types of threat that species face in today's changing world.

The threats to species can be looked at in two different ways. First, there are the immediate threats; and then there are the underlying factors that give rise to these threats. The immediate threats include such factors as loss of habitat; direct over-exploitation; competition with introduced invasive species; and low viability of populations due to their small size. Of these, habitat loss is generally considered to be the most severe. Particular concern has been raised about this issue in relation to the loss of tropical forests and wetlands. However, there is also severe degradation in many other habitats, including grasslands (which are under threat almost everywhere from over-grazing), and most coastal habitats. The direct exploitation of species is a very highly publicized threat, and has had devastating effects on many species. The most widely discussed form of exploitation is that which leads to international trade; however, it is generally considered that the great majority of direct exploitation of species is for local use. Problems posed by introduced, often invasive species are some of the most worrying, since they are probably the most difficult to control. It is likely that the great majority of species extinctions which have taken place on oceanic islands have resulted from the introduction of species that did not originally belong there. It has proven very difficult to eradicate these species, once they become established over a very wide area. The increasing colonization of large continental land masses by such species is therefore of grave concern. Invasive species cause a large number of problems, including out-competing native species, acting as highly efficient predators, changing the structure of habitats (particularly in the case of invasive plants), and spreading disease. The problem of low population viability is a major threat to species that have already become rare. Such species can become subject to genetic erosion as a result of inbreeding, and thus lose their capacity to adapt to changing environments. Even more seriously, such species can often be vulnerable to catastrophic events, especially if they are confined to a very small area.

Conservationists employ a number of different methods to combat all these sorts of threats. Legislation is often a fundamental basis to species conservation efforts, although there are many countries that have good legislation, but lack the capacity to enforce it. Perhaps the most fundamental of all conservation methods is the establishment of protected areas. Many of the world's most valuable sites for threatened species are now within national parks and nature reserves. Another technique frequently used is that of sustainable use. This involves managing the exploitation of species so that it does not cause detriment to their populations. The success of sustainable use programs varies very widely around the world. One of the arguments in favor of sustainable use, especially in the developing world, is the need to provide impoverished local human communities with some form of incentive to conserve species. This has given rise to the concept of sustainable development: that is, the integration of human development and environmental conservation needs, especially at the local level, to ensure that both conservation and development needs can be achieved and reconciled. Other conservation techniques include the eradication of invasive species (particularly those that have become damaging to native species), and various forms of *ex situ* conservation. *Ex situ* conservation can involve breeding species in zoos or botanic gardens; the importance of increasing population of extremely threatened species in captivity is now well recognized, prior to re-introducing them into the wild as a part of coherent recovery program for such species. Underlying all these efforts is the increasing tendency throughout the world to base species conservation efforts on clearly focused recovery plans. Conservationists have learned that by defining goals, and testing different methods, the success of attempts to bring about the recovery of species can be greatly enhanced.

As mentioned above, there are also some more fundamental underlying causes of the disappearance of species. These are very varied. In some parts of the world they are related to poverty. Human communities who are very poor frequently have no option but to destroy the natural habitats and environments around them. It is natural for people to put their own survival above that of other life forms, and this again underlines the need to address development and conservation needs at the same time. In other parts of the world, it is the opposite problem: rapid economic growth leading to damaging forms of development, frequently for short-sighted objectives. When conservation and industrial interests conflict, the latter almost always take precedence. Another problem is one related to economic incentives. Most national economies are managed in such a way as to provide incentives (sometimes unintentionally) to the destruction, rather than the conservation, of natural habitats. Incentives may take many forms, but one of the most common is subsidies to activities, such as agriculture, that are not necessarily economically viable. Conservationists are increasingly arguing for a change in the way that economic incentives work, in order to provide real incentives for people to conserve wildlife, and real disincentives to destructive activities. Related to this is the very low value attached to wildlife in most economic systems. In some countries, where this has been changed so that wildlife is valued

highly, there has been a spectacular participation by local communities in conservation efforts. Other problems include issues such as the lack of education and lack of basic information about what is important to conserve in a particular country. IUCN addresses these fundamental root causes of species loss through its Biodiversity Program. This works very closely with the SSC, and together they provide IUCN with a leadership role in this area.

Readers of this book will find many of its pages to be depressing. However, the book is realistic. The fight to maintain the world's biological diversity, in particular its richness of species, is very far from won. A study of this book will enable readers to get a clearer understanding of the basic issues, which are often more complex than is portrayed in most popular conservation literature. For anyone who would like to follow up these issues in greater depth, they are invited to contact us at IUCN Headquarters.

Simon N. Stuart
Head
Species Survival Program
IUCN Headquarters, Gland, Switzerland

Mammals

Long-beaked echidna

Zaglossus bruijni

Phylum	Chordata
Class	Mammalia
Order	Monotremata
Family	Tachyglossidae
Status	Endangered, IUCN
	Appendix II, CITES
Range	Irian Jaya (Indonesia); Papua New Guinea

Description and Biology

The long-beaked echidna is an unusual looking, egg-laying mammal. Its upper body is covered with spines that are almost obscured by long hair. A short tail and large ear opening are also hidden by the spines and hair. The spines are usually gray or white, but in some individuals can be almost black; the hair is brown or black except on the head, which is lighter. Head and body length averages 18-35 in (46-90 cm), weight 11-22 lb (5-10 kg); males are larger than females. The snout is long and naked with large nostrils at the tip. The echidna uses its long snout to root through undergrowth or debris on the forest floor, locating prey with its acute sense of smell. It feeds at night, primarily on earthworms; a long, flexible tongue with small spines is used to grab the worm and pull it into the mouth. When disturbed or threatened, the echidna rolls itself into a ball with its spikes protruding or digs down into the soil.

This is usually a solitary species. Little is known about reproductive biology, except that the female has a sort of pouch that appears only at breeding time. She lays eggs in the pouch which hatch in seven to ten days; the young stay in the pouch and nurse.

Habitat and Current Distribution

The long-beaked echidna occurs in humid montane forest in New Guinea and possibly on neighboring small islands. In the mid-1970s the total population was estimated to be about 300,000.

History and Conservation Measures

This species is thought to have been distributed widely throughout Australia at one time, but it disappeared from this continent around 10,000 years ago,

Long-beaked echidna.

probably because of climatic changes. Today, its status is uncertain. It is often hunted for food by traditional methods using trained dogs and is considered a great delicacy by New Guinea's indigenous people. Habitat destruction also threatens this species. As montane forests are cleared for cultivation, logging or mining, the long-beaked echidna is forced into inaccessible or marginal areas. This species has been protected in Irian Jaya since 1973. It was designated a "national animal" in Papua New Guinea in 1975 and receives some protection there, although this protection does not prohibit hunting by traditional methods.

Numbat

Myrmecobius fasciatus

Phylum	Chordata
Class	Mammalia
Order	Marsupialia
Family	Myrmecobiidae
Status	Endangered, IUCN
	Endangered, USFWS
Range	Australia

Description and Biology

The numbat, also called the banded anteater, is a very unusual Australian marsupial, belonging to its own family and being diurnal instead of nocturnal as are most other marsupials. It is not much larger than a domestic rat, at 9 in (23 cm) long with a 7 in (18 cm) tail and an average weight of 14-21 oz (400-600 g). Its reddish brown coat with white flecks is accented by a series of black and white bars on the rump. A dark bar bordered with white stretches across the eye from ear to snout. The head is long and flattened with a long snout, and the tail is bushy. The numbat feeds exclusively on termites, digging into termite galleries with its sharp clawed forefeet and then using its long sticky tongue to extricate the termites, which are swallowed whole. A solitary animal except when the female has young, it occupies a home range of 50-120 acres (20-50 ha).

Numbats shelter at night in hollow logs or burrows that they dig for themselves. Nests of leaves, grass, and bark are built in these sleeping places by both males and females. Since the numbat does not have a true pouch, the four young—born in January or February—attach themselves to the female's nipples and cling to the surrounding hair. After six months, the young are deposited in a burrow. The female suckles them at night, moving them between nests by carrying them on her back. The young start to venture out of the nursery burrow in September and are weaned in October but remain in their mother's home range until they disperse in November or December.

Numbat.

Habitat and Current Distribution

The numbat is now restricted to southwestern Western Australia. Population figures are unknown but are believed to be less than 2,000 individuals.

Preferred habitat in its current range is woodland of *Eucalyptus* species susceptible to termite attack, with a plentiful supply of hollow logs. Formerly, it also occupied arid and semi-arid shrublands and grasslands.

History and Conservation Measures

At one time the numbat was widely distributed throughout southern Australia, but it declined from the east until it became restricted to southwestern Western Australia by the 1960s. There it continued to decline until 1980, when research by the Western Australian Department of Conservation and Land Management (CALM) demonstrated that the introduced red fox was the overriding cause of the numbat's decline. Since then, fox control has led to a recovery in numbat populations. CALM has carried out captive breeding research with support from the World Wide Fund for Nature Australia (WWF Australia) and is conducting translocations to areas of former habitat, again with support of WWF Australia.

Kowari

Dasycercus byrnei

Phylum	Chordata
Class	Mammalia
Order	Marsupialia
Family	Dasyuridae
Status	Endangered, IUCN
Range	Australia

Description and Biology

The kowari is a rodent-like marsupial with soft, reddish gray fur and very white underparts and feet. Its average head and body length is 5.3-7.2 in (13.5-18.2 cm), and it weighs about 2.5-4.9 oz (70-140 g). Males are larger and heavier than females. The kowari's tail measures 4.3-5.5 in (11-14 cm); it begins as a reddish color but the terminal half is covered with long black hairs that give the appearance of a brush. This species spends most of its time on the ground, but climbs well and is able to leap almost 18 in (46 cm) vertically. A nocturnal animal, the kowari feeds on insects, arachnids, and such small vertebrates as lizards, rodents, and birds.

Mating usually takes place between May and July, but is possible from April to December. A litter of three to seven young is born after a gestation period of 30-36 days. The young are attached to the mother's nipples for almost two months and continue to nurse for at least another month.

Habitat and Current Distribution

This species occurs in Australia, where it is found near the South Australia-Northern Territory border, in northern South Australia (south and east of the Simpson Desert), and in Queensland between the Simpson Desert, and the Diamantina River south of Boulia. Population figures are unavailable. The kowari inhabits gibber plains and gibber crests in undulating Mitchell grass plains. Little information about the ecological requirements of this species is known and further research is a high priority.

History and Conservation Measures

A recovery plan has been prepared and implementation has commenced. The objectives of this plan include: complete surveys of the current distribution of the species; the declaration of an additional

Kowari.

conservation reserve in suitable habitat north of Birdsville between Diamantina Lakes and Coorbulka Stations and its intensive management; retention of remnant habitats on private and public land and the establishment of corridors when dispersal patterns are known; management and protection of key colonies of this species; and research concerning the special/basic needs of the species.

Chuditch

Dasyurus geoffroii

Phylum	Chordata
Class	Mammalia
Order	Marsupialia
Family	Dasyuridae
Status	Endangered, IUCN
Range	Australia

Description and Biology

The chuditch is sometimes called the western quoll. It has a soft, thick coat that is grayish to reddish brown with lighter underparts and white spots on its back, shoulders, and head. This species has large eyes, pointed ears, and pale gray face. The average head and body length ranges from 11.4-25.6 in (29-65 cm); the average weight is approximately 20 oz (567 g). Its tail, which measures about 10.6-13.8 in (27-35 cm), is black. This animal is active at night and is a good climber; its diet apparently includes insects, small mammals, and birds.

All quolls, including the western quoll, appear to be winter breeders, producing a single litter between May and August. The western quoll produces a litter of four to six young after a gestation period of 16 to 23 days.

Habitat and Current Distribution

The chuditch is now restricted to the southwest of Western Australia primarily in areas of jarrah (*Eucalyptus marginata*) forest. The species is thought to be uncommon and its range has been severely reduced. Population is estimated at 2,500-4,400 individuals.

The habitat of the chuditch formerly included hummock grassland, mallee (land covered by low-growing, shrubby species of *Eucalyptus*), scrub, woodland and forest.

History and Conservation Measures

The chuditch once occurred in every mainland Australian state and territory, from western New South Wales, southwestern Queensland and South Australia, across central Australia and much of Western Australia. There is no information about initial population. The species is believed to have been reduced because of habitat disruption. It is also possible that it has been affected by the introduction of cats and foxes. Further studies will be necessary to formulate specific conservation plans. A recovery plan has been prepared and is now being implemented. The actions include monitoring populations within its known range, determining the effects of fox control and ensuring that timber harvesting does not affect its abundance. A translocation to an area of former habitat has already taken place and another is planned.

Dibbler

Parantechinus (Antechinus) apicalis

Phylum	Chordata
Class	Mammalia
Order	Marsupialia
Family	Dasyuridae
Status	Endangered, IUCN
	Endangered, USFWS
Range	Australia

Description and Biology

The dibbler is a small marsupial that has brownish gray hair flecked with white and gray-white to yellow underparts. It has a long snout and white rings around the eyes. The average head and body length is 5.5-5.7 in (14-14.5 cm) and it weighs 1.5-3.5 oz (40-100 kg). This species' tail is 3.75-4.5 in (9.5-11.5 cm) long, and its hair is tapered. The female's pouch is little more than folds of skin low on the abdomen. A nest is built on the ground in a sheltered area. The dibbler is most active at daylight and dusk and feeds mainly on insects, although nectar is also taken in captivity.

Little is known about its social structure, but the dibbler is apparently a solitary animal. Observations of captive specimens indicate that breeding is seasonal, taking place once a year, with mating in March and gestation lasting 44 to 53 days. Litter size is probably seven to eight, and the young remains dependent on the mother for up to four months.

Habitat and Current Distribution

The dibbler is found in Australia. Currently, it resides on the banks of the Fitzgerald River and Torndirrup National Parks on the south coast of Western Australia from Boullanger and Whitlock Islands to the north of Perth.

History and Conservation Measures

Probably widely distributed in the southwest corner of Western Australia, it was believed to be extinct for more than 80 years before it was rediscovered in 1967 at Cheyne Beach on the south coast of Western Australia. Surveys since then have located the dibbler within heartlands and scrub near Western

The dibbler was not seen in the wild for more than 80 years; it was rediscovered in 1967.

Australia's south coast and on two small offshore islands.

The decline of the population may be due to habitat loss. The reasons for the original decrease in range are unknown, though bush clearing for agriculture and the introduction of predators such as foxes and feral cats are likely to have been important.

The habitat at Cheyne Beach, where it was once collected, has been incorporated into a nature reserve.

Red-tailed phascogale

Phascogale calura

Phylum	Chordata
Class	Mammalia
Order	Marsupialia
Family	Dasyuridae
Status	Endangered, IUCN
Range	Australia

Description and Biology

The red-tailed phascogale has soft, gray fur and white underparts. Its average head and body size ranges from 3.7-4.8 in (9.4-12.2 cm), and it weighs approximately 1.3-2.4 oz (37-68 g). Its tail measures 4.7-5.7 in (11.9-14.5 cm) long and is black, except for a reddish area at the base. This species has a pointed snout, large eyes, and large ears that are only sparsely furred. The female does not have a true pouch, but develops protective skin folds to shelter her young. A nocturnal animal, it spends days sheltered in a nest it builds in trees or on the ground. It has long claws which it uses to catch insects, birds, and small mammals.

Home range is approximately 10-12 acres (4-5 ha). Mating takes place between May and July and, after a gestation period of around 30 days, a litter of usually eight young is born between June and August. The young are at first attached to the mother's nipples for over a month and then are left in the nest for up to five months while they are still being nursed.

Habitat and Current Distribution

The red-tailed phascogale occurs in Australia, where it is now confined to a few isolated populations in nature reserves, a national park, and a state forest in southwest Western Australia. Its population is un-

known, but it is considered to be moderately abundant within its restricted distribution.

Preferred habitat seems to be woodlands of rock oak (*Allocasuarina langellii*) and wandoo (*Eucalyptus wandoo*).

History and Conservation Measures

This species was formerly widely but sparsely distributed in central and southern Australia, occurring in central-northern Western Australia, central Northern Territory and the far western border between New South Wales and Victoria. The range was reported to have contracted to the extreme southwest

Red-tailed phascogale.

by 1941. Causes of the decline are unknown, as apparently suitable habitat is still widespread in its former range; predation by feral cats and, possibly, foxes has been implicated as a possible factor.

The red-tailed phascogale now occurs in several nature reserves, including East Yornaning, Tutanning Dongolocking, Parkeyerring Lake and Boyagin; it also inhabits the Dryandra and Highbury state forests and Fitzgerald River National Park. Despite its presence in these protected reserves, it is still considered at risk because of the very marked contraction of its range and its apparent present restriction to a few small areas, some of which may not be subject to appropriate management practices. Studies are underway to identify factors affecting populations and to determine the causes of the range contraction. Once the species' requirements have been determined, management plans for existing populations can be formulated. The possibility of reintroduction to suitable areas should be considered, as many reserves, especially those in the wheatbelt, are now isolated by large areas of agricultural land and are extremely unlikely to be naturally recolonized.

Julia Creek dunnart

Sminthopsis douglasi

Phylum	Chordata
Class	Mammalia
Order	Marsupialia
Family	Dasyuridae
Status	Endangered, IUCN
Range	Australia

Description and Biology

The Julia Creek dunnart, a mouse-like marsupial, is the second largest of the dunnart species, which usually have a body length averaging 2.8-4.7 in (7-12 cm) and a tail length of 2-5 in (5.5-13 cm). Its soft, dense fur is mostly brown, with pale to buff underparts. It has reddish cheeks, large ears, and a dark stripe on the forehead. As an apparent adaptation to an unpredictable food supply, its thin tail becomes enlarged with fat when food is readily available, to be stored for times of meager food supply. It is probably nocturnal and feeds primarily on insects.

Little is known about social organization or reproductive biology; a female specimen had six juveniles in the pouch, but the date of birth was unknown.

Habitat and Current Distribution

This species occurs in north-central Queensland, Australia, where it has been collected from the vicinity of Julia Creek and Richmond, both in the watershed of the Cloncurry River. Little is known of its habitat, but the area from which it was collected has low annual rainfall. The number of known localities has been increased from three to eleven. Population size is unknown, but it appears to be rare. As of 1992, this species has maximum geographic distribution of over 125 mi (200 km).

History and Conservation Measures

Little is known about the area this species inhabits, and a survey of this region is a major requirement to determine the status and habits of *S. douglasi*. There is presently not enough information to determine whether or not the population of this species has declined and whether or not it is really rare.

Golden bandicoot

Isoodon auratus

Phylum	Chordata
Class	Mammalia
Order	Marsupialia
Family	Peramelidae
Status	Endangered, IUCN
Range	Australia

Description and Biology

The golden bandicoot is one of the short-nosed marsupials. The golden appearance of its coarse fur is caused by yellow-orange hairs mixed with dark brown hairs. Its snout is elongated and the ears short and rounded. The female has a pouch which faces the rear and eight nipples. The average head and body length of this animal ranges from 9-19 in (23-48 cm) and it weighs about 2.4-3 lb (1.1-1.4 kg). Its tail measures 3-8 in (8-20 cm). This species spends its days in a nest built within vegetation on the ground, in a hollow, or in the shelter of a rock pile. Active at night, the golden bandicoot is capable of running very quickly and able to jump straight up into the air and change directions quickly. It is described as pugnacious, and both sexes are very aggressive and combative. Diet includes insects and worms.

Although usually a solitary species, two are sometimes found sharing a nest. Males and females come together only to mate. Little is known about reproductive biology, but gestation is around 12 days and litter size is usually four. Young probably remain in the pouch for up to eight weeks.

Habitat and Current Distribution

The golden bandicoot once occurred across a third of Australia. It has declined drastically and now occurs only in a small part of the Kimberleys of Western Australia and on Augustus, Barrow, and Middle Islands.

Preferred habitats are grassland, sometimes with a woodland overstory.

History and Conservation Measures

Although there are no estimates of initial population, this species was once distributed throughout most of Australia. The exact reasons for its decline are unknown, but it is thought to be due to predation from introduced foxes and cats and to changed fire regimen in its grassland habitat.

Western barred bandicoot

Perameles bougainville

Phylum	Chordata
Class	Mammalia
Order	Marsupialia
Family	Peramelidae
Status	Endangered, IUCN
	Endangered, USFWS
	Appendix I, CITES
Range	Australia

Description and Biology

This marsupial is one of the long-nosed bandicoots. Its back is covered with coarse, dark brown hair flecked with black tipped hairs; its underparts are almost white. This bandicoot has long ears, a long snout, and large eyes. The female has eight nipples and a pouch which faces the rear. The average head and body length is 8-16 in (20-40 cm), and its tail measures 3-7 in (7.6-17 cm). This species weighs 7-8.5 oz (198-241 g). Days are spent in a nest built of vegetation on the ground, in a hollow, or in the shelter of a rock pile. Active at night, the bandicoot can run very quickly and then jump straight up into the air and change directions quickly. It is described as pugnacious and both sexes are very aggressive and combative. Diet includes insects, bulbous roots, and other plant matter; in captivity, it is known to eat rodents.

Although usually a solitary species, two individuals are sometimes found sharing a nest. Its home range may be around 45-100 acres (18-40 ha) for males and 3-10 acres (1-4 ha) for females; females have overlapping ranges. Breeding has been recorded from May to August with litters of two, sometimes three. The gestation period is probably around 12 days.

Habitat and Current Distribution

The western barred bandicoot is now probably extinct on the Australian mainland. The only known populations are now on Bernier and Dorre Islands in Shark Bay, Western Australia. There are no population estimates.

When this species occupied the mainland, its habitat included plains and sand ridges with woodland, shrubland, grassland, or heath. On the islands, it inhabits typical sandhill vegetation and open steppe associations.

History and Conservation Measures

This bandicoot once occurred across a broad belt of arid to semi-arid territory in southern Australia from Shark Bay through central South Australia, along the length of the Murray River in northwestern Victoria to the Liverpool Plains in eastern New South Wales. It was said to have been common along the length of the Murray River around 1857 but to have become extinct there shortly afterwards. The last known specimen from New South Wales was taken in 1867 near the Murray-Darling river junction. The last specimens from the mainland were taken from Western Australia in 1909 and from South Australia in

1922, although there were reported sightings in sub-desert western South Australia up to 1942. A 1959 expedition to Bernier and Dorre Islands described it as extremely common.

The exact reasons for its decline are unknown, but vegetation throughout its mainland range has now been either cleared for crop production or drastically altered by stock grazing, feral goats, and rabbits. Its entire mainland range is also infested with such introduced predators as foxes, feral cats, and, at its eastern end, feral pigs. Conditions on the islands have remained more pristine. Sheep were apparently never introduced to Dorre, and were only temporarily introduced to Bernier at the beginning of this cen-

tury. Feral goats are also absent from Dorre, although there was damage caused in 1959 on Bernier by a herd which was eradicated by 1975. The bandicoot populations on the islands, although regarded as stable, remain potentially very vulnerable to fire or to the accidental introduction of foxes, cats, or rabbits.

Bernier and Dorre Islands are nature reserves; despite this protection, the populations remain at hazard because of their restricted distribution and small numbers. Continued protection of these islands from any form of unnecessary disturbance is vital for the survival of the species. Studies are underway on island populations as a precursor to developing a recovery plan, including reintroduction to the mainland.

Giant bandicoot

Peroryctes broadbenti

Phylum	Chordata
Class	Mammalia
Order	Marsupialia
Family	Peramelidae
Status	Endangered, IUCN
Range	Papua New Guinea

Description and Biology

One of the long-nosed bandicoots, this marsupial has long, soft fur that is dark brown on the back, reddish yellow on the flanks, and almost white on the underparts. This species has long ears, a long snout, and large eyes. Its head and body length averages about 15-22 in (39-56 cm), and its tail measures about 4.5-13 in (11.4-33 cm). The average weight of the giant bandicoot is 10 lb (4.7 kg); the male is larger and heavier than the female. A rear opening pouch extends along the female's abdomen. Days are spent in a nest built of vegetation on the ground, in a hollow, or in the shelter of a rock pile. Active at night, it can run very quickly and then jump straight up into the air and change directions quickly. It is described as pugnacious and both sexes are very aggressive and combative. Diet includes insects, roots, and other plant matter.

Although usually a solitary species, two are sometimes found sharing a nest. There is little information about reproductive biology, but gestation is probably around 12 days and litter size one to three.

Habitat and Current Distribution

The giant bandicoot is found in southeastern New Guinea where it inhabits lowland rainforest and possibly lowland hill forest. There are no estimates of population size.

History and Conservation Measures

Very little is known about the New Guinea bandicoots. There are no estimates of initial population, but they are believed to be in decline. Causes of the decline probably include the introduction of predators such as foxes and cats and changes to habitat caused by grazing animals such as sheep and cattle.

Northern hairy-nosed wombat

Lasiorhinus krefftii

Phylum	Chordata
Class	Mammalia
Order	Maruspialia
Family	Vombatidae
Status	Endangered, IUCN
	Endangered, USFWS
	Appendix I, CITES
Range	Australia

Description and Biology

The northern hairy-nosed wombat, also known as the Queensland hairy-nosed wombat, does, indeed, have a hairy nose or muzzle; it also has poor eyesight, but it smells and hears well. A thick, stocky body, weighing 42-70 lb (19-32 kg) and averaging 3.25 ft (1 m) in length, is covered with a soft, silky brown coat. It has a large head, small eyes, pointed ears, a rearward opening pouch, and powerful legs with strong claws. The strong foreclaws are used to excavate warrens (a warren consists of several burrows), which have complex designs and a number of entrances. Usually only one wombat is found in a burrow, although males and females may sometimes be found together. Warrens are surrounded by a home range of about 14.8 acres (6 ha). A nocturnal feeder, the wombat is a vegetarian that eats mainly grass, especially bunch speargrass.

A single young is born in summer (November to March); it is carried in the pouch for around six months and is nursed for eight to nine months.

Habitat and Current Distribution

The only known surviving population is in the Epping Forest National Park, Queensland, Australia. Population is estimated at 65 individuals.

Habitat is semi-arid, open woodland or grassland. Burrows are dug into sandy areas, sometimes strengthened by tree roots.

History and Conservation Measures

At the time of European settlement, the northern hairy-nosed wombat was almost certainly already rare; there were only three reported populations in widely separated locations in the semi-arid interior of eastern Australia. By 1909 these populations had all died out, and the northern hairy-nosed wombat was considered extinct. In 1937 a small group was discovered west of Clermont in central Queensland.

In the 1970s the last refuge of the northern hairy-nosed wombat was declared a national park. The presence of cattle in the park who grazed on the food source needed by the wombat remained a threat. Steps have been taken to eliminate cattle from the park, but the number of surviving wombats is very low. This small and compact population makes it highly vulnerable to environmental disturbance. It is essential that additional populations be established in other suitable areas to assure the survival of the species.

Woodlark Island cuscus

Phalanger lullulae

Phylum	Chordata
Class	Mammalia
Order	Marsupialia
Family	Phalangeridae
Status	Vulnerable, IUCN
Range	Woodlark Island (Papua New Guinea)

Description and Biology

The Woodlark Island cuscus is a marsupial that looks rather like a monkey. It has thick, woolly fur and has sometimes been regarded as a spotted subspecies of the common cuscus (*Phalanger orientalis*). It has a yellow nose and yellow rims around its protruding eyes. Length of head and body averages 13-24 in (33-61 cm) and it weighs 35-53 oz (1,000-1,500 g). Prehensile tail is 10-14 in (25-61 cm) long; the end of the tail has scales instead of hair. It is mostly arboreal, but sometimes moves slowly on the ground. It is active at night and spends the days sheltered in vegetation, rocks, or tree roots. Diet includes leaves, shoots, and fruits.

Little is known about this animal's reproductive biology. The gestation period and breeding season are likewise unknown. Although litter size may be up to three, only one young may be raised.

Habitat and Current Distribution

This species is endemic to Woodlark Island and Alcester Islands, Milne Bay Province, Papua New Guinea, which contain primary rain forest, secondary forest, and small areas of grassland. It inhabits lowland rain forest. The cuscus population size is unknown.

History and Conservation Measures

This species is only known from eight specimens, four collected in 1896 and four in 1953. It is apparently a relict form with a very limited distribution and is expected to come under hunting pressure, as all cuscuses are game animals in Papua New Guinea. Part of the forest on the island is considered to have potential for commercial logging and the remainder is topographically suitable for agriculture.

Surveys are necessary to determine ecology and population size. It will be necessary to restrict forestry development to the level necessary to satisfy only local needs and agriculture to areas already denuded of forest. The establishment of suitable rain forest reserves is essential; captive breeding and relocation to other islands would be desirable.

Rat-kangaroo species

Bettongia spp.

Phylum	Chordata
Class	Mammalia
Order	Marsupialia
Family	Potoroidae
Status	Endangered, IUCN
	Endangered, USFWS
	Appendix I, CITES
Range	Australia

Description and Biology

These rat-kangaroos are also called bettongs; they have short forelimbs, long, strong hindlimbs, and a strong tail that is used for balance. The head and body length averages 12-30 in (30-65 cm) and tail length is 10-13 in (25-33 cm). Soft, dense fur is gray or grayish brown, underparts are lighter, and muzzle is light and hairless. Feeding is nocturnal and diet usually includes seeds, roots, and tubers, and possibly insects; the brush-tailed species also eats forest fungi.

Rat-kangaroos are generally solitary. Home ranges of 59-90 acres (20-36 ha) have been recorded but vary with species. Breeding can take place at any time during the year and up to three litters per year may be produced. One young is usually born, but twins are not unknown.

Habitat and Current Distribution

The woylie or brush-tailed bettong (*Bettongia penicillata*) is restricted in southwestern Western Australia to four separate populations in nature reserves and state forests (Perup Nature Reserve, Tutanning Nature Reserve, Dryandra State Forest and Batalling State Forest east of Collie). Captive-bred animals have been introduced to Venus Bay and Baird Bay Islands, Wedge Island and St. Peter Island, South Australia. It spends the day in a grass nest and prefers semi-arid scrublands and grasslands or woodland with medium rainfall. There are no current estimates of population.

The boodie or burrowing bettong (*Bettongia lesueur*) is restricted to three islands off the coast of Western Australia: Barrow, Bernier, and Dorre Islands. It digs and lives in burrows that can be simple or very elaborate with many entrances. Boodies inhabit a broad range of habitats from spinifex (grasses with stiff sharp leaves) deserts to woodlands. There are no current population estimates available.

The northern bettong (*Bettongia tropica*) is currently found in northeastern Queensland, restricted to the western edge of Wet Tropics between Cardwell and Daintree above 1,300 ft (400 m) elevation. This species inhabits rainforest margins, tall open forest and grassy woodland. There are no estimates of population.

History and Conservation Measures

The woylie was common over most of the southern half of Australia until the early 1900s. The recently-burned habitat that it prefers was abundant when nomadic Aborigines used small fires for clearing on a sporadic basis; this left sufficient brush

Brush-tailed bettong.

for the species to survive the fire and provided sufficient food in newly burned areas. With the departure of the Aborigines and the expansion of European settlement, brush was either cleared permanently for agricultural development or fires were so widespread that they left no safe areas for fire survival. European settlers also introduced grazing animals that had an adverse impact on rat-kangaroo populations. Fox predation has also contributed to the decline of this species. In refuges in the Perup and Dryandra forests and the Tutanning Reserve, suitable habitat has been preserved and the control of foxes has led to dramatic increases in population. Efforts

have been made to introduce the species onto offshore islands, and other mainland habitats may eventually be repopulated.

The boodie was once found throughout most of Australia but is now restricted to three offshore islands. A number of factors contributed to its decline. Introduced competitors and predators were one of the primary causes; rabbits offered competition for burrows and food, and foxes and cats (particularly on islands) helped to decimate the population. Habitat alteration resulted from changes in the number and extent of fires after the settlement of Aborigines and from clearing to provide grazing land for domestic livestock. The remaining island populations are stable and protected, but still vulnerable to disease and predation. Efforts are being made to reintroduce the species into some habitat on the mainland (especially to Shark Bay peninsulas).

The northern bettong was thought to be extinct until it was rediscovered in the Davies Creek National Park. Reasons for its decline are thought to be introduced predators and habitat destruction as a result of forest clearance, but these require further study. Research into the biology, distribution, and ecological needs of this species is underway.

Long-footed potoroo

Potorous longipes

Phylum	Chordata
Class	Mammalia
Order	Marsupialia
Family	Macropodidae
Status	Endangered, IUCN
Range	Australia

Description and Biology

The common name for this potoroo comes from the fact that its hind foot, at approximately four inches (10 cm) long, is longer than its head. It has grayish to greenish brown fur flecked with lighter hairs to give it a grizzled appearance. The animal has a dark stripe on its face and its underparts are gray. Its tail measures 9-13 in (22.8-33 cm) and is black with a lighter underside. The average head and body length of this animal is 12-16.5 in (30-42 cm); the average weight is 1.7-4.9 lb (759-2,200 g). The potoroo moves along the ground on two or four legs and sometimes leaps, using its powerful hind legs to propel it as high as eight feet (2.5 m). It feeds at night on fungi and other types of vegetation, including grass and roots, by digging a conical pit with its front feet.

Breeding probably occurs throughout the year and a single young is produced. It is attached to the mother's nipple for almost two months and leaves the pouch after four months.

Habitat and Current Distribution

This species is found in southeastern Australia. It is sparsely distributed in the state of Victoria, where 20 colonies have been identified in East Gippsland. A single colony also has been found in New South Wales in the Rockton area of Bondi State Forest. The size of the current population of this species is unknown.

The long-footed potoroo appears to be restricted to riparian vegetation with dense understorys, surrounded by mixed-species *Eucalyptus* forest.

History and Conservation Measures

The long-footed potoroo was first described in 1980, and little is known about its actual range, status, diet, reproduction, or habitat requirements. Further research in all these areas is necessary. This species is probably being pushed to denser areas of its riparian habitat due to predation by feral dogs and foxes, and to increased access to its habitat as a result of forest management practices. Forests adjoining known colonies are threatened by timber extraction that may adversely affect potoroo habitat. Further habitat disruption can also lead to isolation of small potoroo colonies. Protection of known habitat has been strongly advocated, including temporary or permanent restriction of logging activities. Mechanisms are now in place in Victoria to immediately protect new potoroo colonies as they are identified. Predator control could also have a positive impact on the long-footed potoroo population. The establishment of a captive breeding colony at Melbourne Zoo or Taronga is also under consideration.

Rufous hare-wallaby

Lagorchestes hirsutus

Phylum	Chordata
Class	Mammalia
Order	Marsupialia
Family	Macropodidae
Status	Endangered, IUCN
	Endangered, USFWS
	Appendix I, CITES
Range	Australia

Description and Biology

The rufous hare-wallaby, also known as the western hare-wallaby, or mala, is reddish orange above and pale below, with a gray head and very dark gray on the top of its tail and feet. Its body length, including its tail, is approximately 26 in (65 cm), and it weighs up to 4.5 lb (2 kg), with the male smaller than the female. Days are spent protected in "squats" within spinifex (porcupine grass) hummocks or under shrubs or tussock grass or in short burrows. At night, it feeds on spinifex grass seeds, sedges, and perennial shrubs, preferring succulent new growth that also provides its supply of moisture.

Reproduction is continuous under favorable conditions but ceases in drought. The young remain in the pouch for about 124 days.

Habitat and Current Distribution

This hare-wallaby is now present in the wild only on Bernier and Dorre Islands in Shark Bay, Western Australia. Until recently, two populations existed in the Tanami Desert, Northern Territory; however, both of these have disappeared, one because of fox predation and the other due to a wildfire. Captive colonies established from these populations are being used in re-introduction experiments.

Island habitat is heath or open steppe with spinifex; desert habitat is sandplain with spinifex and other shrubs.

History and Conservation Measures

This hare-wallaby was once widespread throughout the arid inland regions of western and central Australia. It provided a food source for the nomadic Aborigines, who regularly burned small areas of desert to manage desert vegetation. This controlled burning provided a regular source of the new growth the hare-wallaby liked to feed on while maintaining the necessary surrounding shrubs it required for shelter.

After the Aborigines settled into permanent homes, vegetative conditions developed that allowed large summer fires to burn out huge areas, rendering them unsuitable for the hare-wallaby and killing any wallabies in the fires' paths. So much habitat was destroyed that the population of hare-wallabies dropped to critically low levels. The island populations are in nature areas, where fire management is being used to preserve necessary habitat, as is control of predators and protection from competition from grazing animals. Captive breeding programs have been instituted to attempt re-introduction into suitable habitat.

Banded hare-wallaby

Lagostrophus fasciatus

Phylum	Chordata
Class	Mammalia
Order	Marsupialia
Family	Macropodidae
Status	Endangered, IUCN
	Endangered, USFWS
	Appendix I, CITES
Range	Australia

Description and Biology

This tiny kangaroo has gray fur with dark bands across the rear body. Its common name comes from the similarity of its locomotion and its body size and appearance to hares. Body and tail length averages 31.5 in (80 cm); average weight is 3-4.5 lb (1.3-2.1 kg). Grasses make up less than half of its diet; the remainder consists of a variety of dicotyledonous plants.

Breeding can take place any time between December and September, but most births occur in the latter half of summer. Although capable of bearing two young, only one is usually raised; it spends up to six months in the pouch and is weaned at nine months. Juvenile mortality is high because of predation by owls, hawks, and goannas, a species of monitor lizard.

Habitat and Current Distribution

The banded hare-wallaby is now restricted to Bernier and Dorre islands in Shark Bay, Western Australia. Exact numbers are unknown, but population is thought to be relatively stable. A population was introduced to Dirk Hartog Island in the 1970s, but it failed to establish.

Daytime habitat is thick acacia scrub, where the hare-wallaby can find shelter; at night it moves to open coastal sand dunes to feed.

History and Conservation Measures

The banded hare-wallaby was once fairly common throughout southwestern Western Australia, but the last mainland specimen was collected in 1906. Its disappearance from the mainland is attributed to clearance of natural vegetation for agriculture. Competition from introduced herbivores such as sheep and rabbits and predation by cats may also have played a role.

The present island populations of this species are believed to be secure, but continued efforts to preserve its required scrub habitat from development or fire and to prevent the introduction of predators and competitors are crucial. Isolated island populations, of course, are vulnerable to sudden decline or extinction.

Bridled nailtail wallaby

Onychogalea fraenata

Phylum	Chordata
Class	Mammalia
Order	Marsupialia
Family	Macropodidae
Status	Endangered, IUCN
	Endangered, USFWS
	Appendix I, CITES
Range	Australia

Description and Biology

This member of the kangaroo family gets its name from a horny spur on the end of its tail. It is silky gray, about 17.7-23.6 in (45-60 cm) in length with a 13.7-19.7 in (35-50 cm) tail, and it weighs about 11 lb (5 kg). During the day this solitary animal rests in a shallow depression under a shrub, small tree, or log; at night it feeds on a variety of grasses and forbs. Dingoes are predators.

Young are raised in the pouch, but little is known of breeding behavior.

Habitat and Current Distribution

The only known population is near the town of Dingo in Queensland, Australia. In the early 1980s, population was estimated at 800 individuals.

Daytime habitat consists of shrubland and woodland; night feeding is usually done in open woodland or grassland.

History and Conservation Measures

This wallaby was once common in inland eastern and southeastern Australia. In the early 1800s, grazing animals, especially sheep, were introduced to its range. The nailtail wallaby was considered a nuisance and a bounty was paid for its scalp. This intentional destruction, along with the reduction of food caused by the grazing animals, and introduced predators, caused such a drastic decline that this wallaby was considered extinct by 1930.

Bridled nailtail wallaby.

In 1973, a population was rediscovered near the town of Dingo, when a resident identified a picture of a presumed extinct species in a magazine article as the wallaby he was seeing in the bush. In the late 1970s and early 1980s, the Taunton Scientific Reserve was established to protect this new population, and the majority of the surviving bridled nailtail wallabies now reside there. Cattle and predators are controlled on the reserve, and captive breeding programs are being established as a back-up to this isolated population.

Prosperine rock-wallaby

Petrogale persephone

Phylum	Chordata
Class	Mammalia
Order	Marsupialia
Family	Macropodidae
Status	Endangered, IUCN
Range	Australia

Description and Biology

Similar in appearance to a kangaroo, the Prosperine rock-wallaby has long, thick fur that is dark or grayish brown in color with lighter shades underneath. The padded hind foot is adapted for gripping rocky surfaces and is edged with stiff hairs. The tail is long, bushy, and black with a reddish area at the base and a white tip. When moving, the tail is arched over the back and used for balance. Head and body length averages 3.3 ft (1 m) and weight is about 11 lb (5 kg); males are larger than females. The main dietary need for this rock-wallaby is grass.

This rock-wallaby is quite agile and can move among rocks with great ease. It can jump up to 13 ft (4 m). Very little is known about this species' reproductive biology, but mating takes place throughout the year.

Habitat and Current Distribution

This species is now known only from northeast coastal Queensland, near Prosperine (where it occurs on private property and state forest), Mt. Dryander National Park, Gloucester Island, and Conway Range National Park. There are no estimates of population size or composition.

The preferred habitat of the species includes rocky outcrops and ranges in, or near, rain forest; the interfaces between closed and open forest may be important feeding areas. The rock-wallaby is mainly nocturnal but sometimes basks in the sun during daylight hours and usually feeds in late afternoon or early evening. In hot weather, it may take shelter in rock crevices or caves.

History and Conservation Measures

Although known to the local people for many years, this species was not scientifically described until the early 1980s. It may once have had a wider distribution, but it now has an extremely limited range. Remaining habitat is isolated by surrounding land that has been cleared and used for agriculture. In addition to an apparently small population and limited range, the Prosperine rock-wallaby faces competition from the more common and adaptable unadorned rock-wallaby, which has apparently taken over some of the former species' feeding and shelter areas. Surveys of distribution, home range, and habitat usage have been initiated to gather vital information which will enable a management plan to be developed and implemented. Identified recovery goals for the Prosperine rock-wallaby include: identification of range, abundance, and conservation status; maintenance of existing range; protection of known rain forest habitats; and identification of ecological requirements. A captive breeding program is also underway to protect against extinction in the wild.

Mountain pygmy-possum

Burramys parvus

Phylum	Chordata
Class	Mammalia
Order	Marsupialia
Family	Burramyidae
Status	Endangered, IUCN
	Endangered, USFWS
	Appendix II, CITES
Range	Australia

Description and Biology

The mountain pygmy-possum is a small creature, brownish gray with lighter underparts. The average head and body length of this species is 4-5 in (10.2-12.7 cm) and weight is 1-2 oz (28-57 g). Its prehensile tail is 5.2-6.3 in (13.2- 16 cm) long and nearly naked except for the base, which is furred like its body. Mainly terrestrial, it is also an agile climber. Active during the night, it forages on the ground and in the trees for seeds, fruit, leaves, and insects and other invertebrates. It is apparently the only marsupial to store seeds for use in the winter, when food is scarce.

A litter of four is born in November, after a gestation period thought to be 13-16 days. The young remain in the mother's pouch for at least three weeks and are nursed for up to nine weeks.

Habitat and Current Distribution

The mountain pygmy-possum dwells in the mountains of eastern Victoria and southeastern New South Wales. The population is believed to be 900 individuals: 500 in Mount Kosciusko National Park in New South Wales and 400 around Mount Higginbotham in Victoria, but other areas of suitable habitat have not been surveyed.

The habitat of this species includes alpine and subalpine zones at an altitude of 5,000-6,000 ft (1,500-1,800 m). It seems to prefer glacial boulder rock screes with dense shrub and shelters near rocks during the day. Because of heavy snow and severe mountain weather conditions, it probably hibernates during the winter.

History and Conservation Measures

Until the 1960s, this species was known only from fossilized remains found in New South Wales. In 1966, a live specimen found in Victoria was identified

Mountain pygmy-possum.

as a mountain pygmy-possum. In the 1970s, further specimens were collected in Victoria and in New South Wales.

Today, a population is protected in Mount Kosciusko National Park in New South Wales and at Bogong National Park in Victoria. The species re-mains vulnerable to habitat destruction caused by the development of ski resorts and to predation by cats and foxes. The greenhouse effect may be a major influence on the future survival of this species, since it may lead to further habitat loss. It will be necessary to survey isolated areas of suitable habitat to determine the presence of populations that need protection.

Leadbeater's possum

Gymnobelideus leadbeateri

Phylum	Chordata
Class	Mammalia
Order	Marsupialia
Family	Petauridae
Status	Endangered, IUCN
	Endangered, USFWS
Range	Australia

Description and Biology

Leadbeater's possum is a small, gray possum 6-7 in (15-18 cm) long and weighing 4-6 oz (120-165 g). It has a narrow, bushy tail. It resembles and is related to the sugar glider, but it has no gliding membrane. Its coat is pale underneath; it has dark patches near the large eyes and a dark band on the back stretching from forehead to rump. This is a nocturnal species that feeds on insects and sap. Using its teeth to notch a hole in tree bark, it increases the flow of gum or sap and licks up the secretion.

A colony consists of up to eight animals, usually comprising a single dominant female and a number of adults and juveniles. When a female reaches breeding age, at about ten months, it is usually forced out of the colony by the dominant female. Breeding takes place at any time during the year and results in a litter of one or two young after a gestation period of 15-17 days. Young are carried in the pouch for three months and then remain in the nest for almost another month.

Habitat and Current Distribution

Southwestern Victoria, Australia, is the only home of this possum. Population figures are un-known, but the total population has been estimated to be between 3,000 and 8,000 individuals.

A very specific habitat is required within mountain ash (*Eucalyptus regnans*) forest, consisting of very old dead or alive hollow-bearing trees for nesting and shelter combined with a dense understory of younger mountain ash trees and wattles.

History and Conservation Measures

This species was first identified in 1867 and then not located between 1909 and 1961, when it was rediscovered near Melbourne. Research then showed that the animal occurred in a number of other locations.

A massive fire occurred in 1939 in Victoria's mountain ash forests; it has been suggested that the species' resurgence in the 1960s may have been in response to the forest's regeneration. The complex habitat requirements of Leadbeater's possum and the predicted natural decline in numbers of hollow-bearing trees mean that the species, even though not uncommon in places at present, is threatened. Careful management of land in reserves and in multiple-use forests will be necessary to protect this possum. Captive breeding at Melbourne Zoo has been successful, and captive breeding colonies now exist at several other zoos in Australia and elsewhere.

Chilean shrew opossum

Rhyncholestes raphanurus

Phylum	Chordata
Class	Mammalia
Order	Marsupialia
Family	Caenolestidae
Status	Endangered, IUCN
Range	Chiloé Island (Chile); Argentina

Description and Biology

The Chilean shrew opossum is a tiny marsupial with soft, dark brown fur. *R. raphanurus*, one of two species of Chilean shrew opossum, is mainly confined to Chiloé Island. These shrew opossums are unique among marsupials in that they have two cusps on the lateral upper incisors.

R. raphanurus has a narrow face with small eyes. The average head and body length is 3.5-5.5 in (9-14 cm) and weight is 0.5-1.4 oz (14-41 g). Its black tail is 2.6-3.5 in (6.5-8.8 cm) long, only slightly shorter than the body. In the autumn, the tail is used to store fat to help sustain the opossum through the winter. In colder months, the width of the tail measures 0.35-0.39 in (9-10 mm), and in the summer it measures 0.15-0.2 in (4-5 mm).

Active at night, the Chilean shrew opossum uses its long snout and tactile whiskers to search for food and sense danger. *R. raphanurus* is chiefly terrestrial, moving about the ground using well-developed trails or runways, but it is also an agile climber. Diet consists mainly of invertebrates (about 55 percent of total diet) and also includes vegetation and fungi.

There is little information available about this animal's social organization or reproductive biology. Reproductively active females have been found in December.

Habitat and Current Distribution

R. raphanurus is found on Chiloé Island and at several sites in the mainland provinces of Llanquihue and Osorno in southern Chile. It has also been recently recorded from southern Argentina. It inhabits humid rain forest up to an elevation of 3,720 ft (1,135 m). It seems to prefer dense cover and often shelters in burrows or near fallen trees. There are no estimates of population size. Until the early 1980s, this marsupial was known only from 17 specimens.

History and Conservation Measures

The Chilean shrew opossum was once considered quite rare, but recent discoveries indicate that the species may be more common than previously thought. However, habitat destruction threatens existing populations, as the dense forest it inhabits is now vulnerable to logging operations. Conservation efforts are currently underway to preserve the rain forests of Chile, which, if successful, would also guarantee the future of a wide range of other species.

Colocolo

Dromiciops australis

Phylum	Chordata
Class	Mammalia
Order	Marsupialia
Family	Microbiotheriidae
Status	Rare, IUCN
Range	Argentina; Chile

Description and Biology

The colocolo, sometimes called the *monito del monte*, is a small marsupial and the only living member of its genus. This species has often been placed in the Didelphidae family, but differences—particularly in teeth structure—have led to its reclassification in the Microbiotheriidae, a nearly extinct family of New World marsupials.

This marsupial has short, dense, silky fur that is brown or gray-brown, with light gray to white patches on the shoulders and rump area. It also has a reddish brown crown and pale to white underparts. The light gray face has a short muzzle; short, furry ears; and dark gray eye circles. Average head and body length is 3-5 in (8-13 cm), and it weighs less than an ounce (16-48 g). Moderately prehensile, the tail is 3.5-5 in (9-13 cm) long and ends in a dark brown tip. The colocolo spends a good portion of its time above ground and is active at night. Days are spent in a nest made of water-repellant bamboo leaves, lined with grasses and moss. Nests are usually found among rocks, fallen branches, or in tree trunks. Its diet consists mainly of insects and other small invertebrates (72 percent of total diet) but also includes seeds and vegetation.

Pairs form during the mating season, between October and December, but the length of their association is uncertain. The length of the gestation period is also uncertain, but females have been observed with young between November and May; litter size is one to five. The young first live in the mother's pouch, attached to her nipples, and are then left in the nest. As they mature, they ride on the mother's back and travel with her.

Habitat and Current Distribution

This species occurs from Concepción south to Chiloé Island in south-central Chile and east into the mountains beyond the Argentine border. There are no recent estimates of population size.

This animal's preferred habitat includes dense, humid thickets, especially those containing Chilean bamboo (*Chusquea* sp). Because this habitat is quite cool in the winter, the colocolo hibernates during the coldest periods. Fat stored at the base of the tail helps sustain it through the winter.

History and Conservation Measures

The history of the Microbiotheriidae, of which the colocolo is a member, is gradually becoming better understood among the scientific community. According to morphological and DNA biochemical studies, this family is believed to be related to the phanalgeroid marsupials of Australia, thus representing a reinvasion of South America with species from Australia. Among the local people of Chile, however, the colocolo is still the object of ignorance and superstition: it is believed that the colocolo's bite is poisonous and causes convulsions in humans. It is also considered bad luck to see one or have it around one's house. Some people have been known to burn their houses to the ground after sighting one inside.

Brazilian three-toed sloth

Bradypus torquatus

Phylum	Chordata
Class	Mammalia
Order	Edentata
Family	Bradypodidae
Status	Endangered, IUCN
	Endangered, USFWS
Range	Brazil

Description and Biology

The Brazilian three-toed or maned sloth is an arboreal animal (although it swims well) that spends most of its life in the trees, hanging beneath branches or sitting in forks. It uses its long, curved claws as hooks to move slowly along beneath branches or to climb trees. This species has a head and body length of 20-24 in (50-60 cm) and a 3-inch (8-cm) blunt tail. It weighs 8-11 lbs (3.6-5 kg). Its limbs are long, its head is round and flat, and its eyes and ears are very small. The maned sloth has coarse grayish brown hair that points downward when the animal is hanging beneath a branch. (The hair of most other mammals grows in the opposite direction.) Algae frequently grow on a sloth's coat, giving the hair a greenish color that helps camouflage the animal in its arboreal home. The sloth has a very low metabolic rate and much weaker muscles than other mammals of comparable size. It feeds nocturnally on leaves, birds, and flowers over a home range of approximately 16 acres (6 ha). Three-toed sloths occasionally (1-2 times per week) descend to the ground to urinate and defecate or to move between trees. On the ground, they crawl slowly on the soles of their feet and their forearms and use their claws (which can inflict severe wounds) for defense if attacked. Predators are ocelots and jaguars.

Breeding can occur at any time during the year. The female gives birth to a single young after a gestation period of 120-180 days. The infant is nursed for about a month and carried by the mother on her stomach for 6-9 months.

Habitat and Current Distribution

The Brazilian three-toed sloth is restricted to the Atlantic coastal forests of eastern Brazil in the states of Bahia, Espirito Santo, and Rio de Janeiro. Population figures are unavailable.

History and Conservation Measures

Since the maned sloth is a slow-moving animal, it is an easy target for hunters. Although this animal has been hunted for meat in the past, it is now protected by law in Brazil and hunting/poaching does not appear to be a major threat. Habitat destruction has probably always been, and continues to be, the major threat to the continued survival of the maned sloth. Humans have cleared all but a tiny fraction of the Atlantic coastal forests to create coffee, sugar cane, cocoa, and eucalyptus plantations, as well as pastures for cattle. Lumbering and charcoal production have deforested other areas, as has industrial development. Unless suitable areas of Atlantic coastal forest are preserved, the maned sloth may not survive.

Existing reserves with populations of maned sloths include the Monte Pascoal National Park; Biological Reserves of Corrego de Veado, Sooretama, and Nova Lombardia; and Serra dos Orgaos National Park in the city of Rio de Janeiro. Studies are recommended to determine further possible reserve areas. The maned sloth appears to have a specialized diet and has not yet been successfully kept in captivity.

Burmeister's armadillo

Chlamyphorus retusa

Pink fairy armadillo

Chlamyphorus truncatus

Phylum	Chordata
Class	Mammalia
Order	Edentata
Family	Dasypodidae
Status	Insufficiently Known, IUCN
	Endangered, USFWS (*C. truncatus*)
Range	Argentina; Bolivia; Paraguay (*C. retusa*)
	Argentina (*C. truncatus*)

Description and Biology

The pink fairy armadillo, also called the lesser pichi ciego, is such an elusive animal that local residents often know only of its existence and nothing of its habits. It is the smallest armadillo with a head and body length of 4.75-6 in (12-15 cm), a tail 0.75-1.25 in (2-3 cm) long, and weighing 3-3.25 oz (85-92 g). Its name comes from the pale pink color of its armor plating. This armor is loosely anchored at one spot on the head and along the ridge of the spine and extends across the top of a body covered with soft white hair.

Burmeister's armadillo, also known as the greater pichi ciego, is slightly larger than the pink fairy armadillo with a head and body length of 5.5-7 in (14-17.5 cm) long and a tail about 1.5 in (35 mm) long. Its armor plates are whitish and yellowish brown and its soft fur is whitish. The head has an armor shield on top, and the tail is partially cover with armor plates. The body armor is attached to the skin along the entire length of the armadillo's back.

The pink fairy armadillo is an excellent digger, constructing burrows to live in during the day and burying itself if threatened by predators. Burmeister's armadillo is not such a good digger—it flattens itself against the ground when surprised in the open. Both species primarily feed on insects and their larvae, although snails, worms, plant material (including underground stems and tubers), small reptiles, and bird eggs are also eaten. The pink fairy armadillo is nocturnal.

Pink fairy armadillo.

No information is available about the social habits or reproductive biology of either species.

Habitat and Current Distribution

C. retusa is found in the Chaco region of western and central Bolivia, in Paraguay, and in extreme northern Argentina. *C. truncatus* occurs only in the desert areas of central and western Argentina. Current population estimates are not available for either species.

Both species inhabit dry grasslands and sandy or stony plains with sparse vegetation of thornbush and cactus. The pink fairy armadillo seems to prefer areas with dry, warm soils.

History and Conservation Measures

Earlier population estimates for these species are unavailable, but both probably inhabit a more limited range than they have in the past. Loss of habitat to agricultural development has probably reduced the numbers of both species. Predation by domestic dogs poses a significant threat to *C. truncatus*, and *C. retusa* may be threatened by overcollection. Neither species has successfully reproduced in captivity. Much more must be learned about the ecology, distribution, and status of these species before conservation measures can be formulated.

Giant armadillo

Priodontes maximus (giganteus)

Phylum	Chordata
Class	Mammalia
Order	Edentata
Family	Dasypodidae
Status	Vulnerable, IUCN
	Endangered, USFWS
	Appendix I, CITES
Range	Argentina; Bolivia; Brazil; Colombia; French Guiana; Guyana; Paraguay; Peru; Suriname; Venezuela

Description and Biology

The heavily armored giant armadillo is much larger than other armadillos. Adults of this species can be distinguished from other armadillos by size alone. A series of 11-13 moveable plates covers the giant armadillo's back, and three to four bands cover its neck. Only a few hairs are scattered between these plates. This animal is dark brown except for the head, tail, and a band around the bottom of shell, which are whitish. At physical maturity, total body and head length is 29.5-39 in (75-100 cm), and tail length is about 19.5 in (50 cm). Weight averages 44-88 lb (20-40 kg). The giant armadillo has prominent, upright ears, and the long claws on its front legs are used to dig burrows for shelter and to dig for food. Since this armadillo cannot completely enclose itself within its armor plates like some other species can, it may try to dig itself into the ground to escape from danger. A nocturnal feeder, it mainly eats ants and termites, although it will also eat other insects, worms, spiders, larvae, snakes, and carrion.

The giant armadillo lines its nest with grass, weeds, and debris. The number of young is thought to be one or two, and the gestation period is reported to be four months. Young weigh approximately 4 oz (113 g) at birth and already have very tough and leathery skin; they nurse for approximately four to six weeks. Young armadillos reach sexual maturity at 9-12 months, and the life span of this species is about 12-15 years.

Giant armadillo.

Habitat and Current Distribution

The giant armadillo is widely distributed in eastern South America from southeastern Venezuela, the Guianas, southern Colombia, and Peruvian Amazonia through Brazil, Bolivia, and Paraguay as far as the northeastern sector of Argentina. Population figures are unknown.

Primary habitat is tropical forest and savanna.

History and Conservation Measures

The overall extent of the giant armadillo's range has not changed substantially, but its distribution within that range has decreased. Causes of the decrease are hunting, human settlement, and in particular, agricultural development. Although the giant armadillo is protected by law against hunting or capture in Argentina, Brazil, Colombia, Paraguay, Peru, and northern Suriname, it is still heavily hunted for food in some areas. More importantly, large areas of savanna and forest are being opened and cleared for residential and agricultural use.

Studies are in progress to plan conservation efforts. Stricter enforcement of hunting restrictions will be necessary, as will expanded protection of habitat. The giant armadillo is thought to occur in a number of national parks and nature reserves in Brazil, Colombia, Peru, and Suriname. Where habitat destruction is unavoidable, the possibility of translocation of animals to protected areas is being explored. Captive breeding plans are also under consideration.

Brazilian three-banded armadillo

Tolypeutes tricinctus

Phylum	Chordata
Class	Mammalia
Order	Edentata
Family	Dasypodidae
Status	Endangered, IUCN
Range	Brazil

Description and Biology

The Brazilian three-banded armadillo is the only armadillo that can roll itself into a sphere when danger threatens. Its vulnerable body parts are protected by tough, bony plates. This animal's general coloring is yellowish brown. Head and body length averages up to 12 in (30 cm), weight is approximately 3-3.5 lb (1.4-1.6 kg), and the thick, fairly inflexible tail measures around 2.5 in (6.4 cm). It walks on its foreclaws and can move rather quickly. Diet includes worms, soft-bodied grubs, insects, and fruit.

Little is known about the habits of the species, but conclusions can be drawn from studies of the closely related *Tolypeutes matacus* in the wild. It is usually a solitary animal, but sometimes groups of up to 12 animals are found together in a shallow nest during the cold season, apparently to conserve heat. One young is usually born between November and January.

Habitat and Current Distribution

This species occurs in central and northeastern Brazil. Its burrows are usually found in and around the bases of large clumps of bushes and small trees in grassy areas with access to water throughout the year. There is no estimate of population size.

History and Conservation Measures

Although little is known about this species, it is believed to be threatened by exploitation for food and is easily captured. It is thought to occur in the national parks of Sete Cidades (Piaui), Ubajara (Ceara), and in the Biological Reserve of Serra Negra (Pernambuco). A study of the behavior, ecology, zoogeography, and taxonomy of this armadillo is needed to direct conservation efforts.

Giant anteater

Myrmecophaga tridactyla

Phylum	Chordata
Class	Mammalia
Order	Edentata
Family	Myrmecophagidae
Status	Vulnerable, IUCN
	Appendix II, CITES
Range	Argentina; Belize (ex?); Bolivia; Brazil; Colombia; Costa Rica; Ecuador (?); French Guiana; Guyana; Honduras; Nicaragua; Panama; Paraguay; Peru; Suriname; Uruguay; Venezuela

Description and Biology

The giant anteater is easily recognized by its appearance. It has a long, narrow body with coarse, shaggy gray hair and a black and silver-white stripe on the shoulders and back. Head and neck are tapered, with a long, cylindrical snout, small ears, and small eyes. Head and body length averages 40-50 in (100-130 cm), weight is 40-86 lb (18-39 kg), and the shaggy tail is 26-35 in (65-90 cm). A number of adaptations equip the giant anteater for food gathering: sense of smell is well developed for locating prey; strong front legs and claws are used to break into termite or ant colonies; and the 24-inch-long (60 cm) tongue is coated with saliva to pluck prey from the nest. It is also a good swimmer and digger. The powerful front legs and claws are used against predators like pumas and jaguars.

Home range has been variously reported as ranging from 1-1.4 sq mi (2.6-3.6 sq km) or from 3.5-9.6 sq mi (9-25 sq km); in semi-arid parts of Venezuela, it has been reported to be as large as 6,000 acres (2,400 ha). Except for mother-young relationships, this is a solitary species, coming together only for mating. Mating is probably possible at any time during the year, although it is reported to occur between March and May in the southern part of its range. After a gestation period of 190 days, a single young is born while the mother is standing. The infant is nursed for up to six weeks and carried on the back of the mother; it remains with her for more than a year.

Habitat and Current Distribution

The range of the giant anteater is huge, extending from Guatemala to northern Argentina. Despite this, an examination of the giant anteater's status reveals that it is endangered, if not extinct, over much of its range. In Guatemala and El Salvador it is almost certainly gone. In Nicaragua, Costa Rica, and Panama, it is endangered, and some scientists believe that this species will be extinct in Costa Rica by the end of the century. In Central America the major cause of the virtually assured extinction of this species is habitat destruction.

In South America, the giant anteater is found in all types of vegetation, from rain forest to grassland but is very sparse in all but open vegetation formations. In many rain forest areas giant anteaters are eaten by indigenous peoples while the habitat itself is being destroyed very rapidly. These facts combine to threaten the anteater's populations over much of the

Giant anteater.

northern portions of South America. In French Guiana the giant anteater is uncommon; in Peru it has always been uncommon but has disappeared from many areas from which it was previously known; in Bolivia it is endangered; and in the Brazilian Amazon it is sparsely distributed and shot on sight. At the southerly end of its distribution, it is reported to be very rare, having disappeared from two national parks in which it used to occur.

The remaining portion of the giant anteater's range consists of the cerrado region of Brazil and the Chaco of Paraguay. In central Brazil giant anteaters are still common in some locations.

History and Conservation Measures

Giant anteaters are hunted in South America for their meat and for trophies (the claws and tail are highly prized). They are also killed because they are mistakenly believed to kill dogs and cattle, attack people, and, perhaps most frequently, because they are easy to kill. More serious than hunting and direct

human predation is fire. Giant anteaters have long coarse hair which burns easily. The large fires which sweep much of central South America during the dry season spell death to many anteaters. Some of these fires are set deliberately to improve grazing for cattle. Almost all animals other than giant anteaters can escape these fires by running, digging, flying, or in some cases, crossing back through the fire line. Giant anteaters are slow, ungainly beasts, and a few years ago in Emas National Park, at least six adult anteaters burned to death during a fire.

This species is found in a number of protected reserves and parks. In Brazil it occurs in at least ten national parks and three biological reserves; in Argentina it occurs in the Pilcomayo National Park; in Costa Rica in the Tortuguero and Corcovada National Parks; in Honduras in the Rio Platano Biosphere Reserve; in Peru in Manu National Park; in Suriname in Sipaliwini Nature Reserve; and in Paraguay it has been reported in Defensores del Chaco National Park. It has also been studied in the Serra da Canastra National Park in Brazil.

Cuban solenodon

Solenodon cubanus

Haitian solenodon

Solenodon paradoxus

Phylum	Chordata
Class	Mammalia
Order	Insectivora
Family	Solenodontidae
Status	Endangered, IUCN
	Endangered, USFWS
Range	Cuba (*S. cubanus*)
	Dominican Republic; Haiti (*S. paradoxus*)

Description and Biology

In appearance, solenodons resemble large shrews but in fact are more similar to hedgehogs in size, being among the largest living insectivores. Their most distinguishing feature is a very long, flexible snout with nostrils on the sides. The Cuban solenodon has a long, fine coat that is gray to brownish black in color with underparts and head ranging from white to tawny. The Haitian or Hispaniolan solenodon has much coarser hair that can either be a mixture of brown and black with a grizzled appearance or reddish brown; flanks and face are yellowish, and there is usually a white spot on the nape. Eyes are small and ears large and partly hairless. Head and body length averages 11-13 in (28-33 cm), and solenodons weigh about 25-36 oz (710-1020 g). The 7-10 in (17-25 cm) tail is mostly hairless and may play a role in the solenodon's balance; forelimbs are strong and end in sharp claws. Senses of smell and hearing are acute, and the sense of touch is especially developed.

The Haitian solenodon and probably the Cuban solenodon secrete toxic saliva, which is used to paralyze prey. Solenodons are proficient climbers but spend most of their time foraging on the ground, using their claws to dig into bark or debris and their snout to locate prey. They feed at night principally on vertebrates and invertebrates. Natural predators include snakes and birds of prey.

Solenodons are usually solitary animals, except

Cuban solenodon.

for mothers and their young. Very little is known about their reproduction in the wild. One or two young are born in a nest constructed under a burrow; females may have two litters each year. Juveniles receive more parental care than most insectivores and remain with the mother for a longer period of time.

Habitat and Current Distribution

Solenodon cubanus is endemic to Cuba where it is now confined to the northeast, west central, and southwest Oriente Province. The second species, *Solenodon paradoxus*, is endemic to the island of Hispaniola in the Caribbean; it is present in undeveloped areas of the Dominican Republic and is confined to the extreme western end of Haiti. There are no estimates of population size for either species.

The Cuban solenodon inhabits areas of dense, humid, primary montane forest. The preferred habitat of the Haitian solenodon appears to be coralline limestone outcrops covered with dense brush or woodland. Here the animals may shelter in the many natural crevices. Vegetation cover can vary from rain forest at an altitude of 10,000 ft (3,000 m) down to semi-arid woodland or even low-lying scrub. Both species shelter in burrows, caves, hollow trees, or beneath logs.

History and Conservation Measures

One of the main reasons for the rarity of both species is deforestation. Expanding human populations have usurped habitat and cleared it for agriculture or settlement. Feral cats have contributed to the problem in Cuba, as have dogs in Hispaniola. Before rats or dogs were introduced to the islands, solenodons were probably near the top of the predator chain in their habitats. As a result they developed a low birth rate. In combination with other threats, however, a low birth rate makes it very difficult for a species to maintain a self-sustaining population.

The solenodon is legally protected in Cuba and efforts are being made to ensure that this protection is enforced. The Jaguani and Cupeyal reserves for fauna and flora have been established in the montane forest of northeastern Oriente Province, near Toa Baracoa, where this species, together with the rare ivory-billed woodpecker (*Campephilus principalis*), occurs. A third reserve has been planned at Duaba Arriba.

Protective laws also exist in the Dominican Republic and, despite shortcomings in local enforcement, prohibition of export has been effective. There are no reserves in either the Dominican Republic or Haiti that protect the solenodon, but suitable conservation areas have been identified, and efforts have been made to establish protected areas.

Additional surveys of these species' distribution, together with studies of ecology, are necessary as a basis for planning further conservation measures. The establishment of reserves is essential to ensure the survival of the solenodon. Captive breeding programs could be a positive step in preserving this species for possible eventual reintroduction into suitable reserve areas, but this should not be seen as an alternative to protecting these fascinating animals and their habitat in the wild.

Large-eared tenrec

Geogale aurita

Phylum . . . . Chordata
Class . . . . Mammalia
Order. . . . . Insectivora
Family . . . . Tenrecidae
Status . . . . Insufficiently Known, IUCN
Range . . . . Madagascar

Description and Biology

This small insectivore has soft fur that is reddish brown with lighter underparts. Its head and body is 2.8 in (7.1 cm) long, and its finely-haired tail measures just over 1 inch (3.2 cm). It feeds at night on a variety of invertebrate prey, with a preference for termites.

Information about the social organization and reproductive biology of this species is minimal. It has been reported that litters of one to five young are born between November and February.

Habitat and Current Distribution

The large-eared tenrec is endemic to Madagascar, where its precise distributions are unknown. *G. a. aurita* has been widely collected in the southwest and as far north as the Tsiribihina River. Recent records indicate that it is abundant at Beza Mahafaly Special Reserve in the southwest, at Morondava in the north, and that it also occurs in the Zombitse Forest near Sakaraha. It has recently been collected in eastern rain forests in the extreme southeast. *G. a. orientalis* is known from a single individual from Fenoarivo in the south central region of the country. There are no estimates of population size for either subspecies.

This species has been recorded from a range of habitats, including spiny thorn bush, deciduous forest, and gallery forest. It seems to prefer dead, fallen timber for sleeping during the day.

History and Conservation Measures

The status of this species has not been determined, and there is no information about conservation efforts. Its small size and tendency to hide in dead timber have, until recently, caused this species to be overlooked by many scientists. As is the case with other endemic species in Madagascar, forest clearance threatens the continued survival of large-eared tenrecs.

Aquatic tenrec

Limnogale mergulus

Phylum	Chordata
Class	Mammalia
Order	Insectivora
Family	Tenrecidae
Status	Indeterminate, IUCN
Range	Madagascar

Description and Biology

The aquatic tenrec is a unique animal on several counts; it is the only aquatic member of its family and is the only species in its genus. In addition, it appears to be one of Madagascar's rarest mammals and it occupies a unique riverine niche on the island. The aquatic tenrec has soft, sleek fur that is a mixture of red, brown, and black; its underparts are yellow-gray. To assist in swimming, *Limnogale mergulus* has webbed feet and a strong tail used for propulsion and as a rudder. Its head and body length measures about five to nearly seven inches (12-17 cm) long; the tail length is usually the same as the body. Diet includes freshwater crayfish, aquatic insect larvae, and small crustaceans.

There is very little information available about social organization or reproductive biology of this species. Breeding is believed to take place in December or January, and the probable litter size is two or three.

Habitat and Current Distribution

The exact range distribution of this species is unknown, but it is thought to be confined to the eastern section of the country. The aquatic tenrec occurs along small streams and rivers in eastern Madagascar at altitudes from 1,500-6,500 ft (450-2,000 m). There are no estimates of population size.

The principal habitat requirement for this species seems to be permanent, clean, fast-flowing water, though many such localities support no aquatic tenrec populations. Another requirement is the presence of certain aquatic plants which harbor many invertebrates within their root systems.

History and Conservation Measures

Limnogate mergulus was first caught in 1965. It was then feared to be extinct until live specimens were captured in 1989. Initially, this species was known from just a few localities on the eastern edge of the central high plateau and the eastern escarpment in Madagascar. In the late 1980s, these areas were surveyed and two of them were found to be undergoing major geological changes, including river sedimentation. During the same survey period, three additional sites were identified where the tenrec was reported to be present by the local people, and these were the only sites in the survey where abundant feeding signs of the tenrec were found.

Fast-flowing rivers featuring the aquatic plants preferred by this species are becoming increasingly fragmented as slash-and-burn agriculture destroys the surrounding forest. Aquatic tenrecs seem to be particularly associated with the aquatic plants *Aponogeton fenestralis* and *Hydrostachis madagascariensis* because of the rich supply of invertebrates found among their tangled roots. *A. fenestralis* is a popular aquarium plant; overcollection has led to its extirpation in some localities. Although aquatic tenrecs seem to have naturally low population densities and patchy distribution, reduction and degradation of suitable habitat, due to these and other activities, seem to pose an immediate threat to the species' survival.

The limited information available on this species, as well as the ever-increasing threat to its habitat, strongly suggest that the aquatic tenrec may be a prime insectivore candidate for a captive breeding program. Such a project could eventually be linked to re-introduction programs, thus ensuring the survival of wild populations in protected areas. The aquatic tenrec conservation plan includes the following: verification of known localities and identification of the physical and ecological characteristics of the aquatic tenrec sites; determination of the tenrec's ecological requirements, e.g., dietary and spatial needs of the species; determination of the current threats to the aquatic tenrec through habitat changes, and promotion of conservation action where necessary and practical; and determination of whether captive breeding is required and, if so, completion of a series of semi-captive trials to establish and evaluate captive breeding techniques.

Shrew-tenrecs

Microgale spp.

Phylum	Chordata
Class	Mammalia
Order	Insectivora
Family	Tenrecidae
Status	Insufficiently Known, IUCN
Range	Madagascar

Description and Biology

Shrew-tenrecs, also known as long-tailed tenrecs, are a genus of small insectivores with shrew-like habits and appearance. The color of their soft fur varies from shades of brown to almost black with lighter underparts. Head and body length ranges from 1.5-6 in (4-13 cm), depending upon the species. Weight also varies according to species; the smallest shrew-tenrec may weigh as little as 0.18 oz (5 g), while the larger forms may weigh up to 2.1 oz (61 g). The tail usually measures about the same length as the body. Insects are the primary food source for most, if not all, shrew-tenrecs.

Scientific expeditions and surveys often overlook shrew-tenrecs due to their small size and secretive lifestyle. Because so few studies have been made, the taxonomic arrangement of this genus is particularly unclear. The number of species included in *Microgale* has fluctuated widely since its discovery; the latest revision, made in 1987, places 11 species in the genus. The social organization and reproductive biology of shrew-tenrecs is also poorly known.

Habitat and Current Distribution

Shrew-tenrecs are endemic to Madagascar. The short-tailed shrew-tenrec (*Microgale brevicaudata*) has been recorded from the village of Antsirabe Avaratra as well as the Manongarivo Special Reserve,

both in Antsiranana Province. The western short-tailed shrew-tenrec (*Microgale occidentalis*), first described in 1931, is only known from one specimen found near Andriafavelo village. In the collection area only patches of western dry forest remain, otherwise having been replaced with human-induced grasslands. The large-footed shrew-tenrec (*Microgale crassipes*) is also only known from one specimen collected near Antananarivo and, not having been seen for 50 years, may be extinct. Drouhard's shrew-tenrec (*Microgale drouhardi*) is known from seven specimens from the region of Antsiranana in the extreme north.

The striped shrew-tenrec (*Microgale melanorrhachis*) has been recorded from eastern rain forests at Andasibé and from the Ambatovaky Special Reserve 125 mi (200 km) to the north. The Taivi shrew-tenrec (*Microgale taiva*) has been recorded from Ambohimotombo Forest. It was thought to be extinct, but specimens that may belong to this species were recently captured at Andasibé. The lesser long-tailed shrew-tenrec (*Microgale longicaudata*) is known from specimens collected at Ankafina, a 5,250 ft (1,600 m) hill south of Ambohimahasoa, and from the extreme western limit of the eastern rain forests. It was also considered extinct, but recent specimens recorded from Ambatovaky Special Reserve may be of this species. Major's lesser long-tailed shrew-tenrec (*Microgale majori*) is known only from speci-

Shrew-tenrec.

mens collected from the same locality as the lesser long-tailed shrew-tenrec and is considered by some to be the same species.

The northern lesser long-tailed shrew-tenrec (*Microgale prolixacaudata*) is known from a single specimen from the Antsiranana region, the same locality as Drouhard's shrew-tenrec; however, it is thought to be the same species as the lesser long-tailed shrew-tenrec. The pygmy shrew-tenrec (*Microgale parvula*) is known from a single immature specimen collected from the Antsiranana region. The greater long-tailed shrew-tenrec (*Microgale principula*) is known from a single specimen from Midongy Atsimo in the southeastern rain forests at 1,640 ft (500 m) altitude. The long-tailed shrew-tenrec (*Microgale sorella*) is known from a single adult male specimen from the forests of Beforona village at an altitude of 1,640 ft (500 m) on the road from Antananarivo to Toamasina. Some experts consider it

the same species as the greater long-tailed shrew-tenrec.

Thomas's shrew-tenrec (*Microgale thomasi*) was originally known from Ambohimotombo Forest, but recently specimens have been captured at Ranomafana Est and at Anjazorobe at altitudes of 2,625-3,940 ft (800-1,200 m) in eastern rain forests. The gracile shrew-tenrec (*Microgale gracilis*) was also originally known from Ambohimotombo Forest, but additional specimens are now known from Andringitra Strict Nature Reserve, Ranomafana Est, and Andasibé; few individuals have been recorded. The dark pygmy or dusky shrew-tenrec (*Microgale pulla*) is a recently described species captured in Andrivola Forest in the northeastern rain forest.

These species occupy a variety of habitats, including dry forest and rain forest, throughout the country and are important predators of small terrestrial invertebrates. No estimate exists of total population size for any of these species.

History and Conservation Measures

Shrew-tenrecs are poorly described in scientific literature, and no specific conservation programs can be formulated until more is known about their biology and habitat requirements. It is possible that shrew-tenrec species are threatened by habitat loss, as are most indigenous species on Madagascar. Ongoing and planned programs for the preservation of the island's forests would, indirectly, benefit all shrew-tenrecs.

Nimba otter-shrew

Micropotamogale lamottei

Phylum	Chordata
Class	Mammalia
Order	Insectivora
Family	Tenrecidae
Status	Endangered, IUCN
Range	Côte d'Ivoire; Guinea; Liberia

Description and Biology

The Nimba otter-shrew is a semi-aquatic insectivore adapted to diving and lunging for its prey in dark, muddy rivers. In appearance, this rotund species has a black head and long, tapering tail. The fur is generally dark brown in color and is composed of outer, water-repellent coarse fur and much softer, thicker underfur. Its tail is round and its feet have no webbing. Head and body length averages 4.7-7.9 in (12-20 cm); tail length is 3.4-5.9 in (10-15 cm); weight is around 4.8 oz (135 g). Active at night, it feeds on insects, insect larvae, worms, fish, frogs, and freshwater crustaceans.

Little is known about the social organization or reproductive biology of this shy, elusive species.

Habitat and Current Distribution

The Nimba otter-shrew is restricted to the Mt. Nimba area spanning the borders of Côte d'Ivoire, Liberia, and Guinea. Almost all known specimens have been captured in an area covering less than 580 sq mi (1,500 sq km). There are no estimates of population size.

Preferred habitat includes swampy areas, small, slow-flowing rivers, and forest streams.

History and Conservation Measures

The Nimba otter-shrew was first described in 1954. A 1983 survey indicated that it was relatively common in the Danané-Man region of Côte d'Ivoire and that populations occur in similar habitats in neighboring Guinea and Liberia.

Because of threats to its habitat, the long-term future of this species seems bleak. Mining activities have devastated the Liberian sector of the mountain. Habitat conservation in the region is generally ineffective. It has been recommended that the small amount of forest remaining on the Liberian side of Mt. Nimba should be conserved and no further expansion of mining operations permitted. There have also been reports of potential expansion of bauxite mining to Guinea. Efforts are in progress to form a Biosphere Reserve on the Guinean side of the mountain. Further research is urgently needed on the behavior, basic ecology, and requirements of this species. Long-term protection schemes should also consider the need for a captive breeding program. Furthermore, public awareness programs should be set in place in each of the countries with Nimba otter-shrew populations.

Golden moles

Chrysochloridae spp.

Phylum	Chordata
Class	Mammalia
Order	Insectivora
Family	Chrysochloridae
Status	Various, IUCN
Range	Mozambique; Namibia; Somalia; South Africa; Zimbabwe

Description and Biology

The golden moles are probably named for their almost iridescent, sleek coats of light yellow to chocolate which gleam in shades of bronze, red, yellow, blue, green, or purple. The fur is thick and made moisture–repellent by its dense undercoat. Head and body length varies with species from 2.8-9 in (7-23 cm). Limbs are short and there is no visible tail. Ears are covered by hair, rudimentary eyes are covered by hairy skin, and nostrils are protected by a fold of leathery skin at the end of the long snout. Skin is tough, and head and shoulders are powerful to allow the mole to burrow by thrusting itself forward. Most species feed primarily on invertebrates, including insects, insect larvae, spiders, earthworms, grubs, slugs, and snails. Predators include snakes, otters, mongooses, jackals, and owls and other birds of prey.

Golden moles are probably solitary, but their social structures are poorly known. They are mostly territorial, aggressively defending their burrows. Very little is known about reproductive biology, but there does not seem to be a distinct breeding season. A litter of one to three young is born in a nest located inside a burrow.

Habitat and Current Distribution

The golden moles are found in Africa, south of the Sahara. There are no estimates of population sizes.

These moles inhabit a wide range of habitats that vary with different species. *Cryptochloris wintoni* inhabits sand dunes. *Chrysospalax villosus* occurs in dry grassy habitats, particularly in areas bordering marshes. *Chrysospalax trevelyani* occurs in forests and valley forests where there are deep soils, leaf litter, and dense shrubs. *Eremitalpa granti* occurs in coastal sand dunes and also inland, showing a preference for areas with scattered clumps of dune grass. *Chlorotalpa duthiae* habitat is typified by alluvial sands and sandy loams. *Chlorotalpa obtusirostris* favors alluvial soils, dry river beds, and coastal sand dunes. *Amblysomus gunningi* appears to be associated with montane forest, but has also been captured in montane grasslands and ploughed land. *Amblysomus iris* appears to be associated with light sandy soils.

History and Conservation Measures

The golden moles are represented by seven genera and 18 species, all restricted to sub-Saharan Africa. Thirteen of these species are classified as threatened—one as vulnerable, four rare, and eight indeterminate. Status information is available about 13 of the species, as follows: De Winton's golden mole (*Cryptochloris wintoni*) is known from specimens collected at Port Nolloth in Cape Province, South Africa; its classification is indeterminate. Van Zyl's golden mole (*Cryptochloris zyli*) is known from several museum specimens and from the type specimen from Lambert's Bay in Cape Province, South Africa; it is classified as indeterminate. The rough-haired golden mole (*Chrysospalax villosus*) occurs in the Transvaal, Natal, and eastern Cape Province in South Africa. In the Transvaal it is uncommon. There is no known area where they can be reliably trapped, and only two specimens have been collected in 15 years; it is classified as vulnerable and requires study before conservation measures can be planned.

The giant golden mole (*Chrysospalax trevelyani*) is limited to a few small areas in eastern Cape Province from the King William's Town and East London districts eastward to Port St. Johns in Transkei, and marginally into Ciskei, South Africa. Its habitat is being cleared and degraded, especially in proximity to human settlements. Clearance and habitat damage occurs largely because of firewood collection, bark stripping, cutting for construction, and livestock ranging in the forest. Dogs prey upon the giant golden mole and only one locality in its range is fenced to provide protection from dogs. This species is classified as rare, and it has been suggested that remaining habitats should be controlled and that a reserve be created to protect a representative sample of the otherwise rapidly degrading habitat.

Visagie's golden mole (*Chrysochloris visagiei*) is known only from a single specimen collected at Gouna in Cape Province, South Africa; it is classified as indeterminate, and there is some doubt about its taxonomic status. Grant's golden mole (*Eremitalpa granti*) occurs in a narrow belt in southwestern South Africa and in the Namib Desert of Namibia; it is classified as rare. It does not occur in any protected area in South Africa, but if the proposed Groen River National Park is established, it will cover part of the species' range. The Namib Desert National Park in Namibia is within the species' range. Duthie's golden mole (*Chlorotalpa duthiae*) occurs in a narrow coastal band between Knysna and Port Elizabeth in southern Cape Province in South Africa; it is classified as rare. It may be locally common, but little is known of its ecology, and few museum specimens exist. Sclater's golden mole (*Chlorotalpa sclateri*) occurs in a series of scattered localities from Cape Province north eastward to southeast Transvaal, with additional sites from eastern Orange Free State and Lesotho. Virtually nothing is known about the species, and its status is indeterminate.

The Somali golden mole (*Chlorotalpa tytonis*) is known only from a single specimen collected at Giohar in Somalia. Limited information and its unusual locality have led to the classification of indeterminate. The yellow golden mole (*Chlorotalpa obtusirostris*) occurs in southern Zimbabwe, southern Mozambique, and northeastern South Africa; it is found in the Kruger National Park. Little is known of its habits and ecology, and it is classified as rare. Gunning's golden mole (*Amblysomus gunningi*) is known only from the Woodbrush Forest and the Agatha Forest, in northeastern Transvaal. Its range is apparently very restricted, and only seven museum specimens are known; it is classified as indeterminate. Zulu golden mole (*Amblysomus iris*) occurs widely from Knysna in Cape Province to Natal, South Africa, but is restricted to a narrow coastal band; it is classified as indeterminate. Juliana's golden mole (*Amblysomus julianae*) is known from only five museum specimens collected from three sites near Pretoria and two in the Kruger National Park, in South Africa. Because insufficient evidence is available to determine its current status, it is classified as indeterminate.

Mindanao gymnure
(moonrat)

Podogymnura truei

Phylum	Chordata
Class	Mammalia
Order	Insectivora
Family	Erinaceidae
Status	Vulnerable, IUCN
Range	Mindanao (Philippines)

Description and Biology

The gymnure, also called the moonrat, is a relative of the hedgehog. Native people call this species *bagobo*, meaning ground pig. It has long, soft fur that is a mixture of gray, red, and brown hairs; underparts are almost white. Head and body length averages 5-6 in (13-15 cm). The lightly haired tail is 1.6-2.8 in (4-7 cm) long and buff-purple in color. Its long snout is blunted at the end. Diet includes insects, worms, and some vegetable matter.

Little information is available about the social structure or reproductive biology of this gymnure. This insectivore is nocturnal and terrestrial and probably remains in burrows (or rock crevices) during daylight. Breeding probably takes place throughout the year. This is a solitary animal which is intolerant of other members of the same species.

Habitat and Current Distribution

This species is endemic to Mindanao, Philippines. It has been collected from Mount Apo, Mount McKinley, and Mount Katanglad at elevations of 5,900-7,500 ft (1,800-2,300 m). There are no estimates of population size.

Often found among tree roots or in dense undergrowth, the Mindanao gymnure inhabits dense forests and wooded valleys, often near water.

History and Conservation Measures

The Mindanao gymnure is considered to be very rare and may be in danger from habitat destruction. Logging has diminished available forest habitat, as has clearance for agriculture. The latter is considered the most serious problem facing the Mindanao gymnure. At the present time, there are no conservation efforts directed specifically at this species, although some moonrats are protected in a few nature reserves. Until more is known of this animal's ecology, little can be done to protect the species. Habitat protection, however, is the best answer; it would also benefit the many other rare and unique small mammals of Mindanao.

Russian desman

Desmana moschata

Phylum	Chordata
Class	Mammalia
Order	Insectivora
Family	Talpidae
Status	Vulnerable, IUCN
Range	Belarus; Estonia; Kazakhstan; Latvia; Lithuania; Russia; Turkmenistan; Ukraine

Description and Biology

Restricted to eastern Europe, the Russian desman is a nocturnal, aquatic insectivore found in slow-moving waters. This desman is a little larger than the related Pyrenean desman; it is about 7-9 in (18-22 cm) long. Its tail is as long as its body and at the base of the tail, glands emit a strong, musky odor. Rings of scales also encircle the tail. The Russian desman's hind feet are webbed and the forefeet are partially webbed; fur color is reddish brown but gray underneath. Like the Pyrenean desman, this species has a long, flexible snout. Diet includes many food items but is made up mainly of insects, crustaceans, molluscs, fish, and amphibians.

The Russian desman is a social creature, and eight animals have been known to share a common burrow, although a pair, or three or four individuals, is most common. It is a sedentary species and some individuals use the same burrow year after year. Burrows are built near the edge of the water with underwater entrances. The Russian desman is thought to give birth just once each year. Breeding takes place in spring and autumn, and three to five young are born per litter.

Habitat and Current Distribution

This species is found in southeastern Europe and central western Asia. It prefers still or slow-moving rivers, lakes, ponds, and canals. An ample supply of freshwater is essential. Population estimates range from 37,000-40,700; the largest population is found in the Volga River basin.

History and Conservation Measures

During the early 1800s the Russian desman was abundant throughout its range until hunting for its fur nearly destroyed the population. In 1929 laws banned the hunting of this creature, and captive breeding efforts were introduced. In 1940, however, limited hunting was allowed but a declining population forced another ban in 1957.

While hunting is no longer a threat to this desman, water pollution and human activity near the desman's habitat have become serious problems. In addition, competition from introduced species such as the muskrat has further pressured the desman population.

Captive breeding and reintroduction to the wild have been very successful. Currently there are five nature reserves and 80 refuges for this desman.

Pyrenean desman

Galemys pyrenaicus

Phylum	Chordata
Class	Mammalia
Order	Insectivora
Family	Talpidae
Status	Vulnerable, IUCN
Range	Andorra (?); France; Portugal; Spain

Description and Biology

A small, semi-aquatic insectivore, the Pyrenean desman is found in fast-flowing, cold mountain streams. This creature is well-adapted to life in the water: it has a 5.5-in (14-cm) cylindrical tail that is used as a rudder; webbed feet; sharp, long claws; and short, thick fur. Its long snout and short neck gives this creature a mole-like appearance. The total head and body length is about 5 in (12.5 cm) long; at the end of the long tail, scent glands release a strong odor which may mark an individual's territory. Pyrenean desmans weigh about 1.2-2.8 oz (35.5-80 g), and no obvious size differences are apparent between the sexes.

This desman is a nocturnal creature and shelters during the day in long, narrow burrows along stream banks. Diet includes crustaceans and insect larvae. It will also eat fish but doesn't appear to prey on them. On land it moves rather clumsily, and terrestrial hunting has not been observed.

Primarily solitary, Pyrenean desmans also form pairs. The male occupies a home range of around 1,400 ft (427 m); the female occupies a smaller area of around 1,000 ft (304 m). A solitary male covers a larger territory. The female gives birth two times a year from February to May; litter size is generally one to five young after a gestation period of 30 days.

Habitat and Current Distribution

This species is found in the French and Spanish Pyrenees, northern Spain, and northern Portugal. It prefers fast-flowing waters, although it also inhabits canals, lakes, and marshes at altitudes of 190-3,900 ft (60-1,200 m). This is a timid creature and it scurries away from any sign of disturbance, making it difficult to obtain population estimates.

History and Conservation Measures

Like most endangered species, this desman is threatened with extinction from habitat degradation and hunting. Water pollution and hydro-electric plants have damaged or fragmented much of this desman's habitat. Fishermen have indiscriminately killed these animals because they are perceived as a threat to their livelihood. Education should be an essential component of any conservation effort.

The Pyrenean desman is currently found within the Parc National des Pyrénées Occidentales and the Parque Nacional de Covadona. It may also occur in the Parque Nacional de Aiguas y Lago de San Mauricio and the Parque Nacional de Ordesa.

Montane tree-shrew

Tupaia montana

Phylum	Chordata
Class	Mammalia
Order	Scandentia
Family	Tupaiidae
Status	Indeterminate, IUCN
Range	Borneo

Description and Biology

The montane tree-shrew is a small mammal that resembles a squirrel; its genus name is derived from the Malay word "tupai," which means squirrel. It has soft hair that can range in color from reddish brown and gray to near black, with lighter underparts. Average weight is 3-7.7 oz (90-220 g); head and body length ranges from 5.5-9 in (14-23 cm). The 5-7.5 in (13-19 cm) tail is covered with long, thick hair and is usually as long as its body. Spending much of the time on the ground, the tree shrew forages during the day. Diet includes insects, fruit, seeds, and other plant material.

Mating probably takes place throughout the year. After a gestation period of 45-51 days, one to three young are born in a tree hollow, in a nest lined with leaves. Most female tree shrews pay very little attention to their young, leaving them in the nest and visiting once a day to nurse. The young leave the nest at around four weeks of age.

Habitat and Current Distribution

Endemic to Borneo, particularly the hills and mountains of the northwest, the montane tree shrew inhabits tropical rain forest, preferring areas with thick brush and fallen trees. There are no estimates of population and little is known of the ecology of this species in the wild.

History and Conservation Measures

There is no information available about the status of this species or about conservation efforts.

Philippine tube-nosed fruit bat

Nyctimene rabori

Phylum	Chordata
Class	Mammalia
Order	Chiroptera
Family	Pteropodidae
Status	Endangered, IUCN
Range	Philippines

Description and Biology

Characterized by massive, blunt jaws and a fleshy nose with tubular nostrils, the Philippine tube-nosed fruit bat attains an average length of 5.5 in (14 cm). Its fur is light brown, except for a slender band of dark brown fur on its back, from the shoulders to the base of its tail. Females are typically lighter in color than males, though markings are similar. Sometimes irregular yellow spots are found on the bat's ears or on the skin over the limbs, fingers or toes.

Though its diet is not known in detail, this fruit bat apparently feeds on figs, as it is often found near trees of the genus *Ficus*, such as *F. chrysolepis*. Males attain sexual maturity at one year of age. At 7-8 months of age, females become pregnant, producing their first offspring 4-4.5 months later. They give birth to only one young per year, in April or early May, and nurse for about three to four months.

The density of this bat's population seems to be fairly low; only one bat per 7.5 acres (3 ha) was found at Lake Balinsasayo.

Habitat and Current Distribution

The Philippine tube-nosed bat is found only on the southern part of Negros Island, where it inhabits primary and dense secondary forest. It is chiefly found at altitudes of 1,968 ft (600 m) to 4,265 ft (1,300 m), though a few individuals have been seen at altitudes as low as 656 ft (200 m). This bat does not occur in urban areas, farmland, or poor secondary forest, as it cannot tolerate habitat disturbance. Breeding populations are found only on the sides or summits of tall forested peaks. There are no estimates of population size.

History and Conservation Measures

The chief threat to the Philippine tube-nosed bat is deforestation. As a result of forest clearance at lower altitudes, the bat is now seldom found below 2,625-2,950 ft (800-900 m); if forest destruction continues at the current pace, most of its habitat will be eradicated within ten years.

If this bat is to survive, remaining forest in southern Negros must be protected to the lowest possible elevation. If this is not done, a captive breeding program may be the only way to prevent the extinction of the species. An effort to find a population of this fruit bat on nearby Panay Island might also be initiated since, as recently as the Pleistocene period, Negros and Panay were connected.

Chuuk flying-fox

Pteropus insularis

Pohnpei flying-fox

Pteropus molossinus

Mortlock Islands flying-fox

Pteropus phaeocephalus

Phylum . . . . Chordata
Class . . . . Mammalia
Order . . . . Chiroptera
Family . . . . Pteropodidae
Status . . . . Endangered, IUCN
                   Appendix I, CITES
Range . . . . Chuuk (Federated States of Micronesia) (*P. insularis*)
                   Chuuk, Pohnpei (Federated States of Micronesia) (*P. molossinus*)
                   Chuuk (Federated States of Micronesia) (*P. phaeocephalus*)

Description and Biology

The Chuuk flying-fox (*Pteropus insularis*) is also sometimes known as the Carolines fruit bat or the Chuuk fruit bat. It has moderately long, soft, silky fur that is dark brown on the back, rump, belly, sides of the breast, and flanks. The back and rump are sprinkled with silvery grayish white hairs, while the underparts are sprinkled with long, pale grayish or buffy hairs. The mantle and sides of the neck vary from buff to a deep tawny color, and there is a more or less distinct buffy pectoral patch that contrasts dramatically with the dark fur of the breast and belly. The size of this patch varies greatly from individual to individual. The ears are moderately sized and exposed. The top of the head is a mixture of buff and dark brown, while the sides of the face, chin, and throat are blackish sprinkled with buffy or grayish hairs. *P. insularis* feeds on the flowers of coconut (*Cocos nucifera*) and has been observed forming colonies of up to 1,000 bats.

The Pohnpei flying-fox (*P. molossinus*) or Pohnpei fruit bat has rather long fur that is uniformly dark brown on the back, rump, and underparts; these areas are also sprinkled with whitish hairs. The fur of the shoulders and mantle is erect; the color is slightly darker brown than the rest of the body, and the sprinkling of whitish hairs is almost completely absent. The ears are small and almost concealed in the fur. The top and sides of the head are the same color as the mantle, and the face has a yellowish tinge. Males have a tuft of rigid orange-buff hair tipped with dark brown on each side of the neck. *P. molossinus* eats the fruits of *Clinostigma* and the flowers of *Ceiba pentandra* and coconut. Researchers have encountered these bats individually and in pairs, an indication that a large number of these bats may roost outside colonies.

The Mortlock Islands flying-fox (*P. phaeocephalus*) or Mortlock Islands fruit bat is similar in appearance to *P. insularis* but is much paler. The fur of the back and rump is golden cream-buff at the tips and brown at the base. The belly, sides of the breast, and flanks are dark brown mixed with buff on the sides of the breast and thickly flecked with long silvery hairs on the belly. The center of the breast is marked with a bright cream-buff patch. The mantle hairs are buffy at the tips and brown at the bases; this buff color gradually shades to yellowish buff on the sides of the neck and to yellow on the foreneck. The top and back of the head are a mixture of buff and brown sprinkled with silvery hairs, and the face, chin, and throat are dark brown thinly sprinkled with silvery hairs.

Habitat and Current Distribution

P. insularis is only known from native forest on the island of Chuuk in the Caroline Islands in the western Pacific Ocean, and from small islands in Chuuk lagoon. The population was estimated at 5,628 in 1986, but the current population is believed to be substantially lower.

P. molossinus has been reported to occur in the Mortlock Islands (southeast of Chuuk Lagoon), but its status and distribution there is unknown; because of the small area of these islands, any population that might occur there would probably not contain more than several thousand individuals. *P. molossinus* was described as locally common in the northern half of Pohnpei in July 1981; it was described as common on Ant Atoll (9 mi [15 km] west of Pohnpei) and Pakin Atoll (18.5 mi [30 km] west of Pohnpei) in the 1950s. However, evidence gathered in 1989 indicated that significant declines in these three populations have taken place in recent years.

P. phaeocephalus has been reported to occur in the Mortlock Islands. Its status and distribution are unknown but, because of the small land area in the Mortlock Islands, any surviving population probably would not contain more than several thousand animals.

History and Conservation Measures

The decline of the Chuuk flying-fox is attributed to commercial hunting and to the conversion of native forest to agricultural land. A large commercial fruit bat trade has existed in Micronesia during the last 20 years, with large numbers of bats captured on a number of islands and exported to the Mariana Islands for use as food. Importation of *P. insularis* from Chuuk to Guam increased dramatically in the late 1980s; in 1988 and 1989 alone more than 3,700 animals of this species were exported to Guam. Although the residents of Chuuk are not known to hunt these bats for local consumption, the commercial trade continues to negatively impact bat populations. Chuuk's dense human population has destroyed much of the native forest on the islands in the Chuuk Lagoon. Remnants of these forests occur on the mountain tops on Moen, Dublon, Fefan, Tol, and other small islands, but most of the lower slopes on the islands have been converted to growing coconut, breadfruit (*Artocarpus altilis*), mangoes (*Mangifera indica*), bananas (*Musa* spp.), and other food crops. This habitat alteration has affected flying-foxes by changing their food sources and reducing colonial roosting sites. *P. molossinus* also is threatened by commercial hunting and deforestation. Between 1979 and 1989, more than 15,000 bats were exported from Pohnpei to Guam, and in 1989, an additional 6,478 animals were exported. Fruit bats have also been exported from the Mortlock Islands to Guam, but the numbers and species represented are not documented. *P. phaeocephalus* suffers from commercial hunting, in combination with periodic habitat destruction and population reduction by typhoons.

No protected areas have been established within the geographic range of these species. Population surveys should be conducted throughout Chuuk and the presence of *P. insularis* on neighboring islands should be investigated. In the Mortlock Islands, population surveys should be conducted throughout the range of *P. molossinus* and *P. phaeocephalus*. CITES regulations pertaining to these species must be enforced, with commercial shipments of bats to Guam inspected to assure compliance with regulations. None of these bats currently receives local protection, and local laws should be enacted to prevent overhunting either by giving bats full protection, allowing them to be hunted at subsistence level only, or by allowing sustainable quotas for commercial harvests if adequate data on reproduction and population structure are available. An environmental education program should be initiated to emphasize the importance of conserving natural resources, including flying-foxes and other wildlife. The biology and ecological role of these species should be studied, with particular attention given to reproduction, population structure, and clarification of taxonomic rela-

tionships. Protected areas should then be created for all three species.

Comoro black flying-fox

Pteropus livingstonii

Phylum	Chordata
Class	Mammalia
Order	Chiroptera
Family	Pteropodidae
Status	Endangered, IUCN Appendix II, CITES
Range	Comoro Islands

Description and Biology

More commonly known as Livingston's fruit bat or the Comoro black fruit bat, the Comoro black flying-fox is distinguished from other members of its genus by its long, black fur and uniquely shaped semicircular ears. The rump and sides of the belly are tinged with golden or tawny hairs; a tuft of tawny hairs on each shoulder may also be visible.

Flying-foxes are long-lived animals with low reproductive rates. Females generally give birth to one young at a time after a four- to six-month gestation period. Although young may fly at three months, they are not usually weaned until they are four to six months old and may remain dependent on their mothers for a year.

Habitat and Current Distribution

This species is known only from remnant forest patches on the islands of Nzwani (formerly Anjouan) and Mwali (formerly Mohéli) in the Comoros. A single roost was located on Nzwani in 1990 that was estimated to contain between 60 and 120 bats. Expeditions in 1988 found no evidence of the species on Mwali or Njazidja (formerly Grand Comore), although there is a possibility of relict populations existing.

History and Conservation Measures

In the late 1800s Livingston's fruit bat was reported as being abundant in the great forests of Nzwani's peaks. By the late 1970s, however, it was reported as extremely rare and threatened by active and progressive deforestation. A colony that had been seen near Dzialandze apparently moved to a new site around 2 mi (3 km) south because of disturbance from people and as a result of cyclone damage in 1989. The forest at the new site is rapidly being cleared, and there is a plan to build a road through the area.

Deforestation in the Comoros is a gradual process of underplanting with fruit, coconuts, manioc, maize, peas, and sweet potatoes. This type of agriculture necessitates the removal of scrub and herbaceous layers and some large trees and, coupled with grazing, severely affects regeneration. It also appears that in this new type of forest, the common Comoro flying-fox (*P. seychellensis comorensis*) competes with *P. livingstonii*. *P. s. comorensis* was formerly confined to areas below 1,300 ft (400 m), but in 1989 roosts were recorded at 2,000 ft (610 m) and 3,280 ft (1,000 m), elevations traditionally inhabited by Livingston's fruit bat.

Once on the edge of the cyclone belt, the Comoro Islands are now within it, and the recent incidence of major cyclones is unprecedented in climatic records for the islands. It seems likely that the Mwali population was wiped out as a result of two major cyclones (1983 and 1984) that destroyed 80 percent of the food crops on Mwali.

There is no legal protection of endangered species on the Comoros and no protected areas have been established. Recommended conservation measures include: assessment of populations on Nzwani, including surveys to locate possible relict populations on Mwali and Njazidja; establishment of forest reserves on Nzwani, Mwali, and, possibly, Njazidja if populations exist; protection of canopy trees and maintenance of biological diversity through controls on logging and underplanting or through re-vegetation; studies on the species' feeding ecology and population biology, particularly as they affect habitat requirements; initiation of educational programs on fruit bats; and the establishment of captive breeding colonies.

Mariana fruit bat

Pteropus mariannus mariannus

Phylum	Chordata
Class	Mammalia
Order	Chiroptera
Family	Pteropodidae
Status	Vulnerable, IUCN
	Endangered, USFWS
	Appendix I, CITES
Range	Guam; Northern Mariana Islands

Description and Biology

Seven identified subspecies of *Pteropus mariannus* inhabit the Micronesian Pacific region, including Belau, Yap, Kosrae, Guam, and the Northern Marianas, as well as the Ryukyu Islands, Japan; the relationships between some of these subspecies remain in dispute.

Perhaps the best known of these subspecies is the Mariana fruit bat, *P. m. mariannus*. This bat, with a forearm length averaging 5.3 in (135.5 mm), has a dark brown back, sides and belly with a small number of silvery hairs. The back and rump are somewhat darker in color than the sides of its belly, while its neck and mantle are a much paler earthy yellow-buff. The teeth of *P. m. mariannus* are slightly larger and heavier than those of its close kin such as *P. m. yapensis*.

Usually gathering in large colonies, especially on cliffs or other isolated terrain, the Mariana fruit bat consumes the fruits and flowers of a large number of plant species; even the twigs and leaves of a few species are eaten. While they normally roost in large numbers, bats on occasion may be seen roosting alone or in small groups.

The Mariana fruit bat mates throughout the year; bats assemble in harems containing 2 to 15 females and a single male. Non-mating males gather in "bachelor groups" or roost singly near a harem. At a given time, 7-20 percent of females in harems can be found with recently-born young.

The bat's movements are poorly understood. Colonies have been observed ranging as far as 6.2-7.4 mi (10-12 km) from their roosting location while foraging for food; in addition, individuals or small groups have been observed flying between islands. Large groups of 50-300 bats have occasionally been observed flying between Rota and Guam or Anguijan, a distance of 37-50 mi (60-80 km). It is thought that hunting may be the cause of these migrations.

Habitat and Current Distribution

The Mariana fruit bat inhabits mangroves, forests and coastal areas. Roosts are usually located on cliffs or at other locations protected from strong winds and human interference.

This bat is found on Guam and the adjoining Northern Mariana Islands of Aguijan, Rota, Saipan, and Tinian. In addition, groups of *P. mariannus* of unknown subspecies have been recorded from a number of other islands in the group; these may also be *P. m. mariannus*. The population of Mariana fruit bats can be estimated as follows: roughly 1,400 bats

Mariana fruit bat.

on Rota, a single colony of 600-650 bats on northern Guam (fluctuating from year to year with migrations from Rota); fewer than 100 individuals on Saipan, roughly 50 bats on Aguijan, and fewer than 25 on Tinian.

History and Conservation Measures

Considered common before the 1920s, the Mariana fruit bat became increasingly rare on Guam after the introduction of guns to the island. The population steadily dropped; in 1958 the island supported a maximum of 3,000 individuals, but by 1978 perhaps only 50 bats remained. In 1980, a new colony appeared at Pati Point, numbering over 500 individuals; this colony may have arrived from Roti. It grew to around 850 bats in 1982 before declining to some 600 the following year. Meanwhile, the island-wide population reached nearly 775 bats the same year, though nearly all the bats inhabited sites owned by the United States Air Force (USAF) in northern Guam. Since 1984, the population has fluctuated from year to year; as of 1988 it stood at about 650.

The island of Rota supported as many as 2,500 bats prior to 1988, but a violent typhoon in January of that year, as well as an increase in poaching, roughly halved the island's population by mid-1989.

The Mariana fruit bat is currently subject to several threats, including predation, hunting for food, and typhoons. Deforestation is not considered to be a major danger at present.

Overall, hunting has probably been the major cause of decline. Fruit bats are a traditional food source over much of the Pacific including the Marianas, where they are savored as a delicacy. In parts of Southeast Asia, the meat of fruit bats is considered medicinal. Guam has served as a major crossroads for trade in fruit bats; it is estimated that over 16,000 bats were exported to Guam from neighboring islands between 1975 and 1989. Although hunting these bats on Guam was banned in 1973, it was listed as endangered by the U.S. Fish and Wildlife Service (USFWS) in 1981; enforcement has not been effective and illegal hunting remains a problem. In the 1980s, for example, only one person was arrested and fined on Guam for hunting the bat, even though many incidents of poaching were recorded. Hunting has also been implicated as a serious cause of decline on other Northern Marianas Islands. Through the 1960s and 1970s, bat populations on Aguijan, Saipan, and Tinian were extensively hunted for local food or export.

In recent years, predation by the brown tree snake (*Boiga irregularis*) on young bats has exceeded the threat of hunting as the most serious threat to *P. m. mariannus* on Guam. This snake, a nocturnal tree-climber, has also devastated the bird population of Guam's forests. Surveys of bat colonies made since the 1980s have demonstrated that juvenile fruit bats rarely reach adulthood due to predation.

Strong typhoons strike the region about every 10-15 years, though they have probably not been responsible for serious declines in bats in the past. However, Guam's single colony of bats could be devastated should a typhoon strike the northern part of the island directly.

A number of conservation steps have been recommended for the Mariana fruit bat. These include: implementing methods to control brown tree snakes in bat roosting areas (as a precursor to a wider snake control program which would take years to put in place); coordinating the efforts of military, civilian, and conservation authorities to enforce sanctions against poaching; expanding conservation education programs; translocating some bats from the colony on USAF property in northern Guam to previously inhabited parts of the island; and upgrading the listing of the *P. m. mariannus* bat population in the Northern Mariana Islands to fully endangered, thereby granting U.S. federal authorities law enforcement status to protect the bats found there.

In late 1993, the USFWS established the Guam National Wildlife Refuge on 370 acres (148 ha) of forest it was granted by the federal government. Containing the single colony of Mariana fruit bats remaining on Guam, this tract of land may eventually be expanded to more than 28,000 acres (11,200 ha) if cooperative agreements can be worked out between the USFWS, the U.S. Navy, the USAF, the government of Guam and other parties now administering land proposed for the park.

Rodrigues flying-fox

Pteropus rodricensis

Phylum	Chordata
Class	Mammalia
Order	Chiroptera
Family	Pteropodidae
Status	Endangered, IUCN
	Endangered, USFWS
	Appendix II, CITES
Range	Rodrigues (Mauritius)

Description and Biology

The Rodrigues flying-fox can range in color from silver to dark brown to black, or it may be shaded yellow, orange, or red on the mantle and head. The fur is rather long and silky and the small, sharply pointed ears are nearly concealed in fur. The ripe pods of tamarinds (*Tamarindus indica*) are very important food source for this fruit bat, but it also feeds on the rose apple (*Eugenia jambos*), mango (*Mangifera indica*), native *Pandanus* spp. and palms (*Hyophorbe verschafeltii* and perhaps *Latania verschafeltii*).

Flying-foxes are generally long-lived animals with low reproductive rates. Female Rodrigues flying-foxes generally give birth to one young at a time after a four- to six-month gestation period. Dependent young are present from late August through to early February. In captivity, births occur from October to April. Young are normally weaned at 10-11 weeks but occasionally suckle at six months and associate with their mother for one year.

Habitat and Current Distribution

This species survives in remnant forest patches on the island of Rodrigues in the Indian Ocean. It has been reported to roost in tamarinds. In 1991, the population was estimated at a maximum of 350 bats. In addition, nine zoos held colonies of captive-bred Rodrigues flying-foxes (totalling more than 250 animals) at the end of 1991.

History and Conservation Measures

Although once probably present on Mauritius and Round Island, the species is now extinct at these locations. In the 1700s and 1800s and until as recently as 1916, it was reported as abundant on Rodrigues. In 1955 there were about 1,000 individuals, but the population was reduced by a cyclone in 1979 to about 70. Numbers rose slowly until the population was again estimated to be greater than 1,000 in February 1990, based on an actual count of 650 animals. By the summer of 1991, however, an expedition counted a maximum of 350 bats.

Deforestation has been and still is a serious threat to this species. Between 1955 and 1968, a stand of over 100 old, mature tamarinds—a favorite food source for these bats—was cleared at a place still known as Tamarins, on the west slope of the Baie aux Huitres valley. There have also been losses of other food and shelter trees at other sites. Cyclones also destroy remaining forest and, with it, essential feeding areas. Cyclones in 1968 and 1972 probably killed a large number of these bats—known to be poor fliers even in moderate wind conditions. Although this species is fully protected under Mauritius wildlife regulations, hunting continues to be a problem.

Recommended conservation actions include: continued monitoring of the wild population to assess long-term trends; research into feeding biology; a ban on further deforestation; and a ban on hunting. Because of the success of the captive breeding program, plans are being formulated to introduce the species to another Indian Ocean island outside the cyclone belt.

Samoan flying-fox

Pteropus samoensis

Phylum	Chordata
Class	Mammalia
Order	Chiroptera
Family	Pteropodidae
Status	Endangered, IUCN
	Appendix I, CITES
Range	American Samoa; Fiji; Western Samoa

Description and Biology

Two subspecies of Samoan flying-fox are recognized: *P. s. nawaiensis* and *P. s. samoensis*. They have dark brown fur sprinkled with gray hair that fades to a lighter shade at the rump. The mantle is tawny, and the center of the breast and belly are dark brown. The sides of the breast, belly, and flanks have longer, coarser buff-gray hairs. Short, half-exposed ears are rounded at the tips, and the face, chin, and throat are blackish in color. The forearm measures 5.6 in (14.3 cm).

P. s. nawaiensis does not form large colonies and is often found roosting alone. Feeding in open areas on nectar or leaf buds of *Pandanus* sp., it is less diurnal than *P. s. samoensis* and has never been observed foraging before late afternoon. This species does not exhibit soaring behavior and has only been seen flying below the forest canopy. It is preyed upon by peregrine falcons (*Falco peregrinus*), for which flying-foxes are an important food item.

Usually found alone or in a small family group comprised of one male, one female, and one young, *P. s. samoensis* inhabits canopy trees. Occasionally, aggregations of 9-40 bats have also been observed. The male and female of individual pairs often roost in separate trees but will fly out together and return to the roost at approximately the same time. Although it has been observed feeding in coconut plantations, in breadfruit trees, and along the forest edge, it appears to prefer fruits and flowers in primary forest. This bat is a major pollinator for *Freycinetia reinecki*. Primarily diurnal—feeding during early morning and late afternoon—*P. s. samoensis* can be seen soaring on thermals, often spiraling upwards in pairs. It is sometimes found with *P. tonganus*.

The reproductive cycle is not known for certain, but *P. s. samoensis* females have been observed carrying young in July and August, and it is probable that the majority of births occur between June and August. Although young may fly at three months, they are not usually weaned until they are four to six months old and may remain dependent on their mothers for up to a year.

Habitat and Current Distribution

P. s. nawaiensis occurs in Fiji, where it was noted as "abundant" on Viti Levu and Vanua Levu in 1978. A survey in the vicinity of Suva and Viti Levu in 1989 located some individuals, but current status, distribution, and population trends elsewhere on Fiji are unknown.

P. s. samoensis occurs in the primary forests of American and Western Samoa. Subsequent to drastic declines in the 1980s, it was estimated that no more than 500 animals were left on Tutuila, the largest island of American Samoa. A 70 percent decline was reported on the large island of 'Upolu between 1896 and 1989. A 1989 survey found 176 animals at 49 survey sites.

History and Conservation Measures

In addition to predation, *P. s. nawaiensis* is vulnerable to typhoons. Samoa experienced at least 39 typhoons between 1831 and 1926, and there have been three severe storms in the past 24 years—1966, 1987, and 1990. Recommended conservation actions for this species include: a survey to determine its distribution and to assess its status, particularly in protected areas; and in-depth studies of its ecology to ensure that land use and wildlife management policies are not detrimental to existing populations.

P. s. samoensis is also vulnerable to typhoons, and anecdotal data after an intense typhoon in February 1990 reported significant mortality, particularly from increased post-storm hunting. However, the primary cause of population declines in Samoa in recent years has been the commercial exportation of fruit bats as a luxury food item to Guam. Between 1982 and 1986, 2,700-8,350 fruit bats were killed and exported. Harvesting for local consumption also poses a threat. This species is considered particularly vulnerable to hunting because it is relatively slow-flying, with poor maneuvering ability, is primarily diurnal, and is not easily alarmed when approached at a roost.

Loss of habitat, due to logging and agricultural conversion, poses the second most significant threat to populations in Samoa. *P. s. samoensis* is currently protected in O le Pupu-Pu'e National Park on the island of 'Upolu. Recommended conservation actions include: a re-assessment of its population status; measures to limit hunting; enforcement of existing laws in American and Western Samoa; in-depth ecology studies; and development and expansion of public awareness programs.

Insular flying-fox

Pteropus tonganus

Phylum	Chordata
Class	Mammalia
Order	Chiroptera
Family	Pteropodidae
Status	Indeterminate, IUCN (*P. tonganus tonganus*)
	Appendix I, CITES
Range	American Samoa; Cook Islands; Fiji; Karkar Island; New Caledonia; Niue; Schouten Islands; Solomon Islands; Tonga; Vanuatu; Wallis and Futuna; Western Samoa

Description and Biology

Also called the Tonga flying-fox, *P. tonganus* is one of the most widely distributed of all *Pteropus* species. Three subspecies are recognized, *P. t. basiliscus*, *P. t. geddiei*, and *P. t. tonganus*; there is a decrease in size across the range of *P. t. geddiei* and *P. t. tonganus* with the Cook Islands population being the smallest. The insular flying-fox is similar in appearance to *P. vanikorensis* but is somewhat larger and has relatively longer wings. The back, rump, breast, belly, and flanks of this bat are blackish or seal-brown with a light sprinkling of white hairs; the fur is darker and more glossy on the back and rump. The mantle is buff, sometimes very pale, sometimes washed with pale yellow or pale yellow-orange. The mantle hair of adult males is shorter, more rigid and oily, while adult females have longer, softer, more spreading mantle hair. In males, the mantle hair seems to be a uniform color from tip to base; in females, mantle hairs have long, concealed, seal-brown bases. The head may be similar in color to the mantle or may be seal-brown; dark headed specimens may have pale russet or buffy russet "spectacles" around the eyes. *P. tonganus* is active from dusk to dawn; only individuals who have been accidently disturbed or who are especially hungry come out earlier in the day. These bats feed on the nectar of the flowers of various indigenous and introduced trees; they probably often act as pollinators, carrying pollen from one flower to another on their fur.

Female flying-foxes generally give birth to one young at a time, and probably do not breed until they are two years old. Young are born after a six-month gestation, during March and April north of latitude 4°, and around September south of latitude 3°. In Niue or Samoa, breeding is apparently not synchronized and young have been reported at different times throughout the year. Although young may fly at three months of age, they usually are not weaned until they are four to six months old and may remain dependent on their mothers for a year.

Habitat and Current Distribution

P. tonganus usually occurs on small, species-poor islands, but is absent from the largest, species-rich islands. *P. t. basiliscus* occurs on Karkar Island off the northeast coast of New Guinea; apparently it also occurs on Koil Island in the Schouten Islands, about 124 mi (200 km) to the west. Its status and population size are not known.

P. t. geddiei occurs on the Loyalty Islands in New Caledonia, where its status is uncertain. How-

Insular flying-fox.

ever, recent reports of the importation of *P. tonganus* from Vanuatu to New Caledonia for food raise serious questions about the size of bat populations in New Caledonia. *P. t. geddiei* also occurs on the islands of Malaita, Rennell, and Santa Cruz in the Solomon Islands, where it is described as not common, but widespread; and in Vanuatu, where it is reportedly the most common bat.

P. t. tonganus is known from American Samoa, where the population is estimated at 10,000-13,000 animals on Tutuila, the largest island; from the Cook Islands, where the population may number fewer than 1,000 on Mangaia, and is considerably lower on Rarotonga; from Fiji, where it is widespread throughout the islands; from Niue, where it is apparently restricted to the Tapu Forest Sanctuary and surrounding Huvalu Forest; from Tonga, where the Kolovai colony has been designated a fruit bat reserve and is protected by the royal family; from Wallis and Futuna, where current status is unknown; and from Western Samoa, where there is a small colony on the Falealupo Peninsula, a colony near the Tafua Peninsula, and reports of a colony of about 100 near Fagafau on Savai'i.

P. tonganus appears to be strongly colonial throughout most of its range, with colonies most often found in large canopy trees, in mangrove or other forests, often near the edge of cliffs. Subspecies are sometimes found roosting singly or in pairs or small groups, but such roosting behavior may be attributable to depleted population levels. On Rarotonga, in the Cook Islands, this species roosts in hilly, deeply forested areas, and in open trees.

History and Conservation Measures

A number of factors threaten this species throughout its range. Flying-foxes are a popular food item, and these subspecies may be threatened by commercial and non-commercial harvesting. Loss of native forest habitat poses a significant threat to flying-fox populations on many Pacific and Indian Ocean islands. Severe tropical storms are also a recurrent threat, with food in short supply for both bats and people after typhoons; the animals are often forced to forage for fallen fruit on the ground, and roost without the concealment of canopy shelter, thus making them vulnerable to hunting. Natural predation, primarily by the peregrine falcon, may also present a threat in parts of the range.

Recommended conservation actions include: surveys to determine current status; studies of the effect of local hunting on flying-fox populations; enforcement of CITES regulations; studies of ecology, with a particular focus on identifying foraging and roosting requirements; consideration of the establishment of reserves; and public awareness programs.

Pemba flying-fox

Pteropus voeltzkowi

Phylum	Chordata
Class	Mammalia
Order	Chiroptera
Family	Pteropodidae
Status	Endangered, IUCN
	Appendix II, CITES
Range	Pemba Island (Tanzania)

Description and Biology

The Pemba flying-fox is closely related to *P. comorensis* but has shorter ears and darker overall color. The back and rump are black and tinged with seal-brown hair; the breast and belly are reddish brown, flanks seal-brown, and upperside of the head dark brown mixed with silver-buff hairs. The chin and throat are brown-black. The forearm measures 5.9-6.3 in (15.1-16.1 cm).

Flying-foxes are long-lived animals with low reproductive rates. Females generally give birth to one young at a time after a four- to six-month gestation period. For this species, mating probably takes place between January and April and births between June and August. Although young may fly at three months, they are not usually weaned until they are four to six months old and may remain dependent on their mothers for a year.

Habitat and Current Distribution

This species occurs on Pemba Island in Tanzania. In 1989 a search located only one group of three bats on the central-west coast at Kisiwani, with an additional four sightings of a single bat in flight at dusk. At Mgogoni, a small colony of about 50 bats was reported in a section of natural forest on one of the steep, inaccessible hills. In 1989, 150-200 roosting bats were reported in northwest Ngezi Forest.

The Pemba flying-fox is very social and until recently occurred in large colonies. It does not appear near human settlements unless large trees are fruiting. It is primarily a forest species and is now restricted to small forest remnants in the northwest corner of the island.

History and Conservation Measures

Evidence suggests that this species may have undergone a serious decline in numbers in recent years, due in part to hunting. In the past, traditional hunting methods, such as the use of long sticks, were employed, but today firearms have become the preferred method. Deforestation has also played an important role in the decline of this species. The western half of Pemba was formerly covered with tropical rain forest, but much of the original forest was cleared in the 1700s; now, even the remnant forest patches are threatened.

Recommended conservation actions include: surveys to locate remaining colonies; research to obtain ecological data as a basis for better conservation planning, with special attention to the relationship between fruit bats as pollinators and seed dispersers and the vegetation as a vital food source; reduction of pressure on the forest remnants and a ban on hunting; educational programs on fruit bats; and a captive breeding program as a support for field conservation efforts.

Bumblebee bat

Craseonycteris thonglongyai

Phylum	Chordata
Class	Mammalia
Order	Chiroptera
Family	Craseonycteridae
Status	Rare, IUCN Endangered, USFWS
Range	Thailand

Description and Biology

About the size of a large bumblebee, this bat—also known as Kitti's hog-nosed bat—is considered among the smallest mammals in the world. It weighs between 0.05-0.10 oz (1.5-3 g), while its head and body length averages 1.1-1.3 in (29-33 mm). The bumblebee bat's wings span 6-6.7 in (15-17 cm) and have long tips adapted for hovering. Two phases of body coloring—reddish brown upperparts or gray upperparts—have been identified, while the wings are darker and underparts lighter. Its ears are relatively large, and its nose resembles that of a pig. The eyes are small and almost completely hidden by fur. The bumblebee bat also possesses a large web of skin between its hind legs, presumably to aid it in flight and in catching insects. However, unlike other bats with similar webs of skin, this species does not possess a visible tail or elongated ankle bones to aid in its control. Nocturnal, the bumblebee bat is believed to feed primarily on small insects gleaned from foliage or caught in flight.

The bumblebee bat has been observed roosting in colonies of 10 to 15 bats. No information about its reproductive biology is currently available.

Habitat and Current Distribution

This bat occurs in western Thailand, where it inhabits small limestone caves located near bamboo thickets and teak plantations and possessing domed or conical ceilings and normal sections. Population is estimated at approximately 200 individuals.

History and Conservation Measures

By the time of the bumblebee bat's discovery in 1974, the once heavily forested area of its occurrence had long since been cleared for agriculture. This habitat alteration probably contributed to the population's decline, though little information exists about specific threats to the species. Studies concerning the bat's food consumption and reproductive habits should be conducted before any specific conservation measures are formulated, as should surveys of existing habitat to determine the species' exact range and population.

Bumblebee bat.

Seychelles sheath-tailed bat

Coleura seychellensis

Phylum	Chordata
Class	Mammalia
Order	Chiroptera
Family	Emballonuridae
Status	Endangered, IUCN
Range	Seychelles

Description and Biology

The Seychelles sheath-tailed bat ranges in color from reddish brown to dark brown and may be slightly lighter underneath. Head and body length averages 2.2-2.6 in (5.5-6.5 cm), weight is 0.36-0.39 oz (10.2-11.1 g), forearm length is 1.8-2.2 in (4.5-5.6 cm), and tail length is 0.47-0.78 in (12-20 mm); females are larger than males. A high and fast flier, this bat forages at night primarily for insects.

This species roosts in colonies but may be divided into harem groups of one male and a number of females. Pregnant females roost away from the rest of the colony; they usually give birth in November, during the rainy season, but they also give birth in April.

Habitat and Current Distribution

There is now only one cave that is known to harbor a colony of the sheath-tailed bat, on the island of Praslin in the Seychelles Islands. They are believed to occur on the islands of Silhouette and, possibly, Mahé, also in the Seychelles. There are no estimates of population size.

Roosting only in caves, this bat is most often found in light areas near the entrance.

History and Conservation Measures

There are reports that this bat was once much more abundant than it is today. A number of factors may have contributed to its decline, with destruction or disruption of habitat the most likely factor. An additional problem is thought to be predation by the introduced barn owl. The remaining bat population has continued to decline, and it is hoped that forest regrowth will allow the sheath-tailed bat population to increase once again.

Ghost bat

Macroderma gigas

Phylum	Chordata
Class	Mammalia
Order	Chiroptera
Family	Megadermatidae
Status	Vulnerable, IUCN
Range	Australia

Description and Biology

This bat has two common names, one of which—ghost bat—comes from its light coloring and the other—false vampire bat—from a mistaken idea that it feeds on blood, as does a true vampire bat. Ghost bats have large canines and strong jaw muscles which are used to catch and devour their prey, including birds, other bats, frogs, lizards, small snakes, and large insects.

A large bat, the ghost bat has an average head and body length of 3.5-5.5 in (9-14 cm), forearm length of 3.7-4.5 in (9.6-11.4 cm), weight of 3-5.5 oz (100-165 g), and wingspan of 24 in (61 cm). Overall body color is usually white or whitish, but hairs on the back are tipped with gray or gray-brown. Eyes and ears are large and there is no external tail. This bat has a small noseleaf and large lips. The ghost bat is nocturnal and roosts during the day in caves or old mines. Food is frequently brought back to the day roost and consumed.

Mating occurs in April and a single young is born between mid-October and late November. The young are initially carried by their mothers but later are left in the nursery caves at night. After young are weaned, colonies tend to disperse, particularly in winter months (May-August).

Habitat and Current Distribution

The ghost bat occurs in northern Australia in Queensland, Northern Territory, and Western Australia, where populations are centered around approximately 10 maternity sites. It is estimated that the total population of ghost bats is around 5,000.

The bat is found in a variety of habitats from arid, stony hills in Western Australia to tropical woodlands and monsoon and vine scrub. Roost sites for maternity colonies are usually in large complex caves or abandoned mines. Other times of the year this bat will roost in caves, rocky overhangs, mines, and occasionally in old buildings.

History and Conservation Measures

Fossil history shows that the genus *Macroderma* has been present in Australia for 25 million years and a number of species have appeared and disappeared. Recent and subfossil deposits have revealed that *M. gigas* was distributed over most of the Australian mainland until recently. In the last 200 years the distribution has retreated northward (from 30°S to approximately 24°S) and the species no longer appears to exist in central Australia. The cause for the contraction in range is not known but may be related

Ghost bat.

to long-term climatic changes. The primary threat today is human disturbance to roosting and maternity sites. The ghost bat is protected by law but due to its mobile nature, it is difficult to protect roost sites. A number of maternity sites are within national parks but several are not, including the largest colony (1,500) at Pine Creek in the Northern Territory. The Pine Creek colony occupies old gold mines, which, like a number of other ghost bat roosts, are now being re-worked. Limestone quarrying has caused loss of roost sites in the past, but due to legislation it is not now regarded as a threat.

Research projects on the genetics, movements, and general ecology of ghost bats are currently underway in Western Australia, Northern Territory, and Queensland. There is also a captive breeding program for the bat at Taronga and Perth Zoos. There is still a need to gather information on critical habitat and the protection and management of maternity roosts.

Big long-nosed bat

Leptonycteris nivalis

Little long-nosed bat

Leptonycteris curasoae (sanborni)

Phylum	Chordata
Class	Mammalia
Order	Chiroptera
Family	Phyllostomidae
Status	Vulnerable, IUCN (*L. nivalis*)
	Insufficiently Known, IUCN (*L. curasoae*)
	Endangered, USFWS
Range	Texas (U.S.A.); Guatemala; Mexico (*L. nivalis*)
	Arizona, New Mexico (U.S.A.); El Salvador; Mexico (*L. curasoae*)

Description and Biology

Named for an elongated muzzle, these bats also have an extremely long tongue that can measure up to 3 in (76 mm) long. Body coloration is grayish brown to reddish brown with cinnamon brown underparts; the coat of *L. curasoae* is shorter and denser. Head and body length averages 2.7-3.7 in (70-95 mm) and weight is 0.6-1.1 oz (18-30 g). The long-nosed bat is a good flier, with excellent maneuverability and speed. The muzzle and tongue are specially adapted for feeding on a diet of nectar and pollen, especially from the flowers of cactus plants and paniculate agaves (century plants); fruits and insects are also included in the diet.

Groups of tens of thousands to over 100,000 *L. curasoae* are known and maternity colonies of 10,000 to over 100,000 female bats have been observed. Litter size is one young; *L. nivalis* gives birth between April and June. Birth times in *L. curasoae* vary geographically with northern migrants giving birth in May; bats in southern Mexico give birth in December. It is likely that females give birth only once a year. Length of gestation period is about four months.

Habitat and Current Distribution

The only currently known roosting site for *L. nivalis* in the United States is a cave in Big Bend National Park in Texas, where 1,000 individuals were reported in 1983. Surveys conducted in the 1980s of historic roosting sites in Mexico yielded only small surviving groups in some of the sites, with the largest group comprised of only 30-50 individuals. Three maternity roosts of *L. curasoae* containing a few thousand to over 15,000 bats are known in southwestern Arizona; a very large maternity colony occurs in Pinacate National Park, and in Sonora, Mexico, just south of the U.S.-Mexican border. Post-weaning roosts of up to 20,000 bats occur in southern and southeastern Arizona; bats migrate south from these roosts in September. Additional large roosts of this species occur in the Mexican states of Sonora, Jalisco, Guerrero, Chiapas, and Baja California Sur.

Large-nosed fruit bats roost during the day in

Big long-nosed bat.

found in arid or desert habitat in the United States and Mexico, where they also occur in thorn scrub and tropical dry forests as well as in montane pine forests.

History and Conservation Measures

L. nivalis once occurred from southwestern Texas and southwestern New Mexico through Mexico to Guatemala, and *L. curasoae* from central Arizona and southwestern New Mexico through Mexico to El Salvador. Populations and distributions of both species have probably declined in recent decades but are poorly documented. Causes of decline are unknown but are unlikely to have involved human harvesting of agave plants for food, fiber, and alcohol production. The bats are nutritionally dependent on the nectar and pollen of cacti (and cactus fruits) and paniculate agaves, but this dependency is not necessarily mutual throughout the ranges of these plants. Occasional roost disturbances and conversion of former wildlands into agriculture and cattle grazing lands have undoubtedly had a negative impact on these bats.

Colossal Cave, which is an historic roosting site for *L. curasoae*, has been renovated in an effort to reattract long-nosed bats. Other critical roosting sites are now known and many of these are under protection in the United States and Mexico.

caves, abandoned mines or tunnels, hollow trees, and buildings, emerging in the evening to feed. They are

Sucker-footed bat

Myzopoda aurita

Phylum	Chordata
Class	Mammalia
Order	Chiroptera
Family	Myzopodidae
Status	Vulnerable, IUCN
Range	Madagascar

Description and Biology

The sucker-footed bat is so named because of the suction discs on its feet and thumbs that allow it to cling to smooth surfaces, including the stems and leaves of trees. It also has a mushroom-shaped structure at the base of the large ears and an upper lip that extends beyond the lower lip. Head and body length averages 2.3 in (5.8 cm), tail length is 1.9 in (4.8 cm), and general body coloration is reddish brown. Presumed to be a solitary species, this bat finds prey by using echolocation (sending out sound waves that are reflected back as echoes). Diet is not known but is thought to include insects.

Habitat and Current Distribution

This species is endemic to Madagascar, where the majority of the sightings have been on the eastern side of the island. There are no estimates of population size.

Primary habitat appears to be rain forest. It is suspected that the traveler's tree (*Ravenala madagascariensis*), a relative of the banana, is a primary roosting site for this bat.

History and Conservation Measures

Although fossil evidence of its presence has been found in Africa, the sucker-footed bat is now found only in Madagascar. It is the only member of its family. For some time, only 15 specimens were known, most of which had been collected before 1900; in the 1970s and 1980s additional specimens were collected, but information about the biology, behavior, and ecology of this bat is still scarce. Due to this lack of knowledge, no specific conservation measures have been formulated for this rare species.

Gray bat

Myotis grisescens

Phylum	Chordata
Class	Mammalia
Order	Chiroptera
Family	Vespertilionidae
Status	Endangered, IUCN
	Endangered, USFWS
Range	central and southeastern U.S.A.

Description and Biology

Distinguished from other species in its genus by its wing membrane, which attaches to the ankle instead of the side of the foot, the gray bat is reddish brown in color, with a forearm length of 1.6 in (41 mm) and average weight of 0.35 oz (10 g). This species feeds at night on insects, especially mayflies and mosquitoes; predators of the bat include owls. The gray bat roosts in caves throughout the year, using a winter cave for hibernation and a summer cave as a maternity roost.

Immediately after mating in the fall, adult females begin hibernating, followed by adult males and juveniles several weeks later. Bats remain in hibernation from November until adult females emerge in late March or early April; other bats emerge between mid-April and mid-May. Females store sperm overwinter and fertilize their eggs when they emerge from hibernation, giving birth to a single young in late May or early June.

Habitat and Current Distribution

The gray bat inhabits parts of the southeastern United States in which limestone caverns are found. It is found in Alabama, Missouri, Kentucky, and Tennessee, as well as some adjoining areas in Indiana, Illinois, Kansas, Oklahoma, Arkansas, Mississippi, Georgia, Virgina, and possibly North Carolina. Its distribution throughout its range is patchy, increasingly so in recent years.

A 1980 estimate placed the population of gray bats at less than 1.6 million; over half the population overwinters in a single cave, and 95 percent of the total population overwinters in only nine caves. More reliable information is required on the population status.

The habitat requirements of the gray bat are very specific; summer maternity caves must be warm (57-77°F [14-25°C]), while hibernating caves must be very cool (43-52°F [6-11°C]). All wintering caves have large spaces below the lowest entrance in which cool air is trapped, while maternity caves have restricted chambers or domed ceilings that trap warm air. Male and yearling bats do not seem to be limited to these hotter caves, and during the spring and fall, all bats use a wider range of caves.

History and Conservation Measures

Many millions of gray bats once occupied the southeastern United States, making it one of the most common mammals in the region. Its history of decline dates from the Civil War, when bat guano was used in the production of saltpeter for gunpowder manufacturing. Human disturbance of roosting caves

Gray bat in flight.

continues to be the major cause of decline. The aggregation of huge populations of bats in a few caves makes them extremely vulnerable, especially during maternity and hibernation. In winter, arousal of a hibernating bat can deplete its fat reserves, causing starvation.

An increase in disturbance has accompanied the rising popularity of caving (spelunking) since the 1950s. A number of important colonies were destroyed by the opening of caves to tourism, as well as by flooding caused by the construction of dams. Between the early 1960s and the early 1980s, the gray bat population declined approximately 80 percent, a drop which may have been exacerbated by mortality from water pollution and pesticides which are absorbed from their insect prey.

Recently, protection of hibernation and maternity caves seems to have stabilized the gray bat population and may in fact be reversing its decline. Measures needed to promote full recovery of the species include: the purchase of caves by government agencies or private organizations; the building of structures to prevent human intrusion into caves without blocking air flow that regulates cave temperature; further research into the possible effect of water pollutants and pesticides on bats; education programs to inform the public about the conservation needs of this species; and preservation of the bat's foraging habitat, much of which has already been altered by human activity.

Indiana bat

Myotis sodalis

Phylum	Chordata
Class	Mammalia
Order	Chiroptera
Family	Vespertilionidae
Status	Vulnerable, IUCN
	Endangered, USFWS
Range	eastern and midwestern U.S.A.

Description and Biology

In overall appearance, the Indiana bat resembles other bats of the genus *Myotis*. About 2 in (50 mm) long not including the tail and weighing between 0.15-0.33 ounces (4.5-9.5 g), this bat can be distinguished from other members of its genus by its dull brown coat, its short ears (which contain a blunt, short tragus), and the distinctive "keel" shape of its calcar, a process supporting the membrane between the leg and tail. The bat's dorsal fur ranges from light to dark brown while its ventral fur is buff or pale gray. The dorsal hairs have distinctive tricolored banding—black at the base, gray in the middle, and brown at the tip.

During the winter months from November to April, Indiana bats hibernate in large colonies in caves or mine shafts at a small number of locations; one study indicated that the 10 largest hibernating sites contained 91 percent of the entire bat population. The sites selected have relatively low temperatures (optimally 39-46.4°F [4-8°C]); typically, only caves that trap cold winter air are suitable.

When they emerge from hibernation in spring, Indiana bats migrate up to 300 mi (480 km) to summer feeding and breeding grounds. Females disperse, forming small maternity colonies in hollow trees, buildings or beneath bridges to raise their young. The movements and range of male bats during the summer is poorly understood, though it is suspected that males roost in caves, including hibernation caves.

Indiana bats.

In the late summer, courtship and mating take place, and in September or October bats begin to return to hibernating sites where mating may continue sporadically until re-emergence from the caves in spring. At this time, female bats ovulate, fertilizing their eggs using sperm stored from mating. They give birth to a single young around the end of June.

The Indiana bat feeds on a variety of flying insects, including moths, beetles, wasps, and flies.

Habitat and Current Distribution

In summer, the Indiana bat frequents floodplains and forested, slow-moving streams through much of the eastern United States, from the Florida panhandle in the south and New Hampshire in the northeast, to Iowa and eastern Oklahoma in the west. Its winter range is restricted primarily to caves in Tennessee, Kentucky, West Virginia, Alabama, Indiana, and Missouri. A population of just over 500,000 bats was estimated to occur in the early 1980s, but it is now believed to have decreased by over half, to about 250,000.

History and Conservation Measures

The population of the Indiana bat continues to decline, chiefly because of human disturbance at hibernation caves. Since it congregates in such large numbers, it is especially vulnerable. For example, a colony of 300,000 bats drowned when a cave flooded in 1937; 60,000 bats were lost when another cave was disturbed by humans; and 80,000 bats died in three caves where intentionally blocked entrances caused excessive increases in temperature. Human disturbance is dangerous to hibernating bats because they store just enough fat to survive the winter months; arousal during hibernation depletes as much as 30 days of fat supply, potentially resulting in starvation before spring.

A number of important caves and mines have already been accorded status as "critical habitat" under federal law and most of the bat's important hibernating sites are on state or federal government property; public access to many of these caves is strictly regulated.

Implementation of several key programs can help ensure the recovery of the Indiana bat population. These include: identifying and preserving summer maternity roosts in riparian habitats; closing hibernating caves to human access, using structures that will not restrict air flow or bat movements; reclaiming caves by removing faulty structures that restrict air circulation; and acquiring and protecting caves situated on private land.

Townsend's big-eared bat

Plecotus townsendii

Phylum	Chordata
Class	Mammalia
Order	Chiroptera
Family	Vespertilionidae
Status	Indeterminate, IUCN
	Endangered, USFWS (*P. t. ingens; P. t. virginianus*)
Range	Canada; Mexico; U.S.A.

Description and Biology

Townsend's big-eared bat is named for its large ears that can measure from 1-1.6 in (25-40 mm). In contrast, head and body length averages 1.8-2.7 in (45-70 mm), tail is 1.4-2.1 in (35-55 mm), forearm is 1.4-2 in (35-52 mm), and weight is 0.18-0.46 oz (5-13 g). Of the five subspecies of Townsend's big-eared bat, two are endangered: the Ozark big-eared bat (*P. t. ingens*), which is gray with white underparts and the Virginia big-eared bat (*P. t. virginianus*), which is predominately gray. The big-eared bat feeds primarily on moths, using echolation to locate its prey.

Townsend's big-eared bat forms seasonal roosting aggregations. Mixed sex aggregations are created in November or December when males and females come together to mate and hibernate. These aggregations are sometimes large, numbering in the thousands, particularly in the eastern United States. In colder portions of their range the animals rely on stored fat reserves to survive the winter, making disturbance of hibernation sites a particularly significant threat. Mating takes place during the fall and winter; however, females store the sperm until spring when

Townsend's big-eared bat.

they ovulate and become pregnant. At this time adult females also form nursery colonies, each giving birth to a single young in late spring or early summer after a gestation period of 56-100 days. Mothers and young then stay together until the nursing aggregations disband in the fall.

Habitat and Current Distribution

Townsend's big-eared bat occurs in southwestern Canada, the western United States, and Mexico, where it inhabits forest or scrub and desert areas. The Ozark big-eared bat is known from only a few caves in the states of Arkansas, Oklahoma, and Missouri; the Virginia big-eared bat occurs in the Appalachian region, where it is found in eastern Kentucky, southwestern Virginia, and eastern West Virginia. The Ozark big-eared bat population is estimated at less than 700; and the Virginia population is believed to number approximately 11,000.

Big-eared bats inhabit caves and abandoned mines throughout the year, but in some areas they also take shelter in buildings. Hibernating roosts and maternity roosts are fairly close to each other and the same sites are used year after year. Favored habitat includes limestone karst and lava flats.

History and Conservation Measures

The primary cause of the population decline in Townsend's big-eared bat is human disturbance of hibernation and nursery roosts. Intolerant of such disruption, the bat has been known to vacate roosts if disturbed during hibernation. It is also subject to starvation if disturbed during this time because it may be forced to use up fat reserves before they can be replenished in spring. To further complicate matters, suitable roosting habitat is limited.

Some of the known caves for this species have been designated as critical habitat by the U.S. Government. As a result federal agencies must ensure that actions authorized, funded, or carried out by them do not result in the destruction or adverse modification of this habitat. The National Speleological Society has also attempted to impose a moratorium on visits to designated caves housing bat colonies, but this has not deterred vandals from entering protected caves. Although creating effective protective gates has been difficult, some designs have proven successful, thwarting vandals while not disturbing resident populations of the species. Studies have been initiated as well to study foraging areas and foraging behavior. However, protecting colonies from human disturbance remains the most important factor in any conservation program aimed at Townsend's big-eared bat.

New Zealand lesser short-tailed bat

Mystacina tuberculata

New Zealand greater short-tailed bat

Mystacina robusta

Phylum	Chordata
Class	Mammalia
Order	Chiroptera
Family	Mystacinidae
Status	Vulnerable, IUCN (*M. tuberculata*)
	Extinct, IUCN (*M. robusta*)
Range	New Zealand

Description and Biology

The New Zealand short-tailed bats belong to the Mystacinidae family, an ancient endemic family with no close affinities with other bat families. The external morphology of both species of *Mystacina* is similar. They have dense velvety brown fur, which is generally frosted in appearance. The elongate head tapers conspicuously forward to prominent nostrils. The ears are simple and separate with long and narrow tragus (the flap in the front of the ear). When not in flight the wings are furled in a slot along the posterior of the forearm and in against the body; the tail membrane is rolled forward beneath the tail. The legs and feet are unusually robust. Together these characteristics are probably adaptations for terrestrial activity. *M. tuberculata* is agile on the ground and on trees and has been observed burrowing through leaf litter while foraging on the ground.

M. tuberculata is the smaller species of the two

bats. Total body length averages 2.4-2.7 in (6-6.8 cm); tail is 0.4-0.47 in (1-1.2 cm); forearm is 1.6-1.8 in (4-4.5 cm); and weight is 0.4-0.6 oz (11-17 g). *M. robusta*'s total body length can reach 3.5 in (9 cm); tail is 0.6 in (1.5 cm); forearm is 1.7-1.9 in (4.5-4.8 cm); and weight is 0.9-1.2 oz (25-35 g).

Little is known about the diet of *M. robusta*. It is presumed to be similar to that of *M. tuberculata*, which is extremely varied. Insects and other arthropods are captured both by gleaning and aerial hawking. Nectar, pollen, and fruit are also important components of these bats' diet. Short-tailed bats pollinate several forest plant species, including the endangered and endemic New Zealand parasitic woodrose *Dactylanthus taylorii*. Both species of *Mystacina* are also reported to be carnivorous, preying on nestlings and scavenging bird carcasses.

M. tuberculata is probably a lek-breeding species: clusters of males sing from individual roosts in trees for several hours each night during summer and early autumn. Young are born in nursery roosts during December and January. Little is known about the breeding behavior of *M. robusta*. *M. tuberculata* usually roosts in hollow trees but has been observed roosting in caves on offshore islands. Colonial roosts with more than 500 bats are common, though individuals frequently roost alone. Most roosts are traditional, but occupancy is erratic. *M. robusta* has only been recorded roosting in caves.

Winter hibernation does not occur, although extended periods of torpor occur during inclement weather.

Habitat and Current Distribution

The lesser short-tailed bat is considered a species of the forest interior and is only found in, or close to, areas of mature indigenous forest. The distribution and status of *M. tuberculata* on the main islands is uncertain, but the species is still present in some forests in Northland and central North Island. There are no recent reports from the South Island or Stewart Island. Populations in excess of 1,000 individuals remain on two offshore islands: Little Barrier Island (north of the North Island) and Codfish Island (northwest of Stewart Island). There are no estimates of the size or viability of other populations.

M. robusta is considered extinct.

History and Conservation Measures

Both species of short-tailed bats were once found throughout New Zealand. Their declines are probably a consequence of the combined impact of forests clearance, forest degradation by introduced mammalian browsers, and predation by introduced predators. *M. robusta* has only been recorded on two small rat-free islands near Stewart Island. It is thought to have gone extinct in about 1965 following the arrival of *Rattus rattus*. There has been a major decline in the distribution and numbers of *M. tuberculata* since the last century, but there is scant information on present trends. Recent observations indicate that one Northland population has declined markedly over the past 20 years. The populations on Little Barrier Island and Codfish Island seem stable and, in the absence of catastrophic events, are probably viable in the long term. Plans to eradicate *Rattus exulans* from the two islands within the next five years may benefit these populations.

Research projects are currently underway on a variety of aspects of the biology and conservation of *M. tuberculata*. A small number is held in captivity for research and to develop husbandry methods. Primary recommendations of a draft recovery plan for New Zealand bats include: surveys for *M. robusta* on offshore islands in the Stewart Island region; research on the biology and conservation of *M. tuberculata*; surveys of mainland forests to assess the distribution of *M. tuberculata*; implementation of programs to monitor trends in existing populations; and establishment of a population of the subspecies *M. t. rhycobia* on a predator-free island.

Hairy-eared dwarf lemur

Allocebus trichotis

Phylum	Chordata
Class	Mammalia
Order	Primates
Family	Cheirogaleidae
Status	Endangered, IUCN
	Endangered, USFWS
	Appendix I, CITES
Range	Madagascar

Description and Biology

The hairy-eared dwarf lemur gets its common name not from its small ears which are concealed in fur, but from the long, wavy hairs that form tufts in front of the ear lobe. General coloration is rosy brownish gray, with gray underparts and narrow dark rings around the eyes. Length of head and body is 5-5.7 in (12.5-14.5 cm), weight is 2.5-3 oz (75-80 g), and the reddish brown tail is 6.5-7.7 in (16.5-19.5 cm). There is no information on the diet of the hairy-eared dwarf lemur in the wild; it has been suggested that it may feed on nectar, as it has a very long tongue and will eat honey in captivity. Species members in captivity have also eaten locusts and fruit.

Little is known about the reproductive biology or social habits of the hairy-eared dwarf lemur. Most of the available information is derived from the observations of local people. They report finding two or three, sometimes six, individuals sleeping in tree holes. A nocturnal species, the hairy-eared dwarf lemur is active at dusk and remains so until the first light of dawn. Births may take place in January or February. It is suspected that some type of hibernation occurs between May and September.

Habitat and Current Distribution

Distribution of this species is probably restricted and patchy; it has been found in only one area of northeastern Madagascar. It appears to occur only in lowland rain forest; it has been reported in degraded primary lowland forest and in virgin primary forest. Population figures are unknown.

History and Conservation Measures

The hairy-eared dwarf lemur is one of the least known of all the lemur species. It was known only from five museum specimens until it was rediscovered in 1989 in lowland forest in northeast Madagascar. It has been suggested that the species once occurred quite widely in the eastern humid forests, but this has been difficult to prove due to the infrequency of either specimens or sightings. In all likelihood, this rarest member of the surviving lemurs probably never existed at high densities.

The main threat to this species is destruction of the rain forest for fuel, timber, and farming. Recent investigations have estimated that 280,000 acres (111,000 ha) of eastern rain forest were cleared each year between 1950 and 1985. Most of the forest cleared was lowland forest, and, if this is indeed the species' only habitat, continued deforestation will probably lead to its extinction.

No specific measures have been suggested for conserving this species, and none can be proposed until more is known about the lemur's ecology and range. However, preservation of the eastern rain forest will likely increase its chances for survival. It has been suggested that the area around Mananara, the only known location of this species, be established as a national park with a surrounding buffer zone. Also extensive surveys should be conducted in order to locate any remaining populations of the hairy-eared dwarf lemur.

Crowned lemur

Eulemur (Lemur) coronatus

Phylum	Chordata
Class	Mammalia
Order	Primates
Family	Lemuridae
Status	Endangered, IUCN
	Endangered, USFWS
	Appendix I, CITES
Range	Madagascar

Description and Biology

The crowned lemur has long, soft fur and a ruff, or crown, between its ears. The male is brownish gray with lighter limbs and underparts, a white face, and a black crown; the female is gray with a light brown crown. Average head and body length is 12-17 in (30-43 cm), tail length is 16-25 in (40-63 cm), and weight is 4-6 lb (2-3 kg). It can move easily through the trees or on the ground, usually on all four limbs. Fruit is the mainstay of the crowned lemur's diet, supplemented by leaves, especially in the wet season.

A typical group is usually comprised of five individuals: two adult pairs and a sub-adult or juvenile. Information about reproductive biology is sketchy. One or two young are most commonly born in September or October, at the beginning of the rainy season; births have also been recorded in mid-January and mid-May. In captivity, the gestation period is 125 days. Infants are initially carried on the mother's front, but as they get stronger, they transfer to her back.

Habitat and Current Distribution

This species is found in the dry forests of north and northeastern Madagascar. The western extent of its range is the Ankarana Massif, between Ambiloband Anivorano Nord. To the east it ranges as far as the Fanambana River, just south of Vohimarina. Its range includes the slopes of Montagne d'Ambre. Population numbers are unknown, but are thought to be declining.

History and Conservation Measures

In 1935, crowned lemurs were reported to be very common in the dry wooded areas of the northern savanna. They were also reported from the dry forest on the slopes of Mt. d'Ambre, up to about 2,600 ft (800 m), but were absent from the higher, humid forests on the summit. However, the species is now reported to occur in these humid forests and it is suggested that this is a recent extension of their range, possibly due to pressure on their preferred habitat.

The area of suitable habitat remaining for crowned lemurs is probably less than 500 sq mi (1,300 sq km) and it is continuing to shrink. Crowned lemurs occur in several protected areas, including Forêt d'Ambre, Analamera, and Ankarana Special Reserves, and in the Montagne d'Ambre National Park, but these refuges are not well protected. Poaching, bush fires, logging, and grazing are problems in the

Sleeping crowned lemurs.

refuges; management plans have been initiated to improve each of these reserves. Wider surveys are also needed to determine both the remaining areas of suitable habitat for crowned lemurs and their population size so that adequate protective measures can be taken.

Mongoose lemur

Eulemur (Lemur) mongoz

Phylum	Chordata
Class	Mammalia
Order	Primates
Family	Lemuridae
Status	Endangered, IUCN
	Endangered, USFWS
	Appendix I, CITES
Range	Comoro Islands; Madagascar

Description and Biology

The mongoose lemur is one of only two lemur species found on both the Comoro Islands and Madagascar. It has long, soft fur and a ruff around the neck and ears. The underparts of both sexes are white, while the upperparts of the male are gray and those of the female gray-brown. Males have a pale face with bushy, reddish brown cheeks and beard; females have a dark face with bushy, white cheeks and beard. Average head and body length is 12-17 in (30-43 cm), weight is 4.5-6.6 lb (2-3 kg), and tail is 16-25 in (41-63 cm). This lemur is nocturnal in some areas and seasons and diurnal in others; the activity pattern appears to be influenced by climatic factors. Diet is composed primarily of flowers, fruit, and leaves. Natural predators include fossas, civets, and birds of prey.

Family groups are usually made up of a male, a female, and their immature offspring. Home range size varies with climate from a recorded low of three acres (1.15 ha) to about 250 acres (100 ha). Information about reproductive biology is limited. Infants are probably born in mid-October after a gestation period of 128 to 135 days. One young is the norm, but twins are not unusual.

Habitat and Current Distribution

The mongoose lemur is found in the forests of northwest Madagascar and on the islands of Nzwani (Anjouan) and Mwali (Mohéli) in the Comoros archipelago. The lemur populations in the Comoros are probably descendants of individuals brought to the islands by fishermen from Madagascar. Population estimates are currently unavailable.

In western Madagascar, this species is found in dry deciduous forests, while on the Comoros it occurs in humid forest. It can also survive in secondary vegetation.

History and Conservation Measures

There are no estimates of population size, but the species is certainly declining in number. In Madagascar, the mongoose lemur is found in only

Mongoose lemur.

one protected area, Ankarafantsika. However, this reserve is being encroached upon by clearance for pasture, by charcoal merchants, and, to a lesser extent, by the need for additional clearing for crops. The reserve is not sufficiently well managed to provide protection to the wildlife of the region. Laws protecting lemurs on the Comoro Islands have been passed, but are not enforced. In recent years, cyclones have hit the Comoros more frequently and may also pose a threat the archipelago's lemur population.

Programs are needed to educate local communities on the Comoros and in Madagascar about the value of forest conservation and the adverse effect of species loss. In addition, reforestation projects on Madagascar are recommended so that villagers living near Ankarafantsika would be able to harvest fuel and lumber from sources outside the reserve. Despite such initiatives, however, adequately guarded and managed forest reserves may be the only way to ensure the survival of the mongoose lemur. Surveys are required to determine the actual range and population of the mongoose lemur should be conducted prior to the formulation of specific conservation measures.

Golden bamboo lemur

Hapalemur aureus

Phylum	Chordata
Class	Mammalia
Order	Primates
Family	Lemuridae
Status	Endangered, IUCN
	Endangered, USFWS
	Appendix I, CITES
Range	Madagascar

Description and Biology

The golden bamboo lemur is a medium-sized lemur covered with soft, pale orange fur with gray-brown guard hairs; its underparts are yellow and it has a black face with golden-yellow eyebrows, cheek, and throat. The sexes are difficult to distinguish. Head and body length averages 10-18 in (25-46 cm), weight is 2.4-5.5 lb (1.1-2.5 kg), and tail is 10-22 in (25-56 cm). It can run quickly on the ground or move through the trees, jumping from branch to branch. The muzzle is short, the ears small and hairy, and the teeth are well adapted to feed on bamboo. As its common name suggests, the species feeds primarily on giant bamboo, but also on bamboo creeper and bamboo grass. Feeding on the base of bamboo leaves and all new growth, the golden bamboo lemur eats high-protein shoots containing toxins which are lethal to most mammals.

This lemur is most active in the early morning and evening, but is probably also active for part of the night. The average group size is from two to six animals—probably family groups composed of an adult male, at least one adult female, and juveniles of various ages. The home range was originally thought to be around 40-45 acres (16-18 ha), but recent investigations found exclusive territory of a group is approximately 200 acres (80 ha). Little is known about reproductive biology, but births have been recorded in the wild in January and February. The gestation period in captivity is 135-150 days; a single young is the norm, although twins are not uncommon.

Habitat and Current Distribution

The golden bamboo lemur is spottily distributed in a small area of rain forest in southeastern Madagascar. The population is thought to be only 200 to 400 individuals.

History and Conservation Measures

This species was only discovered in 1987, near the village of Ranomafana in southeastern Madagascar. It is also known from other bamboo areas south of the Namorona River and northward to the village of Bevoahaza 5 mi (8 km) from Ranomafana. Prior to the early 1960s, the region south of Ifanadiana was probably an important location for bamboo lemurs. Today nearly all of the bamboo and forest in this area has been destroyed and it is unlikely that any surviving lemurs will last for much longer.

Destruction of the forest by slash-and-burn agriculture is the main threat to this species. The forest at Ranomafana is threatened by such destruction around its borders as well as by timber exploitation within the forest interior. It may contain more than 25,000 acres (10,000 ha) of suitable habitat, but the density of the golden bamboo lemur here, or elsewhere, is unknown. An area of 124,000 acres (50,000 ha) around Ranomafana has been proposed as a national park. Detailed surveys of other forests are needed to ascertain if the species does survive anywhere else and to preserve all such forest areas. If this habitat is not preserved, it is possible that the species may well be extinct by the year 2000, just 13 years after its discovery.

Ruffed lemur

Varecia variegata

Phylum	Chordata
Class	Mammalia
Order	Primates
Family	Lemuridae
Status	Endangered, IUCN
	Endangered, USFWS
	Appendix I, CITES
Range	Madagascar

Description and Biology

Found in the eastern rain forests of Madagascar, the ruffed lemur species consists of two subspecies with markedly different coloration: the black and white ruffed lemur (*V. v. variegata*) and the red ruffed lemur (*V. v. rubra*). The coat pattern of the black and white ruffed lemur also varies significantly; scientists recognize four distinct and consistent patterns, and one or more may, with further study, constitute another subspecies. The red ruffed lemur, conversely, is mostly deep rusty red with black extremities, crown, forehead, belly, and tail. A patch of white fur occurs on the neck. The fur of both subspecies is long and soft, and the common name of the ruffed lemur refers to the long fringe of hairs that hides its ears.

Among the largest species in the family Lemuridae, the ruffed lemur averages 20-24 in (51-61 cm) in head and body length and weighs 7-11 lb (3.2-5 kg). Its tail measures between 22 and 26 in (56-66 cm). When moving on the ground, this species uses all four limbs; when moving through the trees, it frequently leaps from tree to tree. Most activity takes place in the morning and late afternoon or evening. Its diet is primarily fruit, supplemented with small amounts of nectar, seeds, and leaves.

Little is known about the habitat and ecology of the red ruffed lemur since to date no studies of this subspecies have been conducted in the wild. However, recently collected data on the black and white ruffed lemur may provide information applicable to both subspecies. Family groups of black and white ruffed lemurs consist of at least one mated pair, together with a variable number of offspring. In one study, scientists determined the home range of one group to be almost 500 acres (197 ha); however much smaller home ranges are found on islands and in isolated forest blocks, probably due to the limited space available.

The reproductive biology of ruffed lemurs in the wild is poorly understood, and most information comes from observations of captive ruffed lemurs. The gestation period is 90 to 102 days; females may produce up to six offspring at a time, though litters of two or three offspring are more common and one infant is not unusual, especially in a mother's first litter. On the island of Nosy Mangabe, an investigation found that most females gave birth to twins from October to November. After being born, infants remain in nests and do not cling to the fur of their mother, as is the case with other lemur species. If they are transported, it is in the mother's mouth. At three weeks of age, infants begin to follow their mother who often leaves them "parked" in high tree

Ruffed lemur.

branches while she feeds. At seven weeks old they are as mobile and active as adult ruffed lemurs.

Habitat and Current Distribution

Scientists are uncertain as to the distribution of the black and white ruffed lemur. Its range may extend through the eastern rain forests from the Antainambalana River in the north to Manakara or to just north of the Mananara River in the south. It is also found on the small island of Nosy Mangabe, where it was introduced in the 1930s. Population figures are unknown, but it does not appear to occur at high densities apart from Nosy Mangabe, where as many as 100 to 150 individuals are estimated to reside.

The red ruffed lemur is restricted to the forests of the Masoala Peninsula in northeastern Madagascar. Numbers are unknown, but it is considered to be extremely rare, and it may even be extinct in the northern part of its small range.

History and Conservation Measures

Like most other lemur species, habitat destruction is the primary threat to both subspecies, as the forests within their range are rapidly being cleared for farming. Considerable destruction has taken place

within the eastern forests and parts of the Masoala Peninsula are heavily degraded. In addition, ruffed lemurs are hunted for food and commonly kept as pets in Madagascar.

The black and white ruffed lemur is present in the nature reserves of Betampona, Zahamena, and Andringitra. It is also found in the Special Reserve of Nosy Mangabe and appears to be recurring in Analamazaotra Special Reserve. Conservationists have also proposed several new protected areas in which the subspecies is present. Before specific measures can be taken, however, surveys are needed to determine whether or not more than one subspecies comprises the black and white ruffed lemur population as well as to determine their exact distribution and number.

The red ruffed lemur is present in a proposed national park on the Masoala Peninsula, but logging is still taking place within this area, and poaching is also common. A study of this subspecies is needed to identify the factors responsible for its limited distribution and to estimate present population size. Since this species has been bred with some considerable success, it may be possible to re-introduce some of the many captive animals to the wild. However, the primary focus of any conservation program must be habitat conservation as re-introduction is extreme and rarely works well.

Indri

Indri indri

Phylum	Chordata
Class	Mammalia
Order	Primates
Family	Indridae
Status	Endangered, IUCN
	Endangered, USFWS
	Appendix I, CITES
Range	Madagascar

Description and Biology

The only member of its genus, the indri is the largest living lemur and the largest of the prosimians. Its head and body length averages 23-35 in (58-89 cm), and its weight varies between 15 and 22 lb (7-10 kg). By contrast, its small tail measures only 2-2.5 in (5-6.4 cm). Considerable variety exists in body coloration and pattern, with the head, shoulders, and back often black and other parts of the body in varying shades of white, gray, or brown. Eyes and ears are large, and the hairless snout is pointed. An erect posture and long limbs give it an ape-like appearance as it moves through the trees, leaping from one tree trunk to another. At night it sleeps in trees from 30-100 ft (10-30 m) above the ground. During the day it feeds on leaves, flowers, and fruit. Natural predators include birds of prey and the fossa.

Indri groups are usually composed of an adult pair and their offspring. A group's territory averages 44 acres (18 ha); the territory is proclaimed by scent marking and by a series of songs or calls. The adult male defends the territory. A single young is born in May after a gestation period of 120-150 days. For the first four to five months, the infant is carried on the front of the female, after which it rides on her back. By eight months of age, the young can move independently of its mother, but will not venture far from her while feeding until well into the second year. Females probably give birth no more than once every two or three years.

Habitat and Current Distribution

The indri is now confined to approximately 310 mi (500 km) of rain forest in northeastern and central-eastern Madagascar from sea level to 5,000 ft (1500 m). Population figures are unknown.

History and Conservation Measures

According to subfossil evidence, the indri maintained a far greater range in the past than it does today, occurring in the interior of Madagascar and at least as far west as the Itasy Massif. The species also figures prominently in Malagasy folklore concerning the origin of humans; a common local name for the indri is "babakoto" meaning "the father of man" or "the ancestor." As recently as 1939, naturalists recorded the species as far south as Maranjary. However, some controversy exists as to its more recent distribution. In the late 1970s and early 1980s, it was reportedly confined to the eastern rain forest from the Mangoro River northward to near the latitude of

Indri.

Sambava, but excluding the Masoala Peninsula. Alternately, it was considered to extend just to Maroantsetra or to the Antanambalana River. In 1982, the indri was considered to be rare or even eliminated from the more northern extremities of its range. In 1989, it was reported from the Anjanharibe-Sud Spe-

cial Reserve. Despite such relatively minor discrepancies concerning the indri's current distribution, naturalists agree that its range has shrunk considerably even within the past few decades.

The most significant threat to the indri is posed by habitat destruction, primarily for farming as well as for timber and fuel. Clearing of rain forest occurs even in protected reserves due to the fact that none are adequately guarded or financed. Malagasy law prohibits the hunting of indris and other lemurs, and taboos against killing the species exist in some local communities. However, hunting continues in both protected and unprotected forest. These factors, combined with the species' slow reproductive rate, make extinction a definite possibility.

Indris inhabit several reserves in Madagascar, including Zahamena and Betampona Natural Reserves and the Special Reserves of Anjanharibe-Sud and Analámazaotra. Funding for better patrol of these reserves as well as for conservation education programs for nearby local communities have been recommended. Yet before specific conservation measures can be taken, surveys must be conducted to accurately assess the distribution of this species. Captive breeding has thus far proved impossible, and individuals do not survive long when caged. Therefore, habitat preservation is considered the primary focus of conservationists, not only to safeguard the indri, but to preserve the biodiversity which originally gave rise to the species.

Diademed sifaka

Propithecus diadema

Phylum	Chordata
Class	Mammalia
Order	Primates
Family	Indridae
Status	Endangered, IUCN
	Endangered, USFWS
	Appendix I, CITES
Range	Madagascar

Description and Biology

The diademed sifaka is a relatively large mammal with four recognized subspecies. Its average body length measures 20-22 in (51-55 cm), tail measures 18-20 in (46-51 cm) long; its weight is 11-18 lb (5-8 kg). This animal's fur is long and soft on the back but shorter on the underparts. Its face is black and hairless. *P. diadema diadema* has a black crown extending onto its neck, shoulders, and for a variable distance along its back. Hindquarters and hindlimbs are usually a light golden color; its tail, forelimbs, forehead, throat, and cheeks are white. Its extremities are black and underparts are light silver or gold. *P. diadema candidus*, also called the silky sifaka, has dense, silky fur that is usually white, but some individuals may have pale to darkish silver-gray tints on the crown, back, and limbs. *P. diadema edwardsi*, Milne-Edwards' sifaka, is almost entirely black or chocolate brown with white patches on the flanks and back. *P. diadema perrieri*, Perrier's sifaka, has long, dense, silky fur of a uniform black color. The sifaka spends most of its time in large trees, using its powerful, long legs to propel it from tree to tree, making leaps of up to 33 ft (10 m). When it descends to the ground, however, it moves on its two hind feet, moving its arms to the side and above the head for balance. Active during the day, the sifaka feeds on leaves, fruit, stems, and flowers.

Diademed sifaka.

The sifaka's home range usually averages from 50-125 acres (20-50 ha). The home range of one group of *P. diadema edwardsi* is more than 620 acres (250 ha) in size. Groups of up to eight individuals vary in composition, from a dominant pair and their offspring to variable numbers of adult males, adult females, and juveniles. Very little information about this species' reproductive biology exists. One young is born after a gestation period of 130-150 days. *P. diadema edwardsi* infants are reported to be born in late June and July. The infant is initially carried on the belly of its mother until it begins to ride on her back at the age of eight weeks.

Habitat and Current Distribution

This species occurs in the eastern rain forest south of Madagascar, ranging southwards from the Mananara River to the city of Antananrivo in the north. The total population figures of the sifaka are unknown. *P. diadema diadema* is the most widely distributed of the four subspecies, though the precise limits of its range are unknown. It is found throughout the eastern primary rain forest from the Mangoky River in the south to Maroantsetra in the north. *P. diadema candidus* occurs throughout the humid forest belt north of Maroantsetra to the Andapa Basin and the Marojejy Massif; it is extremely rare throughout its range. *P. diadema edwardsi* is thought to occupy the eastern rain forest southward from the Mangoro River to, at least, Manakara. The total population number of this subspecies is unknown, but it is reported to occur at very low population densities. *P. diadema perrieri* was until recently thought to be restricted to the forests located south and east of Anivorano Nord, but it has since been recorded in the northern and northeastern part of Ankarana Special Reserve, which extends its range further south and west than was previously thought. Considered to be the rarest of the subspecies, the *P. diadema perrieri* population was reported as 500 in 1972, 100 in 1987, and a maximum of 2,000 individuals in 1988.

History and Conservation Measures

The major threats to all subspecies of the sifaka are habitat destruction and hunting. Agriculture and human encroachment are reducing suitable habitat throughout this species' range. Hunting for food also remains a problem because existing legal protections are difficult to enforce. Studies are needed to determine population numbers, limits of distribution, and ecological requirements.

A number of these sifaka occur in protected reserves. *P. diadema diadema* is found in the Analmazaotra Special Reserve and in Zahamena Nature Reserve. It may also still occur in Betampona Nature Reserve, where it was reported in 1972, but was not seen in a later, 1984 survey. All of these reserves need improved protection. Two new protected areas have been proposed within the range of this subspecies: Mananara Biosphere Reserve and Mantady National Park. It has been suggested that it be introduced to the island of Nosy Mangabe. *P. diadema candidus* is found in the Marojejy Nature Reserve and in Anjanaharibe-Sud Special Reserve. At Ranohafana a national park is being designed in the range of *P. diadema edwardsi*; it is hoped that the area can be adequately guarded to ensure the survival of the lemurs in this region. Most of the population of *P. diadema perrieri* is found within the Analamera Special Reserve. Others have been found in Ankarana Special Reserve. A management program for Montagne d'Ambre National Park, Foret d'Ambre, and the two special reserves is being developed. Suggestions for the area include education and development programs for the local people, better protection of the reserves, prevention of cattle grazing within them, and the cutting of fire breaks. Encouraging tourism in the area would also help protect the lemurs. Ecological surveys to determine the requirements of this subspecies are needed. None of these subspecies have been successfully kept in captivity.

Golden-crowned sifaka

Propithecus tattersalli

Phylum	Chordata
Class	Mammalia
Order	Primates
Family	Indridae
Status	Endangered, IUCN
	Endangered, USFWS
	Appendix I, CITES
Range	Madagascar

Description and Biology

The golden-crowned or Tattersall's sifaka is considerably smaller than the diademed sifaka. On average, it weighs a little over 7 lb (3.3 kg) and is about 14-18 in (35-45 cm) long. It has long, soft hair on its back that gets shorter on the underparts. This animal is mostly white, with a gold or orange crown on its head and a wash of golden-orange across its upper chest and rump. Its facial area is black and hairless, and its ears are completely furred, with long hair tufts extending beyond their tips. The sifaka has short arms and long legs, and a long tail; it uses its powerful legs to jump from tree to tree, making leaps of up to 33 ft (10 m). It spends most of its time in large trees, but when it descends to the ground it moves on its two hind legs. Active during the day, it probably feeds on fruit and leaves. In captivity, it has also been seen to feed at night.

Groups of three to six individuals have been reported, but there is no information available on group composition. Little is known of the reproductive biology of this species.

Habitat and Current Distribution

This species is confined to an oval-shaped area with a diameter of about 15 mi (25 km) around Daraina in northeast Madagascar. It is estimated that there are a maximum of several hundred individuals in existence, occuring in many small, fragmented populations.

The preferred habitat of the golden-crowned sifaka is dry forest, but it also makes extensive use of gallery forest during the dry season.

History and Conservation Measures

The golden-crowned sifaka is a newly described species. In 1974, Dr. Ian Tattersall discovered a population of golden-crowned lemurs in a section of dry forest near Daraina, northeast of Vohimarina, though it was not recognized as a separate species until the sighting was reported in 1982. In 1987, a group of scientists from Duke University's Primate Center found several other individuals in locations east and northeast of Daraina. Local people also reported that the species was also found near Madirabe, a region also located east of Daraina.

No population of this species exists in any protected area; its limited geographical distribution means that it is one of the most severely threatened lemurs. Threats include hunting, brush fires, and clearance of vegetation for agriculture. Although local customs forbid the consumption of lemurs, outsiders attracted to the area by its gold reserves are, however, likely to hunt the species for food.

Much of the area around the gallery forest in which the golden-crowned sifaka was seen in 1988 has already been cleared; fires, some deliberately set to increase grass growth, ensure that regeneration of trees is inhibited. The gallery forest itself is being cleared for agricultural land. This forest may well be critical to the sifaka, particularly during the dry season.

It is suggested that a national park of approximately 50,000 acres (20,000 ha), divided into three different blocks, be established in the Daraina area to protect the golden-crowned sifaka. Programs are needed to educate the local people of the economic and environmental importance of the forests. Surveys to locate further populations are likewise essential, as is an extensive ecological study of the species. A small population now exist in captivity and it has been suggested that a captive breeding program be eventually combined with the relocation of populations in Madagascar; however, there is some question whether such a program could be successful.

Verreaux's sifaka

Propithecus verreauxi

Phylum	Chordata
Class	Mammalia
Order	Primates
Family	Indridae
Status	Vulnerable, IUCN
	Endangered, USFWS
	Appendix I, CITES
Range	Madagascar

Description and Biology

Verreaux's sifaka is one of the larger lemurs. Its head and body length averages about 16-21 in (41-53 cm); its weigh is approximately 4-11 lb (2-5 kg). The tail measures 17-23 in (43-59 cm) long. This species' fur is long and soft on its back and shorter on the underparts. The facial area is hairless and black, but there is considerable variation in body coloring among the three subspecies. *P. verreauxi verreauxi* is predominantly white, often with a black or maroon cap on its head that may extend onto the neck. A slightly darker variant is sometimes called a separate subspecies, *P. verreauxi majori*. *P. verreauxi coquereli* is white, with extensive maroon patches on the front part of the belly and on parts of the thighs and forelimbs. *P. verreauxi deckeni* is usually completely white; a variant sometimes called *P. verreauxi coronatus* has a dark chocolate brown or black head and throat as well as a chestnut-brown breast. Like other sifakas, this species' arms are short and its legs long and powerful. It is capable of jumping from tree to tree. It is active during the day, feeding on leaves, fruit, and flowers, depending upon season and availability of food.

Groups are made up of from three to ten individuals of variable composition; some may be family groups while others contain adult males and females, and juveniles. Home range is usually 17-21 acres (6.8-8.5 ha), but the group spends most of its time in a small portion of the range. Mating between females and dominant males has been reported between January and March. A gestation period of 130-165 days results in the birth of a single young in June, July, and August. At first, the infant clings to the mother's belly, later transferring to her back until it becomes almost independent at six months of age.

Habitat and Current Distribution

Verreaux's sifaka is only found in Madagascar, where it is restricted to the dry western and southern forests (west of Tolanaro [Fort Dauphin] to Antsohihy in the north). *P. verreauxi verreauxi* is found in all types of southern and southwestern forests, from the arid *Didierea* formations to riverine gallery forests. It has also been seen in a small, isolated patch of rain forest in the Andohahela Nature Reserve. It is not, however, found in dense brush or scrub vegetation, nor is it successful in edge vegetation. *P. verreauxi coquereli* occurs in the mixed deciduous and evergreen forests of northwestern Madagascar. *P. verreauxi deckeni* lives in the dry deciduous forests in the west of Madagascar. There are

Verreaux's sifaka.

no estimates of the population size of any of the subspecies.

History and Conservation Measures

The primary threat to Verreaux's sifaka is habitat destruction. Though it has a wide geographic distribution, this species is dependent on the two natural vegetation types found in southern Madagascar (Didiereaceae and riparian forest) and on the deciduous forests of the west. The southern forests are quite restricted in area. Destruction of these forests is, to a great extent, caused by the collection of wood for conversion to charcoal and by the deliberate setting of fires to encourage new grass growth for livestock. Overgrazing, which prevents forest regeneration, is a problem in both the south and the west.

The sifaka is also an easy prey for hunters and has probably been exterminated from some parts of its habitat as a result. In several areas, local custom forbids the killing of the animals but, as the region develops, people from other ethnic groups, without this cultural restriction on hunting, may well hasten the demise of the lemurs in the area. Legal protection is difficult to enforce.

P. verreauxi verreauxi is found in south and southwestern Madagscar, from around Tolanaro to the Tsiribihiwa River; the eastern extent of its range occurs within Andohahela Nature Reserve. One of the most intensely studied lemurs, it has been subject to intermittent scientific investigation at the Private Reserve of Berenty since 1963. It has also been observed near Hazafotsy and Beza Mahafaly Special Reserve. It is also found in Isalo National Park, Andranomena Special Reserve, and Analabe Private Reserve. There are management and conservation education plans underway, or proposed, for many of these reserves.

P. verreauxi coquereli is found in Ankarafantsika Nature Reserve and in Bora Special Reserve. A management program has been drafted and a number of suggestions made for the area, including: motorbikes for guards so that they can patrol the reserve more effectively; development of fire breaks around the reserve; establishment of conservation/education programs; and the development of plantations to supply local people with wood for fuel and construction material.

P. verreauxi deckeni is found in Bemaraha and Namoroka Nature Reserves and reported to be abundant in Ambohijanahary Special Reserve. Bemarivo, Maningozo, and Kasijy Special Reserves are also located within the range of this subspecies, but little information is available on the status of these sites.

A number of suggestions have been made for the conservation of Bemaraha Nature Reserve, including: informing the local people that the area is protected; the posting of notices at access points to mark entry into the reserve and to warn visitors of the legal ramifications of cutting down trees or hunting for animals; the construction of official access paths through the reserve; adding additional guards; and the cutting of fire breaks. Similarly, conservation/education programs for the villagers around Namoroka and Ambohijanahary Reserves would help to protect these areas.

Aye-aye

Daubentonia madagascariensis

Phylum	Chordata
Class	Mammalia
Order	Primates
Family	Daubentoniidae
Status	Endangered, IUCN
	Endangered, USFWS
	Appendix I, CITES
Range	Madagascar

Description and Biology

Among the most unusual looking of the primates, the aye-aye possesses unique physical characteristics that suit it to its evolutionary niche. Long, coarse blackish brown guard hairs overlay a dense layer of relatively short white hair which sometimes shows through and gives a slightly mottled appearance. Length of head and body averages 15-18 in (38-45 cm) and weight averages 4.4-6.6 lb (2-3 kg); the 16-22 in (40-55 cm) tail is bushy. Diet is composed primarily of fruit (especially coconuts) and insect larvae, possibly supplemented by adult insects, bamboo shoots, and small vertebrates. To assist in food gathering and eating, the aye-aye has large, sensitive ears, rodent-like incisors, and elongated, claw-like fingers and toes. It breaks into coconuts or other hard-shelled fruits using its powerful incisors, then scoops out the pulp with its exceptionally long middle finger. The aye-aye uses its sensitive hearing to locate larvae under tree bark, then strips the bark from the tree with its incisors to expose the larvae, which it crushes and extracts with its middle finger. Citing such behavior as evidence, some scientists have suggested that the aye-aye fills the evolutionary niche of woodpeckers in Madagascar.

The aye-aye is a nocturnal creature that builds a complex nest in the fork of a large tree for shelter during the day. It can walk on the ground, but spends most of its time in trees, sometimes hanging by its hind legs and using its middle finger for grooming. Little is known about the social structure or reproductive biology of this species. It is usually seen alone or sometimes in pairs. Home range is estimated to be around 12 acres (5 ha). Gestation period is unknown, but a single young in usually produced every two to three years, between October and March. The young is probably nursed for a year and, during that time, is kept in a nest.

Habitat and Current Distribution

The aye-aye is probably widely but sparsely distributed in the forests of the east, north, and northwest of Madagascar. Population figures are unknown.

This species is very adaptable in its choice of habitat; it has been found in areas of primary rain forest, deciduous forest, secondary growth, cultivation (particularly coconut groves), and may even frequent mangrove swamps and dry scrub forest. It has also been recorded from open brush and low trees, several miles from any real forest.

Aye-aye.

History and Conservation Measures

The aye-aye was once considered to be one of the most endangered mammals in Madagascar. Yet scientists now speculate that its population is higher than first believed and that it is elusive rather than very rare. It is unlikely, however, that this species has ever been found in very high densities.

Apart from some possible natural predation by fossa, the main threat to this species is habitat destruction. It is unknown whether it can survive in degraded areas because it needs large, old trees in which to build its nests. It is also at risk because of a local perception that it is a harbinger of misfortune, even death. Those who consider it bad luck will kill it on sight and sometimes eat it. Local farmers may also kill it as a pest.

This species is found in a number of protected reserves and areas that are designated to become reserves. Most of these areas, however, are in need of protection. A special conservation program for the aye-aye was designed and implemented in 1966 and 1967. In this activity, nine animals were released on a small 1,300-acre (520-ha) island, Nosy Mangabe, located off the east coat of Madagascar. This population has been protected and recent investigations have begun to monitor the results of this program.

Detailed studies have been initiated to determine the habitat requirements of the aye-aye and its ability to adapt to environments modified by humans. Extensive surveys are needed to determine the extent of its present range and its population status. Results of these studies should allow formulation of conservation plans in addition to those already devised. Among the measures environmentalists recommend are educational programs to increase local awareness of the aye-aye and its endangered status; better enforcement of laws already passed against killing aye-ayes; and compensation of local people for damage done to their crops by the species.

Buffy-headed marmoset

Callithrix flaviceps

Phylum	Chordata
Class	Mammalia
Order	Primates
Family	Callitrichidae
Status	Endangered, IUCN
	Endangered, USFWS
	Appendix I, CITES
Range	Brazil

Description and Biology

One of the smallest animals of the primate order, the buffy-headed marmoset is closer in size to a squirrel than a monkey. Its head and body length averages 7-12 in (18-30 cm) and it weighs 8-16 oz (230-460 g). This species has thick, soft fur in shades of light to dark gray and brown, with a lighter yellow to red colored head and ear tufts. Its forelegs are shorter than hind legs; its tail is banded and measures 7-16 in (17-40 cm) in length. It has a keen sense of hearing and vision. Moving through the tropical forest from branch to branch, it feeds during the day on fruit, tree exudates, and insects.

Groups of 4-15 animals live together. Home range varies with the availability of food from 2.5-100 acres (1-40 ha). Marmosets are usually reported to form monogamous pairs, but the female may mate with different males in the group. A gestation period of 130-150 days usually results in the birth of two young, but litter size can range from one to four; births peak between March and May. The father takes an active role in raising the young and all members of the group surrender food for the young and assist in transporting them.

Habitat and Current Distribution

The buffy-headed marmoset is reduced to fragmented populations in southeastern Brazil. Population figures are unknown, but the largest numbers occur in the Nova Lombardia Biological Reserve in Espírito Santo and on the Fazenda Montes Claros protected area.

Preferred habitat is mountainous forest above 1,300 ft (400 m). Most sightings have been in edge habitats, mainly along roads, where the animals range from the understory at about 10 ft (3 m) to the upper part of the canopy at about 100 ft (30 m).

History and Conservation Measures

Historic and present population figures are unknown. Because of habitat destruction, this species survives only in isolated forest patches. These cannot be considered viable populations. Since the 1800s, the Atlantic coastal forests of eastern Brazil have suffered a tremendous increase in human population and widespread, largely uncontrolled forest destruction to make way for coffee plantations; the production of such products as sugar cane, cocoa, and eucalyptus; cattle grazing; lumber extraction; and charcoal production. In recent years, industrial development has also taken its toll on the environment. As a result, the forests have been devastated and only a tiny fraction of the original forest cover remains.

Necessary conservation measures include ecological studies for the eventual planning and implementation of conservation activities; rescue operations to remove isolated groups from remnant tracts of forest slated for destruction; and the institution of a captive breeding program.

Buffy tufted-ear marmoset

Callithrix aurita

Phylum	Chordata
Class	Mammalia
Order	Primates
Family	Callitrichidae
Status	Endangered, IUCN
	Endangered, USFWS
	Appendix I, CITES
Range	Brazil

Description and Biology

Like its relative, *Callithrix flaviceps*, the buffy tufted-ear marmoset is one of the smallest of the primates. The average length of its head and body is 7-12 in (18-30 cm) and it weighs 8-16 oz (230-460 g). This species has soft, thick fur in shades of light to dark brown or black; black throat, head, and cheeks; dark underparts; and small white ear tufts. The face is furless or only sporadically haired. Like other mammals, this species is fastidious in the care of its fur and engages in individual and mutual grooming. The forelegs are shorter than hind legs; the tail is banded and averages 7-16 in (17-40 cm) in length. It has acute senses of hearing and sight. Facial expressions are indicated mainly by lip movement. Other emotions are expressed by movements of the eyelids, ears, and head. Moving through the tropical forest from branch to branch, this species feeds during the day on fruit, tree exudates, and insects. At night, it shelters in trees. Home range varies with the availability of food but is within the range of from 2.5-100 acres (1-40 ha).

Groups of 4-15 animals live together. Marmosets are usually reported to form monogamous pairs, but the female may mate with more than one male in the group. The gestation period of 130-150 days usually results in the birth of two babies, but litter size can range from one to four; births peak between March and May. The father takes an active role in raising the young, and all members of the group surrender food for the young and assist in carrying them.

Habitat and Current Distribution

The buffy tufted-ear marmoset is found in the Atlantic coastal forests of southeastern Brazil. This species was once found at high altitudes in Rio de Janeiro, in both mountains and lowlands in São Paulo, and at low altitudes in Minas Gerais. Population figures are unknown, but surveys in 1979-80 found that it occurred in only two protected areas: the privately-owned Fazenda Barreiro Rico in São Paulo, and the Estacao Experimental de Mogi-Gaucu, a tiny 124-acre (50 ha) forest belonging to the Institute Florestal of the State of São Paulo. It has apparently become extinct in two national parks: Serra dos Orgaos and Itatiaia, in which it once definitely occurred.

History and Conservation Measures

The buffy tufted-ear marmoset once occurred in southeastern São Paulo, western Rio de Janeiro, and adjacent parts of Minas Gerais, but has now disappeared from most of this area, as deforestation has destroyed the majority of suitable habitat. In addition, epidemics have caused some remnant populations to become extinct. Since the 1800s the Atlantic coastal forests of eastern Brazil have suffered a tremendous increase in human population and widespread, largely uncontrolled forest destruction to make way for coffee plantations; the production of sugar cane, cocoa, and eucalyptus; cattle grazing; lumber extraction; and charcoal production. In recent years industrial development has also taken its toll. As a result, these forests have been devastated, especially during the rapid development and economic expansion that began in the 1960s. Only a tiny fraction of the original forest cover now remains.

Necessary conservation measures include: ecological studies necessary to plan conservation activities; surveys in the parks, reserves, and experimental stations of São Paulo; and the institution of a captive breeding program.

Lion tamarins

Leontopithecus spp.

Phylum	Chordata
Class	Mammalia
Order	Primates
Family	Callitrichidae
Status	Endangered, IUCN
	Endangered, USFWS
	Appendix I, CITES
Range	Brazil

Description and Biology

Lion tamarins are distinctive animals that have a golden mane, long, silky fur, and very striking coloration. Three species have been identified. *Leontopithecus rosalia*, the golden lion tamarin, has an overall reddish gold coat; *Leontopithecus chrysomelas*, the golden-headed lion tamarin, has a black coat except for the golden mane, forearms, and rump; *Leontopithecus chrysopygus*, the golden-rumped lion tamarin, is black with a golden mane, rump, and thighs. Average length of head and body is 8-13 in (20-33 cm) and weight is 21-28 oz (600-800 g). The tail averages 12-16 in (30-40 cm) and may have black or brown markings.

Lion tamarins are arboreal species, travelling from tree to tree and feeding during the day on fruit and insects, their diet occasionally supplemented by plant exudates and small vertebrates.

The family group can range from two to eight animals but is most commonly three or four individuals, with a male-female pair at the center of the group. In the wild, births usually take place between September and March after a gestation period of 126-132 days. Litter size can be one to three, but twins are the norm. The mother and father share responsibility for the young and are assisted by juveniles in the group.

Habitat and Current Distribution

All lion tamarin species are very scarce in the wild. The golden lion tamarin is limited to the state of Rio de Janeiro; the population is estimated to be about 550. The golden-headed lion tamarin is restricted to the southeast of Bahia State and probably numbers less than 200 individuals. The golden-rumped lion tamarin is found in two tracts of forest in the state of São Paulo: the Morro do Diabo State Reserve in the extreme west of the state and the Caitetus Reserve in central São Paulo; the population is probably less than 100 animals.

Preferred habitat is primary tropical forest along the Atlantic coast below 1,300-1,600 ft (400-500 m) altitude. The lion tamarin is usually found between 10-33 ft (3-10 m) above the ground, where dense vines, air ferns, and interlacing branches provide cover. Tall primary forest assures the presence of holes in trees and branches where the tamarin can sleep at night.

History and Conservation Measures

The home of this species is one of the most densely inhabited parts of Brazil, where the major cause of its decline has been, and continues to be, forest destruction for lumber, agriculture, pasture,

Golden lion tamarin.

and housing. As a result, all of the lion tamarins are considered extremely endangered and on the brink of extinction. They have always been uncommon and, although their range has not changed, there are now only isolated pockets of forest that provide suitable habitat. Lion tamarins were once heavily captured for the pet trade, for zoo exhibits, and for use in biomedical laboratories, but they are now protected by the CITES agreements.

The Poco D'Anta Reserve was established specifically to protect the golden lion tamarin, but surveys have shown that only a small percentage of the reserve contains suitable habitat. Similar conditions exist on a reserve for the golden-headed lion tamarin in Una and in the Morro do Diabo State Reserve.

The protection and breeding of lion tamarins have been the concern of many national and international organizations. All three species have been bred in captivity and successful reintroduction to the former parts of their range has been implemented. The National Zoo in Washington, D.C. and the Rio de Janeiro Primate Center have exchanged animals in an effort to preserve genetic diversity. Additional reserves in Brazil should be expanded and improved to support other populations of lion tamarins.

Bare-faced tamarin

Saguinus bicolor

Phylum . . . . Chordata
Class . . . . Mammalia
Order. . . . . Primates
Family . . . . Callitrichidae
Status . . . . Endangered, IUCN (*S. b. bicolor*)
Endangered, USFWS
Appendix I, CITES
Range . . . . Brazil

Description and Biology

The bare-faced tamarin, named for its almost completely bare, black face, is sometimes also called the pied tamarin because of the contrast between the front of its body, which is yellow to white, and its hindquarters, which are a darker gray-brown. One of the smallest of the primates, the tamarin has an average head and body length of 7-12 in (18-30 cm) and weight of 8-32 oz (226-900 g). It has long, soft fur and a tail that averages 10-17 in (25-43 cm). Three subspecies of bare-faced tamarin are recognized: *S. b. bicolor*, *S. b. martinsi*, and *S. b. ochraceus*. These tamarins spend most of their time in trees, moving quickly among the branches. They are active only during daylight, feeding on insects, fruit, flowers, and small vertebrates. With the exception of small prey, animals are killed by a bite on the head. Some plant extracts such as resin and gum may also form an important component of this species' diet.

Group size for this species is usually five to ten animals, often led by a mated dominant pair. Home range averages 20-80 acres (8-32 ha). It is usually reported as monogamous, but the female may mate with more than one male in the group. Gestation period of 140-145 days usually results in twins, although litter size may be one to three. The father is present when the mother gives birth and plays a major role in caring for the young.

Habitat and Current Distribution

The bare-faced tamarin is found in northern Brazil, where it occurs only in the state of Amazonas. It is confined to the north bank of the Amazon, between the lower Rio Negro and the lower Rio Paur de Oeste or Cumina. *S. b. bicolor* occurs mostly near the city of Manaus; *S. b. martinsi* occurs between the Rio Nhamundá, east to the Rio Erepecurú, north of the Rio Amazonas. *S. b. ochraceus* is believed to occur on the west bank of the Rio Nhamundá, possibly extending west to the Rio Uatuma, north of the Rio Amazonas. No population figures are available.

Preferred habitat is primary tropical forest, but the species can survive in secondary forest.

History and Conservation Measures

Because the city of Manaus is growing so rapidly, forest destruction is the primary threat to the bare-faced tamarin. Areas around the existing city are already experiencing industrial and residential development, and road building is opening up additional areas for development.

An additional threat to this species may be the invasion of its range by the golden-handed tamarin, *S. midas midas*. Studies have been initiated to determine the ecological relationship between the golden-handed tamarin and the bare-faced tamarin.

The bare-faced tamarin occurs in few officially protected areas. A viable population is thought to occur in the 15,000-acre (10,000 ha) Reserve Ducke located north of Manaus and belonging to the National Amazonian Research Institute. Studies are underway to determine its precise range and to locate the best possible areas for a large reserve. Surveys are necessary to better determine the status and possible threats to the survival of the bare-faced tamarin. A captive breeding program has also been suggested.

White-footed tamarin

Saguinus leucopus

Phylum . . . . Chordata
Class . . . . Mammalia
Order . . . . Primates
Family . . . . Callitrichidae
Status . . . . Endangered, IUCN
Threatened, USFW
Appendix I, CITES
Range . . . . Colombia

Description and Biology

The white-footed tamarin is easily distinguished from other tamarins by its white feet and limbs. Apart from a naked face, the rest of the body is covered with soft, yellowish brown fur, with white to silver hairs on the head. One of the smallest of the primates, the tamarin has an average head and body length of 7-12 in (18-30 cm), weight of 8-32 oz (226-900 g), and a 10-17 in (25-43 cm) tail. Spending most of its time in trees, it feeds during the day on insects, fruit, small vertebrates, leaves, shoots, buds, and flowers.

Group size ranges from 3-12 individuals, often led by a mated dominant pair. Home range averages 20-80 acres (8-32 ha). It is usually reported as monogamous, but the female may mate with more than one male in the group. A gestation period of 140-145 days usually results in twins, born between January and June. As with other tamarin species, the father is present when the mother gives birth and takes a major part in rearing the young.

Habitat and Current Distribution

The white-footed tamarin is found only in northern Colombia, where it occupies a small range stretching from the confluence of the Rio Magdalena and the Rio Cauca in northern Bolivar (including Mompos Island) southward into northeastern Antioquia and along the western bank of the middle Rio Magdalena in the departments of Antioquia, Caldas, and northern Tolima. Population estimates are unavailable.

Preferred habitat is the fringe area of tropical forests, near streams, or in secondary growth.

History and Conservation Measures

Initial population figures are unknown, but the species is thought to have declined significantly in recent years. Its range has been greatly reduced by extensive forest clearance, especially since the 1960s.

No existing parks or reserves are likely to contain a viable population of this species; a survey to locate a suitable reserve site is urgently needed. There is also an urgent need for studies to investigate the ecology of this tamarin and to determine a realistic approach to its conservation needs.

Cotton-top tamarin

Saguinus oedipus

Phylum	Chordata
Class	Mammalia
Order	Primates
Family	Callitrichidae
Status	Endangered, IUCN
	Appendix I, CITES
Range	Colombia

Description and Biology

This striking tamarin is named for the crest of long white hair that extends from the forehead to the back of the head, framing a mostly black face. Underparts are white or yellow, while the back is mottled brown changing to reddish orange on the rump. The reddish tail is 10-17 in (25-43 cm) long and ends in a black tip. Average head and body length is 7-12 in (18-30 cm) and weight is 8-32 oz (226-900 g). The tamarin spends most of its time in trees and feeds during the day on fruit, vines, air plants, insects, new sprouting leaves or buds, leaves, leaf stems, and small vertebrates.

Groups of three to nine animals center most often around a mated dominant pair. Home range averages 20-80 acres (8-32 ha). Although reported as monogamous, the female may mate with more than one male in the group. A gestation period of 125-140 days usually results in twins, most often born between January and June. The father is present when the mother gives birth and takes an active part in caring for the young.

Habitat and Current Distribution

This species occurs in northwest Colombia, between the Rio Atrato in the west, the lower Rios Cauca and Magdalena in the east, and in the departments of Cordoba, Bolivar, Sucre, Atlantico, northwest Antioquia, and northeast Choco. Because there is very limited knowledge of the state and extent of the re-

Cotton-top tamarin.

maining forest in its range, it is impossible to estimate the population size or composition of the cotton-top tamarin.

Habitat ranges from deciduous forest in the northern part of its range to humid tropical forest in the Andes foothills at altitudes from sea level to around 1,600 ft (500 m). It also adapts to secondary forests.

History and Conservation Measures

There are no estimates of initial population size, and it is now thought that the original distribution of this species may have been smaller than is usually believed. An early threat to the species was the animal trade between 1960 and 1975, when it was captured for the pet trade and for biomedical research. Now that it is protected by CITES agreements, the primary threat is deforestation.

By 1966, at least 70 percent of the original forest cover in its former range had been replaced with pasture and farmland. By the mid-1970s, even remote forest areas were subject to clearing and some of the remaining patches of forest were devoid of tamarins, even though they appeared to provide suitable habitat. Since then, several reserves have been established at sites where the cotton-top tamarin could occur, and the establishment of other properly protected reserves is considered high priority.

Muriqui
(Woolly spider monkey)
Brachyteles arachnoides

Phylum . . . . Chordata
Class . . . . Mammalia
Order . . . . Primates
Family . . . . Cebidae
Status . . . . Endangered, IUCN
Endangered, USFWS
Appendix I, CITES
Range . . . . Brazil

Description and Biology

The muriqui, or woolly spider monkey, is the largest of the New World monkeys. The Brazilian common name for this monkey is *mono* or *monocarvoeiro*. Average head and body length is 18-25 in (46-63 cm), and it weighs between 26-33 lb (12-15 kg). It has thick buff-gold fur, a black face, and black extremities. In some areas, the face and extremities are pink or mottled. Its head is round and small in proportion to the body, and its limbs are long; the prehensile tail is longer than the body, averaging 25-32 in (63-80 cm). This monkey lives in the crown of the tallest trees and has never been observed on the ground. It moves through the trees by swinging from branch to branch with its arms (brachiation). Woolly spider monkeys feed during the day mainly on leaves, supplemented by seeds, fruit, and insects.

Small groups of two to four are the most common, but groups of up to 20 or more have been observed. Social structure seems to be dependent on the distribution of key items in the monkey's diet. In some areas it is fluid, with individual monkeys joining together and separating with no set pattern. In these areas, females seem to remain in discrete territories, while males appear to range more widely, moving through the forest alone or in all-male groups of up to eight individuals. In other areas, muriqui form cohesive troops. These monkeys are polygamous and newborns have been observed in February, April, and October.

Habitat and Current Distribution

The muriqui is found in southeastern Brazil, where it is very sparsely distributed in the states of Sao Paulo, Espirito Santo, Rio de Janeiro, and Minas Gerais. Population is estimated at 200-400 individuals.

Preferred habitat is undisturbed high forest, including both lowland tropical and montane rain forest.

History and Conservation Measures

This species at one time probably occurred in all Atlantic coastal forests of eastern and southeastern Brazil. It is estimated that population in the sixteenth century was almost half a million and that the species was still quite abundant in the nineteenth century. In

Muriqui.

largely uncontrolled forest destruction to make way for agricultural development, including coffee plantations, sugar cane, cocoa, and eucalyptus production; to provide pasture land for cattle; and to accommodate lumber extraction and charcoal production. In addition, more recent industrial development has also taken its toll. As a result, forests have been devastated, and only a tiny fraction (2 percent) of the original forest cover remains. This species has been hunted for food in the past and, although protected by law, may still be taken by hunters in some areas.

A population of approximately 50 individuals exists in Minas Gerais on a private coffee plantation called Fazenda Montes Claros. (The monkeys have been protected by the owner for about 40 years, but this tradition may not continue.) The largest single concentration of these monkeys (over 100 individuals) occurs in Fazenda Barreiro Rico, a private ranch in São Paulo. Muriqui may also be found in the Biological Reserve of Nova Lombardi (Espirito Santo), in the state parks of Rio Doce and Carlos Botelho, and in the national parks of Itatiaia, Serra dos Orgaos (Rio de Janeiro), and Caparao.

All known populations are isolated from one another. There is no gene flow among these populations and their habitat is surrounded by development and deforested land. Surveys are necessary to locate other remnant groups, but these small, isolated populations are not viable over the long term and, if located, translocation or reintroduction to other protected areas may be necessary. Survival of this species will depend on protection of remaining populations and habitats. It is extremely difficult to maintain woolly spider monkeys in captivity since little specific information is known about their dietary requirements.

1971, population was estimated at 3,000 and in 1972 at 2,000; today this species is on the verge of extinction.

Since the 1800s, the Atlantic coastal forests of eastern Brazil have suffered a tremendous increase in human population. There has been widespread,

Masked titi

Callicebus personatus

Phylum	Chordata
Class	Mammalia
Order	Primates
Family	Cebidae
Status	Vulnerable, IUCN
Range	Brazil

Description and Biology

The masked titi has a dark brown or black face, black hands and feet, and a reddish brown tail measuring 10-22 in (25-55 cm). Its long, soft hair is dark brown at the base and lighter at the tips. Its belly is reddish brown. The average length of this species' head and body is 11.8-16.5 in (30-42 cm). This monkey lives in the trees, feeding during the day and sleeping in a tree at night. Its diet includes fruits, leaves, and flowers consumed over a home range averaging 45,000-50,000 sq ft (4,000-4,600 sq m). Titi monkeys are generally very difficult to observe because they are fast-moving and very shy.

Groups of two to seven animals include a mated pair, who form strong pair bonds, and their young of various ages. Information about reproductive biology is scarce. One young is usually born, possibly between December and April. The adult male searches for food, leads group movements, and also usually carries the infant when it is not being nursed by the female. The masked titi used a wide range of visual signals and vocalizations for communication.

Habitat and Current Distribution

The masked titi is found in the Atlantic forests of eastern Brazil, from the Rio Itapicuru in northern Bahia to the Rio Tiete in São Paulo. Four subspecies are recognized, the most abundant of which is *C. p.*
nigrifrons. C. p. personatus occurs in two Espírito Santo reserves; *C. p. melanochir* was found to be either very rare or extinct in the northernmost part of its range, where little or no habitat remains, but was still fairly common in remaining forested areas in southern Bahia. Population figures are unknown.

Habitat includes the Atlantic coastal forests, primary and secondary, at elevations from 300-3,000 ft (100-1,000 m). Much of this forest area has been destroyed and the masked titi is considered the most endangered species of its genus. It is also one of the least known of the titi monkeys.

History and Conservation Measures

Because the range of this species coincides with a very high human population density, habitat destruction is the most serious threat to its existence. When not replaced by human settlements, the forests are being cleared for agriculture and grazing land, and for timber and charcoal production. An additional, but less serious, threat is hunting for food.

All of the subspecies occur on protected reserves, but the establishment of additional reserves is necessary to ensure the long-term security of this species in the wild. Other conservation measures include the planning of rescue operations to capture titi groups still living in forest areas identified for destruction, and long-term studies to determine population status.

Yellow-tailed woolly monkey

Lagothrix flavicauda

Phylum	Chordata
Class	Mammalia
Order	Primates
Family	Cebidae
Status	Endangered, IUCN
	Endangered, USFWS
	Appendix I, CITES
Range	Ecuador(?); Peru

Description and Biology

The yellow-tailed woolly monkey gets its common name from a yellow patch of hair on the underside of the last part of its 22-28 in (56-71 cm) tail; the rest of its short, thick coat is a rich brown color. Average head and body length is 20-27 in (51-68 cm) and weight is 12-24 lb (5-11 kg). This species has a large, round head and a relatively heavy body for tree monkeys. Its furless face is almost black in color. The monkey's thumbs and toes are well developed, and the fingers are short and thick with long, pointed nails. The tail is prehensile. *Lagothrix flavicauda* spends much of its time in trees, but often travels on the ground, walking on its hind legs and using its front legs for balance. Its diet consists of fruits and flowers; feeding takes place during the day.

Groups of 4-35, with an average of 13 individuals, include a number of adult males, adult females, and juveniles. Very little is known about their reproductive biology, but one young is believed to be born after a gestation period of approximately 225 days. Newborn animals have been observed in the wild in November. Sexual maturity is reached at 4 or 5 years for females and males, respectively.

Habitat and Current Distribution

The yellow-tailed woolly monkey is endemic to northern Peru, where it has an extremely limited range. It occurs only in patches of montane Amazon rain forest which intrude as finger-like projections into the Andes. Population figures for this species are unknown.

Preferred habitat is humid and very humid montane rain forest of the Amazonian type.

History and Conservation Measures

First described from skins obtained in 1802 by Alexander von Humboldt and then known only from specimens collected in 1925 and 1926, this species was rediscovered by an expedition, which in 1974 obtained four skins, three skulls, and a live specimen that had originally been caught in the upper Rio Mayo area on the eastern edge of its currently known range. Since then, it has been observed in the wild and become the subject of studies. There are no estimates of the initial population, but it is undoubtedly declining.

The major threats to the yellow-tailed woolly

monkey are habitat destruction and hunting. It seems unable to adapt to secondary forests and is therefore particularly vulnerable to human habitat alterations. Large sections of forest have been cleared by settlers who have gained access to the region along newly constructed roads. These roads also open up previously inaccessible areas to hunters, who have always targeted this species for food and skins and for the pet trade. Taking juveniles for the pet trade usually involves killing the mother. *Lagothrix flavicauda* has legal protection, but enforcement of laws is difficult in isolated areas. Several areas have been suggested for designation as protected reserves or national parks; a study in 1980 predicted that the species will be extinct in the wild by 2030 unless effective reserves are established.

Central American squirrel monkey

Saimiri oerstedii

Phylum	Chordata
Class	Mammalia
Order	Primates
Family	Cebidae
Status	Endangered, IUCN
	Endangered, USFWS
	Appendix I, CITES
Range	Costa Rica; Panama

Description and Biology

The Central American or red-backed squirrel monkey has reddish fur that is short and thick on its back and limbs. Its underparts are white to yellow and its face, throat, and ears are white. The muzzle is black and hairless; the tail, which averages 14-18 in (36-46 cm) long, is covered with short, reddish fur that becomes black and slightly tufted at the end. The tail is not prehensile. The average head and body length of the red-backed squirrel monkey is 9-14 in (23-36 cm); its weight is 1-2.4 lb (0.5-1.1 kg). The male is larger than the female. This monkey spends most of its time in trees and feeds during the day on fruit and insects.

Groups of 10-40 animals live together, often combining with other groups to form very large societies. The home range of this species varies widely with habitat; patches of forest as small as two acres (0.8 ha) can support some groups, while other groups may occupy 50-100 acres (20-40 ha) and defend only a small portion of that area as exclusive territory. Dominance is established for mating purposes by fighting; mating is polygamous but with no pair bonds formed. Mating is seasonal in captivity, but possibly not in the wild. One young is born after a gestation period of 152-170 days. It clings to its mother after birth and remains dependent for approximately twelve months.

Habitat and Current Distribution

The distribution of *Saimiri oerstedii* is limited to western Panama and southern Costa Rica, where its lives in forests, shrubby areas, deciduous woodland, or low, bushy secondary growth. The population in Costa Rica has been estimated at 3,000 individuals; figures for Panama are unknown.

History and Conservation Measures

There are no estimates of initial population size, but numbers are believed to have decreased greatly since the 1950s in both Panama and Costa Rica. The primary reason for this decline is deforestation due to clearing land for banana plantations, cattle ranches, sugar cane and rice farms. In Costa Rica, banana

Central American squirrel monkey.

planting and the slash-and-burn agriculture have eliminated much suitable habitat. In Panama, where most shrub cover has been removed for cattle fodder, the human population is growing rapidly. In addition, the implementation of an land reform law in the 1950s and 1960s has led to increasing pressure by the Panamanian government on land owners to make profitable use of forested lands or forfeit their holdings; as a result, the forest cover in the state of Chiriqui was drastically reduced.

From the 1950s through the 1970s, the squirrel monkeys was under siege by exporting for the pet trade and for biomedical research. Animals were taken from the more accessible areas until the species became too scarce to make the business profitable. A protected population lives in the Corcovado National Biological Reserve in southern Costa Rica. The creation of national parks and wildlife refuges in Panama would be of considerable benefit to the species there.

Diana monkey

Cercopithecus diana

Phylum	Chordata
Class	Mammalia
Order	Primates
Family	Cercopithecidae
Status	Vulnerable, IUCN
	Endangered, USFWS
	Appendix I, CITES
Range	Côte d'Ivoire; Ghana; Guinea; Liberia; Sierra Leone; Togo

Description and Biology

Also called the Diana guenon, the Diana monkey is one of 26 species of guenons. Two subspecies are recognized within *Cercopithecus diana*: *C. d. diana* and *C. d. roloway*. The Diana monkey has a bright, multicolored coat; its back is reddish brown flecked with gray, and its hands, feet, tail, and face are black. It has a white stripe on the thigh and a white ruff and beard that frame the face. Average head and body length is 14-26 in (35-66 cm), tail averages 20-40 in (50-100 cm), and these monkeys weigh about 11 lb (5 kg). Active during the day, this monkey is often sighted in the upper layers of the canopy but also forages in the dense understory. It feeds on fruits, leaves, flowers, and arthropods.

Groups size is variable, ranging from 15-40. A group is typically composed of one adult male with six to eight adult females and their immature offspring, who occupy a defended home range of approximately 470 acres (189 ha). Little information is available about reproductive biology.

Habitat and Current Distribution

The Diana monkey occurs in southern Sierra Leone, Liberia, southern Côte d'Ivoire, western and southern Ghana, and the Seredou area of southwest Guinea. *C. d. diana* is found to the west of the Sassandra River and *C. d. roloway* to the east. There are no estimates of total population.

Preferred habitat includes high canopy forests, mature secondary forest, riverine forest, and areas of

Diana monkey.

semi-deciduous forest. Although they are regarded as a crop-pest in some areas, none have been observed to enter cultivated areas or to raid crops.

History and Conservation Measures

Total population numbers for this species is unknown. Hunting and habitat destruction, especially in combination, are the primary threats throughout this monkey's relatively restricted range. Because of its large size, this monkey is an easy and desired prey among hunters. It is also conspicuous in color and vocalizes frequently as it travels in the high canopy, thereby making them easy to spot and hunt. Logging activities have further opened up new, previously inaccessible, areas of forest to hunters.

Large-scale deforestation by logging has resulted in vast reductions in forest cover throughout Sierra Leone, Liberia, and Ghana. The Diana monkey can be found in lightly logged areas, but it is absent when the canopy area is reduced. Replanting with unpalatable species reduces suitable habitat even further. In Ghana, charcoal production, shifting agriculture, and cocoa plantations continue to erode areas of the forest, even within some reserves.

Hunting of the Diana monkey needs to be totally banned or severely restricted in all countries within its range. Remaining areas of habitat require protection and integrated forest management practices need to be established. Conservation education is essential to changing perceptions about these primates as crop-pests or meat species. Further studies on the distribution and status of this species are also necessary.

Red-bellied guenon

Cercopithecus erythrogaster

Phylum	Chordata
Class	Mammalia
Order	Primates
Family	Cercopithecidae
Status	Endangered, IUCN
	Endangered, USFWS
Range	Benin (?); Nigeria

Description and Biology

The red-bellied guenon is sometimes called the white-throated monkey because of its white throat ruff. Although this animal's name implies that the monkey has a red belly, the actual color is gray in the Nigerian species so far located. The average head and body length is 15-21 in (38-53 cm); the monkey weighs around 13 lb (6 kg), and the tail measures 20-40 in (50-100 cm) long. It is arboreal and feeds during the day on fruit and insects.

Although social organization is poorly known, this species is thought to live in groups composed of one male accompanied by several females and their offspring. Foraging groups tend to be around five animals, but groups of more than 30 animals have been reported. Reproductive biology in the wild is unknown.

Habitat and Current Distribution

The red-bellied guenon has one of the most restricted distributions of all African primates. It is found only in lowland forests in southwest Nigeria and, possibly, in southern Benin. The largest population probably lives in the Okomu Forest; 6,000 animals are reported to reside here. Total population figures are unknown.

In the lowland rain forest zone, this species is found in high canopy forests, secondary forests, and in bush and old farmland close to high forests. It prefers dense, tangled vegetation and tends to be found between 6-50 ft (2-15 m) above the ground.

History and Conservation Measures

There are no estimates of initial population, but numbers are now estimated to be small and declining. Timber extraction, farming, road construction, oil exploration, and conversion to plantations have all reduced this monkey's suitable habitat. The forests of southwestern Nigeria have been intensively exploited and now exist only as small, isolated patches. While these patches can support small populations, such tiny, genetically-isolated populations may not be viable over the long term. Hunting of primates for meat is also a threat to the species.

The red-bellied guenon is known to inhabit at least 12 forest reserves, but forest clearing has occurred even within these reserves. Effective management and protection of the reserve areas are essential. Stringent habitat protection and hunting restrictions are needed, as are further data on status and ecology of the species.

Red-eared nose-spotted guenon

Cercopithecus erythrotis

Phylum . . . . Chordata
Class . . . . Mammalia
Order . . . . Primates
Family . . . . Cercopithecidae
Status . . . . Vulnerable, IUCN
                        Endangered, USFWS
                        Appendix II, CITES
Range . . . . Cameroon; Bioko (Equatorial Guinea); Nigeria

Description and Biology

The red-eared nose-spotted guenon, sometimes also referred to as the russet-eared guenon, is a colorful animal with a grizzled brown back and gray limbs. Its face is blue around the eyes, red around the ears and nose, and has yellow cheek fur. Its tail measures 20-40 in (50-100 cm) long and is at least partly red. Average head and body length is 14-20 in (36-51 cm), weight averages 7-11 lb (3-5 kg). This monkey is arboreal but preferences for different canopy heights are unclear. It feeds during the day, possibly on fruit and insects.

Group size ranges from four to over 30, and solitary males have been observed. Little is known about social structure and nothing on reproductive biology.

Habitat and Current Distribution

This species is found in southern Nigeria, in southwestern Cameroon, and on the island of Bioko in Equatorial Guinea, but its distribution within this area is poorly known. Three subspecies are recognized. *C. e. camerunensis* occurs in southeastern Nigeria and northern Cameroon on the upper course of

the Cross River, between the Benue and Sanaga Rivers. *C. e. erythrotis* is endemic to Bioko. The third subspecies, *C. e. sclateri*, occurs between the Niger and Cross Rivers in southern Nigeria. (Some scientists believe that *C. e. sclateri* may be a separate species altogether). No population estimates are available.

Preferred habitat is primary lowland rain forest, but it can also include secondary, immature, and seasonally flooded forest.

History and Conservation Measures

Habitat destruction and hunting are the primary threats to this species. By 1974 rapid deforestation was occurring throughout much of its limited geographical range in Nigeria and Cameroon. A 1988 survey of the Akri area found it to be under heavy human exploitation, including widespread farming, tree cutting for fuel and timber, and hunting. While wildlife in remote areas of Bioko had long been spared agricultural development, new pressures to develop the island's natural resources may threaten remaining areas of habitat.

Protected populations exist within the Douala-

Edea Reserve and Korup National Park in Cameroon, but Douala-Edea is under pressure from proposals for oil exploration. The Cross River National Park contains *C. e. camerunensis* but hunting, although illegal, is still widespread. The integration of conservation priorities with development of resources is essential for Bioko as the pace of development increases. Several conservation projects have been proposed, and educational programs to inform residents of the need to safeguard natural resources have been suggested. Further information on the status, distribution, and ecology of the species throughout its range is urgently needed.

Preuss's guenon

Cercopithecus preussi

Phylum	Chordata
Class	Mammalia
Order	Primates
Family	Cercopithecidae
Status	Endangered, IUCN
	Appendix II, CITES
Range	Cameroon; Bioko (Equatorial Guinea); Nigeria

Description and Biology

This monkey has a head and body length of 15-28 in (38-71 cm). Its fur is a mixture of black, white, and gray hairs that give a grizzled effect to the coat. There are white markings below the eyes and under the chin. Tail is prehensile in juveniles, but in adults it is used for balance. The guenon is reported to be a good swimmer. An eclectic and opportunistic feeder, it eats leaves, fruit, and other vegetation, supplemented by insects and small birds and reptiles.

Groups tend to be small, ranging between two and nine individuals, and composed of a single adult male with one or more females. Little is known about this animal's reproductive biology.

Habitat and Current Distribution

This species occurs only in Nigeria, Cameroon, and on the island of Bioko. There are no estimates of population size.

Preferred habitat is primary and old secondary montane rain forest above 3,200 ft (1,000 m). It can also occur in isolated forest patches in mountainous grasslands.

History and Conservation Measures

The population of Preuss's guenon is thought to be declining as a result of deforestation and hunting.

By 1974 the forests of the Mt. Cameroon area were being logged, drastically reducing available habitat for the guenon and forcing it to higher elevations. Hunting and trapping in this area have reduced populations even further. Although not confirmed, there may be a population in the Oban Hills Forest Reserves of Nigeria. Little information on conditions in Bioko is available, but remote areas with poor soils for agriculture have been left relatively undisturbed. The confiscation of firearms in this region in 1976 have helped reduce hunting pressures for this monkey.

Preuss's guenon is found in the Cross River National Park in Nigeria. In Cameroon, Korup National Park may contain some guenons, although the population density is likely to be low. Remaining areas of habitat on and around Mt. Cameroon need to be strictly protected from encroachment and poaching. The species also occurs in the Takamanda Reserve, but the area remains poorly surveyed. On Bioko, plans have been proposed to integrate conservation priorities with the development of natural resources; conservation education has also been proposed to alert residents to the value of forest resources. Surveys of the status and distribution of Preuss's guenon are needed in all remaining areas where it may occur. Enforcement of protective legislation and restriction of hunting are also essential.

Black colobus

Colobus satanas

Phylum	Chordata
Class	Mammalia
Order	Primates
Family	Cercopithecidae
Status	Vulnerable, IUCN
	Endangered, USFWS
	Appendix II, CITES
Range	Cameroon; Congo; Equatorial Guinea (including Bioko); Gabon

Description and Biology

The black colobus is a slender monkey with an average head and body length of 20-28 in (51-71 cm) and weight of 13-30 lb (6-13 kg). As the common name suggests, its coat is totally black, and its long tail measures 22-39 in (56-99 cm). Active during the day, the black colobus spends most of its time in trees and feeds primarily on seeds, supplemented by leaves.

Group size tends to be small, averaging from 6 to 13 individuals, including one or more adult males. Home range sizes vary from 170 acres (70 ha) in coastal forests to 450 acres (180 ha) in inland forests. Little information about reproductive biology is available, but births probably coincide with seasonal abundance of food.

Habitat and Current Distribution

This species has a very limited distribution and is restricted to southern Cameroon, Equatorial Guinea including Bioko (Fernando Po), western and central Gabon, and probably extending into Congo (Brazzaville); it does not occur in Zaire. There are no estimates of population.

Preferred habitat is coastal evergreen rain forest, typically high in the canopy of dense, primary forest; it has also been found in montane and swamp forests.

History and Conservation Measures

The black colobus monkey was once found throughout the evergreen forest belt between the Sanaga, Bioko, and Zaire Rivers. There is no estimate of initial population. While hunting remains a serious problem, the primary threat to this species' survival is disturbance and destruction of habitat. Vast woodland areas have been cleared for logging and this monkey is apparently unable to survive in secondary forest and requires high canopy habitats. Clearance for agricultural development has also reduced available habitat.

This species occurs in the Douala-Edea Reserve in Cameroon, which is protected from illegal logging. It is also known to occur in the Lop Okanda Reserve in central Gabon and is currently well protected there from logging and hunting pressures. The black colobus is now found only in protected or inaccessible areas. Studies providing information on status and distribution are urgently needed as a basis for further conservation planning.

Preuss's red colobus

Procolobus badius (pennanti) preussi

Phylum	Chordata
Class	Mammalia
Order	Primates
Family	Cercopithecidae
Status	Endangered, IUCN
	Endangered, USFWS
	Appendix II, CITES
Range	Cameroon; Nigeria (ex?)

Description and Biology

This monkey has a dark gray coat that is flecked with brown and a saddle-shaped, reddish brown area on its back and shoulders. Its lower limbs and underparts are orangish brown. Average head and body length is 18-26 in (46-66 cm), weight is 11-25 lb (5-11 kg), and tail length is 20-31 in (51-79 cm); the male is larger than the female. Most of its time is spent in treetops, with only an occasional descent to the forest floor. Its diet includes leaves, flowers, buds, fruit, and seeds.

Groups can be very large, sometimes consisting of 30-80 animals. Home range varies widely from 20-300 acres (8-120 ha). Mating probably takes place at any time during the year, and one young is born after a gestation period of 180-210 days.

Habitat and Current Distribution

Preuss's red colobus monkey occurs only in western Cameroon along the border with Nigeria. Although total population is unknown, one estimate based on observed group sizes of 30 animals in Korup National Park indicates that at least 8,000 survive in all known inhabited areas. However, this estimate is based on a nine-month study carried out in only one small part of Korup National Park.

Primary habitat is coastal lowland evergreen forest, typically in areas with rainfall over 40 in (100 cm) per month.

History and Conservation Measures

There are no estimates of initial population, but the range of this species was thought to have extended from the Cross River to the Sanaga River in coastal forests of Cameroon and in the lowland forests of southeast Nigeria, where it is probably now extinct. The majority of the population is now thought to be found in Korup National Park, with some animals in the Ejhagen Reserve to the north, where logging poses a threat to their continued existence. Due to a dependence on high canopy trees, the animals are particularly vulnerable to logging or activities disrupting the canopy. They are also subject to hunting and are commonly taken for food. Hunting has probably caused local extinctions, such as in the Barombi Mbo Forest. Korup became a national park in 1984 and contains the only protected viable population of this monkey.

Tana River red colobus

Procolobus rufomitratus rufomitratus
(P. badius rufomitratus)

Phylum	Chordata
Class	Mammalia
Order	Primates
Family	Cercopithecidae
Status	Vulnerable, IUCN
	Endangered, USFWS
	Appendix I, CITES
Range	Kenya

Description and Biology

The Tana River red colobus is one of six subspecies of the eastern red colobus. As with the other red colobus monkeys, the Tana River colobus is distinguished by its generally red appearance: the top of its head is red, and the lateral surface of the upper arms is reddish brown. They are about 18-26 in (46-66 cm) long and weigh 11-25 lb (5-11 kg). Their dark gray tail is approximately 20-30 in (51-76 cm) long. The red colobus monkey spends most of its time in trees and seldom descends to the ground. It feeds during the day on young leaves, green fruit, leaf and floral buds, mature leaves, and flowers. Red colobus monkeys demonstrate a variety of vocalizations, including a loud, alarm bark.

Group size ranges between 12 and 20 individuals, with each group containing one or, at the most, two adult males. Each group travels about 2,000 ft (610 m) a day within a home range of 22 acres (9 ha), depending upon the availability of food. Adult and subadult females emigrate between groups and, as a result, group size can vary throughout the year. Mating is apparently possible throughout the year. One young is usually born after a gestation period of 180-210 days.

Habitat and Current Distribution

This species is endemic to small patches of gallery forest along the floodplains of the Tana River in Kenya. Four subspecies of the eastern red colobus—*Procolobus rufomaitratus tholloni, P. r. foai, P. r. ellioti,* and *P. r. oustaleti*—are found in Zaire on the east side of the country. The Uganda red colobus (*P. r. tephrosceles*) is found in southwestern Uganda and western Tanzania.

Primary habitat of the Tana River colobus is small patches of gallery forest, often less than 5 acres (2 ha) in size, which are seasonally inundated by the Tana River. The gallery forest is made up of a mosaic of habitats, and this monkey is found in areas closest to the river.

History and Conservation Measures

In 1972, population was estimated at 1,860 and in 1975 at 1,245-1,700; by 1985 it had declined drastically to only 200-300 individuals. Population declines were associated chiefly with the clearance of the gallery forest for agriculture. However, the loss of trees for canoe construction, fires set to enhance grass production on the surrounding floodplains, and habitat alteration from the grazing of cattle have also contributed to the loss of habitat for this animal. Changes in the water table and flooding regime due to the construction of dams upriver from the Tana River Reserve appears to have drastically slowed the rate of vegetation and tree regrowth. Since the colobus is a selective feeder unable to utilize secondary forest, the absence of mature trees has had a detrimental effect on the species.

The 65-sq-mi (170-sq-km) Tana River Reserve was created along the banks of this river in 1976. However, only 4 sq mi (11 sq km) of this reserve is suitable for the Tana River red colobus, and only 50-60 percent of the remaining population of this species is protected in the reserve. A project has been initiated that aims to deal with the causes of forest destruction and to enhance forest regeneration in the reserve. In addition, intensive management of the red colobus subpopulations is being considered.

Zanzibar red colobus

Procolobus kirkii
(Procolobus badius kirkii)

Phylum	Chordata
Class	Mammalia
Order	Primates
Family	Cercopithecidae
Status	Endangered, IUCN
	Endangered, USFWS
	Appendix I, CITES
Range	Zanzibar (Tanzania)

Description and Biology

As its common name indicates, this monkey has reddish fur with grayish brown underparts and limbs, a dark face, and grayish side whiskers. Average head and body length is 18-29 in (46-74 cm), weight is 13-27 lb (6-12 kg), and tail length is 16-37 in (41-94 cm); the male is larger and heavier than the female. Rarely descending to the ground, it uses all four limbs to travel among tree branches, sometimes leaping or swinging by the arms. Diet has not been described in detail, but it probably consists primarily of leaves, supplemented by flowers, seeds, and fruits.

Groups tend to be large, containing around 35 animals with at least two adult males. Home ranges vary widely from 20-325 acres (8-130 ha) and often overlap; separate groups are often found in close proximity to each other. Mating can take place at any time during the year. One young is usually born after a gestation period of somewhere between 135-195 days.

Habitat and Current Distribution

This species is endemic to Zanzibar, an island off the coast of Tanzania. It is now known to occur at very low densities throughout the island in small, isolated forest patches, while higher densities are found only in four southern forests: Jozani Forest, Muungwi Forest, the Muyuni coastal strip, and Uzi Island. Small populations of translocated animals are found at Masingini, Kichwele, and on Pemba Islands. Total population was estimated in 1981 to be almost 1,500 animals in 75 groups. Largest concentrations are approximately 235 animals in Jozani, 200 in Muungwi, 350 in the Muyuni coastal strip, and 300 on Uzi Island.

Preferred habitat includes areas of ground water, swamp forest, scrub forest, or mangrove swamp.

History and Conservation Measures

The primary threat to the Zanzibar red colobus monkey is habitat destruction as a result of timber felling, charcoal production, clearance for cultivation, and bush burning to facilitate hunting of pigs and duikers. In addition, animals are occasionally shot for food, sport, or as a supposed crop pest; laws protecting this monkey are not well enforced.

The Jozani Forest was designated as a forest reserve in 1960. It has been recommended as a national park and its boundaries expanded to provide larger areas of suitable habitat and to provide access to adjoining forests. Other areas with major populations, such as the Muyuni coastal strip and the southern part of Uzi Island, should also be designated as national parks. None of these monkeys are known to exist in captivity, and no wild populations are currently protected effectively. Jozani Forest Reserve and other remaining areas of habitat require full legal and practical protection if this species is to be saved.

Lion-tailed macaque

Macaca silenus

Phylum	Chordata
Class	Mammalia
Order	Primates
Family	Cercopithecidae
Status	Endangered, IUCN
	Endangered, USFWS
	Appendix I, CITES
Range	India

Description and Biology

The most arboreal of all macaques, the lion-tailed macaque has large tufts of gray hair that frame its face and contrast with its overall brownish black coat. The 10-18 in (25-46 cm) tail from which it gets its common name is covered with shorter hairs and has a slight tuft at the tip. Head and body length averages 18-26 in (46-66 cm) and weight is 13-20 lb (6-9 kg); the male is substantially larger than the female. This species can move easily through the tops of trees but also travels well on the ground and is a good swimmer. It is active during the day and feeds on plants and fruits as well as on insects and small vertebrates. There is even speculation that lion-tailed macaques may act as crop raiders on occasion.

Groups may contain 20-30 individuals, including males, females, and young, and occupy a home range averaging 0.4-2 sq mi (1-5 sq km). Female receptiveness to mating is indicated by perineal swelling, and females usually give birth to a single young after a 180-day gestation period. Young are nursed for at least a year.

Habitat and Current Distribution

The lion-tailed macaque is found in fragmented patches of moist evergreen forest in the Western Ghats (a mountain range) of peninsular India at elevations between 1,600-5,000 ft (400-1,500 m). It is found in the southern part of the range in Kerala and Tamil Nadu and in the northern part of the range in Karnataka. Total population may range from 3,600-5,000 individuals; the largest population is found in Karnataka, where as many as 3,000 may occur.

Lion-tailed macaque.

History and Conservation Measures

In the early 1980s, the total wild population of lion-tailed macaques was estimated at no more than 2,000, but by 1985 a large population was known to exist in Karnataka. The most serious threat to this species is continued loss of habitat through conversion to plantation agriculture, the development of hydroelectric and irrigation projects, road construction, and mining.

Drill

Mandrillus (Papio) leucophaeus

Phylum	Chordata
Class	Mammalia
Order	Primates
Family	Cercopithecidae
Status	Endangered, IUCN
	Endangered, USFWS
	Appendix I, CITES
Range	Cameroon; Bioko (Equatorial Guinea); Gabon (?); Nigeria

Description and Biology

The drill is a highly endangered primate that lives in West Africa. It has a tawny-gray coat and white cheeks and chin hair that contrast sharply with a hairless, black, shiny face. It has a short tail about 3-4 in (7-10 cm) long. Adults are highly sexually dimorphic; males weigh up to 77 lb (35 kg), over twice the size of females. They have pink, red, violet, and blue rump colorations. They are also distinguished by a large, round face with a prominent ridge on either side of the nose and a red streak on the lower lip. Both sexes possess sternal scent glands.

Drills are mainly terrestrial, feeding on fruits, plant material, and invertebrates; they ascend trees to forage and to sleep at night. Typical group size is 15-30 animals, which may contain only one adult male. Solitary adult males are also observed. Groups may split to form foraging sub-groups or coalesce at certain times of the year to form super-groups of 100-200 individuals. Super-group function is unclear but may allow females to emigrate from their natal group. Drills have large home ranges, traveling widely each day. Reproductive biology is not well known, but may

Drill.

correlate with seasonal food availability. One young is normally born, possible in alternate years, after a gestation period of approximately 180 days.

Habitat and Current Distribution

Drills are restricted to the area between the Cross River in southeast Nigeria and the Sanaga River in southwest Cameroon and to the island of Bioko, Equatorial Guinea. Total range is about 15,400 sq mi (40,000 sq km), roughly 80 percent of which lies in Cameroon, but usable habitat is only about half of this due to fragmentation by forest clearance, roads, cultivation, and human settlement. The Bioko population is likely a different subspecies (*M. l. poensis*) from the mainland population (*M. l. mundamensis*). Total population may be several thousand, but the species is thought to be threatened with extinction.

Habitat of the drill is lowland rain forest and mature secondary rain forest to elevations of 3,300 ft (1,000 m); drills seem to prefer stony, steep terrain, but this may be a response to hunting pressure.

History and Conservation Measures

There are no estimates of initial population for this species, but numbers are believed to have de-clined dramatically in recent years. Habitat destruction and hunting within its very limited range are the major threats. Mainland habitat is fragmented into at least 10 permanently isolated habitat islands, with probably two on Bioko. Extensive logging, particularly in Cameroon, is currently destroying and further fragmenting remaining habitats. Logging roads open areas to cultivators, causing further habitat loss, and allow increased access by hunters.

Drills are hunted commercially for their meat, which is preferred for its sweet, fatty flavor. They are peculiarly vulnerable to local hunting methods whereby dogs are used to locate a group and hold it a bay in small trees; in these situations, hunters have been known to shoot an entire group. Hunters report decreased sitings of super-groups, a situation with potentially deleterious genetic consequences.

Drills occur in Korup National Park, Cameroon, and Cross River National Park, Nigeria; portions of these parks are contiguous along 11 miles (17 km) of border. Protected areas have been proposed for Bioko. However, the parks have yet to provide any effective protection from hunting, and outside them hunting and habitat destruction continue unchecked, although the species is protected by law in Nigeria and Cameroon.

Mandrill

Mandrillus (Papio) sphinx

Phylum . . . . Chordata
Class . . . . Mammalia
Order . . . . Primates
Family . . . . Cercopithecidae
Status . . . . Vulnerable, IUCN
Endangered, USFWS
Appendix I, CITES
Range . . . . Cameroon; Congo; Equatorial Guinea; Gabon

Description and Biology

The largest of the monkeys, with a shoulder height of 20 in (51 cm) and males weighing 119 lb (54 kg), the mandrill is easily recognized by its brilliant face coloring. The adult male of the species has prominent ridges on each side of the nose. The ridges are bright blue and a narrow band of red runs down the center of the muzzle to and around the nostrils. The female and juveniles have less pronounced ridges and their face coloring is less brilliant. All mandrills have black muzzles when they are young, and color gradually develops as they mature, remaining somewhat muted in females. Despite its formidable appearance, the mandrill is reported to be gentle.

The mandrill has a beard, crest, and mane. It has a mottled greenish brown coat and lighter underparts. Head and body length averages 26-31 in (66-78 cm) and tail length is 3 in (7 cm). The adult male mandrill usually forages on the ground, and females and juveniles are typically found in mid-level trees. They are active during the day—except in the hot afternoon when they seek shelter—and sleep in the trees at night. The mandrills have a diverse diet, which includes fruits, buds, leaves, roots, insects, fungus, and seeds. Oil palm fruits (*Elaeis guineensis*) are frequently eaten from local plantations and, when food is scarce, the mandrill sometimes raids crops from farms. It has also been observed to eat small vertebrates.

This species is thought to have a flexible social organization and lives in a single-male unit with 20-40 members. Home ranges may be between 12-19 sq mi (30-50 sq km). Little information is available about reproductive biology, but most births take place between December and April. Mating season is believed to be between July and October. Gestation period in captive animals is 168-176 days, but it has not been confirmed in the wild.

Habitat and Current Distribution

The mandrill is restricted to forest areas south of the Sanaga River in southwestern Cameroon, Rio Muni (Equatorial Guinea), western Gabon, and southwestern Congo (Brazzaville). There are no estimates of population size.

Mandrills are found in tropical rain forest, montane forest, thick secondary forest, and thick bush.

History and Conservation Measures

Drastic declines are thought to have occurred in the population of this species in recent years. Habitat destruction and hunting are the main threats to the mandrill and effective protection is lacking in

Female mandrill with her young.

most areas. It is relatively easy to hunt mandrills because they emit loud calls. Dogs are sometimes used to chase mandrills up trees, where they are easily targeted by hunters with guns.

The degree of threat and level of conservation effort exerted on behalf of the mandrill varies with each country in which this monkey occurs. In Cameroon, the mandrill is hunted for food, and much of the forest within its range has been cleared or logged. It does not occur in any current or proposed national parks, but is found in the Campo Reserve; the reserve has been heavily logged, and further use of the land is planned. Effective protection of existing reserves is essential.

In Rio Muni (Equatorial Guinea), the mandrill is considered a source of food by local people. As a result it is heavily hunted and has become extremely rare. Logging removed the majority of commercial tree species by 1972. It is not legally protected in this area.

In Gabon, it is hunted for meat and threatened by the timber industry. Logging also increases the local demand for meat by the timber workers, and many hunt and log illegally inside reserves and parks. It is present in Wonga-Wongué Reserve and in five other reserves, including the large Lopé Okanda Reserve; however, settlements, hunting, and logging still take place within many of these areas. Effective protection of these reserves is essential. In Congo (Brazzaville), game meat is the most important source of protein after fish for the local people, and hunting and poaching of the mandrill (and other species as well) are widespread. Much of the forest has been destroyed and replaced by fire-maintained grassland. Illegal logging occurs within the reserves. Suitable mandrill habitat is now limited to small forest blocks in the south and west. The range of the mandrill should encompass four reserves, but these do not appear to have been formally designated and are primarily fire-maintained grassland, which is unsuitable for the mandrill. It is not known if viable populations of mandrills are found in any of the reserves or if they are adequately protected in these areas.

The mandrill lives at relatively low density throughout its range and is poorly protected. It could be threatened with complete extinction if populations continue to decline under pressure from hunting and habitat disturbance. Surveys are needed to determine where viable populations still exist, and areas containing mandrills should be given immediate protection.

Pig-tailed snub-nosed monkey

Nasalis (Simias) concolor

Phylum	Chordata
Class	Mammalia
Order	Primates
Family	Cercopithecidae
Status	Endangered, IUCN
	Endangered, USFWS
	Appendix I, CITES
Range	Mentawai Islands (Indonesia)

Description and Biology

Like other members of its genus, the pig-tailed snub-nosed monkey (also known as the pig-tailed snub-nosed langur) is fairly thickset and has a distinctive nose. The species occurs in two color variants. The most common is a brownish gray shade with lighter areas on the nape, shoulder, upper back, and upper arms; the hands, feet, buttocks, and face are black, with the face bordered with white hair. Less commonly, body color is cream to yellowish brown. Length of head and body averages 18-22 in (45-55 cm), while weight averages 15-16 lb (6.8-7.2 kg). The tail measures 4-7.5 in (10-19 cm) and is bare except for a small tuft of light brown hair at the tip. Arms are almost as long as legs. This species spends its time in trees, descending to the ground only if disturbed. It feeds on leaves, leaf petioles, flowers, figs, and twig bark.

A family group is usually made up of a male, a female, and up to three of their offspring, who range over an area of 25-75 acres (10-30 ha). The species is sexually dimorphic, with males generally weighing up to 19.4 lb (8.8 kg) and females weighing up to 15 lb (6.8 kg). Some populations are monogamous, while others are polygamous, with one adult male living with up to five adult females. Little is known about reproductive biology, but apparent newborns have been observed in June and July.

Habitat and Current Distribution

The pig-tailed snub-nosed monkey occurs on the Mentawai Islands, west of Sumatra. Population is estimated at fewer than 10,000 individuals.

Preferred habitat is lowland rain forest, swamp forest, and mangrove forest.

History and Conservation Measures

In 1980, the population on one of the larger islands alone, Siberut, was estimated at 19,000 individuals. In general, population is believed to have drastically declined, and this species has become extinct on some of the smaller islands. The chief cause of the decline is hunting of the animal by humans for food. In addition, the primary forest, upon which the species depends, is being cleared for logging.

Because of restricted distribution and isolation, island populations are always most vulnerable to extinction. In 1981, Siberut Island was declared a UNESCO Biosphere Reserve. This step, along with the establishment of the Teitei Batti Sanctuary, may help to protect the species on this island. A second protected area, specifically for primates including the pig-tailed snub-nosed monkey, has been proposed for South Pagai Island.

Proboscis monkey

Nasalis larvatus

Phylum	Chordata
Class	Mammalia
Order	Primates
Family	Cercopithecidae
Status	Vulnerable, IUCN
	Endangered, USFWS
	Appendix I, CITES
Range	Borneo (Brunei; Indonesia; Malaysia)

Description and Biology

The feature that gives this odd-looking monkey its common name is the large, tongue-shaped nose of the adult male. The nose can be as much as 4 in (10 cm) long and sometimes hangs down over the mouth, but extends when the male makes a loud honking noise. In the female, the nose is slightly enlarged but not as pendulous as in the male; in young, the nostrils are upturned. The coat ranges from light to reddish brown with underparts that are gray or cream colored; facial skin is reddish in adults, blue in infants. Average head and body length is 21-30 in (53-76 cm), weight is 16-53 lb (7-24 kg), and tail is 22-30 in (56-76 cm); the male can be up to twice as large as the female, with males typically weighing 44-48 lb (20-22 kg) and females weighing 22-26 lb (10-12 kg). The proboscis monkey moves easily through the branches of trees and, because of partially webbed hind feet, is a good swimmer in and below the water. It feeds during the day on fruit, flowers, leaves, seeds, and aquatic vegetation.

Groups range in size from 3-30 individuals, usu-

Proboscis monkey.

ally based on one adult male and a number of adult females; they occupy a home range of less than one square mile (2 sq km). Large troops often feed together, but individuals usually sleep alone in a tree in fairly close proximity. Mating is probably possible at any time during the year, and a single young is born after a gestation period of around 166 days.

Habitat and Current Distribution

The proboscis monkey is endemic to the island of Borneo. A 1986 study estimated the total population at approximately 250,000 individuals. The current population may be considerably smaller; one researcher recently estimated the total population in all protected areas combined at less than 5,000.

Preferred habitat is mangrove swamp, peat swamp, and riverine forest.

History and Conservation Measures

Because of its inaccessible habitat, the proboscis monkey was safe for many years from human intrusion. Today, even the mangrove swamps are being cleared and the destruction is reducing suitable habitat for this monkey. As the species becomes more accessible, it is vulnerable to hunting by natives who consider its flesh a delicacy.

Studies have been initiated at the Samunsam Wildlife Sanctuary, where the relief of hunting pressure is an urgent priority, and at Tanjung Puting National Park. Its presence has also been established in Kutai National Park in Kalimantan. In Tanjung Puting, human settlement, increased river traffic, river pollution, and poaching are all severe threats to the species. A survey is needed to determine the monkey's distribution and abundance within and outside reserved areas in order to identify populations for which protection can be established. The species is declining very rapidly throughout its entire range.

Grizzled leaf monkey

Presbytis comata

Phylum	Chordata
Class	Mammalia
Order	Primates
Family	Cercopithecidae
Status	Endangered, IUCN
Range	Java (Indonesia)

Description and Biology

The grizzled leaf monkey is also sometimes called the Javan leaf monkey. Its coat is light gray, flecked with black or brown, and its underparts are pale to white. Its hands and crown are dark with an area of white on the brow and around the face. Average head and body length is 16.5-24 in (42-61 cm), weight is 11-18 lb (5-8.2 kg), and tail length is 20-33 in (51-84 cm). Spending most of the time in trees, this monkey feeds during the day on leaves and seeds.

Groups contain an adult male, two or more adult females, and varying numbers of young who occupy a home range of 75-100 acres (30-40 ha). Little information is available about social or ecological behavior or about reproductive biology.

Habitat and Current Distribution

This species is found in patches of tropical rain forests in West and Central Java. Population figures are unavailable, although one 1986 study estimated the total population at 8,040, with 3,650 of those in protected areas.

History and Conservation Measures

There are no recent estimates of initial population, but the grizzled leaf monkey has become highly endangered. Clearing of the forests has reduced suitable habitat and isolated small populations in the remaining patches of forest.

Gunung Halimun Reserve in West Java contains the largest primary rain forest in Java and is regarded as the remaining stronghold for the species.

Tonkin snub-nosed monkey

Pygathrix (Rhinopithecus) avunculus

Phylum	Chordata
Class	Mammalia
Order	Primates
Family	Cercopithecidae
Status	Endangered, IUCN
	Endangered, USFWS
	Appendix I, CITES
Range	Vietnam

Description and Biology

The Tonkin snub-nosed monkey has long, blackish hair on its back and limbs with pale yellow to orange underparts; the forehead and face are cream to yellow and the sides of the neck orange. There is a cream to white area on the rump, back of the legs, and around the 26-36 in (66-92 cm) tail, which is blackish with a light tip. Average head and body length is 20-24 in (51-61 cm). Although it spends most of its time in trees, this monkey sometimes descends to the ground for feeding.

Little is known about the social organization and mating behavior of the species. However individuals may interact in a manner similar to that of other snub-nosed monkeys. Other species of this genus form units of one dominant male, three to five adult females, and various young. These units in turn may combine to form large troops of up to hundreds of animals. Individual groups have non-exclusive home ranges averaging up to eight square miles (20 sq km). One young is usually born to a female snub-nosed monkey in the spring or summer after a gestation period of approximately 200 days.

Habitat and Current Distribution

This species occurs in the bamboo jungles or forests in the limestone hills and mountain areas of northern Vietnam, where only a few hundred are estimated to survive.

History and Conservation Measures

While there are no estimates of initial population, the Tonkin snub-nosed monkey is now considered to be one of the most highly endangered primates in Vietnam. Hunting, in addition to habitat disruption caused by decades of warfare, has reduced the population to a dangerously low level. Fur and various other body parts of the snub-nosed monkey are considered to have valuable medicinal properties and make the species a target of hunters. In addition, sporadic military skirmishes on the border with China may be causing the loss of moist evergreen forest in northern Vietnam. Habitat disruption has also been exacerbated by a rapidly growing human population. Surveys are necessary to provide information on the diversity, distribution, habitat requirements, and status of primate populations in Vietnam, and it will be necessary to strengthen the management and protection of existing reserves and/or to declare new ones.

Guizhou snub-nosed monkey

Pygathrix (Rhinopithecus) brelichi

Phylum	Chordata
Class	Mammalia
Order	Primates
Family	Cercopithecidae
Status	Endangered, IUCN
	Endangered, USFWS
	Appendix I, CITES
Range	China

Description and Biology

Not much is known about the Guizhou snub-nosed monkey. Adult males of this species have been described as having golden hair on the chest, inner arms, and brow; brown on the back; black on the outer limbs and tail; and white on the tips of the ears and tail. It also has a bright patch between the shoulders. Head and body length averages 29 in (73 cm), and this monkey has a long tail averaging about 38 in (97 cm). It appears to spend most of its time in trees but sometimes feeds on the ground. Diet includes fir and pine needles, fruits, leaves, buds, and bamboo shoots.

Groups contain one dominant male, three to five females, and young of various ages who inhabit a home range of almost 8 sq mi (20 sq km). Sometimes groups gather together in troops of hundreds of animals. One young is born after a gestation period of around 200 days; twin births are not uncommon. Most births take place in the spring or summer.

Habitat and Current Distribution

This species occurs only in mountainous northeastern Guizhou in China and may number less than 1,200, perhaps even less than 800, on Mt. Fanjingshan. A relatively warm climate supports broadleaf vegetation, and the species has been found from evergreen forest at 1,600 ft (500 m) elevation to mixed deciduous-evergreen forest at 8,500 ft (2,570 m).

History and Conservation Measures

Following World War II, the expansion of human population, industry, development programs (especially hydrology projects), and agriculture have led to a serious reduction of forest habitat necessary to support primate populations in China. In addition, these monkeys have been subject to intensive hunting for fur and medicinal purposes. In 1978, the Fanjingshan Natural Protected Area was established in part to protect the monkeys and their habitat. It has since been enlarged and declared a Man and the Biosphere Reserve. Although hunting and trapping of monkeys has been stopped by vigorous enforcement, habitat destruction by local people collecting firewood, timber, and wood for charcoal production remains a serious threat.

Black-shanked douc langur

Pygathrix nigripes

Red-shanked douc langur

Pygathrix nemaeus

Phylum	Chordata
Class	Mammalia
Order	Primates
Family	Cercopithecidae
Status	Endangered, IUCN (*P. nemaeus*)
	Indeterminate, IUCN (*P. nigripes*)
	Endangered, USFWS (*P. nemaeus*)
	Appendix I, CITES (*P. nigripes* and *P. nemaeus*)
Range	Kampuchea; Laos; Vietnam (*P. nigripes*)
	China; Kampuchea; Laos; Vietnam (*P. nemaeus*)

Description and Biology

Both species of douc langur are distinguished by vividly colored coats. The back is mottled gray, lighter below, with white rump and tail. In *P. nigripes* the forearms are gray speckled with black, and the shanks of the legs are black. The face is blue to black, with a red-yellow muzzle; the scrotum and inner thighs are blue and the penis red. Length of head and body averages 22-30 in (56-76 cm) and the tail is 22-30 in (56-76 cm). In *P. nemaeus* the forearms are white, and the shanks of the legs are orange-red. The head is brown with a lighter reddish area below the ears. Whiskers are white, and the face is yellow to orange. Length of head and body averages 21-32 in (53-81 cm), and the tail is 22-30 in (56-76 cm). Both species feed during the day on fruits and a variety of leaves.

Only one field study (in 1974) has been undertaken, so information about social and sexual behavior is scarce. It has been suggested that groups of 4-20 individuals usually include one or more adult males, a number of females, and assorted juveniles. Also, births often occur between February and June, when food supply is most abundant. One young is thought to be born after a gestation period of 165-190 days.

Habitat and Current Distribution

The black-shanked douc langur occurs in Vietnam, Laos, and Kampuchea, while the red-shanked douc langur is found in Vietnam, Laos, Kampuchea, and on Hainan Island in the South China Sea. Population figures are not available for either species.

Preferred habitat for both species is tropical rain forest and monsoon forest from sea level to 6,500 ft (200 m), although here again little information is available.

History and Conservation Measures

There are no estimates of initial population sizes, but these species—especially *P. nemaeus*— may be less threatened than previously thought. Nevertheless, habitat disruption has resulted from long-term military conflict. In addition, excessive hunting by local people for food and illegal trade have made serious inroads on the status of the populations. More detailed information about biology and population is necessary to formulate conservation measures.

Sichuan snub-nosed monkey

Pygathrix (Rhinopithecus) roxellana

Phylum	Chordata
Class	Mammalia
Order	Primates
Family	Cercopithecidae
Status	Vulnerable, IUCN
	Endangered, USFWS
	Appendix I, CITES
Range	China; India (?)

Description and Biology

The Sichuan snub-nosed monkey is sometimes called the golden snub-nosed monkey. Its fur is dark brown to black or gray-black over most of the body, and the back is overlaid with long white or silver hairs; underparts and fur around the face and neck are a golden color. Average head and body length is 23-30 in (58-76 cm) and tail length is 21-28 in (53-72 cm). Nose is turned upward, muzzle is white, and upper facial area light blue. The Sichuan snub-nosed monkey spends most of its time in trees, but sometimes feeds on the ground. Diet consists of fir and pine needles, supplemented by leaves, fruits, and bamboo shoots.

Small groups comprised of a dominant male, three to five adult females, and various young join together to form troops of up to hundreds of animals. Home range averages up to eight sq mi (20 sq km). One young is usually born after a gestation period of approximately 200 days. Most births take place in spring or summer.

Habitat and Current Distribution

Isolated populations of Sichuan snub-nosed monkeys have been found in areas extending from Sichuan to southern Gansu, including the Chinese provinces of Hubei, Shaanxi, Gansu, and Sichuan. Overall population is estimated to be 10,000 to 15,000 individuals.

This species is found in conifer and conifer-mixed deciduous/evergreen forest at elevations ranging from 5,000-11,000 ft (1,500-3,400 m), and seasonal migration appears to be a response to the seasonal

Sichuan snub-nosed monkey.

presence of humans at all but the very highest elevations.

History and Conservation Measures

The decline of this species is a result of hunting and habitat destruction. The fur of the snub-nosed monkey has long been believed to have valuable medicinal properties, making it the target of hunters. Destruction of forest in the steep mountains, especially as a consequence of slash-and-burn agriculture, has altered the habitat of primates throughout southwest China. For the most part, this species appears to be surviving human pressures in marginal fringes of vegetation along the high mountain crests. Long-term ecological studies as well as population and status monitoring are needed for all species of snub-nosed monkeys. In addition, authorities should assess the adequacy of reserves in respect to habitat requirements and adequate protection against hunting.

Tonkin leaf monkey

Trachypithecus francoisi

Phylum	Chordata
Class	Mammalia
Order	Primates
Family	Cercopithecidae
Status	Endangered, IUCN
Range	China; Laos; Vietnam

Description and Biology

The Tonkin leaf monkey is also called François' leaf monkey or the Tonkin langur or brow-ridge langur. Six subspecies are recognized and they vary greatly in their appearance. In general, they have a black coat, white facial markings, prominent brow ridges, and a pointed crest. Head and body length averages 10-27 in (51-69 cm), weight is around 13 lb (6 kg), and tail length is 32-36 in (81-91 cm). Diet is vegetarian, consisting mainly of leaves.

Habitat and Current Distribution

This species is known from southeastern to south-central China, northern Vietnam, and central Laos, where it inhabits tropical forests. All six subspecies are of conservation concern. The least threatened is *T. f. francoisi*, which still has a substantial range in Guangxi and Guizhou in south-central China extending into northeastern Vietnam. Even this subspecies is very depleted from habitat loss and overhunting. *T. f. leucocephalus* numbers only 400-600 individuals in Guangxi, China. *T. f. poliocephalus* is known only from extreme northeast Vietnam and might survive only on Cat Ba Island (where numbers are not known but are certainly no more than a few hundred, possibly much less). *T. f. hatinhensis* is known only from a single specimen collected at Xom Cuc in north-central Vietnam. Nothing else is known of this subspecies. *T. f. delacouri* is also known from north-central Vietnam, where it is extremely rare, though a population of 100-150 animals survives in Cuc Phuong National Park. *T. f. laotum* survives in a number of localities in central Laos, though its status is not well known.

History and Conservation Measures

The Tonkin leaf monkey is thought to have been reduced to its present status by excessive hunting and loss of habitat, primarily because of the growing human population. The various subspecies are included in a number of protected areas in China and Vietnam, though in most cases the protection provided is inadequate. The Cuc Phuong National Park has not so far been able to control hunting of *T. f. delacouri*, though strong measures are now being proposed to combat this problem. *T. f. laotum* occurs in a number of proposed protected areas in Laos, but these have not yet been established.

Mentawai gibbon

Hylobates klossii

Phylum	Chordata
Class	Mammalia
Order	Primates
Family	Hylobatidae
Status	Endangered, IUCN
	Endangered, USFWS
	Appendix I, CITES
Range	Mentawai Islands (Indonesia)

Description and Biology

With an upright posture, relatively long legs, and no tail, the Mentawai or Kloss's gibbon has a human-like appearance. Quick and extremely agile like all gibbons, it leaps through the forest canopy using a form of locomotion called brachiation, extending its long arms above the head to swing from one branch to another. Head and body length averages 17-25 in (43-63.5 cm); weight is 9-18 lb (4-8 kg). This is the only gibbon to have an overall black coat. It feeds during the day on ripe fruit, supplemented by small invertebrates. A mated, monogamous pair and two or more of their offspring occupy and defend a home range of 25-85 acres (10-35 ha).

All gibbons engage in singing, but the singing of the Mentawai gibbon—especially that of the female—is particularly noteworthy. The male Mentawai gibbon uses a song or call to proclaim his territory. Lasting from ten minutes to two hours and performed on average every two days, the male's call consists both of whistling notes and longer phrases of about 12 notes followed by a trill. The female's call, performed on average every three or four days, consists of a spectacular series of rising, trilled, and falling notes that announce her claim on her mate. Although nearly all other gibbon singing is done in duet fashion by the male and female—with the pair calling and answering each other in tandem—the singing of the Mentawai gibbon apparently consists of solo acts by the male and female.

A single young is produced every two to three years after a gestation period of seven to eight months. It clings to the mother and is carried during the first year; in the second year, the father may become more involved in its care.

Habitat and Current Distribution

This species is found in rain forests on the Mentawai Islands off western Sumatra in Indonesia. Although population is uncertain, probably fewer than 25,000 individuals remain.

History and Conservation Measures

Habitat disruption has been responsible for a drastic decline and fragmentation in the population of the Mentawai gibbon. In 1977, population was estimated at 84,000 individuals. It has been reduced to present levels because of an increase in human population and the resulting forest clearance for logging, development, and agriculture. Hunting for food and for illegal trade remains an additional threat.

To save this gibbon from extinction, it will be necessary to provide protected reserve areas. Currently, there is one protected area—Teitei Batti Sanctuary on Siberut Island—in the Mentawai Islands, while another protected area has been proposed for South Pagai Island. A captive breeding program would also be of value to provide animals for eventual reintroduction into the wild, although such a measure will be of no use if the remaining habitat is not protected immediately. The mating habits of the gibbon make it difficult to recover from a decreased population: because it is monogamous and because a gibbon without a territory cannot mate, its reproductive capabilities are limited.

Javan gibbon

Hylobates moloch

Phylum	Chordata
Class	Mammalia
Order	Primates
Family	Hylobatidae
Status	Endangered, IUCN
	Endangered, USFWS
	Appendix I, CITES
Range	Java (Indonesia)

Description and Biology

The Javan gibbon, also called the silvery gibbon or moloch gibbon, is considered the rarest and most endangered gibbon species. With an upright posture and no tail, it has a human-like appearance. Agile and quick, it leaps through the forest canopy using a form of locomotion called brachiation, extending its long arms above the head to swing from one branch to another. Head and body length in both males and females averages 33 in (84 cm), while weight in both sexes averages 18-20 lb (8-9 kg). The Javan gibbon has relatively long arms and a dense coat that is silver to blue-gray with a darker chest and cap. It feeds during the day on ripe fruit, supplemented by leaves and small invertebrates.

A mated, monogamous pair and two or more of their offspring occupy and defend a home range of around 42 acres (17 ha). The gibbon performs a type of singing that is instrumental in establishing territory and in maintaining pair bonds: an elaborate, "great" call by the female is followed by a short call by the male. A single young is produced every two to three years after a gestation period of seven to eight months. It clings to the mother and is carried during

the first year; in the second year, the father may become more involved in its care.

Habitat and Current Distribution

The Javan gibbon is confined to forest patches in West and Central Java. Population is believed to be somewhere between 2,400 and 8,000 individuals; a 1986 estimate put the figure at 4,824 individuals.

History and Conservation Measures

Habitat disruption has been responsible for a drastic decline and fragmentation in the population of the Javan gibbon. Perhaps 98 percent of its habitat has been lost to forest clearance as an increased human population leads to increased demand for logging, development, and agriculture. An additional threat to the species is hunting for food and illegal trade.

The mating habits of the gibbon make it difficult to recover from a decreased population. Because it is monogamous, and because a gibbon without a territory cannot mate, its reproductive capabilities are limited. In 1977, population was estimated at 20,000 individuals; its rapid decline to present population levels points out the need for protected reserve areas. Currently, Gunung Hallmun Reserve is thought to contain the largest remaining population, with a 1992 estimate of 852-1,320 individuals. In addition, a captive breeding program would be of value to provide animals for eventual reintroduction into the wild.

Gorilla

Gorilla gorilla

Phylum	Chordata
Class	Mammalia
Order	Primates
Family	Pongidae
Status	Vulnerable, IUCN
	Endangered, USFWS
	Appendix I, CITES
Range	Angola; Burundi (ex?); Cameroon; Central African Republic; Congo; Equatorial Guinea; Gabon; Nigeria; Rwanda; Uganda; Zaire

Description and Biology

The largest of the living primates, the gorilla is considered the most intelligent land animal other than humans. When standing on its hind legs, the male averages 5-5.75 ft (150-175 cm) in height and the female may reach 5 ft (150 cm). Male gorillas can weigh 300-500 lb (135-230 kg), females 200-250 lb (90-110 kg). The coat coloring varies from brown-gray to black depending upon the subspecies. In males, the hair on the back turns silver after 10 years of age; the male also has a sagittal crest—a large bone on top of the skull running from back to front—that supports the animal's massive jaw muscles and produces the distinctive high forehead. Both sexes have small ears and broad nostrils surrounded by nasal rings and black, hairless skin.

Gorillas are active during the day, slowly foraging for herbs, shrubs, and vines that make up the majority of its diet. Groups in West Africa may also eat fruit. During the wet season—from April until June—gorillas may move as little as 1,500 ft (450 m) a day in search of food, while during the dry season—from July until August—they may travel almost a mile (1.6 km). Depending on the group, the yearly range will vary from approximately 2 to 14 sq mi (5-36 sq km). At night, adults and sub-adults build individual nests from branches and leaves on the ground, in low vegetation, or in trees.

Gorillas live in relatively permanent groups led by a mature male—or silverback—and including two to four adult females and two to five young under the age of eight. Social behavior in gorilla groups focuses on the silverback; when resting at midday, females and sub-adults will groom him, but will rarely groom one another. Females also keep their infants nearby him, fostering a bond between the silverback and their offspring while also ensuring his protection from predators and other adult males. Once sexually mature, most young males leave the group to form their own harems; those that remain are often sons of the silverback that will inherit leadership. Females also leave the group upon reaching sexual maturity, joining lone males or other harems. However, they rarely stay with the first male to which they attach themselves.

Females in the wild begin to breed when 10 years old, males from 15-20 years. Breeding can take place any time during the year. Birth of a single young, weighing about 4 lb (2 kg), occurs after a gestation period of 250-270 days. The mother nurses

Gorilla.

the infant for 2.5-3 years and carries it for the first few months of life. At eight or nine weeks it begins to crawl and walks in seven to ten months. Infant mortality in gorilla groups averages about 45 percent, and females successfully raise only two to three young during their life. Adults have been known to live to almost 50 years of age.

Despite its ferocious image, the gorilla is not an aggressive animal. Even in a clash between two adult males, most of the conflict consists of aggressive posturing, roaring, and chest-beating, rather than physical contact.

Scientists have recognized three subspecies of gorillas: the western lowland gorilla (*G. g. gorilla*), the eastern lowland gorilla (*G. g. graueri*), and the mountain gorilla (*G. g. berengei*).

Habitat and Current Distribution

The western lowland gorilla is found in Gabon, Rio Muni (Equatorial Guinea), Congo, Cameroon, Central African Republic, Nigeria, and Angola. The population size is uncertain, but is estimated at 35,000-45,000, with the largest population in Gabon. The eastern lowland gorilla occurs in eastern Zaire. Population is estimated at 3,000-5,000. The mountain gorilla is found in the Virunga volcanoes region of Rwanda, Uganda, and Zaire, and in the Bwindi Forest Reserve of Uganda. Considered highly endangered, probably fewer than 400 survive.

Preferred habitats are forest edges, secondary forest (primary forest to a lesser degree), mountain forest, riverine forest and, in certain seasons, bamboo forest.

History and Conservation Measures

Hunting for capture and food posed the earliest danger to the gorilla. Hunting for capture was particularly damaging to the breeding population as it usually focused on infants and often resulted in the slaughter of the mother. Trade restrictions have diminished the market for animals caught in the wild, reducing hunting for capture. Hunting for food, however, has increased.

Currently, the most serious threat to the gorilla population is habitat destruction. Commercial logging as well as forest clearance for agricultural, pastoral, residential, and industrial use permanently usurps gorilla habitat. Continuing human population growth puts increasing pressure on limited forest habitat.

Conservation efforts to provide protected reserves for the gorilla are made difficult by the economic concerns of an increasing human population. The mountain gorilla has been the focus of an extensive conservation program in Rwanda and Zaire. Political unrest in Rwanda, however, threatens the program as humans retreat to the reserves to escape the violence in cities and villages. Present conservation efforts for the species as a whole should be directed towards implementation of protection laws. Also, laws prohibiting, rather than just controlling, the capture and sale of gorillas need to be passed and enforced in all countries within the species' range. Gazetting of additional reserve areas is desirable. Finally, tourism should be more intensively developed, thus ensuring that gorillas in their natural environment are more valuable than those killed by poachers or captured for zoos.

Pygmy chimpanzee (Bonobo)

Pan paniscus

Phylum	Chordata
Class	Mammalia
Order	Primates
Family	Pongidae
Status	Vulnerable, IUCN
	Endangered, USFWS
	Appendix I, CITES
Range	Zaire

Description and Biology

The pygmy chimpanzee, also called the dwarf chimpanzee or bonobo, differs in build but is not significantly different in body weight or stature from the eastern subspecies of the chimpanzee (*Pan troglodytes schweinfurthii*). The species was originally diagnosed from its cranium which is small and resembles that of a juvenile chimpanzee, hence the misleading common name. Average stature is 46 in (1.2 m) for males and 44 in (1.1 m) for females. Body weights for wild animals range from 81-134 lb (37-61 kg) for males and 59-84 lb (27-38 kg) for females. The skin and pelage is dark, and the face is black from birth except for pink pigmentation around the lips and on the upper eyelids. Head hair is long and parted in the middle. Adults do not bald with age. The ears are small, set close to the head and partially obscured by long cheek whiskers. Relative to the chimpanzee and gorilla, the pygmy chimpanzee has the longest legs and shortest arms.

The pygmy chimpanzee can move long distances through the forest canopy employing quadrupedal locomotion, arm swinging, scrambling, leaping and diving to move from tree to tree. Like the other African apes, it knuckle-walks on the ground. The bonobo also has been known to wade through shallow water. Night nests are built in trees with a median height of 43-56 ft (13-17 m). During the day, it feeds mainly on fruit, supplemented by leaves, pith, flowers, seeds, fungus, invertebrates and sometimes infant duikers or other small mammals such as flying squirrels. Fibrous plant foods appear to be important.

Estimates of community size range from 30-150 animals. Bonobos forage and travel in temporary parties which vary in size from site to site. Temporary parties are most frequently mixed in composition, including males and females of all ages and reproductive status. The total range of one community numbering 65 animals was estimated at 58 sq km with a 66 percent overlap with other communities.

Little is known about this species' reproductive physiology. Life history data is available from the Wamba Reserve. The wild female bonobo undergoes an extended period of adolescent sterility. She begins to menstruate between the ages of seven and nine years, is sexually attractive to adult males, and soon thereafter permanently leaves her natal community. Males, in contrast, remain in their birth groups and maintain close relations with their mothers throughout her life. Females generally give birth for the first time between the ages of 13 and 15 years. Gestation of a single young ranged from 230-241 days for five

Bonobo.

captive females. Birth intervals average 4.7 years at Wamba. Longevity is estimated at more than 40 years. Pygmy chimpanzees employ sexual behavior for both reproductive and social purposes. Females have been observed to mate during all phases of the sexual cycle, and mothers are sexually active during lactation. Homosexual contacts are common, especially among females. Mating is promiscuous.

Habitat and Current Distribution

The pygmy chimpanzee has a discontinuous or patchy distribution in the central Zaire basin and is the only great ape found south of the Zaire River. The species' range appears to be limited by large river systems and forest cover. Although extensive areas of potential habitat are found in this region, viable populations of this species are confirmed from only a few scattered locations. In 1973, population was estimated at 54,000 animals. Since that time, Japanese researchers estimate that numbers have dwindled by more than half due to hunting and habitat destruction, and the population now numbers somewhere between 10,000-20,000. New evidence of populations existing in the southern part of their range warrants further surveys which may increase our estimates of numbers remaining in the wild.

A wide variety of habitats are utilized, including evergreen and semideciduous forest, old and young secondary forests, seasonally inundated swamp forest, swamp grassland, and cultivated areas. While an optimal habitat cannot be identified, high densities occur in the study sites of Wamba (about 60 percent mixed semi-deciduous forest, evergreen and aged secondary forest) and Lomako (87 percent semi-deciduous, evergreen and aged secondary). Bonobos at these study sites feed mainly in the mixed primary forests.

History and Conservation Measures

The greatest threats to the pygmy chimpanzee are habitat loss and hunting. Some may be captured for food, local trade, or for export for zoos and biomedical research.

When surveys were undertaken in the 1970s, distribution was already patchy. Populations have since disappeared from areas where they were formerly common. Competition for resources with the rapidly growing human population of Zaire coupled with economic hardship and the erosion of traditional values in areas where the species was formally protected by local traditions pose the greatest threat to both individual bonobos and their habitat. Although the forest of the Central Basin harbor 50 percent of the remaining undisturbed forest of Africa, both slash-and-burn agriculture and commercial logging are on the rise.

Subsistence hunting for meat and commercial hunting of bushmeat to supply large labor forces employed by companies in the area are widespread in central Zaire, where pygmy chimpanzees and other primates are prized prey. Bonobos are also occasionally hunted for medicinal or magical purposes. Given the late age at first birth and low lifetime reproductive output of females in this species, small isolated populations cannot maintain their numbers or retain genetic diversity in the face of high hunting pressure.

At present, only the Wamba population is protected on the local level. Proposals have been submitted to create a reserve between the Lomako and Yekokora Rivers. Although the Salonga National Park was established in part for the protection of this species, bonobos have only recently been confirmed there, and no estimate of distribution or numbers within the park is possible at this time. The most urgently required conservation measure is, therefore, the establishment of national reserves in areas known to harbor bonobos. Additional surveys remain critical to evaluating the species' status in the wild.

Protective laws exist throughout Zaire but since there is almost no enforcement, a major effort to reduce exploitation of the species and its habitat are necessary. Conservation education and local development projects within the bonobo's range are necessary to encourage the coexistence of humans and pygmy chimpanzees.

Chimpanzee

Pan troglodytes

Phylum	Chordata
Class	Mammalia
Order	Primates
Family	Pongidae
Status	Vulnerable, IUCN
	Endangered, USFWS
	Appendix I, CITES
Range	Angola; Burundi; Cameroon; Central African Republic; Congo; Côte d'Ivoire; Equatorial Guinea; Gabon; Gambia; Ghana; Guinea; Guinea-Bissau (ex?); Liberia; Mali; Nigeria; Rwanda (ex?); Senegal; Sierra Leone; Tanzania; Uganda; Zaire

Description and Biology

Of the three great apes, which includes the gorillas of Africa and the orang-utans of Asia, the chimpanzee is most closely related to humans. There are two chimpanzee species in Africa today, the pygmy chimpanzee (*Pan paniscus)* and the "common" chimpanzee (*Pan troglodytes*). Both are heavily threatened by habitat destruction, population fragmentation, disease, and human persecution.

Humans and chimpanzees share many biological, behavioral, social, and psychological traits. These two groups share 98 percent of the same genetic makeup, and chimpanzees have demonstrated the ability to use and make tools, share and cooperate for common good, express complex emotions, form bonds and friendships, and communicate using sign language.

Three subspecies of chimpanzee are recognized: *Pan troglodytes verus*, generally found in the western region of Africa; *Pan troglodytes troglodytes*, found in central Africa; and *Pan troglodytes schweinfurthii*, found in the eastern region of Africa.

The overall coloring of the chimpanzee is dark, varying from light brown to deep black. Their arms are longer than their legs, and they "knuckle-walk," an adaptation to ground-dwelling. When erect, male chimpanzees can be as tall as 6 ft (1.8 m). Chimpanzees in captivity usually grow faster and reach larger size than those in the wild, and they often become obese from lack of exercise. Hair around the face ranges from light brown to black and grays with age; baldness often occurs in older chimpanzees. Beards are gray regardless of age and white tail tufts mark infants.

Chimpanzees are highly social creatures, living in communities made up of 30 to 60 individuals. They travel on the ground during the day and spend nights in nests on top of trees. Heights of nests vary with available vegetation; heights of 5 ft (1.5 m) to more than 100 ft (30.5 m) have been reported. Chimpanzees are omnivores, much like humans. The primary component of the chimpanzee's diet is fruit, supplemented according to season by insects, leaves, flowers, bark, seeds, resin, eggs, and meat. At times chimpanzees also band together to hunt animals such as antelopes and monkeys.

Female chimpanzee with her young.

Mating can take place at any time during the year, but many female chimpanzees are highly selective about their mate. Unlike some other female primates in the wild who mate only with high-ranking males, female chimpanzees have been known to favor certain male "friends," regardless of their status within the group. Females average fewer than five offsprings per lifetime, and they invest much time and care in their young. Some bonds between mothers and infants last a lifetime. Among the chimpanzees of Gombe, Jane Goodall has observed infants "grieving" over their dead mothers, emitting distress calls, clinging to their mother's body, and demonstrating depressed behavior (not eating, showing no interest in play or grooming).

Habitat and Current Distribution

A few centuries ago, there were several million chimpanzees in equatorial Africa, today there are less than 300,000. In the western region, between 18,000 to 25,100 *P. t. verus* are known to exist; in central Africa there are 62,100 to 95,800 *P. t. troglodytes*; and in the eastern region, 75,100 to 118,600 *P. t. schweinfurthii* are known to exist. Of the 25 African nations that once contained chimpanzees, four now have none at all, 10 have so few that survival is doubtful, and only 11 nations have populations above 1,000.

The spectrum of habitats traditionally occupied by chimpanzees runs the gamut from dense forest to open savanna. However, these habitat areas are quickly disappearing due to human activities. Mining has destroyed chimpanzee habitat in the diamond districts of Sierra Leone and the iron districts of Liberia. Timber exploitation is a major threat mainly in Uganda, and crop cultivation is the major threat in Rwanda and Burundi. The two populations surviving in Tanzania, both on the shores of Lake Tanganyika, are the best protected in the eastern region but are completely surrounded by expanding human settlements. By all accounts, the explosion of human populations in the tropical realm is the main threat to chimpanzees as well as other wildlife.

History and Conservation Measures

The population of captive chimpanzees currently is about 5,000 worldwide. More than half of these are biomedical subjects, the rest are zoo exhibits, entertainer props, and private pets. For each chimpanzee shipped overseas, ten die during transport due to mistreatment and malnutrition. Exports have been heaviest from western Africa, and most "smuggled" chimpanzees end up in North America,

Europe, and Asia. Hunting for bushmeat is not a serious threat in most areas, but it is a cause for concern in Liberia and Côte d'Ivoire. While certain laws prohibit the hunting and sale of chimpanzees, enforcement of these laws is minimal and sometimes difficult. Conservation measures should include stricter enforcement and sanctions on countries that deal in illegal animal trade. Priority areas are Uganda, Liberia, and Congo.

Two sanctuaries for orphaned and confiscated chimpanzees exist in Gambia and Zambia. The establishment of additional protected areas and sanctuaries is vital. The encroachment of agriculture into previously forested areas is a major problem in many African nations, and efforts to balance development with environmental protection are slow and difficult. Most nations have some protected areas and legal protection for chimpanzees; however, parks and refuges are facing increasing pressure from human needs.

Orang-utan

Pongo pygmaeus

Phylum	Chordata
Class	Mammalia
Order	Primates
Family	Pongidae
Status	Endangered, IUCN
	Endangered, USFWS
	Appendix I, CITES
Range	Borneo (Brunei (?); Indonesia; Malaysia); Sumatra (Indonesia)

Description and Biology

Translated from Malay as "man of the woods" or "forest man," the name orang-utan is a true description of this largest living arboreal ape. It is possible that the orang-utan's habit of spending its time in trees and seldom descending to the ground is an ancient adaptation to human interference in its habitat. It is physically better equipped to move through the trees, with long, powerful arms as well as hands and feet adapted to grasping branches. Average head and body length is 30-40 in (76-102 cm), standing height is 45-59 in (114-150 cm), and weight is 85-220 lb (39-100 kg); the male is much larger and heavier than the female. Reddish brown coat is long and soft; face has a high forehead, small ears, and a bulging snout. Although its use of tools is much more limited than that of the chimpanzee, the orang-utan is very intelligent and able to find fruit that is scattered widely throughout the rain forest. Active during the day, it spends nights alone in nests built each day in trees at a height of 35-80 ft (11-24 m). Diet is primarily fruit, supplemented by leaves, shoots, insects, bark, eggs, nestling birds or squirrels, and mineral-rich soil.

The orang-utan is a solitary animal; except for temporary gatherings, the only bond formed is between mother and young. Home range has been reported to be from less than one square mile to four square miles (2-10 sq km); range for females is smaller and overlapping, while the male has a larger range that overlaps that of several females. Breeding can take place at any time during the year. When the female is ready to mate, she locates a male by his call and they may form a consortship, staying together for a few days to a few months until she is pregnant. They then resume their solitary existence and the female bears one young after a gestation period of 233-270 days. She raises the infant alone, keeping it with her constantly for the first year and nursing for up to three years. After the mother bears a second infant, the juvenile becomes increasingly less dependent upon her and eventually begins to live alone at the age of seven or eight years. Although the female is fertile for around 20 years, she usually bears no more than four or five young. In areas of significant human interference, the period between births may average eight years.

Habitat and Current Distribution

The only great ape found in Asia, the orang-utan occurs in Borneo and northernmost Sumatra. In the 1960s, the population was reported to be only 5,000

Orang-utan.

individuals, but that estimate was later believed to be pessimistic and revised to over 150,000; population was later estimated to be 53,000, with 47,000 in Borneo and 6,000 in Sumatra. The most recent population estimates, compiled in January 1993, are 12,300 to 20,571 individuals in Borneo and 9,200 in Sumatra.

The orang-utan inhabits a variety of forest habitats, including peat swamp forest, coastal heath, mangrove forest, lowland fruit trees, lowland dipterocarp forest, and mountain forest.

History and Conservation Measures

For thousands of years, the orang-utan has been the victim of human exploitation. Early humans found it an abundant source of food and hunted it to the point of extinction in some areas. More recently in Borneo, it served as a substitute for humans in head hunting rites. In the 1960s, the population was further decimated by the collection of young animals for zoos and circuses. Despite legal protection by the governments of Malaysia and Indonesia, the capture of young orang-utans has not yet been completely halted.

Today the greatest threat to this species is habitat destruction and disruption. Rain forest is rapidly being logged and cleared for agricultural development and mining on Borneo, leaving only patches of suitable habitat. The orang-utan is very sensitive to human intrusion and, as a consequence, suffers a further reduction of an already low rate of reproduction. For this reason, research on how it responds to alteration of its habitat, especially selective logging, is necessary.

Several protected reserves have already been designated. The Gunung Leuser National Park is considered the last stronghold for the Sumatran orang-utan; surveys of distribution and population trends for the orang-utan population in the park are underway. Kutai National Park in Kalimantan, an Indonesian provence on Borneo, has been damaged by drought and fire; it is necessary to assess the extent of damage to primary moist evergreen forest and to primates. This assessment should be followed by study of the type of secondary growth that occurs and its effect on the recovery of primate populations. Tanjung Puting National Park is the largest and most diverse protected area of coastal heath and peat swamp forest, which formerly covered much of southwestern and southern Borneo. The Gunung Betung Dan Kariman Reserve in Kalimantan, along with Lanjak-Entimau Wildlife Sanctuary, will encompass more than 2,300 sq mi (6,000 sq km) of protected forest. Bukit Raya Reserve is being developed in central Kalimantan. Surveys of existing and proposed reserved areas in Sabah, a Malaysian state on Borneo, have been recommended. A number of other studies have been proposed, including a project to develop methods for translocation of orang-utans from forest being clear-cut to permanent forest areas, and other reintroduction and management programs. To have any hope of saving this species, it is imperative to preserve remaining habitat and manage existing reserves.

Red wolf

Canis rufus

Phylum	Chordata
Class	Mammalia
Order	Carnivora
Family	Canidae
Status	Endangered, IUCN
	Endangered, USFWS
Range	North Carolina (U.S.A.)

Description and Biology

Although this species is called the red wolf, its coat varies in color from light cinnamon-brown to black. Measuring 37-47 in (95-120 cm) long with a 9-10 in (23-25 cm) tail, and weighing 45-65 lb (20-30 kg), it is smaller than the gray wolf and about the size of a large dog. A solitary hunter, the red wolf feeds in the wild on swamp rabbits, nutria, raccoons, birds, and deer. It is also known to take chickens and, occasionally, calves and piglets. Hunting territory averages 30-40 sq mi (80-100 sq km) per mated pair.

This species lives under a complex social order made up of family groups. Individual males and females form a pair bond that is long-lasting, but apparently not exclusive. Mating takes place between January and April. A litter of two to eight pups is born after a gestation of 61-63 days; the birthing den is used year after year.

Habitat and Current Distribution

The red wolf has been declared biologically extinct in the wild. It now exists in captivity and in a small reintroduced population of captive-bred animals in North Carolina.

A variety of suitable habitats includes swamps, wetlands, bushlands, and forests.

History and Conservation Measures

At one time the red wolf ranged from central Texas to the Atlantic coast and from the Gulf of Mexico north to the Ohio Valley and southern Pennsylvania. In the early 1900s, this species disappeared from much of that range and by mid-century, it survived only in scattered remnant populations. Its decline is attributed to persecution by settlers and by modification to its habitat with attendant disappearance of prey species.

With the clearing of forests and the resultant shrinkage of suitable habitat, the previously separate ranges of the red wolf and the coyote began to converge. The resulting hybridization created a new threat to the remaining stock of genetically pure red wolves. A few of the remaining specimens were taken into a captive breeding program begun by the U.S. Fish and Wildlife Service in the 1970s, with the goal of preserving the species and reintroducing it into the wild in some of its previous habitat; by 1989 the captive population had increased to 83 individuals. Beginning in 1988, the first captive-bred wolves were introduced in the Alligator River National Wildlife Refuge in North Carolina.

Another effort begun in 1988 was a project which involved releasing wolves in the Cape Romain National Wildlife Refuge on Bulls Island, South Caro-

Red wolf.

lina, and then capturing their offspring to be released elsewhere. A second island project was initiated in 1989 on Horn Island, off the Mississippi coast and part of the Gulf Islands National Seashore. The Bulls Island project was dealt a serious setback by Hurricane Hugo in 1989, which killed two of the five red wolves on the island. Although the reintroduction program has been successful thus far, the red wolf can still be considered the most endangered canid.

The red wolf was the first species for which the U.S. Fish and Wildlife Service's Office of Endangered Species developed a recovery plan. Adopted in the early 1970s, it has served as a model for subsequent plans for other species in jeopardy.

Simien jackal

Canis simensis

Phylum	Chordata
Class	Mammalia
Order	Carnivora
Family	Canidae
Status	Endangered, IUCN
Range	Ethiopia

Description and Biology

The Simien jackal is sometimes called the Ethiopian wolf or the Simien fox. The male has a bright reddish coat with white patches on the throat, neck, chest, and underside of the tail; females and juveniles have similar markings, but a lighter coat. Its ears are large and its face appears to be pointed due to its long, thin muzzle. The average head and body length of the Simien jackal is 3.3 ft (1 m), shoulder height is 23 in (60 cm), and it weighs 28 to 39 lb (13 to 18 kg). Males are slightly heavier than females, and its black-tipped bushy tail averages 13 in (33 cm) long. Its diet includes mammals ranging in size from hares and the giant mole-rat to small, common species of grass rat. The Simien jackal is considered a key predator in the food chain because of its high altitude ecosystem, assuming an important role in regulating the rodent population.

The jackal usually forages alone during the day, but often joins a group of 2 to 12 individuals in the morning or evening. Mating takes place between August and December; a litter of two to six pups is born in a den after a gestation of around 60 days. Both parents attend the den, and they are assisted by helpers from previous litters. All members of the pack regurgitate food to the young.

Habitat and Current Distribution

The Simien jackal occurs in the Ethiopian highlands at altitudes over 9,800 ft (3,000 m), including the Arssi and Bale mountains of southeast Ethiopia, the Simien mountains, northeast Shoa, Gojjam, and Mt. Guna. Total population is estimated to be well under 1,000 individuals; the only known large population is found in the Bale Mountains National Park and is estimated at 500-600 individuals.

This species is commonly found in open moorlands with low-level vegetation; it is also seen in heather moorlands.

History and Conservation Measures

The Simien jackal population was once widespread throughout the Ethiopian provinces and may

Simien jackal with pup.

ground as agricultural development usurped habitat and drove out prey. Populations have always been small, but they may be declining. Loss of habitat remains the primary threat today, but the remaining populations of jackals now face other threats. Jackals were routinely killed in late 1991 by people who had acquired arms during the war in Ethiopia; it is speculated that the animals were used as target practice. Because of the limited numbers and the single large population, outbreaks of disease could decimate the population. Competition with domestic dogs for prey is a problem, as is the reduction in prey population because of overgrazing. Cross-breeding with domestic dogs threatens to pollute the Bale population gene pool.

The Bale and Simien populations are completely protected by inclusion in national parks and the species is protected in Ethiopia by law. No poaching, hunting, or trade of live animals has been observed. A study was begun in 1988 on the ecology, behavior, and conservation of the species. The Simien jackal has apparently not yet been bred in captivity; a captive breeding program has been recommended to prepare for possible reintroduction into historic habitat in order to establish a second and distinct wild population.

have occurred at lower elevations before human intrusion into its habitat. It apparently moved to higher

Maned wolf

Chrysocyon brachyurus

Phylum	Chordata
Class	Mammalia
Order	Carnivora
Family	Canidae
Status	Vulnerable, IUCN
	Endangered, USFWS
	Appendix II, CITES
Range	Argentina; Bolivia; Brazil; Paraguay; Peru

Description and Biology

This uniquely colored wolf has long, soft, reddish yellow fur with dark hair forming an erect mane down its neck and back, a dark muzzle, and dark stockings on its legs and feet. It has large ears and extremely long limbs. At physical maturity, the maned wolf weighs 44-51 lb (20-23 kg), its head and body measure 49-52 in (124-132 cm), and its tail is 11-18 in (28-45 cm) long. Smaller than true wolves, this species is said to resemble a red fox on stilts. Some scientists have suggested that these extremely long legs are an adaptation for fast running or for traversing swampy ground, but it is more likely that their function is to allow the maned wolf to see above tall grass. The maned wolf is omnivorous with plants making up almost half of its diet; it eats small mammals, lizards, birds, foliage, fruit, and insects; it is also known to take chickens and, very occasionally, newborn lambs and piglets. The maned wolf is not as fast as some other canids, and it does not pursue its prey for long distances. Rather, it stalks and ambushes its prey, usually at night.

Maned wolf.

Monogamous pairs share a territory averaging 10 sq mi (25 sq km), but they usually hunt alone and rarely associate. Mating peaks in May-June and results in a litter of one to five young (usually two) after a gestation of 62-66 days. For reasons unknown, only two pups usually survive to leave the den. Pups are nursed for three to four months and given regurgitated food after the first month. Although maned wolves are sexually mature at one year, they don't breed until their second year. Average life span is 12-15 years.

Habitat and Current Distribution

The maned wolf is found in central and eastern South America, including northern Argentina, south and central Brazil, eastern Bolivia, Paraguay, and southeastern Peru. Population figures are not known, but it is believed to occur at low densities in all parts of its range.

A variety of open habitats are utilized, including savanna, grassland, scrubland, swamps, marshes, and agricultural land.

History and Conservation Measures

The status of this species has shown recent improvement, but it still faces a number of threats, including disease, agricultural expansion in its range, and persecution by people. Disease has been blamed for the decline of the maned wolf population in Bolivia and has often plagued captive breeding attempts. Initial stages of forest clearing for agricultural use may actually be beneficial, but extensive use of land for agricultural purposes may preclude use of that area by maned wolves. Habitat disruption also causes loss of cover and resulting decline or elimination of prey. The maned wolf is not hunted for its fur or meat, but it is frequently killed as a pest, although its reputation as a chicken thief may be exaggerated.

The problems facing the maned wolf must be addressed on a local level. Farming practices that are compatible with wildlife use should be encouraged, as should education programs aimed at minimizing wolf-human conflict. This species is legally protected in Brazil and has been classified as endangered by the Argentine Wildlife Board. Successful captive breeding programs have been established, and reintroduction programs should be explored.

Asiatic wild dog

Cuon alpinus

Phylum	Chordata
Class	Mammalia
Order	Carnivora
Family	Canidae
Status	Vulnerable, IUCN
	Endangered, USFWS
	Appendix II, CITES
Range	Bangladesh; Bhutan; China; India; Java, Sumatra (Indonesia); Kampuchea; Kazakhstan (?); Kyrgyzstan (?); Laos; Peninsular Malaysia; Mongolia; Myanmar; Nepal; North Korea (?); Russia; South Korea (?); Sri Lanka (ex?); Tajikistan (?); Thailand; Uzbekistan (?); Vietnam

Description and Biology

The the Asiatic wild dog is also called the dhole or the red dog; its coat is tawny to dark red with lighter underparts. Its dark, bushy tail is 16-18 in (41-46 cm) long; legs are short and ears round. The dhole averages 35 in (89 cm) in length, 20 in (51 cm) in height at the shoulder, and weighs 22-44 lb (10-20 kg), with the male heavier than the female. Territorial packs of 5-18 animals cover a hunting range of around 15 sq mi (39 sq km). The pack trails prey by scent and then kills it by running it down or by driving it to other waiting dholes. Prey includes wild ungulates, such as deer and pigs, and domestic livestock. Diet is supplemented by berries, insects, reptiles, and rodents. Tender grass is also eaten.

Usually only one female in a pack breeds; mating takes place between September and February in central and northern India and between September and December in southern India. After a gestation period of 60-62 days, the female prepares a den in a hole or cavern and gives birth to an average of five to eight pups. The pack provides food to the lactating mother and the pups. The pups leave the den when

Dhole.

they are about three months old and join active hunting at about eight months.

Habitat and Current Distribution

Packs of Asiatic wild dogs are found in jungles in the Indian subcontinent and southeast Asia, forests and alpine areas in China and the former Soviet Union, and as far east as Korea, as well as on the islands of Java and Sumatra. Total population size is unknown.

Maximum altitude at which dholes are recorded is 7,000 ft (2,100 m) in India and 10,000 ft (3,000 m) in Thailand. Factors which determine the quality of habitat for dholes are prey abundance; water availability; absence of human disturbance; and dens in the form of rock crevices or porcupine burrows.

History and Conservation Measures

The primary reason for the decline of dholes has been human effort to eradicate an unpopular and unwanted predator. Hunters have also considered it a competitor for prey and have used a variety of methods, including shooting, poisoning, and smoking of den sites, in an effort to eradicate the dhole. Other threats include diseases introduced by contact with domestic dogs, continued poisoning as a result of conflict with cattle grazers, and depletion of natural prey. There have also been unexplained declines of population in well-protected areas such as Chitawan National Park in Nepal and Corbett National Park in India that are a continuing cause of concern. The dhole is a species which is unlikely to survive outside of protected areas except in extremely remote regions. Information is urgently required on status, abundance, and distribution throughout its range to facilitate conservation planning.

Gray zorro

Dusicyon griseus

Phylum	Chordata
Class	Mammalia
Order	Carnivora
Family	Canidae
Status	Vulnerable, IUCN
	Appendix II, CITES
Range	Argentina; Chile; Falkland Islands; Peru

Description and Biology

Also called the Argentine gray fox or South American gray fox, the gray zorro has a beautiful coat marked with dark flecks and streaks. Its reddish head is flecked with white, and there is a black spot on the chin. This fox has large ears and a long, bushy tail that measures 11.8-14.2 in (30-36 cm). The average head and body length is 16.5-26.8 in (42-68 cm), shoulder height is 15.7-17.7 in (40-45 cm), and weight is 9.7 lb (4.4 kg).

While the gray zorro occasionally consumes birds and rabbits, 98 percent of its diet consists of rodents. It also eats berries, particularly from *Cryptocarya alba*, *Lithraea caustica*, and *Berberis buxifolia*. There have been unconfirmed reports that the gray zorro killed and ate sheep. In Chile this species controls the population of endemic rodents such as *Octodeon degus* and *Abrocoma bennetti*.

Little is known about the social behavior of this species. Mating occurs from August to September, and a litter of two to four pups is born after a gestation period of 53-58 days.

Habitat and Current Distribution

The gray zorro is found in Argentina throughout Patagonia from the Straits of Magellan to Chubut Province and northward in the lowlands of western Argentina as far as Santiago del Estero and Catamarca. In Chile, it is widespread from the Straits of Magellan northward to the southern half of the II Administrative Region, mainly in the lowlands and foothills of coastal mountain ranges. It is also found on several small islands of the Falklands/Malvinas group and was introduced to Tierra del Fuego in 1951 to control European rabbits. It also occurs in southern Peru and, perhaps, central Peru, although this has not been confirmed.

The gray zorro appears to prefer plains, pampas, deserts, and low mountains. Population size is unknown.

History and Conservation Measures

The status of this species has been the subject of debate between conservationists and hunters for several years. A survey conducted during the 1980s reported 1.3 to 2.5 gray zorros per square kilometer in Chile. Based on this study—which was funded by an association of hunters—the hunting ban was lifted, despite arguments from scientists who contested the methodology and results of this study. A few years later, the population of gray zorros plummeted, and the ban was re-imposed.

The gray zorro is the most traded species among the CITES-listed canids. Between 1980 and

1983, about 381,000 skins were exported from Argentina (where it is still legal to hunt gray zorros) to Germany, Switzerland, and Italy. Despite an export ban, over 7,000 skins were exported from Chile. Aside from the value of its fur, the gray zorro is also killed because it is perceived to threaten livestock. Recent forest and bush clearing in South America has created more habitat for this species, but this may also serve to bring it into conflict with domestic livestock. Efforts are underway to educate people about the conservation needs of this species. Studies have been recommended to better assess the status and distribution of this animal.

African wild dog

Lycaon pictus

Phylum	Chordata
Class	Mammalia
Order	Carnivora
Family	Canidae
Status	Endangered, IUCN
	Endangered, USFWS
Range	Algeria (ex?); Angola; Benin (ex?); Botswana; Burkina Faso; Burundi (ex?); Cameroon; Central African Republic; Chad; Congo (ex?); Côte d'Ivoire; Ethiopia; Gabon (ex?); Ghana (ex?); Guinea; Kenya; Malawi; Mali (ex?); Mauritania (?); Mozambique; Namibia; Niger; Nigeria; Rwanda (ex?); Senegal; Sierra Leone; Somalia; South Africa; Sudan; Swaziland; Tanzania; Togo (ex?); Uganda (ex?); Zaire (ex?); Zambia; Zimbabwe

Description and Biology

The African wild dog is also called the African painted wolf, because of its streaked, multicolored coat. A pattern of tan, black, and white varies with each individual, but the head is usually dark. This dog has very large, rounded ears that are used to signal to other dogs and to control body temperature by radiating heat. The tail ends in a plume that is white-tipped; the jaw contains teeth that are adapted for both shearing and grinding. Legs are long and slim; feet have four toes. Average shoulder height at physical maturity is 24-31 in (62-79 cm), head and body length is 30-44 in (76-112 cm), tail length is 12-16 in (30-41 cm), and weight is 37-79 lb (17-36 kg). Dogs form packs of 2-45 individuals and hunt together in a cooperative effort. Prey includes impalas, antelopes, gazelles (especially Thomson's gazelle), ungulates (e.g. steenboks and elands), zebras, and warthogs, rarely supplemented by rodents and small mammals. Prey is disemboweled and shared by all adults in the pack, who allow pups to eat first.

Hunting dog packs have a very definite social system. Within a pack, all males are related to each other but not to the females; all females are related to each other but not to the males. Both males and females seem to emigrate from packs with equal frequency to join new packs. Mating is thought to take place almost exclusively between the dominant male and the dominant female, although there is no evidence that subdominant males do not breed. In about 10 percent of packs, two females will breed, although the survival rate of the subdominant female's young is frequently low. Births may take place at any time of the year, but the breeding/denning season varies according to location. In Southern Africa, for example, the peak occurs May through July during the winter dry season. The female chooses a den and, after a gestation of approximately 69-72 days, gives birth to up to 16 pups, about 50 percent of which will not survive. Pups are cared for jointly by the pack, initially being fed regurgitated food by the adults. Home range varies widely from 500-1,500 sq mi (1,300-3,900 sq km), contracting to an area as small as 60 sq mi (155 sq km) during the two months when the dogs are denning.

African wild dogs.

Habitat and Current Distribution

African wild dogs are found throughout Africa south of the Sahara. World population is estimated at less than 6,000.

Preferred habitat is bushland or open and wooded savanna.

History and Conservation Measures

Wild dogs were once common throughout the African continent. Growing human population has decreased or degraded suitable habitat and, as a re-sult, also diminished available prey. Road kills and human persecution (hunting and/or vermin control) have also had a negative impact on African wild dog populations. This species is also susceptible to a vari-ety of diseases that are controlled in domestic dogs, including distemper. Captive breeding in zoos has been relatively successful, but all known stock is of Southern African origin, and this is the least threat-ened subspecies.

Conservation of natural habitat must have the highest priority, as the African wild dog suffers in habitats modified by human intrusion.

Bush dog

Speothos venaticus

Phylum	Chordata
Class	Mammalia
Order	Carnivora
Family	Canidae
Status	Vulnerable, IUCN
	Appendix I, CITES
Range	Argentina; Bolivia; Brazil; Colombia; Ecuador; French Guiana; Guyana; Panama; Paraguay; Peru; Suriname; Venezuela

Description and Biology

Although it is a wild dog, this animal resembles a stocky weasel or civet. It is small, with a head and body length averaging 22.4-30 in (57-75 cm), shoulder height 9.8-12 in (25-30 cm), and weight 11-15.4 lb (5-7 kg). Its head and neck are reddish tan to brownish yellow, turning black toward its bushy tail which is only 5-6 in (12.5-15 cm) long. Its underside is dark; there is sometimes a lighter throat patch. Its face is broad, ears small and round, and legs very short; feet are webbed to accommodate semi-aquatic habits. It is active during the day, feeding on birds and rodents, including the rhea (a relative of the ostrich) and the capybara (the largest rodent in the world). When hunting in a pack, it may pursue game as large as deer.

Considered the most social of the canids, the bush dog lives in groups of up to ten. Its breeding season is uncertain, but may be associated with the rainy season. Litters of one to six young are born in a burrow or hollow tree trunk after a gestation period of approximately 67 days. The male helps to take care of the young, hunting for food and protecting both mother and pups.

Habitat and Current Distribution

The bush dog occurs from eastern Panama south through Colombia and Ecuador to eastern Peru and northern Bolivia, and through Venezuela and the Guianas; it has also been discovered in northern Argentina. It is thought to be a naturally rare species, but population figures are unavailable.

Bush dog.

This species is primarily a forest dweller which also visits open country at the forest edge and is generally found close to streams, rivers, or canals. Burrows are usually located under a fallen tree, or in the roots of a large tree.

History and Conservation Measures

Considered rare throughout its range, the bush dog does not inhabit areas used by humans and so is threatened by habitat restriction as more forest is cleared and the habitat in its range irreversibly destroyed. It is apparently not hunted intentionally or sought as a pet, but is often killed if encountered by hunters. Pups are sometimes killed by hunters' dogs, which enter the burrow.

This species occurs in a number of national parks and reserves: in Brazil it occurs in such national parks as Araguia and Tocantins (Goias), Brasilia (Distrito Federal), Emas (Goias and Mato Grosso), and Iguacu, and also in the Cara-Cara Biological Reserve (Mato Grosso); in Peru it may occur in the Manu National Park. Because it has been very poorly studied, no specific conservation measures have been enacted. Legal protection in all countries of its range has been suggested. Studies are necessary to clarify distribution and ecological studies are needed to determine what conditions must be provided in parks and reserves to ensure its survival.

Island gray fox

Urocyon littoralis

Phylum	Chordata
Class	Mammalia
Order	Carnivora
Family	Canidae
Status	Rare, IUCN
Range	California (U.S.A.)

Description and Biology

The island gray fox is similar in appearance to the related North American gray fox (*U. cinereoargenteus*): much of the body is a gray color, apart from the white underparts and throat, and the sides of the neck and underside of the tail, which are a rusty color. Black markings often occur on the face and limbs, and black-tipped hairs form a mane along the back. The island gray fox can be easily distinguished from the North American gray fox by its much smaller tail, which averages between 4.3-11.4 in (11-29 cm), half the size of that of the latter species. Head and body length averages 19-20 in (48-50 cm), shoulder height is 4.7-5.9 in (12-15 cm), and weight is 2.9-6.2 lb (1.3-2.8 kg).

This species spends a considerable time in forests and forages in the early morning, late evening, or at night. Diet is comprised mainly of insects and fruits and also includes small mammals, birds, reptiles, and eggs.

The species' social structure is centered around a mated pair and their pups. The family's home range has been calculated at around 3 sq mi (7 sq km). Mating takes place between December and March; a litter of one to eight young is born after a gestation period of 50-60 days. The young are nursed for about six weeks.

Habitat and Current Distribution

This fox is only found on the six largest Channel Islands off the coast of southern California. However, recent discoveries indicate that some nearby mainland populations may also belong to this species. There are no estimates of total population size.

The island gray fox occupies a variety of habitats, including grassland, coastal scrub, sand dune communities, and forested areas. Dens are found in bushy and woodland areas.

History and Conservation Measures

At the present time, the status of this species appears stable, but the long-term safety of the population is uncertain due to its small size. The primary threat to this species is habitat destruction, combined with competition from introduced feral animals, particularly feral cats (*Felis catus*) on three islands. An additional problem is the possibility of disease introduced by domestic dogs.

The island gray fox is protected throughout its range; the islands' remoteness makes enforcement difficult, but this may also serve to protect the species. Conservation programs include an attempt by the U.S. Navy to eliminate feral cats on San Clemente and San Nicolas and studies of population genetics and disease. The establishment of a captive breeding population is being considered by the Los Angeles Zoo.

Cheetah

Acinonyx jubatus

Phylum	Chordata
Class	Mammalia
Order	Carnivora
Family	Felidae
Status	Vulnerable, IUCN
	Endangered, USFWS
	Appendix I, CITES
Range	Afghanistan (ex?); Algeria (ex?); Angola; Benin; Botswana; Burkina Faso; Cameroon; Chad; Ethiopia; Iran; Jordan (ex?); Kenya; Libya; Malawi; Mali; Mauritania; Morocco (ex?); Mozambique; Namibia; Niger; Nigeria; Pakistan (ex?); Saudi Arabia (ex?); Senegal; Somalia; South Africa; Sudan; Swaziland; Tanzania; Turkmenistan; Uganda; Western Sahara (ex?); Zaire; Zambia; Zimbabwe

Description and Biology

Considered the world's fastest land mammal, the cheetah can reach speeds of 60-75 mph (96-120 kph). The cheetah's name is derivative from the Hindu word *chita,* which means "spotted one." This cat's body measures 4.5-5 ft (1.4-1.5 m) long, weighs 100-145 lb (45-66 kg), and its tail is 24-32 in (61-81 cm) long. Its tawny brown fur is accented by black spots, a distinctive black tear streaks across the cheeks, and pale underparts. In some cats in southern Africa, genetic factors create a uniquely blotched coat; these cats are called king cheetahs. Cheetahs are able to climb trees but not with the same facility as semi-arboreal cats. They can, however, chase their prey at high speeds for short sprints. The cheetah has physical similarities to dogs and, like them, pursues prey animals rather than ambushing them. Its method of killing depends on the size of prey; as in other cats, large prey is throttled while small prey is bitten on the nape. Large prey animals include gazelles, impala, wildebeest, and antelopes; small prey includes warthogs, hares, and ground birds.

Adult females are solitary except when mating or raising cubs. Males often live with littermates in groups of two to four called coalitions. Coalitions have an advantage over solitary males in securing and defending a territory of approximately 15.5 sq mi (40 sq km). Females cover a much larger range while following migrating prey such as Thomson's gazelle. The female's territory may cover as much as 310 sq mi (800 sq km) and often overlaps the territory of other females. Sexual maturity is reached in 20-24 months. Females in heat squirt urine on rocks, trees, and bushes to attract males, then mating occurs frequently over a period of several days. After a gestation period of 90-95 days, a litter of one to eight cubs is born. They are hidden by the mother and moved often to new hiding places in long grass or bushes until they are weaned in three months. Young cubs are especially vulnerable to predation by lions,

Cheetah.

hyenas, jackals, and eagles. The mother brings small, live prey to the cubs to help them develop hunting skills.

Habitat and Current Distribution

The cheetah is now restricted to Africa south of the Sahara. Estimates of total population range from 5,000 to 12,000. An additional population estimated at 200 animals occurs in Iran and possibly in northwest Afghanistan.

Preferred habitat is savanna and arid, open grasslands for hunting prey. It also utilizes bushland as cover for stalking prey, for hiding from predators, and for shade in the heat of the afternoon.

History and Conservation Measures

The cheetah once ranged over much of Africa, Arabia, the Middle East, and northern India. Population was estimated at 28,000 in the mid-1950s and at 14,000 in the early 1970s. Decline in distribution and

population is attributed to a number of factors, including hunting and habitat disruption. Cheetahs are legally protected in most countries, but they are sometimes killed by farmers protecting their domestic animals. They are also hunted for their spotted pelt, although not as often as other cats.

The loss of habitat is the most serious threat to this species. As suitable habitat decreases, so does available prey for cheetahs and for other large carnivores. Other concerns include a cub mortality rate of almost 90 percent and a depleted gene pool that leaves the cheetah vulnerable to genetic defects. The death rate of adult males is also very high as a result of territorial disputes. Despite these obstacles, the cheetah seems to be adapting to its reduced circumstances and resisting extinction.

Captive breeding of this species has not been very successful, with less than 25 percent of captive adults breeding more than once. The American Association of Zoological Parks and Aquariums is sponsoring research through the Species Survival Plan to investigate the causes of breeding failure.

Bay cat

Catopuma (Felis) badia

Phylum . . . . Chordata
Class . . . . Mammalia
Order . . . . Carnivora
Family . . . . Felidae
Status . . . . Insufficiently Known, IUCN
Appendix II, CITES
Range . . . . Brunei; Kalimantan (Indonesia); Sabah, Sarawak (Malaysia)

Description and Biology

The Bornean Bay cat, Bornean red cat, or Bornean bay cat is a very small species of cat, averaging 19-24 in (48-60 cm) in length, with an estimated weight of 4.5-6.5 lb (2-3 kg). Its coat is bright red-brown above and lighter underneath with light spots on the belly and legs. It has a long, red-brown tail averaging between 12-15 in (30-38 cm) with a light streak on its underside. Diet includes small mammals, birds, and carrion.

No information is available about the social structure or reproductive biology of this species. Some scientists believe that this species may be a subspecies of the golden cat (*Catopuma temmincki*).

Habitat and Current Distribution

This cat is found only on the island of Borneo. No estimates of population size are available.

Habitat is apparently dense forest and rocky limestone scrub at the edge of the jungle.

History and Conservation Measures

The Bornean bay cat has never been observed in the wild by scientists; it is known only from a few museum specimens. With no information available about biology or population, no conservation efforts are possible.

Spanish lynx

Lynx (Felis) pardinus

Phylum	Chordata
Class	Mammalia
Order	Carnivora
Family	Felidae
Status	Endangered, IUCN
	Endangered, USFWS
	Appendix I, CITES
Range	Portugal; Spain

Description and Biology

The Spanish lynx or pardel is a small- to medium-sized cat with an average length of 30-40 in (76-101 cm), shoulder height of 20-27 in (50-70 cm), and weight of 25-30 lb (11.3-13.6 kg). The upper body is light brown to reddish, liberally covered with well-defined, round black spots; underparts are pale to white. The face is heavily whiskered and the ears end in black tufts. Its short, black-tipped tail measures 4.75-5.5 in (12-14 cm). Rabbits are the mainstay of this lynx's diet, supplemented by water birds and young deer. It is a strong swimmer and climber, but usually hunts on the ground. Home range varies widely with season and the availability of food, from 4-40 sq mi (10-100 sq km).

This species is solitary except during mating season, usually in January, when the female mates with a single male, the male with a number of females. Average litter is two to three young, born in a secluded den after a gestation period of 63-73 days. The female cares for the young alone, nursing them for three to four months.

Habitat and Current Distribution

The Spanish lynx is found in southwestern Spain and in a few scattered areas in Portugal. Population is estimated at fewer than 1,000 individuals.

Present restricted habitat is comprised of wooded, mountainous areas in central and southern Spain and in scrubs and sand dunes in the Coto Donana, and the Guadalquivir Delta.

History and Conservation Measures

While the Spanish lynx once ranged throughout the Iberian Peninsula, its distribution has now been greatly reduced. Initial population figures are unavailable, but the population has declined and continues to decline. Considered a threat to livestock, bounties were once offered to encourage the slaughter of the lynx. In the 1950s and 1960s, a major decline was attributed to the disease myxomatosis, which infected rabbit populations.

The most serious continuing threat to the Spanish lynx is loss and degradation of habitat. Agricultural development is usurping prime habitat, contributing to the fragmentation of the population and the reduction of prey species. Conservation ef- forts must take into account the habitat requirements for a predatory species. In addition, the public's per- ception of the lynx as a pest needs to be challenged.

Andean cat

Oreailurus (Felis) jacobita

Phylum	Chordata
Class	Mammalia
Order	Carnivora
Family	Felidae
Status	Insufficiently Known, IUCN
	Endangered, USFWS
	Appendix I, CITES
Range	Argentina; Bolivia; Chile; Peru

Description and Biology

Slightly larger than a house cat, the Andean or mountain cat measures between 23-30 in (58-76 cm) and weighs 8-15 lb (3.6-7 kg). Its long, soft coat is silver-gray with dark markings above, pale to white below with black spots. Its bushy tail has a series of dark rings and a pale tip. Diet consists of small mammals, birds, lizards, and rodents.

No information is available about the social structure or reproductive biology of this species.

Habitat and Current Distribution

The mountain cat is found in the high Andes of northern Chile, southern Peru, southwestern Bolivia, and northwestern Argentina. No population estimates have been made, but the species seems to be naturally very rare.

The species' known habitat is the treeless, rocky, arid and semi-arid zone of the high Andes from 10,000-16,000 ft (3,000-5,000 m).

History and Conservation Measures

Very little is known about this rare species. It has been observed in the wild only once when scientists spotted it in Argentina in 1980. Therefore experts cannot tell if the population is declining or if suitable habitat has decreased. Apparently, commercial exploitation has not been an endangering factor. While the species must be further studied before specific conservation measures can be considered, protection of its entire range is highly recommended due to its rarity.

Iriomote cat

Felis iriomotensis

Phylum	Chordata
Class	Mammalia
Order	Carnivora
Family	Felidae
Status	Endangered, IUCN
	Endangered, USFWS
	Appendix II, CITES
Range	Ryukyu Islands (Japan)

Description and Biology

About the size of a domestic cat, the Iriomote cat is approximately 20-23.5 in (50-60 cm) long and weighs 6.5-10 lb (3-4.5 kg); the female is smaller than the male. Its dark brown coat is covered with even darker spots that cluster to form almost-solid lines running the length of its body. White markings line both sides of the nose and the area below the eyes. Legs and tail are short, the tail averaging 8-12 in (20-30 cm) in length. Mainly a nocturnal hunter, the Iriomote cat preys on waterbirds, small rodents, crabs, and fish, especially mud skippers; if active during the day, it preys on skinks and flying-foxes. It is a good climber and swimmer and may also hunt in the water. Home range is approximately one sq mi (2.5 sq km) and overlaps the ranges of other cats.

Mating often takes place in February or March. Two to four kittens are born in April or May, after a gestation period of around two months. The female chooses a secluded area such as a hollow tree or sheltered crevice to give birth. The kittens become independent more quickly than domestic cats.

Habitat and Current Distribution

This cat is found only on Iriomote, a Japanese-owned island in the Ryukyu chain, about 62 mi (100 km) east of Taiwan. Population is estimated at 40-100 individuals.

The cat's preferred habitat is lowland, sub-tropical rain forest close to water, but it can be found in all habitats on the island, including mountains, beaches, and cultivated land.

History and Conservation Measures

The Iriomote cat was declared a new species in 1967. While some experts believe that it may have descended from a leopard cat, decades of isolation on Iriomote have made its origin uncertain. Initial population figures are unknown, but it is thought to have declined drastically since the mid-1970s.

Threats to the Iriomote cat include competition from feral cats, incidental catching in snares set for wild boars, and habitat loss. Prime habitat has been usurped for road construction and agricultural development, though at least a third of the island has been designated a national reserve. The Iriomote cat has been granted full legal protection and has been declared a national treasure by the government of Japan.

Jaguar

Panthera onca

Phylum	Chordata
Class	Mammalia
Order	Carnivora
Family	Felidae
Status	Indeterminate, IUCN Endangered, USFWS Appendix I, CITES
Range	Argentina; Bolivia; Brazil; Colombia; Costa Rica; French Guiana; Guatemala; Guyana; Honduras; El Salvador; Mexico; Nicaragua; Panama; Paraguay; Peru; Suriname; Venezuela

Description and Biology

The jaguar is the third largest living cat and the largest in North and South America. The color of its coat ranges from yellow-brown to auburn, with patterns of black spots and rosettes, many encircling a spot, and white underneath. Its fur may be black or white, but this occurrence is very rare. The average length of an adult jaguar is 4-6 ft (1.2-1.8 m); weight is approximately 75-250 lb (34-113 kg). The jaguar is a good swimmer, runner, and tree climber and an opportunistic feeder. It feeds on aquatic animals, either fresh or carrion, including turtles, capybaras, iguanas, and fish, peccaries, monkeys, birds, dogs, and cattle. A solitary animal, it defends its chosen hunting territory, which is 4-27 sq mi (10-70 sq km) for the female and 8-80 sq mi (20-207 sq km) for the male.

Male and female pair briefly for the mating season. Breeding takes place at any time in tropical areas, in spring in cooler climates. A litter of one to four cubs is born after a 90-110 day gestation. Young are raised by the female and remain dependent for up to two years.

Habitat and Current Distribution

The jaguar is found in parts of Mexico, in Central America, and in South America as far south as northern Argentina. Population figures have been difficult to ascertain because of the secretive, nocturnal nature of this cat, but it is probably the most numerous, together with the lion, of the great cats. The largest remaining population of jaguars is in the Amazon rain forest.

This species' habitat includes tropical and subtropical forests, open woodland, mangroves, swamps, scrub thickets, desert, and savanna. The preferred habitat of the jaguar is densely forested with easy access to water.

History and Conservation Measures

The jaguar once inhabited the southern United States and was fairly common from Mexico to northern Argentina. It is now extinct over much of its former range and greatly reduced in number throughout the reduced range. Historically, the major threat to this cat, as with many others, was hunting. It

Jaguar.

was hunted for sport and, more importantly, for its skin. In the early to mid-1960s, spotted cat skins were in great demand. Legal protection provided by the Convention on International Trade in Endangered Species of Wild Fauna and Flora (CITES) has now virtually eliminated the commercial pelt trade. As human settlements encroach on jaguar habitat, it is more often killed by farmers because it preys on domestic farm animals.

Clearing of forests by loggers and subsequent settlement by ranchers and farmers is rapidly eliminating the jaguar's habitat. The survival of this cat is largely dependent on conservation efforts toward preservation of adequate habitat. Limited populations of jaguars are protected in large national parks in Bolivia, Brazil, Colombia, Peru, and Venezuela, and smaller reserves and private ranches provide protection to isolated pairs or families. The jaguar has been bred successfully in zoos.

Leopard

Panthera pardus

Phylum	Chordata
Class	Mammalia
Order	Carnivora
Family	Felidae
Status	Indeterminate, IUCN
	Endangered, USFWS
	Threatened, USFWS (parts of Africa)
	Appendix I, CITES
Range	Africa (south of the Sahara Desert); southeast Asia

Description and Biology

The leopard is known for its beautiful coat of light to tawny brown with clusters or rosettes of black spots. Some cats, most commonly in southern Asia, are born with a black coat that still retains the characteristic spotting; while still leopards, these cats are commonly called black panthers. The leopard averages 38-75 in (96-190 cm) long and weighs 65-155 lb (30-70 kg). This nocturnal hunter's varied diet includes small to medium sized mammals, birds, rodents, and insects. Prey is killed by a bite to the neck or is seized by the throat and strangled. The leopard often stores its dead prey in trees. Home range averages 4-20 sq mi (10-25 sq km), but can sometimes be much larger because it varies with availability of prey.

A solitary animal, the male leopard associates with the female only for mating. Breeding can take place at any time of year. The female is sexually receptive for several days, during which mating is frequent. Two to three cubs are born after a gestation of 90-105 days; the female cares for the young, hiding them until they are six to eight weeks old. Cubs are nursed for several months and are dependent for 18-20 months.

Habitat and Current Distribution

The leopard is found in Africa south of the Sahara and in southeast Asia. A controversial computer model in 1987 predicted about 700,000 leopards in Africa, but local experts believe there are actually not more than half that number.

With the ability to adapt to almost any habitat, this cat occupies anything from arid semi-desert to dense rain forest, as long as sufficient prey is available.

History and Conservation Measures

This species has historically been a victim of the international fur trade. Its classification as endangered has given it legal protection, but it is still poached for the international market. It is also hunted legally for sport in Africa.

The leopard's adaptability brings it in direct

Leopard.

conflict with humans. As ranching and farming interests usurp its habitat, the leopard is likely to feed on domestic livestock. It is often poisoned in deliberate predator extermination campaigns. Despite its ability to adapt to changing conditions, the leopard population is considered to be in decline. Leopards also reside in national parks, where they are considered a tourist attraction.

Tiger

Panthera tigris

Phylum	Chordata
Class	Mammalia
Order	Carnivora
Family	Felidae
Status	Endangered, IUCN
	Endangered, USFWS
	Appendix I, CITES
Range	Afghanistan (?); Bangladesh; Bhutan; China; India; Indonesia; Kampuchea; Kazakhstan; Kyrgyzstan; Laos; Malaysia; Myanmar; Nepal; North Korea (ex?); Russia; Tajikistan; Thailand; Turkmenistan; Uzbekistan; Vietnam

Description and Biology

Very few animals, by the mere mention of their name, evoke such wonder, fear, and mystery in humans as the tiger. The protection of this magnificent animal has been an international conservation priority since the 1970s and yet it is still faced with extinction in the wild. There are perhaps 5,000-7,500 tigers left today, with most estimates at around 5,000 individuals—a population decline of 95 percent in this century. Once found across Asia from Siberia in the north, Turkey in the west, and Indonesia in the south, the tiger is now found in only a handful of locations.

There are eight tiger subspecies, three of which are extinct: the Bali tiger (*P. t. balica*) became extinct in the 1930s; the Caspian tiger (*P. t. virgata*) disappeared in the 1970s; and the Javan tiger (*P. t. sondaica*) was hunted to extinction in the 1980s. The remaining five subspecies—the Indo-Chinese tiger (*P. t. corbetti*); Siberian tiger or Amur tiger (*P. t. altaica*), South China tiger (*P. t. amoyensis*), Bengal tiger (*P. t. tigris*), and Sumatran tiger (*P. t. sumatrae*)—are fast disappearing in the wild. The color, size, and general appearance of these tigers vary according to subspecies. On average, the head and body length ranges from 4.6-9.2 ft (1.4-2.8 m), weight from 220-660 lb (100-300 kg), and tail length from 24-37 in (60-94 cm). The length of coat varies with geographic region, but the basic pattern of stripes against a lighter-colored background is always present. Underparts are usually white in color; background color ranges from tawny to reddish and, in one variant, white. Striping pattern varies with subspecies.

The tiger is mainly nocturnal, although it is also active during the day. It is an able climber, good swimmer, and fast runner. It can leap up to 32 ft (10 m) and swim up to 18 mi (29 km). In general, most tigers travel between 6-12 mi (10-20 km) a day; the Siberian tiger can travel up to 37 mi (67 km) in one day. The tiger is not always a successful hunter; in fact it fails to catch prey about 90 percent of the time. It hunts by sight and hearing, often stalking its prey and pouncing on the animal from the rear or the side. A tiger can bring down an animal twice its size using its strong shoulders, forelimbs, and teeth. The prey is usually killed by strangulation or a bite to the neck. After the kill, the animal may be dragged to a cover or near water, where it is eaten; the remainder may be hidden until the next feeding. (Some poachers have poisoned the prey remains in an attempt to kill the tigers.) Prey varies with geographic range but often includes such large mammals as wild pigs, a wide variety of deer, and wild cattle; smaller mammals and birds are also hunted. Although the tiger usually

Tigers.

avoids human contact, it has been known to attack and consume humans.

The tiger is a solitary animal, except for mating pairs and females and their young. Home range varies with habitat and food supply from 4-1,500 sq mi (10-4,000 sq km). The home range of the male usually encompasses the ranges of several females. But even among individuals who share the same range, they keep a 1-3 mi (2-5 km) distance between each other. Tigers are not entirely unsociable, however, as they will band together to hunt and share their kill. Mating is possible at any time during the year but seems to occur most frequently between November and April. Two to four cubs are usually born after a gestation period of just over 100 days. The female cares for the young, who nurse for six to eight weeks and then begin to accompany her during kills. The cubs usually remain dependent for around two years, usually leaving after a new litter is born. Cubs are preyed upon by wild dogs and hyenas.

Habitat and Current Distribution

Tigers occupy a wide range of habitats, the few requirements being adequate cover, water, and prey. Tigers are found in rain forests, evergreen forests, mangrove swamps, grasslands, savannas, and rocky country.

It is estimated that there are 650 Sumatran tigers left in the world; 30-80 South China tigers; 150-200 Siberian tigers; 1,000-1,700 Indo-Chinese tigers; and 3,350-4,700 Bengal tigers. The Caspian tiger, once found as far west as Turkey, disappeared in the 1970s. The Bali tiger, the smallest of the eight sub-species, became extinct in 1937. The Javan tiger was last seen in 1983.

The Bengal tiger is found in India, Bangladesh, Myanmar, Nepal, and Bhutan. The Indo-Chinese tiger is found in Kampuchea, Laos, Malaysia, Thailand, Myanmar, and Vietnam. The South China tiger is considered to be almost extinct in the wild, with perhaps as few as 50 individuals surviving in southern China. The Siberian tiger once roamed from Lake Baikal to the Pacific coast and Korea but is now believed to be restricted to North Korea, Manchuria, and Russia. The Sumatran tiger is limited to the island of Sumatra, Indonesia.

History and Conservation Measures

At the beginning of the twentieth century about 100,000 tigers roamed the Asian forests and grasslands. The decline in the tiger population accelerated from the 1940s through the 1960s; in 1972 the population in India dropped below 2,000 animals in the wild. Currently the country of India has about 60 percent of the world's tigers—about 3,750 individuals—and the government has established 21 reserves in an effort to protect them. India's first concentrated effort to save the tigers began in 1972 under Prime Minister Indira Gandhi when she launched "Project Tiger." Under this plan, reserves were established and hunting and trading of tiger products banned. By 1980, reports declared that the tiger population was at safe levels, but it was later revealed that the numbers were highly inflated by government officials. Today, even within protected reserves, tigers face illegal hunting. The Nagarahole National Park, which contains 51 Bengal tigers, is patrolled by 250 guards but poaching still occurs. Between 1989-92, the Ranthambhore National Park in Rajasthan lost 18 tigers to poachers, even as 60 guards patrolled the area. As recently as August 1993, New Delhi police confiscated 850 lb (386 kg) of tiger bone (equivalent to about 42 tigers).

The tiger is revered in the legends, histories, and medical practices of many Asian countries. Historically, the tiger has been hunted for its beautiful skin, as game trophy, and because they threatened livestock and human lives. Later, habitat destruction (forest clearance for logging and for agricultural development) became the primary threat to the species.

This subsequent loss of habitat diminished prey supply, which fragmented the remnant tiger populations. Although habitat destruction remains the primary threat to the tiger's survival, a recent upsurge in poaching is compounding the problem. In China and Taiwan, it is believed that two or three tigers are killed illegally each day. In an effort to save the remaining tigers in these Asian countries, CITES—Convention on International Trade in Endangered Species—has threatened trade sanctions if the governments of China and Taiwan do not shut down the illegal trading and selling of tiger products. Almost every part of the tiger—bones, eyes, and even whiskers—is valued in Oriental medical practices. Tiger parts are used to cure or ease human ailment, enhance longevity, and aid in sexual performance.

Today, even within protected reserves, the survival of the remaining tigers is uncertain. In countries like India, burgeoning human populations are encroaching on protected land, and there are pressures to open up the land for development. Conservation efforts on behalf of the tiger must consider and balance wildlife management with economic development if the tiger is to survive into the next century.

Snow leopard

Uncia (Panthera) uncia

Phylum	Chordata
Class	Mammalia
Order	Carnivora
Family	Felidae
Status	Endangered, IUCN
	Endangered, USFWS
	Appendix I, CITES
Range	Afghanistan; Bhutan; China; India; Kazakhstan; Kyrgyzstan; Mongolia; Nepal; Pakistan; Russia; Tajikistan; Uzbekistan

Description and Biology

This beautiful leopard has a coat of long, pale gray fur with white underneath. Its coat is patterned with solid spots on the head and legs, with dark gray rosettes (larger spots) on the rest of the body. A little smaller than the leopard, the snow leopard averages 48-56 in (122-142 cm) in length at maturity, with a tail length of 32-40 in (80-100 cm) and an average weight of 132-165 lb (60-75 kg). Its adaption to a cold and snowy high altitude terrain can be seen in several features: strong chest muscles for climbing, large and heavily padded forepaws for walking through snow, and a thick coat in winter.

Although this leopard is mostly nocturnal, crepuscular (dawn and dusk) activity has been recorded in some locations. The preferred prey in most parts of its range is the bharal, a kind of goat with sheep-like characteristics. Snow leopards also take Asiatic ibex, yak—which can weigh more than 440 lb (200 kg)—marmots, musk deer, and domestic livestock. Individual home ranges in one snow leopard population in Nepal varied with availability of prey from 5-15 sq mi (12-39 sq km) and overlapped considerably. A superb leaper, this animal has been reported to jump as far as 50 ft (15 m) in a single bound.

Like other big cats such as tigers, snow leopards are generally solitary animals. Males and females associate only for mating, with females giving birth to one to four cubs in a den in spring or early summer; the gestation period is 98-103 days. Cubs nurse for at least two months and remain dependent for nine months to one year.

Habitat and Current Distribution

The snow leopard's range extends over a massive area of almost one million sq mi (2.5 million sq km). The species is found in the Hindu Kush mountains of Afghanistan and Pakistan, along the Karakorum and Pamir mountain ranges. The habitat further extends through the Tien Shan, Altai, and Sayan ranges along the borders of Tajikistan, Kyrgyzstan, Uzbekistan, Kazakhstan, Russia, and Mongolia, continuing south through the Qinghai, Gansu, and Sichuan provinces of China, into Tibet and the Himalayan countries of Bhutan, Nepal, and India. The species occurs sparsely throughout this range; population figures in the wild are unknown, although some biologists put the population as high as 5,000.

Snow leopard.

Snow leopards inhabit alpine and subalpine zones above 9,840 ft (3,000 m), where these zones are closely associated with arid and semi-arid steppe habitats. The species has been seen as low as 1,968 ft (600 m) in some parts of its range and, in the summer months, may be found as high as 18,040 ft (5,500 m). In India and Pakistan, these leopards are known to move down to oak, fir, and rhododendron forests in winter, and in certain parts of their range are reported to remain in conifer forests throughout the year.

History and Conservation Measures

As might be expected, the snow leopard has long been hunted for its handsome coat. Legal restrictions to animal trade instituted by the Convention on International Trade in Endangered Species of Wild Fauna and Flora (CITES) have eliminated much of the demand for leopard fur, but it is still poached and sold on the black market. Enforcement is difficult because of the inaccessibility and isolation of much of the habitat.

Although poaching remains a problem, the primary threat to this species is now the expansion of human activities into its habitat. As the human population grows and habitats are developed for livestock grazing, traditional prey becomes scarce. Snow leopards are then forced to feed on domestic livestock, thus becoming targets for angry livestock owners. Survival of this leopard depends upon the preservation of areas of natural habitat large enough to provide hunting ranges and support sufficient prey. It also depends on improving the living standard of local human populations and ensuring that they benefit economically from the presence of such wildlife in their region.

Since the remaining snow leopards are scattered over a such wide range, they are divided into small, isolated populations. Studies are in progress to determine the effect of this isolation on genetic variability. Scientists are also trying to determine if inbreeding has occured.

Liberian mongoose

Liberiictis kuhni

Phylum	Chordata
Class	Mammalia
Order	Carnivora
Family	Herpestidae
Status	Endangered, IUCN
Range	Liberia; Cote d'Ivoire

Description and Biology

The Liberian mongoose is a quick and agile animal found in northern Liberia and the western Cote d'Ivoire. It has a neck stripe that is dark brown in the middle and banded on either side by lighter brown stripes. The overall coat color is dark brown to black. Head and body length averages 16.5 in (42 cm) and weight is around 5 lb (2.3 kg). The tail averages 7.8 in (19.8 cm) and may have both light and dark brown shadings. Feeding during the day, this mongoose uses its sharp claws and long snout to dig for earthworms and beetle larvae.

Unlike many other mongoose species, which are solitary, the Liberian mongoose is reported to live in groups of three to five individuals and has been sighted in groups as large as 15. Information about this animal's reproductive biology is unavailable.

Habitat and Current Distribution

This species occurs in a small area of northeastern Liberia and western Cote d'Ivoire. There are no estimates of population.

Specimens have been found in areas of dense primary and secondary forest with access to water. It is believed to be restricted to habitats with deep, sandy soil that supports its primary food source. It apparently shelters in burrows or hollow trees.

History and Conservation Measures

Very little is known about the Liberian mongoose, since it has been studied from only 25 specimens. Habitat destruction has contributed to the endangered status of this species, since most of the forest where it has been found is already greatly degraded as a result of logging and settlement by squatter villagers. Its numbers have also been reduced because of heavy hunting.

It is possible—but unlikely—that this species occurs in the Sapo National Park in Liberia; it does occur in the Tai National Park in Cote d'Ivoire. Conservation efforts should include surveys to determine whether populations are sufficient for the long-term conservation of this species. Additional efforts should be made to locate any populations that may exist outside these protected areas. Due to the restricted range of the species and the heavy hunting pressure on it, establishment of a captive breeding colony could be an important safeguard against extinction.

Brown hyena

Hyaena brunnea

Phylum	Chordata
Class	Mammalia
Order	Carnivora
Family	Hyaenidae
Status	Vulnerable, IUCN
	Endangered, USFWS
	Appendix I, CITES
Range	Angola; Botswana; Mozambique; Namibia; South Africa; Zimbabwe

Description and Biology

The brown hyena has a long, brown, shaggy coat with lighter underparts, gray to black face and legs, and dark horizontal bars on the legs. On average, it measures 43-53 in (110-135 cm) in length, 25-35 in (64-88 cm) in height, and weighs approximately 82-104 lb (37-47 kg); males are larger than females. This carnivore feeds on the remains of prey killed by other predators and can crush and digest bone not usually eaten by other predators. It is predominantly a scavenger of mammal remains, but also feeds on other vertebrates, insects, eggs and fruits, as well as the occasional small mammal or bird which it kills. Although the brown hyena has acute vision and hearing, it usually locates its prey by scent. Along the coast it feeds on dead seals and other marine life washed up on the shore. Excess food is often cached in a hole or hidden in bushes or long grass to retrieve later. Its home range averages about 183 sq mi (300 km). It usually covers about 19 sq mi (30 km) per night, but has been known to travel over 31 sq mi (50 km). Lions and spotted hyenas are predators.

Foraging and hunting is usually a solitary activity, but brown hyenas often form clans of up to 10 adults plus numerous cubs. Mating takes place throughout the year and after a gestation of 90-100 days, 1-5 cubs are born. Dens are solitary or communal, where cubs may suckle from females other than their mother. All members of the clan help to feed the cubs by carrying food to the den. Cubs remain attached to den for up to 14 months after birth.

Habitat and Current Distribution

There are no estimates of the number of brown hyenas surviving in southern Africa. Its preferred habitat is arid and includes rocky desert areas with thick brush, open scrub and grassland, and semi-desert. Hunting at dusk or during the night, the hyena requires shelter for the daylight hours, using dense vegetation, sheltering rocks, or a burrow dug by another animal.

History and Conservation Measures

Although there are no initial population estimates for the brown hyena, scientists have determined that its range and population have been greatly reduced, particularly in South Africa. In South Africa it is still found in the northern Cape and parts of the northern and eastern Transvaal, the Orange Free State, and Natal, where it has been reintroduced into the St. Lucia and Itala Game Reserves. It is found over much of Namibia (except for the Caprivi Strip re-

Brown hyena.

gion), and extends into the southwest tip of Angola. The brown hyena can also be found in Botswana, which hosts the largest population, except for the extreme northern region of the country. It also has a sizable population in Zimbabwe. Unlike many endangered species which are the victims of habitat destruction, the brown hyena is the target of intentional killing by human beings who perceive it as a threat to livestock. Since it feeds primarily on carrion, this perception is inaccurate. Despite legal protection, the future of the brown hyena will remain uncertain until people realize that it is a poor hunter who seldom makes a successful kill. Although no specific conservation plans are being implemented, the brown hyena is well protected in several conservation areas such as the Kalahari Gemsbok and Gemsbok National Parks, which together contain a population of about 650 individuals, the Central Kalahari Game Reserve, and the coastal regions of the southern Namib Desert and Etosha National Park.

Congo clawless otter

Aonyx congica

Phylum	Chordata
Class	Mammalia
Order	Carnivora
Family	Mustelidae
Status	Indeterminate, IUCN
	Endangered, USFWS
	Appendix I, CITES
Range	Angola; Burundi (?); Cameroon; Central Africa Republic; Congo; Gabon; Nigeria (?); Rwanda; Uganda; Zaire

Description and Biology

The Congo clawless otter has a brown coat with lighter underparts; some individuals have white markings in the facial area or on the chest. Its head and body length averages 28-35 in (70-90 cm), and its weight ranges from 26-45 lb (12-20 kg). Tail length averages about 17-22 in (44-57 cm). Diet is thought to include fish, worms, insects, mollusc, crustaceans, and amphibians.

There is no information available about social structure or reproductive biology.

Habitat and Current Distribution

The Congo clawless otter is endemic to central West Africa, where it occurs in the rain forest habitats of the Congo River basin, extending eastward to the forests and wetland areas of Rwanda, Burundi, and Uganda. There are no estimates of population.

Preferred habitat apparently includes small montane streams and marshes and lowland swamp forests.

History and Conservation Measures

So little is known about this species that its status has not been determined and its ecology and conservation requirements are unknown. Conservation priorities, however, have been determined. Field surveys are necessary to determine current distribution and status of the Congo clawless otter. Studies on the ecology and conservation requirements should be initiated to identify habitat features that must be conserved. Improved protected area management is needed for all reserves in which the Congo clawless otter occurs, and management plans for these reserves should take the particular needs of this species into account. Habitat management practices outside protected areas should also be carried out in such a way as to prevent population fragmentation. This implies the management of timber concessions in the African equatorial forests on a long-term sustainable use basis, rather than clearance. There is also a need to integrate indigenous people and their needs into the conservation and sustainable management of these forests. In local situations, it might prove necessary to devise a means of reducing the numbers of Congo clawless otters accidentally killed in fish traps. There should be initial attempts to keep and breed this species in captivity, with a view to starting a coordinated captive breeding program.

Marine otter

Lutra felina

Phylum	Chordata
Class	Mammalia
Order	Carnivora
Family	Mustelidae
Status	Vulnerable, IUCN
	Endangered, USFWS
	Appendix I, CITES
Range	Argentina; Chile; Peru

Description and Biology

The marine otter is sometimes called the sea cat. It has coarse, dense hair that is dark brown with lighter underparts. Its physical characteristics include a long body, flat head, small ears, and a broad muzzle which is whiskered. It has short legs and webbed feet to facilitate swimming. The marine otter's head and body length averages 22-31 in (56-76 cm), its tail length is 12-14 in (30-36 cm), and it weighs 7-31 lb (3-14 kg). Diet consists mainly of crustaceans and mollusc, with lesser amounts of fish. Some aquatic vegetation is taken, but it may be ingested accidentally along with shellfish. The killer whale (*Orcinus orca*) is thought to be a predator and there may be competition for food with gulls and sea lions.

Most observations of this species are of single individuals, though occasionally it is seen in groups of three or more. Mating has been observed in December and January. Young are born in autumn and winter, after a gestation period that lasts somewhere between 60-120 days. The normal litter size is two, but up to four or five young in one litter is possible.

Habitat and Current Distribution

The marine otter occurs along the Pacific coastline from equatorial Peru to the southern tip of South America, with the most abundant populations occurring on the Chiloé Islands south of Chile and further south towards Cape Horn. An unconfirmed estimate places total population at less than 1,000 individuals.

This species known habitat includes exposed rocky coastal areas and secluded bays and inlets near estuaries. While searching for freshwater shrimp, it sometimes ascends rivers up to 2,000 ft (650 m) above sea level. The marine otter has been studied in an area characterized by a rocky shore of irregular topography with a heavy swell, constant strong winds, and a dense cover of shrubs and small trees stunted by wind and poor soil extending down to the highwater mark above a heavy growth of seaweed and algae.

History and Conservation Measures

The marine otter originally occurred more or less continuously from northern Peru to Cape Horn,

Marine otter.

and possibly also in Argentinean waters. It has been hunted for its fur in Chile, where it is now considered to be threatened or endangered. It is very endangered in the northern part of the country and rare in central Chile, where it is vulnerable due to limited suitable habitat. In Argentina, the marine otter has always been somewhat marginal, but is now on the verge of extinction. At one time it was abundant in the Beagle Channel, as Charles Darwin observed during his voyages on the HMS *Beagle*, but has now disappeared from the Argentine portion of the Channel. The only known population lives on Staten Island, where its status needs to be evaluated. Populations are probably small and isolated in Peru, where it occurs in discontinuous pockets of suitable habitat all along the Peruvian coast.

Conservation priorities have been outlined for this species. Field surveys should be conducted throughout its range to determine current distribution and status. Beginning in areas of suitable rocky habitat, the surveys should develop into regular monitoring programs. Studies on the ecology and conservation requirements should be continued in order to identify those habitat features that must be conserved

to ensure survival and recovery of the species. Research is also needed on food requirements, and on the impact of human activities such as harvesting of marine resources, including algae. Coastal protected areas need to be established in Argentina, Chile, and Peru.

This species requires strict protection from hunting and persecution in order to prevent the fragmentation of populations. Continued efforts are needed to eliminate the illegal trade in pelts. In local situations, it might prove necessary to devise means of reducing conflicts between marine otters and fisheries, most notably with shrimp harvesters in Peru. The effects of inshore pollution on suitable habitat need to be evaluated, as well as the necessity of stricter controls on the discharge of pollutants into the sea. Public education campaigns are needed in all three countries within its range to draw attention to the plight of the marine otter and to develop support for its conservation. Finally, the possibility of captive breeding should be explored, with the long-term goal of reintroduction of the species into parts of its former range.

Southern river otter

Lutra provocax

Phylum	Chordata
Class	Mammalia
Order	Carnivora
Family	Mustelidae
Status	Vulnerable, IUCN
	Endangered, USFWS
	Appendix I, CITES
Range	Argentina; Chile

Description and Biology

The southern river otter is a freshwater species. It has a velvety coat that is dark brown to very dark brown, turning into a lighter, cinnamon color on its underparts. Its physical characteristics include a long body, flat head, small ears, and a broad muzzle which is whiskered. This species legs are short, claws strong, and feet webbed to facilitate swimming. The head and body length of the southern river otter averages 22-28 in (56-71 cm); its tail length measures 14-18 in (35.6-45.7 cm). Diet is thought to be composed almost entirely of crayfish and freshwater mussels.

The southern river otter has been so poorly studied that no information is available about social structure and the only thing known about reproductive biology is that breeding is probably possible throughout the year.

Habitat and Current Distribution

The southern river otter occurs only in the southern parts of Chile and western Argentina. In Argentina, only one important population remains today, that of the Nahuel Huapí Basin and nearby sub-basins, with occasional sightings in other freshwater Andean systems. The only other known population lives on Staten Island near Tierra del Fuego. In Chile, important populations persist in the southern portion of the country; there are freshwater populations from Aysén to the north. There are no population estimates.

This species is found in estuaries, rivers, and lakes, encompassing fresh and brackish waters. It requires dense vegetation cover near the shoreline.

History and Conservation Measures

The population of the southern river otter is believed to have declined as a result of habitat destruction and fur-hunting. Although it has probably always had a restricted natural distribution in Argentina, this species has disappeared from several areas and remnant populations are isolated. In Chile, this otter has disappeared from the northern fringe of its former range due to excessive hunting and habitat alteration, especially the clearing of riparian vegetation. Since the river otter requires clean water, it is adversely affected by pollution of wetlands.

Conservation priorities for this species have been outlined. Field surveys are necessary throughout its range to determine current distribution and status; the surveys should develop into regular monitoring programs. Studies on the ecology and conservation requirements should be continued to identify those habitat features that must be conserved to ensure the survival and recovery of the southern river otter. Research is also needed on food requirements, and to determine the impact on habitat of human activities such as harvesting of marine and freshwater resources, including algae. Coastal and inland protected areas need to be established for this species in Argentina and Chile; there should be close cooperation between both countries in implementing conservation programs for the southern river otter. Additionally, careful habitat management outside of protected areas is needed to prevent population fragmentation. The clearance of large areas of forest in southern Chile, and of riparian vegetation in central Chile, is of particular concern and needs to be carefully regulated.

Strict protection from hunting and persecution is required in order to prevent the fragmentation of populations. Continued efforts are needed to eliminate the illegal domestic trade in pelts, another issue which depends on close cooperation between Argentina and Chile. When major development projects are being considered (e.g., hydroelectric power development and agricultural expansion around rivers), environmental impact assessments should consider the effect of the project on otters and other species of conservation concern. In local situations, it might be necessary to devise means of reducing conflicts between southern river otters and fisheries. The effects of pollution need to be evaluated, particularly freshwater pollution in central Chile. Public education campaigns are needed in both countries to draw attention to the plight of the species, and to develop support for its conservation. Finally, captive breeding should be attempted, with the long-term goal of reintroduction of the southern river otter into parts of its former range.

Hairy-nosed otter

Lutra sumatrana

Phylum	Chordata
Class	Mammalia
Order	Carnivora
Family	Mustelidae
Status	Insufficiently Known, IUCN Appendix II, CITES
Range	Brunei; Bangka, Java, Kalimantan, Sumatra (Indonesia); Kampuchea; Laos (?); Peninsular Malaysia, Sabah, Sarawak (Malaysia); Singapore; Thailand; Vietnam

Description and Biology

This otter's common name describes its most distinguishing feature; otherwise, except for a darker coat both dorsally and ventrally, it is very much like the Eurasian otter. Short, dense, waterproof fur is dark brown to black above and below with a distinct white throat patch. Its head and body length averages 19-32 in (48-81 cm), and its tail length measures about 13-20 in (33-50 cm). This species' weighs approximately 7-31 lbs (3-14 kg). Its physical characteristics include a long and sinuous body, flat head, and small ears, and its legs are short and feet webbed to facilitate swimming. This species' broad muzzle is surrounded by long, stiff whiskers which are thought to be used in searching for prey. River otters are known to feed on a variety of aquatic invertebrates, fish, rodents, birds, and small mammals; the exact diet of the hairy-nosed otter is unknown.

Although information is available for relatives of the hairy-nosed otter, there has been insufficient study to determine the social structure or reproductive biology of this species.

Habitat and Current Distribution

The distribution of this species is poorly known; it is thought to survive in Sumatra, Kalimantan, and Java (Indonesia), where it inhabits freshwater and coastal areas, especially mangroves. It has been sighted in scattered localities in East Malaysia, but has not been observed in Peninsular Malaysia in recent years. If the hairy-nosed otter still exists in Peninsular Malaysia, it is thought to remain in the rivers at higher altitudes, far from human presence. There are no population estimates.

History and Conservation Measures

The hairy-nosed otter was once found in southern Indochina, Malaysia, and other parts of Indonesia (Sumatra, Java, and Borneo). It has since become the rarest of the Asian otters, now probably verging on extinction in the northern parts of its range, and of uncertain status elsewhere. Decline in the population of this species, as in other otters, is attributed to habitat destruction, especially pollution of wetlands, excessive hunting for pelts, and the fishing industry.

This species has been reported in such protected areas as the Padang-Sugihan Wildlife Reserve (Sumatra Selatan), the Way Kambas Game Reserve (Lampung), and Ujung Kulon National Park (Java). A number of conservation efforts have been recommended. Field surveys should be conducted throughout this otter's range to determine current distribution and status; surveys should begin in those areas where populations are thought to survive and then be conducted in parts of the former range for which there are no recent records, but in which populations might survive. Studies on the ecology and conservation requirements should be initiated in protected areas where the otter is known to occur; such studies should seek to identify those habitat features that must be conserved to ensure survival and recovery of the species.

Improved protected area management is needed for all reserves in which the hairy-nosed otter occurs, and management plans for these reserves should take the particular needs of this species into account. Habitat management practices outside protected areas should also be carried out to prevent population fragmentation; this applies in particular to the draining of wetlands in Sumatra and Kalimantan and to the extraction of gravel from river beds in Sumatra. The use of pesticides in agriculture, and the dumping of toxic wastes from factories and domestic wastes and detergents from human settlements needs to be strictly regulated.

The hairy-nosed otter should have strict legal protection in Indonesia, where it is thought the bulk of the known populations survive. All trade in the pelts of this species should be prohibited by national laws, and there is a need for stricter compliance with the wildlife protection laws in several parts of its range. Initial attempts should be made to keep and breed this species in captivity, with a long-term goal of a coordinated captive breeding program which could lead to eventual reintroduction of the species in parts of its former range.

Colombian weasel

Mustela felipei

Phylum	Chordata
Class	Mammalia
Order	Carnivora
Family	Mustelidae
Status	Endangered, IUCN
Range	Colombia; Ecuador

Description and Biology

The Colombian weasel is a semi-aquatic species with a long, slender body and soft, thick hair. Upper body and tail are dark brown to black; underparts are tan to orange. Head and body length averages 8.3-8.7 in (21-22 cm) and tail length is 3.9-4.3 in (10-11 cm). Feet are bare and webbed to facilitate swimming. Weasels are carnivores and generally feed on rodents, birds, insects, or small mammals; the exact diet of the Colombian weasel is unknown.

There is no information available about social structure or reproductive biology.

Habitat and Current Distribution

Four of the five specimens of the Colombian weasel were collected along rivers between 5,700-8,800 ft (1,750-2,700 m) in the provinces of Huila and Cauca, Colombia; one was obtained from Andean Ecuador. There are no estimates of population size.

Very little is known about the Colombian weasel's habitat. The few specimens have been obtained from an altitude where cloud forests predominate. One specimen was collected from a part of the Suaza River where torrential currents are interrupted by quiet periods.

History and Conservation Measures

The Colombian weasel was first described in 1978; live weasels have never been observed by scientists. If the species depends on riverine habitats within its small range, it must be considered a great conservation concern. It is considered the rarest carnivore in South America.

One of the specimens was collected in the Cueva de los Guacharos National Park; the Parque Nacional de Huila and Parque Nacional de Purace are also close to the collection sites. Immediate protection should be given to any site containing a population of the species.

Black-footed ferret

Mustela nigripes

Phylum	Chordata
Class	Mammalia
Order	Carnivora
Family	Mustelidae
Status	Endangered, IUCN
	Endangered, USFWS
	Appendix I, CITES
Range	Reintroduced in Wyoming (U.S.A.)

Description and Biology

The black-footed ferret is a member of the weasel family, similar in size to a mink. It has a brownish head and a long, slender body with short, pale yellow fur shading to nearly white on its throat and belly. Brown-tipped guard hairs on its back create the appearance of a dark saddle. It has a brownish black mask across the eyes, black feet and a black tip on its tail. The ferret's body length is 18-22 in (46-56 cm), its tail is 4.5-5.5 in (11.4-13.9 cm) and it weighs 18-36 oz (0.5-1 kg).

The only North American weasel considered endangered, the fate of the black-footed ferret is intimately tied to the fortunes of the prairie dog. The ferret preys upon prairie dogs and lives in prairie dog burrows. A nocturnal hunter, it is only occasionally active above ground during the day. After making a kill, the ferret drags the prairie dog below ground before devouring it. Ferrets also eat mice, voles, ground squirrels, gophers, birds, and insects. They are preyed upon by great-horned owls, golden eagles, coyotes, and badgers.

An individual ferret moves nomadically around a range of about 100 acres (40 ha) of prairie dog colony. It marks this territory with musk from scent glands that it rubs against the ground or on bushes.

The male has a larger range than the female and the two sexes live apart except during March and April when breeding occurs.

After a gestation period of 41-45 days, the female ferret produces a litter of three to five kits. The kits do not come out of the burrow until they are six weeks old and have reached three-quarters of adult size. At the end of the first summer, the mother separates the kits into different burrows and then leads one or two kits on increasingly longer trips away from her territory. In the wild, most young

Black-footed ferret.

ferrets do not survive their first year, and few adults live more than several years.

Habitat and Current Distribution

The black-footed ferret is adapted to the prairies of the Great Plains of North America. It once ranged from Texas to southern Saskatchewan, Canada, and from the Rocky Mountains eastward through the Dakotas, Nebraska, and Kansas. Until the release of 49 captive-bred ferrets in the fall of 1991, a black-footed ferret population had not existed in the wild for five years.

History and Conservation Measures

As ranchers and farmers settled the prairies, they waged an active campaign to eradicate prairie dog towns, using these lands for livestock grazing and agriculture. The use of poison, hunting, and habitat destruction reduced the prairie dog population by 90 percent, thus eliminating food sources and habitat for the black-footed ferret. As suitable habitat became more fragmented, ferret groups often became too isolated to breed successfully. Wild ferret populations were further reduced by a severe plague of canine distemper in the 1950s.

From 1972 to 1981, the ferret was thought to be extinct. In 1981, a small breeding population was discovered in Wyoming and it prospered, numbering 130 individuals by 1984. However, in 1985, disease caused a significant decline in the prairie dog population and ferret numbers plummeted. By 1987, only 17 individuals survived in the last known wild ferret population at Meeteetse, Wyoming, and they were captured to form the basis of a captive breeding program. Since a number of these individuals were related, the actual founder population for the captive breeding program was probably only five or six. This lack of genetic diversity may pose long-term difficulties for the recovery of the species. In 1991, 49 captive-bred, juvenile ferrets were released into a prairie dog town in Shirley Basin, Wyoming. Several of these animals survived the winter and have bred successfully. Some 260 black-footed ferrets remain in captivity.

The goal of the captive breeding program is to maintain a viable breeding population of black-footed ferrets in captivity and to return their offspring to the wild. In 1992, another 100 juvenile ferrets has been released. The U.S. Fish and Wildlife Service aims to establish 10 separate wild ferret populations, spread over the widest possible area within their former range. While the first releases of captive-bred ferrets risk high mortality rates, the experience gained will establish successful methods to return the black-footed ferret to its natural habitat.

Giant otter

Pteronura brasiliensis

Phylum	Chordata
Class	Mammalia
Order	Carnivora
Family	Mustelidae
Status	Vulnerable, IUCN
	Endangered, USFWS
	Appendix I, CITES
Range	Argentina; Bolivia; Brazil; Colombia; Ecuador; French Guiana; Guyana; Paraguay; Peru; Suriname; Uruguay (ex?); Venezuela

Description and Biology

The giant otter is the largest and perhaps the rarest of all the otters. Its sleek brown coat is accented by light patches on its chest and throat area. This member of the weasel family is well suited to aquatic life with its waterproofed body hair, webbed feet, and a flat, wedged tail. It is 38-60 in (96-150 cm) long with a 18-26 in (45-65 cm) tail and weighs 53-75 lb (24-34 kg). Scent marking is used to outline territories along stream, river bank, or lake. Along slow-moving rivers, areas are cleared for rest and eating. The giant otter feeds mainly on fish, up to 8 lb (4 kg) per individual per day. Smaller prey are usually eaten at once in the water but bigger fish are taken to shore. Giant otters build dens among rocks and vegetation along riverbanks. During rest, group members groom one another, and play periods of up to one hour have been observed.

The basic social structure of the giant otter is the family unit built around a mating pair; females are dominant. One to four cubs are born normally at the beginning of the dry season (June to August). Cubs stay in the den for up to two months. Often a group member "babysits" while the group is outside fishing. Cubs remain with the parents for around two to three years. Giant otters often fish together but they don't share their prey. Cubs and sub-adults beg very loudly for food and sometimes try to steal food from the adults. Nine different calls are known among giant otters, including loud screams and soft coos. Maximum group size appears to be nine, but it generally averages four to five animals. When old enough, individual members leave their group, travelling large distances before forming a new group or joining another group.

Habitat and Current Distribution

The giant otter is found in South America in Colombia, Ecuador, Suriname, French Guiana, Guyana, Venezuela, Bolivia, Paraguay, Brazil, Peru, Argentina, and possibly Uruguay. Estimates of total population are unavailable.

The giant otter's habitat is rivers and creeks of the greater Amazon Basin. The otter inhabits large rivers and narrow forest creeks in seasonally-flooded and high-forest areas. It prefers areas with fairly shallow water and low, sloping banks with good cover. In broader rivers, it prefers access to shallower areas

Giant otter.

such as rapids or waterfalls, with pools and ponds created by boulders and sandbars.

History and Conservation Measures

This species was once found in most rivers and creeks in the Amazon Basin. It now has only a sporadic distribution within this range. Because of its diurnal habits, group social structure, and curiosity, the otter has been an easy target for hunters collecting its pelt for the international fur trade. Legal protections instituted in the 1970s slowed the slaughter, but poaching continues on a large scale.

To a population already decimated by hunting, habitat loss looms as a new threat. Much of its remote habitat is being invaded and cleared for development, or polluted. Protection of river systems and lakes that still contain giant otter populations is vital if this species is to survive.

Juan Fernández fur seal

Arctocephalus philippii

Phylum	Chordata
Class	Mammalia
Order	Carnivora
Family	Otariidae
Status	Vulnerable, IUCN
	Appendix II, CITES
Range	Juan Fernández islands (Chile)

Description and Biology

The Juan Fernández fur seal, like the related Guadalupe fur seal, has a dense coat of black fur and, in males, a mane of coarse guard hairs tipped with gray. These two seals are distinguished from other species of *Arctocephalus* by their long, slender snout and light-colored whiskers. Male Juan Fernández seals are about 6.6 ft (2 m) long and weigh around 310 lb (140 kg). Females are much smaller at about 4.6 ft (1.4 m) and 110 lb (50 kg). The front flippers are used for swimming, but all four flippers can be used on land for locomotion. Diet includes fish and cephalopods, particularly *Dosidicus gigua*, *Octopotenthis* spp., *Tremoctopus violacens*, *Torades filippovae*, and *Morotenthis banksii*.

On shore, this fur seal rests on solid lava rocks at the base of cliffs, ledges, and caves. Even when swimming, the Juan Fernández fur seal stays close to the rocks, and when threatened, may retreat into sea caves. Sharks, killer whales, and leopard seals are known to prey on this species.

Little information is available about social structure or reproductive biology, but mating is known to occur between November and January. Pups are 26-27 in (65-68 cm) long and weigh 14-15 lb (6.2-6.8 kg).

Habitat and Current Distribution

This species is restricted to the Juan Fernández Archipelago and the Desventuradas Islands off the coast of Chile, where it inhabits rocky shorelines and caves in the summer and autumn; it spends winter and spring at sea in the cold waters of the Humboldt current.

A population survey in 1975 recorded 300 Juan Fernández fur seals on Desventuradas Islands; in 1985, 4,700 individuals were counted over the whole archipelago. A more recent population survey during the breeding season in 1990-1991 found 12,000 animals.

History and Conservation Measures

It is estimated that there were over four million Juan Fernández fur seals until the late 1600s. During the sixteenth and nineteenth centuries, this species was hunted nearly to extinction for its fur and oil. By the 1960s, scientists thought that it was extinct in the wild. However, local fishermen reported small numbers of these animals. In 1965, the species was rediscovered on Alejandro Selkirk Island. In 1968, 50 individuals were found on Robinson Crusoe Island.

Hunting of this species has been illegal since

1965, but it still occurs occasionally. Commercial harvest of the fur seal is rare, but fishermen have been known to kill some seals when they see them remove fish from their gear or cages. Like other sea mammals, the Juan Fernández fur seal is threatened with habitat degradation, pollution, and habitat disturbance from human activities.

In addition to these factors, this species is also hampered by the natural limitations of its habitat. The major calving ground—Alejandro Selkirk Island—is accessible only by land, while two others—Santa Clara and Robinson Crusoe Islands—to which the seals are forced to retreat by human harassment, are located on very rugged parts of the coast. Protection of calving grounds has been recommended as an essential conservation measure. Other protective measures include a census and tagging program; exploration for additional breeding areas and designation of reserves; behavior and reproductive studies; and an educational campaign to increase public awareness of the conservation requirements of this fur seal.

Guadalupe fur seal

Arctocephalus townsendi

Phylum	Chordata
Class	Mammalia
Order	Carnivora
Family	Otariidae
Status	Vulnerable, IUCN
	Threatened, USFWS
	Appendix I, CITES
Range	Mexico; California (U.S.A.)

Description and Biology

Closely related to the Juan Fernández fur seal, the Guadalupe fur seal exhibits certain unique behavioral characteristics among the genus *Arctocephlus*. Unlike most other seal species, this fur seal frequents caves and rocky recesses while on land. Some scientists have theorized that this preference is an adaptation to hunting pressures during the nineteenth century when seals were slaughtered in large numbers. As a survival measure, the Guadalupe seal retreated to caves, a behavior which has since been passed on to current populations.

Physically, the Guadalupe fur seal can be distinguished from other members of the genus—with the exception of the Juan Fernández seal which shares the same trait—by its long, pointed snout and light-colored whiskers. Males can grow up to 6.5 ft (2 m) and weigh 310 lb (140 kg); females are smaller at 4.4 ft (1.3 m) and 110 lb (50 kg). The front flippers are used for swimming, but all four flippers can be used on land for locomotion. Although the diet of the Guadalupe fur seal has not been examined in detail scientists know that it includes squid and lantern fish.

This seal travels widely at sea and has been found 186 mi (300 km) away from its main home range. Unlike other seals, the Guadalupe fur seal may be found on shore all year-round. During the breeding season, males are highly territorial. Dominant

Guadalupe fur seal.

males have a harem of two or three females but may have as many as ten. Mating occurs in May, June, and July and one or two young are born in a cave the next year during the same months.

Habitat and Current Distribution

The only known breeding colony of this fur seal is on the east coast of Guadalupe Island, west of the Baja California mainland, where it inhabits rocky shorelines and caves at the base of cliffs. In 1987, Mexican scientists counted 3,294 individuals on Guadalupe. The total population is now estimated at 6,000 individuals.

History and Conservation Measures

Like most sea mammals, the Guadalupe fur seal was abundant throughout its range until commercial hunting for its fur and oil decimated the population. Over 20,000—and maybe as many as 200,000—seals may have lived on Guadalupe Island alone before hunting in the 1800s nearly drove it to extinction. In fact, this species was considered extinct until 1928,

when two males were caught by fishermen. In 1949, a single bull was found on one of the Channel Islands, San Nicolas and, in 1954, a small breeding colony of 14 seals was discovered on Guadalupe. Since then, several censuses have been taken and indicate that the population is slowly increasing.

The Guadalupe fur seal has full legal protection but, because of its lack of fear of humans, is highly vulnerable. Human activity—noise and cruise ships—has also disturbed breeding, as has the presence of feral goats on breeding grounds. Guadalupe Island was declared a wildlife sanctuary in 1922 and, in 1978, Mexico declared all islands of the Baja California Peninsula and adjacent Sonoran Desert coast as a wildlife reserve.

Despite these measures, the Guadalupe fur seal still needs protection. Regular population censuses are necessary to monitor population recovery, as is research into the life history and ecology of this animal. Since the population recovered from a very limited number of individuals, there may be a lack of genetic diversity; genetic studies should therefore be given high priority.

Hooker's sea lion

Phocarctos hookeri

Phylum	Chordata
Class	Mammalia
Order	Carnivora
Family	Otariidae
Status	Vulnerable, IUCN
Range	New Zealand

Description and Biology

Hooker's sea lion is sometimes referred to as the New Zealand sea lion or Auckland sea lion. Once considered a member of the genus *Neophoca*, this sea lion was defined as a separate genus due to a number of distinctive morphological and behavioral characteristics. Hooker's sea lion is differentiated from the related fur seal species by its thinner underfur, short guard hairs, and blunt snout. The male is blackish brown with a long mane of coarse hair; the female is silver-gray with light cream underparts. Males measure from 8.2-11 ft (2.5-3.5 m) and weigh between 660-990 lb (300-450 kg). Females are much smaller: 6.6 ft (2 m) and about 350 lb (160 kg). Diet includes fish, squid, cuttlefish, octopus, crustaceans, prawns, crayfish, and occasionally, penguins.

Hooker's sea lion does not undergo lengthy migrations and breeds on sandy beaches (mainly on Auckland, Snares, and Campbell Islands). On land, their movements appear awkward, but they sometimes move inland and rest in forest areas or on high cliffs. At the height of the mating season, hundreds of males defend their territory—about a 6.6-ft (2-m) circular area—and the females within it. Mating takes place in November or December, just six to seven days after the birth of young conceived the previous season. Females give birth to one pup after a gestation period of 12 months and nurse for about a year.

Pups are born on beaches and remain on land for the first two months, although they may venture to streams and small pools, before finally joining their mothers in the sea.

Habitat and Current Distribution

Hooker's sea lion occurs mainly on the Auckland Islands but also on Snares and Campbell Islands and the mainland of South Island. Outside of the breeding season it may range into fairly deep waters. The population was estimated at around 5,000 individuals, but recent counts in 1992 found the population to be around 10,000-15,000 animals.

History and Conservation Measures

There are no estimates of previous population size, but this sea lion is thought to have bred throughout New Zealand at one time. During the early 1800s, it was hunted by humans for its skin, meat, and oil. Since afforded legal protection in the late 1800s, it has made a very gradual recovery. The Auckland Islands have been designated as a protected reserve. Despite these efforts, Hooker's sea lion still faces certain dangers: a commercial squid fishery 12-40 nautical miles north of the two largest rookeries is responsible for an annual incidental mortality of 2.4 percent of the female population and an estimated total catch of

Male Hooker's sea lion surrounded by females.

about 100-200 individuals. The presence of rabbit burrows on Auckland Islands has also been linked with juvenile mortality.

The IUCN has urged the New Zealand Government to declare a Marine Mammal Sanctuary and to ban drag-net fishing from the species' feeding grounds or take other measures to protect this sea lion. Recommendations regarding the management of rabbit populations have also been made. Governmental action is still pending.

Hawaiian monk seal
Monachus schauinslandi
Mediterranean monk seal
Monachus monachus

Phylum	Chordata
Class	Mammalia
Order	Pinnipedia
Family	Phocidae
Status	Endangered, IUCN
	Endangered, USFWS
	Appendix I, CITES
Range	Hawaii (U.S.A.) (*M. schauinslandi*)
	Mediterranean and Black Seas (Albania; Algeria; Bulgaria; Cyprus [ex?]; Greece; Sardinia [Italy, ex?] Lebanon [ex?]; Libya; Syria [ex?]; La Galite Island [Tunisia, ex?] Turkey; Yugoslavia); Atlantic coast of northwest Africa (Mauritania; Morocco; Western Sahara); Madeira Islands (Portugal); Canary Islands (Spain) (*M. monachus*)

Description and Biology

Most Mediterranean monk seals are dark brown with lighter underparts, with a distinctive irregular white patch on the belly. Some individuals are very pale and may appear almost white. Adults are 8-8.5 ft (2.4-2.6 m) and may weigh more than 660 lb (300 kg), but most individuals are smaller. The Hawaiian monk seal is slate gray above and silver-gray below. Its length is 7-7.5 ft (2.1-2.3 m) and its weight is 450-550 lb (204-250 kg). In both species, the female is large than the male. Monk seals eat a variety of bottom and reef-dwelling aquatic animals, including fish, eels, crustaceans, and octopuses. Sharks are known to prey upon Hawaiian monk seals.

Although the Mediterranean monk seal has been known to Western civilization far longer than any other seal, very little specific information is available about its behavior or reproductive biology. Historically, Mediterranean monk seals bred on open beaches backed by cliffs or desert and on beaches in caves. Breeding now occurs only in remote caves, probably because of excessive disturbance at more accessible sites. There is some evidence that *M. monachus* may be polygynous and mating seems to take place underwater. The gestation period is about 11 months and births of a single pup occur from May to November with a peak in September and October.

Male Hawaiian monk seals choose a mate by cruising the beaches where females sun themselves. Since there are about three times as many males as females, the females are frequently disturbed. Mating takes place in the water. Pups are born from late December to mid-August, with a peak in births occurring in April and May. Births occur high on the beach

Hawaiian monk seal.

in dry sand, at the water line, and on lava ledges or cobble beaches. A female Hawaiian monk seal nurses her single pup for five weeks, during which time she fasts and remains with her offspring. The pups are weak swimmers at birth and practice swimming under maternal supervision until they are weaned.

Habitat and Current Distribution

During the twentieth century the Mediterranean monk seal has disappeared from the mainland coasts of Spain and France, the Canary Islands, and from many sites in eastern Mediterranean. It is still found in the Madeira Islands, on the Atlantic coast of Morocco, on the Mediterranean coast of north Africa (possibly as far east as Libya), in Greece and Turkey, and at a few sites in the Adriatic Sea and southern Black Sea. It may still occur in Sardinia. The largest single concentration is in southern Morocco. It is unlikely that more than 500 individuals of the species still survive.

The Hawaiian monk seal inhabits the islands and atolls of the northwestern Hawaiian Islands. Breeding occurs primarily on Nihoa Island, Necker Island, French Frigate Shoals, Laysan Island, Lisianski Island, Pearl and Hermes Reef, the Midway Islands, and Kure Atoll. Fewer than 1,000 Hawaiian monk seals remain in the wild. It spends most of its

time in the water along island shorelines where mating takes place and where it feeds. It basks in the sun and gives birth on sandy or gravel beaches. While there is some movement between islands, most Hawaiian monk seals remain fairly close to their home beaches.

History and Conservation Measures

Both *M. monachus* and *M. schauinslandi* were much more common and widespread in the past than they are today. The Mediterranean species has declined due to hunting and disturbance by humans, especially those engaged in commercial fishing and recreational activities. Although this species is protected throughout its range, it is still killed by fishermen who consider it competition and who believe it damages their fishing nets. Some seals do become entangled in fishing nets and drown. If a pregnant female is disturbed by people, she may abort the fetus, and if a lactating female is disturbed, she may be unable to nurse and her pup may die. Overfishing and water pollution may also contribute to the decline of this species. The area around the Northern Sporades Islands in the Aegean Sea has been designated a national marine park by the Greek government, but local fishermen have opposed this designation and strict enforcement is difficult. Orphaned seal pups are also rescued, rehabilitated, and returned to the wild by biologists from the Hellenic Society for the Study and Protection of the Mediterranean Monk Seal.

The Hawaiian monk seal evolved in an environment totally free of people and other terrestrial predators. This made the species very approachable and easily disturbed. (Disturbing a pregnant or nursing female has effects similar to those noted above for *M. monachus*.) It probably once bred throughout the Hawaiian Islands, but commercial sealing in the nineteenth century pushed the species to the brink of extinction. The population rebounded slightly and remained essentially undisturbed in remoter areas until human presence increased during World War II. Today, increased fishing activity in its current range may lead to conflicts between the interests of seals and humans, and seals may also become entangled in fishing gear and drown. Shark predation is responsible for the deaths of many seal pups. In 1940 a number of the islands and atolls in the seal's present range were designated the Hawaiian Islands National Wildlife Refuge, and in 1967 this area was further declared a Research Natural Area. These protective measures limit unauthorized landings on uninhabited islands and decrease the level of human disturbance on seal beaches.

A third species, the Caribbean monk seal (*M. tropicalis*), was hunted relentlessly for its skins and oil after Europeans arrived in the Western Hemisphere, and is now considered extinct by the IUCN.

Red panda

Ailurus fulgens

Phylum	Chordata
Class	Mammalia
Order	Carnivora
Family	Procyonidae
Status	Vulnerable, IUCN
	Appendix II, CITES
Range	Bhutan; China; India; Laos; Myanmar; Nepal

Description and Biology

The red panda, also known as the lesser panda, is a striking animal that has russet fur marked with chocolate brown. It is the only species in its genus and the only Old World representative of its family. The Chinese call this animal "firefox" because of its flame-colored fur. *A. fulgens* has a long, banded tail; short, pointed ears; and a masked face similar to a raccoon's (another member of the Procyonid family). Its legs are short, the feet have hairy soles, and the claws are sharp and semi-retractile. Head and body length averages 20-23.5 in (50-60 cm), weight is 7.7-11 lb (3.5-5 kg), and the tail measures 12-20 in (30-50 cm). The red panda is mainly crepuscular, exhibiting two peaks of activity each day; one beginning just before dawn and ending soon after sunrise, with a second around dusk. It is highly arboreal, spending much of its time eating in the trees. It feeds primarily on the fresh, young leaves and shoots of bamboo and seems to have a strong preference for arrow bamboo. Red pandas also eat grasses, roots, lichens, berries, and fruits, and occasionally supplement their diet with eggs, chicks, birds, or small mammals.

Red pandas seem to be solitary and territorial. Males regularly patrol the perimeter of their territories, while females are more often found in the central portion of their territories. The territory of a single male will overlap the territories of several females. Mating begins around January and February, and the female seems to be receptive for a very short period of time (about 1-3 days). Because the period of female receptivity is so short, a male must regularly monitor the breeding status of the females within his territory and will mate repeatedly with a female when she becomes receptive. Red pandas engage in mutual grooming during courtship, but after mating, the male does not care for the female or her young. Gestation is thought to be between 90 and 145 days. The female selects a secure den site, usually a hollow tree, cave, or rock crevice, and two cubs are usually born (litter size can range from one to four). Newborn pandas are a uniform buff color, are blind, and totally dependent on their mother. They feed exclusively on their mother's milk until they are about five months old when they are gradually weaned to a diet of bamboo leaves. At about six months of age juvenile red pandas begin to disperse from their mother's territory and search for space of their own with a suitable den and food supply.

Habitat and Current Distribution

This species occurs only in the Himalayas in northern India, Sikkim, Nepal, Bhutan, southeastern Tibet, China, and northern Myanmar. It inhabits

Red panda.

mixed mountain forests of spruce and fir with dense bamboo understories at elevations of 6,500-13,000 ft (2,000-4,000 m). In China, the geographical range of the red and giant panda overlap, but the two species do not seem to compete for food or space. The red panda has only been studied extensively in Nepal, where research has indicated that there many be as few as 300 individuals. Other scientists consider this figure to be low since the study was conducted at fairly low altitudes and believe that the species may be more abundant at higher altitudes. The total number of red pandas in the wild is not known, but the species does appear to be very rare and unevenly distributed.

History and Conservation Measures

The red panda population is thought to be declining, primarily because of habitat loss. Forests throughout much of their range are being cleared for agriculture or are being damaged by fuelwood collection and overgrazing by domestic animals. All of these activities are the result of rapidly growing human populations and the pressures these populations exert on the environment. Selective timber cutting can also lead to habitat fragmentation and the creation of "islands" with isolated populations vulnerable to inbreeding, loss of genetic variation due to genetic

drift, and starvation. Because of its attractive fur, this species has been hunted for the fur trade and is also caught accidentally in traps set for other animals such as musk deer. The red panda is listed on Appendix II of the Convention on International Trade in Endangered Species of Wild Fauna and Flora (CITES). It is fully protected in Nepal and China and partially protected in Myanmar. In China, the red panda also benefits from the system of parks and reserves established for the giant panda, although it is not known whether these protected areas support viable red panda populations. Throughout its range, the status of the red panda in existing parks and reserves should be studied and new protected areas considered where suitable, contiguous habitat remains.

Red pandas are displayed in zoos worldwide and they have been bred in captivity with reasonable success. An international effort coordinating successful regional breeding programs (one in North America, two in Europe, one in Australia, one in Japan, and one in China) is underway with the goal of producing a single global management program for captive breeding of the species under the auspices of the International Red Panda Management Group. There is a strong possibility that a viable population of red pandas can be maintained in zoos. In recent years, however, a large number of live red pandas of uncertain origin have appeared in zoos, causing some concern that these animals were taken from the wild. It is imperative that additional live red pandas not be taken from the wild for zoos or other collections. Hopefully, the success of captive breeding efforts will eliminate the impetus for taking wild red pandas into captivity. Public education and the involvement of local people in the design and implementation of conservation programs are also crucial to the survival of this unique animal in its wild and natural state.

Giant panda

Ailuropoda melanoleuca

Phylum	Chordata
Class	Mammalia
Order	Carnivora
Family	Ursidae
Status	Endangered, IUCN
	Endangered, USFWS
	Appendix I, CITES
Range	China

Description and Biology

This famous animal has become a symbol in the fight to save endangered species from extinction. The taxonomic classification of the giant panda has been a subject for debate since its discovery, since various features demonstrate similarity to both the bear and raccoon families, which evolved from a common ancestor.

The giant panda is 4-5 ft (1.2-1.5 m) in length (excluding tail) and weighs 165-330 lb (75-150 kg). It is white with black legs, shoulders, eyes, ears, and, sometimes, tail tip. The panda usually sits upright while eating and uses its sixth digit like a thumb to hold the bamboo that forms the mainstay of its diet. In the wild, its diet is supplemented by grass, bulbs, insects, rodents, and perhaps even large mammals.

A solitary and territorial animal, the giant panda uses secretions from scent glands to mark its home range of 1.5-2.5 sq mi (3.9-6.4 sq km). The female reaches sexual maturity at four to five years of age and is receptive to the male only once each year, usually between March and May. Scent marking increases before the brief mating. Up to three young are born after a gestation of 45 days, although pregnancy lasts 100-160 days due to delayed implantation. The young are very small and helpless, weighing only 3-5 oz (85-140 g) at birth.

Habitat and Current Distribution

This species is found only in central and western China, in the Sichuan, Shaanxi, and Gansu provinces. Population in the wild is estimated at 1,000-2,000 individuals.

The only suitable habitat is forest with a bamboo understory between 5,900-12,500 ft (1,800-3,800 m).

History and Conservation Measures

At one time, the giant panda was common throughout China, but in the last 2,000 years it has disappeared from Henan, Hubei, Hunan, Guizhou, and Yunnan provinces. Armand David, a Jesuit missionary, discovered panda furs in 1869, but the species was not well known in the west until a captive specimen was brought to the United States in the 1930s. In the 1970s, China began a series of studies to determine the status and population of the giant panda. It invited the World Wildlife Fund, which had already adopted the giant panda as its logo, to help develop a strategy to stop the species' decline.

Because the panda is heavily dependent upon one food source, it is vulnerable to any changes or decreases in the supply of that source. Each of the various species of bamboo that provide the bulk of the panda's diet has a life cycle ranging from 40-80

Giant panda.

years or more. This cycle includes flowering, seeding, and dying of the entire crop at once. If this occurs in an area with only one species of bamboo, the giant panda may need to move into a new territory to find food. Such a move can be difficult, however, as human settlement has reduced habitat and isolated panda populations. With fragmented populations, starvation is a danger whenever main crops of bamboo flower and die. Fragmentation caused by habitat destruction also leads to a risk of inbreeding.

The other main threat to the panda is poaching. Although it is legally protected and heavy penalties have been imposed for poaching, the panda is still a target for poachers because of the striking coloration of its hide.

The Chinese have been fairly successful with captive breeding, but using captive-bred animals to restock the wild population is—at best—a long way off. Restocking may not be desirable, because of the risk of introducing animals that are not resistant to pathogens in the local population. At present, captive breeding is probably a drain on wild populations. This makes preservation of habitat a top priority, with special attention given to the possibility of establishing links or corridors between suitable habitat areas. Currently, the World Wildlife Fund and the Chinese Ministry of Forestry have developed a Conservation Management Plan outlining 14 new panda reserves and 5 corridors connecting patches of panda habitat.

Sun bear

Helarctos malayanus

Phylum	Chordata
Class	Mammalia
Order	Carnivora
Family	Ursidae
Status	Vulnerable, IUCN
	Appendix I, CITES
Range	Brunei; China; India; Kalimantan, Sumatra (Indonesia); Laos; Peninsular Malaysia, Sabah, Sarawak (Malaysia); Myanmar; Thailand; Vietnam

Description and Biology

The sun bear is the smallest member of the bear family. Head and body length averages 3.3-4.6 ft (1-1.4 m), shoulder height is 26.6 in (70 cm), weight is 60-140 lb (27-63.5 kg), and tail is 1.2-2.8 in (3-7 cm). This bear's fur is very short and black; face and muzzle are pale to white; and there is a white to yellow-orange horseshoe-shaped chest marking on most individuals. Their soles are hairless, and they have curved and pointed claws. The sun bear's days are spent sleeping or sunning on a platform built on trees 7-20 ft (2.1-6 m) off the ground. An excellent climber, it forages in the trees at night. Strong claws are used to slit into trees to locate larvae or open bees' nests; strong forepaws and a long tongue are used to remove termites from their nests. Diet includes insects, fruits, honey, birds, and small mammals.

This bear does not hibernate. Mating can take place at any time during the year. One or two cubs are born on the ground after a gestation period of 95-240 days; the variation seems to indicate delayed implantation.

Habitat and Current Distribution

The sun bear occurs in Borneo, Sumatra, Malaysia, Vietnam, Laos, Myanmar and southern China.

It may be extinct in India and Bangladesh. There are no estimates of total population.

Sun bear.

Preferred habitat includes tropical or subtropical forest and woodland at all elevations.

History and Conservation Measures

Although information is scarce, it appears that sun bear populations are declining and that its range is shrinking due to destruction of its forest habitat and conversion of this land to agricultural uses. Sun bears are killed and used for food and medicinal purposes. Korean tourists in Thailand seek out special restaurants serving fresh bear meat since it is believed to enhance health and vigor. Bear cubs are sometimes captured and kept as pets.

The sun bear exists in a number of reserve areas throughout its range, but many of these reserves are increasingly isolated by development of surrounding lands. These reserves may be the only areas in many countries where populations of large mammals survive and, thus, serve as magnets to poachers. Since the basic habitat needs of the sun bear are unknown, existing reserves may or may not provide the necessary habitat for long-term survital of bear populations.

Sloth bear

Melursus ursinus

Phylum	Chordata
Class	Mammalia
Order	Carnivora
Family	Ursidae
Status	Vulnerable, IUCN
	Appendix I, CITES
Range	Bangladesh; Bhutan (?); India; Nepal; Sri Lanka

Description and Biology

The sloth bear is distinguished by a yellowish white V- or Y-shaped marking on its dark chest. Its shaggy coat is usually black but can be flecked with gray, brown, or red. The ears are prominent and hairy, the snout area whitish in color. This bear has long, curved claws that enable it to hang upside down like a sloth: hence its name. Average head and body length is 4.6-6 ft (1.4-1.8 m), shoulder height is 2-3 ft (61-91 cm), and weight is 120-320 lb (54-145 kg); males are slightly larger than females. Hearing and vision are not well developed, but the sloth bear's sense of smell is excellent. Diet includes insect, grubs, fruit, flowers, grass, eggs, honey, and carrion, but the most important is termites.

In addition to long claws, the sloth bear also has a long tongue, missing upper center incisors, and mobile lips and snout, adaptations that enable it to easily consume termites. After blowing dust and dirt, this bear forms a kind of vacuum tube with its mouth to suck out the termites from their hole, making a loud, sucking noise in the process.

Mating takes place in June in northern populations and throughout the year in southern populations. One to three young (usually two) are born in a ground shelter after a gestation period of around 190-210 days. The cubs remain in the den and nurse for up to three months; they stay with the mother for two to three years.

Habitat and Current Distribution

The sloth bear occurs in India, Nepal, Sri Lanka, Bangladesh, and Bhutan. It inhabits moist and dry forests at lower elevations, especially in areas with rocky outcrops. Its optimal habitat is the tropical dry forests of central India. Even though the sloth bear is the most common bear in India, there is surprisingly little information available about its numbers. A 1975 population estimate was 7,600-8,400 animals (excluding northern India, Nepal, and Bhutan). A 1982 survey of unknown origin reported in the *New York Times* placed the worldwide population of sloth bears at 10,000 animals.

History and Conservation Measures

This bear is often hunted and killed because it is considered dangerous to humans and a pest to crops. It is sensitive to human intrusion into its habitat and is subject to reduced habitat because of forest clearing for logging, human settlements, and expanding agriculture. Sloth bears are also vulnerable to hunting for market; their gall bladders are used in traditional medicine to cure liver, stomach, and intestinal problems.

Sloth bear.

Thirteen national parks in India report the presence of sloth bears, and three sanctuaries (Ratanmahal, Jessor, and Shoul Paneshwar) have been specifically established for sloth bears. Sloth bears also occur in Chitwan National Park in Nepal. There are laws banning bear killing and the sale of bear parts, but they are ineffective or unenforced. Surveys are needed to determine the current population of sloth bears and their distribution before further conservation measures are proposed. Stronger controls on the exploitation of sloth bears for commercial purposes are also needed.

Asiatic black bear

Selenarctos (Ursus) thibetanus

Phylum . . . . Chordata
Class . . . . Mammalia
Order . . . . Carnivora
Family . . . . Ursidae
Status . . . . Vulnerable, IUCN
Appendix I, CITES
Range . . . . Afghanistan; Bangladesh; Bhutan; Kampuchea; China; India; Iran; Japan;
North Korea; South Korea; Laos; Malaysia (?); Mongolia; Myanmar; Nepal;
Pakistan; Russia; Taiwan; Thailand; Vietnam

Description and Biology

The Asiatic black bear is also called the Himalayan bear or Tibetan bear. This species has a crescent or V-shaped white marking on its black chest. The head tapers to a rather pointed snout; rounded ears are large and prominent. Length of head and body averages 4-6 ft (1.2-1.8 m), weight ranges from 110-330 lb (50-150 kg), and tail is 2.5-4 in (6.4-10 cm); the male is larger than the female. An excellent climber and good swimmer, it usually spends the days sleeping and the nights foraging in the trees; it has also been reported to feed during the day when fruit is abundant. Diet includes fruit, nuts, and buds; intake of insects, invertebrates, small vertebrates, and carrion increases as the bear builds up a layer of fat before winter. Larger mammals, including domestic livestock, are also consumed.

Except for mothers and cubs, this bear is usually solitary, with a reported home range of 1,200-1,500 acres (500-600 ha). In the northern parts of its range, the bear hibernates for four to five months, taking shelter in a cave or a hollow tree. In warmer areas, it may become dormant only during severe weather or not hibernate at all. Mating in northern areas takes place in June or July and births from January through March; in southern areas, mating probably takes place around October and births in February. Two cubs are usually born after a gestation period of seven to eight months. Young are nursed for three to four months and remain with the mother for around two years.

Habitat and Current Distribution

This bear has a widespread distribution from Iran to Japan. There are no estimates of population, but it is considered vulnerable throughout most of its distribution. One subspecies, the Baluchistan bear (*U. t. gedrosianus*), whose historic range is Iran and Pakistan, is considered to be endangered.

Habitat includes temperate and tropical woodlands; hilly or mountainous areas with heavy brush cover are preferred.

History and Conservation Measures

Because it prefers forest habitat, the Asiatic black bear is vulnerable to habitat destruction as the woodlands are cleared for development. It is also considered a nuisance to crops and domestic livestock and a danger to humans, and so is often hunted and killed. The future survival of the Asiatic black bear is uncertain throughout most of its range with the exception of dense forests in Laos, Myanmar and eastern Russia. This species is particularly vulnerable to hunting for market, since it is favored for traditional medicine and unusual cuisine especially in China, Japan, and Korea.

Asiatic black bear.

Spectacled bear

Tremarctos ornatus

Phylum	Chordata
Class	Mammalia
Order	Carnivora
Family	Ursidae
Status	Vulnerable, IUCN
	Appendix I, CITES
Range	Argentina; Bolivia; Brazil; Colombia; Ecuador; Panama; Peru; Venezuela

Description and Biology

This bear gets its common name from its striking appearance: entirely black or dark brown fur interrupted only by white markings around the eyes. These markings are generally circular or semi-circular in shape and sometimes extend onto the neck and chest. The spectacled bear has a small head and a short snout, and its head and body length averages 3.6-6 ft (1.1-1.8 m) at maturity. Its shoulder height averages 26-34 in (66-86 cm), its weight is 110-350 lb (50-160 kg), and its tail length is about 3 in (7.6 cm). This species is sexually dimorphic, as males are substantially larger than females.

Apparently nocturnal, this bear spends its days sheltered among large tree roots, tree trunks, or in a cave. Its diet relies heavily on fruits in addition to various plants, insects, small rodents, and perhaps even livestock. A good climber, the spectacled bear forages in trees and sometimes constructs platforms made of broken branches, which it can rest on while eating.

The spectacled bear is generally solitary except

Spectacled bear.

for females and cubs, although occasionally it will form groups to feed together. Little is known about reproduction, but births are probably higher during seasons of heavy rainfall, when fruits are most plentiful. The bear's gestation period lasts from 180-225 days and results in one to three cubs. Cubs remain in the den for around three months.

Habitat and Current Distribution

The only bear native to South America, this species occurs in Bolivia, Colombia, Ecuador, Peru, and Venezuela; small numbers may also exist in Panama, Brazil, and Argentina, but confirmation of their presence is needed. The spectacled bear occurs in a wide variety of habitats, including low-altitude, near-desert conditions at 650 ft (200 m); dry-deciduous, rain and cloud forests; steppe lands; páramo (high, barren plains); and treeless alpine areas above 13,120 ft (4,000 m). Its preferred habitat is probably rain forest between 6,230-7,550 ft (1,900-2,300 m).

Total population figures are unavailable, and the most recent status surveys were carried out in the late 1970s and early 1980s. These surveys suggested that the bear was considered vulnerable in Bolivia; that in Colombia it was mainly confined to isolated patches of mountainous forest and páramo; that it was still common in remote and inaccessible areas of Ecuador; that in Peru the range was declining but still extensive; and that Venezuela had no more than 100 bears.

History and Conservation Measures

With its ability to adapt to a variety of conditions and habitats, the spectacled bear has thus far avoided a drastic decline in population. It does, however, face a number of threats, chief among them being habitat destruction. As the human population has increased, road systems have spread into previously pristine forest. In turn, that forest has been exploited for natural resources such as timber and minerals or cleared for agricultural use. This bear has also been hunted for meat, for sport, and as a pest, since it is seen as a threat to domestic livestock. These problems, along with a lack of effective conservation practices, put the spectacled bear at risk.

This species occurs in a number of reserves, sanctuaries, and national parks, but many of these areas are poorly protected, are subject to livestock grazing, or are too close to human settlements. Because the bear is so adaptable, it will readily eat crops as natural foods become scarcer, which inevitably leads to increased conflict between humans and bears. The species' survival will depend on better protection in existing reserves and the designation of large national parks and reserves. In addition, buffer zones with controlled human usage should be established around such reserves.

Surveys of distribution and studies of behavior and ecology are needed to serve as a basis for conservation efforts. Where bear populations are in immediate peril, researchers and governments need to give special attention to enforcing forestry laws, controlling grazing practices, and protecting threatened watersheds.

Owston's palm civet

Chrotogale owstoni

Phylum	Chordata
Class	Mammalia
Order	Carnivora
Family	Viverridae
Status	Indeterminate, IUCN
Range	China; Laos; Vietnam

Description and Biology

Owston's palm civet is found in China, Laos, and Vietnam. It has a yellow-brown to gray-brown coat that is accented by a series of four dark bands on its back and a number of dark spots on its neck, forelimbs, and trunk. This animal's common name comes from its reputed liking for the fermented juice of the palm. Head and body length averages 20-24 in (51-61 cm); the tail measures 15-18 in (38-45.7 cm) long, and the terminal two-thirds of its length is black. Largely terrestrial, this civet is thought to feed primarily on earthworms and small mammals.

There is no information available on the ecology or reproductive biology of this species.

Habitat and Current Distribution

This species is known to occur in northern and central Vietnam, northern Laos, and in China in the southern Yunnan and southwest Guangxi provinces. Most museum specimens come from sites in northern Vietnam, but the species could be more widely distributed in Laos and southern China. There are no estimates of population size.

Preferred habitat includes primary and secondary forest in the vicinity of rivers, but areas close to villages are also utilized.

History and Conservation Measures

Little information is available on this species because it is known only from about 20 museum specimens. Like most wildlife in southern China, Owston's palm civet is subject to considerable hunting pressure.

This civet is found in the Cuc Phuong National Park in Ha Nam Ninh province, Vietnam. In China it is thought to survive in the Dasei Mountain National Reserve, Jinping Divide National Reserve, and Huanglian Mountain National Reserve, all in Yunnan. Recommended conservation efforts include surveys to locate additional populations; research to obtain ecological data as a basis for better conservation planning; international assistance to Vietnam to increase protection of the Cuc Phuong National Park and to reduce poaching in the park; and reduction in hunting of this species.

Otter civet

Cynogale bennettii

Lowe's otter civet

Cynogale lowei

Phylum	Chordata
Class	Mammalia
Order	Carnivora
Family	Viverridae
Status	Endangered, IUCN (*C. bennettii*)
	Indeterminate, IUCN (*C. lowei*)
	Appendix II, CITES (*C. bennettii*)
Range	Brunei; Kalimantan, Sumatra (Indonesia); Peninsular Malaysia, Sabah, Sarawak (Malaysia); Singapore (?); Thailand; Vietnam (*C. bennettii*)
	Vietnam (*C. lowei*)

Description and Biology

The otter civet derives its common name from its semi-aquatic habits and its resemblance to the otter. It has a wide, blunt muzzle with nostrils on the top and long, thick whiskers; nostrils and ears can be closed to keep out water. Feet are slightly webbed to facilitate swimming, but the otter civet is also a good climber. Head and body length averages 23-26 in (58.4-66 cm), weight is 7-11 lb (3.2-5 kg), and tail is 6-8 in (15.2-20.3 cm). Fur is short and dense, pale at the base and brown to black at the tips; longer guard hairs tend to be gray and give a grizzled appearance to the coat. Lowe's otter civet (*Cynogale lowei*) is dark brown with a dark brown tail; underparts are whitish. Believed to hunt by lying in ambush in water, the otter civet is thought to feed on crustaceans, fruit, fish, birds, and small mammals.

There is little information available about the social structure or reproductive biology of these two animals. There are records, however, of pregnant otter civets with two and three embryos.

Habitat and Current Distribution

The otter civet is known from museum specimens collected in Borneo, Sumatra, and Peninsular Malaysia; it probably also occurs in the Yala and Pattani Provinces of Thailand. It prefers a riverine habitat and most specimens were taken from the following rivers: Sempang, Kendawangan, Mandawez, and Ulu Rejang in Borneo and from near the mouth of the Gasip River in Sumatra. Lowe's otter civet is known only from the skin of one immature specimen, which was collected in Vietnam. Taxonomists do not all agree that Lowe's otter civet merits full specific rank; some believe that it is a subspecies of *C. bennettii*. There are no estimates of population for either species, but Lowe's otter civet is believed to be extinct or close to extinction.

History and Conservation Measures

Expanding human settlements and agricultural developments threaten the habitat of the otter civet. Lowe's otter civet is also threatened by these factors but, because of its extremely restricted distribution, is probably more heavily impacted.

The otter civet occurs in the Sepilok Forest Reserve, Sabah (East Malaysia), and Padang-Sugihan Wildlife Reserve in Sumatra. There are numerous other conservation areas, some of them quite large, throughout the range of the species, but it is not known whether any of these contain sizable popula-

tion, or even whether the species occurs there at all. Recommended conservation actions include surveys throughout the range of the species to locate surviving populations; a study of the species to identify its exact habitat requirements and its vulnerability to human actions; and an experimental captive breeding project to gather data on the captive maintenance of the species.

There is an unconfirmed and somewhat doubtful report that Lowe's otter civet may occur in the Phu Kradung National Park in Thailand. Recommended conservation actions include field surveys in this park and in other areas with potential habitat in northern Vietnam, Laos, and southern China. Immediate protection should be given to any site where this civet is found, and an ecological study should be initiated.

Captive breeding of both species may be needed as a safeguard against extinction.

Malabar civet

Viverra megaspila civettina
(V. civettina)

Phylum	Chordata
Class	Mammalia
Order	Carnivora
Family	Viverridae
Status	Endangered, IUCN
	Endangered, USFWS
	Appendix III, CITES
Range	India

Description and Biology

The Malabar civet, like other civets, has a long body and short legs and excretes scents from the anal region. It has gray or light brown fur with contrasting black spots; the tail and neck area have black stripes. A crest of long, black hair runs along the center of the back. Head and body length averages 24-37 in (61-94 cm), weight is 11-24 lb (5-10.9 kg), and tail length is 12-18 in (31-46 cm). Although a good climber, the spotted civet hunts mainly on the ground, eating birds, frogs, insects, snakes, and small mammals.

Usually a solitary species, the Malabar civet can mate at any time during the year. One to four young are born in dense vegetation or in a hole or indentation in the ground and are nursed for around a month.

Habitat and Current Distribution

This civet is endemic to southwest India, occurring in the evergreen rain forest belt. It was previously found along the coastal hinterland and in the Western Ghats in southwest India; it has probably disappeared from most of the coastal tracts and its continued existence in various parts of the Western Ghats is threatened. The population is estimated at 100-500 animals.

History and Conservation Measures

The Malabar civet was apparently already rare at the turn of the century and it was thought to be extinct in 1972. In more than half a century, there had been only two possible sightings. In 1987, the continued existence of the species was proven by the capture of three specimens at Elayur, east of Calicut in Kerala. Threats to this animal's survival has been and continues to be habitat loss due to agricultural development and hunting by humans.

The species is thought to occur in the Parambikulam Wildlife Sanctuary in Kerala state and Dandeli Wildlife Sanctuary in Karnataka; a number of other sanctuaries and national parks may contain populations. Recommended conservation steps include status surveys along the Western Ghats to locate surviving populations, particularly within conservation areas; a detailed ecological study at sites where the species still occurs to determine habitat needs; and consideration of a captive breeding program.

Fanalouc

Eupleres goudotii

Phylum	Chordata
Class	Mammalia
Order	Carnivora
Family	Viverridae
Status	Vulnerable, IUCN Appendix II, CITES
Range	Madagascar

Description and Biology

The fanalouc has a long body and a head that looks small in relation to the body; its face is narrow, and its muzzle long and pointed. Fur is soft, thick, and bushy. The eastern fanalouc (*Eupleres goudotii goudotii*) has light brown coloration above and light gray-brown below; males of the western fanalouc (*Eupleres goudotii major*) are brown and females gray. Head and body length averages 18-24 in (46-61 cm) and weight is 4.4-8.8 lb (2-4 kg). Feet are large and claws long; the bushy tail is 8.7-14 in (22-35 cm) long. Fat is stored at the base of the tail to provide nourishment in the cold months of June and July when food supplies are low; some fanaloucs may hibernate during the winter. Active at night, they feed almost exclusively on earthworms and only occasionally take amphibians or insects and their larvae.

This is a solitary species, with consortships forming only during mating season, probably July or August. A single young is the norm, but twins are not unknown; gestation period is uncertain. The newborn is well-developed at birth and nurses for at least two months. It begins to forage with the mother at a very young age and becomes independent before the next breeding season.

Habitat and Current Distribution

E. g. goudotii is endemic to eastern Madagascar, where it inhabits rain forests and marshes. *E. g. major* is found in the undisturbed forest areas and wetlands of northwestern Madagascar. Both subspecies take shelter during the day in dense vegetation or burrows. To date no population estimate of fanaloucs exists.

History and Conservation Measures

The eastern fanalouc is still widespread in remaining suitable habitat, but is nowhere common. The largest population of western fanaloucs appears to be in northwestern Malagasy rain forests. However, the western fanalouc is most at risk today due to its restricted range. The total area of primary forest in Madagascar is already relatively small, and undisturbed forests could be lost completely within one or two decades if present rates of clearance continue; marshes, too, are increasingly being drained. Predation by dogs is an additional threat to the species, as is hunting for meat by the local human population.

The eastern fanalouc is present in a number of reserves including Mananara-Nord Biosphere Reserve, Andohahela Nature Reserve, and Analamazaotra Special Reserve. The western fanalouc is known to exist in the Tsaratanana Nature Reserve and possibly in the Manongarivo Special Reserve.

Recommended conservation actions for both subspecies include improved protection of all reserves known to have fanalouc populations; declaration of further marshlands as conservation areas; nation-wide protection for the species; and initiation of an internationally coordinated captive breeding program.

Bowhead whale

Balaena mysticetus

Phylum	Chordata
Class	Mammalia
Order	Cetacea
Family	Balaenidae
Status	Vulnerable, IUCN
	Endangered, USFWS
	Appendix I, CITES
Range	Oceanic (northern latitudes only)

Description and Biology

The distinctively curved jawline common to right whales—those whales in the Balaenidae family—is especially pronounced in the bowhead whale and inspires its common name. The head comprises 40 percent of total adult body length, which ranges from 36-66 ft (11-20 m); weight ranges from 60-100 tons. This whale's body color is black, with a chin patch that can be white, cream, or ochre-colored. The bowhead has two blowholes and no dorsal fin. Rows of baleen plates, commonly known as whalebone, line the sides of the mouth and facilitate the extraction of zooplankton—primarily small, shrimplike crustaceans—from seawater. Although bowheads usually live alone or in small groups, larger groups may form to feed together where food is plentiful or to migrate; these groups are often segregated by sex, age, or size. Predation by killer whales is uncommon but not unknown.

Females reach sexual maturity at approximately 38 ft (11.5 m). Mating is apparently at random; a receptive female may be surrounded by several competing males. After circling and diving in what may be courtship behavior, one male may help to position the female for copulation with another male. Mating occurs from late winter through early spring, and births take place between March and August, peaking in May; gestation is estimated at 10-16 months. One calf nurses for up to a year.

Habitat and Current Distribution

Bowhead whales inhabit arctic and sub-arctic waters between latitudes 55 and 85 degrees north. With their ability to locate and travel through ice crevices and to break through ice with their heads, the whales are well adapted for living in and at the edges of ice fields. They migrate to northerly feeding grounds in spring and summer, returning to the southern parts of the range in late autumn.

Much of the historical range is no longer used by the depleted populations. Five populations, or stocks, are currently recognized, totaling approximately 8,000 individuals.

History and Conservation Measures

Long a target of the whaling industry, the bowhead whale stocks were hunted for commercial purposes beginning in the eighteenth century. In fact, the common name of the Balaenidae family refers to the fact that early whalers considered these whales the "right" or best whales to hunt because they were

Bowhead whale.

relatively slow, came close to land, had high buoyancy and thus were less likely to sink if killed, and yielded many valuable products. In particular, the bowhead whale was prized because of its large baleen and the thickness of its blubber. By the early twentieth century, when demand for Balaenidae products began to decline, the bowhead whale stocks had been devastated. Of the five stocks, only one—the Bering/Chukchi/Beaufort Seas stock—is now considered a viable population. Its current population is estimated at 7,500 individuals, down from its initial population of 14,000-20,000.

The other four stocks are the Spitsbergen stock, the Hudson Bay stock, the Davis Strait stock, and the Okhotsk Sea stock. Though each of these stocks initially had populations of several thousand whales, they have now been reduced to—at best—a few hundred individuals.

The bowhead whale is protected under a number of international treaties. Exceptions have been made to these treaties to allow a limited amount of subsistence hunting by local, native peoples such as Alaskan Inuits, or Eskimos. Bowhead hunting has long been considered to be of cultural importance to Eskimos, but the level of hunting was not a threat to the population. Now, given the extremely low bowhead populations, there is controversy over exactly how much hunting should be allowed, even by indigenous peoples.

Northern right whale

Eubalaena glacialis

Southern right whale

Eubalaena australis

Phylum	Chordata
Class	Mammalia
Order	Cetacea
Family	Balaenidae
Status	Endangered, IUCN (*E. glacialis*)
	Vulnerable, IUCN (*E. australis*)
	Endangered, USFWS
	Appendix I, CITES
Range	Oceanic

Description and Biology

These whales were given their common name by early whalers because they were the "right" whales to catch: they are slow-running animals often seen along shorelines, making them relatively easy to kill; they don't sink after being killed; and they yielded more valuable products than other whales. Both species weigh about 50 tons at physical maturity, but the average length at physical maturity is somewhat different for the two species—42-60 ft (12.8-18.3 m) for the northern right whale as opposed to 50-54 ft (15.2-16.5 m) for the southern right whale. Sexual maturity is reached at 49-51 ft (15-15.5 m) for both species. In both the northern and southern species, a large head accounts for up to a quarter of total body length, and the female is larger than the male. Body color is black with patches of white callosities around the head area. These patches are skin growths infested with lice, barnacles, and parasites, and they were called "bonnets" by early whalers. Like other baleen whales, right whales strain their food from seawater with the baleen lining the sides of their mouths. Their diet consists mainly of copepods, euphausiids, pteropods, and other small aquatic organisms collectively known as zooplankton.

Right whales usually travel alone or in groups of two or three, except in areas of high food concentrations where they form herds. Right whales do not form pair bonds; a female may be surrounded by several competing males who make a number of low frequency sounds during courtship. After a gestation period of 10-12 months, one 20-foot (6 m) calf is born, generally between May and August. Females have a very strong, protective maternal instinct. This feature was sometimes exploited by early whalers, who first caught the calf, knowing that the mother was then unlikely to escape.

Habitat and Current Distribution

Both species of right whale seem to prefer temperate oceans and are often found in shallow, coastal waters, particularly during the breeding season. Northern right whales are found between about 25

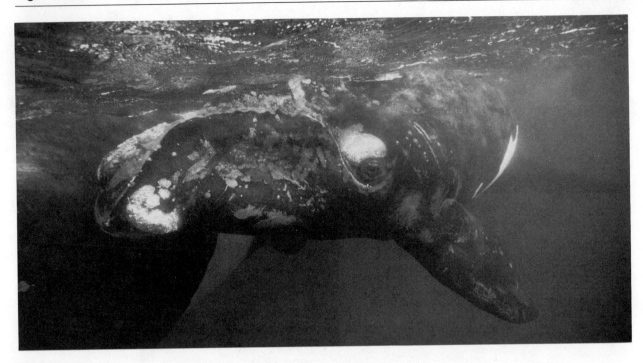

Southern right whale.

and 60 degrees north latitude. They move north to rich feeding grounds in the spring and return to more temperate waters in the fall and winter. In the Atlantic Ocean, the northern species ranges from the northwest coast of Africa, Madeira, the Azores, Bermuda, and Florida to Spitsbergen, Jan Mayen, Iceland, Newfoundland, and the Davis Strait. The North Atlantic population is generally divided into eastern and western stocks. The eastern stock is believed to be near extinction with no more than a few individuals surviving, while the western stock is estimated at 380-1,100 animals. In the North Pacific, *E. glacialis* is found from Alaska and the Aleutians to Oregon and California, and from the Gulf of Anadyr and the Sea of Okhotsk to the Yellow and China seas. There are no estimates of the size of the North Pacific population, but it is also thought to be quite small.

Southern right whales have a circumpolar distribution in the South Pacific and Indian and South Atlantic oceans from about 20 to 50 degrees south latitude. They spend the summer in the southern parts of this range, moving to warmer waters in the winter. At present, there are thought to be at least 1,500 southern right whales in these waters.

History and Conservation Measures

Because of their slow movement and shallow, coastal habitat, right whales were among the first of the large whales to be extensively hunted. These whales were hunted for meat, for oil (used as fuel for lamps and cooking, and as a lubricant), and for baleen (used in the manufacture of umbrella ribs, fishing rods, carriage springs, corsets, and garment supports such as farthingales and hoop skirts). Regular catches began in the tenth century in the Bay of Biscay and eventually extended to Newfoundland, where 25,000-40,000 right whales were killed between 1530 and 1610. American vessels took 70,000-74,000 right whales in the southern oceans between 1805 and 1914. Since commercial exploitation of this species began so early, the initial population size is not known with any certainty, but one estimate has placed it as high as 300,000 for both species. It is evident, however, that right whales were once very abundant and have now drastically declined in numbers. In 1937, right whales received complete protection in accordance with the International Agreement for the Regulation of Whaling, but in the more than 50 years since this protection was granted, right whale populations have showed only modest signs of recovery.

Because right whales prefer temperate coastal waters and depend on shallow coastal bays for giving birth, they may be more vulnerable to the effects of human activities than other whale species. Entanglement in fishing nets and collisions with ships or ship propellers have caused fatalities. Shipping activities, geological changes, and other factors may now exclude right whales from former calving areas. In addition, water pollution may make former habitat unsuitable. Legal protection for both species must be extended and enforced so that no more animals are killed. Research is necessary to identify and overcome continuing threats to the survival of these species. Critical habitat, such as calving and feeding areas, must be protected. Several countries, including the United States, Canada, Russia, South Africa, and Argentina, have established national parks or reserves within the ranges of these species.

Sei whale

Balaenoptera borealis

Phylum	Chordata
Class	Mammalia
Order	Cetacea
Family	Balaenopteridae
Status	Vulnerable, IUCN
	Endangered, USFWS
	Appendix I, CITES
Range	Oceanic

Description and Biology

One of the fastest of whales, the sei whale can reach speeds of up to 30 mph (48 kph). Its streamlined body is steel gray with irregular light ventral markings. Females in the Southern Hemisphere can reach 60 ft (18.3 m) at physical maturity, while females in the Northern Hemisphere can reach 49 ft (15 m) at physical maturity; males are slightly smaller. Average weight for a 50-ft (15.2 m) whale is 53,000 lb (24,000 kg). Baleen plates that line the sides of the mouth are used to strain seawater for plankton. In the Southern Hemisphere, krill is the major food, supplemented by tiny crustaceans called copepods or amphipods. In the North Pacific, copepods are the major food, with krill forming about 10 percent of the diet. Off Norway and Iceland, these whales also consume fish. Sei whales usually travel in groups of two to five individuals, although abundant food may attract much larger groups.

Sexual maturity is reached at an average length of 43-45 ft (13-14 m). In the Northern Hemisphere, mating takes place between November and February; in the Southern Hemisphere, the mating season runs from May through July. One calf, averaging just under 15 ft (4.5 m) long, is born after a gestation of 11 months and is nursed for 6-9 months.

Habitat and Current Distribution

Sei whales have been reported from most oceans and seas, although they appear to favor temperate and oceanic waters. The U.S. National Marine Fisheries Service estimated the population in 1989 at 4,600 in the North Atlantic, 24,000 in southern waters, and 22,000-37,000 in the Pacific, but it has been suggested that these figures may be optimistic.

These whales are deep-water animals, rarely found in marginal sea areas. The winter months are spent in temperate waters, and the summer on higher latitude feeding grounds. The animal is not a deep diver, usually staying under water for only 5-10 minutes at a time.

History and Conservation Measures

Because of its speed and its deep-water habitat, the sei whale did not become a popular target of commercial whaling until populations of more accessible whales had been depleted. No reliable estimates exist for the original population. Exploitation of the sei whale peaked in the 1960s and early 1970s. The International Whaling Commission (IWC) progressively shut down sei whaling operations in the North Pacific and Southern Hemisphere during the 1970s,

Sei whale.

but catches of sei whales off Iceland continued under scientific permit through 1989; no sei whale catches have occurred since. Commercial whaling is currently prohibited under the IWC moratorium, but a few countries—Japan and Norway, for example— continue to take whales under an exemption from IWC regulations granted for scientific research. While the historic objective of commercial sei whaling was oil, meat for human consumption is now the most important product, with Japan being the largest consumer.

Blue whale

Balaenoptera musculus

Phylum	Chordata
Class	Mammalia
Order	Cetacea
Family	Balaenopteridae
Status	Endangered, IUCN
	Endangered, USFWS
	Appendix I, CITES
Range	Oceanic

Description and Biology

The blue whale is believed to be the largest animal ever to have lived on Earth. Average length at physical maturity is 79-88 ft (24-27 m), while average weight at physical maturity is 130-150 tons. Whales in the Southern Hemisphere are at the high end of the height and weight ranges, while whales in the Northern Hemisphere are at the low end. Color is mottled blue to blue-gray, and microorganisms sometimes accumulate—particularly in colder waters—to give the whale a faintly yellow sheen. It is this sheen that is responsible for the term "sulphur bottom," which is sometimes applied to the blue whale. The head is wide and U-shaped, and the dorsal fin is small.

The species' diet is composed mainly of krill, a small, shrimplike crustacean. Like all whales in this family, the blue whale uses the baleen plates that line its mouth to sieve krill from seawater. For many years, it was believed that blue whales fed only in summer in polar waters, consuming several tons daily, and that they seldom ate during the rest of the year. However, recent researchers have suggested that some blue whales (for example, those off the North American coast) may feed year-round, and that earlier reports of whales with empty stomachs outside polar waters may have indicated migrating whales that resumed feeding at "wintering" areas.

Sexual maturity is reached at 70-75 ft (21-23 m) in the Northern Hemisphere and at 75-80 ft (23-24 m) in the Southern Hemisphere. Mating and calving take place in warmer waters, with the gestation period lasting 10-11 months. Peak birthing time is in the spring, which gives the calves all summer to develop a layer of blubber to protect them from colder waters. Females give birth to one calf, which measures 20-23 ft (6-7 m) at birth and which nurses for around seven months.

Habitat and Current Distribution

The blue whale occurs in all major oceans of the world. The Northern and Southern Hemisphere stocks, which generally do not meet or mate with each other, are sometimes regarded as separate sub-species: *B. m. musculus* and *B. m. intermedia*. A third sub-species is recognized; *B. m. brevicauda*, the pygmy blue whale, which is somewhat smaller than the two main sub-species of blue whale, is known mainly from the sub-Antarctic waters of the Indian Ocean and southeast Atlantic. North Atlantic stocks of the blue whale are now estimated at approximately 400, North Pacific stocks at 1,400-1,900, the Antarctic stock at around 400, and the Indian Ocean stock at around 30.

Most blue whales prefer cold waters and open

Blue whale.

seas and do not concentrate in coastal areas. They summer in polar feeding grounds and winter in more temperate breeding grounds. Some, however, do not appear to migrate, and in fact may be resident in tropical coastal areas. Such whales have been noted off the coast of Peru and in the northern Indian Ocean.

History and Conservation Measures

Before commercial whaling decimated the blue whale population, the North Atlantic stocks were estimated at 15,000, the North Pacific stocks at 5,000, and the Antarctic stock at 160,000-240,000. In the early days of whaling, blue whales—because of their speed, size, and strength—were deemed too difficult to hunt. However, beginning in the 1860s and increasing in the twentieth century, improved whaling techniques made blue whales a viable target, and the whales quickly became a prime prey because of their enormous size. It is estimated that more than 280,000

blue whales were taken between the early 1920s and the early 1970s; in the 1930-1931 season alone, nearly 30,000 were taken worldwide. In 1964, full protection was finally extended to the blue whale by the International Whaling Commission.

As the blue whale population decreased, smaller whales, seals, and penguins as well as humans began to take advantage of the surplus of available krill; the resulting competition for this food supply—though still abundant—may be a problem if the blue whale population begins to build back up. Further research is necessary to monitor this species, which is at a dangerously low level.

Because the blue whale is an oceanic species occurring in low density around the globe, there is little hope of aiding recovery through habitat protection. The best chance of recovery is to provide comprehensive protection from catching. In general, the blue whale is very widely protected throughout the world, often through incorporation of international agreements into domestic legislation.

Fin whale

Balaenoptera physalus

Phylum	Chordata
Class	Mammalia
Order	Cetacea
Family	Balaenopteridae
Status	Vulnerable, IUCN
	Endangered, USFWS
	Appendix I, CITES
Range	Oceanic

Description and Biology

The fin whale is second only to the blue whale in length and, being relatively thin, is second only to the sei whale in speed. Its average size at sexual maturity varies with sex and from one population to another, ranging from 58-65 ft (17.8-19.8 m). Its average length at physical maturity is 62-82 ft (19-25 m), while its average weight at that age is 60-85 tons. Animals in the Southern Hemisphere are larger than those in the Northern Hemisphere, and females are larger than males. Body color is dark gray above and white below, with the right side of the head and jaw gray and the left side white. Food is strained from the seawater by a series of baleen plates that line the sides of the mouth. In the Southern Hemisphere, the main food source around the Antarctic is a small, shrimplike crustacean, *Euphausia superba*, which is supplemented by other euphausiids. In the North Atlantic and North Pacific Oceans fish are commonly taken, including capelin, herrings, cod, mackerel, pollock, and sardine, supplemented with squid, euphausiids, and copepods. Prey choice may depend on availability as much as on preference in these northern areas.

Fin whales may be found singly or in pairs, and they may be monogamous. Although mating can take place at any time during the year, it peaks between April and August in the Southern Hemisphere and between December and January in the Northern Hemisphere. After a gestation period of about 11 months, a single calf measuring 21 ft (6.5 m) and weighing up to 2 tons is born. The calf nurses for six to seven months.

Habitat and Current Distribution

The fin whale has been reported from all oceans of the world. This species undergoes lengthy seasonal migrations to temperate waters for mating and to colder feeding grounds in the summer months. It is a deep water, or pelagic, species.

Populations were estimated at 103,000 in the Southern Hemisphere and 20,000 in the North Pacific in 1980 and 1985, respectively. Recent surveys indicate that the numbers may actually be much smaller.

History and Conservation Measures

Estimates of peak population vary widely, but it probably exceeded 500,000 individuals, with the majority in the Southern Hemisphere. Because of its speed, the fin whale was not heavily hunted commercially until other whale stocks were depleted. Power

Fin whale.

boats and factory ships facilitated hunting of the fin whale, until annual catches of 30,000 per year during the 1950s and early 1960s quickly reduced the population. The International Whaling Commission's moratorium on commercial whaling should have ended commercial catching in 1985-1986, but fin whales are still being taken under the auspices of scientific research.

A major threat to this whale is the dumping from industrial barges of waste containing heavy metal ions into the Mediterranean around Corsica, an area rich in euphausiids. Fin whales following these euphausiids may become contaminated and die, or become debilitated and more susceptible to infection or being struck by boats in the area.

Humpback whale

Megaptera novaeangliae

Phylum	Chordata
Class	Mammalia
Order	Cetacea
Family	Baleanopteridae
Status	Vulnerable, IUCN
	Endangered, USFWS
	Appendix I, CITES
Range	Oceanic

Description and Biology

The humpback whale is best known for its acrobatic movements and its distinctive song. Despite a weight of 30-60 tons and a length of 42-52 ft (13-16 m), the humpback performs spectacular leaps and spins, making it a favorite of whale watchers. Its body color is dark gray to black above and lighter below. Wing-like pectoral fins are patterned in white. At 13-16 ft (4-5 m), these fins are approximately one-third of the total body length and are among the largest found in the cetaceans. Baleen plates, commonly called whalebone, line the mouth and are used to sieve food from seawater. The diet of the northern humpback population consists of crustaceans, sand lance, herring, capelin, pink salmon, Arctic cod, walleye pollack, and pteropod and some cephalopod molluscs; in the Antarctic, diet is restricted almost exclusively to krill. Possible natural predators include killer whales and swordfish.

Large schools of humpback whales form when migrating and, occasionally, for feeding. During the breeding season, a female and her young travel with one or more males. It is during this time that single males emit their startling song, considered one of the most intricate in the entire animal kingdom. The song consists of a rhythmic pattern of vocalizations, including moans, cries, grunts, snores, and chirps; each humpback stock appears to have its own distinct dialect, although there is evidence that the whales modify these dialects continually from year to year. In fact, some researchers have postulated that humpback vocalization fills an evolutionary gap between birds, which learn songs through mimicry, and people, who create new songs.

Mating takes place between October and March in the Northern Hemisphere and between April and September in the Southern Hemisphere; no permanent pair bonds are formed. Mating is a frenzied period: a remarkable performance with two whales rising together face-to-face at right angles to the water has variously been interpreted as the act of copulation or as a battle between competing males. The gestation period is believed to be about a year; a single calf nurses for around 12 months.

Habitat and Current Distribution

Humpback whales are found in all oceans from the Arctic to the Antarctic. They feed in colder waters during spring, summer, and autumn, then travel to a winter range, swimming in deep water along coastlines.

Humpback whale.

Current worldwide population is estimated at 25,000.

History and Conservation Measures

Although there are no definite records of population size, humpback population is estimated to have been 150,000 individuals worldwide before hunting began; all stocks since have been seriously depleted by commercial whaling. Heavy commercial exploitation began in the North Atlantic in the late 1800s and depleted the population by the early 1900s; the hunting then moved to the Southern Hemisphere and Pacific Ocean stocks. Protection was instituted by the International Whaling Commission in 1963.

Because this species travels close to the shore, it has been easily exploited. The whales are also vulnerable to shoreline pollution, boat traffic, entanglement in fishing gear, and other human coastline activities.

Hector's dolphin

Cephalorhynchus hectori

Phylum	Chordata
Class	Mammalia
Order	Cetacea
Family	Delphinidae
Status	Indeterminate, IUCN
	Appendix II, CITES
Range	coastal waters of New Zealand

Description and Biology

Hector's dolphin, also known as the white-headed dolphin, is often attracted to, and sometimes follows, boats. It averages 4-4.5 ft (1.2-1.4 m) long and ranges in weight from 80-100 lb (36-46 kg); females are usually larger than males. Its stout body shades from gray to dark gray with black flippers. Gathering in small groups to feed, Hector's dolphin feeds opportunistically, both at the bottom and throughout the water column; a wide variety of fish is taken. Sharks are known predators.

Sexual maturity is reached between 7-9 years, at approximately 4 ft (120-130 cm) in males and 4.5 ft (130-145 cm) in females. After maturity, one 2-2.5 ft (60-75 cm) calf is born every two to three years, typically between early November and March. Mothers with newborn calves are shy and seldom approach stationary or moving boats. Of 60 animals aged from tooth sections, the oldest was 20 years.

Habitat and Current Distribution

Hector's dolphin is found only in New Zealand coastal waters. Total population was estimated in the mid-1980s at 3,000-4,000 animals.

This dolphin prefers shallow waters and is rarely seen further offshore than five nautical miles. It moves close inshore in spring and summer, and there is a general reduction in numbers inshore during winter.

History and Conservation Measures

Incidental catches of this species in coastal gillnets reached high levels in the mid to late 1980s and prompted the establishment of the Banks Peninsula Marine Mammal Sanctuary. The sanctuary is a 725-mi (1,170 km) coastal area within which commercial gillnetting is illegal and amateur gillnetting restricted to specific times and places. Moderately high levels of boating traffic do not appear to negatively affect the dolphin. The impact of gillnetting on dolphin populations outside the sanctuary area is unknown, but any gillnetting in areas dolphins inhabit poses a potential hazard.

Concern today is for incidental catches in coastal gill nets. Commercial fishing in summer is concentrated inshore, in the same areas the dolphins frequent. A high level of activity and boating does not seem to affect the dolphin, but incidental catching or entanglement in nets is a hazard to the population.

Hector's dolphin has full legal protection. Con-

Hector's dolphin.

servation efforts now must be directed to information gathering. The most urgent needs are for further information on reproductive rate, abundance, movements, and fishing mortality.

Vaquita

Phocoena sinus

Phylum	Chordata
Class	Mammalia
Order	Cetacea
Family	Phocoenidae
Status	Endangered, IUCN
	Endangered, USFWS
	Appendix I, CITES
Range	northern Gulf of California (Mexico)

Description and Biology

The vaquita (Spanish for "little cow") is so rare that very little is known about it. An overall gray body is accented by large black eye and lip patches. The dorsal fin is higher and larger than in most other porpoises. This smallest member of the porpoise family has an average length at physical maturity of 4-5 ft (1.2-1.5 m) and a weight of 90-120 lb (40-55 kg), with females being slightly larger than males. Fish and squid are thought to be the primary food.

The vaquita, also known as the Gulf of California harbor porpoise, generally avoids contact with sailing vessels; it is usually seen in small groups of one to four, but aggregations of up to ten animals have been reported. Information about reproduction is unknown.

Habitat and Current Distribution

This species is thought to be restricted to the northern Gulf of California in Mexico. Although sightings have been reported south of this area, they are considered unreliable. The vaquita has the most limited range of any marine cetacean species as well as one of the smallest populations, perhaps in the low hundreds.

History and Conservation Measures

Although it had been known for years to Mexican fishermen who coined its common name, the vaquita was not known to scientists until a skull was found in 1958. There has been no means to estimate the original population size, but it is believed to have been drastically reduced. Approximately 30-40 vaquitas are taken incidentally each year in fishing nets. The majority of recorded incidental takes have been in experimental and illegal nets set for an endangered fish, the totoaba (*Totoaba macdonaldi*), which is sold in the United States. They are also captured in nets for sharks and other fish as well as in shrimp trawls.

Because of its limited range, habitat quality is critical to this species' survival. Unfortunately, the vaquita's habitat—the Gulf of California—has undergone significant alteration. For instance, water flow from the Colorado River was once a major source of nutrients to the gulf; that flow has been drastically reduced by dams in western Mexico and the southwestern United States. In addition, various pollutants may recently have entered the food chain, particularly through contamination of the waters of the Colorado River.

Extensive studies are necessary to gather basic

information necessary to formulate conservation plans. Such studies would include estimates of population size and distribution, studies of food habits and reproductive behavior, and studies of the ecosystem that supports the vaquita. Meanwhile, the most direct way to improve the species' immediate status is to reduce the level of incidental catching. There is sufficient legal provision for such action, but enforcement would be difficult. An educational campaign among fishermen could be effective and should be instituted.

It has been proposed that a national park be established in the Colorado River delta in conjunction with a buffer zone in the upper gulf to protect suitable habitat for the species and encourage limited and controlled tourism. Although the vaquita is not known to have been kept in captivity, the possibility should be explored; it would not only save the species from extinction but also provide biological and behavioral information that could be instrumental in saving the species in the wild.

Chinese river dolphin

Lipotes vexillifer

Phylum	Chordata
Class	Mammalia
Order	Cetacea
Family	Platanistidae
Status	Endangered, IUCN
	Endangered, USFWS
	Appendix I, CITES
Range	China

Description and Biology

The Chinese river dolphin, or baiji, is among the rarest and most endangered of cetaceans. Its body is light blue-gray above and pale to white below. Its average length is 6.75-8.25 ft (2-2.5 m), while its weight ranges from 220-500 lb (100-227 kg). The river dolphin's poor eyesight is an evolutionary response to the muddy conditions of the water in which it lives; eyesight became less important in finding food than echolocation, a process by which the dolphin emits a sound wave which bounces off objects and is echoed or reflected back to the dolphin, indicating the location of prey. By this method, it locates and eats a variety of available freshwater fish with a width smaller than 2.5 in (6.5 cm) and weighing less than 9 oz (250 g).

These dolphins usually travel in pairs or in small groups that make up larger social units of up to ten individuals. Sexual maturity is gained at around 6.5 ft (2 m). Little reproductive information is available. Mating peaks between March and May and again between August and October; gestation period is 10-11 months. In related species, calves are weaned by eight to nine months. A young dolphin may swim behind its mother or the mother may carry the young with her flipper.

Habitat and Current Distribution

The baiji is found only in the Changjiang (Yangtze River) in China. The current estimate for the entire population may be less than 200 individuals, of which about one third are in the lower region of the river.

The river dolphin is distributed chiefly along the middle and lower reaches of the main river. It frequents regions where tributaries enter the main river and where the river is connected to lakes, as well as the vicinity of sandbanks and the ends of islets, because these are all places where fish gather.

History and Conservation Measures

No estimates of past numbers are available, but fishermen believe that the animals were more common in the 1950s than at present. The species is considered to be declining and is liable to become extinct in the wild unless extensive new conservation measures are implemented. The major problems are incidental catching, collisions with boats, use of explosives, extensive habitat damage, and possible food shortage.

The incidental catching is often a result of an illegal type of fishing gear called rolling hooks that

Chinese river dolphin.

are set to snag bottom feeding fish; these traps may account for about half of the known deaths. The problem with boat propellers is greatest in the lower river, where traffic is expected to double by the end of the 1990s. The use of explosives in construction and, illegally, in fishing has been implicated in a number of deaths. Construction of dams and other barriers along the river and its tributaries has led to changes in fish abundance and distribution. Some fish stocks also appear to have been greatly reduced through overfishing, pollution, and a reduction in the size of lakes, which have been drained to create farmland.

The baiji has received a high degree of protection since 1978. Although the skin, meat, and fat of the animal are edible and may also be used in industry and medicine, there seems never to have been an organized fishing operation. The deaths as a result of incidental catching in traditional fishing methods and those as a result of river traffic present a difficult challenge to conservationists, as both are very important to the local economy. The focus of attention now is an educational program and the setting up of reserve areas in the river, where harmful fishing activities would be prohibited and speed limits set for vessels. In view of the serious situation in the wild, a captive breeding program has been proposed in two semi-natural reserves, at Shishou in Hubei Province and at Tongling in Anhui Province,

Ganges River dolphin

Platanista gangetica

Phylum	Chordata
Class	Mammalia
Order	Cetacea
Family	Platanistidae
Status	Vulnerable, IUCN
	Appendix I, CITES
Range	Bangladesh; Bhutan; India; Nepal

Description and Biology

The Ganges River dolphin, or susu, averages between 6.5-8.5 ft (2-2.6 m) long at physical maturity and weighs from 175-195 lb (79-86 kg); the female is larger than the male. Its body is gray above and lighter below, with a long, slender snout that becomes curved with age. The species has small eyes and very poor eyesight, since the rudimentary eye structure lacks a lens. Prey is located using echolocation, a process by which the dolphin emits a sound wave that bounces off objects and is echoed or reflected back to indicate the distance to the prey. The long snout is used to probe the muddy river bottom to find a variety of fish and invertebrates, including shrimp, catfish, freshwater shark, mahseers, gobies, and carp.

This dolphin lives alone or in small groups. Sexual maturity is reached at 5.5 ft (1.7 m) for the male and 6.5 ft (2 m) for the female. Births may take place at any time during the year, with gestation reported to be between 8-12 months. The calf is just under 2.5 ft (70 cm) long and nurses for up to a year.

Currently, the Ganges River dolphin is considered a separate species from the Indus River dolphin, *Platanista minor*, which is found in the Indus River system of Pakistan and India. However, some recent researchers have expressed doubts about this separation and have called for a review of the taxonomy of the *Platanista* genus.

Habitat and Current Distribution

This dolphin is found in the fresh water river systems of the Ganges, Brahmaputra, Karnaphuli, and Meghna rivers in India, Bangladesh, Nepal, and Bhutan. Because there have been no complete surveys of the Ganges river dolphin populations, there are no reliable estimates of current population. Construction of dams for irrigation and hydroelectric power has divided the dolphin population of the Ganges system into small, isolated subpopulations, and some of these subpopulations have disappeared. For instance, the dolphin is no longer found above the Kaptai dam on the Karnaphuli river.

The species prefers deep water in habitats where it is available. There is some evidence of seasonal change in distribution, with animals travelling upstream as the water level rises and entering smaller streams.

History and Conservation Measures

Although there are no accurate estimates of former population, the Ganges River dolphin was apparently quite abundant until the past few decades.

Ganges River dolphin.

There is evidence that populations have severely declined in much of the dolphin's range, with the chief reasons for decline being extensive habitat damage, particularly through dam construction; direct and incidental catching; pollution; and boat traffic.

Conservation and research efforts should include surveys and habitat assessment, action to ameliorate the effects of existing and proposed dams, increased legal protection and more energetic enforcement of existing protective legislation, reserve areas, and education of local people to prevent direct catching.

Indus River dolphin

Platanista minor

Phylum	Chordata
Class	Mammalia
Order	Cetacea
Family	Platanistidae
Status	Endangered, IUCN
	Endangered, USFWS
	Appendix I, CITES
Range	Indus River (Pakistan)

Description and Biology

The Indus River dolphin is physically very much like the Ganges River dolphin; in fact, it has been suggested that they should be considered the same species. It averages between 6.5-8.5 ft (2-2.6 m) long and weighs from 175-195 lb (79-86 kg); the female is larger than the male. Its body is gray with lighter coloring underneath. It has small eyes and very poor eyesight, since the rudimentary eye lacks a lens. Prey is located using echolation, a process by which the dolphin emits a sound wave that bounces off objects and is echoed or reflected back to indicate the distance to the prey. The long, slender snout is used to probe the muddy river bottom to find a variety of fish and invertebrates, including shrimp, catfish, freshwater shark, mahseers, gobies, and carp.

This dolphin lives alone or in small groups. Sexual maturity is reached at 5.5 ft (1.7 m) for the male and 6.5 ft (2 m) for the female. Although births may take place at any time during the year, most occur between October and March; gestation has been reported to be between 8-12 months. The calf is just under 2.5 ft (70 cm) long at birth and nurses for up to a year.

Habitat and Current Distribution

This dolphin is found only in Pakistan; it is known to be present in the Indus River between Jinnah barrage in the Punjab and Kotri barrage in Sind. It also inhabits a short stretch of the Chenab River below Panjnad headworks. Of the present population of about 500 individuals, perhaps 400 are in the dolphin reserve between the Guddu and Sukkur barrages in the Sind, where they are well protected.

The Indus River dolphin moves according to the availability of food and is often seen at the mouth of irrigation canals and side channels. It also seems to be attracted by human activities.

History and Conservation Measures

Although early population figures are unavailable, this dolphin appears to have been reasonably common throughout its original range. It was distributed throughout the Indus River system, from the Himalayan foothills to the sea, and in the main tributaries from the hills to their junction with the Indus. It is now extinct in the parts of its former range in the Indus above Jinnah barrage and in the other rivers above Panjnad headworks. These populations were exterminated by the late 1970s through illegal hunting and the lowering of water levels.

Hunting and entrapment in fishing nets have been a problem for this species. It is hunted directly for its meat and oil, which is used for medicinal purposes. Although it is legally protected, there is a need for stronger law enforcement to prevent further decline in population. Habitat degradation, through the construction of dams or barrages on the rivers since the 1930s, has had a major effect on the dolphin populations. The smaller volume of water, particularly in the dry season, has greatly reduced available habitat. Subpopulations on either side of these barriers are now isolated and hence more vulnerable to extinction through hunting, accident, or environmental change. It may be necessary to explore the possibility of captive breeding if there is no improvement in the wild population.

Dugong

Dugong dugon

Phylum . . . . Chordata
Class . . . . Mammalia
Order . . . . Sirenia
Family . . . . Dugongidae
Status . . . . Vulnerable, IUCN
Endangered, USFWS
Appendix I or II, CITES (depending on population)
Range . . . . Shallow tropical and subtropical coastal and inland waters of the Indian and western Pacific Oceans from east Africa to the Red Sea to Vanuatu

Description and Biology

The dugong, a close relative of the manatee, is also called the sea cow or sea pig. A large gray to bronze sea mammal with lighter underparts, the dugong is up to about 10 ft (3 m) long and weighs up to about 880 lb (400 kg). It has a large head, whiskered muzzle, small round eyes, pinpoint ear openings with no external pinnae, and a pair of nostrils on top of the head which are closed except during inhalation and exhalation. The tusk-like incisors erupt only in adult males and a few very old females. The dugong is easily distinguished from the manatee by its more streamlined body and its tail, which is shaped like that of a whale or dolphin, whereas the manatee's tail is rounded like that of a beaver. The dugong eats seagrasses almost exclusively, favoring soft delicate species which can be rooted up and consumed whole, thus inspiring the name sea pig. While it is not heavily predated except by man, the dugong may be attacked by large sharks, the saltwater crocodile, and the killer whale.

Reproductive maturity is usually reached at about ten years, although in some areas it is delayed until 15-17 years. In populations studied, calving occurs over several months. The reproductive cycle in males is complex and adults do not produce sperm continuously. One calf is usually born after a gestation period estimated to be about 12-13 months. Calves may suckle for up to two years.

Habitat and Current Distribution

The dugong is found along the shallow coastal and island waters of the Indian and western Pacific Oceans. Population figures are unknown but have been roughly estimated at 100,000 individuals, with the largest known population in northern Australia and the Arabian region. There is almost no quantitative information on dugong abundance in other parts of its range. In its habitat of coastal mainland and island waters in tropical and subtropical latitudes, the dugong generally feeds in areas where fine bottom sediments support extensive beds of seagrass at depths to about 66 ft (20 m). Studies of 18 animals fitted with satellite transmitters for two to three months indicate that they have home ranges varying from about 4-46 sq mi (10-120 sq km). One animal journeyed between two bays, over 81 miles (130 km) apart, three times in six weeks.

Dugong.

History and Conservation Measures

The dugong and the manatee are thought to be the inspiration for the myth of the mermaid. This association, however, has not protected the sea cow from being exploited by humans. Hunting over most of its range has drastically reduced the population. The dugong is hunted for food and oil by local subsistence hunters and fishers. The tusks and ribs have been used for jewelry, the tears have been used as aphrodisiacs, and the oil for medicinal purposes. Many animals are now drowned incidentally in gill nets used to reduce shark numbers near swimming beaches or in tropical fisheries. The most serious threat to the dugong in many areas is probably the degradation of its seagrass habitat as a result of coastal development. The magnitude of these causes of anthropogenic mortality are largely undocumented, and it is not known whether dugong numbers are increasing, decreasing, or stable in any area. However, anecdotal evidence suggests that numbers are decreasing.

The reproductive rate of the dugong is too low to support any type of commercial exploitation. The challenge will be to maintain dugongs and restrict hunting throughout their range. Large scale multiple use marine parks such as those developed in the Great Barrier Reef in Australia would seem to be the most suitable approach to dugong conservation.

Caribbean manatee

Trichechus manatus

Phylum	Chordata
Class	Mammalia
Order	Sirenia
Family	Trichechidae
Status	Vulnerable, IUCN
	Endangered, USFWS
	Appendix I, CITES
Range	Bahamas; Belize; Brazil; Colombia; Costa Rica; Cuba; Dominican Republic; French Guiana; Guatemala; Guyana; Haiti; Honduras; Jamaica; Mexico; Nicaragua; Panama; Puerto Rico; Suriname; Trinidad and Tobago; U.S.A.; Venezuela

Description and Biology

There are two subspecies of the Caribbean or West Indian manatee: the Antillean manatee (*Trichechus manatus manatus*) and the Florida manatee (*Trichechus manatus latirostris*). Manatees and their closest living relatives, dugongs, are called sea cows because they graze on marine seagrass meadows. Manatees are large, entirely aquatic mammals with a rounded body in shades of brown or gray and a flattened tail used for propulsion. Average length of adults ranges from 8-13 ft (2.4-4.0 m), weight is from 700-3,500 lb (320-1,600 kg). Eyes are small and there is no external ear pinna. The nostrils are located on the upper surface of the snout and can be tightly closed by valves when the manatee is underwater. Manatees often rest suspended just below the surface, coming up occasionally to breathe. Flexible flippers are used almost like hands for eating, moving through seagrass, touching, holding a suckling calf, and even hugging other manatees. Stiff, bristly hairs line the split upper lip, which is used to grasp food and pull it into the mouth. Manatees lack incisors, but as their molars are worn down, they are replaced by new ones which move forward from the back of the tooth row. Diet consists of a variety of aquatic vascular plants, including seagrasses and true grasses. A variety of algae and small crustaceans are taken incidentally with the vegetation and may provide an additional source of protein. In Florida, seagrass, water hyacinths, and hydrilla are important foods. There may be some predation by sharks.

Sexual maturity is typically reached at seven to nine years of age. When a female is sexually receptive, she is pursued by males and often mates with several of them over the course of a week. There is no particular breeding season, but most births apparently take place in spring and early summer. After a gestation period of 13 months, usually one calf is born; it begins grazing within a few months but nurses and remains with the mother for one to two years.

Habitat and Current Distribution

The Caribbean manatee is found in the coastal waters and rivers of the Caribbean and Atlantic re-

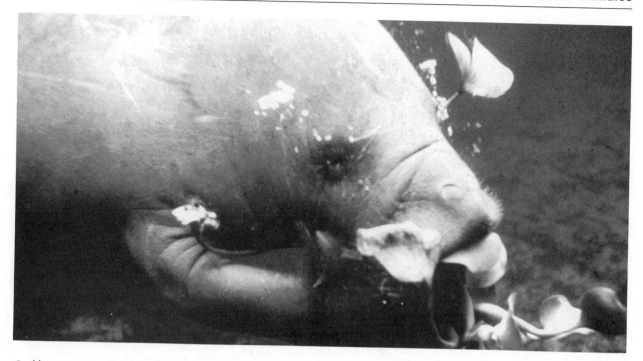

Caribbean manatee.

gions of the Americas, in tropical and subtropical latitudes. Exact population figures are unknown. An intensive statewide survey conducted in Florida in January 1992 produced a minimum estimate of 1,856.

The manatee prefers slow-moving rivers, river mouths, bays, lagoons, shallow coastal waters, and coves to open marine waters. It is adapted to marine, estuarine, and fresh water habitats. This nomadic animal sometimes covers great distances migrating between winter and summer grounds, stopping along the way where feeding conditions and shelter are favorable.

History and Conservation Measures

The manatee and its relative, the dugong, are thought to be the inspiration for the myth of the mermaid. Historic population figures do not exist, but it is now considerably reduced throughout much of its range. Commercial exploitation began in the sixteenth century, with the Spanish colonization of the Caribbean region. The flavor of the meat was highly esteemed and, as it would keep without spoiling for long periods of time, it was especially valuable for extended voyages and expeditions. Because of its low population, commercial hunting is no longer feasible.

Although it is legally protected throughout most of its range, subsistence hunting still reportedly occurs in many areas outside of the United States and continues to pose a substantial threat. Manatees are still reasonably abundant on both coasts of Florida, in Belize and some areas of Mexico, and in Guyana in South America.

Human activities are now the greatest threat to the manatee. Even in areas where they are not deliberately hunted, many undoubtedly drown each year from being trapped in fishing nets; are drowned or crushed by flood gates and canal locks; and are injured by discarded fishing lines, hooks, and trash in the water. Despite the protective measures to regulate boating activity, collision with boats is still the major cause of man-related manatee mortality in Florida. A large proportion of the Florida manatee population bears propeller scars, which are used by biologists to identify individual animals. Manatee protection zones have been established in which boat speeds are restricted; in areas designated as refuges, no boats, swimmers or divers are allowed. Research, public education, and management activities have been initiated in countries throughout the manatee's range.

West African manatee

Trichechus senegalensis

Phylum	Chordata
Class	Mammalia
Order	Sirenia
Family	Trichechidae
Status	Vulnerable, IUCN
	Threatened, USFWS
	Appendix II, CITES
Range	Angola; Benin (ex?); Cameroon; Chad; Congo; Côte d'Ivoire; Equatorial Guinea; Gabon; Gambia; Ghana; Guinea (?); Guinea-Bissau (?); Liberia; Mali; Mauritania; Niger; Nigeria; Senegal; Sierra Leone; Togo; Zaire

Description and Biology

The West African manatee, also known as the African manatee, is an aquatic mammal with a rounded body and wrinkled gray-brown skin sparsely covered with white hairs. Its facial features includes nostrils that appear on top of the squared-off snout, small eyes, and stiff bristles on the upper and lower lip. When its front teeth are completely decayed, new teeth move up from the back of the mouth. The rounded tail fin is used for propulsion, back flippers are lacking, and flexible front flippers are used almost like hands for eating, for moving through seagrass, touching, holding a suckling calf, and even hugging other manatees. The averages head and body length of this species is 10-13 ft (3-4 m) long; average weight is 1,100-2,200 lb (500-1,000 kg). Diet consists of a variety of aquatic vascular plants and grasses, but the manatee feeds primarily on mangroves when inhabiting estuaries. A variety of algae and small crustaceans are taken incidentally with the vegetation and provide a source of protein.

The manatee may travel alone or in groups of up to four to six animals. Reproductive biology is not well known, but breeding may take place throughout the year. One young is usually born after a gestation period of 12-13 months. The juvenile may stay with its mother for one to two years.

Habitat and Current Distribution

This species occurs in West African coastal waters, estuaries, and rivers all the way from Senegal to Angola. It can live in both salt and fresh water, adjusting its diet to available vegetation. This nomadic animal sometimes covers great distances migrating between winter and summer grounds, stopping along the way where feeding conditions are favorable. Crocodiles and sharks are the West African manatee's only natural predators. Estimates of population size are unavailable.

History and Conservation Measures

In some parts of West Africa, manatee hunting is a valued tradition. The manatee population has been depleted primarily by hunting, not on a commercial basis, but by local people as a source of food and protein. It is also sometimes killed for stealing fish from fishing nets, or is accidentally caught in the nets. Changes in water levels as a result of dam building can strand manatees and interfere with their migration patterns. During the dry season, some manatees who migrate upstream may become trapped by falling water levels.

Further studies of the status, numbers, and distribution of this species are necessary for the formulation of conservation plans. Even in areas that have already extended protection to the species, enforcement is difficult when it is hunted and consumed as food. Conservation efforts will have to find a balance the between economic and nutritional needs of the local people and the conservation need to protect the manatee.

Asian elephant

Elephas maximus

Phylum	Chordata
Class	Mammalia
Order	Proboscidea
Family	Elephantidae
Status	Endangered, IUCN
	Endangered, USFWS
	Appendix I, CITES
Range	Bangladesh; Bhutan; Brunei; Kampuchea; China; India; Indonesia; Laos; Malaysia; Myanmar; Nepal; Sri Lanka; Thailand; Vietnam

Description and Biology

Unique among wild animals, Asian elephants have long been domesticated to work predictably and peacefully alongside humans. The elephants have been important in myth and in religious observances, in pageantry, in military operations, and in industry—particularly forestry.

Also known as the Indian elephant, the Asian elephant is smaller than the African elephant and has much smaller ears. Average height at the shoulder is 8-10 ft (2.5-3 m), while average weight is 5,000 lb (2,270 kg) for females and 11,900 lb (5,400 kg) for males. It has a flat forehead and convex back. The trunk is an extension of the nose and upper lip; the tail ends in a tuft of hair. Unlike African elephants, only some Asian elephant males—and no females—have tusks, which are enlarged incisor teeth. This elephant has six molars in each half jaw, which move forward in progression. As one set wears out and falls out, the next set moves forward and comes into use; when the final set is worn out, the elephant can no longer chew food, making death imminent.

With their huge size and feeding habits, Asian elephants require large areas of forest habitats to maintain viable populations. The elephants feed on more than 100 species of plants, including grass, leaves, twigs, and bark; up to 330 lb (150 kg) of vegetation is consumed in a typical day, with the animals spending 17-18 hours a day foraging. Range varies with food and water supply and can extend twice as far in the dry season as in the rainy season.

Elephants have a complex matriarchal social system based on breeding groups of females and young. Mature males live singly or together in a small group but have no permanent contact with females; they associate for mating and sometimes for feeding. Females reach sexual maturity between 9-15 years and produce a single calf after a gestation of 18-22 months. The calf suckles and remains dependent for three to four years.

Habitat and Current Distribution

The Asian elephant occurs in Bangladesh, Bhutan, China, India, Indonesia, Kampuchea, Laos, Malaysia, Myanmar, Nepal, Sri Lanka, Thailand, and Vietnam. Total population in the wild is estimated to be between 34,000 and 54,000, with the largest population in India.

Preferred habitat is forest with access to a permanent water supply and grass.

Asian elephant.

History and Conservation Measures

Because many Asian elephants don't have tusks, ivory poaching is less of a threat than it is for African elephants. Nevertheless, the Asian elephant still faces major threats to its survival, chiefly deforestation for agricultural purposes. Deforestation has had a devastating impact on this species, which needs vast areas of natural range to support its basic requirements. Reduction of the Asian elephant's habitat has resulted in elephant populations becoming pocketed in patches of forest that are surrounded by agricultural land. When this happens, emigration and dispersion become difficult for the elephants and conflict with humans becomes inevitable. Before the incursion of human settlement, the range of the Asian elephant extended from the Euphrates-Tigris river systems in the west through Asia south of the Himalayas to Indochina and most of southern China in the east. The animal's current range is but a fraction of that area.

Survival of the Asian elephant depends on provision of protected areas, uninterrupted by human settlements and roads, that are large enough to sustain viable populations of the animal.

African elephant

Loxodonta africana

Phylum	Chordata
Class	Mammalia
Order	Proboscidea
Family	Elephantidae
Status	Vulnerable, IUCN
	Threatened, USFWS
	Appendix I, CITES
Range	Angola; Benin; Botswana; Burkina Faso; Cameroon; Central African Republic; Chad; Congo; Côte d'Ivoire; Equatorial Guinea; Ethiopia; Gabon; Ghana; Guinea; Kenya; Liberia; Malawi; Mali; Mauritania; Mozambique; Namibia; Niger; Nigeria; Rwanda; Senegal; Sierra Leone; Somalia; South Africa; Sudan; Tanzania; Togo; Uganda; Zaire; Zambia; Zimbabwe

Description and Biology

The African elephant is the largest living land mammal, standing 10-13 ft (3-4 m) at the shoulder and weighing 11,000-13,000 lb (5,000-6,000 kg). Body color is usually a dark, muddy gray. It has huge ears that help to dissipate body heat, upper incisors that form tusks, and a trunk that is an extension of the nose and upper lip. This elephant feeds on various types of vegetation, including tree bark, fruit, grasses, and leaves of trees and shrubs, and requires approximately 300-400 lb (136-181 kg) of food daily. The tusks are used in feeding to strip bark from trees or dig roots; the trunk enables the elephant to eat from the ground or from bushes and trees. The trunk is also used for smell and touch and in drinking, greeting, or throwing dust for frequent dust baths; the finger-like tips at the end of the trunk are sensitive enough to pick up very small objects. Range used for feeding varies with the season and the availability of food and water.

The elephants' complex social system is based on breeding groups of females and young. Adult males live singly or in small groups and have no permanent ties with the females, although they may associate with them for feeding as well as for breeding. After a gestation period of almost two years, the female gives birth to a single young, although twins have been found in the wild. Other females are often present during the birth and help keep predators away. The calf, which weighs from 200-300 lb (90-136 kg) at birth, nurses for at least two years and remains dependent on the mother for four to five years.

Habitat and Current Distribution

The African elephant is found in much of Africa south of the Sahara. Population is estimated at 549,000-652,000, with the largest proportion in central Africa.

Two subspecies of *Loxodonta africana* are recognized: *L. a. cyclotis*, the forest elephant, lives in the rain forests of central and west Africa; *L. a. africana*, the savanna or bush elephant, lives on the plains of east and southern Africa.

African elephants.

History and Conservation Measures

The most serious historical threat to the elephant is still the most serious threat today: the ivory trade. Elephants have been hunted for centuries for their ivory tusks. Early population estimates are unavailable, but the magnitude of the decline is demonstrated by the drop from a population in the late 1970s of 1,700,000 to the present estimate of approximately 760,000 individuals. The African elephant once occurred in North Africa, up to the Mediterranean coast, but it became extinct there during the European Middle Ages.

Rapid growth of human population in Africa is putting the elephant into competition with humans for usable land. Other major factors in the decline of the elephant are desertification and other consequences of human incursion into its habitat.

Steps have been taken to save the African elephant. In 1989, the Convention on International Trade in Endangered Species of Wild Fauna and Flora (CITES) adopted a ban on the sale of elephant ivory. Although poaching is still a major problem, the market for ivory has decreased. The elephant is also being recognized as a tourist attraction; national parks and reserves protect the species and bring in tourist dollars. Conservationists are hoping that the U.S. Fish and Wildlife Service will change this elephant's status from threatened to endangered.

African wild ass

Equus africanus

Phylum	Chordata
Class	Mammalia
Order	Perissodactyla
Family	Equidae
Status	Endangered, IUCN
	Endangered, USFWS
	Appendix I, CITES
Range	Ethiopia; Sudan; Somalia; Arabian Peninsula (?)

Description and Biology

The African wild ass is the smallest member of the horse family, averaging 6.5 ft (2 m) long, 4 ft (1.25 m) high at the shoulder, and weighing 550-600 lb (250-275 kg). Upper body is brownish gray with a darker dorsal stripe; underparts and muzzle are white; legs are pale and banded. Mane is upright, hooves narrow, and the 16.5-in (42 cm) tail is tufted. Wild asses spend the day grazing and foraging for food, resting only in the heat of the afternoon. They consume a variety of grasses and forbs, although browse may be an important part of their diet in some circumstances.

Although some males live alone, most individuals join non-permanent groups whose members change from time to time. Males defend a non-exclusive territory of up to 9 sq mi (23 sq km) and compete for breeding females; no pair bonds are formed. Mating peaks with the beginning of rainy season, and one foal is born after a gestation period of at least one year. Females may associate with males and other females when lactating but otherwise live with their recent offspring in unstable groups of up to 50 animals.

Three subspecies have been accepted, but this classification is based on relatively little material, and further studies may in fact only identify one subspecies. For the moment, the Nubian wild ass (*Equus africanus africanus*), the Atlas wild ass (*E. a. atlanticus*), and the Somali wild ass (*E. a. somaliensis*) are recognized.

Habitat and Current Distribution

The preferred habitat of the African wild ass is remote, arid and semi-arid bushlands and grasslands. No recent sightings have been made of the Nubian wild ass in its historic range, and the free-living asses found in Ethiopia and Sudan are probably feral or cross-bred. The Nubian ass may therefore be extinct.

Aerial counts of Ethiopian populations in 1970-1971 provided an estimate of around 3,000 animals. This may have been an underestimate, however, and the actual numbers may have been much higher (possibly 6,000-12,000). The most recent figures were compiled in 1978 following aerial surveys of part of the area. At this time the population was estimated to be around 1,500.

In Somalia partial counts made during 1988-1989 yielded only 100-250 individuals, indicating that the total population in Somalia may be only a few hundred.

History and Conservation Measures

The original range and population of the African wild ass are not fully known, but experts agree that both are now drastically reduced. Humans have used domesticated animals as beasts of burden for thousands of years due to their ability to survive in the harshest of conditions. However, these domestic animals pose a serious threat to the survival of wild asses. Extensive interbreeding has already occurred and may have led to the disappearance of wild asses from the northern part of their range.

Other threats to the African wild ass include hunting and loss of access to food and water. Hunting has become a major problem due to the political unrest in both Somalia and Ethiopia since automatic weapons are now more readily available. Wild asses are sometimes excluded from certain areas where agricultural development has taken place since they are thought to compete with domestic livestock for grazing and water.

Conservation action is urgently required for the African wild ass. Obviously, political stability in the countries within the species' range is essential to any conservation action. In Ethiopia and Somalia, updated surveys of population size and distribution are crucial to any conservation effort, but attempts to conduct these surveys are often thwarted by unrest. If such surveys could be completed, recommended actions would include increasing the numbers of wild populations and providing for their protection. Improved management of the Yangudi-Rassa National Park in Ethiopia, where a nucleus population of African wild asses occurs, could help ensure that numbers there would build to a viable level. In Somalia a multi-use reserve has been proposed for the Nugaal Valley, where another nucleus group of wild asses exist.

Less than 100 African wild asses are presently in captivity, too low of a number to support a viable breeding program. These captive herds are, however, of great importance and should be carefully managed under a single breeding program which would conserve their genetic diversity and prepare them for eventual interaction with the wild populations.

Grevy's zebra

Equus grevyi

Mountain zebra

Equus zebra

Phylum	Chordata
Class	Mammalia
Order	Perissodactyla
Family	Equidae
Status	Endangered, IUCN (*E. grevyi*)
	Vulnerable, IUCN (*E. zebra*)
	Endangered, USFWS (*E. zebra zebra*)
	Threatened, USFWS (*E. grevyi, E. zebra hartmannae*)
	Appendix I, CITES (*E. grevyi, E. zebra zebra*)
	Appendix II, CITES (*E. zebra hartmannae*)
Range	Ethiopia; Kenya (*E. grevyi*)
	Angola; Namibia; South Africa (*E. zebra*)

Description and Biology

Like other zebras, members of these two species have a startling coloration pattern that sets them apart from other animals on the African continent. Though scientists once speculated that the black-and-white zebra stripes served as camouflage or to confuse predators, recent researchers have suggested that the stripes serve mainly as a socialization feature, helping individuals to recognize each other and leading to group cohesion.

Grevy's zebra is as closely related to the horse as it is to other zebras and, except for its stripes, is similar in appearance to a mule. It is the largest species in the equid family, with a head and body length averaging 8-10 ft (2.4-3 m) at physical maturity, a shoulder height averaging 4.5-5 ft (1.4-1.5 m), and weight ranging from 800-950 lb (360-430 kg). It has a large head, broad ears and a dark, erect mane. The

mountain zebra, by contrast, averages 7-8.5 ft (2.1-2.6 m) in length (head and body), 4-5 ft (1.2-1.5 m) at the shoulder, and weighs 550-800 lb (250-360 kg). It has longer ears, a dewlap below its chin, and hooves adapted to climbing in mountainous terrain.

A beautiful pattern of narrow vertical stripes covers most of the head and body of Grevy's zebra. These stripes curve upward on the haunches but do not widen as they do on the mountain zebra. The belly of Grevy's zebra is white, as is an area on either side of a dark dorsal stripe. The mountain zebra also has narrow stripes over most of its body, but these stripes broaden significantly on its rump, with the black stripes predominating. The mountain zebra's belly is white with a single black stripe.

Both species feed on grasses, but the mountain zebra also eats bark, leaves, and shoots of trees or shrubs. Lions, hyenas, and crocodiles prey upon

Grevy's zebra.

adults and sub-adults of both species, while cheetahs are known to take foals.

Grevy's zebras exhibit social patterns that are unusual among equids. They do not form permanent groups, although nursing females and foals, other females, and solitary males sometimes gather in temporary herds. Some bachelor males are territorial for mating purposes. In such cases, the males defend huge territories of 1-4 sq mi (2.6-10.4 sq km), often for years. Occasionally, they may join other Grevy's zebras on their seasonal migrations, but they usually return to re-establish control of their territory. Males compete for dominance and the right to mate with receptive females. Unlike Grevy's zebras, mountain zebras do form permanent breeding groups; these usually consist of one male and between one and five females. A dominant male may control a group for a number of years until he is defeated in combat by a younger male. Mountain zebra males are not territorial but inhabit home ranges with extensive overlap.

In both species, breeding can occur at any time during the year. Among Grevy's zebras, mating peaks during the rains in July-August and October-November, when dominant males re-establish control of their territories after the seasonal migrations. Among mountain zebras, mating peaks occur between November-April for *E. z. hartmannae* and between De-cember-February for *E. z. zebra*. The gestation period of Grevy's zebra is 390 days, while that of the mountain zebra is somewhat shorter at about one year. Both species produce a single foal. The newborn Grevy's zebra has an eye-catching extension of the mane down its back to the tail and is brown and black in color. Adult coloring develops after four months of age. Offspring of both species may remain with their mothers for up to three years.

Habitat and Current Distribution

Grevy's zebra is found in semi-arid scrub/grassland and subdesert steppe in southern Ethiopia and Kenya. In 1980, about 1,500 individuals remained in Ethiopia. Recent drought and military activity make population estimates uncertain, but they are thought to be declining. Meanwhile, a 1988 survey in Kenya put the population at 4,276, with a core population of 1,500 occurring in the Buffalo Springs/Sambura/ Shaba nature reserves complex.

The mountain zebra, as its common name implies, is found in mountainous regions of southwestern Africa. It is found from the edges of true desert through semi-arid regions to savannah grasslands, preferring mountain grassland at around 6,500 ft (2,000 m) but it may also inhabit plateaus and flats. It

Mountain zebra.

History and Conservation Measures

Although there are no initial population estimates for Grevy's zebra, it has been exterminated in Somalia, and its distribution in Ethiopia and Kenya has been significantly reduced. No recent surveys have been made in Ethiopia, but numbers are thought to be declining. A survey in Kenya in 1977 estimated a population of 13,718. Thus, the 1988 estimate of 4,276 signals a decline of 70 percent in just 11 years. Much of the cause of its decline in early years was hunting for its beautiful skin. It is now legally protected, however, and poaching is not considered a major problem. Instead, the major current threat is the loss of habitat as a result of competition with increasing numbers of livestock and recent irrigation projects in Kenya, which limit the water flow to the arid and semi-arid regions that form the habitat for Grevy's zebras.

The population of Hartmann's mountain zebra was estimated at 50,000 in the 1950s, and earlier populations were probably much larger. It formerly occupied a continuous range extending from southwestern Angola through western Namibia to the border of South Africa. Like the Cape mountain zebra, Hartmann's mountain zebra has declined in the past 20 years mainly because of competition with domestic livestock and hunting by farmers. Animals outside protected areas will always be subject to these dangers. In addition, drought has long been a threat to the subspecies, and water extraction schemes in the Namib Desert have made this threat even worse.

The introduction of Hartmann's mountain zebra into the range of the Cape mountain zebra has brought with it the possibility of hybridization and loss of genetic diversity. To prevent this, landowners in Cape Province are being encouraged to exchange their animals for Cape mountain zebras at no cost to themselves.

A species management plan has been developed to coordinate management of mountain zebra species in the various protected areas, among the main objectives of this plan are: the conservation of genetic diversity of the various subspecies; the natural increase of Hartmann's mountain zebras on public and private lands; and improved monitoring procedures for each of the separate populations.

moves to lower elevations to graze in cold weather and may seek shelter in caves or wooded areas.

There are two subspecies of mountain zebra: *E. z. zebra*, the Cape mountain zebra, from the mountainous regions of Cape Province, South Africa; and *E. z. hartmannae*, Hartmann's mountain zebra, from extreme southwestern Angola and western Namibia. Both subspecies occur in isolated, discontinuous groups over portions of their former ranges. The most recent population estimate of the Cape mountain zebra put its numbers at about 600. Most of these occur in protected areas, particularly in Mountain Zebra Park, which contains 178 individuals. The population of Hartmann's mountain zebra is thought to be around 7,000 in Namibia, of which 4,000 are in protected areas. The latter subspecies has been introduced into the Cape Province, which is outside its historical range, and the population here stands at 350. There are thought to be very few Hartmann's mountain zebras left in Angola.

Asian wild ass

Equus hemionus

Equus kiang

Phylum . . . . Chordata
Class . . . . Mammalia
Order . . . . Perissodactyla
Family . . . . Equidae
Status . . . . Vulnerable, IUCN (*E. k. holderei*)
Endangered, IUCN (*E. h. khur; E. h. kulan; E. h. onager*)
Insufficiently Known, IUCN (*E. h. luteus*)
Indeterminate, IUCN (*E. k. polyodon; E. k. kiang*)
Extinct, IUCN (*E. h. hemippus; E. h. hemionus*)
Appendix I, CITES (*E. h. khur; E. h. kulan; E. h. onager*)
Appendix II, CITES (*E. h. hemionus; E. h. luteus; E. k. polyodon; E. k. kiang*)
Range . . . . Russia; Mongolia; China; India; Turkmenistan; Kazakhstan; Iran; Israel (*E. hemionus*)
China; Nepal; India; Sikkim (*E. kiang*)

Description and Biology

A member of the horse family, the Asian wild ass is known by a number of common names throughout its range: kulan, khur, onager, and dziggetais. The two species of Asian wild ass—*Equus hemionus* and *E. kiang*—share many behavioral and physical traits.

E. hemionus is the fastest equid; it can travel up to 43 mph (70 kph). The color of *E. hemionus*' coat varies according to its distribution and season; generally it has a reddish brown coat that fades to yellowish brown in winter. Underparts and muzzle are white or buff, and a dark stripe edged in white runs down the middle of the back. *E. hemionus* has short legs, small feet, and a 12-16 in (30-40 cm) tail that ends in a tuft of long hair. Average head and body length is 6.5-8 ft (2-2.5 m); height at the shoulder 3.2-4.6 ft (1-1.4 m); and weight averages between 441-573 lb (200-260 kg).

Grazing mainly at night, *E. hemionus* is entirely vegetarian, feeding on grass, herbs, bark, and succulent plants. As with other equids, this animal is capable of surviving long periods of time without water. Wolves are known predators of this species.

Group size and composition vary throughout the year. Large herds have been recorded, particularly in the autumn after the monsoon season: one was even found to contain 135 animals. The breeding season occurs from April to October. One foal is born after a gestation period of 11-12 months and is nursed for one to two years.

E. kiang is the largest wild ass, with a shoulder height of 4.6 ft (1.4 m). Males weigh 882 lb (400 kg), and females average between 551-661 lb (250-300 kg). The coat of this species is bright red in the summer, turning rusty-brown in winter. Like *E. hemionus*, *E. kiang* has a black dorsal stripe. The underparts are white, as are the leg, throat, and sides of the muzzle. It also has white rings around the eyes. Compared to

Onagers (*E. hemionus hemionus*).

E. hemionus, this species has a larger head, broader snout, shorter ears, longer mane, and broader hooves.

E. kiang lives in cohesive herds ranging from 5-400 individuals. Groups are led by a female and are comprised of adult females and their foals. Males live alone or join other males. Unlike horses, *E. kiang* does not engage in mutual grooming: physical contact is minimal. When females are ready to give birth, they leave the herd in small groups of two to five animals and move to the safety of rocky outcrops to give birth. Foals can run and walk within few hours, and they quickly join their mothers in the herd.

Habitat and Current Distribution

Two species and at least eight subspecies of Asian wild ass are currently recognized, although there are many more geographically distinct populations. Six subspecies of *E. hemionus* have been identified: *E. h. hemionus*, also called north Mongolian dziggetais, has traditionally been found in Russia and Mongolia but may now be extinct; *E. h. luteus*, also called the Gobi dziggetais, is found in Mongolia and China. Population size for this animal is estimated in the thousands but no exact figure is available; *E. h. khur*, the Indian wild ass, is found in India and numbers about 2,000 animals; *E. h. kulan*, the kulan, is

found in Turkmenistan and Kazakhstan and numbers about 2,000 individuals; *E. h. onager*, the onager, is found in Iran and Israel and numbers less than 400 animals. The Syrian wild ass, *E. h. hemippus*, became extinct in 1927.

Three subspecies of *E. kiang* have been identified: *E. k. holderei*, the eastern kiang; *E. k. kiang*, the western kiang; and *E. k. polyodon*, the southern kiang. The eastern kiang is found in China and numbers at least 30,000. Several thousand western kiangs are found in Nepal and India. The southern kiang traditionally inhabited China and Sikkim, but this animal may be extinct in the wild.

The preferred habitat of these species are highland or lowland desert, semidesert, or steppe. *E. hemionus* prefers flat country, and *E. kiang* inhabits high, undulating steppe at elevations of 16,405 ft (5,000 m).

History and Conservation Measures

As late as 1900, the Asian wild ass covered most of the continent's steppe and desert regions from the Black Sea to the Ural Mountains in the north and as far east as the Gobi Desert. In the south they occurred in Anatolia, south to the Negev and through the deserts of Arabia, Persia, Afghanistan, and Pakistan to the Thar Desert. Major population declines of virtually every species occurred in the first half of the twentieth century, mainly due to hunting for meat and for its coat. In the latter half of this century the distribution of wild asses has varied considerably, depending upon the population. Only the eastern kiang is considered common in its sparsely inhabited central Asian desert habitat. The status of all other subspecies needs accurate and regular monitoring.

The specific conservation measures required for each subspecies are varied. Habitat loss is a major threat to all species as land is converted for farming and grazing domestic livestock. They also face competition from livestock for water and food sources. In addition, the small population size of most of the subspecies threatens the genetic diversity of future generations.

Attempts have been made to re-introduce this species into areas of former habitat. A number of onagers from Iran were recently introduced into a protected reserve in Israel.

Przewalski's horse

Equus przewalski

Phylum	Chordata
Class	Mammalia
Order	Perissodactyla
Family	Equidae
Status	Extinct (?), IUCN
	Endangered, USFWS
	Appendix I, CITES
Range	China (ex?)

Description and Biology

Przewalski's horse is the only remaining truly wild horse and may be the ancestor of today's domestic horse. The upper body color varies from dark bay to dun with a dark dorsal stripe from mane to tail; the belly and muzzle are much lighter. They may be as long as 8 ft (2.45 m), and height at the shoulder varies from 4-4.75 ft (1.2-1.4 m). Most weigh between 440-750 lbs (200-340 kg).

Przewalski's horse has a compact build with a thick neck and a large head. Unlike the domestic horse, the mane and short hairs at the base of the tail are shed annually. The mane is, therefore, erect and, apart from yellow side hairs, is dark, as are the long hairs of the tail and the legs. Dark stripes can be seen on the lower part of the legs.

Przewalksi's horse feeds on grass and other low vegetation and was probably subject to predation by wolves.

Most information on the social structure of Przewalski's horse is inferred from studies of feral horses. Large breeding groups are headed by a dominant stallion, responsible for most of the breeding; other groups of bachelor horses are less stable, with shifting size and membership. Most young are born between April and June, after a gestation period of 330-340 days and may nurse for up to two years.

Habitat and Current Distribution

The last possible sighting of Przewalski's horse in the wild was in 1966. Chinese biologists believe that there may be a remnant population in northeastern Xinjiang, but it is likely that this species is now extinct in the wild. Captive population in various zoos and reserves is now over 1,000.

Preferred habitat in the wild is open grassland, steppe, and semi-desert areas.

History and Conservation Measures

Przewalski's horse was discovered by the Polish geographer N. M. Przewalski in 1878; this and all subsequent observations have been made in Dzungaria (Mongolia/China), Xinjiang, and Kazakhstan. There are no estimates of initial population size.

By the early 1900s, the population had been greatly reduced by hunting and competition with domestic stock for grazing and water. By the 1950s, the remaining animals were seen in a small area on the border between southwestern Mongolia and China

Przewalski's horse.

called the Takhin-Shara-Nuru (the "mountain of the yellow horses").

Today's captive population descends mainly from animals captured in the late nineteenth and early twentieth centuries. Many years of inbreeding have resulted in a loss of genetic diversity, but several programs are now underway to return this species to its historical range.

Central American tapir

Tapirus bairdii

Phylum	Chordata
Class	Mammalia
Order	Perissodactyla
Family	Tapiridae
Status	Vulnerable, IUCN
	Endangered, USFWS
	Appendix I, CITES
Range	Belize; Colombia; Costa Rica; Ecuador; Guatemala; Honduras; Mexico; Nicaragua; Panama

Description and Biology

The Central American or Baird's tapir is a large animal with a medium to dark brown coat. Head and body length averages 6.5-8 ft (2-2.4 m), height at the shoulder is 36-42 in (91-107 cm), and weight is 550-660 lb (250-300 kg). Body shape is well adapted for moving quickly through the forest, with short legs and a stout body that narrows in front. It is also a good swimmer and spends a significant amount of time submerged in water or wallowing in mud. The Central American tapir has acute senses of hearing and smell, but poor eyesight with small, deeply set eyes. A short, bristly mane on the back of the neck provides some protection from the teeth of feline predators. The nose and upper lip extend to form a short trunk or proboscis which is used to shovel food into the mouth. Diet consists primarily of grass, leaves, and a wide variety of fruit. Jaguars and mountain lions are predators.

Females are receptive to mating at two-month intervals throughout the year; courtship behavior includes squealing, nipping, circling, and sniffing. One young is born after a gestation period of 390-405 days. At birth, the calf has protective coloration and markings which begin to fade within a few months; it may nurse for up to a year.

Habitat and Current Distribution

Remnant populations are found from southern Mexico through Central America to northern Columbia. Population figures are unknown.

The Central American tapir is found in a variety of mostly humid habitats from sea level to at least 11,000 ft (3,350 m), including marshes, mangrove swamps, tropical rain forests, riparian woodlands, monsoon-deciduous forests, and páramo (high, barren tropical plain) above the tree line.

History and Conservation Measures

This species once occurred from southern Mexico through Central America to Colombia and Ecuador. Although initial and current population figures are unavailable, it is now extinct in some areas, and

Central American tapir.

numbers have decreased throughout most of its range. Today the Central American tapir is for the most part confined to reserves in Honduras, Costa Rica, Panama, Nicaragua, Guatemala, and Belize.

Historically, the Central American tapir has been hunted for food, sport, and for its skin. Now legally protected, the species nevertheless continues to be the target of poachers due to lax enforcement. Despite this problem, the most serious threat to the species today is the degradation of its habitat. Vast tracts of land have been cleared for agricultural development, pushing a dwindling population into widely separated remnants of suitable secondary forest. Population and range surveys and ecological studies are necessary before conservation plans, including the establishment of further reserves, can be formulated.

Malayan tapir

Tapirus indicus

Phylum	Chordata
Class	Mammalia
Order	Perissodactyla
Family	Tapiridae
Status	Endangered, IUCN
	Endangered, USFWS
	Appendix I, CITES
Range	Sumatra (Indonesia); Malaysia; Myanmar; Thailand

Description and Biology

The Malayan or Asian tapir is easily identified by a distinctive pattern of coloration which provides camouflage at night in the light and shadows of the jungle. The front part of the body and the forelegs are black, as are the rump and hind legs; the middle of the body is white. Body shape is well adapted for moving quickly through the forest, with short legs and a stout body that narrows in front. It is also a good swimmer and spends much time submerged in water or wallowing in mud. Head and body length averages 6.5-8 ft (2-2.4 m), height at the shoulder is 36-42 in (91-107 cm), and weight is 550-660 lb (250-300 kg). A short, stumpy tail measures only 2-4 in (5-10 cm). The tapir has acute senses of hearing and smell, but poor eyesight with small, deeply set eyes. The nose and upper lip extend to form a short trunk or proboscis which is used to shovel food into the mouth. Diet includes aquatic vegetation, grasses, leaves, fruits, and especially green shoots and new plant growth. Leopards and tigers are predators.

Mating takes place in April or May; courtship behavior includes squealing, nipping, circling, and sniffing. One young is born after a gestation period of 390-400 days. At birth, the calf has protective coloration and markings which begin to fade within a few months. Young remain dependent for six to eight months.

Habitat and Current Distribution

This tapir is found discontinuously in parts of Myanmar, Thailand, Malaysia, and Sumatra (Indonesia). Population estimates are unavailable.

Preferred habitat for the Malayan tapir is tropical forest. It shelters in the forest during the day and ventures out into adjoining grassland at night to feed. Because the tapir often stays submerged for long periods, proximity to water is an important component of suitable habitat.

History and Conservation Measures

The Malayan tapir is a fairly primitive mammal that has changed very little in millions of years. Early estimates are unavailable, but experts agree that the species' population has now declined to dangerous levels. Once hunted for food, sport, and its pelt, the tapir is now legally protected.

Malayan tapir.

The primary threat to this species today is loss and degradation of habitat. Vast areas of tropical forest are being cleared for agricultural development and to provide grazing lands for domestic livestock. Protected reserves like Taman Negara in Malaysia are necessary to preserve suitable habitat and ensure the survival of this species.

Mountain tapir

Tapirus pinchaque

Phylum	Chordata
Class	Mammalia
Order	Perissodactyla
Family	Tapiridae
Status	Endangered, IUCN
	Endangered, USFWS
	Appendix I, CITES
Range	Colombia; Ecuador; Peru; Venezuela

Description and Biology

The mountain tapir is the only one of its kind adapted to a cold climate, its relatives preferring tropical or subtropical habitat. To survive in the Andes mountains, it has developed a thicker, longer outer coat with a warm undercoat. Color is dark brown to black, with white edging on the ears and lips. The mountain tapir is slightly smaller than other tapirs, with an average length of 6 ft (1.8 m), shoulder height of 30-32 in (76-81 cm), and weight of 500-620 lb (227-281 kg). The mountain tapir has acute senses of hearing and smell, but poor eyesight with small, deeply set eyes. The nose and upper lip extend to form a short trunk or proboscis which is used to bring food into the mouth. Diet includes grasses, leaves, and fruit. Mountain lions and jaguars are predators.

The tapir is a solitary animal except during mating; males may compete violently for receptive females. Females are receptive to mating at two-month intervals throughout the year; courtship behavior includes squealing, nipping, circling, and sniffing. One young is born after a gestation period of 390-400 days.

At birth, the calf has protective coloration and markings which begin to fade within a few months; it may nurse for up to a year.

Habitat and Current Distribution

The mountain tapir is found discontinuously in the Andes of Colombia, Ecuador, Peru and Venezuela. Population figures are unknown.

Habitat is rugged mountainous terrain up to the snowline at elevations between 6,500 and 14,500 ft (2,000-4,400 m).

History and Conservation Measures

No estimates of initial population exist for this species, but its numbers today are greatly reduced. Despite legal restrictions on commercial and international trade, the mountain tapir is heavily hunted for its meat by local hunters. It is also being disturbed by human intrusion into its habitat. Because very little is known about this species, studies of its biology, range, and habitat are necessary before conservation efforts can be organized.

Mountain tapir.

Northern white rhinoceros

Ceratotherium simum cottoni

Phylum	Chordata
Class	Mammalia
Order	Perissodactyla
Family	Rhinocerotidae
Status	Endangered, IUCN
	Endangered, USFWS
	Appendix I, CITES
Range	Zaire

Description and Biology

The northern white rhinoceros is also called the northern square-lipped rhinoceros. This rhinoceros derives its common name from the Afrikaans word "weit," which means "wide." A mistranslation rendered "weit" as "white" and thus its other common name "white rhinoceros."

The northern white rhinoceros is one of two races of white rhinoceroses in Africa. The southern white rhinoceros is found in South Africa, Botswana, Zimbabwe, Namibia, Swaziland, Kenya, Mozambique, and Zambia. In 1986, they numbered less than 4,000 in the wild. The northern white rhinoceros is found only in Zaire and number only 33 individuals.

As its alternate name indicates, the northern white rhinoceros has a large, square-shaped mouth that is well-suited for grazing on short grass. This large animal stands 5.5-6 ft (1.7-1.8 m) at the shoulder, with a body length of 12-13 ft (3.7-4 m). It has a 20-28 in (50-70 cm) tail and weighs 5,000-8,000 lb (2,270-3,600 kg). This gray-colored rhino has short legs, broad ears, and two horns; it has a highly developed sense of smell but very poor vision. They are agile creatures and have been known to gallop as fast as 25 mph (40 kph).

Much of the northern white rhino's activity depends on the climate: during cool weather, the rhinos feed and rest throughout the day and night; during hot weather, they rest during the day and feed at morning and evening, even at night. In the heat of the day, they wallow in mud to keep cool—at times searching for water away from feeding areas. These waterholes are often shared with buffalos and warthogs. When no water is available, they roll in dust to keep cool and to keep insects away. Home range varies widely with habitat from less than one square mile (2.6 sq km) to almost 40 sq mi (100 sq km); the female's range is larger than that of the male.

The male is solitary, associating with the female only during the breeding season. The males are also very territorial, with the dominant males defending their territories against other males with displays of strength such as wrestling with horns and charging each other. Average feeding territory is about 0.75 sq mi (2 sq km). Socially inferior males are sometimes allowed to feed with dominant males if they make submissive gestures and sounds.

Females have larger territories than males, averaging about 4 sq mi (10 sq km). A female's feeding area may overlap several male territories. Females are sexually mature at seven years of age, and mating

Northern white rhino.

can take place throughout the year, with peaks in February and June. Courtship activity is cautious and may take five to twenty days before females allow males to mount them. After a gestation period of around 16 months, a single calf is born. When the offspring is two years old, it is chased away by the mother, who is usually ready to deliver another calf. The juveniles form a subadult group and often play and wrestle together. Dominant males appear to tolerate the subadults in their territory.

Habitat and Current Distribution

The northern white rhinoceros is restricted to Zaire. In 1993 the population consisted of 33 animals living in the Garamba National Park.

Preferred habitat is open grassland and savanna with access to water.

History and Conservation Measures

The northern white rhinoceros is one of the most endangered animals in Africa. In 1980, they numbered 821 individuals and just six years later, there were only 17 left in Zaire. Its decline was attributed to hunting and poaching for its horns.

The remaining population of white rhinos in Zaire became the focus of intensive conservation efforts and by 1993, the numbers increased to 33 individuals. Breeding of captive stock is critical to preserving such a reduced population, as is the continued upgrading of its protected habitat. Continued rehabilitation of Garamba National Park is recommended, along with a monitoring program for its population of white rhinos.

Sumatran rhinoceros

Dicerorhinus sumatrensis

Phylum	Chordata
Class	Mammalia
Order	Perissodactyla
Family	Rhinocerotidae
Status	Endangered, IUCN
	Endangered, USFWS
	Appendix I, CITES
Range	India (ex?); Kalimantan, Sumatra (Indonesia); Kampuchea (ex?); Laos (?); Malaysia; Myanmar; Thailand; Vietnam

Description and Biology

The Sumatran rhinoceros is the smallest rhino and, as its alternate name, hairy rhinoceros, implies, the hairiest. It averages 8-10 ft (2.4-3 m) long, stands 3.5-5 ft (1.1-1.5 m) tall at the shoulder, weighs 1,760-2,400 lb (800-1,100 kg), and its dark grayish brown skin is sparsely covered with long, bristly hairs. It has two horns, but one is small and knobby. The Sumatran rhino has an acute hearing but very poor vision. It swims well and spends a lot of time in water and in mud wallows. Wallowing is thought to cool the animal and provide some protection from biting insects. The Sumatran rhino has a prehensile upper lip which it uses to grasp food and draw it into its mouth. Diet includes leaves and twigs from trees and bushes and a variety of fruits. This species seems particularly fond of wild mangoes, figs, and bamboo and eats up to 110 lb (50 kg) of food daily. It feeds before dawn and after sunset and moves primarily at night. Its home range averages just under 12 sq mi (30 sq km) and usually includes a salt lick where the male lingers to encounter females. Tigers and wild dogs prey on young or sick rhinos.

Both males and females are territorial and both are solitary. Adult males and females generally come together only for mating. The gestation period is often reported to be between seven and eight months, but it is more likely to be at least 13 months. A single calf is well developed at birth but remains with the mother for over a year.

Habitat and Current Distribution

The Sumatran rhinoceros presently survives in pockets in Myanmar, Thailand, the Malay Peninsula, Sumatra, and Borneo. The total population is thought to be 500 animals in the wild and about 24 in captivity.

This species occupies a wide variety of habitats with water as the common denominator. It survives in lowland tropical rainforest, lowland swamps, and mountain forests, as well as along forest margins and in secondary growth areas.

History and Conservation Measures

Although estimates of earlier population are unavailable, the Sumatran rhinoceros once had a much wider distribution than it presently has and can be assumed to have had a much larger population. Like other rhinos, it has been a victim of overhunting for

Sumatran rhinoceros.

its horn (thought to have aphrodisiac and medicinal properties) and of habitat destruction. Even with legal protection it remains a target of poachers. This species probably suffers from a higher level of poaching for its horn than any other species of Asian rhinoceros. As suitable habitat is cleared for logging or agricultural uses, rhino populations become smaller and more fragmented, making them more susceptible to disease or natural disasters.

Conservation efforts for this species are guided by several specific objectives including: development of populations of at least 700-1,000 rhinos in each major region of its current range; preservation, management, and, where possible, expansion of all existing populations that have the potential to increase to 100 or more animals; location or establishment of additional viable populations, especially on the mainland and Borneo; development of a captive population of 150 rhinos distributed in zoos in Southeast Asia, North America, and Europe; continuation of efforts to close down the trade in rhino products. An intensive international cooperative program for the conservation of the Sumatran rhino has been started while there is still time to reverse the rapid decline of this species.

Black rhinoceros

Diceros bicornis

Phylum	Chordata
Class	Mammalia
Order	Perissodactyla
Family	Rhinocerotidae
Status	Endangered, IUCN
	Endangered, USFWS
	Appendix I, CITES
Range	Angola; Botswana; Cameroon; Central African Republic (ex?); Chad (ex?); Congo (ex?); Ethiopia (ex?); Kenya; Malawi (ex?); Mozambique; Namibia; Nigeria (ex?); Rwanda; South Africa; Sudan (ex?); Swaziland; Tanzania; Zambia; Zimbabwe

Description and Biology

One of the two species of rhinoceros found in Africa, the black rhinoceros is actually not black, but gray. Despite its huge size, shoulder height 4.5-5.25 ft (1.4-1.6 m), body length 9-12 ft (2.8-3.7 m), weight 2,000-4,000 lb (900-1,800 kg), the rhino can move fairly quickly when it decides to charge. It has poor vision but a highly developed sense of smell, its sinus passages being larger than its brain. A reputation for aggression comes from the high-speed charges it makes upon scenting danger. Of its two horns, the front one is longer and can measure up to 53 in (135 cm). It browses on branches, leaves, and bark, using its prehensile upper lip to grasp branches. Home range varies widely with habitat and climatic conditions from 1-35 sq mi (2.6-90 sq km). Non-human predators include lions, hyenas, and sometimes wild dogs.

Breeding is possible throughout the year, but most births occur during the rainy season. Males and females associate only during breeding season, at which time they are together constantly. The female reaches sexual maturity between five and eight years of age . A single young is born after a 15-18 month gestation, weighing around 88 lb (40 kg). It nurses for up to two years and remains dependent for another year.

Habitat and Current Distribution

The black rhino is found today in Africa in the southwestern desert, in south-central and eastern Africa, and north of the rain forest belt in Cameroon, Chad, and the Central African Republic. Population is estimated at 2000 individuals.

Habitat includes open, arid scrub and savanna or dense thickets and mountain forests.

History and Conservation Measures

The black rhinoceros once ranged widely throughout the savannas of Africa, only avoiding the equatorial forest belt and some of the most arid desert regions. In 1970, an estimated population of 65,000 was distributed over most of its original range. It has now been wiped out in West Africa and severely reduced throughout the rest of Africa. The direct

Black rhinoceros.

cause of this species' decline is the demand for its horn. Rhino horn has been ground and used as an aphrodisiac in India and for medicinal potions in many places in Asia. It has also been used to make handles for the traditional *jambia* daggers worn by men in Yemen. Increased income from oil wealth in the Gulf made it possible for more Yemeni men to afford the expensive daggers, increasing the demand for rhino horn.

Although legal restrictions to trade have been instituted under the CITES treaty in most countries that are major consumers of rhino products, trade has not yet been halted everywhere and poaching continues, especially in Zimbabwe. One desperate effort to alleviate the slaughter of poaching was instituted in Namibia in 1989; "Operation Bicornis" involved tranquilizing rhinos and removing their horns to make them unattractive to poachers.

In the long term, it will be necessary to make the continued existence of the rhino commercially advantageous to the local people. Non-consumptive uses of the animals, such as tourism and photographic safaris, must be developed to make the black rhino more valuable alive than dead.

Javan rhinoceros

Rhinoceros sondaicus

Phylum	Chordata
Class	Mammalia
Order	Perissodactyla
Family	Rhinocerotidae
Status	Endangered, IUCN
	Endangered, USFWS
	Appendix I, CITES
Range	Java (Indonesia); Kampuchea; Laos; Myanmar (ex?); Thailand (ex?); Vietnam

Description and Biology

The rarest large mammal in the world, the Javan rhinoceros has a single horn and tough gray skin that falls into folds at the shoulder, back, and rump. Head and body length is 10-10.5 ft (3-3.2 m), height at the shoulder is 5-5.75 ft (1.5-1.75 m), and weight averages 3,000-4,400 lb (1,360-2,000 kg). The female is larger than the male and often lacks a horn or has only a small knob. This rhino has an acute sense of smell, but very poor eyesight. A prehensile upper lip is used to grasp food, including shoots, twigs, young foliage, and fallen fruit, and bring it to the animal's mouth.

The Javan rhino likes to submerge itself in water with only its face above the surface. Mud wallowing is also a frequent activity. This species is generally solitary except during mating season or when caring for its young. Females seem to be receptive every 46-48 days, and males may compete violently for access to females. After a gestation period assumed to be about 16 months, a single calf is born. The calf is well developed at birth and nurses for one to two years. Young or sick rhinos are preyed upon by tigers.

Habitat and Current Distribution

The Javan rhino is now found primarily in the Ujung Kulon National Park, western Java, where only 50-60 animals survive. Scattered remnant populations may remain in southern Laos, Kampuchea, and southern Vietnam, but further study is necessary to assess the true status of any populations that may still exist in these areas.

This species prefers dense rain forests in low-lying areas with plentiful water and mud wallows. The wooded floodplains of large rivers are also favored sites.

History and Conservation Measures

The Javan rhinoceros was once widespread from India and China south to the islands of Java and Sumatra. As recently as 150 years ago three distinct subspecies existed—*R. s. inermis* in eastern India, Bangladesh, Assam, and Burma; *R. s. annamiticus* in Vietnam, Laos, Cambodia, and eastern Thailand; and *R. s. sondaicus* in southern Burma, Malay Peninsula, Sumatra, and western Java. Of these, the first is almost certainly extinct and the others survive only in scattered remnant populations in Indochina and west Java. The Javan rhinoceros, like other rhino species, has declined due to habitat destruction and hunting for its horn and other body parts, which are thought to have medicinal value. Despite legal protection (the Javan rhino has been protected in Indonesia since 1931), a thriving black market for rhino products continues to make poaching a threat to this species, even in reserves.

Ujung Kulon National Park was set aside specifically for the conservation of the Javan rhinoceros. However, the population is limited by the carrying capacity of the area and is so small that it is highly vulnerable to disease, poaching, and natural disasters. In 1981-1982 an unknown disease killed at least five rhinos (10 percent of the population) in the park. Conservation priorities for this species include preserving remnant wild populations; locating and/or establishing other wild populations; developing a captive propagation program to breed animals for reintroduction in the wild; and continuing efforts to eliminate the trade in rhino products. No Javan rhinos are currently in captivity. The population of the Javan rhino is now at a critically low level, and its future is uncertain despite ongoing conservation efforts.

Great Indian rhinoceros

Rhinoceros unicornis

Phylum	Chordata
Class	Mammalia
Order	Perissodactyla
Family	Rhinocerotidae
Status	Endangered, IUCN
	Endangered, USFWS
	Appendix I, CITES
Range	Bangladesh; Bhutan; India; Nepal; Pakistan

Description and Biology

This rhino, also known as the greater one-horned rhinoceros, has a single horn that can grow as long as 21 in (53 cm). It is believed that this rhino provided the impetus for the legend of the unicorn in medieval Europe.

The great Indian rhinoceros has gray-brown skin that falls in folds, resembling pieces of armor. Short, powerful legs support a body that can weigh 4,000-8,000 lb (1,800-3,600 kg). This rhino measures 5-6 ft (1.5-1.8 m) at the shoulder and averages 11-13 ft (3.4-4 m) long. Despite its formidable size, it generally tends to run away from disturbance rather than attack, although female rhinos have been known to charge and kill humans who have gotten too close to their calves.

Like other rhinos, the great Indian rhino has a highly developed sense of smell but very poor vision. Rhinos mark their territory by urinating and defecating. Both sexes defecate at a communal dung heap, and reportedly males can determine the availability of sexually receptive females by smelling the heap. The great Indian rhino is active at night, early morning, and late afternoon. Although groups are rare except for mothers and calves, these rhinos are often found together in mud wallows during the heat of the day. They eat by grabbing food with their prehensile upper lip. Diet is composed mainly of grasses and shoots, supplemented by fruit, leaves, and cultivated crops.

Home range varies with habitat from 0.75-3 sq mi (2-8 sq km), with dominant males controlling prime territory and the breeding females within it. Dominance is established and maintained with physical superiority: in a clash with challengers, the size of one's tuskes—sharp, lower tusks that are used to bite opponents—and physical size are determining factors. Courtship of females sometimes involves a chase and ends when the female is physically exhausted. After a gestation period of 15-16 months, one young is born. The infant is 3.1-4 ft (96-122 cm) long, 1.8-2.2 ft (56-67 cm) high at the shoulder, and weighs about 145 lb (66 kg). The calf is nursed for about a year and chased away from the mother when she is about to deliver her next calf, which is about three years later.

Habitat and Current Distribution

Restricted mainly to reserves in Assam, west Bengal, and Nepal, population of this rhino is estimated at 1,960. This is considered the highest number of great Indian rhinos in the past 30 years.

Great Indian rhino.

This rhino prefers a habitat of tall, swampy grassland and likes to be near water, where it wallows in mud with other rhinos.

History and Conservation Measures

The range of the one-horned rhinoceros once extended across the floodplains of South Asia's great rivers: the Ganges, Indus, and Brahmaputra. This rhino existed across the entire northern part of the Indian subcontinent from Pakistan to the Indian-Burmese border and included parts of Nepal and Bhutan. It may also have existed in Burma, southern China, and Indochina. As grasslands were converted to agriculture, prime habitat was lost and the rhino became more vulnerable to hunting. The horn and other parts of this rhino are highly valued for their supposed medical properties, and the great Indian rhinoceros has been hunted almost to the point of extinction. During the mid-1980s, a kilogram of powdered horn cost $20,000-$30,000 in east Asia.

At the beginning of the twentieth century, these rhinos numbered less than 100 individuals. In the early 1900s conservation efforts were begun to save this rhino, and the remaining habitat for the few animals who survived was turned into reserves. There has been some success and animals have been translocated to establish new populations in historic habitat.

Because loss of habitat and poaching still threaten the rhino, continued conservation efforts are essential. Conservation objectives include: the maintenance of a wild population of at least 2,000 rhinos in at least six major sanctuaries in the current range of the species; translocation of animals to create new sanctuaries and populations; continued anti-poaching efforts; maintenance of a captive population capable of long-term viability to guard against any unforeseen extinction of the wild population; and reduction in the demand for rhino products in eastern Asia by encouraging the use of substitutes.

Babirusa

Babyrousa babyrussa

Phylum	Chordata
Class	Mammalia
Order	Artiodactyla
Family	Suidae
Status	Vulnerable, IUCN
	Endangered, USFWS
	Appendix I, CITES
Range	Buru, Sula Islands, Sulawesi, Togian Islands (Indonesia)

Description and Biology

The babirusa is the object of great conservation concern in Indonesia because of its unique characteristics. Three living subspecies of babirusa are recognized: *B. b. babyrussa*, also called the "golden" or "hairy" babirusa because of its thick, body hair; *B. b. togeanensis*, the largest of the babirusa subspecies; and *B. b. celebensis*, the only subspecies kept in captivity. These animals are unique among mammals in that their canines emerge vertically through the skin of the nose and curve over the front of the face towards the forehead. The lower tusks also curve and grow toward the face. In females the canines are absent or reduced in size. The exact function of these tusks is not known. It is believed that they are used in fighting and for sexual display, but Alastair Macdonald has observed that the tusks are brittle and rarely used in fighting.

The babirusa averages 33-43 in (84-109 cm) long, measures 26-33 in (66-84 cm) high at the shoulder, and weighs 200-220 lb (90-100 kg). It has acute senses of smell and hearing. An excellent swimmer, it sometimes ventures into the sea. A social animal, the babirusa travels and feeds in troops comprised of up to eight individuals. In captivity, babirusas become sexually mature at five to ten months of age and live for up to 24 years. In the wild, sexual maturity occurs later. Females produce one or two litters a year; gestation period is 155-158 days.

There are few natural predators for this species. Pythons and the Sulawesi civet, however, prey on young babirusas. Diet for the babirusa includes leaves, root, fruit, nuts, and sometimes small mammals. In captivity, adult babirusas have been known to cannibalize the young of other babirusas.

Habitat and Current Distribution

The babirusa is found on Sulawesi, Buru, the Togian Islands, and the Sula Islands of Indonesia. *B. b. togeanensis* is found only on the Togian islands. In 1978, their population numbered between 500-1,000 individuals. *B. b. babyrussa* is found on Buru and the Sula Islands; *B. b. celebensis* is found on Sulawesi. In general it is difficult obtaining a population estimate for this species because of its timid nature and remoteness of distribution.

The preferred habitat for this species is tropical

Babirusa.

rain forest on the banks of rivers and ponds with ample water plants.

History and Conservation Measures

The babirusa has been protected by law since 1931, but hunting and habitat destruction have severely diminished its numbers. Native peoples have hunted this animal for food, and logging activities have cleared forests at an alarming rate.

Currently babirusas occur in wildlife reserves and national parks in Sulawesi but even here poaching still occurs. *B. b. celebensis* has been bred in captivity since the 1800s, but high inbreeding has weakened the gene pool.

Conservation measures for this species include field studies of the animal's ecology, behavior, and status. The establishment of additional reserves in Buru, Mangole, and Sulawesi is vital. The introduction of fresh blood-stock to captive population has also been recommended.

Pygmy hog

Sus salvanius

Phylum	Chordata
Class	Mammalia
Order	Artiodactyla
Family	Suidae
Status	Endangered, IUCN
	Endangered, USFWS
	Appendix I, CITES
Range	Bhutan (ex?); India; Nepal (ex?)

Description and Biology

True to its name, this critically endangered animal is the smallest of all pig species. Apart from its size, the pygmy hog is distinguished from other pig species by its short tail and by the presence of only three pairs of mammae on the female. On average, the pygmy hog is 25 in (65 cm) long at physical maturity, 10 in (25 cm) high at the shoulder, weighs 19 lb (8.5 kg), and has a one-inch (3-cm) long tail. Its hide is covered with coarse dark brown to black bristles. Partly due to its diminutive size and bullet-like shape, the pygmy hog is an extremely agile creature that can move rapidly through its grassland habitat.

The adult male is bigger than the female and has exposed tusks. Males are usually solitary except during the mating season, when they may join small groups of females and juveniles. Births peak at the beginning of the monsoon season, which in the species' current habitat (western Assam) falls in late April and May. The litter size is typically three or four but can range from two to six. Unlike many other pig species, pygmy hogs, both males and females, build and use their nests throughout the year.

Habitat and Current Distribution

The pygmy hog inhabits dense, tall grasslands. The species is now found only in two wildlife sanctuaries in northwestern Assam, in the Himalayan foothills of India. The main population center is the Manas Wildlife Sanctuary, which contains at best a few hundred individuals. Less than 50 are believed to occur in the Barnadi Wildlife Sanctuary. The total population size is estimated at no more than 300 and may be far less.

History and Conservation Measures

The pygmy hog is one of the most endangered mammals in the world and probably the most endangered species in the suborder Suiformes, which includes pigs, peccaries, and hippopotamuses. Owing to its precarious existence, the species and its remaining strongholds have received much attention by the international wildlife community and by the Indian government. For instance, the pygmy hog was included on the first IUCN/WWF list of the 12 most threatened animal species in 1985, and it has been given maximum legal protection by the Indian government under the Indian Wild Life Protection Act. In addition, the Manas Wildlife Sanctuary was designated as a World Heritage Site by UNESCO in 1986, and the Barnadi region was upgraded to a Wildlife Sanctuary in 1981. However, all of these measures have done little to stop the habitat degradation and destruction that has put the pygmy hog in imminent danger of extinction.

Initial population figures for this species are unavailable, but it was once found throughout the Himalayan foothills, in southwestern Nepal, West Bengal, and Bhutan. By 1950, after many years of habitat destruction for land development for the expanding human population, this hog was considered extinct. It was rediscovered in 1971 after a bush fire in the Barnadi Forest Reserve in the state of Assam, and surveys at this same time confirmed its existence in the Manas region as well. Small populations were also discovered in other areas of northwestern Assam, including Corromore, Gohper, and Khalingdaur, but these have since become extinct.

A major reason for these extinctions has been the intentional burning of the grassland forests that make up the pygmy hog's habitat. Due to consistent pressures—clearing land for agricultural use, overgrazing, etc.—that have disrupted the natural replacement of the grasslands, manual burning on an annual or semi-annual basis has become necessary to replenish the habitat. Such activity, however, endangers the pygmy hog for two reasons. First, these fires are sometimes so extensive that they kill pygmy hogs

before the animals can move into other areas. Second, in the period after burning and before the grasslands have re-emerged, the animals are forced into very small grassland areas, where unexpected fires can easily wipe them out, and sometimes into tea plantations, where they are often killed by hunters.

Such habitat degradation poses a major threat to the remaining population in the Barnadi Sanctuary but is less of a problem in the Manas Sanctuary. Unfortunately, the Manas reserve has recently become politically unstable. In 1989, armed extremists from the All Bodo Student's Union (ABSU) took control of the core area of the sanctuary, an action that has opened up the sanctuary to poachers. The extremists still control the area, which makes any government protection of it impossible. Although researchers don't believe the pygmy hog has been seriously affected as yet by this instability, the sanctuary's future is in doubt. Thus, the IUCN has put the Manas reserve on its list of the World's Threatened Protection Areas.

Several conservation measures are recommended for this species. First, the Manas Sanctuary needs to be secured and properly protected as soon as possible. Second, further status surveys and studies on the ecology and requirements of the pygmy hog need to be conducted. Third, while it has not been successful in the past, captive breeding programs should be pursued with the goal of reintroducing the animals into the wild. Fourth, and perhaps most importantly, this species' remaining habitat should be protected from further degradation.

Chacoan peccary

Catagonus wagneri

Phylum	Chordata
Class	Mammalia
Order	Artiodactyla
Family	Tayassuidae
Status	Endangered, IUCN Appendix I, CITES
Range	Argentina; Bolivia; Paraguay

Description and Biology

The Chacoan peccary or tagua resembles a pig, but it has long, thin legs and small hooves. It also has a large head and large ears, and its grayish brown fur is long and bristly. There is a whitish ruff on the jowls and legs. This animal's snout is long and pig-like, with the nostrils placed at the end of the nearly bare tip. The tagua is larger and weighs more than other peccaries. Head and body length averages 36-46 in (91-117 cm), shoulder height is 21-27 in (53-69 cm), weight is 66-97 lb (30-44 kg), and tail length is 1-4 in (2.5-10.2 cm). There is no significant sexual dimorphism.

This peccary's main diet consists of cacti, although it also consumes roots, fruit, forbs, and at times carrion. It also eats and licks mineral-rich soil. The Chacoan peccary has been observed preying upon small mammals. It seldom seems to drink water. Natural predators are jaguars and pumas; ocelots attack young peccaries.

Primarily territorial, this peccary travels in small groups of two to ten individuals. Home range has been estimated at 2,750 acres (1,100 ha). This animal is active at daytime and rests in the evening. Captive females produce young as early as two years old. Litter size is usually two or three but can range from one to four. Young are born between July and December, with births peaking in August and September.

Habitat and Current Distribution

This species is known from the semi-arid Chaco region, a lowland plain area with dense bush and scrub that stretches across parts of Argentina, Paraguay, and Bolivia in South America. It is endemic to western Paraguay, southeast Bolivia, and northern Argentina, some of the hottest and driest places in South America. It seems to prefer the thorn forest but makes excursions into palm and thorn steppe.

During the mid 1970s, the Chacoan peccary was quite abundant throughout its range but within a few years, the population declined drastically. In the late 1980s the Chacoan peccary population in Paraguay was estimated at approximately 5,000 individuals and several thousand in Argentina and Bolivia.

History and Conservation Measures

Previously known only as a Pleistocene fossil, this peccary was presumed extinct until it was found in the wild in 1975, making it one of the most recent mammal discoveries. Field surveys in 1979 and 1980

Chacoan peccary.

in Bolivia and Argentina found the tagua to be rare in both countries, and it is also thought to be declining in Paraguay. Primary threats to survival of the species are habitat destruction and hunting for food. Much of the native vegetation is being replaced by grass to provide pasture for cattle. The peccary is the chief source of meat for hunters, trappers, army personnel in the numerous outposts, and ranchers during the initial stage of land clearance. Hunting for its hide is not a serious problem because it is not highly valued. Livestock diseases such as foot-and-mouth disease and bovine rabies have contributed to the declining number of peccaries.

In Paraguay, the species occurs in the Defensores del Chaco and in Taniento Enciso national parks, but illegal hunting occurs even there. No reserves currently exist in Bolivia. In Argentina, a small population of Chacoan peccaries is protected at the El Copo Provincial Reserve. A captive breeding project has been instituted to guard against possible extinction in the wild and to provide animals for eventual reintroduction into the wild.

Pygmy hippopotamus

Hexaprotodon liberiensis

Phylum . . . . Chordata
Class . . . . Mammalia
Order . . . . Artiodactyla
Family . . . . Hippopotamidae
Status . . . . Vulnerable, IUCN
Appendix II, CITES
Range . . . . Côte d'Ivoire; Guinea; Guinea-Bissau (?); Liberia; Sierra Leone

Description and Biology

The pygmy hippopotamus looks very much like its larger relative, the common hippopotamus, with the exception of its much smaller size. In addition, its head is smaller and rounder than the common hippo and its eyes are on the side of the head instead of on the top. Its coloration is generally black with a greenish tinge on the back, turning to gray on the sides and cream or yellow-gray on its stomach. At physical maturity, the pygmy hippo has an average head and body length of 5-5.7 ft (1.5-1.7 m), a shoulder height of 30-39 in (76-99 cm), a tail length of about 6 in (15 cm), and a weight of 355-600 lb (161-272 kg). (By contrast, the average adult common hippo weighs between 2,425-5,720 lb [1,100-2,600 kg].)

Apart from its size, the pygmy hippo differs from the common hippo in several other important ways. Although it does enter the water at times and spends its days around swamps and rivers, it is less aquatic than the common hippo and its toes are not as webbed. Pygmy hippos are also much more solitary than their larger counterparts, generally being found alone or in pairs. Finally, the pygmy hippo requires heavily forested areas as its habitat, whereas the common hippo needs grassland areas for grazing.

Like the common hippo, the pygmy hippo has glands beneath the skin that secrete a pink, sweat-like substance, inspiring the myth that it "sweats blood." This species avoids the sun, which would damage its skin, by seeking shelter in forested areas near swamps or rivers during the day and feeding only at night. Its diet is strictly vegetarian and consists of leaves, shoots, grasses, roots, and fruits.

Mating usually takes place in the water. Females may give birth throughout the year. With rare exceptions, only one young is born; the gestation period lasts an average of 188 days. Calves are nursed for around eight months.

Habitat and Current Distribution

The pygmy hippo inhabits lowland forests. The stronghold of this species is Liberia, although there are a few animals in Sierra Leone, Guinea, and Côte d'Ivoire. In 1958, a hunter claimed to have shot one in Guinea Bissau, but current researchers believe that the animal was probably a young common hippo. The pygmy hippo also used to occur in Nigeria as a separate subspecies, *Hexaprotodon liberiensis heslopi*, but this subspecies is now considered extinct.

Numbers in Liberia were estimated in 1983 to be several thousand but are now probably decreasing. An estimate in 1979-1980 put the total population in Sierra Leone at less than 100. There are no more

Pygmy hippopotamus.

recent estimates from there or the other countries in the species' range.

History and Conservation Measures

The major threats to this species are deforestation and hunting. Because the pygmy hippo occurs in such low densities throughout its range, hunting is likely to put the species at risk. There is little information available about current or planned conservation efforts, but any such efforts should focus on Liberia, including such protected areas as Sapo National Park. In addition to the wild populations, there is a large captive population of pygmy hippos, numbering about 350 in more than 100 collections throughout the world.

Bactrian camel

Camelus bactrianus (ferus)

Phylum	Chordata
Class	Mammalia
Order	Artiodactyla
Family	Camelidae
Status	Endangered, USFWS
	Vulnerable, IUCN
Range	Mongolia; China

Description and Biology

One of only two living camel species, the bactrian camel is also called the two-humped camel, distinguishing it from its better-known Arabian relative, *C. dromedarius*, which has only one hump. The bactrian camel stands 6-7.5 ft (1.8-2.3 m) tall and weighs 1,000-1,575 lb (454-714 kg). The species' skin has practically no sweat glands; the wild bactrian camel has a short, gray-brown coat, unlike its domestic counterpart, which has a long, woolly coat of dark brown hair. Well adapted to the desert, the bactrian camel has specialized eyelids which wipe sand from the eye's surface, nostrils that close to slits to keep out blowing sand, and feet with specialized broad sole-pads for walking in the sand. The species' eyesight and sense of smell are keen. The bactrian camel is also fast, achieving speeds up to 40 mph (65 kph).

The small, conical humps of the wild bactrian camel store fat. They are erect and plump during plentiful seasons, while they shrink and sag to one side when food is scarce. Despite popular belief, however, the camel's stomach lining does not store water, and the species can go for extraordinary periods without drinking only if it receives sufficient moisture from the plants it eats. Its herbivorous diet primarily consists of low-lying shrubs found in the desert, but may be supplemented by grasses and the branches and leaves of trees occurring near water sources.

A family group is made up of an adult male, a number of females, and various young. The rut generally begins in November and peaks during late January to late February. Competition for females is fierce due to the low ratio between the sexes, and confrontations between males have been known to end in death. During this period a single, dominant male gathers a harem of 10 to 20 females. The gestation period of a single offspring is approximately 13 months, and births occur usually in March and April. Pregnant females often leave the herd just prior to giving birth, and remain alone with their offspring for about two weeks. Young weigh approximately 80 lb (36 kg) at birth and nurse for 1-1.5 years.

Habitat and Current Distribution

In Mongolia, wild bactrian camels are now found only in and around the Great Gobi National Park, a protected area of the Gobi Desert located in the southwestern part of the country. In China, the species' range is restricted to the western provinces of Xinjiang and Gansu, principally the eastern part of the Taklimakan Desert south of the Tian Shan mountains around Lop Nur, a lake and marshland drained for irrigation in the 1960s. Scientists estimate that 500 to 600 camels reside in the Great Gobi National Park. The population in China is believed to be around 500 individuals; however, information on their status is far from complete.

Domestic bactrian camel.

Habitat includes desert and steppe in lowland and mountain areas.

History and Conservation Measures

The bactrian camel was probably domesticated before 2500 B.C. for use as a pack animal in China and Mongolia. Because of its extensive exploitation, the range of the domesticated version of this species extended at one time from Asia Minor to northern China, and wild populations were common through the early 1900s. However, as human populations began to encroach upon their habitat, wild populations were eventually confined to the relatively small areas of their current range.

Habitat loss continues to threaten the bactrian camel; blocking access to only one watering hole in the species' range would adversely effect populations over a wide area. The governments of Mongolia and China have declared the camel a protected species, and three reserves have been established within the species' range: the Great Gobi National Park in Mongolia, the Annanba Nature Reserve in Gansu, and the Altun Mountain Nature Reserve in Xinjiang. However, both countries face challenges in conserving the species. The recently created Chinese reserves lack

field staff and well-developed conservation plans. Also, in-depth studies of bactrian camel populations have yet to be conducted in China. This lack of comprehensive conservation measures, coupled with the pressures associated with increased mineral and oil exploration, have made the survival of the bactrian camel in China questionable.

In Mongolia the species is generally well protected and has been the subject of numerous studies. However, the park's small staff has difficulty patrolling the vast area under its jurisdiction; camels from Gobi Park occasionally stray into Xinjiang where they are killed by humans for food. Park officials have identified wolves as a major predator of bactrian camels—particularly of newborn calves and young—and have initiated a program to control their population. A captive breeding program for bactrian camels has also been established at the Gobi Park.

Conservationists are concerned that the wild bactrian camel population may be diluted by interbreeding with domesticated camels. Domestic animals should be removed from the Chinese reserves and the northern part of the Gobi Park where limited use by pastoralists has been allowed. Hybrid offspring should also be culled from wild populations.

Vicuña

Vicugna vicugna

Phylum	Chordata
Class	Mammalia
Order	Artiodactyla
Family	Camelidae
Status	Vulnerable, IUCN
	Endangered, USFWS
	Appendix I, CITES
Range	Argentina; Bolivia; Chile; Peru

Description and Biology

A member of the camel family, the vicuña is closely related to the llama and alpaca. The coat of the vicuña is light brown above and off-white below, with a patch of longer hair on the throat and chest, the latter serving to keep the animal warm when resting on the ground. The head is relatively small in comparison with body size, and the vicuña has small, prominent ears and eyes. The neck is long. An adult vicuña is 4-6 ft (1.2-1.8 m) long, stands 30-40 in (75-100 cm) at the shoulder, and weighs 88-110 lb (40-50 kg). It feeds on perennial bunch grasses, tubers, and mosses. Predators include the puma and the Andean fox.

The vicuña is a social animal. Territorial males maintain family groups consisting of a number of adult females and their young; non-breeding males live a solitary life or some may join other males and form bachelor groups. The dominant male defends a feeding and sleeping territory averaging 17-74 acres (7-30 ha), which is maintained throughout the year. Males rarely reach sexual maturity before they are four years of age. Sexual maturity in the female is reached in two to three years; mating in March or April, she produces one young after a gestation period of 330-350 days. The young nurses for up to ten months and becomes independent between one and two years of age.

Habitat and Current Distribution

The vicuña is found in the Central Andes of South America, in Argentina, Bolivia, Chile, and Peru. The majority of vicuña are now on protected reserves. In 1981 the population was estimated at almost 150,000 animals, of which some 98,000 occur in Peru.

The preferred habitat of this species is semi-arid grasslands and plains at altitudes of 9,850-15,100 ft (3,000-4,600 m). Groups spend the day in one feeding territory, then move to higher elevations at night to sleep.

History and Conservation Measures

The vicuña is a sought-after species on account of its lustrous wool—often said to be of the finest

Vicuña.

domesticated and historically was not heavily used. The Incas reserved the right to capture and shear wild vicuña for special rituals, and its wool was only used for certain types of clothing. During this period, the Incas were judicious in their use of vicuñas, but when the Spanish overcame the Inca people, all conservation measures were abandoned.

The vicuña population is thought to have been several million individuals before it became the target of hunters. By the 1500s, numbers had been reduced to less than 500,000; by 1965, only 6,500 survived. At that point, conservation efforts were initiated and protected reserves were established for this species. Additional protection was provided by the Convention on International Trade in Endangered Species of Wild Fauna and Flora (CITES). These efforts were successful and resulted in a population of 80,000-85,000 by the early 1980s.

Illegal hunting is still a problem in parts of the animal's range, particularly in Peru and Bolivia. Experiments have begun in Chile and Peru, where viable populations now exist once again, to capture, shear, and release wild animals. Turning a vicuña's coat into commercially valuable cloth on a sustainable basis would not only help the local people, it might also help secure the future of this species in the wild.

quality in the world. Unlike the other South American camelids, the llama and alpaca, the vicuña was never

Musk deer

Moschus spp. (all species)

Phylum . . . . Chordata
Class . . . . Mammalia
Order. . . . . Artiodactyla
Family . . . . Moschidae
Status . . . . Endangered, IUCN (selected species)
Endangered, USFWS
Appendix II, CITES (Appendix I, selected populations)
Range . . . . central and east Asia

Description and Biology

Certain species of musk deer have several very unique features. Their name is derived from the musk gland, a pouch of skin that develops in front of the genitals at sexual maturity and produces a waxy substance. This deer has no antlers, but the male's upper canines develop into narrow, pointed tusks that can be as long as 2.5-3 in (6-8 cm). Coloration varies according to species and subspecies from dark brown to golden brown or grayish; hair is long and coarse. Length of head and body ranges from 28-39 in (71-100 cm), height is 20-31 in (50-80 cm), and weight is 15.5-40 lb (7-18 kg). The hind legs are almost a third longer than the front legs, making the musk deer an agile jumper and allowing it to leap and change directions quickly. Active in the mornings and evenings, it feeds on leaves, flowers, twigs, mosses, grasses, and lichen. In harsher habitat, tree lichens alone make up the bulk of the diet. Predators include the lynx, wolf, fox, and yellow-throated marten; young deer are vulnerable to birds of prey and even crows.

Little is known of the biology and social habits of this deer; it seems to be a solitary animal for most of the year and is strongly territorial. During mating season, which is November and December in the northern parts of its range, the male pursues the female until she becomes exhausted. He may fight with other males for mating privileges, using his tusks to inflict serious injury on opponents. One or two young are born in June or July after a gestation period of 150-198 days. The young are born with spotted coats and attain full growth in around six months.

Habitat and Current Distribution

The musk deer are found in the Himalayas, eastern Asia, and Siberia. They have recently been reclassified into a number of species instead of numerous subspecies, but there is some confusion about the total number of species involved. Estimates of present population vary widely from about 30,000 to 100,000 individuals, but some—like the Lao Bang musk deer *Moschus berezovskii caobangensis*—are very close to extinction.

Musk deer are found in forests at all elevations. Some species are found only in montane forests at elevations of 8,500-11,800 ft (2,600-3,600 m). They

Moschus moschiferus.

prefer dense vegetation and brushland where it can find shelter during daylight hours.

History and Conservation Measures

The musk gland that makes these deer unique has also made them the target of hunters and thus led to a decline in the population. This deer has never been valued for its coat or its meat but has been hunted only for its musk, which is valued as a base for perfume and as an ingredient in medicinal preparations. Destruction of forest habitat has also contributed to a decline in numbers.

Because musk deer do not have to be killed in order for musk to be extracted, a breeding program was begun in China in 1958 which attempted to raise deer and extract their musk. After some initial failures, the Chinese program was successful and other programs were begun in Russia, India, and Nepal. Other programs have attempted to briefly capture wild males to extract the musk.

Calamian hog deer

Axis calamianensis
(A. porcinus calamianensis)

Phylum	Chordata
Class	Mammalia
Order	Artiodactyla
Family	Cervidae
Status	Endangered, IUCN
Range	Calamian Islands (Philippines)

Description and Biology

The Calamian hog deer is called such because, unlike other deer that hurdle obstacles, this deer runs through underbrush with its head held low as is the manner of hogs. It has brownish coloration that can vary in shade depending upon the time of year; it has a white patch on the throat and a white marking on the face that resembles a moustache. Head and body length averages 3.3-6 ft (1-1.8 m), shoulder height is 26-37 in (66-94 cm), and weight is 65-110 lb (30-50 kg). It is presumed to be active in the morning and late afternoon, as are related species, and to feed on a variety of vegetation.

Habitat and Current Distribution

This species is known only from the Calamian Islands in the Philippines, where it inhabits grasslands, plains, or open forest and is seldom found in jungle or dense forest. Population size is known to be fewer than 800 individuals, with the largest subpopulation of 550 animals on Calanit Island.

History and Conservation Measures

The very limited distribution of the Calamian hog deer makes it vulnerable to any further loss of habitat. It is also known to be threatened by poaching and by a movement of local people to settle the Calanit Island Game Preserve and Wildlife Sanctuary. The species is further threatened by competition from almost 600 introduced African antelopes, giraffes, and zebras brought to Calanit in 1976. Attempts to remove some or all of these African ungulates are now being made, and other conservation activities are being carried out under the auspices of a project funded by the Zoological Society of San Diego.

Bawean deer

Axis kuhli (A. porcinus kuhli)

Phylum	Chordata
Class	Mammalia
Order	Artiodactyla
Family	Cervidae
Status	Endangered, IUCN
	Endangered, USFWS
	Appendix I, CITES
Range	Bawean Island (Indonesia)

Description and Biology

The Bawean deer, also called Kuhl's hog deer, has a coarse, dark brown coat with light underparts and a bushy tail. Average head and body length is 40-70 in (100-175 cm), height is 24-40 in (60-100 cm), and weight is 60-240 lb (27-110 kg). It rests in the afternoon and is active in the morning and late afternoon, feeding on grass, leaves, and forbs. The python is a known predator.

This deer is a solitary animal except during mating season, when males compete for available females. Mating can take place at any time during the year but usually occurs between July and November. One young is born between February and June, after a gestation period of 180-210 days.

Habitat and Current Distribution

Approximately 200-500 individuals are thought to remain on Bawean Island in the Javan Sea, but no status survey has been conducted in the past ten years. Preferred habitat is forest and grassland with

Bawean deer.

open areas for grazing and dense vegetation for cover.

History and Conservation Measures

There is some speculation that this species is actually a descendent of the hog deer (*Axis porcinus*), which may have been introduced at some point to its island habitat by humans. The population of the Bawean deer has been greatly reduced by habitat destruction and excessive hunting. Increasing human population on the island is also threatening the continued existence of the Bawean deer.

Marsh deer

Blastocerus dichotomus

Phylum	Chordata
Class	Mammalia
Order	Artiodactyla
Family	Cervidae
Status	Vulnerable, IUCN
	Endangered, USFWS
	Appendix I, CITES
Range	Argentina; Bolivia; Brazil; Paraguay; Peru

Description and Biology

The largest deer in South America, the marsh deer averages 3.5-4 ft (1.1-1.2 m) at the shoulder and weighs 180-330 lb (80-150 kg). The males have double-forked antlers with each branch bearing two sharp points. Their coat is long and coarse and coloration varies with season: in summer it is a bright red-brown that fades to a darker shade in winter. The band on the muzzle and the lower leg is black. This species has broad ears and a bushy tail that is yellow-brown above and black below. Hidden among trees during the day, it emerges in the evening to forage for grass and reeds and may also wade into water in search of aquatic plants. Jaguars and domestic dogs prey on adult deer; wild dogs, cats, and boas sometimes prey on fawns.

The marsh deer may live alone or in a small group led by a mature male and containing two females with young. Males are not known to fight one another for access to females. Little reproductive information is available, but mating seems to peak in October and November, with most young born between May and September. Gestation period appears to be about nine months.

Habitat and Current Distribution

This species occurs in central South America, with the largest population in Pantanal, Brazil; smaller populations are known to exist in Argentina, Bolivia, Peru, and Paraguay. The total population of the marsh deer is estimated at slightly over 20,000 individuals. Another survey conducted by researchers of the Centro de Pesquisa Agropecuária do Pantanal estimated a population between 31,000-41,000 animals in Pantanal alone.

Marsh deer prefer wet savannas with high grass, marshes, damp forest edges, and seasonally flooded areas along rivers.

History and Conservation Measures

This species once ranged south of the Amazon River into northern Argentina but now survives only in scattered populations throughout its former range as a result of hunting, habitat loss, and disease. In some places, poaching for meat, trophies, and sport still continues, despite legal protection. It is the principal source of meat for laborers on many cattle ranches in Bolivia and is hunted extensively in

Argentina. Because its limited habitat preference severely restricts its distribution, the marsh deer is seriously affected by the drainage of marshlands for agriculture. During the rainy season, floods force the deer to higher grounds, where it competes with domestic cattle for food and is exposed to diseases carried by the domestic stock.

Conservation measures for the marsh deer include enforcement of protective laws and the establishment of well-guarded reserves. The creation of reserves is difficult due to the deer's habitat requirements, which often conflict with ranchers' and farmers' plans for the land. Continued monitoring and ecological study of the deer are needed throughout its range, especially in its Pantanal stronghold.

Visayan spotted deer

Cervus alfredi (C. unicolor alfredi)

Phylum	Chordata
Class	Mammalia
Order	Artiodactyla
Family	Cervidae
Status	Endangered, IUCN
	Endangered, USFWS
Range	Visayan Islands (Philippines)

Description and Biology

The Visayan spotted deer has a fine but very dense and soft dark brown coat on its upper body that is accented by lighter spots on the back and flank; underparts are pale to white. Shoulder height averages around 25 in (64 cm) and weight is 80-130 lb (36-59 kg). Ears and tail are relatively short, as are the male's antlers. Diet includes a wide variety of vegetation.

Habitat and Current Distribution

This species is known only from the Visayan Islands in the Philippines, where it utilizes both dense and open forest. The largest surviving population is on Panay; there is also a population on Negros. Population in the wild is estimated at fewer than 300 individuals.

History and Conservation Measures

The Visayan spotted deer once inhabited six islands in the central Philippine archipelago, but it is now extinct on four of the islands and known with certainty from only two islands. Its population was drastically reduced as suitable habitat was cleared for logging and for agricultural development; the clearing of land also allowed freer access for settlers and hunters, who hunt the deer for food.

Less than five percent of the original forest cover remains on the Visayan Islands. The few remaining forest patches are controlled by a guerilla force. Due to these problems, effective conservation of the species in the wild is difficult at present, but education programs and forest protection schemes are nevertheless being carried out. A captive breeding program was also initiated in 1990 as a safeguard against extinction.

Swamp deer

Cervus duvauceli

Phylum	Chordata
Class	Mammalia
Order	Artiodactyla
Family	Cervidae
Status	Endangered, IUCN
	Endangered, USFWS
	Appendix I, CITES
Range	India; Nepal

Description and Biology

The swamp deer is also called the barasingha, a word that means "six-pointer" in central India, but the 36-40 in (90-100 cm) antlers can have ten or more points. Body color is brown above and paler below in winter and lighter overall in summer, when light spotting can sometimes be seen. The male is darker than the female. Average length of head and body is 4-6 ft (1.2-1.8 m), height at the shoulder is approximately 4 ft (1.2 m), and weight varies from 375-620 lb (170-281 kg). The swamp deer grazes on grasses and aquatic plants during the day or at night and has an average range of 8 sq mi (20 sq km). Tigers and leopards are predators.

Small, sex-segregated groups of 12-20 animals may sometimes gather into larger herds. During the mating season (September to April), new, non-permanent groups of males and females form and males compete for mating rights. Dominant males have priority access to harems of up to 30 females. One young is usually born after a gestation period of 225-250 days.

Habitat and Current Distribution

The barasingha occurs today in scattered populations in Nepal, north India, Assam, and central India. Population figures are 4,500-5,000 for the North Indian barasinghas (*C. d. duvauceli* and *C. d. ranjithsini*) and over 600 for the South Indian barasingha (*C. d. branderi*).

The northern Indian populations prefer marshy grassland and floodplains, while the southern population prefers drier woodlands and fields.

History and Conservation Measures

In the nineteenth century, there were probably thousands of marsh deer living along the major rivers in India. Although peak populations figures are unknown, the population of *C. d. branderi* was documented at 3,000 in 1938. Today, most marsh deer live in protected reserves: the Sukla Phanta Preserve in Nepal, the Dudhwa National Park in north India, the Kaziranga Preserve in Assam, and the Kanha National Park in central India.

Barasingha.

Although habitat destruction is the primary cause of the decline, other factors have also come into play. Illegal hunting remains a threat as does competition from other deer species, especially axis deer (*Axis axis*), for food and habitat. Moist grassland is now at a premium and conservation efforts have been directed to protecting grasslands from fire and using dams on small rivers to keep the water level from dropping. These measures have had a positive effect on the population of marsh deer.

Eld's deer

Cervus eldi

Phylum	Chordata
Class	Mammalia
Order	Artiodactyla
Family	Cervidae
Status	Vulnerable, IUCN
	Endangered, USFWS
	Appendix I, CITES
Range	China (ex?); India; Kampuchea; Laos; Myanmar; Thailand; Vietnam

Description and Biology

Eld's deer is also called the thamin or the brow-antlered deer; the brow tine of the antlers and the beam form a curve that is bow-shaped. Depending on the subspecies, this deer's coat is brown, yellowish, or reddish brown. The coat of the female is lighter in color than that of the male. Average length of head and body is 5-6 ft (1.5-1.8 m), height at the shoulder is 3.5-4.25 ft (1-1.3 m), and weight is 180-330 lb (81-150 kg). The mature male has a neck mane. Its diet is primarily grasses supplemented by leaves and fruit. Tigers and crocodiles are predators.

Solitary males join the herd during mating season between February and May and compete for females. In most cases, a single calf is born after a gestation period of approximately 242 days and is nursed for about seven months.

Habitat and Current Distribution

One subspecies of Eld's deer, *C. e. thamin*, still has a fairly large population (over 2,000 individuals) in Myanmar (Burma). Two other subspecies are considered particularly endangered: *C. e. eldi* and *C. e. siamensis*. Some 80 *C. e. eldi* survive in Manipur. Over 200 Eld's deer survive on Hainan (an island in the South China Sea belonging to China); some believe that these animals may represent a subspecies on their own, *C. e. hainanusi*. Numbers of *C. e. siamensis* in Kampuchea (Cambodia), Laos, and Vietnam are not known, and it is probably extinct in Thailand.

The preferred habitat of Eld's deer includes low-lying swampland, grasslands near water, and savanna. It may be found at the forest edge, but it usually avoids dense vegetation.

History and Conservation Measures

The decline of Eld's deer can be attributed to hunting and to habitat loss. Despite legal protection, illegal hunting continues. Suitable habitat has diminished because of logging operations and clearing of land for agricultural development and to improve grazing for livestock. As the deer's habitat shrank, it invaded cultivated fields where it became an easy target for hunters.

Little information is available about initial population size. Most of the Eld's deer surviving in the wild live in national parks or sanctuaries. This deer breeds well in captivity, and breeding groups of three of the subspecies are found in several zoos around the world, though only *C. e. thamin* has a genetically viable population in captivity.

Père David's deer

Elaphurus davidianus

Phylum	Chordata
Class	Mammalia
Order	Artiodactyla
Family	Cervidae
Status	Endangered, IUCN
	Endangered, USFWS
Range	China

Description and Biology

Père David's deer is easily distinguished by its characteristic antlers; the rear tines of the branched antlers face backward instead of forward, sometimes growing almost parallel to the deer's back. Its hooves also make a unique clicking or cracking sound when the animal walks. This deer averages 6-7 ft (1.8-2.1 m) long, stands 4-4.5 ft (1.2-1.4 ft) at the shoulder, weighs 300-500 lb (136-277 kg), and has a longer tail than any other deer (up to 20 in or 51 cm) with a dark tassel on the end. The winter coat is light gray to brown, with throat and lower legs darker; the summer coat is rich red-brown with a darker stripe along the spine. Its diet is mainly grasses, supplemented by herbs and aquatic plants in the summer. In the wild, the leopard is a predator.

During mating season, which begins in June, the male fasts and fights rival males for available females. One or two young are born after a gestation period of 270-300 days.

Habitat and Current Distribution

Extinct in the wild for centuries, Père David's deer survives in zoos and nature parks around the world with the largest population (approximately 1,500) found at Woburn Abbey in England. From captive stock, the species has been reintroduced into its historic habitat in China.

In the wild, this deer prefers swampy plains and marshlands.

History and Conservation Measures

This deer once ranged throughout northeastern and east-central China, roaming the lowlands by the thousands. There is evidence that it probably still survived in substantial numbers into the third century and at least in remnant populations until the seventeenth century. In the eighteenth century, it was discovered that a herd survived in China's Imperial Hunting Park, where it was maintained until a flood in 1894 killed many animals and allowed the rest to escape into the wild, where they were hunted during a famine and killed during the Boxer Rebellion.

The deer is named for Père Armand David, a French Lazarist missionary who, in 1865, acquired the remains of two deer from guards at the Imperial Hunting Park and sent them to Europe to be identified. Chinese authorities then allowed a number of wild specimens to be sent to several zoos in Europe. Around the time the herd in the Imperial Hunting Park died out, the Duke of Bedford gathered captives from several zoos and established a herd at Woburn Abbey. In 1985, 22 descendants of this herd were

Père David's deer.

reintroduced into a 250 acre (100 ha) area that was originally part of the Imperial Hunting Park. One of the aims of this reintroduction effort is to increase the herd's size to provide animals for release in other parts of China.

North Andean huemul

Hippocamelus antisensis

South Andean huemul

Hippocamelus bisulcus

Phylum	Chordata
Class	Mammalia
Order	Artiodactyla
Family	Cervidae
Status	Vulnerable, IUCN (*H. antisensis*)
	Endangered, IUCN (*H. bisulcus*)
	Endangered, USFWS
	Appendix I, CITES
Range	Argentina; Bolivia; Chile; Peru (*H. antisensis*)
	Argentina; Chile (*H. bisulcus*)

Description and Biology

For both species, the average length of the head and body is 4.5-5.5 ft (1.4-1.7 m), tail length is 4.5-5 in (115-130 mm), shoulder height is 2.5-3 ft (78-91 cm), and weight is 100-143 lb (45-65 kg). The north Andean huemul has a coarse coat that is speckled yellowish gray-brown above and white below year-round and its brown tail features a white underside. *H. antisensis* also has a black Y-shaped marking on the face. The south Andean huemul's coarse coat is light colored in the winter and darker brown with light underparts in the summer. It has a brown spot on the rump and its tail has a brown underside. The males of both species have simple antlers that usually branch only once. Both species have canine teeth developed into tusks, but unlike those of musk deer, the tusks of huemuls do not project below the lips. The north Andean species feeds on lichens, mosses, herbs and grasses, while the south Andean species eats primarily leaves and grasses. Predators of *H. antisensis* include the puma and the Magellan fox, and pumas have also been known to prey upon *H. bisulcus*.

The social organization of the two species differs. *H. antisensis* is rarely solitary and is usually found in groups composed of several adult males, adult females and associated offspring. The maximum size of these groups appears to be about 30 individuals. Females about to give birth move away from males, and smaller, all-male groups have also been observed. Mated pairs of *H. bisulcus* stay together for most of the year, inhabiting a range of 90-200 acres (36-81 ha). Solitary individuals are common, but there are no all-female groups and all-male groups are rare. Courting behavior of *H. bisulcus* males includes thrashing of vegetation with the antlers and scent-marking; threatening and sparring with other males; and emitting a rapid, laughing call.

South Andean huemul.

fringes and alpine grasslands. *H. bisulcus* is found at lower elevations between 4,300-5,600 ft (1,400-1,700 m). In summer, this species moves to temperate forest and dense shrubland in the higher areas of its range, while in the winter it moves down into open valley areas above and below the treeline.

History and Conservation Measures

There are no initial population estimates for either species, but both have declined throughout their ranges. Huemuls are still hunted for their meat, despite legal protection. Dogs are sometimes used for hunting, and they often prey upon and harass huemuls. Habitat destruction is a serious threat, particularly at lower elevations as land is cleared for logging, mining, agricultural or recreational activities. Huemuls also face increased competition from domestic sheep, cattle and llamas for grazing land and are susceptible to diseases transmitted by domestic stock.

Both of these species enjoy legal protection throughout their ranges, but levels of enforcement vary widely. The northern Andean species is found in several national parks and reserves in Argentina, Bolivia, Chile, and Peru. The principal conservation priority for *H. antisensis* is effective enforcement of existing laws. The southern Andean species is also found in national parks and informal reserve areas in Argentina and Chile, but protection of the species outside these areas (and sometimes within them) is ineffective. Long term conservation goals for *H. bisulcus* include establishment of areas where these huemuls are free from poaching, uncontrolled use of fire, over-exploitation of vegetation and range, and hazards posed by domestic animals. These areas must be large and varied enough to support a huemul population that is resistant to destruction by local catastrophes or by chance and must be contiguous so that huemuls can disperse, breed with other groups, and recolonize vacant habitat.

In both species, a single fawn is born after a gestation period of seven months.

Habitat and Current Distribution

The north Andean huemul is widely, but sparsely, distributed at high altitudes in the northern Andes of Argentina, Bolivia, Chile and Peru. The south Andean huemul is found in scattered localities in the southern part of the Andes Mountains in Chile and Argentina. The total population of the northern species is unknown, while the population of the southern species is estimated at 1,300 individuals. *H. antisensis* is definitely a high altitude species, found principally at elevations of 8,200-16,400 ft (2,500-5,000 m). It has been observed in a wide variety of habitats from semi-arid steep-sided mountains separated by broad, marshy valley bottoms to montane forest

Black muntjac

Muntiacus crinifrons

Fea's muntjac

Muntiacus feai

Gongshan muntjac

Muntiacus gongshanensis

Phylum	Chordata
Class	Mammalia
Order	Artiodactyla
Family	Cervidae
Status	Vulnerable, IUCN (*M. crinifrons*)
	Endangered, IUCN (*M. feai*)
	Endangered, USFWS (*M. feai*)
	Appendix I, CITES (*M. crinifrons*)
Range	China (*M. crinifrons*)
	Myanmar; Thailand (*M. feai*)
	Tibet; China; Myanmar (*M. gongshanensis*)

Description and Biology

Muntjacs are also known as barking deer for a warning sound they make when sensing a predator in the area. All three muntjacs—Gongshan, Fea's, and black—are relatively small deer. Fea's muntjac averages 2.9-4.5 ft (89-135 cm) long, 1.3-2.1 ft (40-65 cm) high at the shoulder, and weighs 33-77 lb (15-35 kg). Precise length and weight ranges are not available for the black and Gongshan muntjacs. These deer are covered with short, soft hair ranging in color from deep brown to yellowish or grayish brown. In *M. crinifrons* the head is lighter colored than the rest of the body. Males have short antlers (rarely more than 6 in [15 cm] long) and upper canines that grow into sharp tusks used for fighting. *M. feai* has a tuft of yellow hair at the base of each antler. Muntjacs are omnivorous and their diet may include grasses, leaves, herbs, fruits, bird eggs, small animals, birds, and carrion. Tigers, leopards, dholes, jackals, crocodiles, and pythons are thought to prey on muntjacs.

Muntjacs are solitary or found in small groups, and they are territorial except during mating season. Knowledge of reproductive biology is scanty, but mating season seems to occur sometime between December and March for *M. feai*. After a gestation period of 180 days, one or two young are born. *M. crinifrons* also has a gestation period of about 180 days. Newborns of this species have been seen in April, implying a somewhat earlier mating season than that of Fea's muntjac. Young muntjacs are hidden in dense vegetation until they are able to follow their mothers.

Fea's muntjac.

Habitat and Current Distribution

The black muntjac is found in four provinces of east-central China. The Gongshan muntjac occurs in a triangle covering southern Tibet, China, and adjacent Myanmar (Burma). Fea's muntjac occurs in peninsular Myanmar and adjacent parts of Thailand. There is no estimate of the present population of Fea's or Gongshan muntjacs; a maximum of 5,000 black muntjacs are believed to exist.

Muntjacs prefer woodlands, rain forests, or monsoon forests with dense vegetation and ready access to water.

History and Conservation Measures

Earlier population estimates are not available for these species. For many years the black muntjac was only known from three specimens, but in the 1970s it was discovered in four Chinese provinces. Fea's and Gongshan muntjacs are now found only in small numbers in restricted habitats. All species are hunted for their meat and hides. Muntjacs are also vulnerable to habitat disruption due to their solitary habits and low population density.

Muntjacs thrive in captivity and can easily be raised in zoos, but only a few black muntjacs exist in Chinese zoos and breeding groups of Fea's muntjac exist in three Thai zoos.

Pampas deer

Ozotoceros bezoarticus

Phylum	Chordata
Class	Mammalia
Order	Artiodactyla
Family	Cervidae
Status	Insufficiently Known, IUCN
	Endangered, USFWS
	Appendix I, CITES
Range	Argentina; Bolovia; Brazil; Paraguay; Uruguay

Description and Biology

The pampas deer is a medium-sized, delicately built deer with a characteristic scent that is not so delicate. Interdigital glands on its rear hooves exude a substance that smells like onions. The color of short, smooth coat varies geographically from pale red-brown to tawny brown to deep reddish brown. The face is somewhat darker than the rest of the body, the underparts are white, and the tail is dark above and white below. The hair forms two distinctive whorls—one at the base of the neck and one between the shoulders and the middle of the back. The head and body length of the pampas deer is 3.6-4.6 ft (1.1-1.4 m), its tail length is 4-6 in (10-15 cm), its height at the shoulder is 2.3-2.5 ft (70-75 cm), and its weight is 55-88 lb (25-40 kg). Only males have antlers, typically with three tines. The exact diet of the pampas deer is unknown, but it has been observed eating new green growth, seed-heads of grasses, shrubs, and herbs. Puma and jaguar prey upon pampas deer, while foxes, smaller cats and wild pigs are reported to have killed newborn, weak or unattended fawns.

Pampas deer live in small groups rarely exceeding 5-6 individuals that are fluid in size and composition. Males mix with females throughout the year and during mating season adult males compete for receptive females. Courtship behavior includes thrashing vegetation, scent marking, and fighting with antlers or forefeet. There is no evidence that pampas deer form lasting pairs or harems. Births have been recorded throughout the year but seem to peak from

Pampas deer.

September to November. The female leaves the group to give birth to a single spotted fawn after a gestation period of seven months; she defends the fawn and keeps it with her for at least a year.

Habitat and Current Distribution

The pampas deer is now found in Brazil to the south of the Amazon River, eastern Bolivia, Paraguay, Uruguay, and northern and central Argentina. Three subspecies are usually recognized. *O. b. bezoarticus* occurs in eastern and central Brazil south of the Amazon and in Uruguay. Although its numbers are known to have declined, its overall distribution in the northern parts of its range is largely unchanged. Its range has been greatly restricted elsewhere, especially in Uruguay, where about 1,000 animals survive in nine isolated sites. *O. b. leucogaster* is found in southwestern Brazil, southeastern Bolivia, Paraguay, and northern Argentina. Populations of this subspecies are scattered and numbers are declining. *O. b. celer* once ranged across the Argentinian Pampas from the Atlantic Ocean almost to the foothills of the Andes. This subspecies is now restricted to two isolated populations in Argentina—one in the coastal margin of Buenos Aires province and one in central San Luis, 600 mi (1,000 km) inland. Only 400-500 *O. b. celer* remain in the wild.

The pampas deer occupies a variety of open grassland habitats at low elevations.

History and Conservation Measures

The pampas deer was once one of the most widely distributed and abundant deer in the New World. It played a role in the culture of the native peoples of Argentina and Uruguay similar to that played by the bison in the culture of the Plains Indians of North America. This species has declined due to loss or degradation of habitat, competition for food and space with domestic livestock, diseases transmitted by domestic animals, and commercial hunting. Especially in the nineteenth century, pampas deer skins were exported in large numbers and the stomach stones from these animals were valued for medicinal purposes. It is estimated that from 1860 to 1870 more than 2 million pampas deer pelts were exported in Argentina and many more were traded in other countries. In spite of legal protection, poaching for trophies still takes a toll on pampas deer populations.

Two reserve areas, one federal and one private, have been established for the subspecies *O. b. celer* in Argentina. In areas where it is protected from poaching, the population has rebounded, demonstrating the species' natural capacity for recovery. Other conservation priorities for this most endangered subspecies include habitat protection, creation of other park or reserve areas, reintroduction of captive-bred animals, and relocation of wild populations from areas where they are seriously threatened.

Okapi

Okapia johnstoni

Phylum	Chordata
Class	Mammalia
Order	Artiodactyla
Family	Giraffidae
Status	Indeterminate, IUCN
Range	Uganda; Zaire

Description and Biology

A member of the giraffe family, the okapi has a short body with low hindquarters and long legs. Like the giraffe, it has a long neck in relation to the body. Head and body length is about 6 ft (2 m), shoulder height is about 5 ft (1.5 m), and weight is 440-550 lb (200-250 kg). It uses its long tongue to pluck plants, leaves, fruits, and seeds. The okapi's hair is short and reddish brown to almost black in color; the sides of buttocks and upper legs have transverse black and white stripes. Tail averages 12-17 in (30-42 cm) long and ends in a tuft. The male has short horns that are covered with skin.

Primarily diurnal, the okapi is also active shortly after dusk and before dawn. Males are fairly sedentary; two radio-collared males had home ranges of 2.3 sq mi (6 sq km). Usually a solitary species, it also forms pairs and travels in small family groups. A single calf is thought to be born between August and October when rainfall is heavy.

Habitat and Current Distribution

The okapi occurs in northeastern Zaire, from the Ubangi River in the west eastward to the Uele River and Semliki River between Lakes Albert and Edward and southward to Katako-Kombe in Sankuru district. The northern limit corresponds to the limit of equatorial forest. Its range extended into western Uganda in the Semliki area. It appears to favor open primary forest at altitudes greater than 1,640 ft (500 m). Studies in the Ituri forest, one of the major areas still supporting okapis, estimated a population density

Okapi.

of one per 0.8 sq mi (2 sq km). Total numbers are unknown and are difficult to estimate in its dense forest habitat, but the species' total range covers about 38,600 sq mi (100,000 sq km). Total numbers are therefore likely to be at least in the thousands and conceivably in the low tens of thousands. Population trends are unknown, but its range may be retracting in the east and northwest because of habitat destruction.

History and Conservation Measures

The okapi was first described by scientists in 1901, but it was a source of food to the pygmies for many years prior to its official discovery. Subsistence hunting was never a threat to the species, but incidental capture in traps set for smaller game has become a serious problem. The okapi has been protected by law since 1933. The recently established national park in the Ituri forest also gives legal protection to one of its major strongholds. It has been recorded in Maiko National Park and north of Virunga National Park, but its current status in these areas is unknown.

International trade appears not be a significant threat to this species, and effective protection of Ituri should ensure its continued survival. Captive breeding has also been highly successful with this animal.

Addax

Addax nasomaculatus

Phylum	Chordata
Class	Mammalia
Order	Artiodactyla
Family	Bovidae
Status	Endangered, IUCN
	Appendix I, CITES
Range	Chad; Mali; Mauritania; Niger

Description and Biology

The addax is a large antelope with a coat that is gray-brown in winter and almost white in summer. Its forehead has a patch of black hair and its 10-14 in (25-35 cm) tail ends in a black tuft. The average length of the addax is 5-5.5 ft (1.5-1.7 m) and its average height at the shoulder is about 3 ft (95 cm). Typically, the animal weighs about 132-287 lb (60-130 kg). Its spiral horns are long and thin with two or three twists. The addax is well-adapted to life in the desert, requiring no water other than that it gets from the plants it eats. Body temperature is variable to minimize the need for water. It has a long stride and splayed hooves to facilitate crossing vast areas of desert in order to locate sparse vegetation that has been stimulated by infrequent rains.

The addax travels at night in groups of 5-20 individuals. Although little is known of reproductive biology, it is believed that one young is born after a gestation period of 8-9 months.

Habitat and Current Distribution

Numbers surviving in the wild probably do not exceed a few hundred and could be substantially less. The surviving animals occur in northeastern Niger, northern Chad, and along th Mauritanian/Mali border.

The addax thrives in sand dune regions with no water source and meager vegetation.

History and Conservation Measures

Although there are no estimates of initial population, the addax once ranged from the Western Sahara and Mauritania to Egypt and Sudan. This slow and tame animal, which was once domesticated by the ancient Egyptians, is easily caught by hunters who value its flesh and its hide. Excessive hunting was an early cause of the decline in population; despite legal protection, it remains a threat today. Additional problems now faced by the addax are drought and interference in their habitat by tourists using vehicles to track and chase them. Information about conservation measures is unavailable.

The 4,943-sq-mi (12,806-sq-km) Aïr and Ténère National Nature Reserve in Niger protects a sufficiently large area of good addax habitat to enable a small population to survive in the wild. The park has clearly delineated boundaries protected by patrols, and tourist or other human activity is prohibited within the reserve. The addax has been present in

Addax.

this area for centuries, but its numbers here are currently very low. Reintroduction of 50-75 captive-bred addax into this reserve area was proposed over a three-year period beginning in 1991, but has been delayed by political problems. There are currently more than 1,000 addax held in captivity in the United States, Europe, and the Middle East, including 550-600 animals in managed captive breeding programs.

Dibatag

Ammodorcas clarkei

Phylum	Chordata
Class	Mammalia
Order	Artiodactyla
Family	Bovidae
Status	Vulnerable, IUCN
Range	Ethiopia; Somalia

Description and Biology

The dibatag, the only species in its genus, has a slender body with a very long neck and long legs. The coat is reddish gray or reddish purple with white underparts and rump and chestnut markings on the face. Head and body length averages 46-66 in (117-168 cm), shoulder height is 30-35 in (76-89 cm), and weight is 50-75 lb (23-34 kg). Tail is black and around 12-14 in (30-36 cm) long. The peculiar tints of the rufous coat blend well with the surrounding so that the dibatag is often difficult to see. The male has horns that measure 6-12 in (15-30 cm) long and curve backward at the base, then forward towards the tip. The long neck facilitates browsing in high trees and shrubs. They often stand on their hind legs, reaching as high into a tree as possible.

Sometimes solitary, the dibatag can also be found in family groups of three to six individuals. Little information is available about reproductive biology, but young are thought to be born in October or November after a gestation period of around 200 days.

Habitat and Current Distribution

The dibatag occurs only in Ethiopia and Somalia; it is found mostly in the arid southeastern lowlands in Ethiopia, and local concentrations occur in the coastal hinterland of central Somalia. It inhabits grassy plains, semi-arid bush, and open scrub. There are no estimates of population size or composition.

History and Conservation Measures

The population of the dibatag seems to be relatively stable in Ethiopia, but it is declining in Somalia because of poaching, habitat degradation caused by drought, and competition with domestic livestock for grazing land. In Ethiopia, antelopes and other large mammals have suffered severely in the past from the effects of overhunting by the heavily armed local populace, military operations, drought, and habitat destruction. In Somalia, long-term habitat destruction and desertification have occurred as a result of overgrazing and increasingly frequent droughts. Resulting food shortages have been intensified by civil unrest and have led to uncontrolled slaughter of wildlife.

In Ethiopia, this species is legally protected from hunting; yet it does not occur in any protected area. The creation of a reserve in the Ogaden area of Ethiopia has been recommended to provide refuge for this species.

Barbary sheep

Ammotragus lervia

Phylum	Chordata
Class	Mammalia
Order	Artiodactyla
Family	Bovidae
Status	Indeterminate, IUCN Appendix II, CITES
Range	Algeria; Chad; Libya; Mali; Mauritania (ex?); Morocco (ex?); Niger; Sudan; Tunisia (ex?)

Description and Biology

The aoudad or Barbary sheep is found in rough, rocky, arid country. Because of its tawny coloring, which blends with the environment, this animal is difficult to spot. The face lacks a beard, but there is a long, soft mane of hair on the underside of the neck extending to the chest and upper forelegs. Total head and body length averages 4.3-5.4 ft (1.3-1.6 m), shoulder height is 30-60 in (76-152 cm), and weight is 90-310 lb (41-141 kg); males usually weigh up to twice as much as females. The tail is fringed and 6-10 in (15-25.4 cm) long; horns are thick, relatively smooth, and curved, measuring 16-33 in (41-84 cm), being largest in males. This sheep is an agile climber, moving and leaping among rocky cliffs with ease. Its diet includes grasses, herbs, and shrubs.

Females and young usually live in small groups, but males live separately and can be solitary. Males compete with each other, clashing heads and pushing each other to obtain access to females during the mating season. Mating is usually between September and November, and one to two young are born after a gestation period of 154-161 days.

Habitat and Current Distribution

The aoudad occurs in the rugged mountains of North Africa and as far south as the mountains of the Sahara and Sahel regions. Its habitat is arid and rocky, with limited water supplies. There may be several thousand still in Algeria, and between 800 and 1,000 in Morocco, but for most other areas, population estimates are not available, although numbers are generally believed to be small and decreasing.

History and Conservation Measures

The population of the aoudad has declined drastically due to excessive hunting and competition from livestock. They are protected by law in about half the countries they occur in, and as many as 14 protected areas in North Africa may contain Barbary sheep. However, the level of protection varies considerably among countries, and overall they are threatened. Logistical problems of working in remote arid regions, together with political unrest, make conservation efforts almost impossible in many countries with aoudads. Population censuses, new protected areas, and enforcement or creation of anti-poaching laws have all been recommended for the conservation of this species. A population introduced into the southwestern United States in the 1900s appears to be thriving but to the detriment of some native species.

Barbary sheep.

American bison

Bison bison

European bison

Bison bonasus

Phylum	Chordata
Class	Mammalia
Order	Artiodactyla
Family	Bovidae
Status	Vulnerable, IUCN (*B. bonasus*)
	Endangered, USFWS (*B. bison athabascae*)
	Appendix I, CITES (*B. bison athabascae*)
Range	Canada; U.S.A. (*B. bison*)
	Reintroduced in Belarus; Lithuania; Moldova; Poland; Romania; Russia; Ukraine (*B. bonasus*)

Description and Biology

The bison, commonly called the buffalo in America, is easily identifiable by its massive body and shoulder hump. Body hair is short over most of the body but is long and shaggy on the head, neck, shoulders, and forelegs. There is usually a beard under the chin. The American bison has an average head and body length of 7-12.5 ft (2.1-3.8 m), shoulder height of 5-6.5 ft (1.5-2 m), and weight of 700-2,200 lb (320 -1,000 kg); the male is larger than the female. The tail is fairly short, measuring 12-35 in (30.5-89 cm), and tufted. The head is large and the neck thick; horns are present in both males and females and curve upward and inward, ending in a short point. In American bison, especially the plains bison (*B. bison bison*), there is a marked contrast between the light color of the shaggy hair forming a "cape" on the animal's shoulders and the dark, almost black, color of the rest of the body. The shorter hair on the animal's hindparts is usually very dark or black. The

wood bison (*B. bison athabascae*) tends to be less variegated.

The European bison is slightly smaller than the American bison but has stronger hindquarters. In European bison there is little color contrast between the long hair on the head and forequarters and the shorter hair elsewhere. The bison is a fast runner, a good swimmer, and has an acute sense of smell. It is active during the day and night, grazing on grasses and sedges; the European bison also browses on leaves, twigs, and tree bark.

Herds have a fluid composition of females, young, and immature males; males may be solitary or join herds of up to 30 bulls, but even the solitary males join the larger herds as rutting season approaches. There is often aggression between bulls to determine dominance for mating privileges. Breeding season lasts from June to September, with most activity in late July or early August. The gestation period of the American bison averages 285 days, while that of the European bison is 254-280 days.

American bison.

relatively pure woodland bison stock. The taxonomic identity of the remaining animals is currently being studied.

Taxonomists have recognized three subspecies of European bison: *B. bonasus bonasus* from the Bialowieza Forest, *B. bonasus hungarorum* from the Carpathian Mountains and Transylvania, and *B. bonasus caucasicus* from the Caucasus Mountains. The European bison became extinct in the wild during the first quarter of the twentieth century; beginning in the 1950s captive-bred animals were released in the Bialowieza Forest, Poland, and the species has subsequently been re-introduced in Belarus, Lithuania, Moldova, Romania, Russia, and Ukraine. In 1986, about 2,900 European bison were known to exist, and this number was expected to grow to 3,600 by the end of 1990. About half of these animals are in free-ranging herds, the largest of about 500 animals occurring in the Bialowieza Forest. This herd is similar in size to the herd found there in the 1880s.

The American bison is normally considered to be an animal of the plains and grasslands, but it was once also common in forested areas. The European bison inhabits deciduous and mixed forest areas with undergrowth and near-open grazing areas.

Births peaks in late April and early May. *B. bison* calves are reddish brown; *B. bonasus* calves are brownish gray. Calves nurse for seven months to one year.

European bison and American bison interbreed easily, and a number of scientists do not believe that there is any sound biological reason to maintain *B. bison* and *B. bonasus* as separate species. In addition, some scientists favor combining *Bos* and *Bison* into one genus on the basis of morphological and genetic similarities.

Habitat and Current Distribution

The American bison is usually divided geographically into two subspecies. *B. bison bison* survives primarily in Yellowstone National Park, where the population is estimated at 1,500-2,000 individuals. There are smaller, isolated populations in other parks and reserves and on private ranches in the western United States. *B. bison athabascae* survives in a number of sanctuaries in Canada, including Mackenzie Sanctuary and Wood Buffalo National Park. The population may total more than 5,000 individuals, but of these only 2,500 are thought to have descended from

History and Conservation Measures

The American bison was once distributed from Alaska and western Canada throughout the United States and into northern Mexico. The majority of the population was the subspecies *B. bison bison*, which was the most widespread with an estimated population of 50 million individuals. *B. bison athabascae* occurred in Canada, but there are no reliable estimates of the peak population. In 1800 the total population of this subspecies was estimated at 168,000 animals. The bison was integral to the culture of many native American tribes, who depended upon it for food and hides. With European settlement, the bison became a target of commercial hunters and, by the late 1800s, both species were virtually wiped out. Numbers of *B. bison bison* had fallen to a few hundred by 1890; Yellowstone National Park is the only place where a wild herd of *B. bison bison* has existed continuously.

By 1891 only about 300 *B. bison athabascae* survived in northern Alberta and adjacent areas of the Northwest Territories. The Canadian Government established Wood Buffalo National Park in 1922 to protect this remnant population. Unfortunately, thousands of *B. bison bison* were released in the park during the 1920s; these introduced animals genetically swamped the small number of wood bison and created a hybrid population. In 1957, about 200 animals, thought to be genetically very close to *B. bison athabascae*, were found in an isolated herd in the northern part of the park. This herd has now grown to more than 2,500 animals, partially as the result of a selective breeding program. These and other conservation efforts have proven successful in preserving herds of both subspecies in protected areas; re-introduction of captive-bred animals has played an important role in many of these efforts.

B. bonasus was formerly widespread throughout western, central, and southeastern Europe. By the late 1800s, the bison was restricted to the northwestern Caucasus Mountains and the Bialowieza Forest; its distribution was reduced because of expanding human population and spread of agriculture. Hunting for food and sport also played a significant role in its decline, and the transmission of diseases from domestic cattle contributed to the extinction of the Caucasus population (*B. bonasus caucasius*). World War I and the Russian Revolution dealt the final blows to these wild populations. By 1919 the bison was extirpated from the Bialowieza Forest, and it disappeared from the Caucasus Mountains by 1927. Only

54 European bison, most representing the lowland subspecies (*B. bonasus bonasus*) from the Bialowieza Forest, survived in zoos. (The third subspecies, *B. bonasus hungarorum* became extinct earlier, probably in the late eighteenth century.) One pure Caucasus bull was bred in captivity with *B. bonasus bonasus* females, producing a hybrid line, but pure *B. bonasus caucasius* became extinct.

The future of the European bison appears brighter now than at any time since the species became extinct in the wild. Goals of the recovery plan include strict protection and maintenance of the species by planned breeding in zoos, parks and forest reserves; distribution of these animals over a large number of breeding centers (mostly in Europe); and future releases of captive-bred animals into the wild. In spite of the successes already achieved, however, a number of challenges remain to be overcome. All pure *B. bonasus bonasus* are descended from only 17 animals, so the world population of European bison is highly inbred. This inbreeding has resulted in decreased vitality of young bison and shorter lifespans. Future management programs must work to maintain and maximize the genetic diversity of the species.

European bison.

Gaur

Bos gaurus

Phylum	Chordata
Class	Mammalia
Order	Artiodactyla
Family	Bovidae
Status	Vulnerable, IUCN
	Endangered, USFWS
	Appendix I, CITES
Range	Bangladesh; Bhutan; China; India; Kampuchea; Laos; Peninsular Malaysia; Myanmar; Nepal; Thailand; Vietnam

Description and Biology

The gaur or seladang is the largest of the wild cattle, averaging 8.25-10.75 ft (2.5-3.3 m) long, 5.25-7.25 ft (1.6-2.2 m) high at the shoulder, and weighing 1,550-2,200 lb (704-1,000 kg); the adult male is substantially larger than the female. Body color ranges from red-brown to dark brown to black with white stockings. Short, sturdy legs support a massive body and large head; there is a small dewlap below the chin and a large one between the forelegs. The male has a large hump over the shoulders and 24-45 in (60-115 cm) horns. Diet includes green or dry grasses, fruits, and shoots from trees and bushes. Tigers and leopards are predators, particularly of calves. Home range of a herd averages 30 sq mi (78 sq km).

Gaurs travel in groups of 8-11 animals, usually consisting of one mature bull, adult cows, and young of various ages. Bulls may be solitary or form small groups with other males. During mating season, they join maternal herds. Dominance is established by size rather than competition. During courtship, the bull emits a roaring sound that may last for hours. Mating can take place at any time during the year, but it is usually between November and May. The mother leaves the herd to give birth to one young, usually in August or September, after a gestation period of 270-280 days. She nurses the calf for nine months.

Habitat and Current Distribution

Scattered herds of gaur are found in Bangladesh, Bhutan, China, Kampuchea, India, Laos, Myanmar, Malaysia, Nepal, Thailand, and Vietnam. Population figures are unavailable. (The gayal, a domestic form of gaur used for work and meat production, is found in eastern India and Myanmar.)

Primary habitat of the gaur is forest adjoining grassy clearings or glades at elevations up to 6,000 ft (1,800 m). Mountain forests have become habitat for the gaur as lowland forest habitats disappear.

History and Conservation Measures

The gaur is still present in much of its historical habitat but in greatly reduced numbers and scattered

Gaur.

distribution. It is the victim of a number of threats, including sport hunting, which continues despite legal protection. An additional serious threat to the wild gaur is the transmission of diseases from domestic cattle who usurp grazing lands. Information on conservation plans is unavailable.

Banteng

Bos javanicus

Phylum	Chordata
Class	Mammalia
Order	Artiodactyla
Family	Bovidae
Status	Vulnerable, IUCN
	Endangered, USFWS
Range	Bangladesh (ex?); Kampuchea (?); Bali, Java, Kalimantan (Indonesia); Laos; Sabah (Malaysia); Myanmar; Thailand; Vietnam

Description and Biology

A species of wild oxen native to Southeast Asia, the banteng varies widely in color, with the females and young bulls tending toward brown or reddish brown and mature bulls ranging from dark brown to shiny black. Both sexes have white stockings, a white rump patch, a white patch over the eyes, and a white band around the muzzle. Head and body length is 6-10 ft (1.8-3 m), height at the shoulder is 4-6.5 ft (1.2-2 m), and weight is 1,330-2,000 lb (600-900 kg); males are substantially heavier than females. Bulls have a bald patch between their horns and a humped back. During the wet season, the banteng feeds on new shoots and leaves of bushes and trees including bamboo shoots; in the dry season it grazes on grass. Bantengs may be active at any hour but have become nocturnal in areas where they are disturbed by people. They are very wary and shy.

Very little is known about the social habits of this species. It is usually found in groups of 2-40 animals, generally led by a mature bull; other males are either solitary or live in bachelor groups. Mating seems to be possible throughout the year but probably takes place in May or June in the wild. One or two young are born after a gestation period of 270-300 days.

Habitat and Current Distribution

The banteng is found in isolated populations in Myanmar, Thailand, Laos, Kampuchea, Vietnam, and on the islands of Borneo, Bali, and Java. Several thousand individuals are thought to survive in the wild, but the populations are severely fragmented and are declining in most areas. There are also some 1.5 million domesticated banteng in Indonesia which are used as work animals and for meat production.

Preferred habitat includes dense vegetation, forest, or bamboo jungle with access to open glades for grazing. It is sometimes found in sparse forest up to an elevation of 6,400 ft (2,000 m), especially during the monsoon.

History and Conservation Measures

The banteng was probably domesticated in prehistoric times on Bali and Sumbawa and was taken from there to other East Asian islands and northern Australia. Feral herds have been established in Australia and some other areas.

Estimates of earlier wild populations are unavailable, but the banteng has certainly suffered a population decline and distribution reduction. Factors affecting its decline in the wild include dimin-

Banteng.

ished habitat due to human encroachment, excessive hunting, and hybridization with domestic cattle (*Bos taurus*). Because the banteng has not been the sub-ject of much scientific investigation, conservation plans are still being developed.

Wild yak

Bos mutus (grunniens)

Phylum	Chordata
Class	Mammalia
Order	Artiodactyla
Family	Bovidae
Status	Endangered, IUCN
	Endangered, USFWS
	Appendix I, CITES
Range	Afghanistan (?); Bhutan (?); China; India; Nepal

Description and Biology

Although there are millions of domesticated yaks in the world today, the wild yak is a rare and little-known animal. Its huge body is covered with coarse, shaggy, dark brown to black hair that hangs from its underside almost to the ground. Muzzle is white; curved horns are dark and up to 3 ft long (91 cm) in the male and smaller in the female. The male averages 10.75 ft (3.3 m) long, 6.5 ft (2 m) high, and weighs 1,800-2,200 lb (820-1,000 kg); the female is substantially smaller. Legs are short, the drooping head very large, and the shoulders humped. At high altitudes, it uses its rough tongue to feed on lichens and mosses; at lower elevations it feeds on mosses, herbs, and grasses. Because vegetation is sparse in its habitat, it often covers long distances looking for food. A known predator is the Tibetan wolf.

Males and females congregate in separate herds except during mating season, when the males join the female groups. Beginning in September the males compete for available females, making a loud grunting sound as they fight. One young is born in June after a gestation period of 258 days; the calf nurses for almost a year.

Habitat and Current Distribution

Only a few hundred of these animals survive in isolated patches of alpine tundra on the Tibetan Plateau.

The wild yak is found at elevations between 13,500 ft and 20,000 ft (4,000-6,000 m). In warmer months, it climbs up to desolate steppes and icefields where there is snow.

History and Conservation Measures

At one time, the yak's range extended all the way to northern Siberia. Although there are no estimates of early population, in the early 1900s there was still an extensive wild population. It has since been reduced to a dangerously low level by excessive hunting. It has always been valued for its meat, hide, and

Wild yak.

coat. Even though it has legal protection, hunting persists today; the Chinese government has been known to offer sport hunting of this species to foreign hunters. Enforcement of existing protection is almost impossible because of its remote and inaccessible mountain habitat. Also for this reason, it is almost impossible to formulate conservation plans for further protections, leaving the surviving population in grave danger.

Kouprey

Bos sauveli

Phylum	Chordata
Class	Mammalia
Order	Artiodactyla
Family	Bovidae
Status	Endangered, IUCN
	Endangered, USFWS
	Appendix I, CITES
Range	Kampuchea; Laos; Thailand (ex?); Vietnam

Description and Biology

The kouprey or gray ox is one of the most seriously threatened large mammals in the world. It is lighter in build than other wild cattle with an average length of 7-7.25 ft (2.1-2.2 m), a height of 5.50-6.25 ft (1.7-1.9 m), and a weight of 1,550-2,000 lb (700-900 kg). Males are dark brown; adult females and young animals are gray with lighter underparts and darker chest, neck, and forelegs. Males have a pronounced dewlap that may even drag along the ground and wide-spaced, tapering horns with characteristic fraying near the tips. Koupreys occasionally dig in the mud with their horns, which may be one reason for the frayed tips. The horns of the female are lyre-shaped. Both sexes have a very long 40-43 in (100-110 cm) tail and notched nostrils. The diet of the kouprey has been only partially studied but is known to include tall and short grasses, particularly bamboo grasses, ploong grass, and koom grass; sedges; some browse from the leaves of trees and bushes; and some mineral-rich soils eaten or licked at salt licks or termite mounds.

Unstable herds consist of females and their young. For part of the year, both mature and young bulls form bachelor herds, but in the dry season bulls mix freely with the female herds. The animals rest in the early afternoon and may travel 3-9 mi (5-15 km) in a night. Mating takes place in April, and young are born between December and February, before the hottest part of the dry season. Mothers leave the herd at the time of birth and regroup with the herd when the calf is about one month old.

Habitat and Current Distribution

The kouprey is confined to the Indochinese peninsula, centered on the northern plains of Kampuchea (Cambodia), but it also ranges through the southernmost provinces of Laos. It may also range into the Dongrak mountains of eastern Thailand as well as the western edge of Vietnam along the Kampuchean border. Population is estimated at between 100 and 300 individuals.

Preferred habitat is open forest, open parkland savanna on poorer soils, tree and orchard savanna, gallery forest, and patches of dense monsoon forest. The dense forest is utilized for shelter during hot weather and the open areas for grazing. Herds tend to move up into higher, hilly terrain during the wettest times of the year.

History and Conservation Measures

From the time of its discovery in 1937, the kouprey has always been considered rare. There is some evidence that the species might have ranged as far as Yunnan in southern China in ancient times, but it has been estimated that the total population never exceeded 2,000 animals in recent times. Total numbers were estimated at around 1,000 in the 1940s, 500-800 in the 1950s, and 100 in the late 1960s. Because of the difficulties of conducting surveys in the main strongholds of the kouprey in Kampuchea, these estimates are very crude.

There is no hard information on any principal threats to the kouprey; studies have been difficult because of extended human warfare in all of the species' range. Various factors may come into play, including hunting by local people or guerrilla armies, habitat clearance, or inbreeding in small, inviable populations.

In 1960, the kouprey was declared the national animal of Kampuchea, given protected status, and conserved on three major reserves. Because much of the reserve territory is in a military security zone, it is difficult to assess the success of the reserve program. A major field study is necessary to provide ecological, biological, and distributional information that can be used to formulate conservation plans. Until then, general goals are to save the habitat of the kouprey and save the gene pool of the species. To preserve the habitat, it would be most desirable if the kouprey could be restored to population levels that would allow local people to derive direct economic benefit from its existence. Survival of the kouprey will probably be closely linked to the establishment of well-managed, protected areas that have the support of the local human populations. To preserve the gene pool, it has been proposed that a captive breeding herd should be established while the numbers in the wild are still sufficient to allow the removal of a few founder animals without greatly affecting survival chances of the wild population. It has been proposed that the species could be a useful domestic animal in the future, and that hybrids with domestic cattle might benefit from accelerated growth rates, better adaptation to local environments and food resources, and natural disease resistance.

Wild water buffalo

Bubalus arnee (bubalus)

Phylum	Chordata
Class	Mammalia
Order	Artiodactyla
Family	Bovidae
Status	Endangered, IUCN
	Appendix III, CITES
Range	Bhutan; India; Nepal; Thailand

Description and Biology

The wild water buffalo inhabits swampy areas and likes to wallow in mud, often acquiring a mud coat as protection against biting insects. It also escapes insects by submerging itself in the water so that only its nostrils are exposed. Larger than the domestic buffalo, the wild water buffalo averages 7.75-10 ft (2.4-3 m) long, 5-6.25 ft (1.5-1.9 m) high at the shoulder, and weighs 1,550-2,650 lb (700-1,200 kg). Its body is covered with long, coarse hair that grows forward toward the head. Wild water buffalo vary in color from ash gray to black. Both sexes have horns with a wider span than the domestic buffalo, long, narrow faces, and small ears. The horns are heavy at the base, curve backward and inward, and are marked with wrinkles. A fast, aggressive animal, it eats aquatic vegetation and grasses and other vegetation along the shores of lakes and rivers. In some areas, tigers are predators; leopards prey on young animals.

Breeding season can vary with habitat. A single young is born after a gestation period of 310-340 days and is nursed for up to nine months.

Habitat and Current Distribution

The remaining population of the wild water buffalo is scattered throughout its original range. Approximately 1,000 individuals survive in India and Nepal, but less than 100 of them are believed to be free of any genetic influence from domestic or feral buffalo. (In contrast, there are at least 130 million domestic water buffalo living in India, Southeast Asia, and the islands of the East Indies.)

The preferred habitat of the wild water buffalo is swampy or wet grassland, or river valleys with dense vegetation.

History and Conservation Measures

The wild water buffalo has disappeared from much of its original range for several reasons. Excessive hunting has reduced wild populations, and much of the water buffalo's habitat has been converted to agricultural use. Wild water buffalo must compete with domestic cattle for grazing land and are subject to diseases transmitted by domestic livestock. Herds are protected in two national parks in India.

Wild water buffalo.

Lowland anoa

Bubalus depressicornis

Mountain anoa

Bubalus quarlesi

Phylum	Chordata
Class	Mammalia
Order	Artiodactyla
Family	Bovidae
Status	Endangered, IUCN
	Endangered, USFWS
	Appendix I, CITES
Range	Sulawesi (Indonesia)

Description and Biology

Sometimes called dwarf buffalo, anoas are the smallest of the wild cattle. The average head and body length is 5.25-5.75 ft (1.6-1.72 m), height at the shoulder is 27-42 in (69-106 cm), and weight is 330-661 lbs (150-300 kg). Young anoas are covered with thick, woolly yellowish brown hair, but older individuals have darker (dark brown to blackish), much sparser hair. Males are generally darker than females. Anoas frequently have white markings on the face, throat, chest, and lower forelegs. Both species have very thick hide, short limbs and a rather plump body. The lowland anoa has white forelegs, a long tail (7-16 in or 18-40 cm), and flattened, wrinkled, longer horns (7-14 in or 18-36 cm) that are triangular in section. The mountain anoa has legs the same color as its body, more hair than the lowland anoa, a shorter tail and smooth, shorter horns (6-8 in or 15-20 cm) that are rounded in section. Anoas feed in the morning and rest in shady spots during the afternoon. Their wide-ranging diet includes grasses, leaves, ferns, fruits, saplings, palms, and ginger.

Instead of forming herds like most other cattle, these species are frequently seen alone or in pairs. Their preferred gait is a walk or trot, and they try to escape danger by leaping. Very little is known about the biology of anoas, but they are thought to breed at any time of the year and to produce one calf after a gestation period of 275-315 days.

Habitat and Current Distribution

Anoas are basically forest animals. The lowland anoa is found in the swampy lowland forests or swampy woodlands of Sulawesi (Celebes Island). The mountain anoa inhabits the high altitude forests of this island. Population figures for both species are unknown but are almost certainly in the thousands, though probably declining. They survive in reasonably healthy numbers in the larger forest blocks. The lowland anoa is probably more threatened by habitat loss and hunting than is its mountain counterpart.

Lowland anoa.

History and Conservation Measures

Estimates of initial population size are not available for either species of anoa. Their ranges have been restricted and their numbers have no doubt been reduced, primarily due to hunting and loss of habitat. Parasitic diseases may also contribute to the decline of wild populations. Captive breeding of anoas still presents difficulties, but various zoos, including

Mountain anoa.

the San Diego Zoo, are trying to improve captive breeding success. However, the main conservation strategy depends on the establishment and management of protected areas. Key reserves for these species include the Rawa Aopa-Watumohae National Park, the Gunung Tangkoko-Dua Saudara Nature Reserve, Lore Lindu National Park, Morowali Nature Reserve, Dumoga-Bone National Park, and Gunung Anubang Nature Reserve.

Tamaraw

Bubalus mindorensis

Phylum	Chordata
Class	Mammalia
Order	Artiodactyla
Family	Bovidae
Status	Endangered, IUCN
	Endangered, USFWS
Range	Mindoro (Philippines)

Description and Biology

The tamaraw is the Philippines' largest and possibly most endangered mammal species. It is a small buffalo with a coat that ranges from dark brown to grayish black. Shoulder height averages 3.3 ft (1 m) and weight is about 660 lb (300 kg). Horns are short and stout, measuring 14-20 in (36-51 cm). Reported to be nocturnal, the tamaraw grazes on vegetation.

Adults are usually solitary but may be found in pairs or in groups comprised of a female with a varying number of young. Young are thought to be born in the rainy season, between June and November, after a gestation period of 276-315 days.

Habitat and Current Distribution

The tamaraw is endemic to the island of Mindoro in the Philippines, where it utilizes dense forest vegetation for cover and open grassland for grazing. In 1987 population in the wild was roughly estimated at approximately 350 individuals, with the largest population in the Mt. Iglit Baco National Park, although the accuracy of this figure has been questioned. In any case, the population is certain to be very small.

History and Conservation Measures

In the early 1900s, there were an estimated 10,000 tamaraws on Mindoro; because of excessive hunting and loss of habitat, the population had decreased to less than 150-200 animals by 1971. In 1979 a program was begun to try to halt the decline of the tamaraw. The program's immediate objective was to save the species from extinction by establishing protective measures for the tamaraw in the wild, by preserving its habitat, and by initiating a captive breeding program. Its long term objective was to develop the animal and its habitat as economic resources.

A captive breeding facility was established in the southern part of the Mt. Iglit Baco National Park, which still harbors the largest population of wild tamaraws. The captive breeding program has achieved very limited success. Armed aggression and guerrilla warfare have greatly hampered management efforts in the breeding facility. Because of this and other problems, the captive herd has been moved to a new, more secure location on the island. There is no real evidence that the wild population has increased since conservation measures began. There is still no effec-

Tamaraw.

tive protection of the tamaraw in the wild, and poaching remains a problem.

Mt. Iglit Baco National Park is an important focus of conservation plans. It needs protection from the encroachment of cattle ranching, cultivation for agriculture, logging activities, poaching, and human settlement. Other areas of Mindoro should be assessed to determine population and distribution of wild tamaraws, to further determine habitat use and requirements, and to provide more information on the biology of the species. The Philippine government is developing a revitalized conservation program for the species and is seeking external financial assistance for its implementation.

Takin

Budorcas taxicolor

Phylum	Chordata
Class	Mammalia
Order	Artiodactyla
Family	Bovidae
Status	Endangered, IUCN (*B. t. bedfordi*)
	Indeterminate, IUCN (*B. t. taxicolor*)
	Insufficiently Known, IUCN (*B. t. tibetana*; *B. t. whitei*)
	Appendix II, CITES
Range	Bhutan; China; India; Myanmar

Description and Biology

A member of the goat family, the takin is a heavy, oxlike animal with ribbed horns. It has a long, shaggy coat that varies in color with subspecies from almost white to dark brown. Its skin is oily and gives off a strong odor. Head and body length averages 5.6-7.2 ft (1.7-2.2 m), shoulder height is 3.3-4.3 ft (1-1.3 m), and weight is 550-770 lb (250-350 kg), with males much heavier than females. Takins have fairly short legs with broad hooves. Tail length averages 3-18 in (8-20 cm); horns average 10-20 in (25-50 cm) and curve sideways and then toward the back. Feeding in the early morning or late afternoon, this species has a diet that varies with season, including grasses, herbs, leaves, bamboo shoots, and forbs in the summer and leaves and twigs from evergreen trees in winter. Bears, wolves, and snow leopards are predators.

In winter, groups are fairly small, ranging from 10-20 animals. In summer, however, groups can include as many as 150 individuals. In most areas, mating takes place between June and September and births between March and May, after a gestation period variously reported as 200-240 days or 300-330 days. A single young is usually nursed for around nine months.

Habitat and Current Distribution

The takin occurs in western China and the Himalayas (especially India and Bhutan) at altitudes of 3,300-11,000 ft (1,000-3,350 m). It spends the days sheltered in dense vegetation and often frequents salt licks. The large herds congregate at high altitudes in the summer, then break up into smaller groups and descend to lower elevations in the winter. There are no general estimates of population.

History and Conservation Measures

This species has long been a source of food for local peoples. Its population is believed to have declined because of excessive hunting and habitat destruction. The species occurs in over 20 protected areas, including 13 in China and 3 in India. *B. t. tibetana* has been bred successfully at the Chengdu Zoo.

Takin.

Markhor

Capra falconeri

Phylum	Chordata
Class	Mammalia
Order	Artiodactyla
Family	Bovidae
Status	Endangered, IUCN
	Endangered, USFWS
	Appendix I, CITES
Range	Afghanistan; India; Pakistan; Tajikistan; Turkmenistan; Uzbekistan

Description and Biology

The markhor is one of the largest members of the wild goats. Its coat varies in length and in coloration with seasonal climatic changes. While the color is generally reddish gray with a dark dorsal stripe from the shoulders to the tail, in winter it is longer and grayer and in summer it is shorter and more yellowish buff. Males have a large beard and a long shaggy mane on the underside of the neck and shoulders; females only rarely have a small beard. Total head and body length averages 55-70 in (140-178 cm), shoulder height is 26-40 in (66-101 cm), weight is 70-240 lb (32-110 kg), and tail length is 3-5.5 in (8-14 cm); males are substantially larger than females. Active during the day, markhors graze on grasses and herbs or browse on shrubs and low trees depending on seasonal availability. Predators include wolves, leopards, snow leopards, and possibly lynx. Golden eagles may pose a threat to young markhors.

Groups are usually comprised of 10-12 individuals and include females and young, but mixed groups of up to 35 animals have been seen. Except for the mating season, males live separately from females and are usually solitary, although they may form small groups. Males compete with each other for social status and access to females. Mating takes place in winter and one or two young are born after a gestation period of around 155 days.

Habitat and Current Distribution

This species occurs in various mountain ranges at the western end of the Himalayas in northwest India (Jammu and Kashmir) and northeast Pakistan, in the more southerly ranges in northwestern Pakistan and adjacent northern and northwestern Afghanistan, and in the ranges north of the Amadur'ya (Oxus River) in southern Tajikistan and Uzbekistan. In these mountains it inhabits rocky areas, open forested slopes, and meadows. Three subspecies are recognized: the straight-horned markhor (*C. f. megaceros*) of Afghanistan and Pakistan, the flare-horned markhor (*C. f. falconeri*) of northeastern Pakistan and northwestern India, and the Tajik markhor (*C. f. heptneri*) of southern Uzbekistan and Tajikistan. Less than 3,200 flare-horned markhors are believed to remain in Pakistan and India, less than 2,000 straight-horned markhors in Pakistan and less in Afghanistan, and no more than 700 Tajik markhors remain. All three exist only in small scattered popula-

Markhor.

History and Conservation Measures

The primary cause of the decline of the markhor is excessive hunting, primarily for its horns, but also for meat and hides. In addition, increasing human populations have brought more domestic sheep and goats, agricultural demands, and fuel and timber harvesting, all of which have negatively impacted on the markhor and its habitat. A total of 27 protected areas occur in the markhor's range, but the level of protection is often severely limited due to political unrest and military activity. In addition, most populations are very small, scattered, and often isolated from each other. All of these problems make conservation efforts extremely difficult. The main recommendations which have been made for the conservation of the markhor include strict control of poaching, halting habitat destruction and livestock competition, and creating new protected areas. With adequate census data and appropriate management plans, small numbers may eventually be able to be hunted and revenues used to support conservation efforts and benefit local peoples.

tions and are considered endangered throughout their range.

Spanish ibex

Capra pyrenaica

Phylum	Chordata
Class	Mammalia
Order	Artiodactyla
Family	Bovidae
Status	Endangered, IUCN (*C. pyrenaica pyrenaica*)
	Rare, IUCN (*C. pyrenaica victoriae*)
	Endangered, USFWS
Range	Spain

Description and Biology

The Spanish ibex is a wild goat that inhabits rocky, mountainous areas. It has a reddish brown coat; head and body size averages 40-55 in (100-140 cm), shoulder height is 26-30 in (66-76 cm), weight is 77-176 lb (35-80 cm), and tail is 4-6 in (10-15 cm). Males are larger than females. The male has a beard and curving horns that average around 30 in (75 cm) long. Diet includes herbs, grasses, and lichens.

Group composition changes throughout the year; males and females are separated except during mating season, which generally falls in November and December. Young males court females, but only dominant older males are allowed to mate. After birth, the mother and young remain together for several days and later join a group of other mothers and young. Foxes and eagles prey on juveniles.

Habitat and Current Distribution

The Spanish ibex is found in Spain, where it inhabits rocky cliffs, grassy meadows, and forests. Four subspecies are recognized. *C. p. lusitanica* has been extinct in Portugal since the late 1800s. *C. p. victoriae* and *C. p. hispanica* were in danger of extinction but have recovered to current populations estimated at 3,300 and over 16,000 individuals respec-

tively. *C. p. pyrenaica* survives in the Pyrenees, but its population is estimated at fewer than 15 individuals.

Spanish ibex.

History and Conservation Measures

Hunting has been the major threat to the Spanish ibex. *C. p. pyrenaica* occurs only within the Ordesa National Park, Spain. *C. p. victoriae* occurs within one protected area, whereas *C. p. hispanica* is in ten protected areas.

Walia ibex

Capra walie

Phylum	Chordata
Class	Mammalia
Order	Artiodactyla
Family	Bovidae
Status	Endangered, IUCN
	Endangered, USFWS
Range	Ethiopia

Description and Biology

A wild goat, the Walia ibex has a reddish brown coat with a black strip on the front of each leg and light underparts. The male develops a black beard which grows larger as he matures; at maturity, he also has a black chest, a black marking on the back, and horns that average 45 in (114 cm) long. Shoulder height ranges from 35-43 in (89-109 cm) and weight from 175-275 lb (80-125 cm); the male is larger than the female.

Herds of up to 35 animals have been reported, but they may be even larger when joined by the males in rutting season, which is possible throughout the year, but peaks between March and May. One young is usually born after a gestation period of 150-165 days.

Habitat and Current Distribution

This wild goat makes its home in the Semien Mountains of Ethiopia, where it inhabits rocky terrain with steep cliffs at elevations of 9,200-11,200 ft (2,800-3,400 m). The dry season is spent at lower elevations and the wet season at higher ones. Population in the wild was estimated at approximately 400 individuals in 1989. The species was formerly more widespread in the Semien Mountains, but it is now concentrated within the Semien Mountains National Park, with four small populations outside the park.

History and Conservation Measures

Considered rather common until around 1930, the Walia ibex declined because of a number of factors. Hunting has taken a drastic toll, as has conversion of habitat to agricultural uses. Civil unrest and prolonged periods of drought have created unfavorable conditions. In addition, when the ibex moves to lower elevations in the dry season, it has to compete with domestic animals for food; it is also then subject to diseases transmitted by the domestic animals.

The total population of the species has increased slightly since the Semien Mountains National Park was established in 1969, despite civil war and the abandonment of the park by the government authorities during the worst part of the war. Although the species is known to survive, there has been no census since 1989.

Jentink's duiker

Cephalophus jentinki

Phylum	Chordata
Class	Mammalia
Order	Artiodactyla
Family	Bovidae
Status	Endangered, IUCN
	Endangered, USFWS
	Appendix I, CITES
Range	Côte d'Ivoire; Liberia; Sierra Leone

Description and Biology

A type of antelope, the duiker gets its common name from an Afrikaans word that means "diver" or "diving buck," which refers to the way these extremely shy animals lunge into dense vegetation when frightened. Jentink's duiker has a black head and neck, a white collar around its shoulders, and a mixture of black and white hair on its back and rump. The species' head and body length averages around 53 in (135 cm), and its tail measures about 6 in (15 cm); an adult may weigh up to 155 lb (70 kg). A tuft of hair on top of the head nearly hides the short horns that appear on both males and females. These horns are used to defend the animal against predators or when fighting others of the species. Its legs are short in relation to body size, and the hooves are pointed. Duikers have acute senses of hearing and sight. Usually nocturnal, they feed on fruit, seeds, leaves, and tubers from a variety of forest plants.

This species is generally seen singly, and occasionally in pairs. Young are probably born between March and June. The length of the gestation period is uncertain. A single young, born with a dark brown coat, is usually kept hidden in deep vegetation for several weeks.

Habitat and Current Distribution

Jentink's duiker is now confined to parts of Liberia, southwestern Côte d'Ivoire, and Sierra Leone. Surveys indicate that it occurs widely in eastern Liberia. Population size is uncertain, but estimated at several thousand and declining. In Côte d'Ivoire, it is restricted to the Taï National Park and some adjacent forest reserves; population figures are unknown, but thought to be rather low. The presence of this very rare and little-known species in Sierra Leone has recently been confirmed in the southern part of the Freetown Peninsula. It may also occur in the Gola forest and other areas in Sierra Leone.

This species occurs in a variety of habitats including high forest, secondary bush, and on the edges of plantations and cultivated areas.

History and Conservation Measures

Thought to be one of the world's rarest and most threatened antelopes, Jentink's duiker was not described until 1892. Because it is extremely wary, very little has been discovered about it since. The reasons cited for its rarity are forest destruction, un-

Jentink's duiker

controlled hunting for meat, and low population density.

Jentink's duiker occurs in a number of protected areas. In Liberia, it is known from Sapo National Park and the Krahn-Bassa and Gola National Forests. An individual duiker was seen in the Gobi National Forest in an area of partially logged and primary forest. The species probably also occurs in other areas of the country, such as the Grebo National Forest. Maintaining viable populations within Liberia's parks and reserves is critical to the overall conservation of this antelope species. Research programs to better assess the status and distribution of Jentink's duiker are needed to formulate habitat conservation plans. Educational programs for local communities centering on selective hunting methods are also needed, as are captive breeding programs.

The westernmost population of Jentink's duiker is believed to be in the southern part of the Western Area Forest Reserve in Sierra Leone. To preserve this population, programs are urgently needed to educate local farmers and hunters about the rarity of this duiker and its protected status, facts that are often not adequately communicated at this level. An added threat to the reserve, and therefore to the duiker, is loss of forest for fuelwood. To combat this problem, buffer zones intended for the sustainable harvest of fuelwood should be established on the reserve's periphery for use by the surrounding community.

In Côte d'Ivoire, the population density of Jentink's duiker is extremely low, even in suitable habitats. Because of extensive cocoa farming in the region, the species is now primarily confined to Taï National Park, where a moderately viable population exists. Apart from Taï National Park, the species is only known to occur in three other areas in the country: the Scio, Cavally-Gouin, and Haut Dodo Forest Reserves. More effective conservation measures are needed at these sites to ensure the survival of this rare antelope.

Hunter's antelope

Damaliscus hunteri

Phylum	Chordata
Class	Mammalia
Order	Artiodactyla
Family	Bovidae
Status	Endangered, IUCN
Range	Kenya; Somalia

Description and Biology

Hunter's antelope—which is also known as Hunter's hartebeest, hirola, and sassaby—has a fairly soft coat in shades of light or reddish brown and a white marking between the eyes that gives the appearance of spectacles. Head and body length averages 3.9-6.6 ft (1.2-2 m), shoulder height is 36-50 in (91-127 cm), weight is 150-330 lb (68-150 kg), and tail length is 5-20 in (13-51 cm); males are larger and heavier than females and have larger horns. Limbs are long and slender, muzzle long, and horns approximately 22-28 in (56-71 cm) long, curved, and ringed. The hirola is a grazer, feeding mainly on grasses.

Males are solitary and compete for mating rights with available females. Mating takes place in March or April; a single young is born in October or November after a gestation period of seven to eight months.

Habitat and Current Distribution

This antelope occurs only in southeastern Kenya and a small part of adjacent southwestern Somalia. It inhabits grassy plains; in Kenya, the inhabited plains area consists of a narrow strip lying between waterless thornbush to the north and coastal forest-savanna mosaic to the south. Population numbers are uncertain but are estimated at fewer than 10,000 individuals, with the majority of the population in Kenya.

History and Conservation Measures

Although there are no estimates of initial population, this antelope is now thought to be confined to just a small portion of its former range. In the mid-1970s, there were an estimated 12,500 animals in Kenya and 1,000-2,000 in Somalia. A drought in 1984 is believed to have reduced the population. Within its very restricted range, it is believed to be threatened by competition from livestock and development of the cattle industry, with prolonged drought intensifying the threats.

Arawale National Reserve in Kenya is situated in one of the hirola's two major concentration areas. Effective protection of the population in this reserve is considered vital for its long-term survival, as livestock development programs have inevitably affected the rest of its habitat. Following its introduction in the 1960s, a population has become established in Tsavo National Park, south of the species' natural range.

Ecological and biological studies are necessary to establish priorities for conservation efforts. Long-term conservation will be dependent upon management of the antelope and other large mammals, along with their habitat, as valuable natural resources that play a part in the economy of developing nations.

Hunter's antelope.

Beira antelope

Dorcatragus megalotis

Phylum	Chordata
Class	Mammalia
Order	Artiodactyla
Family	Bovidae
Status	Insufficiently Known, IUCN
Range	Djibouti (?); Ethiopia; Somalia

Description and Biology

The beira antelope, the only species in its genus, has coarse hair that shades from red-gray on the back to yellow-red on the head and yellow-white on the underparts; there is a dark line or band on each side. An agile climber and leaper, it has long legs, a short body, and padded or rubbery hooves that are adapted to rocky terrain. Head and body length averages 28-34 in (71-86 cm), shoulder height is 20-28 in (51-71 cm), and weight is 20-24 lb (9-11 kg). Ears are noticeably large and wide; the male has widespread horns that are almost straight, curving only slightly forward. It is apparently a very selective feeder and its distribution may be related to that of its food plants. Its diet is not well known, but it has been seen feeding on some grasses and mimosa leaves, from which it seems to be able to extract enough water for survival.

This antelope is often found in groups of up to seven animals, including at least one male. No information is available about its reproductive biology.

Habitat and Current Distribution

The beira is found in Djibouti, Ethiopia, and Somalia, where it inhabits hills and mountains that are dry, stony, and rugged. There are no estimates of population size. It has been observed only twice in Ethiopia, in 1899 and 1970. It probably still occurs widely, but with a patchy and local distribution, in northern Somalia, including the Marmar Mountains on the Ethiopia/Somalia border adjacent to southeastern Djibouti. If it is present within Djibouti, the population is probably small and localized.

History and Conservation Measures

The status of the beira is uncertain, probably because much of its habitat is inaccessible. Loss of suitable habitat is most likely a threat to this species, as is uncontrolled hunting. Although it seems to need little water, long periods of drought are sure to have a detrimental effect on the population of this species. Reports suggest that there was a marked decrease, at least in Somalia, during the 1975 drought and that its numbers have not recovered. The beira is protected from hunting to some extent by its inconspicuousness, its coloring merging closely with the stony hillsides on which it occurs, but it may be affected by habitat deterioration, as much of its range is overgrazed. At present, it is not known to occur in any protected areas.

Dama gazelle

Gazella dama

Phylum	Chordata
Class	Mammalia
Order	Artiodactyla
Family	Bovidae
Status	Endangered, IUCN
	Appendix I, CITES
Range	Algeria (?); Burkina Faso; Chad; Mali; Niger; Sudan

Description and Biology

The dama gazelle, found in Saharan Africa, has long legs, a long neck, and fairly short, sharply curved horns. At physical maturity, its head and body length averages 40-67 in (100-170 cm), its shoulder height averages 35-42 in (89-107 cm), its horns average 13-15 in (33-38 cm), and its weight averages 90-185 lb (41-84 kg). The dama gazelle's neck and most of its back are reddish brown (except for a white spot on the neck), while the underparts, rump, and head are white. The tail, which is white with a black tip, measures 9-12 in (23-30 cm). Like most gazelles, this species has very acute senses of hearing and smell. The dama gazelle is a browser, feeding on shrubs and on trees such as acacias and desert date.

This species is usually found alone or in small groups, and it moves seasonally to search for food. Births probably occur at the end of the wet season, with the gestation period lasting between 160-220 days. Generally, one young is born, but twins are not unusual.

Habitat and Current Distribution

The dama gazelle ranges across several countries in Central and West Africa, including Burkina Faso, Chad, Mali, Niger, and Sudan. The species is either very rare or extinct in Algeria and is probably extinct in Mauritania and Nigeria. It is also extinct in the wild in Senegal. In Mali, it has been reduced to very small and scattered populations; in the early 1980s, the population there was estimated at several hundred to 1,000 individuals, but the population is probably far lower now and continuing to decline. The largest surviving population in Niger is in the Termit region; the total population in this country is unknown but is probably less than 1,000 and declining. Chad has the largest population of dama gazelles—between 6,000-8,000 in the late 1970s but undoubtedly fewer now. In the Sahel region (an area south of the Sahara characterized by periodic drought) between Burkina Faso and Mali, the population has been reduced to very low levels, with survi-

Dama gazelles.

ving animals seen more often on the Mali side of the border.

In its range, this gazelle occurs mainly in the arid grassy zone between true desert (the Sahara) and true Sahel. The species prefers stony or rocky terrain, especially around the edges of hills. During dry conditions, the animal often seeks temporary streams or creeks that provide green forage and shade.

History and Conservation Measures

The decline of this gazelle is chiefly due to illegal hunting, habitat destruction, and drought. Increasing use and disturbance of the gazelle's habitat by grazing animals has been a serious problem, and droughts have forced considerable numbers of dama gazelles to move south of their usual range in search of food. Such movement brings the species into greater contact with humans, with a corresponding increase in hunting.

In the mid-1970s, this species' last stronghold throughout its entire continental range was in Chad, especially in the Ouadi Rime-Ouadi Achim Faunal Reserve. Now, its survival in Chad is threatened because there is no effective protection even in the reserve. Elsewhere in the gazelle's range, the situation

is no better. In Mali, hunting, especially from motor vehicles, is a major threat. A few dama gazelles probably still exist in Mali's Ansongo-Menaka Reserve, and small numbers may also survive in the Elephant Reserve. In Niger, meanwhile, the only protected population occurs in the Aïr and Ténère National Nature Reserve, although this reserve is in need of a viable management plan. A protected area also needs to be established in Niger's Termit region very soon to ensure the species' survival in this country, although such a measure might need to be supplemented by initiating a captive breeding group and a reintroduction program. In Burkina Faso, the dama gazelle has probably been eliminated from most, if not all, of its range, and its survival is unlikely without immediate and effective protection of the proposed Seno-Mango Biosphere Reserve.

A reintroduction program has been established in Senegal. In 1984, seven individuals were introduced to the Gueumbeul Faunal Reserve. Once this initial population has increased in the reserve and the animals have adapted to Senegal's environment, additional gazelles may be introduced into the population. Researchers also hope to establish a free-living population of dama gazelles on the sandy plains adjacent to the Ferlo River in Senegal's central Ferlo region.

Slender-horned gazelle

Gazella leptoceros

Phylum	Chordata
Class	Mammalia
Order	Artiodactyla
Family	Bovidae
Status	Endangered, IUCN
	Endangered, USFWS
	Appendix III, CITES (Tunisia)
Range	Algeria; Chad (?); Egypt; Libya; Mali; Mauritania (?); Niger; Sudan; Tunisia; Western Sahara (?)

Description and Biology

This graceful, nomadic gazelle occupies sandy desert areas. It has long, slightly curved horns, and its coat is a very light fawn color above and whitish below. At physical maturity, its head and body length averages 30-65 in (76-165 cm), its shoulder height is 20-40 in (51-102 cm), its tail is 6-10 in (15.2-25.4 cm), and its weight is 30-180 lb (13.6-81.6 kg); males are larger than females. It has a slender body, large ears, and long legs, and it has acute senses of hearing and sight. In general, gazelles are grazers or browsers, but the exact diet of the slender-horned gazelle is not known.

This species lives in groups of 5-30 animals, although groups sometimes combine to form aggregations of hundreds or—in previous times when the population was larger—even thousands of animals. A group can be comprised of females and young, bachelor males, or territorial males. Although breeding is possible throughout the year, it is thought to peak in the wet season. One young is usually born, but twins are not unusual. The gestation period typically is between 160-220 days.

Habitat and Current Distribution

This gazelle is found in sandy and stony desert areas from Egypt to Algeria, where it is well adapted to sandy dunes. The largest population of this species is found in Niger, where it occurs sporadically in the Aïr and Ténère National Nature Reserve. It may occur in Mauritania, but if so it is very rare. In Mali, it has been reported in desert bordering the Aïr Massif and may be present in other parts of the desert zone; the population is thought to be less than 1,000 individuals. Historically, this gazelle has been recorded from the extreme north of Chad, below the northern edge of the Tibesti Massif, and east of Tibesti; it may also occur elsewhere in the deserts of northern Chad. Its presence in Chad has not been confirmed recently, however, and its status there is unknown. There are no estimates of total population for the species.

History and Conservation Measures

The population of the slender-horned gazette is thought to be dangerously low, and the species may be on the verge of extinction. Hunting by humans for

Slender-horned gazelle.

food is the historic cause of population decline; an additional factor is drought in much of its range.

This gazelle formerly occurred in the Erg d'Iguidi (an area of sand dunes in the Sahara) within Algeria, and its range may have extended into the southwestern part of the Erg d'Iguidi in northeastern Mauritania. Any remaining animals in Mauritania are probably endangered because of the effects of hunting and prolonged, extreme drought. In Mali, it does not occur in any of the country's conservation areas. In Chad, its survival is certainly threatened by uncontrolled hunting, military activity, and the effects of recent, prolonged droughts. It is not protected within any of Chad's official conservation areas, and security problems make any conservation efforts in the remote northern border region impossible.

Surveys of the desert regions of the Aïr and Ténère National Nature Reserve and of the Termit area, Niger, are needed so that researchers can assess the slender-horned gazelle's status. Discovery of a viable population of this species in the Termit area, for example, would increase the likelihood of a protected area being established there. In addition, researchers need to begin a captive breeding program for this species in Niger so that animals can be reintroduced into protected areas.

Arabian tahr

Hemitragus jayakari

Nilgiri tahr

Hemitragus hylocrius

Phylum	Chordata
Class	Mammalia
Order	Artiodactyla
Family	Bovidae
Status	Vulnerable, IUCN
	Endangered, USFWS (*H. jayakari*)
Range	Oman; United Arab Emirates (?) (*H. jayakari*)
	India (*H. hylocrius*)

Description and Biology

The tahr is a short-horned wild goat that varies in color with species; two of the three species are of conservation concern. The Arabian tahr (*H. jayakari*) has a grayish brown coat with a dark dorsal stripe. Its hair is short and shaggy, and there is a long mane, especially in males, around the neck and shoulders that extends onto the back and forelegs. This is the smallest of the tahr species with a total head and body length averaging 36-43 in (91-124 cm), shoulder height of 32-43 in (81-110 cm), and weight around 50 lb (22.7 kg) The Nilgiri tahr (*H. hylocrius*) has a dark brownish black, short and bristly coat with a saddle-shaped silver-gray area on the back and white markings on the legs. Total head and body length averages 50-59 in (127-150 cm), shoulder height is 23.5-30 in (60-76 cm), and weight is 110-220 lb (50-100 kg); males are larger and heavier than females. The Arabian tahr feeds often at night and during early morning and late evening on a diet of grasses, herbs, fruits, and shrubs. The Nilgiri tahr feeds mainly during day-light hours, especially around dawn and dusk, on grasses and herbs. Predators of Arabian tahrs are leopards; leopards and wild dogs (dholes) prey on Nilgiri tahrs.

The Arabian tahr lives alone or in small groups of up to five individuals. Nothing is known of their social behavior, but a single young is born after a gestation period of at least 150 days. The Nilgiri tahr is found in groups of females and young that range from 20 to more than 100 individuals; males generally live separately except for the mating season. Although young have been reported throughout the year, the peak of births coincide with the beginning of the monsoon season in July and August. One young is born in January or February after a gestation period of around 180 days.

Habitat and Current Distribution

The Arabian tahr occurs in the mountains of Musandam and through the Hajar Mountains of

Nilgiri tahr.

The Nilgiri tahr occurs in the Western Ghats, a mountain range in the extreme southwest of the Indian peninsula. There, in an area of high rainfall at around 6,000 ft (2,000 m), it inhabits grassland hills down to the forests. Population is estimated at between 2,000 and 2,500 individuals. Both species are believed to be decreasing in numbers.

History and Conservation Measures

Very little is known about the Arabian tahr because it inhabits such remote and rugged areas and lives in such low densities. Although legally protected, it is still the target of poachers. Competition with livestock, primarily domestic goats, has also contributed to their decline, as have the periodic naturally occurring droughts. A small captive breeding population is held in Oman, with the hope that in the future surplus animals will be released.

There are 17 known populations of Nilgiri tahrs; the two largest are located in the Nilgiri hill country and in the Eravikulam National Park. Low population figures are attributed to poaching and habitat destruction, but the two largest populations are believed to be fairly secure. Hydroelectric projects and expanding agricultural development also destroy their habitat. An additional concern is the possibility of a low reproductive rate in small population groups.

northern Oman, where it inhabits steep arid cliffs with only scattered scrub vegetation at elevations of 3,300-6,000 ft (1,000-1,800 m). Population is estimated at no more than 2,000 individuals.

Red goral

Nemorhaedus baileyi

Phylum	Chordata
Class	Mammalia
Order	Artiodactyla
Family	Bovidae
Status	Insufficiently Known, IUCN (*N. b. cranbrooki*)
	Endangered, IUCN (*N. b. baileyi*)
Range	China; India; Myanmar

Description and Biology

A member of the goat family, the red goral is found along rugged mountain sides and wooded slopes. It has long, coarse hair that varies from brownish gray to reddish or dark brown, with a dark to black stripe down the back and on the forelegs, a white area on the throat, and light underparts. Head and body length averages 32-50 in (81-127 cm), shoulder height is 22-30 in (56-76 cm), weight is 48-77 lb (22-35 kg), and tail length is 3-8 in (8-20 cm) long. Both male and female have horns that curve backward and average 5-7 in (13-18 cm). Long, strong legs are necessary for climbing and jumping in its rugged habitat. This goral feeds on a variety of vegetation.

Although older males sometimes live alone, the red goral usually gathers in groups of up to 12 animals. During mating season, which varies from September to December with geographic location, males may stake out a territory of approximately 60 acres (24 ha). One or two young are born after a gestation period of six to eight months.

Habitat and Current Distribution

This species is found in a small area of the eastern Himalayas on the borders of Tibet, India, and Myanmar, where it inhabits a rugged terrain of heavily wooded mountains and steep slopes at elevations of 3,300-13,000 ft (1,000-4,000 m). *N. b. baileyi* occurs in Tibet where counts revealed a population of 810-1,370 animals in 1987-88; this subspecies is considered to be endangered. *N. b. cranbrooki* occurs in India and Myanmar, but there is insufficient information as to its status.

History and Conservation Measures

The red goral is subject to hunting in Tibet, primarily due to an increasing number of immigrants with modern hunting weapons. A hunting ban which has been in effect for the last five years has not proved effective, and poaching is still common. Habitat loss is also an increasing problem due to rapid forestry expansion since economic reforms were introduced in Tibet in the early 1980s. The species occurs in at least three protected areas in Tibet, and there is a captive breeding population in the Shanghai Zoo. There is no recent information on the status of this species in India and Myanmar.

Nemorhaedus goral cranbrooki.

Scimitar-horned oryx

Oryx dammah

Phylum	Chordata
Class	Mammalia
Order	Artiodactyla
Family	Bovidae
Status	Endangered, IUCN
	Appendix I, CITES
Range	Chad

Description and Biology

The common name of this oryx comes from the scimitar or curved shape of its two horns, which extend back from its head in a long, sweeping arc. The animal's body is a light tawny color with a darker brown chest and brown markings on the face; the light color helps to reflect some of the intense heat from the desert sun. This oryx has short and rounded ears, large hooves, and a tuft of hair below the chin. It also has a short mane extending from its head over its shoulders. At physical maturity, the scimitar-horned oryx's head and body length averages 60-90 in (152-230 cm), its shoulder height averages 40-55 in (100-140 cm), and its weight averages 250-460 lb (110-200 kg). Its horns average 30-55 in (76-140 cm) in length, while its tail averages 18-35 in (46-89 cm); the tail ends in a tuft of hair. This animal feeds during the day, grazing on grass and desert vegetation and moving over long distances to find new vegetation after rain. Its predators include the large cats and hyenas.

This oryx often gathers in herds of 20-40 animals, but when populations were larger, herds sometimes joined together to form groups of up to 1,000 individuals. Births may occur throughout the year, but they peak during the late cold/early hot season (February-April) and the late rainy/early cold season (September-November). One young is usually born after a gestation period of 220-253 days.

Habitat and Current Distribution

The scimitar-horned oryx inhabits rolling dunes, grassy steppes, and wooded interdunal depressions in the subdesert steppe, an arid grassy zone between desert and Sahel (a region south of the Sahara characterized by periodic droughts) areas. It is thought to be extinct in much of its former range, including Mauritania, Mali, Senegal, Nigeria, and probably Niger and Burkina Faso. Chad is now the only country with a viable population of scimitar-horned oryx. The size of this population is unknown, but it has probably been reduced to a few hundred.

History and Conservation Measures

This species was once quite common in the areas surrounding the Sahara. In 1936, for example, a researcher reported seeing a single herd of 10,000 scimitar-horned oryx. In the past few decades, however, uncontrolled hunting by humans, drought, desertification, and competition with domestic livestock for scarce food supplies have all combined to eliminate this oryx from most of its former range.

The earliest extinction in the scimitar-horned oryx's range probably occurred in northern Senegal, which lies at the southern end of the range. There, the species was hunted to extinction by 1914. Hunting was also responsible for the species' disappearance

A herd of scimitar-horned oryx.

from Burkina Faso in the 1950s. Recent sightings have been reported from this area, but they are unconfirmed.

In Mauritania, the story is the same: uncontrolled hunting leading to extinction. In Mali, where this oryx was once widespread in the Sahel and along the southern edge of the desert, the species has probably been extinct since 1981. Again, hunting was a major factor, although competition with domestic livestock also played a role.

The scimitar-horned oryx was fairly numerous in Niger's Sahel zone, but by the 1970s it was largely confined to the southern fringe of the Sahara. The total population declined to less than 200 by the early 1980s, and there have been no reliable reports of this species since a herd of four was seen between the Aïr Mountains and Termit in 1983. In addition to the usual factors of hunting and competition with livestock for food, the creation of deep permanent-water

bore-holes for livestock impacted the species' feeding grounds.

By the mid-1970s, almost all of the region's scimitar-horned oryx, then numbering several thousand, were confined to a single place: the Ouadi Rime-Ouadi Achim Faunal Reserve in Chad. Established in 1969, the reserve was a suitable, well-protected habitat area, and it probably contained 4,000-6,000 individuals by 1978. With the onset of civil war in 1978, however, protection for the reserve ceased. The population level has decreased significantly since then, and herds have been split into small groups and scattered.

Until this reserve once again has effective protection, the status of the scimitar-horned oryx will be in jeopardy. In addition, captive breeding programs are needed so that animals can be reintroduced into the wild.

Argali

Ovis ammon

Phylum	Chordata
Class	Mammalia
Order	Artiodactyla
Family	Bovidae
Status	Indeterminate, IUCN
	Endangered, USFWS
	Appendix II, CITES
Range	Afghanistan; China; India; Kazakhstan; Mongolia; Nepal; Pakistan; Russia; Tadjikistan

Description and Biology

The argali is the largest of the wild sheep. Coat color varies among subspecies from light brown to dark gray or grayish brown, with pale underparts, and the white rump patch also varies in size between subspecies. The male has massive spiral horns that measure 65-75 in (165-190 cm) in length; the female has small horns that are only slightly backward-curved. Average total head and body length is 50-75 in (127-190 cm), shoulder height is 30-50 in (76-127 cm), and weight is 210-440 lb (95-200 kg). The diet of argali includes grasses, sedges, herbs, and low shrubs. Predators include leopards, snow leopards, and wolves, while golden eagles may prey on juveniles.

Herds may be as large as 100 individuals, but most are smaller. They include females, young, and immature males; mature males mainly live separately, joining the females in the mating season. In fights between males for social status and mating privileges, opponents interact frequently, often raising up on their hindlegs and clashing their horns against each other. Mating occurs in the autumn and early winter; one or two young are born each year in spring after a gestation period of about 150-180 days. Lambs are nursed for around three to four months.

Habitat and Current Distribution

The argali has a widespread distribution from the Pamir northeast through the Tien Shan, Kara Tau, Kazakhsky Melkosopochnik, Krebet Tarbagatay, and the Altai Mountains, through parts of the Gobi Desert and into Inner Mongolia. They also occur east from the Pamir through the Himalayas, Kunlun Shan, and Altun Shan of the Tibetan Plateau. There are at least seven subspecies, and possibly more. It is found at elevations of 4,300-20,000 ft (1,300-6,100 m) and prefers dry climates and steppe and open grasslands on rolling hills and mountains. There is no reliable estimate for the total population, but numbers probably do not exceed 60,000. However, many populations are small (less than 500) and scattered.

History and Conservation Measures

The status of the argali is uncertain but many populations and subspecies are threatened. All subspecies are highly prized for their magnificent horns, and hunting has been and remains a major threat. However, argalis face additional threats, including competition for food and water with livestock, the potential of disease transmission from domestic sheep, and habitat loss and poaching due to increasing human populations.

In most countries argali are protected by law and there are at least 29 protected areas throughout their range. However, the level of actual protection that argalis receive is often limited due to logistical constraints and/or political will. Because of their great value to foreign hunters, many countries with argalis are interested in developing trophy hunting programs, but such programs require adequate population data to be collected before sustainable-use management plans can be developed. In recent years, stricter controls on hunting, poaching, and livestock grazing and the creation of new protected areas have all been recommended to protect argalis.

Mountain nyala

Tragelaphus buxtoni

Phylum	Chordata
Class	Mammalia
Order	Artiodactyla
Family	Bovidae
Status	Endangered, IUCN
Range	Ethiopia

Description and Biology

The mountain nyala has a shaggy, grayish brown coat and brown mane; there are white markings on the back, between the eyes, and on the side of the face. The female has a redder coat and more clearly defined markings than the male. Head and body length averages 6.5-8.5 ft (2-2.6 m), shoulder height is 36-50 in (91-127 cm), and weight is 150-400 lb (68-180 kg); males are larger and heavier than females. The male has spiral-shaped horns that average 26 in (66 cm) long.

Browsing on a diet of vegetation, including herbs, bushes, and lower tree branches, the nyala is most active in the mornings and evenings.

This species is sometimes solitary, but groups of an average of nine animals are more common; groups sometimes combine to form large herds of almost 100 individuals. Males are found in bachelor and/or family groups. Mountain nyalas are not territorial, but groups do exhibit a distinct dominance hierarchy. Very little information is available about its reproductive biology, but one young is produced, usually late in the wet season.

Habitat and Current Distribution

The mountain nyala occurs only in the eastern highlands of Ethiopia at altitudes above 9,500 ft (2,900 m), where it inhabits forests, woodlands, areas of dense vegetation, and associated grassland and moorland. Population in the wild is estimated at 2,000-4,000 individuals, around 1,250-1,400 of which are protected in the Bale Mountains National Park. Mountain nyalas exhibit some degree of seasonal movement, using thicker habitat, such as woodlands and heather, more in the dry season. They avoid extreme cold and hot weather by resting in woodlands.

History and Conservation Measures

Since its discovery in 1908, the mountain nyala's population has experienced a steady decline. Numbers were estimated at 7,000-8,000 in the 1960s, but since then, population has been reduced by at least half. Reasons for the decline are thought to be excessive hunting and forest clearance for agricultural development. Optimum habitat for this species has already been increased around Bale Mountains National Park, providing additional sanctuary for this species in this critical protected area. It has been suggested that a second conservation area be established in the Arssi or Harerghe Mountains.

Mountain nyalas.

Mexican prairie dog

Cynomys mexicanus

Phylum	Chordata
Class	Mammalia
Order	Rodentia
Family	Sciuridae
Status	Endangered, IUCN
	Endangered, USFWS
	Appendix I, CITES
Range	Mexico

Description and Biology

A large, stout squirrel with a short tail and short legs, the Mexican prairie dog averages 12-16 in (30-40 cm) and weighs 1.5-3 lb (.7-1.4 kg); the male is larger and heavier than the female. It has a grizzled appearance, and the pelage is tinted with black, white, red, and yellow. The tip of the tail is black. This squirrel undergoes two complete moults a year. Like other members of the genus, the Mexican prairie dog is active above ground throughout the year and is strictly diurnal, feeding on grasses and other plants. Badgers, coyotes, weasels, eagles, hawks, and snakes are its main predators.

Prairie dogs excavate large burrows with several entrances, where a coterie made up of one or two adult males, one to four adult females, and a variable number of young and yearlings live together. The reproductive season varies from one site to another, depending on food availability. The breeding season is believed to begin as early as late January and extend into July. After a gestation period of about one month, the female produces one litter a year.

Habitat and Current Distribution

Endemic to Mexico, this animal's distribution is extremely limited and restricted to southern Coahuila and northern San Luis Potosi (northeastern Mexico), where it inhabits open plains, valleys, and plateaus at elevations of 5,200-7,200 ft (1,600-2,200 m). There are no estimates of population size.

History and Conservation Measures

The Mexican prairie dog may always have had a restricted distribution and was long known from only one colony. Because of its limited range and apparently small population, it is extremely vulnerable to habitat loss. Expanding human population, increased agricultural activity, and grazing livestock have diminished or destroyed this animal's former habitat. Some colonies have been intentionally poisoned because they were perceived as pests that destroyed crops and grazing land. Specific conservation measures cannot be formulated until more is learned about this species' basic biology. Habitat preservation and public education programs will undoubtedly play major roles in the conservation of this animal.

Vancouver Island marmot

Marmota vancouverensis

Phylum	Chordata
Class	Mammalia
Order	Rodentia
Family	Sciuridae
Status	Endangered, IUCN
	Endangered, USFWS
Range	Vancouver Island (Canada)

Description and Biology

The marmot is a thick-bodied burrowing squirrel with coarse fur and a bushy tail measuring 4-10 in (10-25 cm). Its coat is unique among marmots, being a rich brown, almost black. Head and body length averages 12-23.5 in (30-60 cm) and weight is 6.6-16.5 lb (3-7.5 kg). The marmot is a true hibernator, spending six to nine months sleeping in a den, huddled together with its family group, only occasionally emerging in mild weather or to urinate or defecate. Their diet consists of plants, especially the flowering parts of alpine plants.

Marmot colonies average about eight individuals, excluding newly born young. The adults are usually paired. Mating occurs in April or May; a litter of two to six young is born after a four- to five-week gestation period. When the young emerge from the burrow, they are protected by the family group.

Habitat and Current Distribution

This marmot is endemic to Vancouver Island, British Columbia, Canada. It inhabits the higher parts of the coastal mountains that characterize central and southern Vancouver Island. Most of the known colonies are in a small area between Green Mountain and Butler Peak in the southern part of the island. In 1984,

the population was estimated at 231 individuals, including 68 young.

The alpine and subalpine habitat preferred by

Vancouver Island marmot.

this species lies at elevations of 3,280-6,560 ft (1,000-2,000 m) and is characterized by steep slopes, rocks, and open meadows. Steep slopes, cleared of snow by avalanches, appear necessary to provide early foraging in spring. Avalanches also maintain the herbaceous plant communities favored by the marmot by inhibiting or preventing tree growth.

History and Conservation Measures

The Vancouver Island marmot was discovered in 1911. The major factor in the species' decline since that time has probably been direct or indirect interference by man. Development of ski resorts has destroyed some suitable habitat, and logging may have removed important migration corridors to existing or potential colony sites, exposing dispersing marmots to predation and preventing natural establishment of further colonies. Recent evidence also suggests that low-elevation logging creates environments that are superficially attractive to dispersing marmots since these mimic certain alpine conditions. When these animals become permanent residents, however, they find themselves ill-adapted and unable to survive in such environments.

Inbreeding may also pose a long-term threat in isolated colonies. Hunting and collecting for scientific purposes were probably important factors in the past, and there is evidence that some wanton killing continues today. An additional problem is that most colonies are on privately owned land, which is difficult to protect from logging and recreational development. In some cases, the owners have protected habitat and provided buffer zones between logging areas and colonies but, because of private ownership, long-term protection cannot be guaranteed. Active and vocal conservation efforts, especially from the Vancouver Island Marmot Preservation Society, have stimulated public interest and governmental action, including field research, establishment of a management plan, acquisition of land, and captive breeding programs. As a result, there has been an increase in marmot population and distribution since the 1970s. The establishment of protected reserves for this marmot would give the species further protection from encroachment by the logging and mining industries and from new recreational developments.

African pygmy squirrel

Myosciurus pumilio

Phylum	Chordata
Class	Mammalia
Order	Rodentia
Family	Sciuridae
Status	Vulnerable, IUCN
Range	Cameroon; Bioko (Equatorial Guinea); Gabon; Nigeria

Description and Biology

Considered the smallest squirrel in the world, the African pygmy squirrel resembles a mouse more than a squirrel. It weighs a little over half an ounce (16.5 g) and has a head and body length of 2.3-2.9 in (5.9-7.4 cm). Its narrow tail is nearly as long as its body, measuring 2-2.3 in (5.1-5.8 cm). The pelage of this squirrel has a greenish tint, with almost white underparts; there are white edges around its ears. African pygmy squirrels are solitary animals. This species eats fungi which it obtains by pulling the bark from tree trunks and branches.

Habitat and Current Distribution

The African pygmy squirrel is found in Nigeria, Cameroon, Gabon, and Bioko. It appears to occupy a wide range of forest types and is found at various tree levels. Population figures are unknown but are thought to be low.

History and Conservation Measures

Classified as vulnerable, the African pygmy squirrel may be affected by the widespread deforestation now taking place in West Africa. There is no information available about its conservation needs or efforts being made to protect this species.

Usambara squirrel

Paraxerus vexillarius

Phylum	Chordata
Class	Mammalia
Order	Rodentia
Family	Sciuridae
Status	Rare, IUCN
Range	Tanzania

Description and Biology

The Usambara squirrel is an African bush squirrel with a soft, thick coat of brown fur. It has large eyes, pointed ears, and a bushy tail with a large, orange-buff tip. Not much is known about this species.

Habitat and Current Distribution

This squirrel occurs exclusively on the west Usambara Mountains of northeastern Tanzania. There are no estimates of population, but it is common in rain forest habitat at altitudes between 3,280 and 7,550 ft (1,000-2,300 m). The total population is thought to be several thousand.

History and Conservation Measures

The taxonomic status of this species has been unclear in the past; it was considered by some to be a hybrid between *Paraxerus lucifer* and *P. palliatus*, but more recent studies have confirmed that this is not the case. The natural forests in which the Usambara squirrel occurs are diminishing as a result of encroachment for subsistence agriculture. While a number of the forest patches are in forest reserves, the protection of these is not yet adequate.

European souslik

Spermophilus citellus

Phylum	Chordata
Class	Mammalia
Order	Rodentia
Family	Sciuridae
Status	Insufficiently known, IUCN
Range	Southeast Germany; Czech Republic; Slovakia; Southwest Poland through Southeast Europe to European Turkey; Moldova; Ukraine

Description and Biology

The European souslik, also known as the European ground squirrel, is usually brown to gray with lighter underparts. Adult body length is 7.5-8 in (19.3-20.4 cm), and its tail measures 1.5-2.3 in (3.8-6 cm). The weight of European sousliks varies between 3-35 oz (85-1,000 g). The species feeds primarily on vegetation, nuts, seeds, and grains; however, individuals may also consume small invertebrates.

Habitat and Current Distribution

The range of this species extends from southeastern Germany, the Czech Republic, Slovakia, and southwest Poland through southeastern Europe to European Turkey, Moldova, and western Ukraine. This range is divided into smaller, isolated areas; in particular, the eastern Carpathians divide the range into northwestern and southeastern sections. No estimates of population currently exist.

History and Conservation Measures

Intensification of agriculture in Europe has contributed greatly to the decline of the European souslik and the fragmentation of their range. For example, in Silesia, a region now part of Poland, souslik populations expanded considerably during the early nineteenth century. However, technological advancements and the resulting intensification of land exploitation resulted in the drastic reduction of the souslik's range by the 1960s. The species may now be extinct in this area. The species is protected in Hungary and Poland, but throughout its range, edge populations are steadily decreasing. As colonies become more isolated, the European souslik could easily become extinct as agriculture intensifies and suitable habitat is lost.

California kangaroo rats

Dipodomys spp.

Phylum	Chordata
Class	Mammalia
Order	Rodentia
Family	Heteromyidae
Status	Endangered, IUCN (*D. gravipes; D. heermanni morroensis; D. nitratoides exilis; D. nitratoides nitratoides; D. stephensi*)
	Indeterminate, IUCN (*D. ingens*)
	Rare, IUCN (*D. elator*)
Range	Mexico; California (U.S.A.)

Description and Biology

The kangaroo rat has a tail that is longer than its body and long hind legs that it uses for hopping, thus inspiring its common name. Body coloration varies with each species, ranging from brown to yellowish brown with white underparts. The head and body lengths of these animals average 4-14 in (10-35.6 cm). The kangaroo rat's tail measures 4-8 in (10-20 cm) long and ends in a tuft of hair. Its average weight is 1.2-6.3 oz (34-179 g). The giant kangaroo rat (*Dipodomys ingens*) is the largest of the kangaroo rats and the Tipton kangaroo rat (*Dipodomys nitratoides nitratoides*) is the smallest. Diet includes seeds, leaves, stems, and buds of young plants, supplemented by insects. This rodent seldom drinks water, obtaining moisture from the vegetation it eats and conserving water by foraging only at night. Despite its limited intake of fluids, the kangaroo rat produces a very concentrated urine.

Most of these species live in underground burrows, where they store food for the winter months. Breeding is possible throughout the year, but peaks in mild weather. Two to five young are born after a gestation period of around a month.

Habitat and Current Distribution

At least seven species of kangaroo rats are of conservation concern in southwestern North America.

The most critical example is the Morro Bay kangaroo rat (*Dipodomys heermanni morroensis*), now limited to less than 60 animals on a site of less than 50 acres (20 ha) in San Luis Obispo County, California. It requires low, sparse vegetation and is classified as endangered.

The giant kangaroo rat (*Dipodomys ingens*) is now restricted to an area of less than 5 sq mi (13 sq km) between the Carrizo Plain and the city of Taft located in west-central California. It requires annual grassland on sandy loam soil and is classified as indeterminate.

The Stephens kangaroo rat (*Dipodomys stephensi*) occurs only in western Riverside County, California, and is classified as endangered.

The Fresno kangaroo rat (*Dipodomys nitratoides exilis*) and the Tipton kangaroo rat (*Dipodomys nitratoides nitratoides*) both occur in the southern half of the San Joaquin Valley in California. *D. n. exilis* is in upland areas; *D. n. nitratoides* is

California kangaroo rat.

restricted to the valley floor of the Tulare Basin. Both are classified as endangered.

The San Quintin kangaroo rat (*Dipodomys gravipes*) occurs only in a 60 mi (100 km) coastal strip of low vegetation and little topographic relief in northern Baja California, Mexico. It is classified as endangered.

The historical distribution of the Texas kangaroo rat (*Dipodomys elator*) has been reduced from ten to five counties in Texas and from two to zero counties in Oklahoma. This species is listed as threatened by the U.S. Fish and Wildlife Service and as a threatened nongame species by the state of Texas.

History and Conservation Measures

The common threat to all these animals is habitat destruction due to burgeoning human populations. Residential and commercial development, oil exploration, agricultural development, the use of pesticides, and predation by domestic cats have contributed to the degradation of historical habitat for these rodents.

The habitat of the Morro Bay kangaroo rat has been usurped by suburban housing development. Captive breeding of this species has thus far been unsuccessful, but efforts are ongoing. A survey of sites that may be suitable for the reintroduction of translocated and/or captively bred animals has been initiated. In addition, efforts are currently being made to purchase the acres of private land where the remaining population now resides.

Conservation efforts for the giant kangaroo rat include the acquisition of suitable habitat in Kern and San Luis Obispo Counties in California, and surveys of extant habitat for the species' presence and distribution. Conservation objectives for the Stephens kangaroo rat include the institution of a system of viable preserves within the historic range of the animal. Surveys of potential and extant habitat for the Tipton kangaroo rat and the Fresno kangaroo rat are now underway to determine the species' presence and distribution. Long-term goals include the establishment of protected reserves for the species. Studies are necessary on the distribution and habitat of the San Quintin kangaroo rat and the Texas kangaroo rat before suitable conservation programs can be formulated. Recent recovery plans include the identification of several protected areas, among them Copper Breaks State Park, that could be managed to increase population density of the species. The maintenance of short grasses and bare ground are critical features of such a plan.

African gerbils

Gerbillus mauritaniae

Gerbillus muriculus

Gerbillus nancillus

Gerbillus rosalinda

Gerbillus acticola

Dipodillus maghrebi

Microdillus peeli

Tatera minuscula

Ammodillus imbellis

Phylum	Chordata
Class	Mammalia
Order	Rodentia
Family	Muridae
Status	Insufficiently Known, IUCN
	Rare, IUCN (*G. rosalinda*; *T. minuscula*)
Range	Ethiopia; Mauritania; Morocco; Somalia; Sudan

Description and Biology

The gerbil is a burrowing rodent with long hind legs and a hairy tail. Gerbils in the genus *Gerbillus* are slender with long ears and claws; the tail is furred and often has a darker tuft at the tip. Body coloration varies with the species and can be tan, gray, brown, or reddish brown with a darker linear marking on the back. Many of the African species that are of conservation concern are very poorly known; detailed descriptions are available for only a few.

Microdillus peeli has light yellow-brown fur with light to white underparts, hands, and feet, and a whitish spot behind each ear. Head and body length averages 2.4-3.1 in (6-7.9 cm) and the tail is 2.2-2.4 in (5.6-6 cm). *Tatera minuscula* has a stocky body, and its head and body length averages 3.5-8 in (9-20 cm), weight is 1-8 oz (28-227 g), and tail is 4.5-9.7 in (11.4-24.6 cm). *Ammodillus imbellis*, also referred to as the walo, has reddish tan fur that is tipped with black at the ends; underparts are light to white, as are its hands, feet, chin, and cheeks. White marks at the bases of ears and above the eyes distinguish this gerbil. The 5.3-6.3 in (13.5-16 cm) tail is lightly haired, and the feet and hands appear almost bare but they are also lightly furred. Head and body length of this species averages 3.3-4.2 in (8.4-10.7 cm).

Most gerbils are primarily nocturnal and spend the day in burrows. Diet is not known for all species, but it mainly consists of seeds, roots, grasses, nuts, and sometimes insects.

There is very little information available about the social structure or reproductive biology of these species. Females are known to be in estrous many times during the year, and breeding can take place at any time. Gestation period for most species is 20-22 days, and the litter size ranges from 1-8 young, although 4-5 is most common.

Habitat and Current Distribution

Gerbillus mauritaniae is currently known from just one specimen that originated from southern Mauritania; nothing is known about its life history.

Gerbillus muriculus is one of a number of poorly known, small gerbils found in Sudan. It is only known from two specimens from western Sudan.

Gerbillus nancillus is the smallest species of the hairy-footed gerbil. It is known only from seven specimens collected from central Sudan, and no information is available on its reproductive biology, habitat requirements, or distribution.

Gerbillus rosalinda is a dark-colored gerbil that was described in 1929 from seven specimens originat-ing from west-central Sudan; it was reported from central Somalia in 1978.

Gerbillus acticola is known only from northern Somalia; it is poorly known in this region, and nothing is known of its life history.

Dipodillus maghrebi is known from seven specimens from the type locality in northern Morocco; nothing is known of the population status or the biology of this species.

Microdillus peeli is known from three localities in northern and central Somalia, where it occurs in subdesert steppe. Nothing is known about population levels or the life history of this species.

Tatera minuscula is known from two localities, the type locality of Sheik Hussein in eastern Ethiopia and the lower Omo Valley, Ethiopia. Its taxonomy and distribution are poorly known, but it seems to be rare within its area of occurrence.

Ammodillus imbellis is known from seven localities in eastern Ethiopia and northern and central Somalia, where it occurs in subdesert steppe.

History and Conservation Measures

Because so little is known about these gerbil species, it is difficult to assess their status or the conservation efforts necessary to preserve them. Further studies are necessary to determine these rodents' biology, population size, areas of distribution, and habitat needs.

Greater stick-nest rat

Leporillus conditor

Phylum	Chordata
Class	Mammalia
Order	Rodentia
Family	Muridae
Status	Rare, IUCN
	Endangered, USFWS
	Appendix I, CITES
Range	Franklin Island (Australia)

Description and Biology

This rodent is called the greater stick-nest rat to distinguish it from the lesser stick-nest rat (*Leporillus apicalis*), which is probably extinct. Because of its similar size and rounded ears, the greater stick-nest rat resembles a rabbit, although it has a long tail. It has a brown coat with lighter shading underneath; it averages about 16 in (41 cm) long, including its tail, and weighs approximately 12 oz (350 g). Leaves and fruits of succulent plants form the bulk of the rat's diet; it depends on the high moisture content of these plants for water.

As its name implies, this rat builds elaborate stick-nests or "wurlies," which can be as large as 3 ft (1 m) high and 10 ft (3 m) across. Inside the nests are interconnected grass-lined chambers where a number of rats (usually between 10 and 20) live together, protected from predators and from temperature extremes. Breeding season varies with seasonal and climatic conditions. One to four young are born after a gestation period of 42-44 days and are weaned at four to eight weeks.

Habitat and Current Distribution

This species is found only on Franklin Island, off the coast of western South Australia. Population size is uncertain, and estimates during the 1970s have varied from 1,500-5,000 individuals. In 1991, estimated population size was less than 2,500 individuals.

The preferred habitat of this species is semi-arid or arid shrubland and low steppe. Perennial shrublands—containing succulent and semi-succulent plant species—are especially favored.

History and Conservation Measures

The stick-nest rat was once at least locally common on the Australian mainland, but its former range and population are unknown and it has not been reported on the mainland since 1933. It was already reduced in numbers by the mid-1800s. Since then this species has suffered a range reduction of at least 90 percent and subsequently its population has been reduced by as much.

A number of factors combined to reduce this species to a remnant island population. Introduced rabbits, sheep, and cattle rapidly reduced the available supply of food. In addition, successive years of drought have had a detrimental effect on this and other species. Predation by foxes and cats further reduced the numbers, as did hunting by humans for food.

This rat is preyed upon by owls and snakes, but

the population appears to be stable. It is also threatened by introduced plants which suppress native vegetation. Careful control of predators and competitors on this island refuge will be necessary for the survival of the stick-nest rat. Franklin Island is part of the Nuyts Archipelago Conservation Park under the control of the South Australian National Parks and Wildlife Service.

A captive colony has been established near Adelaide, and about 190 captive-bred animals have been released to nearby islands in the past four years. There are further plans to increase the geographic range of this species by introducing the greater stick-nest rat to adjacent offshore islands and possibly onto the mainland.

Madagascar rodents

Macrotarsomys ingens

Eliurus minor

Gymnuromys roberti

Hypogeomys antimena

Phylum	Chordata
Class	Mammalia
Order	Rodentia
Family	Muridae
Status	Insufficiently Known, IUCN (*M. ingens, E. minor, H. antimena*)
	Rare, IUCN (*G. roberti*)
Range	Madagascar

Description and Biology

Madagascar has some unique rodents that are of conservation concern, but there is very little information available about their population size or composition, habits, or reproductive biology. As a result, it is difficult to determine the conservation requirements, if any, of these species. *Macrotarsomys ingens* is a small species which resembles a gerbil externally, with fawn-colored fur and light to white underparts; its eyes and ears are large. Head and body length averages 4.7 in (12 cm) while the tail measures 8.3 in (21 cm) and is slightly tufted at the end. It is a nocturnal species that appears to be primarily arboreal, although burrows in the ground have also been observed. *Eliurus minor* has a soft grayish fur that is tipped with fawn color on the back. Head and body length averages 3.2-7 in (8-17.8 cm), weight is 1.2-3.6 oz (34-102 g), and tail is 4.3-8 in (11-20 cm). It is nocturnal and arboreal. *Gymnuromys roberti* is a slender rodent with a body length averaging 5-6.3 in (12.7-16 cm). It is dark to blackish gray with light yellow to white underparts. The tail is almost naked and averages 6-7 in (15.2-17.7 cm) long. *Hypogeomys antimena* is a giant rat, the largest in Madagascar, with a head and body length averaging 11.8-13.8 in (30-35 cm). Its coat varies in color from gray or gray-brown to reddish brown with white underparts, hands, and feet. The tail is furred and measures 8.3-9.8 in (21-25 cm) long. It is a nocturnal species and is described as a jumping and running rat.

Habitat and Current Distribution

Macrotarsomys ingens was described in 1959 and, to date, is only known from the type locality, between Tanarive and Majunga in the forest of Ankarafansika in northwestern Madagascar. It is classified as insufficiently known. *Eliurus minor* is known from just six scattered localities in the eastern rain forest and eastern plateau. It is not a burrowing species. It is classified as insufficiently known. *Gymnuromys roberti* was described in 1896 and is known from less than a dozen specimens. It is known from just five localities in the forests of eastern

Madagascar and is classified as rare. *Hypogeomys antimena* is known from three localities in western Madagascar, where it lives in sandy coastal forest. It is classified as insufficiently known.

History and Conservation Measures

There is concern about the status of these rodents but very little information is available about their numbers or distribution, making it difficult to assess the threats to their survival. *Eliurus minor* apparently is under some competitive pressure from the introduced rat (*Rattus rattus*). The other species are probably at risk from forest clearance, but surveys and studies are necessary before conservation programs can be planned or implemented.

Thornton Peak melomys

Melomys hadrourus

Phylum	Chordata
Class	Mammalia
Order	Rodentia
Family	Muridae
Status	Indeterminate, IUCN
Range	Australia

Description and Biology

Also known as the large-tailed melomys, the Thornton Peak melomys is a rodent with soft, thick fur that is reddish brown above and lighter underneath. Head and body length averages 3.5-7 in (9-18 cm) and weight is 1-7 oz (30-200 g). The long tail is scaly and almost naked, averaging 4-7.8 in (10-20 cm) long. Diet includes fruits and berries.

Breeding season is not certain but may span the entire year with peaks in certain months. One to five young are nursed by the mother for around 20 days.

Habitat and Current Distribution

This species is probably restricted to discontinuous blocks of upland tropical rain forest in north Queensland; populations are known to occur in the Thornton Peak-Cape Tribulation National Park, Daintree National Park, and in the Bellenden Ker-Mt. Bartle Frere complex, all part of the Wet Tropics of Queensland World Heritage area. There are no estimates of population size.

History and Conservation Measures

The Thornton Peak melomys has only been known since 1973 and was described in 1984 from six specimens collected at two localities less than six miles (10 km) apart in north Queensland. Populations are known to have declined in the Atherton Tableland, a plateau region on the northeast coast of Queensland, due to clearing and fragmentation of rain forest patches. Several conservation measures have been recommended on behalf of this species: determine the distribution and abundance of this rodent in areas where it is known to occur; assess its status and habits; and determine the species' natural history. Biological studies of the species in the Mt. Bartle Frere area are currently underway.

Northern hopping-mouse

Notomys aquilo

Phylum	Chordata
Class	Mammalia
Order	Rodentia
Family	Muridae
Status	Insufficiently Known, IUCN
	Endangered, USFWS
	Appendix II, CITES
Range	Australia

Description and Biology

The northern hopping-mouse, also known as the Australian native mouse, has soft brown fur with white undersides. It has long hind feet that propel the mouse forward, giving the appearance of a hopping motion. Although the mouse measures up to 11 in (28 cm) long, more than half of that length is the tail. This rodent is thought to be nocturnal, feeding on grass seeds, vegetable matter, and insects.

The hopping-mouse lives in a communal nest burrowed into sand dunes. Although little is known of breeding behavior, young have been observed in June, and litters are thought to consist of three to five young.

Habitat and Current Distribution

The northern hopping-mouse is found in northern Australia, on Groote Eylandt in the Gulf of Carpentaria, Northern Territory, and on the eastern coast of Arnhem Land. It is assumed to be rare, but population figures are not available due to insufficient surveys and collecting in its remote habitat.

Habitat is light, sandy soil in coastal dunes covered with heaths, acacia shrub, and spinifex. This mouse has also been found along Cadell River, close to rocks with sandy substrate and with spinifex and shrubs among the vegetation.

History and Conservation Measures

This species was reported on the Cape York Peninsula in northern Queensland around 1860, but the reliability of the identification has been questioned, since it was not found there in subsequent searches. In 1948 and in 1975, it was reported and collected on Groote Eylandt in the Gulf of Carpentaria. A specimen was caught in Arnhem Land, Northern Territory, in 1979, and it is suspected that others exist in the remote areas of this region.

The status of this hopping-mouse is uncertain and cannot be determined without further research. Preliminary surveys of Groote Eylandt and northwestern Arnhem Land were completed in 1992. Its numbers are believed to have declined, probably due to habitat destruction or degradation. A captive breeding colony is currently being established through the cooperation of Groote Eylandt Mining Company and Territory Wildlife Park.

Dusky hopping-mouse

Notomys fuscus

Phylum	Chordata
Class	Mammalia
Order	Rodentia
Family	Muridae
Status	Vulnerable, IUCN
	Appendix I, CITES
Range	Australia

Description and Biology

This mouse has white underparts and a light orange cast to its soft coat. Head and body length averages 3.6-7 in (9-18 cm) and weight is 0.8-1.8 oz (23-51 g). The tail is long, measuring 5-9 in (13-23 cm) and ending in a slight tuft. Eyes are large and hind feet very long and strong. As suggested by its common name, this mouse moves with a hopping motion. A nocturnal feeder, the dusky hopping-mouse eats seeds, roots, shoots, berries, leaves, and insects.

Groups of up to five mice inhabit a burrow which may be over 3 ft (1 m) deep and extend into an underground tunnel up to 16 ft (5 m) long, with a varying number of escape tunnels leading to the surface. Breeding is possible throughout the year, but it is most common in times of sufficient rainfall. Two to five young are born after a gestation period of 32-38 days and nursed for around a month. Due to its high fertility rate, population size can fluctuate widely.

Habitat and Current Distribution

The dusky hopping-mouse is found among dune systems in far southeastern Queensland and the adjacent part of South Australia, where it burrows in the tops of dunes. This mouse has experienced a great reduction in its habitat range, and population size is estimated to be less than 10,000 individuals.

History and Conservation Measures

This species now inhabits only a fraction of its former distribution in inland Australia. Although there are no estimates of initial population, it was

Dusky hopping-mouse.

once common enough to be hunted for food by the Aborigines. The reason for its decline is not fully known, but a number of factors may have contributed. Changes in fire regimes from Aboriginal and European land management practices and over-grazing of domestic stock have degraded available habitat, as has an abundance of introduced rabbits. Natural and introduced predators, including foxes and cats, may also have contributed to the decline.

Detailed ecological studies of these rodents in relation to the dynamics of their habitats are urgently needed before conservation programs can be planned or implemented. Currently, studies are underway to survey the distribution, habitat requirements, population size, reproductive behavior, and social structure of this species.

Silver rice rat

Oryzomys palustris nator
(O. argentatus)

Phylum	Chordata
Class	Mammalia
Order	Rodentia
Family	Muridae
Status	Indeterminate, IUCN Endangered, USFWS
Range	Florida (U.S.A.)

Description and Biology

The silver rice rat is a small rodent, 10 in (25 cm) long, with coarse fur and a long tail of 5 in (13 cm). The species is named for and identified by the silver-gray color of its back. It is a good swimmer and a nocturnal feeder, consuming seeds, the succulent parts of plants, insects, and small crabs over a range of 50 acres (20 ha). Predators include foxes, skunks, snakes, birds of prey, and raccoons.

Although little is known of breeding behavior in the wild, it is thought that one to five young are produced after a gestation of approximately 25 days.

Habitat and Current Distribution

Although the silver rice rat occurs throughout Florida, it is the population in the lower Florida Keys in Monroe County that is endangered. Because of its nocturnal nature and resistance to trapping, no estimate of the population in the lower Florida Keys is available. The species occurs in low densities on Big Torch, Johnston, Middle Torch, Raccoon, Saddlebunch, Little Pine, Summerland, and Water Keys. A population occurring on Cudjoe Key is believed to have recently become extinct.

In addition to freshwater marshes, this rat is known to inhabit flooded mangrove swamps, saltmarsh flats, and—for nesting—elevated, seldom-flooded areas with abundant vegetation.

History and Conservation Measures

Taxonomic classification of the silver rice rat is a subject of debate. It is variously described as a separate species, *Oryzomys argentatus*, or as a geographic population of *O. palustris natator*.

Distribution and population level of the silver rice rat was probably originally reduced with the changing water levels that resulted in the formation of the Florida Keys. The scattered and isolated populations are now vulnerable to increasing habitat reduction as a result of wetland clearance for commercial and residential development.

Although the silver rice rat is preyed upon by a number of species, the raccoon is the most serious predator. Because of the availability of garbage as a food source on developed Keys, raccoons—native to the area—are present in unnaturally high numbers. Also, the introduced Old World rat (*Rattus rattus*) competes with the silver rice rat for space and food on several of the Keys. Preservation of remaining habitat is the first step toward preserving the silver rice rat.

Bavarian pine vole

Pitymys (Microtus) bavaricus

```
Phylum . . . . . . . . . Chordata
Class . . . . . . . . . . Mammalia
Order . . . . . . . . . . Rodentia
Family . . . . . . . . . Muridae
Status . . . . . . . . . Extinct, IUCN
Range . . . . . . . . . Austria; Germany
```

Description and Biology

A small rodent, the Bavarian pine vole has a stout body and a short tail. Head and body length averages 3.5-4 in (9-10.6 cm) and the tail is 1-1.5 in (3.4-4 cm) long. The snout is rounded and its ears are small, with fur almost completely concealing them. The coloring of this vole's soft fur is gray-brown with lighter underparts. The species' senses of smell and hearing are acute. Fossorial (adapted to digging) and nocturnal, this species feeds on grasses, leaves, seeds, and nuts.

Many voles can breed throughout the year and females often give birth several times each year. Little information is available about social organization or reproductive biology of the Bavarian pine vole.

Habitat and Current Distribution

This species has only been found in two areas: Garmisch-Partenkirchen, in the German state of Bavaria (where it was first described), and Biberwier, in the Austrian state of Tyrol. Both areas possess moist meadow, the favored habitat of the Bavarian pine vole. Only 23 specimens are known, and experts suspect that the species has become extinct in Garmisch-Partenkirchen.

History and Conservation Measures

The status of this species is unclear. Construction of a hospital in Garmisch-Partenkirchen destroyed the Bavarian pine vole's only known habitat in the area. The species may still exist in Biberwier, but no specimen has been caught either there or in Germany since 1962. Furthermore, the taxonomy of this animal is equally unclear; some scientists consider the Bavarian pine vole to be a subspecies of *Microtus multiplex* rather than its own distinct species. Nevertheless, status surveys are urgently needed to determine whether or not individuals are still present in the wild.

Cameroon mountains rodents

Praomys hartwigi

Praomys morio

Lemniscomys mittendorfi

Phylum	Chordata
Class	Mammalia
Order	Rodentia
Family	Muridae
Status	Rare, IUCN
Range	Cameroon

Description and Biology

Praomys hartwigi, *P. morio*, and *Lemniscomys mittendorfi* are found in the mountains of Cameroon in West Africa. Rodents in the genus *Praomys* have soft, gray fur with shades of red, brown, and yellow, depending on the species. As with other members of the genus, *P. hartwigi* and *P. morio* have an average head and body length of 3.5-5.5 in (9-14 cm), weight of 0.7-2.0 oz (21-57 g), and a lightly haired tail averaging 4.3-6.5 in (11-16.5 cm). They have slender bodies with pointed heads and rounded ears that appear naked but which are in fact covered with fine hair. Their diet includes vegetation, fruits, seeds, and insects. Members of the *Praomys* genus bear a litter of three to four young and reach adult size in 10-12 weeks. *Lemniscomys mittendorfi* is an African striped grass rat that was originally described as a subspecies of the widespread *L. striatus* but which is now thought to be a distinct species. Rodents in the *Lemniscomys* genus have thinner, but rougher and coarser, fur than those of the *Praomys* genus. While not much is known about *L. mittendorfi*, some information can be inferred from the related *L. striatus*. *L. striatus* is a light brown rat with a darker stripe on its back and pale spots; its head and body length averages 3.2-5.5 in (8.2-14 cm), weight is 0.6-2.4 oz (16-68 g), and tail length is 2.9-6.2 in (7.4-15.7 cm). Its diet is primarily vegetarian but sometimes includes insects. Rodents in the *Lemniscomys* genus are largely terrestrial and active during the day. They build nests of grass and leaves near the ground and construct elaborate runways around the nest. Members of this genus have a short life expectancy, usually just two years.

Habitat and Current Distribution

P. hartwigi and *P. morio* are known from a few specimens from the mountains of western Cameroon. There are no estimates of population size for either species. *Lemniscomys mittendorfi* also occurs in the mountains of western Cameroon. It is known only from the type locality near Lake Oku at about 7,500 ft (2,300 m). There are no estimates of its population size.

History and Conservation Measures

Despite 20 years of extensive field work, no additional specimens of *P. hartwigi* have been found. Little is known of the life history of these three species. As a result, conservation measures cannot be extended until more is known about the status, biology, ecology, and distribution of these rodents.

Shark Bay mouse

Pseudomys praeconis

Phylum	Chordata
Class	Mammalia
Order	Rodentia
Family	Muridae
Status	Rare, IUCN
	Endangered, USFWS
	Appendix I, CITES
Range	Australia

Description and Biology

The Shark Bay mouse is sometimes called the shaggy mouse or shaggy-haired mouse because of its long, multicolored coat in shades of brown and yellow. Total body and tail length is approximately 9 in (23 cm); weight is 1-1.75 oz (30-50 g). A vegetarian, this mouse eats the flowers of *Olearia* and leaves and stems of various plants.

Little is known of this species' breeding behavior in the wild. In captivity, the oestrus cycle is approximately 14 days, and litters of three to four young are born after a gestation period of 28-30 days. The young attach themselves to the mother's nipples for almost two weeks; they are weaned after four weeks.

Habitat and Current Distribution

This mouse is restricted to Bernier Island in Shark Bay, Western Australia, but it is possible that it may still exist on the adjacent Peron Peninsula, although a 1989 survey was unsuccessful in locating the mouse. Population figures have not been ascertained.

Known habitat is sand dune areas at the base of cliffs, sheltered with dense mats of *Spinifex longifolius* and *Olearia axillaris*. The Shark Bay mouse is also occasionally found among *Triodia-Acacia* heath in the center of Bernier Island.

History and Conservation Measures

The Shark Bay mouse was first collected in 1858 on the Peron Peninsula of the Western Australia mainland but is now restricted to Bernier Island. This rodent's range has been reduced by more than 90 percent, and subsequently, its population has also been drastically reduced. To help protect the species, a number of specimens were captured on Bernier Island in 1975, and a captive breeding program has been successfully implemented. In 1993 the Shark Bay mouse was translocated to Doole Island.

Although the size of the population on Bernier Island is unknown, it is believed to be relatively secure as long as no new predators are introduced. Introduced goats which grazed on island plant life have been removed. Future conservation efforts will depend upon further study, but protection of existing habitat is crucial. It has been proposed that the mainland around Shark Bay be surveyed to determine whether any mice of this species remain. Translocation of these animals to the mainland and other islands to increase geographic range has also been recommended.

False water-rat

Xeromys myoides

Phylum	Chordata
Class	Mammalia
Order	Rodentia
Family	Muridae
Status	Rare, IUCN
	Endangered, USFWS
	Appendix I, CITES
Range	Australia

Description and Biology

This rodent is related to the common water-rat but does not have webbed claws. It is also slightly smaller, at approximately 8.5 in (22 cm) long (including the 3.5-inch [9 cm] tail) and weighs 1.75 oz (50 g). Upper body and limbs are dark gray; underparts are lighter. Although it is a good swimmer and has a water–repellent coat, the false water-rat is only semi-aquatic, living along the edge of the water. It feeds on hard-shell aquatic animals, especially crabs. A ritualized technique is used to incapacitate the crab by biting off its claws, eyestalks, and legs; it is then consumed in its entirety.

A mounded nest of leaves and mud is built in the base of mangroves. Breeding habits are unknown.

Habitat and Current Distribution

The false water-rat is probably confined to coastal areas of Queensland, including Stradbroke Island, and the Northern Territory, Australia. Population figures are not available; inaccessible areas that have not yet been surveyed may harbor a larger population than previously suspected.

A variety of swampy habitat is suitable for this species, including permanent reed swamps with thick covers of grass shrubs, freshwater lagoons, closed canopy mangrove forests, salt marsh grasses in mangrove forests along tidal rivers, and sedge swamps. The presence of shallow water, either tidal or fresh, close to the coastline also characterizes all the preferred sites of the false water-rat.

History and Conservation Measures

Reliable information on the false water-rat has been scarce because of the inaccessible habitat it shares with saltwater crocodiles. It is known from less than 20 specimens collected in vegetated swamps or tidal mangroves. One of the specimens was captured on the Cooloola Fauna Reserve. Studies are necessary to determine current patterns of distribution and to learn about this rodent's reproductive biology and general ecology. A survey of coastal areas of Queensland and Northern Territory has been recommended.

A growing threat to this species is the degradation of its habitat by introduced cattle, feral buffalo, and pigs. It will also be affected by the clearing and development of swampland and mangroves for agricultural and residential use.

Southwest Asian garden dormouse

Eliomys melanurus

Turkish dormouse

Dryomys laniger

Phylum	Chordata
Class	Mammalia
Order	Rodentia
Family	Myoxidae
Status	Rare, IUCN
Range	Turkey; Syria; Iraq; Jordan; Lebanon; Saudi Arabia; Egypt; Libya; Algeria; Morocco (*Eliomys melanurus*) Turkey (*Dryomys laniger*)

Description and Biology

The head and body length of the Southwest Asian garden dormouse averages 3.9-6.8 in (10-17.5 cm), and its weight is 1.6-4.2 oz (45-120 g). Its tail measures 3.5-5.3 in (9-13.5 cm). The coloring of the species differs from region to region. Those occurring in North Africa resemble *E. quercinus*, a dormouse that inhabits northwestern Europe. The upperparts of these individuals are gray to brown with cream or white underparts. Its tail is tri-colored—cinnamon brown nearer the body, then black with a white tuft. Black markings are usually present on the face. Indeed, some scientists contend that the Southwest Asian garden dormouse actually represents the more southerly distribution of *E. quercinus* and does not constitute a separate species. Individuals on the Arabian Peninsula have the same coloring as those in North Africa; however, their tails are brownish white nearer the body, then black to the end. Diet of the Southwest Asian garden dormouse includes nuts, fruits, insects, and small birds and rodents. A litter of two to eight young is born after a gestation of 22-28 days.

The Turkish dormouse has a grayish coat with shades of buff and lighter underparts. Head and body length averages 3.1-5.1 in (8-13 cm), weight is 0.6-1.2 oz (18-34 g), and tail length is 2.3-4.4 in (6-11.3 cm). It feeds nocturnally on seeds, fruits, buds, insects, eggs, and small birds. Two to seven young are born after a gestation of around 30 days.

Habitat and Current Distribution

The range of the Southwest Asian garden dormouse includes southern Turkey, Syria, Iraq, Jordan, Lebanon, Saudi Arabia, Egypt, Libya, Algeria, and Morocco. In North Africa, the species inhabits Mediterranean steppes and oases in the desert. No population estimates currently exist.

Dryomys laniger is endemic to Turkey and is now known only from a few localities in the southwest. It inhabits densely forested areas at elevations up to 5,250 ft (1,600 m) and hibernates in underground burrows or hollow trees. No population estimates currently exist.

History and Conservation Measures

Both of these species are assumed to be rare, probably due to habitat loss. Their status is not well defined, and no information is available about conservation efforts.

Thin-spined porcupine

Chaetomys subspinosus

Phylum	Chordata
Class	Mammalia
Order	Rodentia
Family	Echimyidae
Status	Vulnerable, IUCN
	Endangered, USFWS
Range	Brazil

Description and Biology

Also called the bristle-spined porcupine, this spiny rat gets its common names from the thin, bristly spines that cover its body. The spines on the animal's head and shoulders are rather short—0.6 in (1.5 cm)—and kinky, while those on its upper back, legs, and tail are longer—up to 2 in (5 cm)—and wavier. Unlike true porcupines, the thin-spined porcupine has no spines on its lower back. Its body is generally brownish or grayish with reddish underparts and with dark feet and tail, but its spines are typically tricolored, ranging from a pale yellow at the base to dark brown in the middle and back to pale yellow at the tip.

The head and body length of this species at physical maturity averages 15-18 in (38-45 cm), while the tail averages 10-11 in (26-27.5 cm). All four limbs each have four digits, which end in long, curved claws; the claws' sharpness helps make this animal a terrific climber, as evidenced by its ability to scale stone walls. The lengthy, curling tail is thick and scaly at the base but thin and naked at the tip. The species' vocalization consists of strident puffing sounds.

The bulk of this nocturnal animal's diet consists of fruits, including nuts from cocoa trees. There is no information available about the social structure or reproductive biology of this species.

The thin-spined porcupine was formerly classified in the Erethizontidae family, which includes true porcupines, but in 1984 it was switched to the Echimyidae family of spiny rats.

Habitat and Current Distribution

The thin-spined porcupine occurs only in southcentral and southeastern Brazil, in the states of Bahia, Sergipe, Rio de Janeiro, and Espírito Santo. It inhabits the edges of Atlantic coastal forests near open or cultivated areas. There are no estimates of population, but the species is thought to be quite rare.

History and Conservation Measures

The primary threat to this species is habitat loss due to forest clear-cutting. Inadequate knowledge of South American rodents has limited any attempt to develop preservation or conservation efforts for specific species, either through captive breeding or habitat protection. Like many other poorly known species, the thin-spined porcupine's best chance for survival rests with strategies that preserve the entire ecosystem of which it is a part. Conserving its forest ecosystem will also result in protection for other highly endangered species, such as the golden lion tamarin (*Leontopithecus chrysomelas*) and the woolly spider monkey (*Brachyteles arachnoides*).

Crestless Himalayan porcupine

Hystrix hodgsoni

Phylum	Chordata
Class	Mammalia
Order	Rodentia
Family	Hystricidae
Status	Indeterminate, IUCN
Range	Central and eastern Himalayas to China and Southeast Asia

Description and Biology

True to its common name, this porcupine is a crestless animal, but on occasion it possesses a few bristles that are slightly longer than the spines on the back of its neck. A fairly large rodent, this species has a head and body length of about 18.5 in (47 cm) and a tail length averaging 10.6 in (27 cm). Its body and limbs are covered with short and grooved spines; intermixed with them are also a few longer spines of 8-10 in (20-25 cm) on the loins and rump. It has a dark brown body with blackish limbs, and a band of white-tipped spines forming a collar in front of the neck. The medial portion of the quills is dark brown; the tip, the base, or both are white. This animal's feet are powerful with strong claws. Nocturnal and seclusive, it forages on vegetative matter, such as roots, tubers, and bulbs.

The crestless porcupine lives alone in a burrow. It is monogamous, breeds in the spring, and has a typical litter size of two.

Habitat and Current Distribution

Within the Indian sub-continental limits, this species is known from the central and eastern Himalayas at elevations up to about 5,000 ft (1,500 m), ranging from Nepal through Sikkim to Nagaland and Manipur. The crestless porcupine is also said to occur in lower Bengal and occurs in Myanmar and other countries of southeastern Asia, including China. It lives in burrows that it digs in hill slopes or in flat ground among bushes. Population figures are unknown.

History and Conservation Measures

The population of the crestless Himalayan porcupine has declined greatly, primarily due to indiscriminate killing for its much esteemed meat and quills. There is no information available about conservation efforts on behalf of this species.

Long-tailed chinchilla
Chinchilla lanigera
Short-tailed chinchilla
Chinchilla brevicaudata

Phylum	Chordata
Class	Mammalia
Order	Rodentia
Family	Chinchillidae
Status	Indeterminate, IUCN
	Endangered, USFWS (*C. brevicaudata*)
	Appendix I, CITES
Range	Argentina (?); Chile (*C. lanigera*)
	Argentina; Bolivia; Chile; Peru (ex?) (*C. brevicaudata*)

Description and Biology

Two species of chinchilla are recognized: *Chinchilla brevicaudata* and *Chinchilla lanigera*. These nocturnal animals have soft, silky fur, large ears, and bushy tails. They average between 9-15 in (23-38 cm) in length, and their tail is about 3-6 in (7.5-15 cm) long. The female is larger than the male, the female weighing up to 28 oz (800 g) and males 18 oz (500 g). The pelage is generally gray in color with yellowish white fur underneath. The chinchilla's hind feet are much larger than its forepaws, a trait that makes the species agile jumpers.

When eating, chinchillas stand erect and hold the food—which includes leaves, seeds, fruits, and other vegetation—with their forepaws. Females produce from one to six young in a litter, but the average is two to three. *C. lanigera* lives an average of five years in the wild; in captivity it may live up to 12 years.

Habitat and Current Distribution

Both species of chinchilla were widespread throughout their range until hunting for the fur trade decimated their population. Between 1895 and 1900,

Chinchilla lanigera.

about 1,680,000 chinchilla skins were exported from Chile alone. *C. lanigera* is currently found in Chile, along the foothills of the Andes mountains at elevations of 2,625-5,576 ft (800-1,700 m). *C. brevicaudata* prefers higher elevations of over 6,560 ft (2,000 m) in mountainous regions of Peru, Bolivia, and Argentina, as well as Chile. These animals inhabit barren areas with dense shrub cover and bunch grasses and live among crevices and rocks. Several pairs of chinchillas have been found to share the same shelter.

In 1989 the *C. lanigera* population in the wild was estimated at 7,000-12,000 individuals within and around the Chinchillas National Reserve in north-central Chile. A few other populations of this same species are also known to exist in the area. The population of *C. brevicaudata* in the wild is unknown, although far fewer are thought to exist than *C. lanigera*. *C. brevicaudata* is considered in serious danger of extinction because of hunting pressures for its fur. However, there is little reliable information available to assess the status of either species in the wild.

History and Conservation Measures

Historically, chinchilla fur has been highly prized by humans. Coats made of this animal's soft fur have been sold for over $100,000. It is estimated that hundreds of thousands, even millions, of chinchilla have been bred in farms since the 1920s for the fur industry and, to a lesser extent, the pet industry. Captive breeding of *C. brevicaudata* has proven more difficult than breeding *C. lanigera*. However, due to high inbreeding, *C. lanigera* males are usually sterile.

While the hunting of chinchillas is illegal, this activity still threatens the survival of these animals in the wild. An even greater threat to *C. lanigera* is habitat destruction; overgrazing by goats has destroyed *C. lanigera*'s habitat and reduced food supply. Mining activities also surround this species' habitat. Habitat destruction is not a serious threat to *C. brevicaudata* at the present time because it inhabits remote areas.

Conservation measures for chinchillas include the establishment of reserves, careful management of grazing activity of domestic animals, and stricter controls on hunting. Captive-bred *C. lanigera* have been released to the wild, but inbreeding is thought to have affected their survival chances. Additional captive-breeding efforts with wild chinchillas are currently underway.

Cuban hutias

Mesocapromys (Capromys) spp.

Mysateles (Capromys) spp.

Phylum	Chordata
Class	Mammalia
Order	Rodentia
Family	Capromyidae
Status	Various, IUCN Endangered, USFWS
Range	Cuba

Description and Biology

Thirteen distinct varieties of the Cuban hutias have been identified, some of which are known only from skeletal remains. There are slight variations in size and color among the species, but in general, a Cuban hutia is a fairly large rodent with dense, short fur and longer, coarser guard hairs. It has a broad head, small ears, and short legs with broad feet and claws. Head and body length averages 8.5-20 in (21.6-51 cm) and weight is 1-15 lb (.5-6.8 kg). It has a hairy tail which averages 6-12 in (15.2-30.5 cm) long. Fur color varies with species from tan or yellow-red to brown or black. Some species are nocturnal and others diurnal, but all feed on leaves, fruit, shoots, and bark.

Some of the species build communal nests. For many of them, breeding is probably possible throughout the year, with one to three young born after a gestation period which varies from 90-140 days.

Habitat and Current Distribution

The dwarf hutia, *Mesocapromys (Capromys) nanus*, is the smallest of the hutias. No specimens have been reported since 1937, but it may still survive in the Zapata Swamp, where it inhabits small, dry,

bush-covered islands which are dotted about the marshes and mangroves that surround the swamp. It is classified as endangered by the IUCN.

Cabrera's hutia, *Mesocapromys (Capromys) angelcabrerai*, was discovered in 1974 and is restricted to the mangrove swamps of Cayos de Ana Maria in south-central Cuba. It is classified as endangered by the IUCN and may already be extinct.

The large-eared hutia, *Mesocapromys (Capromys) auritus*, was described in 1970 and is known to exist only on Cayo Fragoso, a small, low island off the north-central coast of Cuba. Total population is expected to be small because of its very limited range. This animal is classified as endangered by the IUCN.

The little earth hutia, *Mesocapromys (Capromys) sanfelipensis*, was discovered in 1970 and is found in the low, dense vegetation of Cayo Juan Garcia and nearby Cayo Real of southwestern Cuba. Classified as endangered by the IUCN, it may already be extinct.

Garrido's hutia, *Mysateles (Capromys) garridoi*, was described in 1970 from a single specimen. It is believed to occur on small islands in the Banco de los Jardins y Jardinillos of the Archipelago de los

Cannaroes south of the Zapata Peninsula and east of the Isle of Pines. Population is expected to be low because of its very restricted distribution. This species is classified as endangered by the IUCN.

Chapman's prehensile-tailed hutia, *Mysateles (Capromys) gundlachi*, is an arboreal hutia restricted to the northern part of Isla de la Juventud (formerly known as the Isla de Pinos). It is classified as indeterminate by the IUCN.

The bushy-tailed hutia, *Mysateles (Capromys) melanurus*, is large and dark-colored; it is arboreal and inhabits the humid montane forests of eastern Cuba. It is classified as rare by the IUCN.

The Isla de la Juventud tree hutia, *Mysateles (Capromys) meridionalis*, is a recently discovered, arboreal hutia that is restricted to the southwestern region of the Isla de la Juventud. It is classified as indeterminate by the IUCN, but a recent survey indicated that it is now very rare or possibly extinct.

History and Conservation Measures

The primary threat to the hutias of Cuba is hunting, although some of them are also in danger from habitat destruction. Fishermen who land on the cays and islets can take many hutias in a single raid. When disturbed, the hutias leave the nest and take refuge in the water, where they are easily caught because they are slow and clumsy swimmers. In addition, they also have a slow reproductive rate, making it difficult for the hutias to maintain a healthy population size. The recent shortage of food in Cuba is resulting in a renewed effort to hunt hutias for food, and some populations are now heavily exploited. Some meat is even sold to tourists as "wild game."

A number of conservation measures have been proposed, the most important of which are the strict enforcement of existing protective legislation and the establishment of additional reserves in critical habitats. Access to the offshore cays where hutias occur should be restricted so that fishermen do not kill the animals found there or introduce predators such as cats or mongooses. Education programs emphasizing the uniqueness of the endemic mammals of Cuba could have beneficial effects in improving the chances of survival of the remaining endemic rodents.

Jamaican hutia

Geocapromys brownii

Phylum	Chordata
Class	Mammalia
Order	Rodentia
Family	Capromyidae
Status	Indeterminate, IUCN
Range	Jamaica

Description and Biology

The Jamaican hutia, sometimes called the Indian coney, is a large rodent with rough fur, a broad head, small ears, and short legs. Head and body length averages 13-18 in (33-46 cm), weight is 2-4.5 lb (1-2 kg), and tail length is 1.4-2.5 in (3.5-6.4 cm). This animal is usually brown or grayish brown in appearance. A good climber, it can move quickly when disturbed or threatened. It hides in shelters during the day, feeding at night on leaves, bark, and twigs.

No information is available about the social structure of this species. It mates throughout the year and may produce two or more litters each year. One to three young are born after a gestation period of around 120 days.

Habitat and Current Distribution

This hutia is endemic to the island of Jamaica, where it inhabits forests and places where massive deposits of exposed limestone offer an abundance of hiding places in natural fissures and solution cavities. There are no estimates of population.

History and Conservation Measures

The population of the Jamaican hutia has experienced a decline in the past 30 years, chiefly due to excessive hunting and the clearing of forests for agricultural development. It is still present in several regions of Jamaica, but it may be at risk over the next few decades unless some large areas of suitable habitat are set aside from human activities. A successful captive breeding program was instituted for the Jamaican hutia at the Jersey Wildlife Preservation Trust, but reintroduction of the species in captivity has been difficult. The best captive breeding program is now underway at the Hope Zoo in Kingston.

Conservation efforts for this species should begin with education. All hunting should be prohibited and efforts should be made to create protected areas.

Jamaican hutia.

Since many of the remaining populations of this species are still safe from immediate exploitation, a long-term educational program could have beneficial effects on the status of the animal in the coming decades.

Bahamian hutia

Geocapromys ingrahami

Phylum	Chordata
Class	Mammalia
Order	Rodentia
Family	Capromyidae
Status	Rare, IUCN
Range	Bahamas

Description and Biology

This hutia is a rather large rodent with rough fur, a broad head, small ears, and short legs. Head and body length averages 13-18 in (33-46 cm), weight is 2-4.5 lb (1-2 kg), and tail length is 1.4-2.5 in (3.5-6.4 cm). Its coloration is usually brown or grayish brown, with lighter undersides. A good climber, it can move quickly when disturbed. It hides in shelters during the day, feeding at night on leaves, bark, and twigs.

Little is known about this species' reproductive biology, but litter size is thought to be one.

Habitat and Current Distribution

This hutia is abundant on East Plana Cay, a small island in the eastern Bahamas. The hutias from East Plana Cay have been introduced onto two additional islands in the Exuma Cays Land and Sea Park: Little Wax Cay and Warderick Wells Cay. Total population is uncertain.

History and Conservation Measures

The Bahamian hutia was once widespread throughout the Bahamas. The reason for the initial population decline is uncertain, but the status of the species is improving and should get better if efforts to introduce it to other islands and cays are successful.

There are no known negative factors influencing the populations of Bahamian hutias on any of the three small islands where they now occur. Because the range of the species is limited to such small low-lying islands, however, the animals are vulnerable to a chance introduction of cats or dogs or to the disaster of a tropical storm. In the absence of these hazards, there is a reasonable chance that the animal can survive the threat of extinction in spite of a very limited distribution. Additional reintroductions to different parts of the Bahamas have been recommended, but the Bahamas National Trust opposes these reintroductions because hutias are so destructive of the natural vegetation on small islands and cays.

Bahamian hutia.

Hispaniolan hutia

Plagiodontia aedium

Phylum	Chordata
Class	Mammalia
Order	Rodentia
Family	Capromyidae
Status	Rare, IUCN
Range	Dominican Republic; Haiti

Description and Biology

The Hispaniolan hutia, also known as Cuvier's hutia, is a large, terrestrial rodent that lives in forests and plantations. It has dense, rough fur, a broad head, small ears, and short legs. Head and body length averages 12 in (30 cm), weight is around 45 oz (1,275 g), and tail is 6 in (15 cm) long. It is brown or grayish brown in color, with lighter underparts. It shelters on the ground during the day and feeds at night on fruit, roots, and bark.

The Hispaniolan hutia is thought to form pairs and to occupy burrows in groups of three or four. In captivity a single young is born after a gestation period of 119 days, and a female bears only one litter per year. Little is known of their behavior in the wild.

Habitat and Current Distribution

The Hispaniolan hutia occurs in forests in Hispaniola, an island in central West Indies, divided between the Republic of Haiti on the west and Dominican Republic on the east. This species prefers hilly areas at altitudes up to 6,500 ft (2,000 m). There are no estimates of total population.

History and Conservation Measures

The Hispaniolan hutia is now very rare in most parts of its original range. Growing human populations in Haiti and the Dominican Republic have re-sulted in widespread deforestation for human settlements and for agricultural expansion, resulting in reduced habitat for this species and exposing it to predation by dogs and introduced predators, including the mongoose. The hutia is also subject to hunting in some parts of the Dominican Republic, but it is relatively safe from hunting in Haiti.

In Haiti, many of the known populations of the species have been significantly reduced in numbers since 1980. Educational programs and strict laws have had little effect on conservation efforts for the Hispaniolan hutia, partly because most people who live near the remaining areas of suitable hutia habitat are remote from any areas of authority. The highest conservation priority in Haiti should be to finish the creation of a national parks program and to promote and protect the habitat within the boundaries of the two existing parks. Because the parks are in regions that are important for water and soil conservation, their protection can be important not only to the preservation of the hutia, but also to the quality of life for people living near the parks.

In the Dominican Republic, the Hispaniolan hutia is rarely encountered in most of its previous range. A lowland swamp forest east of Sabana de la Mar was cut down and turned into rice fields, possibly leading to the extinction of a separate subspecies, *P. a. hylaeum*. An immediate survey of the status and distribution of this subspecies is needed to establish whether any animals or suitable habitat remain.

Kozlov's pika

Ochotona koslowi

Phylum	Chordata
Class	Mammalia
Order	Lagomorpha
Family	Ochotonidae
Status	Vulnerable, IUCN
Range	China

Description and Biology

Kozlov's pika is the largest and most morphologically distinctive of all the pikas. It has thicker and denser fur than any other pika. They are pale, whitish buff in color with reddish backs. Their underparts are white and thickly furred, as are their feet. Their ears are yellow with white tips; there is no visible tail. The pika is active during the day and apparently does not hibernate. Most pikas feed on a variety of vegetable matter, but the exact diet of this species is unknown.

Little is known about their social structure or reproductive biology. It is known, however, that Kozlov's pika lives in groups and is reported to produce one young per year.

Habitat and Current Distribution

This species's only known habitat is the Arkatag Range, a spur of the Kunlun Mountains west of the junction of Xinjiang, Xizang, and Qinghai Provinces in China. There are no estimates of population.

This pika occupies alpine meadow tundra and digs holes in the swelling mounds of saline loess (loam) on the Guldsha Pass.

History and Conservation Measures

The original specimens of Kozlov's pika were collected by Polish geographer N. M. Przewalski in 1884, and a few specimens were later collected from the identical locality in 1890. The species was not seen again for nearly one hundred years. A recent expedition to the type locality failed to find any Kozlov's pikas. It is considered a potentially threatened species because of its limited distribution and apparent rarity. A thorough survey is needed to assess the status of this species. Habitats in the Arkatag Range are already known to be severely impacted, and conservation and management measures will almost certainly be necessary.

Riverine rabbit

Bunolagus monticularis

Phylum . . . . Chordata
Class . . . . Mammalia
Order . . . . Lagomorpha
Family . . . . Leporidae
Status . . . . Endangered, IUCN
Range . . . . South Africa

Description and Biology

The riverine rabbit, also called the Bushman rabbit, is very swift and agile. It has a soft, gray coat and reddish coloring on the neck. The chin is white and tinged with yellow on the sides; tail is brown and has an average length of 3-4 in (7.6-10.2 cm); their long ears measure 4.2-4.9 in (10.7-12.4 cm). A dark brown stripe runs along the lower margins of the jaw toward the base of the ear. Head and body length averages 14-18 in (35.6-45.7 cm), and the rabbits weigh 2.2-3.3 lb (1-1.5 kg). A nocturnal feeder, it consumes flowers, leaves, and, in the wet season, grasses.

This is a solitary species with a polygamous mating system. The male has a home range of 45-58 acres (18.2-23.5 ha) that can overlap the female home range of 19-45 acres (7.7-18.2 ha). One or two young are born between August and May. The young probably remain in the breeding nest for a relatively long time before going out to forage independently.

Habitat and Current Distribution

The riverine rabbit has a distribution limited to the Southern African subregion and is endemic to the central Karoo Desert of South Africa's Cape Province. Population size is estimated between 300-800 rabbits.

Preferred habitat is dense growth along seasonal rivers in the central Karoo. A 1989 investigation to determine typical habitat revealed that 68 percent of the remaining riverine rabbit vegetation is found to be associated with an interconnected network of rivers, principally the Sak, Klein Sak and Riet, and Klein Riet in the central Karoo.

History and Conservation Measures

The initial cause of this species' decline was clearance of riverside vegetation for a program to cultivate wheat on the banks of the rivers. The project failed by 1950 because of a lack of irrigation water, but not until 60 percent of the original riparian vegetation had been destroyed. Remaining habitat is not considered to be at risk, but there is concern that even preserving the remaining habitat may be insufficient to ensure the long-term conservation of the species, since the population numbers are so low and the distribution appears fragmented along the rivers. Fragmentation makes the isolated populations more susceptible to local extinctions and contributes to the possible disruption of gene flow between adjacent subpopulations.

No national reserve has yet been proclaimed for this species, but recent additions to the Karoo National Park may prove suitable for relocation of the species once the vegetation has recovered from the effects of overgrazing. Continuation of status surveys is recommended, as is continuation and expansion of a riverine rabbit awareness program that was initiated among the farmers of the central Karoo.

A captive breeding program has been developed with the eventual goal of reintroduction of the riverine rabbit into suitable habitat. Unfortunately, this program has been plagued by lack of proper biological monitoring, and in the future, maintenance of genetic diversity in the captive stock and proper reintroduction techniques should be invoked.

Hispid hare

Caprolagus hispidus

Phylum	Chordata
Class	Mammalia
Order	Lagomorpha
Family	Leporidae
Status	Endangered, IUCN
	Endangered, USFWS
	Appendix I, CITES
Range	Bangladesh; India; Nepal

Description and Biology

The hispid hare, sometimes called the Assam rabbit or the bristly rabbit, has a coarse, bristly coat with a combination of black and brownish hair. The chest hair is light brown and its abdomen is white in color. Average head and body length is 16-19 in (41-48 cm); the average weight is 4-5.8 lb (1.8-2.8 kg). Its brown tail averages about 1-2 in (2.5-5.2 cm) long. This species' ears are short and broad, measuring 2.2-2.8 in (5.6-7.1 cm), and its eyes are small. The hispid hare's teeth are fairly large, and its claws are strong and straight. Most active at night, the hispid hare feeds on shoots, roots of grasses, and, sometimes, cultivated crops. Predators include Indian foxes (*Vulpes bengalensis*), golden jackals (*Canis aureus*), and birds of prey.

Hispid hares probably live as pairs, but the male has a larger home range than the female; mean home range for the male is around 10,000 sq yd (8,200 sq m) and for the female, 3,300 sq yd (2,800 sq m). Breeding is thought to be monogamous and to take place during January and February. Litters are probably small, and the gestation period, while uncertain, may be 37-43 days.

Habitat and Current Distribution

This species survives in only a few isolated pockets across its former range in northern India and southern Nepal. There are no estimates of remaining population.

The hispid hare is dependent upon dense, tall grasslands, commonly referred to as elephant grass or thatchland. These grasslands are a feature of the succession between primary colonizing grasses through deciduous riverain forest to the sal (*Shorea robusta*) forest climax. Tall grasslands may also form an understory during later stages of the succession, particularly near rivers, or in forest clearings and abandoned cultivation and village sites. In relatively undisturbed areas, the tall grasslands are maintained by prolonged inundation during the monsoon or by periodic burning; in disturbed areas, they are maintained by regular burning, grazing, or regular harvesting for thatch and domestic animal fodder. Burrows are utilized, but not dug by the hare.

History and Conservation Measures

Historically, this species has been recorded in tracts along the southern Himalayan foothills from

Uttar Pradesh through Nepal, and West Bengal to Assam, extending southward as far as Dacca in Bangladesh. For many years, there were no confirmed sightings and the hispid hare was suspected to be extinct. Later specimens were recorded from the North Kheri, Uttar Pradesh/Nepal border in 1951; from Chuka Dhaya, Pilibhit Forest Division, Uttar Pradesh in 1960; the Goalpara District of southwest Assam and the Rajagarh areas of the Mangaldai subdivision of Darrang District of northwest Assam in 1971; and Kauha National Park in 1991.

Since its rediscovery, the population of the hispid hare has declined dramatically as a result of the loss of its tall grassland habitat to agriculture, commercial forestry, flood control schemes, and human settlement. The few pockets of tall grassland habitat which remain are located within national parks, wildlife reserves, and sanctuaries, but the isolated, relict populations remain at risk because of the continuing degradation of habitat, even within protected areas. Habitat is lost to overgrazing by domestic stock, human exploitation of thatch and cane material, and the often uncontrolled, regular burning of grassland during the dry season.

A number of conservation measures have been proposed. Status surveys are necessary in tall grassland areas that have not yet been investigated. Relict populations could be protected by a shift from uncontrolled dry season burning to careful rotational burning, leaving large areas of suitable cover and food available throughout the year. Long-term research is necessary to examine the effects of the different factors contributing to habitat degradation in order to formulate appropriate management plans for these remnants of tall grassland. Further long-term studies of behavioral ecology and reproductive biology of the species are also required. In addition to protecting the hispid hare, effective protection and long-term management of tall grass-shrub habitat would also benefit other endangered species, such as the pygmy hog (*Sus salvanius.*)

Sumatran rabbit

Nesolagus netscheri

Phylum	Chordata
Class	Mammalia
Order	Lagomorpha
Family	Leporidae
Status	Endangered, IUCN
Range	Sumatra (Indonesia)

Description and Biology

A rare species, the Sumatran rabbit is easily recognized by its unusual striped coloring. The general color is yellowish gray accented by wide black or dark brown stripes, including a middorsal strip from snout to tail. The fur on the underparts, below the chin, and on the inside of the legs is whitish in color. Head and body length averages 14.5-16.4 in (36.8-41.7 cm), and they weigh around 3.3 lb (1.5 kg). Ears are black and short, measuring only 1.3-1.8 in (3.4-4.5 cm). The tail is so short that it is normally not visible. Coloration is variable between individuals; fur is soft and rather short, and the skin is delicate. Active at night, this rabbit feeds on leaves and stems of certain forest plants.

There is no information available on social organization or reproductive biology.

Habitat and Current Distribution

The Sumatran rabbit is restricted to montane forest in the Barisan Mountains, west and southwest Sumatra. The most recent confirmed sighting was in 1972 in Gunung Leuser National Park in northwest Sumatra, and there may have been a sighting in 1978 near Mt. Kerinci.

This species lives only in remote forest habitat; it seems to require rich, volcanic soil and feeds in the forest understory, not in openings or clearings. It hides during the day in dark places at the base of trees, in burrows, or in holes in the ground. Nearly all sighting records are from coffee or tea estates where rabbits were seen as the forest was felled.

History and Conservation Measures

For many years, this species was known only from about a dozen museum specimens that were collected between 1880 and 1916. Since then, there have been sightings in the wild. It is considered to be the rarest lagomorph and has probably never been abundant anywhere in its range, but population estimates are difficult because of its remote habitat and nocturnal habits. Searches have been conducted without success, but local people have reported sightings. There is much concern about its continued survival because much of the forest has been cleared for tea and coffee plantations, and forest clearing is continuing rapidly as people settle in Sumatra from Java. Forests are threatened by the felling of timber, planting of vegetables, and settling of immigrants from Java through the transmigration program.

The survival of the Sumatran rabbit depends on the continued existence of its mountain forest habitat. The highest conservation priority is to locate this rabbit in the wild through a thorough status survey. Once a population has been found, it will be possible to carry out detailed studies on its habitat requirements. Until a population is located, management of existing protected areas where it might occur is a priority. Gunung Leuser and Barisan-Selatan National Parks are now protected areas and a new National Park has been proposed for Mt. Kerinci-Seblat. A management plan for this park should include appropriate forms of buffer-zone development in the surrounding area.

Amami rabbit

Pentalagus furnessi

Phylum	Chordata
Class	Mammalia
Order	Lagomorpha
Family	Leporidae
Status	Endangered, IUCN
	Endangered, USFWS
Range	Ryukyu Islands (Japan)

Description and Biology

The morphologically primitive Amami rabbit, also referred to as the Ryukyu rabbit, has thick, woolly, dark fur; in fact, the Japanese have a name for it that means "the black rabbit of Amami." It has been suggested that its dark coloration may be related to the darkness of the forest it inhabits. The Amami rabbit's eyes are small and its ears are fairly short, measuring 1.6-1.8 in (4.1-4.5 cm). Its head and body length averages 16.5-18.5 in (41.8-47 cm), and its tail measures 0.4-1.4 in (1.1-3.5 cm). The rabbit's snout is long and its limbs short, with relatively large nails measuring 0.4-0.8 in (1-2 cm) that are used for digging nest holes. Active at night, this rabbit feeds on leaves of the Japanese pampas grass, runners of the Japanese sweet potato, bamboo sprouts, and the bark of a variety of forest trees.

Little is known of the social organization of this species. Amami rabbits frequently use passages through the undergrowth or climb up and down on steep slopes along forest roads. They make clicking sounds when communicating with each other. Burrows are used for dens and nests. Mating behavior most often occurs in November and December, and kits first appear above ground in April or May.

Habitat and Current Distribution

Pentalagus furnessi is found only on Japan's Amami Island and Tokuno-shima, which is part of the Ryukyu Island chain. A survey in 1992-93 estimated that less than 600 animals occupied Amami Island; the percent of range and density was less on Tokuno. Between 1985-86 and 1989-90, Amami rabbits declined in 87 percent of sampled localities. Population levels declined by 70-80 percent during that short period. By 1992-93, Amami rabbits had disappeared from an additional 43 percent of the area counted, and populations were rare on 70 percent of those remaining areas containing rabbits. In the past 15 years the Amami rabbit has declined more than 90 percent throughout its range.

The preferred habitat of the Amami rabbit is probably primary forest, but this rabbit is also found in cut-over areas and forest edges covered by Japanese pampas grass. Droppings have frequently been found along forest roads that run through young secondary forests and in the boundaries between young forests and primary forests.

History and Conservation Measures

This rabbit is considered endangered because of its small, isolated population and its limited distribution. It is designated as a special natural monument by the Japanese government. To ensure the survival of this species, conservation priorities have been set in the areas of habitat conservation and management, control of introduced species, and research and monitoring programs.

A habitat mosaic of mature oak forests and young second-growth stands is required for the Amami rabbit, enabling it to obtain important food supplies throughout the year. In order to maintain this mosaic, careful habitat management is necessary; certain forests should be set aside to become mature, since such old forests are now greatly reduced in area.

The Amami rabbit suffers greatly from introduced predators such as feral dogs, feral cats, and mongooses. As a result, the species tends to be absent from areas near human settlements. Populations of introduced predators should be controlled in important habitat areas.

Although some research has been conducted on population estimates, food habits, and nest site selection for this species, ongoing monitoring is necessary to assess conservation and management needs for the species. The islands inhabited by the Amami rabbit have many endemic terrestrial vertebrate species and subspecies. Amami Island is very important for endemic species conservation and the Amami rabbit is a representative of the unique biocommunity of the island.

Volcano rabbit

Romerolagus diazi

Phylum	Chordata
Class	Mammalia
Order	Lagomorpha
Family	Leporidae
Status	Endangered, IUCN
	Endangered, USFWS
	Appendix I, CITES
Range	Mexico

Description and Biology

The volcano rabbit is found in a small mountainous area in Mexico. This rabbit is a relict species that is characterized by its ancestral morphological features and primitive parasites. It has short, dense dark brown to black fur. Head and body length averages 10.6-13 in (27-33 cm), and weight is 14-18 oz (400-500 g); females are slightly larger than males. Ears are small and rounded, measuring 1.6-1.7 in (4-4.4 cm), hind legs and feet are short, and tail is inconspicuous. Active mainly during the day, but sometimes also at night, it feeds on bunch or zacaton grasses (various wiry grass species that grow in Mexico and the southwestern United States), selecting the green and tender young leaves of the grasses and biting the base and lower edges of the clump. Predators include long-tailed weasels, bobcats, and rattlesnakes.

Social structure has not been studied in the wild, but the volcano rabbit has been reported in groups of two to seven animals. Abundance of volcano rabbits varies significantly among vegetation communities. Group size and density are highest in subalpine bunchgrass communities to which its biology is tightly linked.

Most reproduction appears to occur between January and April; gestation period is 38-40 days. Litters of one to five have been recorded, but two seems to be the most common size.

Habitat and Current Distribution

The volcano rabbit is endemic to central Mexico, with a distribution now restricted to three discontinuous areas of core habitat on the slopes of four volcanoes: Popocatepétl, Iztaccíhuatl, El Pelado, and Tláloc. There are no reliable estimates of population available for the entire distribution area. A population estimate of El Pelado volcano showed considerable variation (range 2,478-12,120 individuals).

This species is found in pine forests with dense undergrowth of zacaton grass and rocky substrates at altitudes of 9,000-14,000 ft (2,800-4,250 m). Most of the areas where the rabbit is found have winter drought and summer rains. It constructs elaborate burrows in sandy, loamy, deep soils; entrances are hidden in the base of grass clumps. Abandoned pocket-gopher burrows, hollows between rocks and boulders, and large boulder-strewn sinkholes are used as temporary daytime retreats. Nesting chambers appear to be constructed in burrows among boulders, in old tree stumps, holes left by fallen trees, or even in shallow depressions beneath the bunch grass or zacaton. Unlike most rabbits, the volcano rabbit maintains an intricate system of surface runways through the thick grass.

History and Conservation Measures

The population of this species is believed to have decreased drastically to about 10 percent of the original distributional range because of hunting and habitat destruction and fragmentation. It has traditionally been hunted for food and for sport and, although hunting is now illegal, there is little enforcement of protective legislation. Factors contributing to the degradation of habitat include forest fires, overgrazing by cattle and sheep, encroachment by agriculture and property developments, over-exploitation of timber, and cutting of zacaton grasses for thatch and brush manufacture. Many of the forest fires are the result of uncontrolled burning of zacaton to promote new growth of pasture for cattle and sheep. Each of the remaining volcano rabbit populations lies within a 45-minute drive of Mexico City, now the world's largest city, with a rapidly growing population of 20 million people. A substantial area of original volcano rabbit habitat has already disappeared as a result of city expansion, but the rapid growth of rural settlement areas around core habitats also presents a continuing threat. Only 16 patches of suitable habitat contain volcano rabbits at the present time.

Conservation priorities include general habitat conservation and management, protected area management, education programs, and captive breeding. The survival of the species revolves around the control of fire and over-grazing in the prime zacaton habitats and the enforcement of laws that prohibit the catching, sale, and hunting of the animal. Forest areas where the volcano rabbit is found are significant not only for this species, but also for other endemic species. They are also crucial as water catchment zones and could be exploited on a sustainable basis for timber and other renewable resources.

Part of this rabbit's present distribution lies within protected areas, including Izta-Popo and Zoquiapan National Parks, but habitat destruction continues, even in the protected areas. Volcano rabbit habitats are disappearing so fast that it is important to select a number of areas as new reserves, in addition to those already established. Where possible, these reserves should be connected with corridors of suitable habitat and located across the species' geographic range to ensure the preservation of the highest possible genetic diversity.

Golden-rumped elephant-shrew

Rhynchocyon chrysopygus

Phylum	Chordata
Class	Mammalia
Order	Macroscelidea
Family	Macroscelididae
Status	Vulnerable, IUCN
Range	Kenya

Description and Biology

This elephant-shrew has unique characteristics, some of them indicated by its common name. It is similar to true shrews in its diet of invertebrates and has an unusual physical appearance that includes a long snout resembling the trunk of an elephant, long legs, large eyes, and a long, rodent-like tail that measures 8-10 in (20-25.4 cm) long. Head and body length averages 9-12 in (23-30 cm) and weight is around 19 oz (540 g). Except for the yellowish rump, body color is a mixture of red-brown and black with slightly lighter underparts; the tip of the tail is white. The elephant-shrew is active during the day, feeding in the leaf litter. Nights are spent in nests scraped into the soil and covered with leaves.

Male and female elephant-shrews live as pairs on a home range averaging 3.5-5 acres (1.4-2 ha); the territory is scent-marked and defended against neighboring pairs. Mating can take place at any time of the year; one or two young are born after a gestation period of around 42 days. The young stay in the nest for around two weeks and then near the mother for almost another week before they become independent.

Habitat and Current Distribution

The golden-rumped elephant-shrew is endemic to Kenya and occurs in forest patches north of Mombasa as far as the Boni Forest. The Arabuko-Sokoke Forest is an important site for the species. There are no estimates of population size.

Preferred habitat includes coastal forest and woodland. There is some evidence that this species might occur in coastal scrub and fallow agricultural land adjacent to undisturbed forests.

History and Conservation Measures

The coastal forests that provide habitat for the golden-rumped elephant-shrew are subject to deforestation for pole-cutting and for urban and agricultural development. The species is also threatened directly by trapping and killing for meat by local people. Further study is necessary to determine the status of this elephant-shrew.

In order to plan conservation efforts for this species, research is necessary to provide information on distribution, habitat preference, and abundance. It will also be necessary to evaluate the effect of subsistence hunting on the status of the species. With more reliable status information, more effective conservation strategies for species and habitat preservation can be developed and implemented. These activities will contribute to the conservation of some of eastern and central Africa's most unique forests, which support numerous other endemic plants and animals.

Yellow-eyed penguin

Megadyptes antipodes

Phylum	Chordata
Class	Aves
Order	Sphenisciformes
Family	Spheniscidae
Status	Vulnerable, IUCN
Range	New Zealand

Description and Biology

The only member of its genus, the yellow-eyed penguin is a flightless, aquatic bird that is unique among penguins in its appearance and social behavior. Like most other penguins, it is mainly gray and white, but it has a striking crown of yellow plumes and bright, yellow eyes. The chin and throat are distinguished from the white underparts by a brown tint on the surface. The cheeks are pale yellow, and the bill and feet are beige in color. Both sexes are similar in appearance; adults can reach 30 in (75 cm) and weigh 11 lb (5 kg). The yellow-eyed penguin's torpedo-shaped body enables the bird to travel swiftly in water and catch squid, crustaceans, and small fish. On land it shuffles along on well-used paths from the sea to grassy cliffs, headlands, and forest inlands, covering more than half-a-mile (0.8 km) a day.

Unlike other penguins, this penguin is not gregarious and is only mildly sociable, although it may live in colonies made up of a few birds or as many as 50 pairs. Penguins may remain with one partner, but mate-swapping has also been observed. Breeding season occurs from late September to mid-October. Two eggs—the second laid four days after the first—are usually laid in nests made of sticks and coarse grass. Nests can be found in holes in the ground, among rocks, or hidden within scrubs. Incubation lasts about six weeks, with both parents taking turns. When the chicks hatch, they are watched over constantly and fed regurgitated food at least once a day. Chicks have fine, short, dark brown down and as they grow older, they show signs of an emerging yellow crown. At about six weeks, the chicks are left alone in the nest, and they may venture out to sea shortly thereafter. Most females breed at age three and males at five or six years. Some females over 20 years old have also been known to breed successfully.

Habitat and Current Distribution

This species occurs on South Island, Stewart Island, Codfish Island, Campbell Island, and Auckland Islands. Population is estimated to be between 1,500-1,800 pairs, with a total population of 5,000-6,000 individuals.

Shallow coastal waters are home to this penguin; it feeds in inshore waters and roosts on sandy beaches.

History and Conservation Measures

The primary threat to this species has been the disturbance or degradation of its nesting habitat; much of the habitat has been usurped for agricultural use and some of the area has been degraded by grazing livestock. Introduced predators such as dogs, cats, and pigs have also taken a toll on the population.

Commercial fishing presents an additional hazard since the penguins sometimes get entangled in fishing nets. Biotoxins in the food chain have also caused massive penguin mortality.

Active conservation and management programs are currently underway on behalf of this bird. Wildlife organizations in New Zealand have bought nesting sites in order to preserve some of the remainder of this penguin's habitat. Within it, they have removed predators, excluded grazers, and begun reforestation efforts. During periods of food shortages, eggs and chicks have been raised in captivity and released when conditions have been more favorable.

Yellow-eyed penguin.

Puna grebe

Podiceps taczanowskii

Phylum	Chordata
Class	Aves
Order	Podicipediformes
Family	Podicipedidae
Status	Endangered, IUCN
Range	Peru

Description and Biology

Of all the bird species in South America, the Puna or Junín grebe is the most likely to become extinct during the 1990s. The species is a diving, flightless waterbird that is grayish brown above with light underparts and neck. Its average length at physical maturity is 13-15 in (33-38 cm). It has a long neck and a fairly long, pointed bill. Its diet consists primarily of fish, supplemented by insects when food supplies are low.

This species is highly sociable, spending most of the year in small close flocks of fewer than 12 birds. The flock is often arranged in twos, followed by one or two singles. Females lay eggs between November and March, and the clutch size is usually two but can vary from one to three. After hatching, the young are carried by the male. This leaves the female free to dive, feed, and in turn to feed the young.

This grebe breeds in patches of tall vegetation in deep water, and during the breeding season it forages along the coast in open water. In the dry season the grebe moves into the deeper central parts of the lake. Nests are placed in colonies on semi-floating vegetation beds, with 8-20 nests per colony; the nests are generally situated 3-13 ft (1-4 m) apart. The Puna grebe appears to have difficulty breeding successfully. In a major study conducted in 1977-1978, more than 60 percent of apparently adult grebes had no young.

Habitat and Current Distribution

This species is restricted to Lago de Junín (Lake Junín) in the highlands of west-central Peru. Lake Junín is a large, shallow lake at an altitude of 13,000 ft (4,000 m) bordered by extensive reed beds. The Puna grebe population, estimated to be between 200-300 birds during the 1980s, had slumped to about 50 by 1993.

History and Conservation Measures

At one time there were probably several thousand Puna grebes occurring on Lake Junín. In 1938 the species was still abundant, and in 1961 there were still thought to be around 1,000 birds. By the 1970s population was less than 400 birds, and by the early 1990s it had dropped to its present level.

The primary cause of the decline of this species is the pollution of Lake Junín, mostly as a result of poisons washed into the lake from nearby copper mines. In addition, water levels have fluctuated as a result of regulation to supply water to the mines. Abrupt changes in water levels have been known to leave bird nests and fish spawning grounds above the water. 1992 was the driest year yet recorded, with open water left only in the center of the lake and very little remaining suitable nesting habitat. Additional threats include competition from the more numerous white-tufted grebe and the supplanting of native fish species by introduced trout.

Because of the dwindling population and the general deterioration of Lake Junín, an effort was made in 1985 to translocate four adult birds to Lake Chacacancha. Unfortunately, the lake also contained trout, and local fishermen believe that the grebes were caught in nets intended to catch trout. By 1987 all four birds had disappeared. Most larger lakes are considered unsuitable for this grebe, so the search continues for a translocation site.

Research projects have been proposed to continue grebe counts and studies of seasonal movements. The studies may help determine the extent to which declines can be attributed to food shortage, competition, or habitat degradation, as well as the effects of water fluctuation.

Short-tailed albatross

Diomedea albatrus

Phylum	Chordata
Class	Aves
Order	Procellariiformes
Family	Diomedeidae
Status	Endangered, IUCN
	Endangered, USFWS
	Appendix I, CITES
Range	Japan; Russia; Taiwan; Alaska, California, Hawaii, Oregon, Washington (U.S.A.)

Description and Biology

The albatross is an ocean bird that spends most of its time gliding over open sea, coming ashore only to nest. The short-tailed or Stellar's albatross is a large bird with a 7 ft (2.1 m) wingspan. It has a white body, neck, and head, a dark brown tail tip, and dark brown wings; the immature bird is dark brown. Preferred food includes fish, squid, and shrimp.

Nesting takes place on the volcanic ash slopes of Torishima, Japan in September or October, after elaborate courting rituals that include dancing, stamping, and special greeting calls. The nest is built in clumps of tall grass, if available, or in a depression in the volcanic surface. One large white egg is guarded and incubated by both parents until it hatches after two to three months. Both parents participate in rearing and feeding the chick, which is accomplished by regurgitating partially digested food directly into the chick's beak. The young albatross is out of the nest by mid-summer but is not fully mature for eight to nine years.

Habitat and Current Distribution

The only known nesting sites of the short-tailed albatross are on Torishima, one of the Izu Islands, south of Tokyo. In 1986, the population stood at 146 adults and 77 chicks.

It nests among clumps of tall grass on the slope of the volcano. The birds' guano enriches the soil and helps to establish the grass they use to nest.

History and Conservation Measures

In the 1800s, this bird was abundant over a wide area, numbering in the hundreds of thousands and nesting on islands throughout the northwestern Pacific. Its range at one time included the west coast of North America, where it was a food source for Indians.

The beautiful, snowy-white breast feathers of the short-tailed albatross were highly valued by hunters. In the late 1800s and early 1900s, hunters killed untold numbers of breeding birds, reducing the population to 1,400 birds by 1929. Feather gathering was outlawed by the Japanese government in 1903, but the practice continued until the mid-1930s, ending only because of the scarcity of the birds. Earthquakes in 1902 and 1939 destroyed villages and buried nesting grounds but apparently did not harm any birds directly. By the end of the Second World War, the bird was considered to be virtually extinct, but in 1949

Short-tailed albatross.

breeding birds were again observed. Since that time, the short-tailed albatross has made a gradual recovery. Programs have been initiated to remove feral cats from the island habitat. While its population will remain threatened because of its restricted nesting area and low reproductive capacity, there is hope that the bird will survive, although it will most probably never exist in its previous large numbers.

Bermuda petrel

Pterodroma cahow

Phylum	Chordata
Class	Aves
Order	Procellariiformes
Family	Procellariidae
Status	Endangered, IUCN
	Endangered, USFWS
Range	Bermuda

Description and Biology

The Bermuda petrel, or cahow, is a graceful seabird about 16 in (41 cm) in length, with long, beautiful wings. Colored in shades of black, gray, or brown and white, it is actually a petrel but derives its alternate name from its eerie mating call. Like the albatross and shearwater, it has large nostrils enclosed in a tube along the top of the beak. An open ocean bird, it dives under water in pursuit of food, usually small squid.

Most of this bird's time is spent gliding over water, but it returns to land to build a nest in October, often returning to previous nesting sites. By December breeding results in one white egg, which is cared for by both parents during the incubation period of 40-60 days. The chick remains in the nest for two to five months, spending much of its time alone as the parents search for food.

Habitat and Current Distribution

In 1985, the population was believed to be 35 breeding pairs which fledged 21 young.

The cahow nests and breeds on rocky islets off the east coast of Bermuda.

History and Conservation Measures

At one time, hundreds of thousands of petrels may have nested throughout Bermuda. With the ar-rival of settlers in the early seventeenth century, they became a valuable food source, and excessive hunting reduced population levels so severely that the species was thought to be extinct.

In 1951, a survey found 18 pairs nesting on the islets off Bermuda that are still their breeding grounds. The birds had been driven from their mainland nesting sites not only by over-collecting, deforestation, and erosion, but also by predators introduced by settlers. Even on the islets, they had to cope with predation by rats and, in the 1960s, with a new threat when DDT contaminated their food supply. In 1967, 22 pairs nested and produced only six young. Oil slicks further polluted the oceans and affected their food supply.

When these birds moved from the mainland to the islets, they had to compete for nesting grounds with the aggressive white-tailed tropicbird. The young chicks were particularly vulnerable while their parents were out searching for food. Conservation efforts have addressed this problem by constructing artificial nesting burrows with baffles to keep out the slightly larger tropicbirds. Rat poisoning programs also exist to keep predators under control. From 17 pairs in 1963 to 35 in 1985, the Bermuda petrel has begun a gradual recovery, but low reproductive potential and dangerously low population keep its future uncertain.

Fiji petrel

Pterodroma macgillivrayi

Phylum	Chordata
Class	Aves
Order	Procellariiformes
Family	Procellariidae
Status	Indeterminate, IUCN
Range	Fiji

Description and Biology

Description and ecological information unavailable.

Habitat and Current Distribution

This petrel, sometimes called MacGillivray's petrel, occurs on Gau Island, Fiji, where it apparently inhabits undisturbed mature forest. Total population size is not known, but it is considered very small.

History and Conservation Measures

For many years, the Fiji petrel was known from only one specimen that was collected in 1855 on Gau Island; subsequent searches did not locate any other birds until 1984 and 1985, when two birds were found. The habitat on Gau Island is apparently still undisturbed, so the species probably has sufficient breeding grounds available, but it may be adversely affected by introduced animals, especially feral cats. Studies are necessary to determine the population, distribution, possible threats, and ecological needs of this species. Meanwhile, the forest habitat must be protected to ensure suitable breeding grounds for this bird.

Dalmatian pelican

Pelecanus crispus

Phylum	Chordata
Class	Aves
Order	Pelecaniformes
Family	Pelecanidae
Status	Vulnerable, IUCN
	Appendix I, CITES
Range	Afghanistan; Albania; Armenia; Azerbaijan; Bangladesh; Bulgaria; China; Egypt; Greece; Hong Kong; India; Iran; Iraq; Kazakhstan; Lebanon; Mongolia; Pakistan; Romania; Russia; Syria; Turkey; Turkmenistan; Ukraine; Uzbekistan; Yugoslavia

Description and Biology

The Dalmatian pelican is the largest member of the pelican family, measuring 5.2-5.9 ft (1.6-1.8 m) and weighing 22-29 lb (10-13 kg); males are slightly larger than females. Wingspan is 10-11 ft (3-3.4 m) and the long, straight bill averages 14-17.5 in (36-45 cm). This pelican has elongated and curly feathers on the nape of its neck. Overall plumage is white-gray with dark finger-like tips on the edge of the wings; legs and feet are gray-black. The pouch is yellow all year-round except early in the breeding season, when it is orange-red.

The pelican is a strong swimmer and a good flyer. The takeoff for flight begins with a heavy running start, but once in the air, the Dalmatian pelican is fast and soars easily. The pelican waddles and moves awkwardly on the ground because of its large, webbed feet, a feature, however, which makes the bird an excellent swimmer. Feeding mainly by plunging its head into the water, the Dalmatian pelican feeds on a variety of fish. While this bird does not dive, it has been known to drive fish into a shoal before consuming them. A flock of pelicans have also been observed lining up and driving fish to the shore.

Breeding occurs in colonies from February to early April, depending on the breeding location, and lasts for four months. One to four eggs are laid. The female builds the nest, assisted by the male, and they both incubate the eggs for 31-32 days. Chicks fledge between 77 and 84 days but remain dependent for around three more weeks. Crows, magpies, and gulls prey on the pelican's eggs.

Habitat and Current Distribution

This pelican breeds from Yugoslavia (Montenegro) to Mongolia and winters from Albania to China. Total world population is estimated between 3,225-4,370 breeding paris, and between 80 to 84 percent of the Dalmatian pelican world population breeds in the former USSR.

This species occurs in estuaries, lagoons, rivers, deltas, lakes, and coastal waters. Nests—made of reed stalks, grass, and branches—have been found in overgrown reeds and in places where access is diffi-

Dalmatian pelican.

cult along seasides, lakes, deltas, and lower reaches of river.

History and Conservation Measures

The Dalmatian pelican was once found throughout Asia and Europe and numbered in the millions; in fact, in 1873, there were apparently millions of pelicans in Romania alone. A steady but gradual decline occurred in the last century, and the majority of the population disappeared.

Persecution by fishermen who view the Dalmatian pelican as a competitor for fish has undoubtedly been a factor in the decline of this bird. It has also been hunted for food and for the skin of its pouch. Subject to massive habitat loss, as wetlands have been cleared throughout its range for the development of agriculture, the pelican is facing more problems as human settlements encroach upon its remaining habitat and nesting colonies. Electric power lines, erected to service the growing human population, have also caused numerous pelican deaths.

Breeding colonies are protected in reserves or national parks in a number of areas, but all surviving colonies should be protected, as well as known feeding areas. Further surveys of nesting colonies have been recommended. In some areas where flooding has endangered nesting sites, artificial nests on flood-proof platforms have been constructed.

Spot-billed pelican

Pelecanus philippensis

Phylum	Chordata
Class	Aves
Order	Pelecaniformes
Family	Pelecanidae
Status	Indeterminate, IUCN
Range	Bangladesh; China; India; Java, Sumatra (Indonesia); Kampuchea; Laos; Peninsular Malaysia; Myanmar; Nepal; Sri Lanka; Thailand; Vietnam

Description and Biology

The spot-billed pelican is a fairly small pelican, averaging around 4-5 ft (1.2-1.5 m), with males slightly larger than the females. Its long, thin bill is yellowish with dark markings and measures 11-13.8 in (28-35 cm). Plumage has a grayish or brownish tint and legs are correspondingly dark. It is a good swimmer and feeds alone or in small groups on a variety of fish.

Breeding is usually communal, often with other pelican species, and occurs between October and April. Male and female share responsibility in the 30-day incubation period of three to four eggs; chicks fledge at around four months.

Habitat and Current Distribution

A survey in 1982 found this species in southeastern India, where fewer than 400 pairs bred in four colonies, and in Sri Lanka, where around 900 pairs bred in 23 colonies. Reports of breeding in China and Myanmar have not been confirmed. Breeding is suspected in Sumatra. The total world population is less than 10,000 birds, with about 2,000 breeding pairs.

Primary habitat includes many types of wetlands, such as rivers, marshes, lagoons, lakes, creeks, flooded fields, and coastal waters. Trees are used for roosting, and large trees are used for nesting. Nests are made up of branches, twigs, and vegetation.

History and Conservation Measures

The initial population of this pelican is described as being in the millions. Its decline apparently did not begin until the early 1900s, but once begun it declined drastically. Reasons for its rarity are similar to those for other pelican species: loss of wetland habitat; reduced supply of fish prey; hunting; destruction of nesting and roosting habitat; and effects of pesticide on reproductive success.

Additional surveys are necessary to better determine the status, distribution, and ecology of this species before conservation measures can be planned.

Abbott's booby

Papasula (Sula) abbotti

Phylum	Chordata
Class	Aves
Order	Pelecaniformes
Family	Sulidae
Status	Endangered, IUCN
	Endangered, USFWS
	Appendix I, CITES
Range	Christmas Island (Indian Ocean)

Description and Biology

The Abbott's booby is a large black and white seabird closely related to the gannet. It is approximately 31 in (79 cm) long, weighs around 3 lb (1.4 kg), and has a wing span of approximately 6 ft (2 m). The female is slightly larger than the male. Its sharp, saw-toothed bill is brightly colored, gray in males and pink in females. A distinctive deep and loud call is used as a greeting and in courtship.

Breeding behavior is unknown, but this species is the only gannet or booby to nest at the top of tall trees instead of on the ground. The nest is substantial and bulky, able to hold a very large white egg. The female lays the egg between May and July and incubates it for 42-55 days. Both male and female tend the chick, which is helpless and needs careful guarding for the first three weeks. The chick grows slowly and does not take its first flight until it is five or six months old. Even after its first flight, the chick remains dependent on its parents for another six to eight months before it heads for the open sea. Food items include fish and squid. Life span is estimated at 25-30 years.

Habitat and Current Distribution

The Abbott's booby nests only on Christmas Island, a tiny island in the Indian Ocean south of Java. Population is estimated to be less than 2,000 breeding pairs.

Nests are built at the top of very tall rain forest trees on the western part of the island plateau. At sea, the species forages to the northwest of Christmas Island.

History and Conservation Measures

This booby was first studied by scientists in the late 1800s, and population was estimated in 1967 at 2,000-3,000 pairs. A number of factors have combined to bring this species to its endangered status. Early settlers of the island named this bird "booby" because of its extreme tameness, which was mistaken for stupidity. It was easily approached by predators and sailors who clubbed it for food.

Extended breeding habits make reproduction slow and uncertain. Because of the long dependent period of the chicks, pairs usually mate only every two years, sometimes skipping an extra year. Chicks are in the nest during monsoon season when high winds pose a threat, and they are vulnerable to predators. Survival rate of chicks is estimated at 10-20 percent.

The greatest threat to this species is deforestation. Clear cutting of mature trees to mine phosphate has reduced the bird's habitat. There is evidence that Abbott's booby once nested on other islands, but deforestation has forced the bird to its present site on Christmas Island. Since 1987, mining activities have been limited to cleared areas, and funds have been procured to reforest some areas. Moreover, there are plans to extend areas of Christmas Island as a national park.

Galápagos flightless cormorant

Phalacrocorax (Nannopterum) harrisi

Phylum	Chordata
Class	Aves
Order	Pelecaniformes
Family	Phalacrocoracidae
Status	Rare, IUCN
Range	Galápagos Islands (Ecuador)

Description and Biology

The flightless cormorant is a fairly large seabird with a long neck and a long bill that is slightly hooked at the end. Head and body length averages around 35 in (89 cm), weight 5.5-11 lb (2.5-5 kg). Its plumage is dull black, but slightly lighter below, and it has large, webbed feet. As its common name indicates, this bird cannot fly; it is also highly sedentary, rarely straying from its usual breeding area. It feeds by diving into the sea to catch prey; fish, eels, and octopus make up the bulk of its diet.

This bird nests in small colonies of just a few pairs, mainly during the cold season from July to October. Mating is thought to be possible throughout the year, however, with some pairs nesting several times. Clutch size is one to six and incubation 22-26 days. Chicks remain in the nest for up to 28 days and may be guarded by either the male or the female.

Habitat and Current Distribution

This species is endemic to the Galápagos archipelago off the coast of Ecuador, where it is restricted to around 230 mi (370 km) of coastline on Fernandina and Isabela Islands. Population is estimated at approximately 1,000 adult individuals.

The flightless cormorant prefers the coldest, richest waters within around 300 ft (100 m) of shore. Nesting takes place along the rocky coastline, with the nests placed very close to the water.

History and Conservation Measures

Population in the early 1970s was estimated to be 700-800 pairs. After a drop in 1983, attributed to heavy mortality and lack of breeding due to disturbance of its food supply brought on by the cyclical appearance of the warm El Niño ocean current, the population seems to have leveled off.

Because of its very restricted distribution and small population, this species is very vulnerable to changes in its environment, such as human disturbance or oil pollution. Until now, commercial fishing for crawfish and lobster has been primarily by divers, but over-exploitation has led to a decline in catch, which could prompt an increase in net fishing, known to drown cormorants. Feral dogs on Isabela have been a threat, but they have now been almost eradicated.

Continued monitoring of this species is essential. Net fishing must not be allowed in the cormorant's range and human disturbance must be

Galápagos flightless cormorant.

minimized; in addition, the removal of feral dogs must be completed. While reasons for its very restricted range remain unknown, this species appears to be relatively stable, at least in the short term. Any drastic or long-term changes to its environment could put it at risk.

Christmas Island frigatebird

Fregata andrewsi

Phylum	Chordata
Class	Aves
Order	Pelecaniformes
Family	Fredatidae
Status	Vulnerable, IUCN
	Endangered, USFWS
	Appendix I, CITES
Range	Christmas Island; Indonesia; Malaysia; Singapore; Thailand; Vietnam

Description and Biology

This aerial seabird is alternately known as Andrew's frigatebird, Christmas frigatebird, and Christmas Island frigatebird. Like other frigatebird species, it is sometimes called the pirate of the sea because of its habit of swooping down on other birds to steal a meal. In addition to searching out carrion on the beaches and catching surface fish and squid, this bird will often surprise a booby or tern that has just secured a meal, overpower it, and abscond with its food.

The Christmas Island frigatebird is about 35-40 inches (89-102 cm) long but has a wing span of up to 8 ft (250 cm). Breeding males are black with white patches on the breast, and they have a red throat patch. Females and immatures are mostly dark brown with white underparts and white markings under the wings. The bill is large, pink, and hooked.

Courtship behavior is elaborate, with the male returning to previous nesting sites, puffing up its scarlet throat pouch, extending its wings, and letting out a raucous cry. If this display attracts a female, they build a nest together and prepare for the breeding season. One white egg is laid between March and June and incubated by both parents for 44-54 days. Chicks are carefully guarded for up to six months and are fed by the parents throughout most of the first year.

Habitat and Current Distribution

The breeding range of this species is restricted to Christmas Island in the Indian Ocean, although there have been unconfirmed reports of nesting on the Anambas Islands. The population in 1988 was estimated at less than 1,600 pairs.

The frigatebird covers wide expanses of open sea for feeding and nests high in trees along the shoreline. Nests are grouped in colonies on the north end of Christmas Island, very near human settlements, including a golf course and phosphate mining operations. Non-breeding birds disperse widely, reaching Indonesia, Malaysia, Thailand, and Kenya.

History and Conservation Measures

Since the 1930s, the number of breeding individuals has varied between 1,000 and 2,000 pairs. Population figures have remained fairly steady, even as the Christmas Island frigatebird has been threatened by loss of habitat and by hunting. In 1946, 225 acres (90 ha) of breeding habitat were cleared, but most of the habitat is now protected in the Christmas

Island National Park, which was extended in 1989 to include the most important areas. Poaching has now virtually ceased. The breeding sites remain vulnerable to cyclones, however, and disturbance from phosphate mining operations and from tourists remains a concern. The Australian Nature Conservation Agency has developed a recovery plan for the species, which includes protection and monitoring of the breeding colony.

Ascension frigatebird

Fregata aquila

Phylum	Chordata
Class	Aves
Order	Pelecaniformes
Family	Fregatidae
Status	Rare, IUCN
Range	Ascension Island (South Atlantic Ocean)

Description and Biology

The frigatebird is a large, aerial seabird with long wings and a long, hooked bill. The Ascension frigatebird averages 35-38 in (89-97 cm) long, has a wingspan of 77-79 in (196-200 cm), and weighs around 44 oz (1.2 kg); females are larger than males. The male is usually all black, with a greenish sheen to the feathers; the female is black with a brown collar and breast band. Feeding is often accomplished by aerial pursuit, catching flying-fish or stealing food from other seabirds; it is also done by dipping to snatch food from the surface of the water or from surfacing birds who feed by diving, such as the brown booby. Adult females and immatures most often steal food from other birds. Fish and flying fish are eaten, as are young green turtles and tern chicks.

Breeding is possible throughout the year, but there is an identifiable breeding season between April and November or December, and a peak of activity in October. Clutch size is one, incubation period 44-50 days, and fledgling period six to seven months. Young remain dependent on the parents for around three to four months.

Habitat and Current Distribution

The Ascension frigatebird is now entirely confined to the top of Boatswainbird Islet, a steep-sided flat-capped rock rising to 330 ft (100 m) off the north-east coast of Ascension Island. Its distribution is apparently confined to the waters around Ascension, probably because of a rather limited area of nutrient-rich surface water. Population was estimated in the 1950s at 9,000-12,000; around 5,000 birds were visible in 1976, with others obviously out of sight. In 1984 the population was estimated to still be healthy on the basis of the number of immature birds.

Most feeding is done at sea, probably within around 500 ft (150 m) of shore. Breeding takes place among the stones and guano deposits of the rough basalt cap, but also on ledges and paths in steeper areas; on the top of the islet, birds prefer slightly sloping ground with hollows and boulders.

History and Conservation Measures

This species was very plentiful on Ascension Island in the eighteenth century, but was wiped out there after human settlers introduced cats to the island in 1815. There was an effort in the 1960s and 1970s to control or eliminate feral cats on the island, but it was unsuccessful and the population of humans and domestic animals on the island has increased.

During the 1960s and 1970s there was increased disturbance to Boatswainbird Islet consisting of sightseeing visits to the islet. During the 1970s, there were efforts at local education in conservation and pleasure trips to Boatswainbird were prohibited.

Ascension frigatebird.

In the 1980s, there was increased activity on Ascension and concern that disturbance on Boatswainbird would also increase.

Further education and conservation effort is required to maintain the stability of seabird populations on Ascension and on Boatswainbird Islet. Boatswainbird Islet should be given protected area status to safeguard the breeding area for this species and for other seabirds. The number of domestic dogs and cats on Ascension should be controlled and an effort made to control or remove feral cats; such actions could result in the recolonization of Ascension by many seabird species, including the frigatebird, that formerly bred there. A study should be initiated to determine other possible threats to wildlife on the islands.

Chinese egret

Egretta eulophotes

Phylum	Chordata
Class	Aves
Order	Ciconiiformes
Family	Ardeidae
Status	Vulnerable, IUCN
	Endangered, USFWS
Range	China; Hong Kong (?); Brunei; Japan; Malaysia; North Korea; Philippines; Russia; Singapore; South Korea; Taiwan

Description and Biology

The Chinese egret is a tall wading bird with long legs, a long serpentine neck, and a long pointed bill. Its plumage is pure white, with a crest of long feathers forming a showy plume along the top and back of the head and neck. Average size is 25.5-27 inches (65-68 cm). Feeding alone or in small groups, this egret wades in shallow water to catch fish, shrimp, and crabs.

Pairs are monogamous and breed in colonies that can be quite large and may include other species. Two to five eggs are incubated primarily by the female for just over a month.

Habitat and Current Distribution

This species breeds on offshore islands along the western coast of North Korea and of eastern China. In winter, birds migrate to the Philippines and Malaysia. Total population is estimated at around 1,000 pairs.

Coastal habitats include estuaries, bays, tidal mudflats, and lagoons, where the egret wades in shal-low water to feed. Breeding occurs on offshore islands where nests are placed in trees or in low vegetation.

History and Conservation Measures

Once a plentiful and wide-ranging species, the Chinese egret, like a number of related species, was reduced almost to the point of extinction by hunting for the feather and plume trade. When the demand for feathers for the fashion industry increased in the 19th century, the egret, with the beautiful white plumes it bears in the breeding season, became a tempting and easy target for hunters. Hunting was finally brought under control around the turn of the century, but the species has never recovered to its previous numbers.

The surviving Chinese egrets are now threatened by loss of habitat as wetlands are usurped for rice cultivation. Collecting of eggs is now prohibited, but has not been completely halted. There is no information available about any current conservation efforts on behalf of the species.

Greater adjutant

Leptoptilos dubius

Phylum	Chordata
Class	Aves
Order	Ciconiiformes
Family	Ciconiidae
Status	Endangered, IUCN
Range	Kampuchea (ex?); India; Laos (ex?); Myanmar (ex?); Vietnam (ex?); Nepal; Thailand

Description and Biology

The greater adjutant is a large stork with long legs and a long, strong beak. Average length is 4-5 ft (1.2-1.5 m). Body color is dark, lightening to grayish on the lower edge of the wings. There is a v-shaped white marking on the neck; the throat and bare head are reddish yellow. A wading bird, the greater adjutant feeds on large fish, carrion, reptiles, frogs, crustaceans, and large insects.

Pairs form for the breeding season and breeding takes place in colonies between October and January. Clutch size is two to four eggs, most commonly three. Both parents share in providing food for the young.

Habitat and Current Distribution

The only breeding grounds for the greater adjutant known to exist with certainty are in Assam, in northeastern India. In 1993, 126 nests were found in Assam indicating that the population there may be 250-350 birds. The species formerly also bred in Southeast Asia, including Vietnam; a few birds are reported in Vietnam each year, so a small population may persist there as well.

Primary habitat includes marshes, lakes, and wetlands, but the adjutant is sometimes found in drier grasslands and open forest. Large nests are built high in tall trees or on high, jutting rocks.

History and Conservation Measures

Although still fairly common in some areas (especially Myanmar) through the mid-1900s, the greater adjutant has suffered a drastic decline. The primary cause of the decline is thought to have been loss of habitat, as nesting and roosting areas have been degraded.

Conservation efforts are geared toward preservation of remaining nesting and roosting sites. Surveys have also been undertaken in an effort to find other surviving populations. Awareness campaigns and the distribution of informative posters have been carried out in Assam.

Greater adjutants.

Northern bald ibis

Geronticus eremita

Phylum	Chordata
Class	Aves
Order	Ciconiiformes
Family	Threskiornithidae
Status	Endangered, IUCN
	Endangered, USFWS
	Appendix I, CITES
Range	Algeria; Morocco; Saudi Arabia (?); Yemen (?)

Description and Biology

Averaging 27.5-31.5 in (70-80 cm) in length, the northern bald ibis, also known as the waldrapp, has an odd vulture-like appearance brought about by its naked red head and a fringe of dark feathers around its neck. The bird's feathers, chiefly black in color, exhibit an iridescent bronze greenish gloss; a patch on the forewing or "shoulder" is a shade of shiny bronze-purple. The ibis uses its long bill to probe for a wide variety of invertebrates (especially beetles and grasshoppers) and small vertebrates.

The ibis nests in small colonies, usually on rocky cliffs or ledges in semi-arid areas near water. Breeding season begins in February; a clutch of three to four (sometimes two) eggs is laid in late March or April in a nest made of straw, grasses, twigs and sometimes fragments of paper. Not long after fledging, often by the end of June, immature birds depart the nesting grounds with their parents. Soon after, juvenile birds form their own flocks, remaining separate from breeding birds for as long as six years.

Ravens sometimes prey upon nestlings or eggs, and falcons have been reported to attack nesting birds.

Habitat and Current Distribution

A single population of the northern bald ibis remains in northwest Africa, mainly in Morocco, with some birds still found in Algeria. Though most birds remain in Morocco during the winter, wintering birds occasionally wander into Tunisia, Mauritania, Western Sahara or Mali. Once thriving, the breeding population of bald ibis at Birecik, Turkey is now extinct. A few recent sightings of birds in Yemen and southwest Saudi Arabia could be captive-bred birds released at Birecek or birds from another breeding colony at an isolated, unknown location.

The northern bald ibis inhabits rocky, semi-arid regions, often with running water nearby. Ibis feeding habitat includes sea coasts, edges of streams, river beds, flats and marshes, sand banks, or other damp ground with sparse and low vegetation. Nesting takes place on steep rocky inclines such as ledges, overhangs or cliffs; such locations limit the access of predators that might otherwise take eggs or young.

The current population is stable and is estimated at approximately 450 birds. Some 60-70 pairs nest yearly in six or seven colonies along the Atlantic coast of Morocco.

Northern bald ibis.

History and Conservation Measures

The northern bald ibis once ranged widely through southern Europe, the Middle East, and northern Africa, including the Red Sea coast. As late as the seventeenth century, the ibis could be found in Austria, Italy, Germany, Switzerland, Hungary and portions of the Balkan Peninsula. Over a period of several centuries, the ibis vanished from Europe, the Middle East and most of Africa. Reasons for its disappearance from specific locations can be cited: in Europe, for example, the removal of young from nests for food has been reported as contributing to the birds' demise there, while its more recent extinction in Syria has been attributed to widespread hunting of adult birds for food as well as uncontrolled collection for zoos. In Turkey, the use of pesticides (especially DDT) beginning in the 1950s decimated the colony in Birecek and led to its extinction there by the 1990s.

Overall, it appears that large-scale climatic changes may have played an important role in the decline of the bald ibis. Long-term cooling in Europe after the mid-1500s, increasing desertification in northern Africa and drought in parts of the Middle East may account for the slow and steady decline of the ibis over nearly all of its original range, even in regions where major human interference with the ibis and its habitat does not seem to have taken place. But the pressure exerted upon the ibis by these climatic changes, possibly combined with other unknown environmental factors, has no doubt been magnified by human pressures such as those listed above.

The conservation efforts for the northern bald ibis in Morocco are centered around the newly established Massa National Park, a 40-mile (65 km) belt along the Atlantic coast between Agadir and Tiznet. This wetland site is home to roughly half of the breeding ibis population remaining in Morocco and is also a major wintering area. The programs carried out here include a dune-stabilization effort and the prevention of pesticide application. Other Moroccan breeding areas and feeding grounds have also been protected, sometimes with the aid of local people who have built nesting areas where natural rock ledges have collapsed.

The northern bald ibis breeds well in captivity. As of 1981, over 400 birds could be found in the collections of 33 zoos. In addition, stocks of captive birds are maintained in Birecek, Turkey and at Tel Aviv University, Israel. Release of captive birds at a number of locations is being discussed, including Italy and Spain, where certain undisturbed areas may prove suitable for the ibis.

Crested ibis

Nipponia nippon

Phylum	Chordata
Class	Aves
Order	Ciconiiformes
Family	Threskiornithidae
Status	Endangered, IUCN
	Endangered, USFWS
	Appendix I, CITES
Range	China

Description and Biology

The crested ibis, sometimes called the Japanese ibis, is a large, wading bird related to herons but distinguished by a long, slender, downward curved bill. Mostly white, this ibis has orange-brown flight and tail feathers, an orange-red face, and a crest of long, white feathers. The species averages between 22-31 in (56-79 cm). Diet includes fish, amphibians, crustaceans, molluscs, and insects.

The breeding season occurs between February and March, and clutch size appears to be two or three eggs. Incubation period is 25-30 days and nestling period is 14-21 days.

Habitat and Current Distribution

This bird survives in Quinling Shan in south Shaanxi, China, where the wild population is estimated to be approximately 40 individuals. It utilizes a variety of habitats, nesting in pine woodlands and feeding in swamps, marshes, and cultivated land.

History and Conservation Measures

This bird was once common in Asia until the late 1800s but is now among the rarest birds in the world. It once bred in southeastern Siberia, eastern Manchuria, China, and Japan but now survives in only a portion of its former range.

The primary cause of the decline in population was hunting for its feathers; in the nineteenth and early twentieth centuries, it was hunted almost to extinction. Furthermore, loss of habitat has compounded the problem for this bird. Because it uses more than a single habitat, this ibis has been affected by deforestation of its woodland nesting areas and by conversion of its marshy feeding grounds to agricultural uses.

The crested ibis has full legal protection and is the subject of several conservation studies. A captive breeding program was attempted on Sado Island, Japan, in 1965 but was unsuccessful. A subsequent attempt was made in Beijing, China, where chicks were successfully hatched for the first time in 1992.

Black-faced spoonbill

Platalea minor

Phylum	Chordata
Class	Aves
Order	Ciconiiformes
Family	Threskiornithidae
Status	Endangered, IUCN
Range	China; Hong Kong; Japan; Kampuchea; North Korea; Taiwan; Vietnam

Description and Biology

The black-faced spoonbill is a long-legged wading bird with a long neck and a characteristic bill that is long, flat, and wide at the end. The wings are long and wide and the tail is short. The plumage is white and legs, bill, and face are black. Average length is 23.5-31 in (60-79 cm). The spoonbill feeds in groups, sometimes with other species, by wading in the water and swinging or sweeping its head from side to side, using its bill to catch fish, shellfish, crustaceans, and aquatic insects.

The breeding biology of this species is poorly known.

Habitat and Current Distribution

The only known breeding colony for the black-faced spoonbill is a single small colony in North Korea; it is suspected that these birds also breed in nearby northeast China. Known wintering grounds include Hong Kong, Taiwan, and Vietnam, but birds have been reported over a wider range. The population is estimated to be just over 300 birds, based on winter counts.

Feeding habitat includes such wetlands as marshes, ponds, mangrove swamps, and estuaries. Wintering habitat includes estuaries and ponds.

History and Conservation Measures

Although historic population figures are unknown, this species was once much more widespread and was common throughout its range. The primary cause of its decline was habitat loss and degradation, especially wetland wintering grounds. Habitat has been cleared for agricultural use and for industrial development and, in some surviving wetlands, pollution is becoming a problem. Feeding habitat has been disturbed by commercial fishing. Warfare in the species' range has probably also been a contributing factor in the decline.

The known breeding grounds for this spoonbill are now well protected, but wintering grounds are not necessarily well-protected. The Red River delta in Vietnam is protected, as is the Mai Po marsh in Hong Kong, but the Tsen Wen River estuary (where two-thirds of the known population winters) is not protected. Surveys to determine distribution and discover other breeding colonies are logical next steps in formulating additional conservation measures.

Giant ibis

Pseudibis gigantea

Phylum	Chordata
Class	Aves
Order	Ciconiiformes
Family	Threskiornithidae
Status	Rare, IUCN
Range	Kampuchea (ex?); Laos; Vietnam

Description and Biology

A large, silver-gray bird with lighter upper wings and long legs, the giant ibis averages around 3.3 ft (102 cm). Its bill is long, slender, and downwardly-curved. It may feed in pairs or in small groups primarily on crustaceans, but also on other semi-aquatic invertebrates.

Little information is available on social organization or reproductive biology.

Habitat and Current Distribution

The last stronghold of this species appears to be an inland delta in southern Vietnam, where probably fewer than 100 birds survive. Its status is unknown in Laos and Kampuchea, and it is thought to be extinct in Thailand.

Preferred habitats include wetlands, open wooded plains, marshes, paddy fields, and humid forest clearings.

History and Conservation Measures

The giant ibis has always been considered rare throughout its range in Thailand, Kampuchea, Laos, and Vietnam, but it is now probably nearing extinction. It was still considered to be numerous in Kampuchea in 1927, but its numbers have since plummeted. The last confirmed sighting in Thailand was in the early 1900s. It was still known to inhabit the Saravane district in Laos in 1925, but its present status is uncertain. There is a possibility that it still survives along the border of Laos and Kampuchea, but there have been no surveys to confirm its presence.

The primary cause of this species' decline is the loss of its wetland habitat. Throughout its range, wetlands have been drained for agricultural development. Hunting may also have been a contributing factor to its scarcity. Long-term political unrest in much of its range has not only contributed to its decline, but has also made it difficult to initiate proper surveys and carry out research on this species. Apparently, there have been no conservation efforts extended on behalf of the giant ibis; a survey of its present status is essential before any such measures can be planned.

Andean flamingo

Phoenicoparrus andinus

Puna flamingo

Phoenicoparrus jamesi

Phylum	Chordata
Class	Aves
Order	Ciconiiformes
Family	Phoenicopteridae
Status	Indeterminate, IUCN
	Appendix II, CITES
Range	Argentina; Bolivia; Chile; Peru

Description and Biology

Adapted for filter-feeding with a unique bill and a body structured for wading, the flamingo is a tall, elegant bird with long legs, a long curved neck, and distinctive pink plumage. The flamingo moves gracefully, whether walking or flying. Using a stocky, decurved bill with hair-like lamellae at its rim, the flamingo strains food items such as diatoms from the mud as it wades.

The Andean flamingo averages 40-43.5 inches (102-110 cm) tall and weighs 4.4-5.3 pounds (2-2.4 kg). Plumage extending from its head to its upper breast is tipped in a shade of light red and it has a red marking on its face in front of the eye. the Andean flamingo's legs and feet are yellow; its yellow bill is tipped in black. The smaller Puna flamingo averages 35-36 inches (89-91 cm) tall and weighs 4-4.4 pounds (1.8-2 kg). It has black flight feathers, deep red legs, and a yellow bill tipped in black.

The flamingo's breeding season, which extends from December to January-February, is preceded by elaborate, ritualized courtship displays which may be performed in unison. Long term pair bonds may be formed. A single egg is incubated by both parents for 27-30 days. The chick leaves the nest within 12 days, but is sometimes carried beneath the adult's wing.

Habitat and Current Distribution

Both species occur in the Andes of Argentina, Bolivia, Chile, and Peru, usually above an altitude of around 11,500 feet (3,500 m). Only one major breeding site has been identified for the Andean flamingo in northern Chile; the most important breeding area for the Puna flamingo is in southwestern Bolivia. The population of each species is estimated at no more than 50,000 individuals.

Both species inhabit salt lakes, the Puna flamingo generally at higher altitudes than the Andean flamingo. Breeding occurs on small islands in the salt lakes.

History and Conservation Measures

For a long time, the Andean flamingo was considered to be quite plentiful, while the Puna flamingo was so seldom seen that it was considered extinct from the mid-1920s until it was rediscovered in 1957.

Andean flamingo.

Although exact estimates are difficult to make because of the inaccessibility of habitat, both species are now considered in jeopardy as alterations to the environment caused by human activities begin to impact their habitat.

As humans move into previously inaccessible areas, flamingo populations can be depleted by egg collecting and by introduced predators such as the fox. Activities like mining can also bring pollution to flamingo habitat, and introduced wildlife species compete for food and degrade habitat. Efforts were begun in the 1980s to protect known breeding habitats of the Andean and Puna flamingos.

Laysan duck

Anas laysanensis

Phylum	Chordata
Class	Aves
Order	Anseriformes
Family	Anatidae
Status	Endangered, USFWS
	Appendix I, CITES
Range	Hawaii (U.S.A.)

Description and Biology

A relative of the mallard, the Laysan duck possesses light brown to ruddy or dark brown plumage. A white patch surrounds the eyes and extends to the ear opening. The male's bill is green and the female's is brown. Both sexes have a purplish green speculum (a patch on the secondary wing) outlined in black and white feathers. Average length is 16 in (41 cm). Relatively tame, the Laysan duck only flies short distances on the small island it inhabits. The species is nocturnal, feeding on insect larvae and small crustaceans in the lagoon from sunset to midnight.

The breeding season lasts from February to August, with nesting taking place in spring and early summer. A clutch of at least three pale green eggs is laid in a nest built on the ground within clumps of grass.

Habitat and Current Distribution

This species is found on Laysan Island in the northwestern Hawaiian Islands, where it inhabits the island's lagoon and marshes. The population is estimated at 500 and is considered stable.

History and Conservation Measures

The earliest cause of decline in this species was hunting for sport and for food, but its more serious decline to near extinction was caused by habitat degradation. Rabbits were introduced to Laysan around the turn of the century and rapidly denuded the island of vegetation. By the time the rabbits were eliminated in the 1920s, the duck population had fallen to a desperately low level. As the vegetation recovered, the duck population grew, and by the late 1950s, it had increased to 400-600 ducks. After wide fluctuations in the 1960s and 1970s, it has leveled off at around 500 birds, apparently the largest number that the island's habitat can comfortably support.

Laysan Island is a part of the Hawaiian Islands National Wildlife Refuge, and human access to the island is strictly limited. Even though the present population is stable, the species will probably always be considered threatened because of the vulnerability of its limited habitat to natural and man-made catastrophes. Previous efforts to introduce the duck to other islands have failed, but may be attempted again in the future. Surveys and studies of behavior are ongoing.

Laysan duck.

Madagascar pochard

Aythya innotata

Phylum	Chordata
Class	Aves
Order	Anseriformes
Family	Anatidae
Status	Endangered, IUCN
Range	Madagascar

Description and Biology

The Madagascar pochard is a freshwater diving duck with brown plumage, shading to white on the underparts; head and chest are brown. It has a dark gray bill, gray legs, and dark brown tail. This is a shy species and rarely flies, hiding instead among aquatic vegetation. Body length averages 18-22 in (46-56 cm). It feeds by diving into the water; diet probably includes aquatic invertebrates and vegetation.

This duck is often solitary but is sometimes seen in pairs. Nesting in March or April, it produces a clutch of two eggs. In captivity, incubation takes between 26-28 days.

Habitat and Current Distribution

Endemic to Madagascar, this species is apparently confined to lakes and pools in the northern central plateau. Any remaining ducks are thought to be in the Lake Alaotra region, but the population is certain to be extremely small.

Primary habitat for feeding has been lakes, pools, and freshwater marshes with open water. Nesting is in marshy areas, in a large tuft of reeds or aquatic vegetation.

History and Conservation Measures

This species was common at Lake Alaotra around 1930, when many live birds were captured. Since that time, it has grown increasingly rare; several sightings of flocks were reported in the 1960s, a pair was reported in 1970, and a single bird was captured in 1991.

The primary reason for the dire condition of this species is large-scale duck-shooting. Another factor in its decline may be the introduction of bass and other exotic fish species which may feed on young and/or alter the state of vegetation in the lake and affect food supplies. Adults may also be caught in gillnets used to catch exotic fish.

It may be impossible to save the Madagascar pochard from extinction. No conservation measures have apparently yet been taken, but legal protection of the duck and protection of its habitat are essential. Captive breeding has been suggested as the last hope for the species, but it is impossible unless more wild specimens are found. A survey is currently underway to determine the status and needs of this species.

Hawaiian goose

Branta (Nesochen) sandvicensis

Phylum	Chordata
Class	Aves
Order	Anseriformes
Family	Anatidae
Status	Vulnerable, IUCN
	Endangered, USFWS
	Appendix I, CITES
Range	Hawaii (U.S.A.)

Description and Biology

The Hawaiian goose or nene is distinctively colored and patterned: its gray-brown feathers have white tips, forming bars that are widely spaced on the back and closer together on the underside. The sides of the neck are reddish brown with black and white markings; bill, face, cap, and back of the neck are black. Average size is 22-30 in (56-76 cm) and weight 4.2-5 lb (1.9-2.3 kg). The goose has excellent senses of hearing and sight and has strong legs and wings. It grazes on vegetation, including grasses, leaves, herbs, and berries.

Breeding begins in October or November and extends through February. Pairs nest on the ground, usually in a patch of vegetation on otherwise barren lava, but occasionally in grasslands. Three to five eggs are incubated for 29 or 30 days and young fledge in 10-12 weeks.

Habitat and Current Distribution

This species is found in the mountains of Hawaii and in a reintroduced population on the island of Maui. Population in the wild is estimated at 350-400 birds.

The nene breeds at elevations of 5,000-8,000 ft (1520-2440 m). Water is not always plentiful in its habitat, but the species can survive without water for long periods by feeding on vegetation with a high water content.

Hawaiian goose.

History and Conservation Measures

Before 1800 the Hawaiian goose was common at all altitudes on the islands of Hawaii and Maui, and its population was estimated at 25,000 birds. It was hunted by Polynesians, but subsistence hunting apparently had little effect on the population. With European settlement came an increase in hunting and the introduction of predators to the island. Introduced cats, rats, and mongooses preyed on eggs and on vulnerable flightless goslings, rapidly having an effect on a population already hampered by a low reproductive rate. By around 1900, the nene occurred only in remote areas at high altitudes on Hawaii and was extinct on Maui. Habitat loss, with a resulting reduction in the availability of food plants, has exacerbated an already dismal outlook for the species. By 1952, only 30 birds survived.

Captive breeding was initiated early in the 1900s, but was not initially successful. However, a similar program begun in 1949 eventually provided birds for reintroduction on Maui and Hawaii. The introduced geese have survived well but have not bred as successfully as scientists had anticipated, requiring continued supplementing of the wild population with captive birds. Programs for controlling or eliminating predators and protecting the habitat from grazing animals are essential to the survival of the Hawaiian goose.

White-winged wood duck

Cairina scutulata

Phylum	Chordata
Class	Aves
Order	Anseriformes
Family	Anatidae
Status	Vulnerable, IUCN
	Endangered, USFWS
	Appendix I, CITES
Range	Bangladesh; India; Sumatra (Indonesia); Kampuchea; Laos; Myanmar; Thailand; Vietnam

Description and Biology

In addition to its wings, from which it gets its common name, this duck has a white head with black speckles. Overall plumage is dark brown to black, with a chestnut-brown underside. Average size is 26-32 in (66-81 cm) and weight 4.2-8.5 lb (1.9-3.9 kg). Active at night, this duck feeds in shallow water on aquatic vegetation, fish, and snails.

Breeding coincides with the rainy season, when 6-13 eggs are laid and then incubated for just over a month.

Habitat and Current Distribution

This species occurs in widely scattered populations. Small numbers exist in Thailand, India, Bangladesh, Myanmar, Vietnam, and Indonesia. The total known population is only 210 birds.

Preferred habitat for this duck is marshy areas in tropical or swampy jungle.

White-winged wood duck.

History and Conservation Measures

This duck was once common throughout Southeast Asia, but is now extinct or rare in all parts of its range. The decline has been caused by hunting and by clearance of its tropical forest habitat.

Only a small number of the remaining population of this species inhabit protected areas; the most urgent need for survival of the species is the establishment of sufficient preserves where habitat is protected and hunting is prohibited.

White-headed duck

Oxyura leucocephala

Phylum	Chordata
Class	Aves
Order	Anseriformes
Family	Anatidae
Status	Vulnerable, IUCN Appendix II, CITES
Range	Afghanistan; Albania; Algeria; Bulgaria; China; Corsica (France) (ex?); Cyprus; Egypt; Greece; India; Iran; Iraq; Italy; Kazakhstan; Morocco; Pakistan; Romania; Russia; Spain; Syria; Tajikistan; Tunisia; Turkey; Turkmenistan; Uzbekistan

Description and Biology

As its name suggests, this duck has a white head, with black markings around the eyes and medium to reddish brown plumage. Average length is 17-19 in (43-48 cm), wingspan is 24-28 in (61-71 cm), and weight is 18-29 oz (510-822 g). The white-headed duck dives to feed on aquatic invertebrates, which are its most important food source, and it also feeds on aquatic vegetation.

Clutch size averages 5-8 eggs, which are incubated for 22-24 days. Chicks fledge after approximately two months.

Habitat and Current Distribution

This species breeds from the southwestern Mediterranean basin through northwestern China. The Mediterranean population is non-migratory; the eastern population migrates in winter to the Middle East and China. In 1992 the world population was estimated at 19,000 birds.

In breeding season, platform nests are built in vegetation near such wetlands as ponds, lakes, lagoons, and marshes.

History and Conservation Measures

The range of this species has become increasingly fragmented. Its population was declining for a long time, especially in the Mediterranean, but now has apparently leveled off. Loss of suitable wetlands was partly responsible for the decline, and hunting has had a negative impact, but hybridization of the species is regarded as the most serious problem. In recent decades the spread of the more aggressive North American ruddy duck (*Oxyura jamaicensis*) and hybrids of the two species has threatened to eliminate the white-headed duck in areas where it previously thrived. The most important conservation measure for this species involves halting the spread of the ruddy duck and hybrids across the Palearctic region. Efforts have also been made to designate protected areas of suitable habitat.

California condor

Gymnogyps californianus

Phylum	Chordata
Class	Aves
Order	Falconiformes
Family	Cathartidae
Status	Endangered, IUCN
	Endangered, USFWS
	Appendix I, CITES
Range	California (U.S.A.)

Description and Biology

The California condor is the largest bird in North America and one of the largest flying birds in the world, with a wingspan of up to 9.5 ft (2.9 m) and a possible weight of up to 25 lb (11.3 kg). The condor's plumage is a dull gray-black, with a diamond-shaped patch of white on the underside of the wings. The bird's neck and head are bare, with gray, yellowish, or orange-red skin. When searching for food the condor covers vast distances—sometimes as much as 140 mi (225 km)—soaring on warm thermal updrafts at speeds of 35-50 mph (56-80 kph) at altitudes of up to 15,000 ft (4,600 m). Like all vultures, it feeds on carrion, preferring the carcasses of deer, cattle, or sheep, but also taking rodents, fish, and birds. Much time is spent in bathing and preening.

The condor can live as long as 40-50 years. Sexual maturity is reached at five to eight years; pairs mate for life. Breeding is possible from December through spring. Clutch size is one egg, but another egg may be laid if the first is damaged or lost. The egg is incubated by both the male and female for around 50-56 days; the young bird fledges within six months but may remain dependent for more than a year. Because of this long period of dependency, a pair is thought to breed only once every two years.

Habitat and Current Distribution

After the last wild California condors were taken into captivity in 1987, eight captive birds were released into the wild at the Sespe Condor Sanctuary in the Los Padres National Forest, and, of these, seven survive. The captive population stands at 62 birds, divided between the San Diego Wild Animal Park and the Los Angeles Zoo.

Nesting habitat in the wild includes caves or cavities in cliffs and mountainous terrain. Foraging habitat is mostly open grassland or savanna. The condor usually roosts on rocky outcrops or on tall, exposed trees.

History and Conservation Measures

According to fossil evidence, the California condor once occurred throughout most of North America, from the west coast to the east coast, feeding on the carcasses of large, Ice-age mammals. Beginning about 8000 B.C., the species began declining, around the time that many of North America's large mammals became extinct. By the time of European settlement, its range was already restricted to the western coast and mountains. With the growth of human population in the region, the condor population rapidly declined; by 1850 condors had vanished

California condor.

shot in carrion; DDT and other pesticides and poisons have also negatively effected the condor. Nesting condors are very sensitive to disturbance, and human activities in nesting areas have affected reproductive success. Development has also caused a shortage of foraging areas and the availability of large carrion. The condor has long fed primarily on cattle, but modern farming methods leave few carcasses in the wild.

In 1979, a program using techniques developed during studies of the related Andean condor (*Vultur gryphus*) was initiated for the California condor. Because wild condors can lay a second egg if the first is lost, biologists collected the first clutch to incubate artificially, and the first condor was born in captivity in 1983. Over the winter of 1984-85, four of the five remaining breeding pairs in the wild disappeared, and scientists captured the remaining condors to raise in captivity.

The captive-breeding program has been successful thus far, and re-introduction into the wild has begun. In January of 1992, two condors were released at the Sespe Condor Sanctuary; one ingested poison and died, but the other survives. In December of 1992, six more birds were released and are slowly acclimatizing to their new environment. Certain aspects of the program remain controversial: for example, the birds will be encouraged to eat carcasses provided by biologists, thus avoiding poisons in the environment, but preventing the condors from surviving entirely on their own.

Additional birds will be introduced into the wild, probably on an annual basis, perhaps utilizing a second, more remote location with a goal of establishing separate populations of at least 150 birds each. Though the species has received a reprieve from extinction for the time being, its long-term survival will depend upon continued intensive management as well as conservation of sufficient wild habitat to sustain a viable breeding population.

from areas north of California, and by the mid-20th century, its range was restricted to an area of central California surrounding the southern end of the San Joaquin Valley. The condor's population declined from about 100 in the early 1940s to 50-60 in the early 1960s and 25-30 by the late 1970s.

In modern times, the most serious factors leading to the condor's decline have been hunting and lead poisoning suffered by condors that ingest lead

Galápagos hawk

Buteo galapagoensis

Phylum	Chordata
Class	Aves
Order	Falconiformes
Family	Accipitridae
Status	Rare, IUCN
	Endangered, USFWS
	Appendix II, CITES
Range	Galápagos Islands (Ecuador)

Description and Biology

This rare hawk is dark brown to black with lighter markings on flanks and belly, and it has a gray tail with dark bars and a yellow, dark-tipped bill. At physical maturity, the hawk has an average length of 21-23 in (53-58 cm). While young marine iguanas form the staple of its diet, this bird also preys on a variety of birds, rats, lizards, and invertebrates, and it will feed on carrion. It soars to great heights and descends in a zig-zag pattern.

The species' territory includes favorite roosts where it sleeps or cleans itself. Territories generally include polyandrous groups consisting of up to four males and one female, although some monogamous pairs are found. In addition to these territorial groups, island populations often include many non-breeding, non-territorial birds, mainly immature birds and adult females. Breeding takes place year round, with peak activity occurring between May and July. Females usually lay one to three eggs, and males care for the young after they hatch.

Habitat and Current Distribution

The species occurs only in the Galápagos Islands, on Isabela, Española, Santiago, Fernandina, Pinta, Santa Fé, Marchena, and Santa Cruz. Popula-

tion figures are unknown, although Santiago Island is thought to have about 250 resident birds.

The bird's habitat includes all types of environ-

Galápagos hawk.

ments on the Galápagos Islands, but nesting is confined to more limited areas—low trees or rocky outcrops. Much of the hawk's range lies within the Galápagos National Park.

History and Conservation Measures

Until the 1930s, this hawk was very common on almost all of the Galápagos Islands, and it was even considered a hazard to domestic chickens. Eventually its numbers began to decline, due mainly to human persecution and disturbance of its habitat, although predation by feral cats has also occurred. Introduced predators have also reduced the amount of suitable food available for the hawks, and this may have caused the decline or disappearance of this bird in some islands. It is now considered extinct in Floreana and San Cristóbal (some experts have questioned whether it was ever present in these islands), as well as in Seymour, Daphne, and Baltra. Since fairly large, non-breeding populations of the Galápagos hawk are present in some islands, it has been suggested that some of these birds be reintroduced to islands that previously supported hawk populations. Some scientists argue against this for ecological reasons, and such reintroductions have not yet been attempted.

Hawaiian hawk

Buteo solitarius

Phylum	Chordata
Class	Aves
Order	Falconiformes
Family	Accipitridae
Status	Rare, IUCN
	Endangered, USFWS
	Appendix II, CITES
Range	Hawaii (U.S.A.)

Description and Biology

The Hawaiian hawk, also called the io, is the only native Hawaiian hawk. It varies in color from dark brown-black to tawny brown to almost white, with dark spots on the underparts. Immature birds are usually lighter in color with mottled underparts. This species' average length at physical maturity is 16-18 in (41-46 cm), with the female larger than the male. The Hawaiian hawk performs aerial displays at great heights, often flying on thermal currents above volcanos. To hunt, the bird generally perches in a tree before swooping down on its prey. Large insects and birds originally made up its diet, but it has adapted to species introduced by settlers and now feeds largely on rodents.

Nests are reused by mated pairs and improved with sticks and branches every year; they are built fairly low in trees and become quite large—as much as 40 in (102 cm) wide and 30 in (76 cm) deep. Nesting begins in March, and then the female lays a single egg in April or May and incubates it for approximately 38 days, while the male hunts and gathers food. Even after fledging at eight to nine weeks, the chick remains dependent for several months. The

Hawaiian hawk.

hawk is very protective of its nest and fights off intruders.

Habitat and Current Distribution

The population is estimated at approximately 2,000 birds. The species breeds only on the island of Hawaii but is known to wander to Maui and Oahu.

The Hawaiian hawk is found from sea level to 8,500 ft (2,600 m) but generally prefers elevations from 2,000-5,000 ft (600-1,500 m). It adapts to various habitats, including light woodland, forests, and cultivated areas bounded by trees.

History and Conservation Measures

This species has been threatened by human encroachment into its habitat. Lowland areas have been developed for commercial, urban, or agricultural purposes, and higher elevations have been subject to logging activities and subsequent use as pasture land. Pesticide contamination and the introduction of non-native plant species have also disrupted suitable habitat. Illegal shooting has also reduced the population, but to a lesser degree. Competition from cats may reduce available prey.

In the mid-1970s, population was estimated at only a few hundred birds. Since that time, there has been a substantial recovery. The Hawaiian hawk will likely benefit from efforts being made to acquire or secure a number of areas for endangered forest birds. It is possible that this bird will soon be considered by the U.S. Fish and Wildlife Service for a change in status from endangered to threatened.

Cape vulture

Gyps coprotheres

Phylum	Chordata
Class	Aves
Order	Falconiformes
Family	Accipitridae
Status	Rare, IUCN
	Appendix II, CITES
Range	Botswana; Lesotho; Mozambique; Namibia; South Africa; Swaziland; Zimbabwe

Description and Biology

The Cape vulture or Cape griffon has a long, bare neck, and a tongue specially adapted to feeding inside the carcasses of sheep, cattle, pigs, goats, and horses. It roosts colonially, departing its roost early in the morning and returning at mid-afternoon in small groups. Unlike most large birds of prey, the Cape vulture does not use thermals (rising warm air currents) to become airborne; rather, it makes use of the swift air currents present around the cliffs it uses as roosting sites. Once a consumer of the carcasses of large migratory mammals, the Cape vulture now depends upon dead livestock for its survival.

Cape vultures begin nest-building in early March; the nest is constructed of grass with a rim of feathers and sticks. Nesting usually takes place on south-facing cliffs having suitable crags and ledges, and nests are sometimes used for several years in succession. Birds lay a clutch consisting of a single egg between April and July. The young are fed mainly on muscle meat, but also on bones when these are available. Chicks and eggs face several natural hazards, including chilling by clouds which settle on south-facing cliffs, and predation by black eagles (*Aquila verreauxii*) and white-necked ravens (*Corvus albicollis*).

Habitat and Current Distribution

This species is restricted to southern Africa, occurring in South Africa, Lesotho, Swaziland, Botswana, Namibia, Zimbabwe, and Mozambique, with occasional birds wandering north to Zambia and Zaire. There are two main centers of breeding distribution, the larger, estimated at 2,300 pairs, is in Transvaal (South Africa) and eastern Botswana, and the smaller, estimated at 950 pairs, is centered on Transkei and Natal Drakensberg (South Africa) and Lesotho. Because immature birds habitually live and forage away from the breeding colonies, the geographical range of the species is much wider than the breeding range, and birds can be seen in almost any part of southern Africa. As much as a quarter of the total Cape vulture population is made up of immature birds; the world population in 1983 was estimated at 10,000 individuals.

The Cape vulture prefers open spaces, foraging

Cape vulture.

with the flesh they are fed, but as large carnivores (which crush the bones of animals later fed upon by vultures) have declined in southern Africa, the flesh fed to chicks no longer supplies sufficient calcium.

Secondary threats to the vulture include disturbance to breeding colonies as a result of human activities, mining, and fire, as well as the electrocution of birds on pylons in western Transvaal and in the Kimberley area.

It has been theorized that much of the initial decline of the species was caused by the widespread shooting and baiting of birds with poisoned carcasses; these forms of human persecution are primarily the result of misconceptions about the bird. These beliefs include the idea that vultures prey upon sheep, spread anthrax, and contaminate the water in drinking troughs intended for cattle. While some reports of vulture attacks on sheep seem to be authentic, most informed ranchers agree that such attacks are exceptional and probably involve livestock which, due to illness or injury, would not have survived anyway. The cape vulture's reputation as a vector for anthrax has also been called into question, for its efficient scavenging of carcasses greatly reduces the population of blowflies, a serious agricultural pest that is responsible for the spread of disease.

The Cape vulture has full legal protection throughout its range. Efforts of conservation groups and the media have aroused considerable sympathy for the bird among landowners and the general public; a media campaign against the practice of poisoning carcasses has also been initiated. Local conservation measures are focused upon enlisting the cooperation of owners of breeding or roosting sites. A number of vulture "restaurants" have been established, where carcasses with smashed bones are put out for the birds; the availability of these has apparently helped to increase calcium intake and reduce the incidence of osteodystrophy in vulture chicks. Studies are underway to further determine calcium requirements, feeding ecology, and breeding biology as well as to monitor population. Stricter protection is needed for the breeding colonies which are highly vulnerable to disturbance, and more research and conservation work needs to be carried out in core areas of the vulture population.

over grassland, thornbush, macchia, karoo, desert, and other sparsely vegetated regions, while it avoids large forested areas. In Tranvaal, Cape vultures are seen foraging far more often in the lowveld than in other areas.

History and Conservation Measures

Common through much of southern Africa during the last century, the Cape vulture has apparently suffered a serious decline in numbers. Early declines have been attributed to massive cattle losses in the 1898-1903 rinderpest epidemic and to declines in stock between 1950 and 1971. There is very little evidence that food supply presents a serious problem to the species today, but a more serious immediate threat is a decline in food quality rather than quantity. Vulture chicks require dietary calcium in order to avoid osteodystrophy, a disease causing deformation and breaking of the bones. Ordinarily, this dietary need would be supplied by bone flakes found mixed

Madagascar fish eagle

Haliaeetus vociferoides

Phylum	Chordata
Class	Aves
Order	Falconiformes
Family	Accipitridae
Status	Endangered, IUCN
	Appendix II, CITES
Range	Madagascar

Description and Biology

The Madagascar fish eagle is one of the rarest birds of prey in the world. With an average length at physical maturity of 27.5-31.5 in (70-80 cm) and a wingspan of 79 in (200 cm), this bird is the largest raptor on Madagascar. Its coloration is very dark, and both its upperparts and underparts are brown; its head is tan, while its tail is white.

This species spends much of its time perched in trees or on posts. From these positions, the birds can eye their prey (mostly surface fish) before swooping down to kill. They either eat their prey on the spot or take it back to the perch and consume it there. In addition to its large size and dark coloring, this bird is marked by its shrill, startling call, which is similar to a gull's call.

Commonly found alone or in pairs, this fish eagle breeds in the dry season towards the start of the rains. Nesting generally occurs between May and September, and although two eggs are usually laid, only one chick is raised. Nests are quite large—47 in (120 cm) in diameter—and consist of large branches supporting a central area of fresh leaves.

Habitat and Current Distribution

This species is confined to the west coast of central to northern Madagascar, where population has been estimated at only 50 pairs. The lakes and marshes between Antsalova, Bekopaka, and the ocean are regarded as critical habitat if the species is to survive. This area has been proposed as a national park or biosphere reserve, but it has not yet been declared as such.

The Madagascar fish eagle favors aquatic habitats near rocky shorelines and forested areas. This habitat provides suitable perching spots from which the bird can hunt in the waters below. Although largely a coastal species, the bird does range among large rivers and lakes up to 56 mi (90 km) inland.

History and Conservation Measures

The Madagascar fish eagle was not uncommon in the nineteenth and early twentieth centuries. By 1940, however, it was considered rare, and now it is one of the most endangered raptors in the world. Researchers are uncertain about the reasons behind the species' decline but suspect that hunting by humans and deforestation are factors.

Efforts are underway to build up a captive stock population without harming the wild population of Madagascar fish eagle. The second chick—normally killed by the other chick in the wild—is removed from the nest and raised in captivity. Conservationists hope to reintroduce these birds back to their natural habitat.

Harpy eagle

Harpia harpyja

Phylum	Chordata
Class	Aves
Order	Falconiformes
Family	Accipitridae
Status	Indeterminate, IUCN
	Endangered, USFWS
	Appendix I, CITES
Range	Mexico south to Argentina

Description and Biology

This eagle is a terrific predator with huge feet and talons, perfect for hunting monkeys, sloths, porcupines, reptiles, and large birds. A forest-dwelling species, the harpy eagle is adept at gliding through the canopy and plucking its prey out of trees. Mature adults have a black upper body, white underparts banded with black, a gray head and neck, and a divided crest on the head; juveniles are mostly white. At physical maturity, this eagle is 35-40 in (89-102 cm) long and weighs up to 15.5 lb (7 kg).

Mating pairs build large nests in the tops of large trees for one to two eggs. Incubation takes eight weeks, with one chick usually surviving and remaining in the nest for up to five months. Mating usually takes place every other year.

Harpy eagle.

Habitat and Current Distribution

This species is found from southeastern Mexico through Central and South America to Paraguay and northern Argentina. Population figures are uncertain.

Preferred habitat is virgin forest in lowlands and subtropics to heights of approximately 5,250 ft (1,600 m). Each pair of eagles requires a vast area of forest as habitat, but exact range is uncertain.

History and Conservation Measures

The harpy eagle is widespread but scarce throughout Central and South America, although it was considered fairly common in some areas in the 1800s. Since it prefers virgin forest, its numbers have decreased wherever there is regular human access to its forest habitat. Forest destruction has substantially reduced its habitat.

Illegal hunting is common throughout the eagle's range. It has been accorded legal protection in several countries, including Brazil, Surinam, and Panama, but that protection is difficult to enforce because of the remote and inaccessible nature of its range. Hunting also reduces the available prey. Captive breeding of this species has been attempted, but its future is uncertain unless the rate of forest destruction is brought under control. Fortunately, it has been declassified as rare by the IUCN, as it is now being found fairly commonly in its range.

Great Philippine eagle

Pithecophaga jefferyi

Phylum	Chordata
Class	Aves
Order	Falconiformes
Family	Accipitridae
Status	Endangered, IUCN
	Endangered, USFWS
	Appendix I, CITES
Range	Philippines

Description and Biology

One of the rarest and most endangered birds of prey in the world, the Great Philippine or monkey-eating eagle is a huge and powerful bird. It is 34-40 in (86-102 cm) long, with short wings and a long tail. It hunts from the treetops or glides across the forest canopy, watching for monkeys. It also feeds on large birds and small deer.

Home range is estimated to be about 40 sq mi (100 sq km) under optimal conditions; in greatly reduced habitat, it can be as small as 4.5-10 sq mi (12-25 sq km), which greatly affects breeding success and survivorship.

Habitat and Current Distribution

Population size for this eagle is estimated at fewer than 200 birds throughout its range on Luzon, Leyte, Samar, and Mindanao. Habitat is primary rain forest and sometimes secondary forest from the lowlands to 6,600 ft (2,000 m).

History and Conservation Measures

Hunting and trapping were the primary historical threats to this species. While these threats are still very real, deforestation has become a bigger threat to this eagle. The forests of the Sierra Madre mountains in Luzon are the largest remaining stronghold. Loss of habitat will continue to threaten this bird unless conservation measures are implemented. Proposed

Great Philippine eagle.

conservation efforts include enforcement of existing protective laws, selective logging, reforestation, and conservation education. Captive breeding programs have also been introduced, and a single chick was hatched in 1992 in captivity from an artificially seminated egg.

Mauritius kestrel

Falco punctatus

Phylum	Chordata
Class	Aves
Order	Falconiformes
Family	Falconidae
Status	Endangered, IUCN
	Endangered, USFWS
	Appendix I, CITES
Range	Mauritius (Indian Ocean)

Description and Biology

This small falcon is reddish brown, with a whitish breast punctuated by dark heart-shaped markings. It has short, rounded wings that allow it to maneuver in the forest canopy, darting after prey. Geckos are the primary food item, but the kestrel also takes insects (dragonflies, cicadas, cockroaches, crickets), small birds such as native gray white-eyes (*Zosterops borbonicus*), or introduced common waxbills (*Estrilda astrild*), and introduced Indian house shrews (*Suncus murinus*).

Home range has been estimated at 370-740 acres (150-300 ha). Breeding includes courtship displays, which usually begin in September or October, and a clutch of three eggs is laid between October and January. Young birds may remain with the parents until the next breeding season.

Habitat and Current Distribution

The Mauritius kestrel is confined to remote areas in the southwestern part of the island of Mauritius, in the Indian Ocean. In the early 1980s, no more than five or six pairs were located in the wild and none in captivity.

This species inhabits lower montane evergreen forest with a canopy height of around 50 ft (15 m). Nesting is usually on a cliff where the birds make a scrape, although recently pairs have been nesting in artificial nest boxes placed in trees.

History and Conservation Measures

When Mauritius was heavily covered in forest, the kestrel was abundant throughout the island. In the 1850s it was found chiefly in the extensive forests of the center of the island, and by 1900 it was reported as fairly widespread in the central and southwestern forests; by the 1950s, however, it was confined to the remote forests of the southwestern plateau. By the 1970s, some estimates placed the population at fewer than 10 birds, and extinction of the species seemed inevitable.

A number of interrelated factors are apparently responsible for the near extinction of this species. The fundamental problem has been, and remains, chronic loss of native forest habitat; almost all of the native vegetation has been cleared and much of what remains has been degraded by grazing livestock and invasion of alien plants. Endemic birds in these forests all suffer, in varying degrees and combinations, from introduced species such as monkeys, rats, cats, and mynahs, which compete for food and nest sites, and contribute to predation, and greater exposure to diseases. Hunting and human persecution have also been contributing factors, as have pesticides in the environment and a decline in prey population caused by habitat loss and degradation. With such a critically low population, a small gene pool must also be considered a serious problem.

Conservation efforts have focused on legal protection for the kestrel, preservation of its habitat, public education and awareness, and a captive-breeding program. The Macabé-Bel Ombre Nature Reserve was created in 1974, which covers 8,880 acres (3,594 ha). A national park linking this and other areas was declared in 1993. A captive-breeding program was begun in the 1970s, not only to save the species from extinction, but to provide birds for reintroduction into traditional habitat and perhaps onto the neighboring island of Réunion. Additional studies are under way to study the birds' movements and their habitat utilization, their ecology, and their life history.

Mauritius kestrel.

Maleo

Macrocephalon maleo

Phylum	Chordata
Class	Aves
Order	Galliformes
Family	Megapodiidae
Status	Vulnerable, IUCN
	Endangered, USFWS
	Appendix I, CITES
Range	Indonesia

Description and Biology

A relative of turkeys, pheasants, and other fowl, the maleo is a chicken-sized megapode with a strange, helmet-like structure on its head. It has dark plumage, with beautiful salmon underparts.

The birds nest communally on beaches or in forest clearings where the sand is warmed by sunlight or by volcanically-heated underground streams. The eggs are buried up to 3 ft (1 m) deep and left there by the female; they take between 60 and 80 days to hatch, depending on soil temperature. By the time the young emerge from the eggs and make their way up through the sand, they are independent and ready to fly.

Habitat and Current Distribution

The maleo is endemic to the island of Sulawesi (formerly Celebes) in Indonesia, where it is now most often found in the northern part of the island. Population size is unknown, but 85 nesting grounds exist, most of which are threatened or abandoned.

This species feeds in lowland rain forest and nests on coastal beaches or in forest clearings where the sand is warm enough to bury and incubate eggs.

History and Conservation Measures

Though it once may have been widespread over the island of Sulawesi, this species has become extinct in some parts of the island. The primary cause of its decline has been the collecting of eggs from the nest mounds and destruction of habitat and nesting grounds. Easily found, its large eggs are valued as food by humans as well as by pigs, monkeys, and lizards.

Current laws banning egg-collecting are not well enforced. Some reserves have been established, but further protection of nesting beaches is necessary for the survival of this species. Areas of primary lowland rain forest that serve as feeding grounds also require protection. It has been suggested that protection of the species would not preclude a certain amount of egg collecting or harvesting, if the nesting areas were properly managed.

A two-phase project, carried out in 1985 and 1990 at the Dumoga-Boue National Park, involved protecting eggs by incubating them in enclosed hatcheries at several nesting grounds, then releasing chicks upon hatching. In all, around 1,500 chicks were released. Periodic repetition of such projects may help to offset losses caused by the poaching and predation of eggs.

Polynesian megapode

Megapodius pritchardii

Phylum . . . . Chordata
Class . . . . Aves
Order . . . . Galliformes
Family . . . . Megapodiidae
Status . . . . Vulnerable, IUCN
Range . . . . Tonga (southwestern Pacific Ocean)

Description and Biology

A small megapode related to turkeys, pheasants, and domestic fowl, the Polynesian megapode or Niuafo'ou scrubfowl averages around 11 inches (28 cm) in length. It is slate gray, with a rufous or olive brown back and wings, red bare skin on the head and neck, and yellow beak and legs.

Nesting communally, the Polynesian megapode buries its eggs in areas of volcanic ash that are warm enough to incubate the eggs. The eggs are abandoned by the female, and by the time the young hatch, they are well enough developed to be independent.

Habitat and Current Distribution

This species is found only on the tiny volcanic island of Niuafo'ou, Tonga, where its population has been estimated to be around 200 pairs of birds. Formerly, it was found on nearby islands.

History and Conservation Measures

Because its eggs are prized for their food value, the Polynesian megapode's nesting grounds are raided by humans; the birds are also subject to predation by feral cats. Legal protection exists for the species, but is not well enforced. Protection of nesting areas will be essential for the long-term survival of this bird; any species with a small island population is always subject to sudden disasters or population declines.

This species' eggs and chicks are currently being reintroduced to the nearby islands of Late and Founalei as part of a long-term conservation project. If successful, the enlargement of the species' range will serve as a hedge against decimation at a single site.

Alagoas curassow

Mitu (Crax) mitu

Phylum	Chordata
Class	Aves
Order	Galliformes
Family	Cracidae
Status	Endangered, IUCN
	Endangered, USFWS
	Appendix I, CITES
Range	Brazil

Description and Biology

Similar in some respects to a turkey, this large bird has an average size of around 35 inches (89 cm). Its plumage is very deep black, with light brown underparts and white-tipped wings. Legs and bill are red; long feathers on the head form an erectile crest. A fruit-eater, it feeds on the ground, primarily on the fruit of a large tree known regionally as "castelo" (*Phyllanthus*).

In related species, clutch size is two to four, and incubation period is 22-34 days.

Habitat and Current Distribution

This species is only known in recent decades from a few patches of lowland, primary forest in Alagoas, northeast Brazil. It is now probably extinct in the wild; the captive population in 1984 stood at only 11 birds.

History and Conservation Measures

Known since the early 1600s, the Alagoas curassow was long thought to be extinct. At the time scientists rediscovered the bird in 1951, it was being reported as fairly common by hunters. But during the following decade, the bird once again declined until it was presumed extinct in 1960. Since that time, there have been reports of its continued survival in small numbers, but this has not been confirmed.

Because it was considered a prime game bird, the curassow was ceaselessly hunted, even when it was extremely scarce and difficult to find. In addition, its lowland forest habitat has been almost completely cleared, largely for the expansion of sugar cane plantations; the clearance has continued as recently as the 1980s.

In an unusual turn of events in 1977, a bird enthusiast in Rio de Janeiro obtained a few specimens of the Alagoas curassow from a local bird-keeper and from the wild; his captive stock (numbering 11 in 1984) constitutes the only known population of the bird. Seldom has the only population of an endangered species been held by a private individual; the signing of a formal agreement with governments or organizations to provide for the birds' management and propagation must be pursued with some urgency. At least in the short term, captive breeding appears to be the only hope for the survival of this species. Although little concrete information is known about the reproductive history of this single captive population, there are grounds for optimism regarding the potential for successful captive breeding. The razor-billed curassow, a close relative of the

Alagoas curassow, has shown good reproductive potential in captivity.

In addition, a detailed population survey of this curassow should be undertaken to determine if it actually survives in the wild. Although a suitable site needs to be located before reintroduction into the wild can be contemplated, there are almost no habitat areas left, and reforestation would be a long, slow process. An area of almost 2,000 acres (800 ha) at São Miguel dos Campos may possibly hold a few birds and should be investigated and protected.

Horned guan

Oreophasis derbianus

Phylum	Chordata
Class	Aves
Order	Galliformes
Family	Cracidae
Status	Vulnerable/Rare, IUCN
	Endangered, USFWS
	Appendix I, CITES
Range	Guatemala; Mexico

Description and Biology

Also known as the Derby Mountain guan, the horned guan is a large forest bird (about 35 in or 89 cm) that is easily identified by its remarkable, bright red, knobby horn on top of its crown. This turkey-like bird has black plumage with white underside streaked with small, black stripes. The belly and flanks are grayish brown. The horned guan has a large, fan-like black tail with a white bar across the median. Its bill is pale brown to bright yellow. This bird appears to be terrestrial, although it roosts and feeds in trees. Diet includes fruit, leaves of various plants, buds, shoots, and perhaps invertebrates, although some scientists believe that these birds are strictly vegetarian. There is strong evidence that the highland guan (*Penelopina nigra*) competes with the horned guan for the same food sources. The horned guan has a low-pitched, booming voice that travels a long distance. This bird appears not be wary unless frequently disturbed.

Except when breeding, guans form groups which may be made up of families. Males appear to be polygamous, and the breeding season coincides with

Horned guan.

the low rainfall months, February and March. Nests have been found in trees, on cliffs, tops of rocks, and on the ground. Clutch size is two, with an incubation period of about 35 days. The female alone feeds and cares for her young.

Habitat and Current Distribution

The horned guan is restricted to the Sierra Madre in southern Mexico and adjacent western Guatemala. There is also one record of its occurrence in eastern Guatemala. The bird may also be in Honduras, although this has not been confirmed. Population size is uncertain but was estimated in the late 1970s to be less than 1,000 birds.

This bird is found in humid mountain forest or at the edge of forests. In Mexico it is found at altitudes of 5,200-8,850 ft (1,600-2,700 m); in Guatemala it is most often found between 7,870-10,200 ft (2,400-3,100 m).

History and Conservation Measures

Although there are no estimates of early population size, this species was once considered quite common. In Guatemala, a decline was evident by the 1930s, although it remained abundant in some areas, especially Tajumulco (which may still hold the largest remaining population) into the 1960s. In Mexico, the decline became apparent in the mid-1960s.

Subsistence hunting was an early cause of the decline of this species, and it remains a problem today. Although this guan is protected by law from hunting or capture in both Mexico and Guatemala, the laws are seldom enforced. The most serious threat, however, is habitat loss, due mainly to deforestation. Habitat has been lost to volcanic activity and cleared for marble mining; it has also been degraded by livestock grazing in the forest undergrowth. Food competition from the highland guan may also affect the horned guan's population.

Currently this guan is protected in several reserves, and more sites have been proposed for protection. A 25,000-acre (10,000-ha) reserve established in El Triunfo in 1972 has been expanded to protect this and other species. This is an important site, not only for the horned guan, but also for the threatened resplendent quetzal (*Pharomachrus mocinno*) and the azure-rumped tanager (*Tangara cabanisi*). Other reserves in the Sierra Madre de Chiapas include the proposed La Sepultura Ecological Reserve, Le Frailescana Forestry Reserve, Pico el Loro-Paxtal Cloud-Forest Reserve, and a proposed reserve in the Volcán Tacaná region. Reserves in Guatemala that hold the species remain virtually unmanaged due to political and military activities.

White-winged guan

Penelope albipennis

Phylum . . . . Chordata
Class . . . . Aves
Order . . . . Galliformes
Family . . . . Cracidae
Status . . . . Endangered, IUCN
Endangered, USFWS
Appendix I, CITES
Range . . . . Peru

Description and Biology

The white-winged guan, a Peruvian forest bird, weighs about 3 lb (1.5 kg) and is about 22 in (56 cm) long. It is mostly dark bronzy brown, but it has white wings, as its name implies. The feathers of its neck and underparts have indistinct whitish streaks. This guan shelters in dense thickets and is active at dawn and dusk, feeding on various vegetation. Diet consists of fruit, berries, pods, flowers, leaves, buds, and possibly a few insects. The main predator for this species is the black-chested buzzard-eagle (*Geranoaetus melanoleucus*), as well as other eagles and hawks. This guan generally avoids flights in open air; ascending flights are made using noisy, powerful wingbeats.

This guan is usually found in pairs or small family groups, but during the non-breeding season as many as ten individuals may be seen together. During the breeding season, loud calls can be heard over a half-mile (1 km) away. Breeding has been reported in December and January, and clutch size is thought to be two or three.

Habitat and Current Distribution

This species is restricted to a small area of north-west Peru, where its exact distribution is uncertain. Population is estimated at approximately 100 individuals.

Preferred habitat includes the valleys of the Andean foothills at altitudes of around 980-2,000 ft (300-900 m). The guan typically inhabits forested slopes with small permanent streams and dry deciduous forest with ample cover and food plants. The only confirmed nest of the species was found up in a vine-covered tree in dense forest.

History and Conservation Measures

This species was originally described from a specimen collected in 1876; it had been reported to be quite common in the 1850s, but by the time it was scientifically described, it was considered rare and even on the verge of extinction. There were no further reports for 100 years until the species was rediscovered in 1977. At that time population was estimated to be a few hundred birds at most. Since then, estimates have ranged from around 200 to less than 100.

Hunting has long been identified as the main cause of this species' decline and its current restriction to the Andean foothills. Habitat destruction, however, is the main threat today, as there is ever-increasing pressure from humans looking for wood, water, and new areas to cultivate. Compounding this problem is climate change (chronic extreme drought) and the low fecundity of the species.

White-winged guan.

This species is now completely protected by law but enforcement is poor. A reserve has been established at Quebrada Negrohuasi, and the Cerrode Amotape National Park in Piura may harbor the species. Further reserves are necessary. A captive breeding program has been established with the eventual goal of reintroducing the white-winged guan into natural habitats.

Cauca guan

Penelope perspicax

Phylum	Chordata
Class	Aves
Order	Galliformes
Family	Cracidae
Status	Rare, IUCN
Range	Colombia

Description and Biology

This fairly large, turkey-like game bird is about 35 in (89 cm) long. The feathers of its breast and back are olive brown edged narrowly all around with gray. Its lower back and belly are reddish brown, and its legs are red. The crest feathers on its head are narrower and longer than those of the crested guan (*P. purpurascens*). Nests with two eggs have been reported, and birds forage and roost in flocks of up to 16 individuals.

Habitat and Current Distribution

The Cauca guan is endemic to the upper tropical and subtropical zones of western Colombia, where it is restricted to the middle and upper Cauca River valley. There are no available estimates of numbers, but the population is considered small but stable. Preferred habitat is humid forest at 4,200-6,900 ft (1,300-2,100 m). The species is known to occur both in primary forest and secondary growth, including cultivated areas and groves. Flocks roost from low trees and shrubs at a height of around 10 ft (3 m) almost to the canopy at up to 65 ft (20 m).

History and Conservation Measures

Most of the known specimens of Cauca guan were taken between 1898 and 1918; at that time the species was considered not uncommon. After that time there was massive forest destruction in the Cauca valley, resulting in a drastic decline of this species. The large-scale habitat destruction—combined with an absence of sightings—led to the conclusion that the species was probably approaching extinction, but a number of sightings, beginning in the mid 1980s, indicate that a small population still survives.

Today the species occurs in the Basque de Yotoco Reserve, where squatters have been effectively excluded and hunting and logging prohibited. It also occurs in the Ucumari Regional Park and in small numbers in Munchique National Park. All three sites are well protected. Surveys and studies have been initiated to gather data on habitat, food preferences, and population density of this bird. Conservation efforts should continue to focus on the three protected areas and the elimination of poaching.

White-breasted guineafowl

Agelastes meleagrides

Phylum	Chordata
Class	Aves
Order	Galliformes
Family	Phasianidae
Status	Endangered, IUCN
	Appendix III, CITES
Range	Côte d'Ivoire; Ghana; Liberia; Sierra Leone

Description and Biology

A shy bird, the white-breasted guineafowl feeds mainly on invertebrates in the undergrowth of the dry closed-canopy forest it inhabits, often beneath fruiting trees. Named for its white breast feathers, it has white markings on its dark plumage and a bare, red head. Although it has sometimes been reported in pairs or groups of four to five birds, it usually congregates in groups of 15-20 birds that range over territories about 0.6 square miles (1 sq km) in size.

The white-breasted guineafowl's mating season apparently occurs during the winter, as immature birds have been spotted between November and May. Although its nest has not been seen, it is believed to be made on the ground beneath a cover of dense vegetation, with a clutch size of around a dozen eggs.

Habitat and Current Distribution

The white-breasted guineafowl may now survive in viable numbers in only one or two adjacent areas of Liberia and Côte d'Ivoire (Ivory Coast). A study of the bird conducted in 1989-1991 in Taï National Park, Côte d'Ivoire, estimated 30,000-40,000 birds there. Accurate counts for populations in other areas are not available.

Found in the thin undergrowth of primary lowland rain forest, the white-breasted guineafowl does not inhabit the thicker understory found in secondary forest, and seldom leaves the security of forest cover.

History and Conservation Measures

At one time, the white-breasted guineafowl ranged throughout the rain forest of the Upper Guinea region between Sierra Leone and Ghana. It has apparently always been a very rare bird, generally occurring at low densities. Although the type-specimen was collected in Ghana, there have been no records of its occurrence there since the early 1960s despite thorough searches by several ornithologists. There is only one record from Sierra Leone. At one time, the guineafowl probably inhabited all of Liberia, and definitely populated Mount Nimba, but quickly vanished when mining operations began there in the late 1950s and early 1960s. Recent reports indicate that guineafowl still inhabit several locations in southeastern Liberia.

The primary causes of the guineafowl's decline have been hunting and the destruction of habitat. The primary forest required by the species to survive can now be found in only a few places in West Africa. The Gola Forest in Sierra Leone is seriously threatened by timber exploitation, and the Taï National Park in Côte d'Ivoire is also suffering from illegal encroachment. Even in some places where suitable conditions exist, such as Liberia, unchecked trapping and shooting of wildlife has pushed the bird to the edge of extinction. The sensitivity of the species to changes in its environment, such as those that occurred at Mount Nimba, underscores the importance of undertaking conservation efforts as rapidly as possible.

To ensure the survival of the white-breasted guineafowl, large tracts of remaining primary forest must be preserved, and hunting must be curbed. The chief immediate focus for conservation should be the Taï National Park in southwestern Côte d'Ivoire and adjoining Liberian forests at Tchien and the Cavally River, including the Grebo National Forest and the Sapo National Park.

Cheer pheasant

Catreus wallichii

Phylum	Chordata
Class	Aves
Order	Galliformes
Family	Phasianidae
Status	Endangered, IUCN
	Endangered, USFWS
	Appendix I, CITES
Range	India; Nepal; Pakistan

Description and Biology

The male cheer pheasant is rather striking in appearance; it is silvery-gray on the neck and upper back, rufous on the lower back, and the 18-24 in (45-60 cm) long tail is heavily barred. The male measures 35-47 in (90-120 cm) overall; the female is slightly smaller at 24-30 in (60-75 cm) and less dramatically marked. This pheasant is largely vegetarian as an adult, digging for roots and seeds with its stout feet and beak and plucking at leaves, shoots, and berries in the ground layer and shrubs. The chicks probably subsist on invertebrates for a few weeks after hatching.

During the non-breeding season, families may come together to form flocks of 15 or more birds. In spring, breeding pairs, and in some cases trios thought to consist of a pair with a yearling male offspring, defend territories of 38-100 acres (15-40 ha) by calling together at dawn and dusk and by fighting invading birds. Eggs are laid in clutches of 8-10 in a shallow nest on the ground amongst boulders and scrub. After an incubation period of 26-28 days, both parents and the young move as a group when

Cheer pheasant.

foraging, and families stay together until the following spring.

Habitat and Current Distribution

The cheer pheasant is only known recently from one locality in Pakistan, but there are more than 20 sites in the Indian state of Himachal Pradesh. As in the past, its distribution still extends as far east as the Kali-Gandaki Valley in central Nepal. It lives on grassy hillsides with scattered patches of oak and pine along ravines, and not in continuous forest, at 3,281-10,663 ft (1,000-3,250 m) in the foothills. Populations are often found on grazings close to hill villages, and the birds make some use of cultivated terracing for foraging.

History and Conservation Measures

Being both sedentary and social, this bird makes an easy hunting prey, and it is widely shot and trapped using snares despite having legal protection status throughout its range. Paradoxically its open habitats are probably maintained only as a result of regular disturbance, in forms such as grazing by domestic animals, hay making, and burning. The present trend towards converting such open hillsides into fire-resistant pine plantations seem detrimental to this bird.

Habitat protection from human disturbance in the Margalla Hills National Park in Pakistan has allowed a dense thorn scrub to obliterate the extensive grasslands formerly inhabited by cheer pheasants there. Unsurprisingly, therefore, a re-introduction project at this site, with eggs imported from the European captive stock of this species, has not been successful. The effective control of hunting, combined with sensitive habitat management, will greatly improve future prospects for this bird, whose small and scattered populations must otherwise be extremely vulnerable to extinction.

Ochre-breasted francolin

Francolinus ochropectus

Phylum	Chordata
Class	Aves
Order	Galliformes
Family	Phasianidae
Status	Endangered, IUCN
Range	Djibouti

Description and Biology

This ground-dwelling game bird, also known as the Djibouti francolin, has short wings and strong legs and feeds on seeds and fruit. Breeding is known to take place from December to February, but little information about reproductive biology is available.

Habitat and Current Distribution

The ochre-breasted francolin is confined to the small relict Foret du Day in Djibouti, at an altitude of around 5,000 ft (1,500 m). Sightings in relict secondary forest at Mabla have been confirmed as this species. The population is estimated at around 5,000 birds.

This francolin inhabits both primary and secondary forest. Its main requirements are reported to be areas of dense cover for roosting and possibly for breeding and areas with appropriate grasses and fruits for feeding. It is a sedentary species.

History and Conservation Measures

Population size for this species was estimated in the 1950s to be no more than a few hundred, but this was clearly too low since a study in 1984 found a population of around 5,000 birds. In that study, the francolin was found to be present at six sites: Garrab, Adonta, Afambo, Wadriba, Goh, and Bankouale, in addition to Mabla.

Despite the relatively high population numbers, this species is considered to be in imminent danger of extinction because of habitat loss. A slow, natural desiccation of the region is being compounded by extensive human interference. Over a period of 2,000 years, the primary forest on the Goda massif was reduced from almost a million acres (400,000 ha) to only 7,400 acres (3,000 ha) in 1977; from 1977 to 1984 the relict area on the Plateau du Day was reduced by more than half to only 3,400 acres (1,400 ha). Causes of habitat loss have included overgrazing and trampling by livestock, cutting of trees to create pasture and firewood, setting of fires to create pasture, and clearance for agriculture and road building. Unless these activities are curtailed quickly, the remaining forest land will be lost.

Immediate efforts must be made to control factors responsible for accelerating habitat loss in the Foret du Day. The loss of Djibouti's only remaining forested area would mean the loss of most of its associated wildlife, much of which is unstudied and could contain species new to science. As a stopgap against extinction, captive breeding and/or translocation of the ochre-breasted francolin to other potential forests should be considered.

Edward's pheasant

Lophura edwardsi

Imperial pheasant

Lophura imperialis

Vo Quy's pheasant

Lophura hatinhensis

Phylum	Chordata
Class	Aves
Order	Galliformes
Family	Phasianidae
Status	Indeterminate, IUCN (*L. hatinhensis*)
	Vulnerable, IUCN (*L. edwardsi; L. imperialis*)
	Endangered, USFWS (*L. edwardsi; L. imperialis*)
	Appendix I, CITES (*L. edwardsi; L. imperialis*)
Range	Vietnam

Description and Biology

Edward's, imperial, and Vo Quy's pheasants are endemic to Vietnam, and surveys conducted in 1993 indicate that all three species are seriously threatened with extinction. Physical and biological information on these birds is scarce; it is known that a black crest distinguishes the imperial pheasant from the other two Vietnamese pheasants. There also appears to be much similarity between Vo Quy's and Edward's pheasants, and some scientists believe Vo Quy's pheasant is a subspecies of Edward's pheasant.

Habitat and Current Distribution

Edward's pheasant has always been known from a small area in the Annamese lowlands in Vietnam. Recent fieldwork in its historical range failed to find the species and revealed the area to be almost completely deforested. It may, however, still exist in small numbers (less than 1,000 individuals). Between 130-420 individuals are believed to be in captivity.

Vo Quy's pheasant is found in north Vietnam, confined to the forests of the level lowlands of northern central Annam. At Cat Bin it is found in level or gently sloping terrain covered by secondary lowland evergreen forest with well-developed understory of palms and rattan interspersed with patches of bamboo. The population in 1992 was estimated to be between 100-10,000 birds. Ten survive in the Hanoi Zoo.

The only recent record of the imperial pheasant is that of a live bird trapped by rattan collectors 7.5 mi (12 km) west of Cat Bin in 1991 in secondary lowland forest at 164-328 ft (50-100 m). The historical assertion that the species occurs in central Laos is probably erroneous. The population of this bird is estimated to be 100-10,000. None are known to exist in captivity.

History and Conservation Measures

Edward's pheasant and the imperial pheasant were both first described in 1924; Vo Quy's pheasant was discovered in 1964. For many years it was very difficult to assess the status of these birds because of continuing military activity in their range. It is suspected that the birds suffered from the defoliants used in the war in Vietnam, through direct poisoning and through the destruction of the dense vegetation that is vital to these birds. Today the pheasants are threatened by habitat destruction and, in the cases of Vo Quy's and imperial pheasants, by over-exploitation for food.

Specific recommendations have been proposed on behalf of these pheasants, one being the need to evaluate sites for the establishment of protected areas; three sites have been especially targeted for protection: Thanh Thuy in Nghe Tinh Province, Vu Qhang, also in Nghe Tinh Province, and Dong Phong Nha in Binh Tri Thien Province. One or more of the three target species are known to be present in these areas. Other localities which may be suitable for protection include Cat Bin forest near Ho Ke Go in Ha Tinh Province, which holds both imperial and Vo Quy's pheasants, and areas in Thua Thien and Quang Tri Provinces. The last two provinces may hold forest suitable for Edward's pheasant, for which no suitable habitat has yet been located.

Another conservation measure involves the management of the Cat Bin forest area. This is the only site known to contain the two species which have recently been recorded, but both the imperial and Vo Quy's are threatened by trapping and habitat loss in this area. Wise use of forest resources is essential if these pheasants are to remain in the Cat Bin region. A third recommendation involves educating and raising conservation awareness of these rare pheasants in and around the project areas.

Edward's pheasant.

Western tragopan

Tragopan melanocephalus

Phylum	Chordata
Class	Aves
Order	Galliformes
Family	Phasianidae
Status	Endangered, IUCN
	Endangered, USFWS
	Appendix I, CITES
Range	China; India; Nepal (?); Pakistan

Description and Biology

A colorful pheasant, the male western tragopan has a naked crimson eyepatch, blue skin at the throat, and deep red nape and bib feathering. The black crest is tipped with red; the breast is white spotted on a black and deep red background; and the back and wings are similarly spotted on a brownish background. The dark tail is short and wedge-shaped. During the frontal courtship display, two bright blue fleshy horns become engorged, and a lappet inflates from the throat: it is purplish in the center and pink with blue indentations on the margins. The male weighs between 3.9-4.4 lb (1.8-2 kg) and has a wing span of 10-11 in (25.5-29 cm). The female western tragopan is much smaller, with brownish gray plumage above and paler breast and belly; there is a rufous tinge to the head and neck but no naked eye patch. The female weighs between 2.8-3 lb (1.25-1.4 kg) and has a wing span of 8.8-9.8 in (22.5-25 cm).

Diet is probably comprised mostly of leafy vegetation from understory shrubs and trees, particularly oaks. This pheasant also digs for roots and seeds and eats berries in season. The yellow-throated marten, leopard, and fox are believed to be predators. Larger birds of prey do not seriously threaten this species because it is difficult to find among the dense forest understory.

During the mating season, males emit a call resembling that of a young lamb—loud wailing cries—during May and early June. Nests are sometimes found in trees. Clutch size and incubation period are not known.

Habitat and Current Distribution

This pheasant inhabits moist temperate forests in the front ranges of the Western Himalayas from Indus Kohistan (Pakistan) to Himachal Pradesh (India). They live in the dense understory under coniferous or oak forests and move from winter quarters at 6,500-9,200 ft (2,000-2,800 m) to breeding areas at 9,200-12,000 ft (2,800-3,600 m) each spring as snow melts. This movement is reversed in October with first snowfall. Major centers of population are presently in Indus Kohistan, on both sides of the Indo-Pakistan ceasefire line in Kashmir, and in both the Kullu and Shimla Districts of Himachal Pradesh.

Population is estimated to be under 5,000 birds. This bird never seems to have occurred at high densities. Surveys of calling males in spring in the Palas

Valley in Indus Kohistan suggest that there may be approximately one male per 25 acres (10 ha).

History and Conservation Measures

The western tragopan was once abundant throughout northwestern India and Pakistan. Substantial numbers were captured and shipped to Europe in the latter part of the nineteenth century (along with all other Himalayan pheasants). People have traditionally valued these birds for their plumage and as a food source. Hunting today is less of a threat than it used to be, due to the lack of financial incentives and better legislation and enforcement. Nonetheless, habitat degradation still threatens this bird. Conservation of near primeval forests within the pheasant's range is the key to its survival. Excessive clearance has fragmented these ancient habitats, and grazing by domestic animals can further render areas uninhabitable for this bird.

The Great Himalayan National Park in Kullu and several wildlife sanctuaries and game reserves in India and Pakistan currently hold populations of the western tragopan. A major forestry project is also underway in the Palas Valley in Indus Kohistan. This bird has rarely been brought into captivity and may never have been bred successfully. There is no captive breeding program in progress at the present time.

Whooping crane

Grus americana

Phylum	Chordata
Class	Aves
Order	Gruiformes
Family	Gruidae
Status	Endangered, IUCN
	Endangered, USFWS
	Appendix I, CITES
Range	Canada; Texas (U.S.A.)

Description and Biology

The whooping crane, so named because of the trumpeting or whooping sound it makes, is the tallest North American bird, standing as high as 5 ft (1.5 m) with a wing span of 7.5 ft (2.3 m) and a weight of 15-16 lb (6.8-7.3 kg). This marsh bird has a white body, white wings with black tips, long dark legs, black feet, red face, and a long pointed yellow bill. The species is migratory, flying south for the winter season. Diet consists of crabs, crayfish, frogs, insects, and plants, which are acquired throughout the 300-400 acre (121-162 ha) range each pair requires.

Courtship behavior begins in late winter and consists of strutting, leaping, head bobbing, wing flapping, and loud calls. In early spring, it builds its nest on the ground among vegetation; two light tan to green eggs with dark markings are laid. Both parents incubate the egg for approximately four weeks and tend the young for another three to four weeks. Whooping crane mates for life and sometimes returns to previous nesting sites.

Habitat and Current Distribution

The original population of whooping cranes nests in Wood Buffalo National Park in Northwest Territories, Canada. It winters in the Aransas National Wildlife Refuge on the Gulf Coast in Texas. In 1989 this population numbered 138 birds.

Preferred nesting grounds are wetlands, marshes, and transitional areas; winter habitat includes coastal lagoons and fresh and brackish marshes.

History and Conservation Measures

Although the whooping crane population was probably always small, at one time they could be found on the Great Plains and on both coasts of the United States. Before the West was settled, they nested from Illinois to southern Canada and wintered from the Carolinas to Mexico. By 1941, fewer than 20 whooping cranes existed in the world. As agricultural development displaced the cranes, they found refuge in the far north at Wood Buffalo National Park in Canada's Northwest Territories, where their breeding grounds were discovered in 1955. Hunting was once a threat to the species, but the crane is now legally protected, although many still die from collisions with power lines. Recovery goals call for a wild population of 90 nesting pairs. Although the current whooping crane population fluctuates from year to year, the crisis seems to have passed due to massive conservation efforts undertaken on its behalf.

Whooping cranes.

Captive breeding efforts have slowly increased the population of the whooping crane. A captive flock has been established at the International Crane Foundation in Baraboo, Wisconsin. Patuxent Wildlife Research Center and the International Crane Foundation host a program in which one of the crane's two eggs is gathered from each nest and artificially incubated. This egg would otherwise be lost, since in most cases only one of the two chicks survives to maturity. An attempt to introduce a population to Gray's Lake National Wildlife Refuge in Idaho failed when no pairs formed. Plans have been made to release captive-reared birds at Kissimmee Prairie and other reintroduction sites in Florida in an effort to start a non-migrating flock. Other efforts will be in the area of habitat management to promote wetland conservation.

Red-crowned crane

Grus japonensis

Phylum	Chordata
Class	Aves
Order	Gruiformes
Family	Gruidae
Status	Vulnerable, IUCN Endangered, USFWS Appendix I, CITES
Range	China; Japan; Russia; Mongolia; North Korea; South Korea

Description and Biology

Also called the Japanese or Manchurian crane, the red-crowned crane is a long-legged marsh bird with a white body, red crown, and green bill. Wings are white with black outermost areas. Cheeks and neck are black in males, gray in females.

The species feeds upon plants and such animals as fish, snakes, tadpoles, and frogs. Pairs require 1-4 sq mi (2.5-10 sq km) of marshland for breeding. The mating season is of limited duration, usually occurring in April and sometimes May. Clutch size is thought to be two eggs, the second of which is laid 2-4 days after the first. Both sexes incubate the eggs and feed the young.

Habitat and Current Distribution

In 1992, the total population of this species was estimated at approximately 1,800 birds in the following distribution: Japan, 500 birds; Russia, 150-200 birds, including 35-40 breeding pairs; and China, 980 birds. Of these, 500 winter in Japan, 750 in China, 300 in North Korea, and 130 in South Korea.

The red-crowned crane breeds in wide expanses of open wetlands, and winters on wetlands bordered by agricultural fields, where it forages on gleanings.

Red-crowned crane.

History and Conservation Measures

Historical range and population size for this species is not well known. The red-crowned crane seemed to have disappeared in Japan after 1870, but a group of 20 birds was discovered in 1924. In China during the 1940s, numerous small flocks of up to 50 birds were observed in migration patterns. In 1964, the entire population in Siberia was estimated at 200-300. In North and South Korea, where the crane is given government protection, historical population figures vary.

Loss of nesting habitat is the main threat to the species as development continues to eliminate marshlands; international cooperation is required to ensure its survival. In Japan, fatal collisions with electric power lines have prompted the proposal that wires near winter feeding areas be marked to help the birds avoid collisions. The red-crowned crane has been declared a Special Natural Monument in Japan, and feeding by farmers and school children is not only encouraged, but subsidized. Feeding stations dispensing corn attract crowds of people who gather to watch the cranes. This guaranteed food supply has led to a gradual increase in the population of cranes in the region.

Siberian crane

Grus leucogeranus

Phylum	Chordata
Class	Aves
Order	Gruiformes
Family	Gruidae
Status	Rare, IUCN Endangered, USFWS Appendix I, CITES
Range	Afghanistan; China; India; Iran; Mongolia (?); Pakistan; Russia

Description and Biology

The Siberian crane, or Siberian white crane, is as beautiful as it is rare, with long, reddish pink legs, red-orange face, and a snowy white body with black areas on its wings. Its height averages 47.25-55 in (120-140 cm). Young cranes eat insects, frogs, and small rodents; adults feed on the roots and tubers of aquatic plants.

Early spring courtship behavior includes ritual dancing and flutelike calls. Breeding pairs require vast amounts of territory and build nests approximately 15.5 mi (25 km) apart from other pairs. Both parents participate in the incubation of two eggs for approximately four weeks. Usually only one chick lives to maturity; it leaves the nest soon after hatching but remains with its parents until it fledges at two to four months.

Habitat and Current Distribution

The Siberian crane is now restricted to two breeding areas: one in northeastern Siberia between the Yana and Kolyma Rivers, and another to the west on the lower reaches of the Ob River. The breeding

Siberian cranes.

population of approximately six birds that nests on the Ob River winters in the Keoladeo Ghana Bird Sanctuary in Bharatpur, Rajasthan, India; another flock winters in the Caspian lowlands of Iran. The larger population of about 2,700 birds winter at Poyang Lake, China's largest freshwater lake.

Breeding habitat includes marshy and lightly wooded tundra; winter is spent in freshwater wetlands and shallow ponds.

History and Conservation Measures

Early population estimates are not available, but Siberian cranes are known to have once nested throughout much of Siberia. Seldom observed during migration, the whereabouts of their wintering grounds long remained a mystery. The Poyang Lake site was discovered in 1981. The major threat to the Siberian crane is hunting along the migration path in Iran and Afghanistan and the reduction of wetlands along the migration route and in wintering areas in South Asia.

Programs are under way in the United States, Germany, and Russia to carry eggs produced by captive Siberian cranes to the nesting grounds of wild cranes near the Ob River, where they are hatched in an electric incubator and hand-reared in visual isolation from man with the use of hand puppets and crane-costumed keepers.

Black-necked crane

Grus nigricollis

Phylum	Chordata
Class	Aves
Order	Gruiformes
Family	Gruidae
Status	Vulnerable, IUCN
	Endangered, USFWS
	Appendix I, CITES
Range	Bhutan; China; India; Myanmar; Vietnam

Description and Biology

The black-necked crane is a medium-sized crane with a stocky appearance. Its body is mostly gray, with white underparts and a black tail; head and neck are black, with a red crown; legs are black; and bill is green or gray with a yellow tip. This crane has a larger body and shorter neck and legs than those of related species, perhaps as an adaptation to the extreme cold of the Tibetan Plateau, where it is found.

Like other cranes, this species has various calls and displays that include threat postures and courtship dances. During breeding season, pairs exclude other cranes from their territories. Females usually lay two eggs. Black-necked cranes nest in wetlands, and during the day adults frequently lead their young to open upland grasslands and pastures where they feed on insects, seeds, and vegetation.

Habitat and Current Distribution

During the breeding season the black-necked crane usually frequents shallow wetlands, many of which are associated with streams and lakes, at altitudes ranging from 12,500-15,000 ft (3,800-4,550 m).

Black-necked crane.

In autumn they gather in flocks and migrate to lower altitudes. Through the winter they feed both in natural wetlands and in agricultural fields. In the wetlands they excavate the fleshy tubers of aquatic plants, while in the fields they feed on gleanings. In Tibet, barley gleanings are their primary food.

Today it is estimated that a minimum of 5,500 black-necked cranes survive. The majority of these spend the entire year in Tibet and in the adjacent provinces of Chinghai, Ganzu, Sichwan, Yunnan, and Guizhou. In addition, there are two to three pairs that breed in Ladakh, India, and about 300 cranes migrate from Tibet to spend the winter in three valleys of Bhutan. Birds have not been reported to winter in Myanmar (Burma) or Vietnam for many decades.

History and Conservation Measures

In recent years in Tibet, much information about the distribution, biology, and conservation of the black-necked cranes have been assembled through comprehensive field studies. Since Tibetan people protect and revere the cranes, if the traditional life of the Tibetans is maintained, the cranes are relatively safe. However, there are plans to modernize Tibet, and much of it involves altering or destroying the crane's habitat. Conservation efforts should focus on preserving this bird's habitat and overseeing land development plans that affect this and other species in the area.

Okinawa rail

Gallirallus (Rallus) okinawae

Phylum	Chordata
Class	Aves
Order	Gruiformes
Family	Rallidae
Status	Vulnerable, IUCN
Range	Okinawa (Japan)

Description and Biology

Almost flightless, the Okinawa rail averages around 11 inches (28 cm) in length. It is a ground-dweller that feeds on insects and other invertebrates. At night, it ascends the sloping trunks of trees by fluttering or climbing to roost on the bare branches. Clutch size is usually four; no other information is available about its reproductive biology.

Habitat and Current Distribution

This species occurs in the northern part of the island of Okinawa, where it inhabits upland forests with dense undergrowth. Its population has been estimated at 500-1,500 birds.

History and Conservation Measures

The Okinawa rail was not fully described until 1981, although it had been observed on a few earlier occasions. It is at risk because of habitat destruction, as areas of its limited habitat are steadily cleared. The Okinawan branch of the Wild Bird Society of Japan is pressing for better conservation of these forests.

Guam rail

Gallirallus (Rallus) owstoni

Phylum	Chordata
Class	Aves
Order	Gruiformes
Family	Rallidae
Status	Vulnerable, IUCN
	Endangered, USFWS
Range	Guam (western Pacific Ocean)

Description and Biology

A flightless, ground-dwelling bird, the Guam rail averages 11 inches (28 cm) long. Plumage is brown above and black and white below; there is a brown stripe in the eye area and a gray stripe above the eyes.

Habitat and Current Distribution

This species is endemic to Guam, where it was distributed in most types of habitat throughout the island, including forests or woodlands, marshes, grasslands, and cultivated areas. It is now extinct in the wild, but a captive population has been introduced to the island of Rota.

History and Conservation Measures

The rail was apparently widely distributed on Guam until it began a steep decline in the 1970s. It was once hunted for food, and was protected beginning in 1976. Despite the presence of introduced pigs, cats, and dogs, this flightless bird survived on the island for many years; the introduction of the brown tree snake (*Boiga irregularis*), however, finally spelled the end of its days in the wild. The population was estimated at around 2,000 birds in 1981, but had been reduced to fewer than 100 within a few years. However, the species breeds very well in captivity.

An attempt has been made to establish an ex-

Guam rail.

perimental artificial population on the island of Rota. Twenty-two rails were introduced, but the majority of the birds died. A further release of 50-100 birds has been attempted, but it is too early to know the long-term results. If reintroduction experiments prove successful, they will be extended to historical habitat on the island of Guam.

Lord Howe rail

Gallirallus (Tricholimnas) sylvestris

Phylum	Chordata
Class	Aves
Order	Gruiformes
Family	Rallidae
Status	Endangered, IUCN
	Endangered, USFWS
	Appendix I, CITES
Range	Lord Howe Island (Australia)

Description and Biology

The Lord Howe wood rail, also called the Lord Howe Island woodhen, is a flightless brown bird with dark brown and black stripes on its wings. Averaging around 14 in (36 cm) long, it has a strong, curved bill and red eyes. Aging birds turn gray around the neck and sides of the head. The wood rail's food in the wild includes worms, insects, and grubs; in captivity, it has been fed poultry pellets and cheese. The rails live in territories 7.5 acres (3 ha) in size. Predators include feral pigs and owls.

Mating for life, the Lord Howe wood rail breeds in the late spring or summer. The nest is built on the ground; clutch size is one to four eggs. Newly hatched young are black.

Habitat and Current Distribution

This bird's home is the island from which it takes its name, Lord Howe Island in the southwest Pacific, off the mainland of Australia.

A few lowland and mountain closed forests provide remaining habitat; in the lowlands, the bird chiefly inhabits kentia palm (*Howea fosterana*) forest

Lord Howe rail.

rather than rain forest, while in the uplands, a formation unique to the mountain summits called Gnarled Mossy Forest is preferred habitat. Population of the species, which was as low as 30 birds in 1980, had increased to roughly 170-200 birds in 1990.

History and Conservation Measures

At the time of the island's discovery in 1788, the wood rail or woodhen was found throughout the island. When whaling ships began to visit the island, the flightless bird was so easily captured that it became an abundant food source. By 1850 there were permanent settlers on the island and the remaining wood rails, decimated by introduced predators and by habitat disturbance caused by feral pigs and goats, could be found only on the mountaintops. By the late 1800s, the bird was well on its way to extinction.

In 1963, the population of the rail was thought to be 150-200 pairs; by the mid-1970s, this number had dwindled to less than 30 birds. At this time, conservationists began taking steps to eliminate introduced predators such as the wild pig, as well as initiating a captive breeding program in 1980 using three of the remaining rail pairs. The captive rails reproduced readily, and in the succeeding four years, 85 birds bred in captivity were released into the wild. As of 1990, the wild population had increased to 40-50 breeding pairs and 170-200 total individuals.

Current conservation efforts are focused on the control of feral pigs, cats and domestic dogs, all of which have played a significant role in the near disappearance of the wood rail. In addition, the masked owl (*Tyto novaehollandiae*), introduced to the island in the 1920s as rat-control predator, is a major threat to the rail today.

Neither forest clearance nor human predation is considered to be a major threat at present; the respectful attitude of the island residents for the endangered bird is expected to make its recovery more likely. A careful annual census of the bird's population has begun, with the aim of closely monitoring the bird's status.

Takahe

Porphyrio (Notornis) mantelli

Phylum	Chordata
Class	Aves
Order	Gruiformes
Family	Rallidae
Status	Endangered, IUCN
Range	New Zealand

Description and Biology

The takahe is a stocky, flightless rail with short wings and a very stout orange-red bill. Its plumage is iridescent, with a dark blue to black head and chest, a green back and sides, and an orange-red face and feet. Its average size is 24.8 in (63 cm). This rail eats primarily the bases of grass shoots and seedheads of tussock; in winter, it consumes grasses, herbs, and ferns.

The takahe mates for life, and a pair defends a territory of 5-140 acres (2-57 ha).

Habitat and Current Distribution

This species is restricted to the Murchison Mountains, South Island, New Zealand, where it inhabits montane tussock grassland and moves into adjacent woodland in winter. Total population was estimated in the late 1970s to be around 250 birds.

History and Conservation Measures

The takahe was not described scientifically until 1849, and it was already considered extinct by 1900. Rediscovered in 1948 on South Island it has been declining in numbers since the 1960s. The cause of this species' decline is the introduction of predators and competitors to the island. A major cause of mortality for the species is the predation of eggs and young by the introduced ermine. In addition, the takahe has difficulty competing for grasses and vegetation with the growing deer population on the island.

Many conservation efforts have been made on

Takahe.

behalf of the takahe. The Fiordland National Park now provides protection to habitat in its range. Programs have been initiated to control the number of deer and thus preserve the forest understory. A captive breeding program has provided birds for a rein-troduction program to a neighboring island. Finally, ecological studies have been ongoing to determine the needs of the species and to better facilitate conservation efforts.

White-winged flufftail

Sarothrura ayresi

Phylum	Chordata
Class	Aves
Order	Gruiformes
Family	Rallidae
Status	Indeterminate, IUCN
Range	Ethiopia (ex?); South Africa; Zambia; Zimbabwe

Description and Biology

The white-winged flufftail is a small rail. As with other species in this genus, it exhibits strong sexual dimorphism. In adult males, feathers on the top of the head and nape are blackish with chestnut bases. The sides of the head are chestnut with fine black scaling and the cheeks are blackish. The back and sides of the neck are dark chestnut, shading to lighter chestnut on the lower throat and sides of the breast. The rest of the bird's upperparts are black with fine white streaks, and the tail is barred in chestnut and black. The center of the breast and the belly are white, and the rest of the underparts are streaked white and black. The bill is purplish brown, and the legs and feet are purplish. The adult female is similar to the male, but is blacker, exhibiting less rufous color on the head and neck. The female's breast is rufous brown scaled with dark brown, and its flanks are white spotted with black. This species is distinguished from most other flufftails by a white wing patch that is clearly seen when the bird is in flight.

The white-winged flufftail's diet is known only from examination of two specimens, one of which had eaten aquatic insects and the other seeds and vegetation.

Habitat and Current Distribution

The white-winged flufftail is known from the Ethiopian highlands, South Africa, Zambia, and Zimbabwe. It currently appears to be restricted to Ethiopia and South Africa, although it may be extinct in Ethiopia. Studies of sighting records have led to the conclusion that it is a nomadic opportunist with a distribution that never stabilizes. There is no estimate of population size, but numbers are thought to be extremely small.

Preferred habitat is marshland, but a "dry" type of marshland. This bird doesn't seem to require a specific type of vegetation, but the species has most often been seen in areas without standing water or in areas that are only partly submerged during the rains. It apparently has no definite seasonal movement but moves in relation to rainfall.

History and Conservation Measures

The white-winged flufftail was first described from two birds shot in 1876 in eastern Cape Province. Records of sightings for this species are mainly from southern Africa between 1877 and 1901 and from

1955 to the present, as well as from Ethiopia between 1905 and 1957.

The reason for the rarity of this species is not well known, but it may be the result of competitive exclusion by the streaky-breasted flufftail (*Sarothrura bohmi*). Destruction of habitat is not thought to have been a problem in the past, but the loss of marshland due to drainage, damming, pumping, burning, and grazing has increased and may have a negative impact on the species in the long-term.

Other than protection by provincial and homeland conservation ordinances, no conservation measures have been taken. The nomadic behavior of the species makes it difficult to plan protection, as it is not known to occur consistently or reliably in any site. Preservation of remaining South African marshland should be of benefit to this rail and to other threatened birds, as would regulation of marsh water levels to maintain or create suitable conditions. Studies should be initiated to gather information on the species' biology and ecology.

Kagu

Rhynochetos jubatus

Phylum	Chordata
Class	Aves
Order	Gruiformes
Family	Rhynochetidae
Status	Endangered, IUCN
	Endangered, USFWS
	Appendix I, CITES
Range	New Caledonia (South Pacific)

Description and Biology

The kagu is the only member of the family Rhynochetidae. Resembling a short heron, it is actually related to the rails. It is 22-24 in (56-61 cm) long, slate to ash gray, with black, red, and white bars on the flight feathers. Its legs and bill are orange-red and it has a long, tufted crest. Essentially flightless and ground-dwelling, its short wings are used more for courtship display than for flight. It probes the ground with its large bill for worms, grubs, snails, and other invertebrates. A nocturnal bird, its strong, yelping call can be heard mostly at night. Predators include those introduced by humans: rodents, pigs, cats, and dogs.

During courtship displays, the kagu extends its wings, fanning them to show the barred pattern, and raises its crest. A single, pale colored egg with brown and gray spots is incubated by both parents for 36 days. The chick becomes independent after nine to fourteen weeks.

Kagu.

Habitat and Current Distribution

The kagu is found only in New Caledonia, both in valleys of the central mountain range and in northern forest, where it dwells in dense forest and brush. Population is estimated at 500-1,000 birds.

History and Conservation Measures

For centuries the untouched forests of New Caledonia sheltered unique species which evolved to fit their secluded and protected environment. The kagu, lacking natural predators, has been severely impacted by introduced ones such as rodents, pigs, cats, and dogs.

In addition to the threat of these predators, the kagu is suffering from loss of habitat. It was once plentiful throughout New Caledonia, but is now restricted to those areas that are least accessible to humans. Forests throughout New Caledonia are being destroyed rapidly for timber, agriculture, and nickel mining.

The kagu has been bred in captivity; it is prized by zookeepers and is a popular pet. Legal protection exists, but that protection needs to be enforced.

Great Indian bustard

Ardeotis (Choriotis) nigriceps

Phylum	Chordata
Class	Aves
Order	Gruiformes
Family	Otididae
Status	Vulnerable, IUCN
	Endangered, USFWS
	Appendix I, CITES
Range	India; Pakistan

Description and Biology

The great Indian bustard is a large, heavy, ground bird, standing about 4 ft (1.2 m) tall and weighing up to 40 lb (18 kg). Somewhat resembling a young ostrich, this bustard carries its body at right angles to its bare, stout legs. Its upperparts are deep buff, finely lined with black, and its lowerparts are white with a broad black gorget on the lower breast. It has a conspicuous black crown on its head. Both sexes are alike in appearance, but the female is smaller. This species primarily eats insects, including locusts, grasshoppers, and beetles, but its diet also includes grain, tender shoot of cultivated plants, lizards, and small snakes.

The great Indian bustard appears to be polygynous, and the males perform a distinctive mating ritual. To attract females, male birds inflate a large white pouch on the throat, then expel their breath, uttering a booming call. This species breeds chiefly between March and September, although some breeding appears to occur throughout most of the year. The female lays a single egg, incubating it and rearing her chick alone. Juvenile birds often remain with their mothers through the following breeding season.

Habitat and Current Distribution

This species occurs in western India, especially Rajasthan, where it inhabits arid and semi-arid grasslands, scrub areas, and cultivated land. Population is considered very small, but stable.

History and Conservation Measures

There are no estimates of early population for the great Indian bustard, but it is thought to have been fairly common at one time. Though its range has not diminished in the last two centuries, it is certainly far less numerous than it once was. By the late 1960s, hunting and trapping had reduced the bustard's population to 750 birds. A conservation program begun in 1981 established a group of reserves around India, and the population of the bird soon reached between 1,500 and 2,000.

The bustard still faces a number of threats, including poaching as well as habitat destruction through grazing of domestic stock and agricultural cultivation. Although population is still quite low, conservation efforts have been successful in stabilizing the remaining population.

Bengal florican

Eupodotis (Houbaropsis) bengalensis

Phylum	Chordata
Class	Aves
Order	Gruiformes
Family	Otididae
Status	Endangered, IUCN
	Appendix I, CITES
Range	Bhutan (?); Kampuchea (?); India; Nepal; Vietnam

Description and Biology

The Bengal florican is a distinctively colored bustard that averages around 26 in (66 cm) in length. The male's upper body is a grizzled black and brown, as are the base of the wings; the balance of the wings are white with black tips, and the head, neck, and underparts are black. The female is slightly larger and lighter colored, with more black on the wings.

Due to its highly secretive behavior, little is known about the behavior and habits of the Bengal florican. Before breeding, the male performs a dramatic courtship display, vaulting as high as 30 ft (9.1 m) into the air and then dive-bombing with wings outstretched and clapping, emitting humming and croaking noises. After mating, the female nests by herself.

Habitat and Current Distribution

The Bengal florican is found in Assam, northeast India and along the border of India and Nepal, where its population is estimated at only several hundred birds and is certainly less than 500. It also occurs in Kampuchea and in Vietnam, but has seldom been seen there and has never been counted.

This species utilizes a monsoon grassland habitat. Short grass is used for courtship displays and nesting, while longer grass provides shelter.

History and Conservation Measures

The primary cause of the decline of the Bengal florican is massive habitat destruction, including the cultivation of its grassland habitat for agricultural uses or degradation of grassland by grazing livestock. Much of the surviving population occurs in national parks or preserves, but habitat areas outside these reserves are rapidly dwindling. Even within the protected regions, habitat is threatened by poor management practices.

Great bustard

Otis tarda

Phylum	Chordata
Class	Aves
Order	Gruiformes
Family	Otididae
Status	Rare, IUCN
	Appendix II, CITES
Range	Afghanistan (?); Austria; Azerbaijan; Bulgaria; China; Czechoslovakia; Germany; Hungary; Iran; Iraq; Kazakhstan; Kyrgyzstan; Moldova; Mongolia; Morocco; Portugal; Romania; Russia; Spain; Syria (?); Tajikistan; Turkey; Turkmenistan; Ukraine; Uzbekistan; Yugoslavia

Description and Biology

The great bustard is one of the world's heaviest flying land birds. Lighter females average around 11 lb (5 kg), but a heavy male can weigh as much as 40 lb (18 kg). The bustard's plumage is golden brown with black bars above and white below. In breeding plumage, males develop a chestnut breast and moustachial plumes. The bird's neck and legs are long, and its body is solid but tapered. The great bustard's diet includes plants and invertebrates.

Large flocks of birds, often made up of only one sex, travel together in search of food. During mating season, males visit display grounds and perform by inflating a throat pouch, spreading their tails, and twisting their wings to expose their white undersides. Clutch size is usually three eggs, which are incubated for 20-25 days. Chicks leave the nest shortly after hatching and fledge at around five weeks.

Habitat and Current Distribution

This species inhabits undeveloped farmland and steppe over a wide but increasingly patchy distribution. Population is estimated at approximately 20,000 individuals, scattered throughout portions of

Great bustard.

Europe, southern Russia, Ukraine, Mongolia, and China, as well as Turkey and parts of the Middle East. It is most numerous in Spain, where it numbers between 8,000-12,000 birds.

History and Conservation Measures

The primary threat to the great bustard is destruction of its grassland habitat. Conservation measures are generally taken throughout the bird's range, including establishment of protected areas (Hungary, Russia, Germany), rear and release programs for eggs abandoned in cereal fields (Germany, Russia, Ukraine), and landscape-scale environmental farming support schemes which, in Spain, cover over 3.7 million acres (1.5 million ha) of great bustard habitat.

Black stilt

Himantopus novaezealandiae

Phylum	Chordata
Class	Aves
Order	Charadriiformes
Family	Recurvirostridae
Status	Endangered, IUCN
Range	New Zealand

Description and Biology

Considered the world's rarest wading bird, the black stilt is also called kaki and is found only in New Zealand. This bird has black plumage and long, red legs. The black stilt stands about 12 in (30 cm) tall and has a long, black bill that is used to forage for food in riverbeds, streams, swamps, and river deltas. Its diet includes mayflies, fly larvae, small fish, and worms. Black stilts begin breeding at two or three years of age. Nest are built near water, and four eggs are usually laid, and if the eggs are destroyed, a second or even third clutch can be laid. Both parents take turns incubating the eggs.

Habitat and Current Distribution

The black stilt prefers to nest and feed along braided river systems. This bird is restricted during its breeding season to a protected area in the upper Waitaki Valley on South Island, New Zealand. The bird is usually sedentary, but some juveniles migrate to North Island during the winter. Population is estimated at around 80 birds.

History and Conservation Measures

The black stilt was once common throughout New Zealand, but its numbers had dropped drastically by the 1800s due to predation by introduced cats, ferrets, and stoats. (Hawks and gulls also prey on these birds.) Habitat destruction has also greatly reduced the number of black stilts on the island. Agri-

Black stilt.

cultural and hydroelectric developments have degraded rivers and disturbed food sources.

Along with these problems, the survival of pure black stilts is now threatened by interbreeding with the pied stilt (*Himantopus leucocephalus*), a closely related species. As the black stilt population gets smaller and the number of available mates declines, hybridization has become more common. (Interestingly, the black stilt mates with the pied stilt with the darkest plumage.)

This species survives only by careful management of its breeding habitat. Since 1981 there has been a concentrated effort to preserve the black stilt. Conservationists have enclosed breeding areas with electric fences to keep predators away from the eggs. Artificial incubation and the removal of first clutches for foster parenting are being utilized to help stabilize the population. These efforts will be futile, however, if development usurps remaining habitat.

Jerdon's courser

Rhinoptilus (Cursorius) bitorquatus

Phylum	Chordata
Class	Aves
Order	Charadriiformes
Family	Glareolidae
Status	Indeterminate, IUCN
Range	India

Description and Biology

Jerdon's courser is a fairly small, terrestrial bird with long legs. Its plumage is mottled white and tan above and white below, with an orange tan throat divided from the belly by dark bands. It forages on the ground at night to feed on insects.

Nesting on the ground, the courser incubates two to four eggs for 17-31 days. Juveniles leave the nest very quickly and are fed by the parents for only a few days.

Habitat and Current Distribution

This species occurs in central and southeastern India, where it inhabits scrublands with rocky soil. There are no estimates of population size.

History and Conservation Measures

Jerdon's courser has always been poorly known and exceedingly rare; by around 1900 it was considered extinct. Since it was rediscovered in Andhra Pradesh in 1986, there have been a number of sightings reported.

Information on this bird's status and distribution, as well as threats to its survival, is urgently needed before conservation measures can be formulated.

Piping plover

Charadrius melodus

Phylum	Chordata
Class	Aves
Order	Charadriiformes
Family	Charadriidae
Status	Vulnerable/Rare, IUCN (depending on population) Threatened, USFWS Endangered, USFWS (Great Lakes)
Range	Bahamas; Barbados; Bermuda; British Virgin Islands; Canada; Cuba; Dominican Republic; Haiti; Mexico; Puerto Rico (U.S.A.); U.S.A.; U.S. Virgin Islands

Description and Biology

The piping plover is a shorebird that gets its common name from its distinctive call. It is a sandy beige above and white below, with a short black bill and yellow legs. In breeding season, the piping plover develops black markings on its forehead and throat area; at this time its bill turns orange except at the tip, which remains black and its legs also turn bright orange.

The diet of the piping plover includes crustaceans, molluscs, and insects. Predators include raccoons, foxes, opossums, gulls, skunks, rats, and feral dogs and cats.

Breeding occurs between March and August after a courtship period which includes aerial and ground displays by the male. Four eggs are incubated by both the male and female for around 30 days; chicks fledge in approximately 30 days.

Habitat and Current Distribution

The piping plover is found on open beaches, sandflats, and alkali flats in North America. It breeds primarily in three regions: the Atlantic coast from

Piping plover.

southern Canada to North Carolina, along rivers and wetlands in the Great Plains from southern Canada to Nebraska, and in the western Great Lakes. In winter, the plovers migrate to coastal areas and sandflats from the Carolinas to Yucatán, Mexico, as well as the Bahamas and the West Indies. Overall, less than 2,500 pairs were known to exist in 1991. Of these, around 1,372 pairs were found on the Great Plains, 946 pairs were recorded on the Atlantic coast, and only 16 pairs were located in the Great Lakes.

History and Conservation Measures

Although there are no estimates of initial population size, the piping plover was certainly much more plentiful in the early part of this century than it is today. The earliest cause of its decline was excessive hunting, which severely threatened the species until it was controlled. Habitat disturbance is the primary threat today; because the plover is a ground nester that utilizes coastal beaches, its nesting habitat is often usurped for development and for recreational use. Inland nesting areas have also been affected by changing water levels as a result of water control efforts.

Current conservation efforts are geared to preserving the plover's habitat by protecting nesting sites, restricting the use of off-road vehicles in plover habitat, building of predator barriers around nests, control of plover predators, both avian and mammalian, encouraging governments to modify water-level control policies damaging to plover habitat, control of vegetation, and even the creation of artificial habitat. Continued investigation and protection of nesting, foraging, and wintering sites are priorities, as are information and education activities.

New Zealand shore plover

Charadrius (Thinornis) novaeseelandiae

Phylum . . . . Chordata
Class . . . . Aves
Order. . . . . Charadriiformes
Family . . . . Charadriidae
Status . . . . Endangered, IUCN
            Endangered, USFWS
Range . . . . Chatham Islands (New Zealand)

Description and Biology

The New Zealand shore plover is a wading bird with dark feathers tinged with white at the tips. It has white underparts and a white band around its crown. The short, orange-red bill tapers to a dark tip. The bird measures about 8 in (20 cm) in length.

This bird is a sedentary species and tends to roost and feed in small groups, except during mating season when pairs will defend their territory vigorously. Nests are built within crevices of boulders, logs, or within dense vegetation. Two to three eggs are usually hatched. This bird feeds on small crustaceans.

Habitat and Current Distribution

Once this shore plover was found throughout New Zealand but is now found only on one small island in the Chatham Islands, east of New Zealand. It was extinct in New Zealand by the late 1880s and was extirpated on most of the Chatham Islands, mainly because of introduced cats and rats. Current population size is estimated at around 120 birds.

Preferred habitat includes mud flats, inlets, sand spits, rocky shorelines, and salt meadows.

History and Conservation Measures

In addition to predation by introduced species, this bird has been subject to collection by commercial hunters. Habitat destruction or modification has not been a major problem for this species.

Until the 1950s, sheep and cattle grazed in the salt meadows favored by this bird, keeping the grass short. When the sheep and cattle were removed from the island, the meadows quickly became overgrown; much of the area may now be too overgrown to accommodate the bird.

In 1954, South-East Island of the Chatham group became a Reserve for the Preservation of Flora and Fauna. An attempt was made to introduce the shore plover to Mangere, a predator-free island, but the bird's homing instinct to South-East Island made this unsuccessful. Subsequent attempts to introduce partially wing-clipped adults have also proven unsuccessful.

Because it is confined to a single island, even a stable population of shore plovers is vulnerable to natural disaster, epidemic, or any catastrophic event. Further attempts at reintroduction with young birds are currently underway.

New Zealand shore plover.

St. Helena plover

Charadrius sanctaehelenae

Phylum	Chordata
Class	Aves
Order	Charadriiformes
Family	Charadriidae
Status	Rare, IUCN
Range	St. Helena

Description and Biology

This small plover is also called the St. Helena sandplover or the wirebird. The adults of both sexes closely resemble the Kittlitz sandplover (*Charadrius pecuarius*) which is found throughout most of Africa except for the Sahara, the Congo Basin, and north-eastern Africa. The St. Helena plover has a white forehead terminated by a black band; a blackish streak runs from the base of the bill to the eye, down the side of the neck, and back around to the base of the back of the neck. The feathers at the base of the upper bill are black in the St. Helena plover, while they are white in the Kittlitz sandplover. The feathers on the crown of the head are brown with sandy edging; a white stripe extends from the back of the eye around the back of the head to form a collar. The feathers of the upperparts are blackish brown with slightly buff-colored margins. The breast is white, and the wings are rounder than the wings of the Kittlitz sandplover. The tail feathers are white except for a pair of central blackish feathers. The bill is black, and the legs and toes are greenish gray. The fact that this species is restricted to St. Helena Island should eliminate confusing it with other small sandpipers of similar appearance.

The St. Helena plover is usually found in pairs, but juveniles are occasionally seen in small groups. It seldom flies. Although the foods eaten by this species have not been specifically studied, its diet is thought to be similar to that of the Kittlitz sandplover, which includes insects and their larvae, crustaceans, and molluscs. Breeding coincides mainly with the drier months of the year (September through February), but the peak may vary from year to year, depending on conditions; breeding has been recorded in all months. Clutch size is two, and double brooding may be frequent.

Habitat and Current Distribution

This species is found only on the island of St. Helena in the southern Atlantic Ocean, where it is widespread in open grasslands at medium elevations. It is most often sighted around the edge of the island between 1,100-1,600 ft (350-500 m); some former breeding areas in the west of the island have been lost to urban development. The population in 1989 was approximately 500 birds.

The St. Helena plover predominantly lives and breeds in the drier parts of the island. It inhabits upland pastures, ploughed fields, and large vegetable gardens and is often seen foraging on freshly-worked ground. It also occurs in semi-desert areas at lower density.

History and Conservation Measures

The small size of this bird's island habitat places some limits on its population. The population was estimated as slightly less than 1,000 birds in the mid-1960s, but it is now estimated at around 500 birds and considered stable. As human development expands, habitat usurpation may become a problem. The St. Helena plover is protected by law and is a popular bird on the island. Research on population dynamics and ecology has been carried out to determine the importance of particular areas that may require protection, but continued monitoring of numbers and distribution is necessary.

Spoon-billed sandpiper

Eurynorhynchus pygmeus

Phylum	Chordata
Class	Aves
Order	Charadriiformes
Family	Scolopacidae
Status	Indeterminate, IUCN
Range	Bangladesh; China; Hong Kong; India; Japan; North Korea; Russia; South Korea; Singapore

Description and Biology

The spoon-billed sandpiper is a small shorebird, averaging 5.5-6.3 in (14-16 cm) long. The plumage is patterned in black, white, and brown, with reddish areas on the wings, throat, and forehead. The tip of the bill is broadened in the shape of a spoon and used to forage in water and mud for food.

Clutch size is four; the male is thought to incubate the eggs and to care for the young after hatching.

Habitat and Current Distribution

This species breeds in tundra from Chukotka to Kamchatka and is thought to winter on coasts and lagoons in China, Hong Kong, India, Japan, North Korea, South Korea, Thailand, and Singapore. The total population has been estimated at 2,000-2,800 pairs but may actually be lower.

History and Conservation Measures

The status of this species is uncertain and there is no information available about conservation measures.

Eskimo curlew

Numenius borealis

Phylum	Chordata
Class	Aves
Order	Charadriiformes
Family	Scolopacidae
Status	Endangered/Extinct, IUCN
	Endangered, USFWS
	Appendix I, CITES
Range	Brazil; Canada; French Guiana; Guyana; Paraguay; Suriname; Alaska (?)
	(U.S.A)

Description and Biology

The Eskimo curlew has also been called the prairie pigeon or the doughbird because of the layer of fat it builds up for winter migration. The smallest of the American curlews, it averages 11.5-14 in (29-36 cm) in length. This shorebird has a dark brown back with a lighter breast and a pale to white throat. The upper breast and underwings have dark brown streaks, the legs are gray, and the eyes are dark brown. The 2-in (5-cm) black, curved bill is rich in nerve endings that allow a feeding bird to detect vibrations caused by underground insects and worms. It also feeds on snails and berries.

Breeding begins in May and June. The three to four green-brown eggs and nest of straw and leaves are well hidden in a hollow in the ground. Incubation period is 18-30 days; chicks are cared for by both parents until they fledge.

Habitat and Current Distribution

Because it was only rediscovered in the 1980s, status surveys for the Eskimo curlew are still in progress. Population estimates vary from 35-150 birds. Studies are being made in St. Michael, Alaska, for late summer or fall migrants, in the Barbados Island wetlands for fall migrants, and on the southwest Texas coast for spring migrants.

Habitat for the breeding season is arctic tundra; for the winter the habitat is the pampas of Argentina, and for north-bound migrants it is the tall grass prairies of the Mississippi valley.

History and Conservation Measures

In the nineteenth century, this was a common bird numbering in the millions. It was hunted along its migratory path so intensely that by the 1900s it was thought to be extinct. Additional factors may have contributed to its decline. Agricultural development of pampas and prairies may have reduced food supplies; it is also thought that climatic changes may have forced these birds off course on migration and adversely affected their reproductive success. Predators and disease may have been factors, but to what degree is unknown.

Sightings of the Eskimo curlew in the 1980s have prompted new interest in the species. The largest sighting was of a flock of 23 in Texas in 1981; others were reported in 1983, 1985, and 1987 in the United States and in Canada. It is uncertain whether the Eskimo curlew will survive, even though a recov-

Eskimo curlews, female in front.

ery program was developed in the late 1980s and an advisory group was formed in 1990 to plan its management. The population of the species is very low, and its small numbers probably should not be affected by hunting. Yet the species continues to decline, indicating that ecological factors may be contributing to its disappearance.

Tuamotu sandpiper

Prosobonia cancellatus

Phylum	Chordata
Class	Aves
Order	Charadriiformes
Family	Scolopacidae
Status	Vulnerable, IUCN
Range	Tuamotu Archipelago (French Polynesia)

Description and Biology

The Tuamotu sandpiper is a small 6.5 in (16.5 cm), tropical shorebird weighing 1-1.5 oz (32-44 g). The plumage of the upper body is generally umber brown; these feathers are extensively tipped or edged with white or a reddish color. The head is primarily buff or ash colored; the crown of the head is umber brown. There is an ashy white stripe above and behind the eye and a dark stripe from the base of the bill through the eye and along the upper ear coverts. The umber brown tail feathers are relatively long and are barred with irregular, incomplete, narrow bands of ashy or pale reddish white. The wings are relatively short (about twice as long as the tail) and are rounded. Wing feathers are uniformly umber brown; inner primaries and secondaries have narrow white edging. The underparts of this sandpiper are generally white with an ashy tinge. The breast, sides, and under-tail coverts have brown spots or bars; this barring is most pronounced on the sides and flanks. The slender, straight bill is blackish, and the legs and feet are gray, grayish brown or yellowish; there is slight webbing between the middle and outer toes. Variations in darkness of the plumage seem to be due to individual rather than sexual differences.

The Tuamotu sandpiper is believed to eat insects primarily, but its feeding and foraging behavior are not well documented. Its social behavior and reproductive biology are also poorly known. *P. cancellatus* is non-migratory and seems to have quite a long breeding season (April to June or later). Only two breeding records exist for this species; in one case a nest was found on the shoreline of a lagoon containing two rather heavily blotched eggs.

Habitat and Current Distribution

The Tuamotu sandpiper has most recently been recorded from Marutea Sud, Maturei Vavao, and Tenararo, in the Tuamotu Archipelago, South Pacific Ocean. There are no estimates of total population, and the species may occur on other atolls in the archipelago.

P. cancellatus has been reported from a variety of habitats throughout the Tuamotu Archipelago; it occurs most commonly where there are stretches of gravel or open shingle beach.

History and Conservation Measures

The type-specimen for this species was collected on Christmas Island, but the birds no longer occur there. The introduction of predators such as cats and rats to many of the islands has forced the bird to take refuge on smaller atolls. Studies are needed to determine which islands still support the sandpiper; these islands should be protected and kept free of introduced predators.

Further research into this bird's biology, its susceptibility to external factors, and its ability to move from one island to another is also needed to formulate comprehensive conservation plans.

Nordmann's greenshank

Tringa guttifer

Phylum	Chordata
Class	Aves
Order	Charadriiformes
Family	Scolopacidae
Status	Indeterminate, IUCN
	Endangered, USFWS
	Appendix I, CITES
Range	Bangladesh; China; Japan; Kampuchea (?); Laos (?); Malaysia; Myanmar; North Korea; Philippines; Russia; South Korea; Thailand

Description and Biology

Very little is known about this rare shorebird, also known as the spotted greenshank.

Habitat and Current Distribution

The only known breeding site for this species is on Sakhalin Island, but it may also breed in Kamchatka, in the Bering Islands, and possibly in other areas in northeastern Siberia. It is recorded to visit Japan, Hong Kong, and Thailand in the winter. There are no estimates of population size, but numbers are probably small.

This species frequents a range of wetland habitat, including lagoons, swamps, and wet or flooded lowlands.

History and Conservation Measures

The reasons for the apparently low numbers of Nordmann's greenshank are unknown, but threats to this species include habitat destruction and increased nest predation by crows (*Corvus corone*), which have followed human expansion in the vicinity of the greenshank's breeding grounds.

Olrog's gull

Larus atlanticus

Phylum	Chordata
Class	Aves
Order	Charadriiformes
Family	Laridae
Status	Insufficiently Known, IUCN
Range	Argentina; Brazil; Uruguay

Description and Biology

This seabird feeds on crabs obtained from mudbanks at low tide and on mussels plucked from rocky coasts. More rarely, it has been reported feeding on waste from boats and scavenging inside a sealion colony. Judging from the size of chicks found in early November, nesting is presumed to start in September or October.

Habitat and Current Distribution

Olrog's gull breeds along the Atlantic coast of Argentina and winters along the coast of Uruguay and south along the Patagonian coasts. The current population is estimated to be fewer than 1,400 breeding pairs.

The species occurs along the coasts on beaches, rocky coasts, harbors, coastal and brackish lagoons, and estuaries. Nesting colonies are established on flat sandy islands just above water level, where grasses and plants are scarce.

History and Conservation Measures

The overall population of Olrog's gull has probably always been small, despite reports that it was locally common. Because the number of known breeding sites is very small, the chief cause of concern for this species is its extreme vulnerability in the breeding season. At the nesting sites in Buenos Aires Province, egg collecting for food already occurs regularly and there is danger from the possible development of tourism, increase in fishing traffic, petroleum exploitation, and other human activities. Diseases or contamination of feeding areas could cause a shortage of prey.

The species occurs in a number of provincial reserves, and some islands have also been declared as reserves, although in practice the islands are not effectively protected. Rigorous protection is necessary for existing colonies and should involve the exclusion of unauthorized persons and potential domestic predators, such as dogs and cats, at least during the breeding season. Surveys should be initiated to locate the most important nesting and feeding areas and to locate any unreported breeding colonies. Details of the species' feeding requirements and of the conservation status of its main staples should be conducted to detect and prevent possible threats and food shortages.

Audouin's gull

Larus audouinii

Phylum	Chordata
Class	Aves
Order	Charadriiformes
Family	Laridae
Status	Rare, IUCN
	Endangered, USFWS
Range	Mediterranean Sea (Algeria; Cyprus; Corsica [France]; Greece; Sardinia [Italy]; Morocco; Spain; Tunisia; Turkey)

Description and Biology

A moderately large gull, Audouin's gull is pale gray and white with black wing-tips and a black and red bill. More specialized than many members of its family, it feeds primarily on fish it plucks from the sea while in flight.

Audouin's gull breeds between April and June, laying a clutch of two or three eggs in a scraped depression lined with bits of plant matter or other debris. Incubation lasts about 28 days and is done by both parents. Young are fed and raised by both parents, and fledge after about 35 to 40 days; immature birds become completely independent at three to four months of age.

Habitat and Current Distribution

Audouin's gull breeds primarily in the western Mediterranean. Colonies are known to occur in Cyprus, France, Italy, Greece, Turkey, Tunisia, Algeria, and Spain. Total population is estimated at approximately 5,500-6,000 pairs, with the largest population on the Chafarinas Islands off the coast of Morocco.

This species usually feeds over water not far

from land. It nests on small, low islands with grass or low bushes.

Audouin's gull.

History and Conservation Measures

There are no early estimates of population for this gull. In the late 1960s and 1970s, population was estimated to be between 600-1,000 pairs, but those figures were thought to exclude the large Chafarinas population.

The primary threat to this species is disturbance of breeding areas by people, including fishermen, tourists, and shepherds. Eggs are regularly collected from breeding colonies, which are in unprotected areas. A long-term threat is pollution of feeding areas with heavy metals, which may affect breeding success.

Protection of gull colonies during the breeding season is probably the most important conservation measure that can be taken to sustain this species. Establishment of protected reserves has also been advocated.

Relict gull

Larus relictus

Phylum	Chordata
Class	Aves
Order	Charadriiformes
Family	Laridae
Status	Rare, IUCN
	Endangered, USFWS
	Appendix I, CITES
Range	China; Kazakhstan; Mongolia; Russia; Vietnam

Description and Biology

The relict gull is similar in appearance to black- and brown-headed gulls (*L. ridibundus* and *L. brunnicephalus*) but is slightly larger, averaging approximately 15.8 in (40 cm) in length. It has a brown head, brown and black neck, dark red bill, and a distinctive white half-moon over each eye.

Diet consists primarily of insects, small fish, and aquatic invertebrates. The species nests on the ground, in close groupings of approximately 20 pairs; three speckled white eggs are laid in May.

Habitat and Current Distribution

The relict gull is known to breed at Lake Alakol in southeastern Kazakhstan, Lake Barun-Toray in the Transbaikal (Russia), and Tatsain Tsagaan Nuur in Mongolia. It nests on level, open lake islands. The species is migratory, wintering in China. The combined population in Russia and Kazakhstan is estimated at approximately 2,000 pairs. There are no estimates of the size of the Mongolian population.

History and Conservation Measures

This gull was first described in 1931. It is judged to be very rare because of the scarcity of recorded sightings, but the reasons for its rarity are not known. It is believed that some conservation measures have been enacted around breeding sites.

Relict gulls.

Purple-winged ground-dove

Claravis godefrida

Phylum	Chordata
Class	Aves
Order	Columbiformes
Family	Columbidae
Status	Endangered/Extinct, IUCN
Range	Argentina; Brazil; Paraguay

Description and Biology

The purple-winged or purple-barred ground dove derives its common name from the three wide purple bars on its wings. The male has dark bluish gray plumage with lighter underparts; its tail is gray in the center and has white edges. The female is reddish brown with lighter underparts and has a brown tail with black and pale yellow edges. Average length is 9 in (23 cm). Bamboo seeds are the most important component of this bird's diet, but it also feeds on fruit, sedges, and grass seeds.

The purple-winged ground-dove is typically seen in small flocks except during the breeding season, which begins in November or December during the flowering of the bamboos.

Habitat and Current Distribution

This species is endemic to the Atlantic forest region of southeastern South America, where it was once found in Brazil, in eastern Paraguay, and in Misiones, Argentina. There are no estimates of population size, and the species is considered extremely rare or possibly extinct, though there are still occasional sightings from widely scattered locations.

Preferred habitat appears to be in dense forest and forest borders near bamboo, or simply in forest edges and adjacent shrubbery; the species apparently prefers hillier, more broken terrain. Nests are placed in a thick, bushy tree.

History and Conservation Measures

This ground-dove has apparently always been rare throughout its range, but it is now close to extinction. Although it has been observed eating other types of seeds, it is primarily dependent upon bamboo seeds, which are only infrequently and irregularly available; even moderate deforestation extends the intervals between major bamboo crops. Such a specialized feeder must be able to range widely and may not be able to survive in the fragmented lowland and montane forests in southeast Brazil. The species has legal protection and is thought to exist in very small numbers in some parks and reserves along the Serra do Mar in Brazil and at Iguazú National Park in Argentina; unfortunately, its particular needs are so poorly understood that no special measures have been taken on this bird's behalf in those parks. A better understanding of its requirements is probably crucial to its long-term conservation.

The purple-winged ground-dove has been so rare that it only occasionally appears in the cage-bird trade and in captivity, but a complete ban on its capture in the wild has been recommended. Effective control in existing forest reserves, mainly during periods of bamboo flowering, would almost certainly

enhance the survival chances of this and other species. The identification and protection of additional

areas where the species exists are also of paramount
importance.

Ring-tailed pigeon

Columba caribaea

Phylum	Chordata
Class	Aves
Order	Columbiformes
Family	Columbidae
Status	Vulnerable, IUCN
Range	Jamaica

Description and Biology

The ring-tailed pigeon, also known as the Jamaican band-tailed pigeon, is named after the distinctive black band around its gray tail. It has a light purple-pink head, breast, and underside; bluish gray upperparts; black bill; and red feet and legs. As it feeds, the pigeon moves from tree to tree, often dispersing seeds and thus helping to regenerate certain fruit-bearing trees. This bird is usually found in groups of six to eight individuals.

Nesting occurs in the spring and summer months. Little else is known about this bird's reproductive biology.

Habitat and Current Distribution

This species is endemic to Jamaica, where it is restricted to the forests in Cockpit Country, Blue Mountains, and John Crow Mountains, areas relatively undisturbed by people. There are no estimates of population size, but the pigeon is considered scarce.

Habitat for this pigeon includes forested mountain areas and hills up to almost 6,500 ft (2,000 m); in autumn and winter, it descends to lower elevations, from 500-1,000 ft (150-300 m). Nests are built on top of trees and are constructed with tangles of twigs, leaves, and bark.

History and Conservation Measures

Although reported to be abundant and locally common throughout the late 1800s and early 1900s, the ring-tailed pigeon has suffered a dramatic decline in numbers, mainly due to habitat disturbance, hunters and trappers, and natural disasters. After Hurricane Gilbert swept across Jamaica in 1988, local people reported seeing far fewer birds, although official census did not confirm this observation. This pigeon has long been subjected to hunting for food as well, despite laws outlawing it. Seasonal concentrations at known localities have made it especially vulnerable to illegal shooting. Trapping for the pet trade has also been reported.

Legal protection for this species has not been well enforced, even in areas designated as forest reserves. The Blue and John Crow Mountains National Park is being established; a wide variety of activities, including felling of trees, will be prohibited or restricted, but the degree of enforcement remains uncertain.

White-tailed laurel pigeon

Columba junoniae

Phylum	Chordata
Class	Aves
Order	Columbiformes
Family	Columbidae
Status	Rare, IUCN
Range	Canary Islands (Spain)

Description and Biology

This fairly large pigeon is about 15 in (38 cm) long. Its forehead, chin, back, and rump are gray. The crown, nape, and lower throat are metallic green and violet, shading to purple toward the back and breast. Its wings are brown, and its underparts are a purplish, reddish brown. The tail is gray, shading to white at the tip. The legs are red, and there is a red circle around the eye. The laurel pigeon spends much of its time foraging on the ground, escaping to the trees when it is in danger. Primary food appears to be laurel fruits, but cultivated fruit and grain are also consumed, usually when preferred food supplies are low.

Breeding begins in May and lasts throughout the summer. One white egg is usually laid, although nests with two eggs have been reported. Incubation for pigeons is usually 13-28 days, and nestling period is 12-36 days.

Habitat and Current Distribution

The white-tailed laurel pigeon occurs in laurel forest on Tenerife, La Palma, and Gomera in the Canary Islands. There are no detailed population estimates, and population varies with each island: on Tenerife it is scarce and very local; on La Palma it is thought to be fairly common and widespread; and on Gomera it is common only in the single remaining patch of laurel forest on the island.

This species prefers scrub areas that occur above and below major stands of laurel. At higher levels it occurs in the mixed pine/laurel shrub forest that forms the transition zone between pure laurel and the higher pine forests. At lower levels it is most frequent near steep slopes and sheer, deep ravines, ledges, rock faces, and cliffs. On La Palma, it also occurs in heavily degraded areas on the edge of cultivations. Nests are built on ledges or stumps.

History and Conservation Measures

This species maintained healthy numbers on Tenerife as recently as 1972. On Gomera, it was fairly abundant in 1888 but reported as very rare by 1949. Destruction of the endemic Canarian laurel forests was considered to have been a serious factor in the depletion of birds on both La Palma and Gomera during the first half of this century, and deforestation for charcoal was continuing in the 1950s. These factors are no longer considered a concern for the species.

Hunting has been prohibited since 1973 and, since 1980, the species has been on a list of fully protected Spanish wildlife whose hunting, capture, maintenance in captivity, trading, and exportation are strictly forbidden, as is the taking of their eggs or young.

On Gomera, almost 10,000 acres (3,875 ha) of

forest, including the best representation of the island's laurel forest, is now the Garajonay National Park. On La Palma, around 1,200 acres (511 ha) of laurel forest with a good population of this species is included in the IUCN network of Man and Biosphere Reserves. Biological studies are underway in both of these protected areas. A network of protected areas has been proposed for the island of La Palma, and some of these areas encompass habitat for this species and for the dark-tailed laurel pigeon (*Columba bollii*).

Pink pigeon

Columba (Nesoenas) mayeri

Phylum	Chordata
Class	Aves
Order	Columbiformes
Family	Columbidae
Status	Endangered, IUCN
	Appendix III, CITES
Range	Mauritius (Indian Ocean)

Description and Biology

This forest-dwelling pigeon is relatively large but lightweight for its size, with an average weight of 9.6-11.3 oz (275-325 g). It has a fairly long, broad tail and broad, rounded wings. The bird's common name suggests its coloration: the back is dusky pink, while the abdominal region is pale pink, becoming paler toward the neck and off-white at the head. Tail and wings are brown; feet, cere (base of the bill), and eye areas are coral red.

Highly agile, the pink pigeon is adept at climbing and hanging upside down in trees. It feeds on leaves, young shoots, buds, flowers, fruit, and seeds of primarily native and some exotic plants. Seasonal changes in its food supply are significant, with a fall-off in the availability of preferred fruits and flowers and other food from August to mid-November; in early summer, December, or January, following the onset of the rains, the species feeds on flowers, and leaves are eaten throughout the year in moderate amounts. Macaque monkeys and black rats are nest predators. On the ground, introduced mongooses and feral cats are predators.

Breeding occurs chiefly from December to June with a peak in May, though activity may be postponed in bad weather or lengthened in the event of repeated nest failures. The variation in onset and length of the breeding season is also affected by food availability, with birds starting to breed the month after the start of the summer rains. Clutch size is one or two.

Habitat and Current Distribution

The pink pigeon is found only on the island of Mauritius in the Indian Ocean. It is restricted to the native montane evergreen forest and scrub that occurs in the southwestern part of the island. For nesting and roosting during the breeding season, the species currently favors a grove of introduced Japanese red cedar (*Cryptomeria japonica*) surrounded by degraded native forest and scattered copses of introduced swamp mahogany (*Eucalyptus robusta*). Nests are built 13-59 ft (4-18 m) up in trees.

The wild population now numbers about 25 birds. In addition, there is a released population of 21 captive-bred birds. The captive population numbers between 160-200 birds.

History and Conservation Measures

Although it probably once ranged more widely over forested areas, this species is thought always to have been localized and was considered rare even in the 1860s. Before the end of the nineteenth century, it was feared to be on the verge of extinction. In the

Pink pigeon.

early 1900s, the population was believed to have increased slightly to a fairly stable level of 40-60 birds. Beginning in 1960, however, its numbers took a drastic fall. In 1960, Cyclone Carol decreased the population by approximately one-half. Another cyclone in 1975, together with the destruction of large tracts of habitat between 1973-1981, caused a severe decrease in the remaining population from which the species has never fully recovered.

Besides cyclones and habitat destruction, the most important factors affecting the pink pigeon are late winter food shortages and nest predation. Nest predation by introduced mammals is a critical obstacle to breeding success. It is also possible that inbreeding now plays a part in limiting the population.

Because of the species' precarious position in the wild, a captive propagation program was instituted by the Jersey Wildlife Preservation Trust in collaboration with the government of Mauritius. At the end of 1990, the captive population stood at 164 birds in 20 collections. The release of birds into their original range was always an aim of the captive-breeding program, and since 1984, 72 birds have been released. A trial release of 22 pigeons was undertaken in the Pamplemousses Botanical Gardens in Mauritius, and subsequently 51 birds were released into native forest. The released population now numbers 21 birds, and the program is ongoing. The released birds have bred in the wild, with two young successfully reared.

In addition, the remaining wild population is intensively managed. For instance, researchers have assisted the wild birds by supplementing their food supply and by eliminating some rat populations. This assistance resulted in 18 young successfully fledged during the 1991-1992 season, as opposed to only 3-4 per season from all previous years. However, predation of both juvenile and adult birds by feral cats and mongooses still restricts any significant increase in the wild population.

Much of the pink pigeon's present range is now incorporated into the Black River Gorges National Park. In addition to this measure, researchers continue to monitor the wild and released populations very closely. In 1991, a Population Viability Assessment was conducted by the Captive Breeding Specialist group of the Species Survival commission of the IUCN. In the same year, an international studbook for the pink pigeon was produced by the Jersey Wildlife Preservation Trust and the Mauritius Government.

Polynesian imperial-pigeon

Ducula aurorae

Phylum . . . . Chordata
Class . . . . Aves
Order . . . . Columbiformes
Family . . . . Columbidae
Status . . . . Vulnerable, IUCN
Range . . . . Society Islands, Tuamotu Archipelago (French Polynesia)

Description and Biology

Also known as the Society Islands pigeon or the Tahitian pigeon, this bird is larger than the average feral pigeon. Plumage is gray on the head, neck, and underparts; upperparts are dark green interspersed with blue and purplish blue. Its bill is black, and its legs and feet are bright red. It has a long tail which is slightly fork-shaped.

The Polynesian imperial-pigeon feeds chiefly on the seeds of the vine *Freycinetia arborea*, wild figs, and guavas. It hops from branch to branch and sometimes hangs nearly upside down while feeding. Little else is known of this bird's ecology or biology.

Habitat and Current Distribution

This species is found in forests on the French islands of Tahiti in the Society Islands and Makatéa in the Tuamotu Archipelago. The population on Makatéa was estimated in the mid-1970s to be ap- proximately 500 birds, but a survey in 1986-87 esti- mated the population to be between 100 and 500 birds. The population on Tahiti was estimated at 10 birds in 1972, but no birds were found on the island in a 1984 search, and the species may now be near extinction there. This pigeon once inhabited the island of Moorea and possibly other islands, where its extinction may have been the consequence of the increase in the population of swamp harriers (*Circus approximans*).

History and Conservation Measures

The Polynesian imperial-pigeon is now consid- ered stable on the island of Makatéa, but its status on the island of Tahiti is much less certain. The reason for its scarcity on Tahiti is not well understood, but probably involves a combination of such factors as hunting and habitat destruction. There is an existing nature reserve in Papenoo Valley, and establishment of additional reserves has been recommended.

Marquesan ground-dove

Gallicolumba rubescens

Phylum	Chordata
Class	Aves
Order	Columbiformes
Family	Columbidae
Status	Indeterminate, IUCN
Range	Marquesas Islands (French Polynesia)

Description and Biology

This dove's head, neck, and breast are light gray, while its back, as well as upper wing coverts, is intense purple. The rest of its plumage is black, with a greenish hue above. The tail and the wings have characteristic white areas. It feeds on seeds and mealworms. The female usually lays two eggs, and the incubation period is 13-15 days.

Habitat and Current Distribution

The Marquesan ground-dove is restricted to the islets of Hatutu and Fatuhuku in the Marquesas Islands, where it inhabits areas of dense vegetation and open ground in forested areas. The population on Hatutu has been estimated at approximately 225 birds; population on Fatuhuku is considerably smaller.

History and Conservation Measures

The type-specimen for this species was apparently collected from the island of Nuku Hiva; the ground-dove may once have inhabited other islands but now survives only on two. The islands of Hatutu and Fatuhuku are uninhabited and predator-free, with the exception of the Polynesian rat. Human activity on the islands or the introduction of non-native plants and predators such as rats, cats, dogs, or pigs could endanger the surviving population of the Marquesan ground-dove.

Rapa fruit-dove

Ptilinopus huttoni

Phylum	Chordata
Class	Aves
Order	Columbiformes
Family	Columbidae
Status	Rare, IUCN
Range	Tubuai Islands (French Polynesia)

Description and Biology

The Rapa fruit-dove has green to blue-green plumage, with a pinkish purple head, throat, and belly, greenish gray neck and breast, yellow bill, and red feet. Feeding and nesting habits are unknown.

Habitat and Current Distribution

This fruit-dove is endemic to Rapa Island in the Tubuai or Austral Island chain in French Polynesia, where its habitat is restricted to wooded hills and valleys.

History and Conservation Measures

There is no estimate of how large the population of Rapa fruit-doves may once have been, but it has certainly experienced a decline. The population was estimated in 1974 at approximately 250 birds, and in 1989-1990 at 274.

The primary cause of this species' initial decline is the disappearance or degradation of its habitat. Forest clearance has continued unabated on the island, and fires and the grazing of goats and cattle have degraded remaining forest. The fruit-dove has legal protection, but that protection has apparently not been well-enforced, and there are no other known conservation efforts on behalf of this species.

Socorro dove

Zenaida graysoni

Phylum	Chordata
Class	Aves
Order	Columbiformes
Family	Columbidae
Status	Endangered, IUCN
Range	Mexico

Description and Biology

The Socorro dove, also known as Grayson's dove, is grayish brown with a reddish brown underside, black bill, red feet, and a long pointed tail with white-tipped feathers. It averages 12 in (30.5 cm) in length. This terrestrial dove feeds on fruits in the wild. The species apparently breeds in May, and it is presumed that male and female Socorro doves, like other species of doves, take turns incubating eggs and tending their young.

Habitat and Current Distribution

This species is endemic to the island of Socorro in the Revillagigedo Islands, Mexico, located southwest of Baja California. While it was once common in the island's forests, there have been no sightings in the wild since 1958, and it is possible that the species survives only in captivity. Captive population is approximately 200 birds.

History and Conservation Measures

In 1958, there were no obvious indications that the population of the species was declining, but despite specific searches there have been no subsequent sightings. Since there has been no systematic search of the entire island, including the remote, heavily wooded northern end, there is still hope that a few individuals survive.

The demise of this species is attributed chiefly to predation by cats, which became feral on the island in the 1950s. A contributing factor was the reduction of forest vegetation in the southern parts of the island by grazing sheep. Fortunately, the Socorro dove breeds well in captivity, and captive-bred birds might one day be reintroduced to the island. Before that can be attempted, however, an effort must be made to eradicate cats and sheep and to restore the natural vegetation cover by replanting native trees.

Ultramarine lorikeet

Vini ultramina

Phylum	Chordata
Class	Aves
Order	Psittaciformes
Family	Loriidae
Status	Rare, IUCN
	Appendix II, CITES
Range	Marquesas Islands (French Polynesia)

Description and Biology

The lorikeet has a brush-tipped tongue that it uses to feed on nectar and pollen. It is frequently seen in small groups of up to six birds. Very little information about reproductive biology is available, but clutch size in captivity is two.

Habitat and Current Distribution

The ultramarine lorikeet occurs on the French Marquesas Islands of Ua Pou, Nuku Hiva, and Ua Huka. Total population is estimated at less than 1,000 birds, most of them at Ua Huka.

This lorikeet occurs in montane forest and high valleys between 2,300-3,300 ft (700-1,000 m); it also apparently makes seasonal visits to banana plantations and flowering trees at lower elevations.

History and Conservation Measures

In 1975, the population of lorikeets on Ua Pou was estimated at 250-300 pairs, but it has since almost completely disappeared. In 1984, population on Nuku Hiva was estimated at 70 birds on the northwestern end of the island. The reason for its decline is predation by rats, *Rattus rattus*.

This species was introduced to the island of Ua Huka, where close to 1,000 birds now exist. However, rats have also been introduced to the island and may result in increased predation levels unless controlled. More recently, the Zoological Society of San Diego, in cooperation with local authorities, initiated a translocation program of lorikeets to Fatu Hiva. The first pairs were translocated in 1992.

Black-cheeked lovebird

Agapornis nigrigenis

Phylum	Chordata
Class	Aves
Order	Psittaciformes
Family	Psittacidae
Status	Rare, IUCN
	Appendix II, CITES
Range	Botswana; Namibia (?); Zambia; Zimbabwe (ex?)

Description and Biology

The black-cheeked lovebird has a dusky-red forehead and crown; sides of the face and throat are black. Diet includes seeds, grass seeds, and leaves. Breeding occurs in November and December.

Habitat and Current Distribution

The black-cheeked lovebird is confined mainly to the extreme southwestern part of Zambia. It occurs (or occurred) outside southern Zambia only along the Zambezi River in northern Zimbabwe, in the very northernmost tip of Botswana, and the eastern tip of the Caprivi Strip in Namibia. Population figures are unavailable, but the species appears to be very local within the range of available habitat, and most recent sightings in Zambia are of small flocks of only a few dozen birds each.

This species occurs in medium-altitude, deciduous woodland dominated by mopane (*Colophospermum mopane*) and *Baikiaea plurijuga*. Total habitat range is about 2,300 sq mi (6,000 sq km).

History and Conservation Measures

Although there are no estimates of the initial population size, this species has been declining due to capture for the cage-bird market; as many as 16,000 birds were reported captured in only four weeks during 1929. In 1982 it was still thought to be reasonably common along the Ngwezi River, but it has been sparse, sporadic, or very local throughout most of its habitat.

Despite legal protection in Zambia, this lovebird is still subject to illegal trapping and remains a common cage-bird. Its current local status appears to indicate that it never recovered from the massive exploitation for trade which it endured in the 1920s. Although it breeds well in captivity, much of today's captive population has been hybridized with Lilian's lovebird (*Agapornis lilianae*).

Habitat destruction does not appear to be a threat at the present time since much of the bird's habitat is considered unsuitable for agriculture. A coordinated survey to establish the status and distribution of the species in the wild is now needed and should be followed by regular monitoring. The maintenance of a pure-bred captive population should also be considered.

Black-cheeked lovebirds.

St. Vincent parrot

Amazona guildingii

Phylum	Chordata
Class	Aves
Order	Psittaciformes
Family	Psittacidae
Status	Rare, IUCN
	Endangered, USFWS
	Appendix I, CITES
Range	St. Vincent

Description and Biology

The St. Vincent parrot is a very colorful bird with yellow-green underparts, a whitish head, multi-color wings and a tail banded in blue. It feeds during the day on flowers, fruit, and seeds.

Birds mate in February or March and breed in April or May; eggs have even be reported as early as January or February. A breeding pair defends its nest site, but tolerates the close proximity of, and often feeds and roosts with, other pairs. Clutch size is two, very rarely three. In captivity, incubation takes around 24 days and fledging occurs at 67-69 days. In the wild only one or two young are raised even in the best years and breeding may be curtailed or skipped in rainy years. Nests are located in tree cavities, especially those found in the tabanuco tree (*Dacryodes excelsa*).

Habitat and Current Distribution

This parrot is endemic to the island of St. Vincent, where it survives on the upper slopes to the east and to the west of the central ridge of the island. Population is estimated at 440-500 individuals.

Primary habitat is mature moist forest that extends from between 410-1,640 ft (125-500 m) up to 3,300 ft (1,000 m) altitude. Within this range, it shows some preference for lower elevations where trees grow that are large enough to nest in. It is reported to make occasional visits to partially cultivated areas outside the main mountain core and to feed in a garden among the hills.

History and Conservation Measures

The status of the St. Vincent parrot has been uncertain through most of its history. In the late 1800s, it was reported to be both quite common and scarce. Though its population seemed diminished by a hurricane and a volcanic eruption that devastated the island around the turn of the century, by 1908 it appeared to be recovering. From the 1920s through the 1950s, its numbers were thought to be in decline, but estimates lacked precision and certainty. A decade long series of studies begun in 1973 sought to obtain more precise population figures, yielding estimates ranging from a few hundred to a few thousand birds. In 1988, a pair of studies using a repeatable methodology was carried out, giving a provisional estimate of 440-500 birds.

Habitat destruction is identified as one of the causes of the bird's decline. Some reports conjecture that the forest on the western side of the island once reached almost to sea level, indicating that the species' range on the island must have contracted and fragmented substantially in the past hundred years. Commercial lumbering and clearing for agricultural development have been responsible for some loss of habitat. This parrot has for many years been in demand for the cage-bird trade on a local and international level; it was also subject to hunting for food in the 1950s and 1960s, but this is no longer considered to be a problem.

A number of natural threats to the parrot also exist. Volcanic eruptions of Mount Soufrière and fairly frequent hurricanes have occurred, but the species has apparently had the capacity to recover from them quite rapidly. Opossums are natural predators of birds and/or nests, as are hawks, thrashers, and rats to a lesser degree. Nest site competition from bees has also been reported.

Legal protection has been in place for this species since 1920, but it has not been well enforced; recently, there have been improvements and enforcement of laws. Ecological studies of the parrot were conducted in the mid-1970s. Registration of all captive birds on St. Vincent was implemented in the early 1980s, and a captive breeding consortium established. Proposals for forest conservation have been made, stressing the need to preserve large trees at lower altitudes and to establish suitable reserves.

To insure the survival of this parrot, continued monitoring of its population will be needed as well as strong enforcement of CITES provisions authorizing the return of illegally held birds to St. Vincent.

St. Vincent parrot.

Imperial parrot

Amazona imperialis

Phylum	Chordata
Class	Aves
Order	Psittaciformes
Family	Psittacidae
Status	Endangered, IUCN
	Endangered, USFWS
	Appendix I, CITES
Range	Dominica (West Indies)

Description and Biology

The largest parrot of its genus, the Imperial parrot is greenish above and violet below. It feeds on seeds, fruit, young shoots, vines, and shrubs.

Breeding season lasts from February to June, with peak breeding occurring between March and May; this coincides with the dry season and results in nestling and fledgling periods during periods of greater food abundance. Defense of a nesting territory probably occurs throughout the year, indicating that pairs rarely leave this territory for long periods. The parrot's reproductive rate is low, with two eggs probably laid every second year; pairs seldom raise more than one young per clutch.

Habitat and Current Distribution

Endemic to Dominica, West Indies, the Imperial parrot is apparently confined to the east, north, and west slopes on the upper reaches of Morne Diablotin in the north of the island, though populations may exist elsewhere. It is chiefly confined to elevations between 1,500-3,300 ft (450-1,000 m), but there are now regular sightings within the newly acquired nature reserve at less than 1,000 ft (300 m). Because much of its habitat has been difficult to access, population estimates have varied widely, proba-bly reflecting the degree of habitat penetration. Population in 1992 was estimated at 80 to 120 birds.

This species occupies primary rain forest canopy on the slopes of interior mountains. Records of nest sites are from high in the trunks of the dominant forest trees, chataignier (*Sloanea berteriana*) and gommier (*Dacryodes excelsa*), although they also have also been reported from a spur high enough to be in the elfin forest zone. Reports of nests in the top of dead palms have not been confirmed. Roosting is at traditional sites, commonly large gommier or chataignier trees.

History and Conservation Measures

This parrot was probably originally found throughout the mountain chain of Dominica as far as Morne Anglais; its center of abundance has most likely always been Morne Diablotin. Estimates of its population were at first highly speculative because its range was once quite inaccessible. Thus, the earliest accounts considered the Imperial parrot to be very rare, but thorough investigation found it to be abundant in the late 1800s. The isolated southern population based around Morne Anglais began suffering a marked decline around 1970; on Morne Diablotin itself, parrot populations have steadily if unevenly re-

Imperial parrot.

Early threats to this species included hunting for food, for sport, and for the pet trade. A road through the forest in the 1880s allowed access to hunters, and hunting remained the most serious factor limiting the population into the 1970s. Certain natural threats to the species may have also played a part in its scarcity. The opossum is an introduced predator that may pose a serious threat, as may rats, boas, and hawks, to a lesser degree. Competition from pearly-eyed thrashers and from the red-necked amazon may play a role, but probably not to any serious degree. Because of its remote range, habitat destruction was not considered a potential hazard to the parrot until recently. Beginning in the 1980s, however, prime forest land bordering this species' habitat has been sold, cleared, and converted for agricultural use. There have been reports that aerial spraying of banana crops on converted land has led to parrot mortality in adjoining habitat.

Following Hurricane David in 1979, officials imposed a total ban on hunting of all wildlife; patrols of the forests to enforce the prohibition have resulted in decreased hunting pressure. Efforts are being made to raise funds to acquire privately owned parrot habitat before it can be cleared. Initiatives have begun to create a new conservation consciousness in Dominica, particularly in relation to parrot protection and habitat conservation. Studies, surveys, and monitoring of birds have been proposed to establish more precisely their range (including a survey in the south to determine whether any more parrots dwell there), habitat requirements, and diet. A plan is now in progress to designate one of the most important areas of habitat at Morne Diablotin as a national park. Replanting of areas lumbered for timber or charcoal with slow-growing native trees might also prove useful to the species and to the local economy.

treated from lower to higher elevations. Hurricanes in 1979 and 1980, which destroyed millions of trees in the southern forests, reduced the southern population to unviable status; by 1985 all birds away from Morne Diablotin had apparently disappeared and the northern population was thought to have been halved.

St. Lucia parrot

Amazona versicolor

Phylum	Chordata
Class	Aves
Order	Psittaciformes
Family	Pisttacidae
Status	Rare, IUCN
	Endangered, USFWS
	Appendix I, CITES
Range	St. Lucia (West Indies)

Description and Biology

The St. Lucia parrot is greenish above and greenish brown below, with a blue face, a reddish patch on the throat, blue and red wing markings, and a banded tail. It feeds during the day on a variety of flowers, fruits, and seeds.

Breeding occurs during the dry season from February to August, and most eggs are laid from the end of February through March. A typical clutch consists of two eggs, laid within a deep cavity in a tree, though only one young is usually reared. Incubation period is 28 days, and the first young hatched in captivity flew at 81 days. Indigenous predators are hawks and boas, and introduced predators include rats, mongooses, and opossums, but none of these are considered a serious problem.

Habitat and Current Distribution

This parrot is endemic to St. Lucia in the West Indies. While its distribution within its range may vary with season, the parrot is most abundant in the southwestern parts of its forest range; forests in the northeast area support very few birds. Population is estimated at 300-350 individuals.

The St. Lucia parrot inhabits the canopy of tropical moist forest in the montane interior of the island. Early in the morning, the parrot moves from the heart of the forest toward the periphery of its habitat, sometimes ranging into adjacent tracts of secondary growth. In the late afternoon or early evening, it returns to the center of the forest to roost.

History and Conservation Measures

The St. Lucia parrot was considered relatively abundant before 1850 and was probably not uncommon through the turn of the century. Thereafter, it experienced a decline before making a slow recovery. An estimated 1,000 birds existed around 1950, but by the 1960s it was becoming rare. Surveys in 1975 estimated a population of 100-150 birds, and by 1977 the total population was probably no more than 100. By 1980, an upward trend began, although it was slowed by Hurricane Allen that year. Subsequent surveys have revealed a steady increase in numbers, with estimates of 200-250 in 1982, 250-300 in 1988, and 300-350 in 1990.

The earliest cause of decline in this species was hunting for food and trapping for the pet industry; around 1910, the St. Lucia parrot was thought to have been hunted to the verge of extinction. Through the 1970s, hunting remained a problem. But the chief

St. Lucia parrot.

cause of the parrot's overall decline has been habitat destruction. Between 1950 and 1975, the species' habitat was reduced from over 100 sq mi (295 sq km) to only 25-27 sq mi (65-70 sq km). Although the forests were under protection by 1975, shifting cultivation was causing considerable forest fragmentation and making inroads into forest reserves. Hurricane Allen in 1980 apparently killed at least two birds and severely damaged the nature reserve established chiefly for the parrot. Uncontrolled felling of trees since the 1950s may have led to a scarcity of trees preferred by the parrot for nesting, thus forcing it to compete with the pearly-eyed thrasher (*Margarops fuscatus*) for suitable sites. The thrasher was rare on the island in 1950, but it has now become numerous in the forests and may represent a considerable threat to the parrot.

In an effort to conserve the St. Lucia parrot, several key proposals were enacted on its behalf. In 1980 the parrot was declared a national bird, and a new Wildlife Ordinance raised the fine for killing a parrot. A nature reserve was also created and an educational program initiated. Following Hurricane Allen, recommendations were made to protect forests against encroachment by new farmers; efforts are also underway to replant the damaged areas with native trees. Further study of the parrot's feeding and nesting requirements would be helpful in maximizing the conservation measures already in place.

Puerto Rican parrot

Amazona vittata

Phylum	Chordata
Class	Aves
Order	Psittaciformes
Family	Psittacidae
Status	Endangered, IUCN
	Endangered, USFWS
	Appendix I, CITES
Range	Puerto Rico (U.S.A.)

Description and Biology

The Puerto Rican parrot averages 12 in (30 cm) long and has a green body, blue wing feathers, and a red forehead. Its feet and bill are pale. Diet consists of fruits, seeds, and leaves. Rodents and red-tailed hawks prey upon eggs and young, and pearly-eyed thrashers (*Margarops fuscatus*) compete for the parrot's nest holes.

Pairs form stable bonds and stay together except when nesting. They return to the same tree each year and nest in a cavity. Two to four eggs are incubated for approximately 26 days by the female while the male gathers food; chicks fledge in around nine weeks.

Habitat and Current Distribution

The range is restricted to a single site on Luqillo Mountains at the northeastern end of Puerto Rico. Only 32 parrots survive in the wild.

Habitat includes both mountain and lowland forests and stands of mangroves. Lowland habitat has been largely eliminated, forcing parrots into the less suitable mountain forests. Their preferred nesting tree is the palo colorado (*Cyrilla racemiflora*).

History and Conservation Measures

This parrot was at one time common throughout the forested areas of Puerto Rico. Estimates of peak population vary widely from 100,000 to over one million birds. Over hundreds of years, the lowland forests were cleared for settlement and development, and the bird's population began a corresponding decline. By 1912, only a small population could be found; in the 1950s flock size was estimated at 200 birds; by 1960 the wild population consisted of 20 birds.

Habitat destruction was the direct and indirect cause of this parrot's decline. Clearing of lowland forests directly eliminated habitat and forced the parrot to upland forests where it had a new threat to confront. Rainfall is heavier in the mountain rain forests and nest sites in colorado trees frequently flood. In addition, Hurricane Hugo in 1989 destroyed about half of the island's wild parrots.

Competitors and predators threaten the surviving birds. Rats prey up on eggs and chicks and red-tailed hawks (*Buteo jamaicensis*) on adult and juvenile birds. The pearly-eyed thrasher, which has become abundant on Puerto Rico, competes for nest sites and preys on eggs or young. Puerto Rican parrots have been successfully bred in captivity, and the

Puerto Rican parrots.

captive population—established in 1970—now stands at 60 birds. A second aviary for captive breeding has been established in the Rio Abajo Forest. A slow but steady increase of the wild population was disrupted by Hurricane Hugo. The lowland forests are being revived, but it will take decades before a suitable habitat develops; until then, the parrot's future is extremely uncertain. Long-term recovery goals call for two separate, self-sustaining wild populations of 500 birds each. The U. S. Fish and Wildlife Service has established a Recovery Team under the Endangered Species Act to coordinate the conservation efforts for this species.

Lear's macaw

Anodorhynchus leari

Phylum	Chordata
Class	Aves
Order	Psittaciformes
Family	Psittacidae
Status	Endangered, IUCN
	Endangered, USFWS
	Appendix I, CITES
Range	Brazil

Description and Biology

The Lear's macaw is also known as the indigo macaw because of its beautiful purplish blue color, which is accented by a yellow patch at the base of its bill and grayish green on its breast and head. Its average length is 30 in (76 cm).

The bird uses its bill as well as its feet for climbing. Preferred food is the small nut that grows on the licuri palm (*Syagrus coronata*). Each day before sunrise, the flock is awakened by the loud cawing of individual "scout" macaws before leaving the nesting area for feeding grounds.

Habitat and Current Distribution

The only known nesting site of the Lear's macaw is Rasa da Catarina in Bahia State in northeastern Brazil. The size of this recently discovered population is estimated at 65 birds.

Habitat is comprised of deep canyons and dry, desert-like plateaus. They nest in narrowly burrowed tunnels in the sandstone cliffs of the region and sometimes roost on cliff faces or ledges.

History and Conservation Measures

The first specimens of Lear's macaw were discovered in a shipment of hyacinth macaws (*Anodorhynchus hyacinthinus*) from South America to North America. While similar in appearance, the Lear's macaws were noticeably smaller than the hyacinth macaws and their origin was uncertain. The bird was known only in captivity until 1979, when biologists discovered a wild population in a remote area of Brazil. Fewer than ten Lear's macaws exist in captivity, and perhaps only two pairs are breeding.

Habitat destruction is the major threat to the Lear's macaw. Cattle, which also feed upon the nut of the licuri palm, have prevented the regeneration of the bird's primary food source. The Lear's macaw has always been hunted by local people for food, and an additional threat lies in the trapping of live birds for the pet trade. The remote location of this macaw's nesting ground provides some protection, but the population is confined to a very small and privately owned area and could easily be wiped out by trappers. A detailed plan for land acquisition and/or the establishment of reserves has been developed.

Lear's macaws.

Blue-throated macaw

Ara glaucogularis

Phylum	Chordata
Class	Aves
Order	Psittaciformes
Family	Psittacidae
Status	Endangered, IUCN
	Appendix I, CITES
Range	Argentina (?); Bolivia; Paraguay (?)

Description and Biology

The blue-throated macaw has a distinct blue coloring on the upper portion of the body and yellow coloring on the bottom. The throat and crown are blue, and there are four or five blue-green horizontal lines on the face. It is described as inquisitive and has a high trilling call. Diet has been reported by traders to be primarily palm nuts.

Nesting takes place from November to March. Two eggs are laid, one two days after the other; incubation period is 28 days for each egg and the young leave the nest 90-94 days after hatching.

Habitat and Current Distribution

For many years sightings of the blue-throated macaw have been rare. In 1992 field ornithologist Charlie Munn sighted this bird in Bolivia. There have been additional sightings in Argentina and Paraguay, but they have not been confirmed. Total population is estimated to be between 500 and 1,000 birds.

This bird inhabits tropical savanna with scattered groups of trees that remain above the water line when the savanna is inundated by rains from October to April. This bird also inhabits ribbons of gallery forest along the watercourses. It is found at elevations between 650-820 ft (200-250 m). Nests are built in tree cavities.

History and Conservation Measures

Apart from data on three museum skins, all information about this species has come from trappers and dealers in the cage-bird trade. Trade and capture have been prohibited within Bolivia since 1984. The species' greatest protection is afforded by the remoteness of its habitat and its elusiveness. It is not known to what extent trapping continues at present.

The first priority with this species is to assess its ecological needs, status, and the pressures upon it to determine necessary conservation measures. The captive population needs to be managed carefully to maintain genetic diversity, and a studbook is being established. Development of a large captive population through aviculture may stem illegal pressure on wild birds and build a good reserve until more can be learned of the wild population.

Golden-capped parakeet

Aratinga auricapilla

Phylum	Chordata
Class	Aves
Order	Psittaciformes
Family	Psittacidae
Status	Vulnerable, IUCN
	Appendix II, CITES
Range	Brazil

Description and Biology

The golden-capped parakeet, also called the golden-capped conure, is about 12 in (30 cm) long. Adults have generally dark green plumage shading to a more yellowish color on the cheeks, ear-coverts, throat, and upper breast. The forehead, lores (spaces between the bill and the eyes), and the regions around the eyes are orange-red; the forecrown or cap is golden-yellow. The feathers of the abdomen and lower breast are red with green bases, and the feathers of the rump and lower back are variably edged with red. The wings are blue and orange-red. The upper side of the tail is olive-green tipped with blue and the underside is gray. The bill is gray-black and the legs are gray. The subspecies *A. a. aurifrons* can be distinguished by the absence of the yellowish tinge on the sides of the head, throat, and upper breast; the feathers of the rump and lower back do not have red margins. The golden-capped parakeet feeds on fruits and seeds. It likes corn (maize) and has been reported as a pest in corn plantations. It is usually seen in groups of 2-20 birds. Reproductive biology is poorly known.

Habitat and Current Distribution

This species is endemic to central southeastern Brazil, from eastern and central-southern Bahia and eastern Goiás through Minas Gerais to Espírito Santo, Rio de Janeiro, São Paulo, and northern Paraná. *A. a. auricapilla* is confined to northern and

Golden-capped parakeet.

central parts of Bahia; birds from southern Bahia tend to be intermediate between this race and *A. a. aurifrons*; the race *A. a. aurifrons* occupies the rest of the range from Minas Gerais and southern Goiás, south to northern Paraná. In general the golden-capped parakeet has become rare, but it is still common in certain parts of its range. Because the range is so widespread, there may be some populations that have not yet been discovered. There are no estimates of current population size.

This is a forest-based species that occurs on the Atlantic Forest borders and also extends through generally much drier inland regions in semi-deciduous forest. Primary forest is important to the golden-capped parakeet; while it favors fringes and small clearings, at least a patch of forest must be nearby.

History and Conservation Measures

This species has experienced a very substantial decline in recent decades, but this decline may have been in progress for 200 years. Even reports from the 1800s call it common in some areas of its range and rare in others. However, the golden-capped parakeet is certainly now rare in many areas where it was common in the late 1800s. Those areas in which it is still common are thought to host small, isolated populations; it has become extinct in many regions and extremely local in others.

Loss of forest habitat has clearly played a role in the decline of the golden-capped parakeet. Extensive land clearance in the southeastern parts of its range has had a major impact, and its present distribution is now heavily fragmented. The forest patches that remain are not protected and degradation will continue at these sites. The impact of this increasing fragmentation is unclear and will depend on the carrying capacity of remaining protectable forests, their distance from each other, and the dispersive ability of the species. It is thought that some populations may be able to stay in contact through the use of riverine forest corridors. This bird has apparently not been persecuted as a pest in corn plantations, but is exploited for the cage-bird trade. It is relatively common in illegal markets in Brazil and is offered for sale in lots of up to 15 birds.

This parakeet occurs in several protected areas, including Monte Pascoal National Park in Bahia and the Rio Doce State Park, Fazenda Montes Claros (Caratinga Reserve), Serra da Canastra National Park, and Serra do Caparaó National Park in Minas Gerais. It has also been found in or very close to the Chapada Diamantina National Park in Bahia (at Lençóis and Andaraí). Comprehensive studies and surveys are necessary to plan conservation efforts. Research into its population dynamics and dispersal capacity, and a detailed analysis of its habitat and feeding requirements should be initiated. Efforts should also be made to locate major new populations and to define the limits of its range. Certain sites in eastern Minas Gerais deserve particularly urgent investigation since they appear to hold populations of other threatened birds. This species should also be protected by Brazilian law.

Golden parakeet

Aratinga (Guaruba) guarouba

Phylum	Chordata
Class	Aves
Order	Psittaciformes
Family	Psittacidae
Status	Vulnerable, IUCN
	Endangered, USFWS
	Appendix I, CITES
Range	Brazil

Description and Biology

Some Brazilians have suggested that the golden parakeet, also known as the golden conure, be adopted as their national bird because its coloring—yellow and green—is the same as the national flag. This distinctive bird forages in the treetops for fruits, berries, seeds, and nuts; it also feeds on some cultivated crops and favors corn (maize). Toucans are predators of eggs and nestlings in clearings, and monkeys and snakes are predators in the forest.

The golden parakeet is gregarious, roosting with up to nine birds in a single tree-hole, and moving in flocks of up to thirty between roosting and feeding areas. Breeding usually lasts from December to April, but some seasonal variation has been observed, possibly due to changes in weather conditions. Apparently, breeding and rearing of young is communal. Several females lay their eggs in a single clutch located in the cavity of an isolated tree 50-100 ft (15-30 m) tall, usually in the highest part of the trunk or a high, thick branch. In captivity, clutch size of a single pair was two to three. However, a group of three males and three females all cared for fourteen chicks. In captive birds, incubation lasts around 30 days.

Habitat and Current Distribution

The range of the golden parakeet in northern Brazil extends from northwestern Maranhao west through Pará along the Trans-Amazonian Highway as far as the Tapajós (Amazonia) National Park. Recent evidence of a population in Rondônia in western Brazil suggests that previous estimates of range must be expanded and that further populations may yet be discovered. No estimates of population size currently exist.

The habitat of the golden parakeet is tropical rain forest, primarily in the canopy of dryland forest in hilly upland areas. It has also been seen in riverine grasslands, and in seasonally or permanently flooded forest. It uses tall forest during the dry, non-breeding season, but seeks out cleared areas with isolated trees near forests in breeding season.

History and Conservation Measures

Ornithologists have long considered the golden parakeet rare, but some suggest that early European explorers were unable to penetrate deeply enough into the species' habitat to accurately assess its num-

Golden parakeet.

bers. Where good forest remains, the bird may still be seen regularly, but overall numbers have declined very seriously.

Habitat destruction is the primary threat to the golden parakeet. Wholesale clearing of tropical forest as a result of road construction and settlement has fragmented the bird's distribution in Maranhao. Major development projects such as railroad construction, lumbering, cattle ranching, and gold mining have also contributed to the decline of habitat.

Another significant threat to the golden parakeet is the fact that it is among the most highly prized birds in the world, selling to collectors for upwards of $15,000. Despite legal protection, it is still smuggled within Brazil and on an international scale. Ironically, legal protection of the species may have worked against the parakeet by identifying it to dealers as being of special value, a situation that could be overcome by a conservation awareness campaign. In addition to live capture, the species is hunted for food or sport and killed as a pest to corn crops.

The only nature reserve currently in the species' western range is the Tapajós (Amazonia) National Park in Pará. The Gurupi Biological Reserve, created in 1988, needs to be demarcated and wardened to protect this and several other important species. Areas between Tapajós and Gurupi must be protected and managed so that populations can survive and interbreed. Studies are also necessary to better determine the golden parakeet's distribution, population, and habitat, as are measures to control the bird's exploitation by illegal traders.

Little blue macaw

Cyanopsitta spixii

Phylum	Chordata
Class	Aves
Order	Psittaciformes
Family	Psittacidae
Status	Endangered, IUCN
	Endangered, USFWS
	Appendix I, CITES
Range	Brazil

Description and Biology

The little blue macaw, or Spix's macaw, is considered an exceptionally beautiful species. At a length of about 22 in (56 cm), it is a medium-sized macaw, and as its name suggests, it is predominantly blue. The back, wings, and upper side of the tail are a darker blue, the breast and abdomen are slightly tinged with green, and the underside of the tail is dark gray. The forehead and ear coverts are gray, tinged with blue, and the remainder of the head and neck are grayish blue. The bill is gray-black and the legs are dark gray. Diet consists of seeds and fruits.

This bird is normally found in pairs, although in the past it also occurred in flocks of up to 15 birds. Breeding was reported to take place from November to March but was variable with rainfall. The number of young is two or three. In captivity, the incubation period is 26 days, and the fledgling period is two months. Young are fed by the parents for up to three months after fledging.

Habitat and Current Distribution

The little blue macaw is endemic to the arid interior of east-central Brazil and is known with certainty from just one site in northern Bahia, at which a single bird survived in 1992. Known captive population at that time stood at 27 birds.

This species is believed to be associated with gallery woodland in which mature specimens of caraiba trees (*Tabebuia caraiba*) dominate, within the coatinga or dry scrub zone of the Brazilian interior. The caraiba tree is important for nesting and roosting; the birds habitually occupy the same branches and reuse breeding holes.

History and Conservation Measures

This species can truly be said to stand on the very brink of extinction in the wild. Even when originally described in 1819, it was considered rare. Between 1819 and the mid-1980s, the species was recorded only twice in published sources. At the beginning of the 1900s, the population was estimated at approximately 30 pairs. By 1985, no more than five birds were reported remaining and in 1986 only three remained; by 1987 all known birds had been captured or had died, and the bird was considered extinct in the wild. In 1990 a single bird was discovered living in the wild.

The single most immediate threat to this species in the recent past has been trapping for the caged bird trade; because of its rarity, extravagant prices have been offered for the bird. Most of the surviving little blue macaws are privately owned, and unfortunately the owners have not been cooperative in helping to preserve the species. Additional threats include hunting for food, which has been a danger to all edible wildlife in interior Brazil and may have been a problem for this species in the Curaçá region in the past. A hybrid strain of African bee, which may compete for traditional macaw nesting holes, has been reported to attack incubating macaws. Habitat destruction over the centuries is almost certainly a major factor in the rarity of this species. It is estimated that there are only 18 sq mi (30 sq km) of *Tabebuia caraiba* woodland remaining; the habitat, an area favored for the cultivation of subsistence crops such as maize, is fast disappearing due to human incursions.

Searches for the little blue macaw have been made in areas of suitable habitat without success, but further searches are necessary. Attempts have been made to bring together the holders of captive birds to establish guidelines for captive breeding, but this has met with little success. If the remaining wild bird can be protected, it may ease the introduction of captive-bred birds, including a mate, into the wild. Conservation of remaining gallery woodland is essential if birds are to be released there in the future. A local education program has been successful, and there is now great local pride and interest in the species.

Orange-bellied parakeet

Neophema chrysogaster

Phylum	Chordata
Class	Aves
Order	Psittaciformes
Family	Psittacidae
Status	Rare, IUCN
	Endangered, USFWS
	Appendix I, CITES
Range	Australia

Description and Biology

This brilliantly colored parakeet is a migratory bird that averages 8.25 in (21 cm) long. Sometimes called the orange-bellied parrot, its upper body is bright green, brow and wings are blue, belly is orange, and underparts are green and yellow. Its diet consists of fruits and seeds of grasses, shrubs, and salt-loving plants. Predators include introduced cats and foxes, and it competes with introduced starlings from Europe, goldfinches, and sparrows.

Birds pair before reaching the nesting ground and then work together to prepare the nest in the hollow of a live tree. The female lays four to six white eggs in November and incubates them for about six weeks. The chicks fledge in four to five weeks and gather with other young birds to migrate.

Habitat and Current Distribution

The orange-bellied parakeet breeds in western Tasmania, Australia, and migrates to the southern coast of the Australian mainland for the winter. Population figures are uncertain but are estimated at 150 birds.

Breeding habitat is heath and sedgelands; the winter months are spent feeding on saltmarshes and coastal dunes.

History and Conservation Measures

In the late 1800s and early 1900s, the orange-bellied parakeet may have numbered in the thousands. Until the 1960s early estimates of population were uncertain because the same flock of birds was being counted in nesting and wintering grounds as two separate populations. Today, changes in fire regime within the breeding habitat has been identified as the primary cause of decline of this species. Salt marshes and coastal dunes are being developed for saltworks and sewage farms. Breeding grounds are also being disrupted by mineral exploration, stock grazing, and trapping. Competition from common species is another threat to the orange-bellied parakeet. Starlings compete for nesting grounds, and goldfinches and sparrows compete for food.

This species has been the subject of ongoing conservation projects for several years and, as a result its numbers have been stable. Considerable success has been achieved in preserving and actively managing habitat in Tasmania, on King Island, and in Victoria. A well-managed captive-breeding program is also in place.

Scarlet-chested parakeet

Neophema splendida

Phylum	Chordata
Class	Aves
Order	Psittaciformes
Family	Psittacidae
Status	Rare, IUCN
	Endangered, USFWS
	Appendix II, CITES
Range	Australia

Description and Biology

The scarlet-chested parakeet is sometimes known as the splendid parakeet or parrot because of its beautiful colors. It has a green upper body, blue wings and face, yellow underparts, and a brilliant red throat patch. It feeds on the ground, using its foot to bend a grass stem and bring the seed within reach of its beak.

Breeding takes place only after rain, when food is most available. Nests are made of soft wood chips, and are constructed in tree crevices or logs. The female carries green leaves from aromatic plants to the nest, transporting them by tucking them among her rump feathers. Sometime between August and January she lays three to six white eggs and incubates them alone for three weeks.

Habitat and Current Distribution

This bird occurs very locally in the southern interior of Australia. Population size is unknown.

The preferred habitats of this species are arid saltbush and scrubland or spinifex plains.

History and Conservation Measures

While it is thought to have always been rare, the population trend of this species is still uncertain. It is well adapted to the dry scrublands where it lives and, after wet weather, it breeds rapidly and is fairly common. The birds then disperse, and population levels seem to decline until the following wet season. At peak times, hundreds of birds may be seen flocking together. In successive dry seasons, these parakeets may be seen only in pairs if at all.

Since it breeds well in captivity, there should be no need for trapping wild birds. Captive-bred birds are sold for as little as $20, and more than 25,000 birds are kept in captivity in Australia alone. Nonetheless, enforcement of existing legal protection is important, as is refuge offered by the establishment of several large national parks in the interior of Australia.

Because its population waxes and wanes, the future of the scarlet-chested parakeet will always be uncertain. Its nomadic habits make it hard to monitor, and it could be at severe risk if its habitat deteriorates or the climate becomes more arid.

Scarlet-chested parakeet.

Night parrot

Pezoporus (Geopsittacus) occidentalis

Phylum	Chordata
Class	Aves
Order	Psittaciformes
Family	Psittacidae
Status	Indeterminate, IUCN
	Endangered, USFWS
	Appendix I, CITES
Range	Australia (ex?)

Description and Biology

Also called the Australian parrot, the night parrot is colored in patterns of green, black, and yellow, which helps the species blend in with the surrounding environment. Average body length is 9.5 in (24 cm). Nocturnal and cautious, it feeds on seed plants, including spinifex, an Australian grass with spiny seeds or stiff, sharp leaves. Predators include cats and foxes.

Breeding is assumed to be erratic. The nest is built on or near the ground in spinifex or samphire vegetation. Clutch size is thought to be two to five eggs, but very little is known about incubation or fledging rates.

Habitat and Current Distribution

Sightings have been reported in western and southern Australia, but the night parrot is considered very rare.

During the day, this parrot is thought to hide in the spinifex and on samphire flats. It is usually sighted near sources of fresh water.

History and Conservation Measures

It is thought that the night parrot was common throughout the interior of Australia until the late 1800s. Converting arid regions to grazing land has destroyed much of this species' nesting habitat and food sources. Predators may also have played a part in the decline, but to what extent is unknown.

Because of the remote nature of the night parrot's habitat and its nocturnal habits, it is very difficult to assess its status. The bird may be more numerous than expected in yet unexplored areas of central Australia. Several large national parks established in the interior of Australia may also harbor this species as well.

Ground parrot

Pezoporus wallicus

Phylum	Chordata
Class	Aves
Order	Psittaciformes
Family	Psittacidae
Status	Endangered, IUCN
	Endangered, USFWS
	Appendix I, CITES
Range	Australia

Description and Biology

Except for an orange-red band on its forehead, the ground parrot is perfectly camouflaged with a pattern of green, black, and yellow that blends in with surrounding vegetation; males and females are similarly colored. Averaging approximately 6 in (15 cm) in length with a 6.5 in (16.5 cm) tail, the ground parrot feeds on vegetation in grass and sedge areas. Most active at dusk, this species is thought to be nocturnal.

The ground parrot builds a nest on the ground from leaves and stems for spring and summer breeding. Three to four white eggs are incubated for about three weeks; chicks fledge after a further three weeks.

Habitat and Current Distribution

Two ground parrot subspecies exist: the western *P. w. flaviventris* and the eastern *P. w. wallicus*. Both subspecies inhabit swamps and grasslands that provide a thick cover of heath and a high density of food plants. The ground parrot chooses heathland in a particular stage of recovery from fire.

Two populations of *P. w. flaviventris*, totalling less than 450 individuals, exist in Western Australia; these populations are found in Fitzgerald River National Park and Cape Arid National Park. *P. w. wallicus* is found in isolated areas in Victoria and New South Wales; its population has not been determined.

History and Conservation Measures

Both ground parrot subspecies were at one time more widespread. Loss of habitat has been the single most important contributor to their decline. Swamp and wetlands have been drained; heath and grasslands have been cleared. Urban and agricultural growth has also disrupted the natural cycle of fires, affecting the availability of food.

Repopulation of previous habitats is very complicated because of the necessity for fire management. Both subspecies have been given legal protection. The eastern ground parrot occurs in nature reserves and national parks in Queensland, New South Wales, and Victoria. Preservation of the existing population can only be accomplished with aggressive habitat protection.

Golden-shouldered parakeet

Psephotus chrysopterygius

Phylum	Chordata
Class	Aves
Order	Psittaciformes
Family	Psittacidae
Status	Rare, IUCN
	Endangered, USFWS
	Appendix I, CITES
Range	Australia

Description and Biology

The golden-shouldered parrot or parakeet is also known as the golden-winged parrot or the anthill parakeet or parrot. It is a beautiful bird: its back, tail, and top of head are brown; belly, breast, and sides of head are green; and a splash of golden color decorates its wings and forehead. The female is less conspicuously colored in green to blue-gray. Average length is 10 in (25 cm). Diet consists of grass and herb seeds.

Breeding season is April through July. The nest is built at the end of a tunnel burrowed into a termite mound. Four to six white eggs are incubated by the female for three weeks; chicks fledge after five weeks.

The golden-shouldered parakeet and the hooded parakeet (*Psephotus dissimilis*) are sometimes considered to be variations of the same species.

Habitat and Current Distribution

The golden-shouldered parakeet is found in the southern portion of the Cape York Peninsula in northern Queensland. It is now restricted to the eastern edge of its original distribution, a strip 75 mi wide and 140 mi long (120 km by 225 km), centered around Musgrave and Koolburra. There are also a few recent records from the west coast. No accurate census figures exist, although the total population probably numbers in the low hundreds.

The preferred habitat of this species is semi-arid

Golden-shouldered parakeet.

savanna woodland. In the breeding season, this species uses terrestrial termite mounds on alluvial flats.

History and Conservation Measures

Nesting sites of this parakeet were not discovered until the 1940s. Once located, the bird was heavily hunted and trapped for the pet trade during the 1950s and 1960s. Trading in this species is now prohibited, but smuggling may continue.

Other possible threats include habitat deterioration as a result of overgrazing by livestock and an altered fire regime, predation by feral cats (*Felis cattus*), and disturbance by tourists. Because the population of this bird is so small, it remains at risk. Captive breeding has been successful; captive stocks can be found in Australia, Europe, and in the United States. The Australian Native Conservation Agency has developed a recovery plan, which includes research, monitoring, control of trapping, fire management, public education, and protection in the Staaten River National Park.

Hooded parakeet

Psephotus dissimilis

Phylum	Chordata
Class	Aves
Order	Psittaciformes
Family	Psittacidae
Status	Insufficiently Known, IUCN Endangered, USFWS Appendix I, CITES
Range	Australia

Description and Biology

The hooded parakeet is also known as the hooded parrot, the anthill parrot or parakeet, and the black-hooded parrot or parakeet. Head and tail are brown, and the head is capped in black. Breast and sides of the face are turquoise; yellow flecks are present on the red belly and upper wings. The female is of a more uniform green to blue-gray shade. Average length is 11 in (28 cm). Diet consists mainly of grass seeds. This species gathers in flocks of over 100 birds around water and in seeding grassland during non-breeding seasons.

Nesting takes place between April and July. The nest is built at the end of a tunnel burrowed into a termite mound. Four to six white eggs are incubated by the female for three weeks; young fledge after five weeks.

The hooded parakeet and the golden-shouldered parakeet (*Psephotus chrysopterygius*) are sometimes considered to be variations of the same species.

Habitat and Current Distribution

The hooded parakeet is found in the Northern Territory of Australia, on the Melville Peninsula from the South Alligator River and Pine Creek, southeast to the Macarthur River, and the southwestern shores of the Gulf of Carpentaria. No estimates of population size are available.

Hooded parakeet.

Preferred habitat is dry open forest where termites nest.

History and Conservation Measures

The hooded parakeet is still found throughout its historic range but in reduced numbers (except perhaps on the Arnhem Plateau) because of a combination of threats. In the past this beautiful species has been a target of trappers for the cage-bird market and although this is now controlled, the trade might have been the cause of the initial decline. Habitat deterioration is a more current threat. Many areas within its range are suitable for cattle grazing and are regularly burned during the dry season, often as the grasses are seeding, thus resulting in an overall deterioration in habitat quality for the hooded parakeet.

This parakeet has been successfully bred in captivity. Its future in the wild depends on protection of its habitat and enforcement of its legal protection.

Mauritius parakeet

Psittacula echo

Phylum	Chordata
Class	Aves
Order	Psittaciformes
Family	Psittacidae
Status	Endangered, IUCN
	Endangered, USFWS
	Appendix I, CITES
Range	Mauritius (Indian Ocean)

Description and Biology

One of the world's most endangered birds, the Mauritius parakeet has dark green plumage with a black collar. Males have a red beak whereas females and juveniles have black beaks. It is arboreal, usually found in upper tree branches. Feeding during the day, it mainly eats fruit and flowers, supplemented by leaves, seeds, buds, shoots, twigs, and bark; more leaves are eaten in the winter when fruit is scarce.

Breeding usually takes place between September and February. Clutch size is two to four, although two young are usually raised. After fledging, the young remain dependent for around two months.

Habitat and Current Distribution

This parakeet is endemic to the island of Mauritius in the Indian Ocean, where it is confined to the southwestern part of the island. *P. e. eques* was once endemic to the neighboring island of Réunion; this subspecies is now extinct. Total population is thought to be around 18 birds.

The Mauritius parakeet primarily inhabits native upland forest and scrublands (dwarf forest); it also occurs in areas of native lowland and middle-altitude forest. It roosts in sheltered areas, including hillsides and ravines, and spends most of its time in dense, mature stands of trees. Remaining birds center their activities on the Macabé ridge and favor some of the largest native trees left on Mauritius. Nests are located at least 32 ft (10 m) up in rain-sheltered tree holes.

History and Conservation Measures

In the 1700s and early 1800s, this parakeet was apparently very common on Mauritius. Between the 1870s and 1900s, the population was noted to be gradually falling, and, by the 1950s, it was considered very close to extinction. Surveys in the early 1970s estimated the population at 50-60 birds and reported very limited nesting success. Initial population on Réunion is unknown, but the parakeet was probably extinct there before 1800.

The reasons for the extinction of this bird on the island of Réunion are not fully known, but hunting pressure is thought to have been a factor, aggravated by clearing of the native lowland forest. A number of factors have been implicated in the decline of the parakeet on Mauritius. The single most critical factor is habitat loss; clearance in 1971-1974 of half of the upland dwarf forest at Les Mares on Plaine Champagne for plantation forestry was probably responsible for the drastic decline of the species. Nest predation by monkeys was also thought to have been a factor, but even when this problem was controlled, the bird's reproductive success remained poor. Competition for nest sites from introduced birds such as the ring-necked parakeet (*Psittacula krameri*) and the Indian mynah (*Acridotheres tristis*) is thought to be a problem, but to what extent is unknown. Food shortages at the end of winter are attributed to the gradual degradation of native forest and to competition for and destruction of fruit by black rats and monkeys.

Captive breeding attempts were begun in the 1970s, but without success. The first two captive-bred parakeets were born in 1993, one of which still survives. Because captive breeding has long been considered the only hope for saving this species, efforts are continuing; if they prove successful, re-introduction of captive-bred birds to suitable habitat will be considered. In 1974 remaining native forest habitat received almost complete protection when the Macabé-Bel Ombre Nature Reserve was created by linking a number of smaller reserves. However, unless intensive management of the forest is undertaken, the parakeet's habitat will continue to become increasingly degraded.

Thick-billed parrot

Rhynchopsitta pachyrhyncha

Phylum	Chordata
Class	Aves
Order	Psittaciformes
Family	Psittacidae
Status	Vulnerable, IUCN
	Endangered, USFWS
	Appendix I, CITES
Range	Mexico; Arizona (U.S.A.)

Description and Biology

The thick-billed parrot is a green bird with red markings on the forehead and forewing. It has a long, pointed tail and a black, hooked bill. Average length is 16 in (41 cm) and wingspan is 8-10 in (20-25 cm). It feeds on pine cones, juniper berries, and acorns, and may travel 6-12 mi (10-19 km) to find food.

The breeding season seems to vary slightly to match the peak availability of pine seeds. Egg-laying has been recorded as early as May and as late as October. Nests are built in tree cavities, where typically 2-4 eggs are laid and 1-3 young are fledged.

Habitat and Current Distribution

This parrot is found in the Sierra Madre Occidental, Mexico. No population censuses have been carried out, but the species is considered to be in decline and is unlikely to number more than a few thousand birds. In the United States, a breeding population has been reintroduced to its former range in Arizona. This flock, numbering 12-14 birds, now winters in the Chiricahua Mountains and summers on the Mogollon Rim of central Arizona.

Preferred habitat is mature mountain conifer forests from 4,000-12,000 ft (1,200-3,600 m).

History and Conservation Measures

The thick-billed parrot was once common throughout Mexico and was even evident in northern Arizona. Large flocks of over 100 birds were often sighted: in 1917, 1,500 were counted in the Chiricahua Mountains of southern Arizona. In the early 1900s, it is believed that miners and woodsmen in the United States eliminated the population by hunting it for food and cutting down its nesting trees for use in mining operations.

In northeastern Mexico, the species is now vulnerable for a number of reasons, including logging and trapping. Even in selective logging ventures, tall pines used by the parrot for nesting and feeding are being felled. Easier access to its mountain refuge also increases its vulnerability to trappers in the cage-bird trade.

The thick-billed parrot is protected in Mexico, but enforcement is difficult because of its remote habitat. The population that was introduced into Arizona in 1986 was made up of birds confiscated from smugglers. Losses to birds of prey have been offset by the release of additional parrots. Sightings of immature birds bred in the wild are encouraging. The captured and parent-reared birds have apparently adapted to their new environment, while a group of hand-reared birds did not. A number of zoos are now cooperating with wildlife officials to provide a supply of parrots to add to the wild population.

Thick-billed parrots.

Maroon-fronted parrot

Rhynchopsitta terrisi

Phylum	Chordata
Class	Aves
Order	Psittaciformes
Family	Psittacidae
Status	Vulnerable, IUCN
	Appendix I, CITES
Range	Mexico

Description and Biology

A sociable species, the maroon-fronted parrot is a dark green bird of moderate size with maroon markings on its head. The parrot forms communal roosts throughout the year, even during the breeding season when nesting pairs may roost during the day while remaining at the nest during the night. It feeds mainly on the seeds of a large number of pine species such as the Aztec pine (*Pinus teocote*), Arizona pine (*P. arizonica*), and Mexican pinyon (*P. cembroides*), supplemented by other seeds as well as acorns and agave nectar.

These parrots nest in colonies in cliffs; one to four young have been reported per nest. Egg laying has been reported in July and August, with variations in timing evidently related to abundance of pine seeds. Incubation is assumed to be around 26 days and fledging period two months. The parrots are nomadic outside the breeding season, and evidence indicates that large numbers of parrots migrate from north to south within their range during the dry winter months.

Habitat and Current Distribution

This parrot is confined to a small area of northeast Mexico in a narrow section of the Sierra Madre Oriental covering southeast Coahuila, west-central and southern Nuevo León, and southwest Tamaulipas. In almost 7,000 sq mi (18,000 sq km) of range, only 1,300-2,700 sq mi (3,500-7,000 sq km) contain appropriate habitat. Population counts have been problematic because of seasonal movements; at times migrating birds may have been counted twice. Population is estimated at roughly 2,000 birds, but that estimate is thought to be too conservative by some.

Prime habitat appears to be mixed conifer forests, mostly at higher elevations; the species is most frequently encountered between 6,500-11,500 ft (2,000-3,500 m) altitude. Roosting is in trees and cliffs; nesting occurs in holes in limestone cliffs near areas of mixed-conifer forest.

History and Conservation Measures

Habitat destruction has long been considered the primary threat to the maroon-fronted parrot. Fires in the 1970s claimed around half of the available habitat in Sierra de la Marta and Cerro Potosí, two of the parrot's prime areas; much of this pine forest was regenerating by the early 1990s. Logging activity at Las Cuevas in 1989 resulted in breeding failure that year and in considerable devastation to habitat; heavy grazing by goats and other livestock has prevented pinewood regeneration in some areas. There has been considerable clearing of forest in the northern part of the range, while the forests in the south have not been as heavily cleared. If the parrot is indeed migratory between the two, its survival will depend on the preservation of areas of forest in both regions. At present, the bird appears to be under little pressure from hunting or the caged-bird trade.

A large part of the parrot's range is contained within the Cumbres de Monterrey National Park, the largest such park in Mexico, but it is poorly protected and damage to habitat through tree clearance ap-pears to be extensive. The preservation of a number of very large tracts of forest where the species occurs has been urgently recommended, as has formal protection of its nesting cliffs and feeding areas. Research to determine what level of sustained-yield logging the parrot can tolerate may benefit not only the species, but local people who depend on the forests. An education campaign has been urged to develop interest in protecting the species and awareness of the heritage of the region's forests.

Kakapo

Strigops habroptilus

Phylum	Chordata
Class	Aves
Order	Psittaciformes
Family	Psittacidae
Status	Endangered, IUCN
	Endangered, USFWS
	Appendix I, CITES
Range	New Zealand

Description and Biology

Critically endangered, this nocturnal, flightless member of the parrot family was once thought to be extinct. The kakapo is also called the owl-parrot because of the stiff feathers around the eyes that give it an owl-like appearance. The largest and heaviest of all parrots, it is 24-25 in (61-64 cm) long; the male can weigh up to 7.75 lb (3.5 kg), while the female is much lighter, up to 3.3 lb (1.5 kg). Its plumage is patterned in yellow and light green; the tail is darker and barred. The kakapo feeds on many different kinds of plants and flowers, chewing the food with its heavy, serrated bill, instead of grinding it in its gizzard as do other birds.

The breeding habits of the kakapo are complex, mysterious, and not very effective. The male develops a series of trails between odd bowl-shaped depressions in the ground; every few years in January or February, it uses these depressions to broadcast a booming sound which can be heard for over 0.5 mi (1 km). The call sounds throughout the night, for months at a time, while the female tries—often in vain—to discover the location of the male. Once mat-

Kakapo.

ing has taken place, the female lays two to four eggs in a nest of vegetation and raises the chicks alone.

Habitat and Current Distribution

Originally widespread in North, South, and Stewart Islands in New Zealand, the kakapo remains in diminished numbers on Stewart Island, Little Barrier Island, and Codfish Island. No chicks were raised for a number of years until 1991, when an artificial feeding program was instituted on Little Barrier Island. This effort resulted in successfully raising two chicks. In 1992 three chicks were hatched on Codfish Island. The total population is 52-54 birds.

Dense scrub-forest and sub-alpine grasslands are both important to the kakapo, the forests for nesting and shelter, the grasslands for feeding.

History and Conservation Measures

The kakapo's eccentric breeding behavior once served as a natural population control in an environment where the bird had no natural predators and no competition for food. The introduction of competitors such as possums, deer, and chamois, and of predators such as cats, rats, and stoats, have reduced the population to a level where it was considered extinct in the early 1970s.

A breeding population was discovered on Stewart Island in 1976, but its numbers have been greatly reduced by introduced cats. Most remaining birds have been transferred to Codfish Island and Little Barrier Island. Even in this protected environment—and despite intensive management programs—it is uncertain whether the kakapo will survive.

Bannerman's turaco

Tauraco bannermani

Phylum	Chordata
Class	Aves
Order	Cuculiformes
Family	Musophagidae
Status	Endangered, IUCN
Range	Cameroon

Description and Biology

Bannerman's turaco is one of the most beautiful members of its genus. Its back, breast, and wings are golden green. The top of its head and long crest are blood-red and its cheeks and chin are gray. Its underparts are grayish black and its tail is a glossy purplish blue. It has a powerful bill that is yellow with a dark red culmen (edge of the upper bill). Bannerman's turaco is an arboreal rain forest bird that feeds on fruits and berries. Breeding is known to take place in March, but there is little information available about reproductive biology.

Habitat and Current Distribution

This species is only known from the Bamenda-Banso Highlands in western Cameroon, where it is restricted to montane forest, especially in ravines and crater rims. Throughout much of its habitat north of the lowland forest, it is the only turaco to be found. Within its very restricted range, this turaco is fairly plentiful, but it is unlikely that more than a few thousand of these birds exist.

History and Conservation Measures

The type-specimen for this species was collected in the Banso Mountains north of Kumbo in 1922; this and subsequent specimens were taken between altitudes of 6,000-8,000 ft (1,830-2,400 m). Since 1984, Bannerman's turaco has been recorded from Mount Oku, the Sabga Pass, the Bafut-Ngemba Forest Reserve (including Lake Bambulue), the Bali-Ngemba Forest Reserve, and the Bamboutos Mountains. The great bulk of the population occurs on Mount Oku, where the largest area of forest remains.

Forest clearance is a very serious threat to this bird. All of the small remaining tracts of forest in the Bamenda Highlands are now badly damaged; they are being cleared for cultivation, used for wood-cutting, damaged by fires, and overgrazed by cattle, goats, sheep, and horses. Even the more extensive surviving forest on Mount Oku is rapidly being cleared. A major conservation project, coordinated by Birdlife International, has been undertaken on behalf of this species since 1987. This has centered on obtaining the support of local people for forest conservation, and ensuring that the people themselves benefit from both the forest and the turaco.

Congo bay-owl

Phodilus prigoginei

Phylum	Chordata
Class	Aves
Order	Strigiformes
Family	Tytonidae
Status	Indeterminate, IUCN
	Appendix II, CITES
Range	Burundi (?); Zaire

Description and Biology

The bay owls are a poorly known group of species. One species is distributed in Southeast Asia; the other—the Congo bay-owl, a much rarer species—is confined to central Africa. Bay owls have dark chestnut plumage, spotted with black and white; their tail is heavily barred. Their facial disk is whitish, and their beak is compressed. Because the Congo bay-owl is known only from one type-specimen, there is no information about ecology or reproductive biology for this species. Bay owls are thought to be nocturnal, their short wings and tail enabling them to hunt small mammals, birds, and bats through dense forests.

Habitat and Current Distribution

The type-specimen of the Congo bay-owl was collected at Muusi at an altitude of almost 8,000 ft (2,430 m) in the Itombwe Mountains of eastern Zaire; it was found sleeping in the grass of a mountain forest clearing. Population size is unknown.

History and Conservation Measures

Since the type-specimen was collected in 1951, this species has not been located again, despite repeated searches. A possible sighting was reported from the Rwegura Tea Estate in Burundi in the mid-1970s, but it was not confirmed. The owl might possibly occur on other mountains in central Africa.

Given the probability that the Congo bay-owl is very rare, any forest clearance in its supposed habitat could endanger the species' survival. A conservation plan for the forests of the Itombwe Mountains has been prepared for the government of Zaire but has not yet been implemented. Researchers need to undertake a systematic search for this owl in the Itombwe Mountains and other areas in the central African highlands. Once its status is determined and its distribution pinpointed, appropriate measures can be taken to protect its habitat.

Usambara eagle owl

Bubo vosseleri

Phylum	Chordata
Class	Aves
Order	Strigiformes
Family	Strigidae
Status	Rare, IUCN
	Appendix II, CITES
Range	Tanzania

Description and Biology

Very little is known about this large forest owl, also called *nduk* by the local people. Breeding may occur in holes in old trees and appears to be concentrated between November and February. Its diet is thought to include squirrels, galagos, bats, and insects.

The plumage of this species is pale in appearance. Blotching occurs on the breast, and the bars on the underparts are widely spaced. The facial discs are wide and dark; the face yellowish in color; and crown and ears orange-brown, spotted with blackish brown. There are distinctive blackish brown spots on the sides of the upper breast and white spots on the shoulders. Upper parts are flecked with orange-brown.

Habitat and Current Distribution

The Usambara eagle owl is restricted to the East and West Usambara Mountains in northeastern Tanzania, where most records are from altitudes of 2,900-4,900 ft (900-1,500 m). Some have also been found at an altitude of about 985 ft (300 m). All specimens have come from the Amani area, East Usambaras; it has also been recorded on the eastern side of the West Usambaras. Estimates of population vary from a low of 200 birds to a more optimistic estimate of 1,000 birds.

Primary habitat is evergreen montane forest. Several young birds, however, have been found on the ground in areas cleared for cardamom (which is generally grown under an intact forest canopy), suggesting that undisturbed forest may not be essential for its survival.

History and Conservation Measures

After the Usambara eagle owl was first described in 1908, there were no further records of its existence until 1962. It was recorded on nine occasions from 1962 until 1977, and there have been a number of observations since then. Because it is very elusive, it is possible that it may occur in other rain forests in eastern Tanzania. While the population was never considered large, it has probably declined as a result of forest destruction.

Considerable forest clearance has taken place in the forests of the Usambaras, particularly between 1880 and 1935. Originally, the clearance was for subsistence farming; more recently it has been for tea and cardamom cultivation. Other, less significant concerns for the species are the relative scarcity of old trees with holes in which to nest and possible competition for such sites from the widespread silvery-cheeked hornbill (*Bycanistes brevis*).

Many of the remaining forest areas within the species' range are in forest reserves, but the reserves may not be adequately protected. A forest conservation program for the East Usambaras is in process, and population and distribution surveys have been recommended.

Sokoke scops-owl

Otus ireneae

Phylum	Chordata
Class	Aves
Order	Strigiformes
Family	Strigidae
Status	Endangered, IUCN
	Endangered, USFWS
	Appendix II, CITES
Range	Kenya; Tanzania (?)

Description and Biology

This small owl is usually seen perched 10-13 ft (3-4 m) above the ground. It calls most frequently two hours before dawn and two hours after dusk but is sometimes heard throughout the night. Diet is comprised mainly of insects such as crickets. Information on reproductive biology is unavailable.

The Sokoke scops-owl is tawny gray above, with dark facial disks and a blackish area extending from below the eye into the auricular region. The throat and breast are blackish brown, the abdomen and belly paler brownish gray. Black bars line the wings, and prominent white spots decorate the outer webs of the wings. The tarsi feathering is mottled with blackish brown, and the undertail coverts are creamy in color and lightly barred with blackish brown. Bill is pale pink-gray. Wing measures 0.44 in (1.12 cm), with a tail length of 2.6 in (6.5 cm).

Habitat and Current Distribution

The Sokoke scops-owl is known chiefly from the Arabuko-Sokoke Forest in coastal Kenya, where it inhabits lowland *Cynometra-Manilkara* forest. About 43 sq mi (111 sq km) of suitable habitat occurs within the Arabuko-Sokoke Forest Reserve, in which there are estimated to be between 1,000-1,500 pairs. The owl is known to occur in patches of forest to the west and south of the reserve, but these areas are being cleared rapidly. In 1991 a small population believed to be this species was found in the foothills of the Usambara Mountains, Tanzania.

History and Conservation Measures

The first specimen of this species was collected in 1965 in the Arabuko-Sokoke Forest. By 1979 seven specimens had been collected and in recent years it has been seen regularly. All of its habitat has been affected to some degree by logging activities, but the owl has thus far withstood the disturbance. In 1992 the National Museum of Kenya began a study to better understand this species' ecology and behavior.

Since 1989 an international collaboration between Birdlife International (ICBP) and various departments of the Kenyan government has resulted in several conservation actions: forest management policies have been reviewed; nurseries rehabilitated; new bird plantations established; and a broad visitor program instituted. Beginning in 1994, this collaboration will continue with wider interventions such as on-farm tree plantations and conservation education targeted at villages and schools in the area.

Comoro scops-owl

Otus pauliani

Phylum	Chordata
Class	Aves
Order	Strigiformes
Family	Strigidae
Status	Rare, IUCN Appendix II, CITES
Range	Comoro Islands

Description and Biology

The scops owls are a highly diverse group of birds which are widely distributed in western North America, sub-Saharan Africa, northern Europe, and southeast Asia. Scops owls evolved to fill a wide range of niches, which range from open grassland to dense woodland. Many of these species are poorly known; the Comoro scops-owl is only known from a single specimen. Once considered a subspecies of *O. rutilus*, the Comoro scops-owl is known as *ndeu* by the local people. This small owl apparently feeds on insects such as beetles. Nothing is known about the behavior or ecology of this bird.

Habitat and Current Distribution

The Comoro scops-owl is restricted to Grand Comoro, in the Comoro Islands, where it is known only from two locales on Mount Karthala: La Conva-lescence on the west side of the volcano and Kourani on the south side of the volcano. There is no estimate of population size, but numbers are thought to be low. The species' habitat is a forest/heath intergradation zone on Mount Karthala.

History and Conservation Measures

The only specimen of this species was taken from La Convalescence in 1958. Since then, however, the bird has been heard calling both there and above Kourani on the south side of Mount Karthala.

Although its population size is uncertain, this species must be considered at risk because of its highly restricted range; an island population is always vulnerable to disease, habitat disturbance, or natural disaster. Habitat destruction is not considered a problem at the present time.

Northern spotted owl

Strix occidentalis caurina

Phylum . . . . Chordata
Class . . . . Aves
Order . . . . Strigiformes
Family . . . . Strigidae
Status . . . . Indeterminate, IUCN
Threatened, USFWS
Appendix II, CITES
Range . . . . Canada; Washington, Oregon, California (U.S.A.)

Description and Biology

One of three subspecies of the spotted owl (*Strix occidentalis*), the northern spotted owl has chocolate brown plumage that is spotted with white or light brown spots. This owl has a round face and dark eyes surrounded by light facial disks. It averages about 16-19 in (41-48 cm) long, and the wings span to around 42 in (107 cm). The female is slightly larger than the male; these owls are thought to be monogamous and mate for life. Typical clutch size is two, but four have also been observed. Females incubate the eggs and males hunt for food. Juveniles leave the nest in three to five weeks but are cared for by one or both of the adults.

Northern spotted owls have exceptional senses of sight and hearing. Although it is sometimes active during the day, the spotted owl is primarily nocturnal, perching on trees and swooping down to catch their prey. Diet includes birds and insects, but 90 percent of the northern spotted owl's diet is mammals, especially the northern flying squirrel (*Glaucomys sabrinus*). Predators include the great horned owl (*Bubo virginianus*), the northern goshawk (*Accipiter gentilis*), and the red-tailed hawk (*Buteo jamaicensis*); the common raven (*Corvus corax*) preys primarily on juveniles.

Home range is quite large, but it can vary widely with geographic location, food availability, and the amount of suitable habitat available within the range; median figures vary from below 2,000 acres (800 ha) to over 14,000 acres (5,700 ha).

Habitat and Current Distribution

This owl is found from southern British Columbia, Canada, south to Marin County, California; it ranges eastward to the edge of the Palouse prairie in Washington and the Great Basin shrub steppe in Oregon and California. It is found from sea level up to elevations of 5,000 ft (1,500 m) in the northern part of the range and to 7,500 ft (2,300 m) in the southern end. This owl lives almost exclusively in old-growth forests among Douglas fir, western hemlock, and redwood that are over 200 years. They appear to prefer multi-layered canopy. Nesting is dependent upon naturally occurring nest sites, such as broken-top trees and cavities in older forests; in younger forests, which are used less frequently, platforms such as abandoned raptor nests or squirrel nests are used. Roosting is usually in areas of high canopy forest with dense vegetation; the owl can adjust to temperature changes by moving about within the roosting habitat. Feeding habitat is the most variable,

Northern spotted owls.

since it is dependent upon the distribution and abundance of prey. Population is estimated at around 4,000-6,000 individuals.

History and Conservation Measures

The northern spotted owl has been at the center of a heated controversy between environmentalists and timber interests. Timber from old-growth forests is highly valued, and it has been estimated that approximately 80 percent of the old-growth forest in the western Pacific Northwest region had been cleared by the early 1980s. Most of the forest that was on privately owned land has been logged, and the majority of remaining suitable habitat is on public land, where its management is the subject of debate.

Efforts to protect the northern spotted owl have been difficult. Timber industries have argued that conserving old-growth forests will have dire economic consequences. It has been suggested that as many as 12,000 jobs may be lost in the region if laws prevent the cutting of old-growth forests. Environmentalists contend that timber companies are merely postponing the inevitable—at the rate at which they are cutting trees, the old-growth forests will soon

disappear, eventually leaving just as many people unemployed.

The reasons for the spotted owl's preference for old-growth forest are not fully understood; it is obvious, however, that the population is declining as the mature forest is logged. Increasing fragmentation of habitat is resulting in the isolation of populations, and the change in forest composition is facilitating the invasion of a number of predators. For example, the barred owl is better adapted to new growth forest, but it is invading the spotted owl's habitat, resulting in displacement of the spotted owl and increasing the potential for hybridization.

A recovery plan for this species has been recommended. The plan calls for a network of designated areas to be protected as habitat for the spotted owl until the species has reached a healthy number. It also recommends guidelines for forest management on federal lands outside those areas, sets standards for judging when the species has reached recovery, recommends contributions from nonfederal forest lands, and outlines monitoring and research programs to provide further information on the northern spotted owl and its habitat.

Purple-backed sunbeam

Aglaeactis aliciae

Phylum	Chordata
Class	Aves
Order	Apodiformes
Family	Trochilidae
Status	Indeterminate, IUCN Appendix II, CITES
Range	Peru

Description and Biology

A small hummingbird, the purple-backed sunbeam is named for the shade of its lower back and rump. Much of the plumage is dark brown with white and yellow-green markings; the tail is white at the base, turning to reddish brown at the tips. The bird averages just over 2 in (5.2 cm). Nectar is taken from alders (*Alnus* sp.), from an orange-red flowered mistletoe (probably the loranthacean *Tristerix longebrachteatum*), and from a white-flowered leguminaceous bush with oleander-like leaves.

There is no information available about social organization or reproductive biology.

Habitat and Current Distribution

This species is known from specimens taken from the upper río Marañón valley, La Libertad Department, in western Peru. There are no estimates of population size.

Primary habitat is montane shrubbery or wooded grassland at altitudes of 8,000-10,500 ft (2,450-3,200 m).

History and Conservation Measures

The purple-backed sunbeam is known from specimens collected in 1895 and 1932. At the time of the collections, the species was noted to be fairly common. The continued presence of the species near the type-locality was confirmed in 1979, but the status of the population today remains undocumented.

Because of its extremely limited range, this hummingbird would appear to be vulnerable to habitat destruction, but the condition of its habitat is unknown. Other related species have adapted well to human presence and feed from areas near agricultural fields and settlements, so it is possible that the purple-backed sunbeam can tolerate some degree of habitat alteration. No conservation measures have been taken on behalf of this species; its status and habitat should be investigated, as should the extent to which it can thrive in secondary habitats.

White-tailed sabrewing

Campylopterus ensipennis

Phylum	Chordata
Class	Aves
Order	Apodiformes
Family	Trochilidae
Status	Vulnerable/Rare, IUCN
	Appendix II, CITES
Range	Trinidad and Tobago; Venezuela

Description and Biology

The white-tailed sabrewing is a large humming-bird, averaging just over 6 inches (16 cm) in length. It is bright green, with a purple throat and a white tail with a black base; the female, with grayish underparts, is somewhat less conspicuous. This sabrewing eats nectar from a variety of flowering plants and also feeds on small insects.

Only a few observations have been made about the bird's reproductive biology. Its breeding has only been observed on the island of Tobago, where sabrewing nests were found, and females were observed incubating their eggs, in the month of February. At this time, male birds were in song. But singing also was prominent during April in Tobago, while in Venezuela males exhibited territoriality during July-September, at which time female birds were seldom encountered, as they were presumably nesting.

Habitat and Current Distribution

The white-tailed sabrewing is found in Venezuela as well as the island of Tobago off the northeastern Venezuelan coast. In Venezuela, it is restricted to two areas: the Cordillera de Caripe, an eastern coastal mountain range which runs along the borders of Anzoátegui, Monagas, and Sucre provinces; and the mountains of the Paria Peninsula. There are no esti-

mates of population, but the species seems to be plentiful in areas containing suitable habitat.

This sabrewing's primary habitat is montane forest, a woodland ecosystem found on moist upland slopes. Often recorded in mature secondary growth and in plantations at lower altitudes, the bird also flourishes in various forest types at higher altitudes. Precise habitat requirements of the species are unknown. Birds have been seen perching on exposed twigs in open areas as well as shrubs in the dense understory of closed-canopy forests.

History and Conservation Measures

This hummingbird has a history of abundance on the Paria Peninsula, where it is still abundant in suitable habitat. In the Cordillera de Caripe, it was historically common, but its status today is not well known. Formerly a common resident of hill forest on Tobago, the sabrewing population was negatively affected for at least a decade by Hurricane Flora in 1963, which devastated all but a few bits of the bird's habitat.

This species is only one of several within its range which are considered threatened by habitat destruction. In the Corcillera de Caripe, widespread clearing of montane forest for agriculture under increasing population pressure is reducing available habitat. On Tobago, the effects of the hurricane are still being felt; as forest regenerates, suitable habitat for the hummingbirds may continue to increase, provided that forest destruction for cash-crop agriculture can be held in check there.

Three national parks exist within this species' range, El Guácharo National Park and Paria Peninsula National Park in Venezuela, and East Tobago National Park. Unfortunately, the parks provide little protection from cultivation or hunting.

The most essential step in preserving the white-tailed sabrewing remains the protection of remaining habitat. On the mainland, an approach considering the needs of all the threatened native bird species is probably wisest; but since the species are poorly understood, a great deal of study will be required to determine what these needs are. In Tobago, protection will best be achieved by curbing the encroachment of agricultural and grazing land. Habitat preservation there could also benefit a threatened endemic variety of the striped owl (*Asio clamator oberi*).

Black-breasted puffleg

Eriocnemis nigrivestris

Phylum	Chordata
Class	Aves
Order	Apodiformes
Family	Trochilidae
Status	Endangered, IUCN
	Appendix II, CITES
Range	Ecuador

Description and Biology

Although this hummingbird appears almost black, the female actually has shades from light to deep greenish blue, and the male is a deep, almost purplish blue. Head and body length averages just under 4 in (10 cm). The black-breasted puffleg takes nectar from a wide variety of vegetation and catches small insects.

Although nothing is known about its reproductive biology, most hummingbird species in the region breed between October and March.

Habitat and Current Distribution

The black-breasted puffleg is restricted to two adjacent volcanoes in northwest Ecuador, Volcán Pichincha and Volcán Atacazo. From April to June, it can be found at altitudes of 9,000-10,000 ft (2,745-3,050 m), and from November to February it inhabits altitudes of 10,000-15,000 ft (3,100-4,570 m). There is no estimate of population, and the only recent sightings were of three birds on Pichincha in 1992.

Black-breasted puffleg.

Dwelling in humid temperate forests and forest edges, the puffleg prefers undergrowth abundant with flowering plants, especially the understory found on the crests of mountain ridges.

History and Conservation Measures

Although there are no estimates of its initial population, the large number of specimens collected in the past suggests that this puffleg may have been fairly abundant once. It is probably vanishing rapidly as its specialized habitat is destroyed by human activity. In the region of Ecuador inhabited by the black-breasted puffleg, the tops of mountain ridges are cleared rapidly because they provide some of the only flat ground available for cultivation. Even on Cerro Pugsi, the primary site with recent records, clearing is now progressing.

No conservation efforts have yet been made on behalf of the black-breasted puffleg. Protecting its remaining habitat is crucial, as is conducting research about its ecological requirements, including its breeding sites and seasonal movements between altitudes. The species could become extinct if conservation action is not taken soon.

White-tailed hummingbird

Eupherusa poliocerca

Phylum	Chordata
Class	Aves
Order	Apodiformes
Family	Trochilidae
Status	Insufficiently Known, IUCN
Range	Mexico

Description and Biology

The white-tailed hummingbird is distinguished from other members of the genus by its larger size and by the color pattern of its tail. Its secondary feathers are reddish in color. The slender bill is used to take nectar from flowering plants in the forest. Breeding season apparently peaks between February and May and then again in September and October.

Habitat and Current Distribution

This species is found on the Pacific slope of the Sierra Madre del Sur, in Guerrero and westernmost Oaxaca states, Mexico. Although population size is unknown, it is generally considered to be fairly common but extremely localized in distribution.

Habitat includes cloud forest, evergreen subtropical forest, semi-humid forest, and forest edges. The species may engage in seasonal movements and is probably marginal or seasonal at lower altitudes of around 4,000 ft (1,200 m) in tropical semi-deciduous forest. It seems to require virgin forest and, in some areas, is most commonly found in heavily vegetated humid canyons.

History and Conservation Measures

For a time after its discovery in 1875, this hummingbird was thought to be quite rare, but later assessments determined it to be very local and to be common within a limited distribution. It inhabits one of the largest tracts of virgin cloud forest left in Mexico, but it is threatened by forest destruction. Forest in the lower altitudes of the species' range is rapidly being cleared for cultivation, and higher elevation forest is being logged at an alarming rate.

The white-tailed hummingbird is apparently common within the Omiltemi State Ecological Park, and it also may occur in the Guerrero National Park, but this park is poorly protected and suffers from extensive habitat degradation. Any remaining cloud forest habitat in the Para-so-Chilpancingo-Putla de Guerrero region needs to be given some form of protection from indiscriminate cutting and burning, and priority should be given to the areas where the species is currently known to occur. Surveys should be undertaken in all suitable habitat to determine the actual distribution of the species and the extent of remaining habitat, which is also important for a number of other threatened birds.

Hook-billed hermit

Ramphodon (Glaucis) dohrnii

Phylum	Chordata
Class	Aves
Order	Apodiformes
Family	Trochilidae
Status	Vulnerable/Rare, IUCN
	Endangered, USFWS
	Appendix I, CITES
Range	Brazil

Description and Biology

This hummingbird is called a hermit because of its preference for closed-canopy forests. It is a small bird, about 4 in (10 cm) in length with a bill typically about 1 in (2.5 cm) long. The upperparts of the hook-billed hermit are bronze green and the underparts are cinnamon with dusky speckles on the sides of the abdomen. Its rump feathers are fringed buff, and it has a conspicuous white postocular streak on its head. This hermit's tail is reddish bronze; in the male, each tail feather is tipped in white. The hook-billed hermit is an agile flier, able to hover and fly backwards. It consumes nectar from ornamental flowering trees and lemon trees and seems to prefer *Heliconia* plants in particular.

Clutch size is thought to be one or two. Incubation period is between 14-16 days and fledgling period somewhere from 20-30 days.

Habitat and Current Distribution

This species is endemic to the Atlantic forest region of southeastern Brazil from Bahia, south of Salvador, to Espírito Santo and possibly eastern Minas Gerais and Rio de Janeiro state. There are no reliable estimates of population, but it is considered to be on the verge of extinction.

The hook-billed hermit inhabits lowland primary forest. It has been observed in the interior of closed-canopy forest and has been found in damp areas along stream beds.

Hook-billed hermit.

History and Conservation Measures

While it was once certainly more abundant than it is today, this species was probably always rare. In the 1960s it was considered the most endangered hummingbird species; it was said to be restricted to the Córrego do Veado Biological Reserve, where no more than 50 birds were believed to exist (and where it has not been found subsequently). In the 1970s, the Fazenda Klabin forest was considered its stronghold and sheltered an estimated population of 20 birds; that population was estimated at 40 in the 1980s. It is no longer found there today. A population was discovered in 1986 in the CVRD Porto Seguro Reserve, where its status has not been confirmed.

Massive deforestation has and continues to threaten the survival of this species. Even where it occurs in reserves, it is apparently not secure. The privately-owned forest at Fazenda Klabin, now the Córrego Grande Biological Reserve, was reduced in the 1970s and 1980s from 10,000 acres (4,000 ha) to only 3,000 acres (1,200 ha) and now includes no significant watercourse except along its periphery. The Monte Pascoal National Park is also under severe pressure. The CVRD Porto Seguro Reserve, although generally well maintained, has been under severe pressure from squatters and has suffered from fire and the construction of forest roads. Fire spreading from the surrounding farm land is a permanent threat to the Córrego do Veado Biological Reserve.

Remnant populations can probably survive if their habitat is preserved. Support for known key sites is imperative. Searches for additional populations should also be conducted.

Juan Fernández firecrown

Sephanoides fernandensis

Phylum	Chordata
Class	Aves
Order	Apodiformes
Family	Trochilidae
Status	Vulnerable/Rare, IUCN
Range	Juan Fernández Islands (Chile)

Description and Biology

This hummingbird is named for the patch of iridescent ruby red on its forehead and crown. Males are a uniform rusty rufous, while females are green and white. In addition to being a nectar eater, it takes small insects from leaves or while in flight.

Habitat and Current Distribution

Native to the Juan Fernández archipelago in the eastern Pacific, off the coast of Chile, the Juan Fernández firecrown is now limited to a 2,700 acre (1,100 ha) tract on Isla Robinson Crusoe (Masatierra). Population was estimated in 1989 at fewer than 700 birds.

This hummingbird prefers native forest with a large proportion of endemic plants, but the firecrown sometimes utilizes exotic plants in urban areas, especially in the fall and winter when fewer forest flowers are in bloom.

History and Conservation Measures

The Juan Fernández firecrown once also occurred on Isla Alejandro Selkirk (Masafuera), but it has not been recorded there since 1908 and is considered extinct; it was also once more plentiful than today on Isla Robinson Crusoe (Masatierra). Reasons for the species' decline include degradation of the natural vegetation cover as a result of human activity, introduced plants, and animals such as cattle, rats, cats, and the coati.

About 90 percent of the archipelago lies within the Archipielago de Juan Fernández National Park, where a program has been established to protect and propagate the endemic endangered vegetation, to conduct education campaigns, and to carry out an ongoing survey of the hummingbird. More information on how introduced plants and predators affect this hummingbird are needed. In addition, elimination of introduced predators such as coatis, as well as control of other predators and competitors, may aid the recovery of the species.

Resplendent quetzal

Pharomachrus mocinno

Phylum	Chordata
Class	Aves
Order	Trogoniformes
Family	Trogonidae
Status	Indeterminate, IUCN
	Endangered, USFWS
	Appendix I, CITES
Range	Mexico; Guatemala; Honduras; El Salvador; Nicaragua; Costa Rica; Panama

Description and Biology

This beautiful forest bird was worshipped by Mayan and Aztec civilizations as god of the air. Although both males and females have brilliant green upperparts, the coloration of the rest of the body differs by gender. Females have brown breasts and bellies with fairly short, black and white tails. Males, by contrast, have orange-red breasts and bellies and a magnificent, 3 ft (1 m) long tail that matches the green on the upperparts. This tail was used in religious ceremonies by both the Maya and the Aztec and was incorporated into the image of the god Quetzalcoatl.

The resplendent quetzal averages 13.75-15 in (35-38 cm) in length at physical maturity. It feeds mainly on fruit—perhaps only certain kinds—but supplements the fruit with the occasional invertebrate or small vertebrate. The bird usually stays in the canopy of the humid cloud forest that makes up its habitat, with its green upperparts providing perfect camouflage. These territorial birds occupy a home range of 15-25 acres (6-10 ha), which is patrolled by the male each morning and evening.

The male flutters his long tail during courtship displays. Nests are built in natural cavities of tree stumps, and the female lays two blue eggs between March and June. Both birds are responsible for caring for the eggs during the incubation period of 17-19 days.

Habitat and Current Distribution

The resplendent quetzal's range includes Mexico, Guatemala, Honduras, El Salvador, Nicaragua, Cost Rica, and Panama. Population estimates are unavailable.

The bird's preferred habitat is wet, tropical cloud forest, usually from 4,000-10,000 ft (1,200-3,000 m) elevation, although it occasionally wanders into partially cleared areas or pastures adjacent to the forest.

History and Conservation Measures

Although the resplendent quetzal has long been revered by people throughout its range for its beauty and religious significance, its survival has been threatened by the clearing of its cloud forest habitat. Legal protections exist but are difficult to enforce because of the remoteness of the bird's habitat. However, the quetzal has been designated as Guatemala's national bird, and cloud forests are now protected in various areas in Mexico, Guatemala, and Costa Rica.

In addition, the quetzal has recently been delisted by both the IUCN and Birdlife International (ICBP). These measures suggest that this bird now has a safe habitat and a stable population.

Resplendent quetzal.

Helmeted hornbill

Buceros (Rhinoplax) vigil

Phylum	Chordata
Class	Aves
Order	Coraciiformes
Family	Bucerotidae
Status	Indeterminate, IUCN Endangered, USFWS Appendix I, CITES
Range	Brunei; Kalimantan, Sumatra (Indonesia); Peninsular Malaysia, Sabah, Sarawak (Malaysia); Myanmar; Thailand

Description and Biology

The helmeted hornbill is a large bird with a distinctive casque on its long bill. An unmistakable bird, the hornbill measures about 47.3 in (120 cm) with central elongated tail streamers measuring another 19.7 in (50 cm). Hornbills may weigh more than 6.5 lb (3 kg). General color of the bird is brown, with white underparts, a white tail banded in black, and two long, light brown tail feathers. Its neck and head are greenish; its casque and bill are deep red. This red pigment is secreted from a gland at the base of the tail and wiped by the bird onto its casque and bill. An unusual call includes a series of loud hooting noises. Each pair requires a large range of 740-1,200 acres (300-500 ha). Diet includes fruit, small mammals, small birds, and insects. The heavy bill is useful for reaching fruits, catching prey, and probing foliage for insects.

The female lays one white egg in a cavity excavated in a tree. She remains in the tree with the egg, and the entrance to the nest is sealed—except for a small opening—with mixed and hardened mud and saliva. The male passes food through this opening using its long bill. The mother and chick stay in the nest for 12-14 weeks. The immature hornbill does not leave its parents for two to three years, at which time the pair breeds again.

Habitat and Current Distribution

Population figures are unknown. It may be fairly abundant in parts of Sumatra and in southern Thailand but is believed to be declining in southern Myanmar, Peninsular Malaysia, Borneo, and Sumatra, though it is still common in some of these areas.

Habitat includes primary forest and closed canopy forest in lowlands and in hills up to an altitude of 5,000 ft (1,500 m).

History and Conservation Measures

The very uniqueness of this bird has always made it vulnerable to threats from humans. Hornbill ivory has been collected and carved by forest people for adornment for thousands of years and is valuable as a trade item. It is legally protected in Indonesia and Malaysia, but hunting pressure remains.

An even greater threat to this bird's existence is loss of habitat. Primary forests are being destroyed at an accelerating rate for lumber and agricultural development. The closed canopy forests necessary for the helmeted hornbill's survival are disappearing over most of its range.

Imperial woodpecker

Campephilus imperialis

Phylum	Chordata
Class	Aves
Order	Piciformes
Family	Picidae
Status	Endangered/Extinct, IUCN
	Endangered, USFWS
	Appendix I, CITES
Range	Mexico

Description and Biology

The imperial woodpecker, if it still exists, is the largest woodpecker in the world. It reaches up to 22 in (57 cm) in length and has a black and white body. The male has a bright red crest; the female has a black crest that curls forward. Both sexes have yellow eyes and a strong, heavy bill. The bill is used to strip bark from dead trees and to dig into the wood to capture and feed on insects and grubs.

Because of the rarity of this bird, breeding activities have not been studied. It is probable that, like the ivory-billed woodpecker (*Campephilus principalis*), the imperial woodpecker uses its bill to excavate nests in mature pine trees and that both sexes share in incubating and raising the young.

Habitat and Current Distribution

Sporadic sightings of the imperial woodpecker have been reported in its former territory in the highlands of northwestern Mexico. The continued existence of the species is uncertain.

Habitat is mature forest of pine and oak trees at an altitude above 6,500 ft (2,000 m) in the north and 8,200 ft (2,500 m) in the south.

History and Conservation Measures

Because each pair requires as much as 20 sq mi (25 sq km) of territory, this bird was probably never common, but it did range from northwest Chihuahua to Michoacan. The last confirmed sighting was in 1958, and there were unconfirmed reports of sightings until the mid-1970s.

The causes of the decline of this species are interrelated. Logging in the forests has disturbed the bird's habitat, but the forest has been harvested selectively, leaving some mature trees for nesting. While theoretically this should preserve habitat, in reality logging roads open up the forests to humans, who then hunt the imperial woodpecker for food. These twin factors may have pushed the imperial woodpecker into extinction.

Surveys are needed to confirm whether the species still survives. There are three general areas that appear most likely to harbor the species: 1) the area around the Sonora-Chihuahua border; 2) the main part of the Sierra Madre Occidental in northern Durango, north and west of Santiago Papasquiaro; and 3) the southern part of the Sierra de los Huicholes, north of the Rio Grande de Santiago in northern Jalisco.

Ivory-billed woodpecker

Campephilus principalis

Phylum	Chordata
Class	Aves
Order	Piciformes
Family	Picidae
Status	Endangered/Extinct, IUCN
	Endangered, USFWS
Range	Cuba; U.S.A.

Description and Biology

The ivory-billed woodpecker is the largest North American woodpecker. It averages up to 19.5 in (50 cm) in length and has a black and white body. Males have a bright red crest; females have a black crest. The strong, heavy bill is used to strip bark from dead or dying trees to feed on the larvae of engraver beetles. Pairs occupy a large territory of up to 4,000 acres (1,600 ha).

For nesting—a season that lasts from March to June—the woodpecker uses its bill to excavate a cavity high up in a tree. Two to three eggs are incubated by both parents for about 20 days; young are cared for by both parents until they fledge at around 35 days.

Habitat and Current Distribution

This woodpecker is extremely rare in Cuba and may be extinct in the United States. The Cuban subspecies (*Campephilus principalis bairdii*) may still survive in very small numbers in eastern Cuba, although it is possibly extinct. In the southeastern United States, unconfirmed sightings of *Campephilus principalis principalis* have encouraged the hope that a remnant population might possibly survive somewhere in remote forests in Louisiana, South Carolina, Mississippi, Georgia, or Florida.

In the United States, the ivory-billed woodpecker occupies mature bottomland hardwood swamp forest and, on occasion, pinewoods and second growth forest. In Cuba, the bird has been found in mixed pine and hardwood forests.

History and Conservation Measures

In the United States, this species has always been considered rare throughout its range. It declined rapidly from the late 1800s and early 1900s. In 1941, the population was estimated at 24 birds in five scattered localities; in 1948 the last identified population disappeared from a tract in Louisiana when the land was cleared for soybean cultivation.

In Cuba, the ivory-billed woodpecker is thought to have once occurred over much of the suitable habitat on the island. By 1956, only 12-13 birds were thought to survive. In 1986, three birds were observed in eastern Cuba. Surveys during the early 1990s in the Sierra de Moa—the bird's last known refuge—proved fruitless; however, in 1991 some evidence of damaged tree bark was found, suggesting the possible presence of woodpeckers.

The primary cause of this bird's decline is loss of suitable habitat. Logging and clearing of virgin swamp forests have made it difficult for a bird requiring a large territory to survive. This species does not seem to be able to adapt to smaller forest areas,

Ivory-billed woodpecker.

and it usually dies out when suitable habitat disappears. Hunters and trappers also contributed to its decline. Long-term survival in the United States is unlikely and, in Cuba, doubtful. No conservation plans have been formulated, as sighting reports are being evaluated in an attempt to determine whether the ivory-billed woodpecker survives or is already extinct.

Helmeted woodpecker

Dryocopus galeatus

Phylum	Chordata
Class	Aves
Order	Piciformes
Family	Picidae
Status	Vulnerable/Rare, IUCN
Range	Argentina; Brazil; Paraguay

Description and Biology

This woodpecker is named for the reddish tan coloration that seems to form a helmet on its head and the bright red color of its crest and nape. It is predominantly black above, except for the lower back and upper tail, and yellow-brown below; there are black lines on the sides of the head and black bars on the underparts. Body length averages around 12 in (30 cm). Diet has not yet been reported.

Very little is known about this species' social organization or reproductive biology. It was thought to breed between November and February, but the only confirmed breeding record is from late September and early October.

Habitat and Current Distribution

The helmeted woodpecker is endemic to the southern Atlantic Forest region of southeast Brazil, eastern Paraguay, and northeast Argentina. The population in the adjacent Iguaçu and Iguazú National Parks in Brazil and Argentina seems likely to be the largest and safest, but the bird is rare even there. It also occurs in the Serra de Paranapiacaba and on Ilha do Cardoso, where there appears to be a very small but stable population.

Preferred habitat includes misty cloud forest, valleys, and mountains. Despite isolated sightings at higher elevations, the bird is primarily restricted to forest at 130-650 ft (40-200 m). Many recent sightings have been from very modified areas, some of them adjacent to towns, but the species still appears to need patches of pristine forest or at least logged forest which still retains some characteristics of pristine forest.

History and Conservation Measures

The status of the helmeted woodpecker is not well known. Long believed to be a rare or very rare species, perhaps on the verge of extinction, this woodpecker has been reported more frequently in recent years, leading to the speculation that it may not be as rare as had been feared. The historical rarity of the bird may be linked to its particular habitat specialization. It was once assumed that this bird required large tracts of forest, but it has recently been observed in fairly small, and sometimes disturbed, forested areas, suggesting that habitat loss may not be as serious a threat as suspected.

Protected under Brazilian law, the woodpecker has been recorded in Carlos Botelho State Park, Ilha do Cardoso State Park, and Iguaçu National Park in Brazil; the Itabo Reserve in Paraguay; and Iguazú National Park and Araucaria Provincial Park in Argentina, where it probably also occurs in Urugua-í and Moconá Provincial Parks. In Argentina, it also occurs in four areas that are proposed for protection.

Red-cockaded woodpecker

Picoides (Dendrocopos) borealis

Phylum	Chordata
Class	Aves
Order.	Piciformes
Family	Picidae
Status	Endangered, IUCN
	Endangered, USFWS
Range	Alabama, Arkansas, Florida, Georgia, Louisiana, Mississippi, North
	Carolina, South Carolina, Texas (U.S.A.)

Description and Biology

The red-cockaded woodpecker is black with white bars above and white below with black-flecked sides. A black crown and a prominent black band from the bill down the side of the neck nearly encircle a large white patch on the sides of the woodpecker's head. The male possesses tiny red patches, or "cockades," on the sides of its head, which the female lacks. About 7 in (18 cm) in length, the red-cockaded woodpecker feeds on insects in and below tree bark, as well as fruits, berries, and seeds.

These woodpeckers are unusually social, nesting colonially in groups called clans, which are composed of a breeding pair, their fledglings, and immature male offspring from previous years called "helpers." These helpers assist in incubating and raising the young. Clans forage over territories of approximately 100-200 acres (40-80 ha). This bird is the only woodpecker which chisels its nesting holes only in living pine trees; in April or May, two to five eggs are laid in these nesting cavities and incubated for approximately ten days.

Habitat and Current Distribution

The red-cockaded woodpecker is found in the southeastern United States from Texas and Arkansas to the southern Atlantic Coast. The largest concentrations can be found in Florida and South Carolina. Population is estimated to be around 7,400 birds.

Habitat for nesting and roosting is old-growth pine forest with a low or open understory that is maintained by recurring natural fires. Trees selected for nesting are usually infected by heartwood fungus, which weakens the wood, aiding the bird's nesting effort.

History and Conservation Measures

This woodpecker was once considered abundant throughout a range that stretched from Oklahoma, southern Missouri, Kentucky, Virginia, and Maryland to the Gulf Coast states and Florida. At the turn of the century, the bird's numbers began to decline, fragmenting into a number of local populations. Before 1989, population was estimated at 2,000 colonies, but the largest group of colonies (in the Francis Marion National Forest, South Carolina), comprising as much as 25 percent of the bird's population, was devastated by Hurricane Hugo in late 1989. A program to erect artificial nest cavities helped to reduce the hurricane's destructive impact, but since the hurricane, the Apalachicola National Forest in Florida, with at least 33 percent of the remaining population, has been considered the woodpecker's major stronghold.

Habitat for this species has steadily declined as forests have been clear cut and replanted with faster growing hardwood trees. Woodpecker colonies require sizeable tracts of old-growth forest with little understory and trees 75-100 years old suitable for nesting; current Forest Service policy, which supports the harvesting of younger trees and discourages the incidence of fire which clears undergrowth, does little to insure that necessary habitat will be maintained.

A conservation plan for the red-cockaded woodpecker must attempt to preserve and increase the extent of old-growth pine forest as well as protect corridors between tracts of forest. Such a program could include measures such as a ban on clear-cutting near active woodpecker colonies, fostering old-growth by extending cutting rotations to 75 to 90 years, and cutting of hardwoods that compete with pines.

Red-cockaded woodpecker.

Okinawa woodpecker

Sapheopipo noguchii

Phylum	Chordata
Class	Aves
Order	Piciformes
Family	Picidae
Status	Endangered, IUCN
Range	Okinawa (Japan)

Description and Biology

Description and information on reproductive biology unavailable.

Habitat and Current Distribution

This species is restricted to Yambaru, in the northern part of Okinawa, Ryukyu Islands, where it inhabits moist, evergreen hill forest. It appears to prefer undisturbed forest but has been known to forage in secondary forest. The population has been reported to be as low as 40 and as high as 200 birds, but the latter figure is probably optimistic.

History and Conservation Measures

This woodpecker apparently has been quite rare since the early 1900s and has been restricted to the northern part of Okinawa. Its population has decreased and its range contracted and fragmented because of forest clearing and burning; much of the clearing has been a result of agricultural development and woodcutting for fuel. The establishment of forest reserves is essential to this species, which is thought to be nearing extinction.

African green broadbill

Pseudocalyptomena graueri

Phylum	Chordata
Class	Aves
Order	Passeriformes
Family	Eurylaimidae
Status	Rare, IUCN
Range	Uganda; Zaire

Description and Biology

The African green or Grauer's broadbill is a stout green bird with a broad head, flat bill, and large eyes. It readily approaches human settlements, but is difficult to see as it is well camouflaged in the foliage of trees. Therefore, the species is usually first identified by its characteristic call. The bird, however, makes no sound while flying short distances of 30-100 ft (10-30 m) between trees. At times foraging in mixed-species parties, the African green broadbill primarily feeds on fruit and insects, though the exact types vary by location.

Little is known of reproductive biology, but breeding season is thought to be prolonged.

Habitat and Current Distribution

The African green broadbill has been located in three mountain ranges: the Itombwe Mountains, the mountains west of Lake Kivu in eastern Zaire, and the mountains of the Impenetrable (or Bwindi) Forest in southwestern Uganda. No population estimates currently exist, but the species is considered common in parts of the Itombwe Mountains.

In the Itombwe Mountains, members of the species can usually be observed in small groups of three to ten birds in the middle story and canopy of the forest edge up to 65 ft (20 m) off the ground. The African green broadbill may also inhabit isolated trees in clearings and fields, and it appears to avoid the densest parts of the forest. Although the overall range in Itombwe is from 5,700-8,100 ft (1,760-2,480 m), most specimens have been observed between 6,300-7,800 ft (1,940-2,390 m). In the Impenetrable Forest, the African green broadbill lives about 6-10 ft (2-3 m) above the ground in the upper portions of the forest interior's undergrowth, though it may occasionally fly up to the canopy.

History and Conservation Measures

In 1908, ornithologists collected the type-specimen for the African green broadbill in the Itombwe Mountains. The pattern of specimens collected since then indicates a rather localized distribution in these mountains. In 1959 the bird was located in Uganda when a specimen was collected at 6,500 ft (2,000 m) near the Bwindi Swamp in the Impenetrable Forest.

Forest destruction is currently considered the primary threat to the African green broadbill. In the Itombwe Mountains of Zaire, the town of Kamituga has become an important mining center, a development that may lead to further economic exploitation of the area. However, a greater threat may be posed by clearance around villages higher in the mountains. No recent information on the conservation status of these forests exists.

The Kahuzi-Biega National Park in Zaire is

thought to protect a population of this species in the mountains west of Lake Kivu. Plans exist for the conservation of the forests on the Itombwe Mountains, but have not yet been implemented. The Impenetrable Forest recently has been declared a national park and is now the focus of a very effective conservation project that includes local human communities. Measures to protect these habitats will also be important for other threatened bird species.

White-browed tit-spinetail

Leptasthenura xenothorax

Phylum	Chordata
Class	Aves
Order	Passeriformes
Family	Furnariidae
Status	Endangered, IUCN
Range	Peru

Description and Biology

The white-browed tit-spinetail is predominantly black with white markings on the back and throat; the top of the head and upper back are reddish in color, and its underparts are gray. This bird's common name is derived from the white markings around the eyes. The tit-spinetail forages in pairs or in family groups of three or four individuals. Its diet is comprised mainly of insects plucked from the bark of trees, branches, moss, and lichens. Little is known about this species in the wild. It has been observed chasing away other birds from its feeding area. This trait may be natural but it may be exaggerated by the lack of habitat and diminishing food supply. Both sexes vocalize frequently. It is not known if this bird builds a nest; it occupies abandoned nests of canasteros and thornbirds or holes in tree trunks or other crevices. The breeding season is uncertain.

Habitat and Current Distribution

This species is known from a very small area in Cuzco and Apurímac provinces in south-central Peru. It prefers a habitat with abundant *Polylepis* trees. There are no estimates of total population size, but there are recent estimates of known individual populations. In 1987 the population southwest of Abra Málaga was estimated at 15 families or around 50 birds; Chaiñapuerto held 10 families or around 35 birds; in 1989 the wooded area of Yanacocha was estimated to hold 20 families or around 70 birds. Canchaillo held only one family of three birds and none were found in the wooded region north-north-east of Abra Málaga. Other small woodlands in the Vilcanota mountains may contain additional populations. In the woodlands southeast of Abancay, the bird occurs at very low densities, and in 1989 only 25 pairs were estimated to occur in the entire region.

Almost all observations of the white-browed tit-spinetail are from *Polylepis* and *Polylepis-Gynoxys* trees. The woodland at Chaiñapuerto is in a semi-humid glacial valley with *Polylepis weberbaueri* forest at the valley bottom. The wood southwest of Abra Málaga is semi-humid, comprising mainly of *Polylepis*. In Apurímac, birds were found primarily in patches of dense, mature woodlands of *Polylepis incana* and *P. subsericans*.

History and Conservation Measures

Once considered the same species as the rusty-crowned tit-spinetail (*L. pileata pileata*), the white-browed tit-spinetail was first discovered in 1915 and was not seen for the next 59 years. It presumably occurs in any patch of *Polylepis* between or near the known localities, but the size and exact location of these patches have not yet been defined. A survey to assess possible additional populations of this bird has been recommended. The major threat to the white-browed tit-spinetail is habitat destruction. *Polylepis* species are collected almost daily by the local people for firewood. Regeneration of the trees has proven difficult due to animal grazing and fires resulting from grass burning. In Urubamba, native tree species have been replaced by commercially valuable *Eucalyptus*.

Conservation priority for this bird is the protection of its remaining habitat, and reforestation with *Polylepis* has been recommended in several key areas, including woodlands in Apurímac province. This area is also inhabited by two other threatened *Polylepis*-adapted bird species: the ash-breasted tit-tyrant (*Anairetes alpinus*) and royal cinclodes (*Cinclodes aricomae*), and both birds could benefit from the protection of the *Polylepis* trees.

Alagoas foliage-gleaner

Philydor novaesi

Phylum	Chordata
Class	Aves
Order	Passeriformes
Family	Furnariidae
Status	Endangered, IUCN
Range	Brazil

Description and Biology

The Alagoas foliage-gleaner is usually found in pairs or in small groups among mixed-species flocks. An insectivore, it forages on the leaves, branches and trunk, and under the bark of trees. The reproductive biology of this species has not been examined.

Habitat and Current Distribution

This species only occurs in Murici in Alagoas, northeastern Brazil. Population size is unknown, but it is thought to be very small.

The Alagoas foliage-gleaner has been observed in the forest interior, from the undergrowth to the canopy of the mid-story trees. It also frequents areas of secondary growth, such as selectively-logged and old secondary forests.

History and Conservation Measures

First identified from two specimens collected in 1979, this species is only known from these and four additional specimens collected in the same area in the 1980s. The only additional reports are a few sightings from the early 1990s. The Alagoa foliage-gleaner has never been seen in the nearby lowland forests on the coast, although these have been explored by ornithologists.

The greatest threat to the upland fauna of Alagoas is the destruction of forest in the vicinity of Murici. All of the forest at lower altitudes has been cleared for the cultivation of sugarcane, while the remaining forest at high altitudes is under pressure from logging operations, firewood removal, and small-scale cultivation. One critical area for the Alagoas foliage-gleaner, once over 17,000 acres (7,000 ha) in size, is nearly gone. The remaining 3,700 acres (1,500 ha), while protected by law from further destruction, was still being damaged by small-scale logging operations in 1992.

This species is protected under Brazilian law, but the best hope for its survival is the protection of its remaining habitat. This is now happening through the alliance of a number of non-governmental organizations working with support from the World Wildlife Fund.

Táchira antpitta

Grallaria chthonia

Phylum	Chordata
Class	Aves
Order	Passeriformes
Family	Formicariidae
Status	Endangered, IUCN
Range	Venezuela

Description and Biology

This antpitta is about 6.5 in (17 cm) in length. The crown and nape of its head are gray, its throat is brown, its back is olive scaled with black, and its breast and sides are whitish, lightly barred with gray. Nothing is known of social structure or reproductive biology.

Habitat and Current Distribution

The Táchira antpitta is known from only four specimens collected in the Andes of westernmost Venezuela. There is no estimate of population size. The specimens were found between 5,900-6,900 ft (1,800-2,100 m) in the dense cloud forest of the subtropical zone.

History and Conservation Measures

This antpitta has been found only at a single location in Hacienda La Providencia, where four specimens were collected in 1955 and 1956. It has apparently not been sighted since these collections, despite some specific searches carried out in 1990.

Since next to nothing is known about the distribution or ecological requirements of this antpitta, threats to the species are difficult to evaluate. Though the bird's only known habitat lies in El Tamá National Park, which contains essentially virgin forest above 5,200 ft (1,600 m), deforestation in the region has been taking place rapidly and the park itself is at risk.

The distribution, population status and ecological requirements of the Táchira antpitta will have to be studied before its conservation needs can be fully understood. In the meantime, enforced preservation of forests in this region needs to be initiated. Studies and conservation programs begun on behalf of the Táchira antpitta should be merged with those carried out for other threatened species in the region.

Ash-throated antwren

Herpsilochmus parkeri

Phylum	Chordata
Class	Aves
Order	Passeriformes
Family	Formicariidae
Status	Endangered, IUCN
Range	Peru

Description and Biology

The ash-throated antwren is a relatively large bird measuring about 4.5-5 in (11.5-13 cm) in length and weighing around 0.40 oz (11.5 g). The male of the species is generally gray in appearance; the crown to upper midback is black and eyebrows are pale gray-white, as is the chin. The throat and breast are gray, intermixed with white; side and flanks are light gray. The center of the abodomen is white, and the undertail coverts are gray-white. Dark gray to black scapulars are edged with white webs. The rump is gray with dark-gray uppertail coverts. Wings are black, and the tarsi and feet are bluish gray. The female antwren is similar in appearance to the male with the exception of several features. The female has a rusty-orange forehead and orangish spotting throughout its feathers. The eyebrows extending from the side of the bill over to the back of the crown is clay-yellow in color. The chin, throat, and breast are yellow-gray. The color of the lower mandible in males is gray but in females, it is light gray.

These birds usually travel in pairs, often within mixed-species flocks. Most breeding probably takes place during the drier parts of the year, from May to October; other aspects of its reproductive biology are unknown.

Habitat and Current Distribution

The ash-throated antwren is known with certainty from only a small area northeast of Jirillo in northern Peru, where it was reported to be fairly common. There are no estimates of population size.

The locality in which the antwren is found includes tall cloud forest, a savanna-like habitat, a ridge habitat with poor, sandy soils and short, dense vegetation, and diverse, somewhat stunted, forest at the transition between savanna-like vegetation and cloud forest. The antwren has been reported most commonly in the canopy and middle levels of the tallest closed-canopy forest, but it has also been reported as fairly common from the mid-levels to the canopy of stunted forest with dense undergrowth and a slightly closed canopy. A few have been seen in low savanna shrubs bordering the stunted forest.

History and Conservation Measures

The ash-throated antwren was discovered in 1983 on a low, isolated mountain ridge in San Martín Department, northern Peru, at an altitude of 4,400 ft (1,350 m). It was recorded again in 1987 and was considered common in the area.

The very limited geographic range of this species makes it vulnerable to the deforestation that has almost stripped the lowland areas in the Huallaga Valley to the west of the ridge where this species occurs. Widespread clearance of forest is taking place throughout the Amazonian slopes of the Andes, and forest clearance for the cultivation of cash crops poses a serious threat to many species unique to the zone.

No conservation measures have yet been taken on behalf of this species. Creation of a reserve surrounding the antwren's habitat in the low, isolated mountain range east of Moyobamba would help not only the antwren but also several other threatened endemic bird species. Furthermore, a study of the bird needs to be undertaken to determine its distribution, population, and ecology.

Slender antbird

Rhopornis ardesiaca

Phylum	Chordata
Class	Aves
Order	Passeriformes
Family	Formicariidae
Status	Vulnerable, IUCN
Range	Brazil

Description and Biology

The slender antbird has a wing measurement of 2.9 in (73.5 mm) and a tail length of 3.4 in (85.5 mm). The upperparts of this bird are pale gray-brown, with gray on top of the head and mantle. Its rump and upper wing coverts are tawny, as are its underparts. The bill is depressed and ridged, and the tail is steeply graduated. Males of the species have a black chin and throat. The female is distinguished by a tawny-brown head and hind neck, which forms a well-defined cap. The chin and throat are white.

A ground-dwelling species, this antbird feeds on a variety of insects on the ground as well as in low vines and on tops of low plants. Pairs of slender antbirds roam over small territories about 164 ft (50 m) across and up to 300 ft (100 m) apart from other pairs. Diet includes small grasshoppers, crickets, cockroaches, and small spiders.

Breeding activity apparently peaks between October and December. No specific information is available about reproductive biology. This species has a simple, loud song, usually sung in the early morning. Males often sing to locate their mates; one male bird is known to have sung for two hours until his partner called back. Males also sing in boundary disputes, and several different alarm calls have been recorded.

Habitat and Current Distribution

This species occurs only in south-central Bahia, Brazil, where it has been found near Ipaoté, Irajubá, Ituaçu, Jequié, and Boa Nova. There are no estimates of population size.

The slender antbird inhabits dry deciduous forest called *mata-de-cipó*; this type of forest is characterized by a fairly open understory interspersed with woody vines and patches of giant bromeliads. The bird has been observed in this undergrowth near the borders of dry forest and thorny scrub (*caatinga*) or between dry forest and pastures.

History and Conservation Measures

This species was first described from a specimen collected in eastern Brazil in 1831 and two birds found in 1928. It was known from only these three specimens until the 1970s, when it was found in small tracts of suitable habitat near Boa Nova. Although it has been described as easy to find in some areas, it must be considered rare because of its limited distribution and restricted habitat.

Primary dry forest in the region is being cleared for cattle pasture. During the initial stages of this clearance, the forest edge ecotones probably suit this antbird, but as remaining patches of forest decrease in size, the quantity of forest edge also diminishes. Widespread clearance has put the species at high risk of extinction.

Though it is protected under Brazilian law, the creation of suitable forest reserves for this and other threatened bird species is necessary. Further study of the biology of this bird is essential for its long-term management.

Kinglet cotinga

Calyptura cristata

Phylum	Chordata
Class	Aves
Order	Passeriformes
Family	Cotingidae
Status	Endangered/Extinct, IUCN
Range	Brazil

Description and Biology

This is the smallest of the cotingas, with an average size of only around 3 inches (7.6 cm). Its bright plumage is light green above and on the throat; its face, underparts, and the base of its tail are yellow. The bird has a bright red crown bordered in black, and dark wings with two white wing bars. Its diet includes fruits, insects, and seeds.

There is little ecological information available about this species aside from reports that it has a loud call, lives in pairs, and climbs about vines and clumps of bromeliads (*Tillandsia*) in search of food.

Habitat and Current Distribution

The range of the kinglet cotinga is known entirely from a few dozen specimens collected in the nineteenth century in Rio de Janeiro state, Brazil, around the areas of Cantagalo, Rosário, and Nova Friburgo. It has not been recorded for over a century and may be extinct. An early report characterized the bird as inhabiting inland mountains and preferring higher and wilder places in virgin forest, but it was more often found in second growth forest in aban-doned clearings where it frequented the middle-height foliage.

History and Conservation Measures

In the nineteenth century, the kinglet cotinga apparently was not uncommon, but it has not been reported for over 100 years and was not found during a survey in 1981 and 1982; the survey covered an area of around 3,000 acres (1,200 ha) at elevations of 2,800-4,900 feet (850-1,500 m) at Serra da Sibéria, around the highest peaks in the Nova Friburgo area.

It has been suggested that this was a very local species of intermediate elevations which was exterminated during the main forest clearances earlier this century. Clearance has been particularly extensive in the Nova Friburgo region, with very little now left below 3,300 ft (1,000 m) anywhere in the area; there is also virtually no forest left around Cantagalo.

Renewed surveys are needed in the hope that the kinglet cotinga still survives. A systematic and thorough search for any remaining kinglet cotingas could also function as a source of data about other threatened species in the area.

Fork-tailed pygmy-tyrant

Hemitriccus (Ceratotriccus) furcatus

Phylum	Chordata
Class	Aves
Order	Passeriformes
Family	Tyrannidae
Status	Rare, IUCN
Range	Brazil

Description and Biology

Named for its gray, forked tail which is edged in black and has a diagonal white tip, this small flycatcher has a gray body and breast with a greenish back, white underparts, and a reddish brown head and throat. The female's tail is much less forked than the male's. The bird's average length is 4 in (10 cm). The pygmy-tyrant eats a variety of insects.

Habitat and Current Distribution

The fork-tailed pygmy-tyrant, sometimes called the fork-tailed tody-tyrant, has only been found on the coasts of the states of Minas Gerais, São Paulo, Rio de Janeiro, and very recently, Bahia, Brazil. One of the "bamboo specialists" found in the Atlantic Forest, this bird primarily occupies bamboo thickets in forest undergrowth. It seems to prefer large-leaved bamboo species and may be completely absent from stands of smaller-leaved bamboo. It also seems to occur in lower numbers where bamboo thickets are less dense. There is no estimate of population size, but its limited range and specialized habitat requirements make it likely that populations of the bird are very local and probably quite small.

History and Conservation Measures

The status of this species is uncertain. Seldom recorded in recent years, it inhabits dense vegetation where it is difficult to locate. The scarcity of sightings may be due to an extremely low population or it may be the result of insufficient surveys of habitat. Although no specific threats to the survival of the fork-tailed pygmy-tyrant have been identified, it is assumed that forest clearance would have a negative impact on its population. The species is protected by Brazilian law and occurs in at least one national park, Itatiaia National Park on the border of the states of Minas Gerais and Rio de Janeiro. It may also occur in other protected areas. Surveys are needed to confirm the bird's presence in Itatiaia National Park and to investigate its status in other areas including Bocaina National Park (on the border between Rio de Janeiro and São Paulo states), Desengano State Park (Rio de Janeiro state), and along the lower slopes of Serra do Mar. This information can then be used to formulate conservation plans.

Gurney's pitta

Pitta gurneyi

Phylum	Chordata
Class	Aves
Order	Passeriformes
Family	Pittidae
Status	Endangered, IUCN Appendix I, CITES
Range	Myanmar (ex?); Thailand

Description and Biology

Gurney's pitta, also known as the jewel thrush, is a small, colorful bird with an average length of 8.3 in (21 cm). Characterized by bright, beautiful plumage, the male has a blue hindcrown and nape and a black forecrown. Its throat is white, and a yellow band extends across the upper breast. The lower breast and belly are black, while the flanks are yellow with black bars. The wings are reddish brown, and its tail is turquoise blue. The female, whose coloring is less brilliant, has an ochre crown and nape. It feeds on the forest floor, probably eating snails, slugs, worms, and insects.

Little information is available about this bird's behavior or reproductive biology. The species apparently breeds from May to November.

Habitat and Current Distribution

This species is known from lowland rain forest in southern Tenasserim, Myanmar, and Peninsular Thailand. Total population is estimated at 25 to 35 pairs which survive in small remaining pockets of the rain forest. The area with the largest population is Khao Nor Chuchi, a mountain in southern Thailand.

History and Conservation Measures

Regarded as quite common in Thailand until 1920, this species has been reduced by habitat destruction, particularly deforestation, to a precarious and critically endangered status. It was thought to be extinct in the early 1950s but was rediscovered in 1986. The small habitat that supports a remnant population is threatened by deforestation. The species has also been reduced by trapping.

Birdlife International (ICBP) has initiated studies on distribution and habitat to provide information necessary to formulate conservation measures. Local conservation projects have been initiated with the support of Thai authorities and area inhabitants.

Yellow-bellied sunbird-asity

Neodrepanis hypoxantha

Phylum	Chordata
Class	Aves
Order	Passeriformes
Family	Philepittidae
Status	Indeterminate, IUCN
Range	Madagascar

Description and Biology

The yellow-bellied sunbird-asity, also known as the yellow-bellied asity or the small-billed asity, is very difficult to distinguish from the wattled sunbird-asity (*Neodrepanis coruscans*). Its bill is approximately 0.7-0.8 in (1.8-2.1 cm) long and slightly curved. Total length averages 3.6-3.9 in (9-10 cm). Male plumage is dark blue on the head, tail, and upperparts; underparts are dull yellow. Females have green head with yellow cheeks and throat; upperparts are green to greenish gray and underparts are yellow. In the breeding season, female plumage becomes brighter, while the head of the male takes on a metallic sheen and its underparts become golden yellow. The sunbird-asity is a nectar feeder, but has been observed catching termites and feeding them to nestlings.

Breeding plumage has been reported from September through November, providing some indication of the breeding season.

Habitat and Current Distribution

This species is found only in eastern-central Madagascar in forests east and perhaps south of Antananarivo and in the Sihanaka forest. The population size is unknown.

The yellow-bellied sunbird-asity inhabits rain forest, where it is typically found alone or in pairs. It feeds at flowering bushes in forest clearings. Nests have been observed 13-16 ft (4-5 m) up in thick forest.

History and Conservation Measures

This sunbird-asity was recognized as a distinct species in 1933; specimens collected before that time are thought to be wattled sunbird-asities. No specimens have been collected since, although sightings were reported in 1973 and 1976. The species was once thought to be extinct, but based on evaluation of specimens taken before its recognition as a separate species and on recent sightings, it is now thought to survive, if only in small numbers.

Destruction and disturbance of primary rain forest is the most serious threat to this and many other species in Madagascar. No conservation measures are known to have been taken on its behalf, but immediate and effective protection of remaining rain forest is the most urgent measure required to assure its survival.

Noisy scrub-bird

Atrichornis clamosus

Phylum	Chordata
Class	Aves
Order	Passeriformes
Family	Atrichornithidae
Status	Endangered, IUCN
	Endangered, USFWS
	Appendix I, CITES
Range	Australia

Description and Biology

The noisy scrub-bird is a small brown-topped bird with white and red-brown markings on its underside. Its average length is 9 in (23 cm), it has long legs and tail, and its wings are short and rounded. It spends more time on the ground than flying and has a territory of around 15 acres (6 ha). The male defends its territory with the loud calls and imitations of other birds which give the bird its common name. It eats frogs, lizards, insects such as crickets and cockroaches, and seeds.

A domed nest is built in shrubs close to the ground of rushes and decayed wood. Breeding occurs in September or October and the female incubates the one or two eggs for approximately five weeks. Young fledge within four weeks.

Habitat and Current Distribution

The population of noisy scrub-birds is found within a 19 mile (30 km) stretch of land east of Albany in southwest Australia. A census undertaken in late 1991 counted 291 singing males.

The scrub-bird's habitat is dense coastal shrubland, including damp and densely vegetated gullies draining seaward and stunted gum trees on the flat heathland between the gullies.

History and Conservation Measures

The noisy scrub-bird was first discovered in 1842 in the Darling Mountains in Western Australia. For nearly a century from 1889, it was believed to be extinct. Burning of forest and shrublands to support cattle grazing had eliminated most of the bird's habitat, and the introduction of cats to the area in addition to several years of drought were thought to have wiped it out. But in 1961, the scrub-bird was rediscovered by a fisherman near Mt. Gardner in Two Peoples Bay, in an area that was slated for development. The area where it survived had been protected by rocky outcroppings from fire and had apparently harbored a very small population in relative isolation. The planned development was relocated and the area was turned into a reserve. Part of this reserve is kept completely isolated; the remaining part is open, under very controlled conditions, to the public.

Under the protection enacted after its rediscovery, the bird naturally spread to a new site at the Angove River in 1979. In addition, populations were translocated to three new sites beginning in the 1980s: Mt. Manypeaks, Denmark-Walpole, and Mt.

Taylor. The population of scrub-birds, which stood at around 50 birds in 1970, increased to between 70-80 pairs in the mid-1980s, and by 1992, 291 singing males had been surveyed.

A conservation program including careful habitat management to protect the shrublands from fire or other disturbances, as well as a translocation plan with the aim of maintaining six to eight separate populations of scrub-birds, is currently being carried out. In addition, protection of natural corridors to allow dispersal of birds between populations should be considered. If the present population increase of scrub-birds can be maintained, it may become feasible to down-list the bird from endangered to vulnerable in the near future.

Rufous scrub-bird

Atrichornis rufescens

Phylum	Chordata
Class	Aves
Order	Passeriformes
Family	Atrichornithidae
Status	Rare, IUCN
Range	Australia

Description and Biology

A small bird with long legs and a long tail, the rufous scrub-bird measures 6.5-7 in (16.5-17.8 cm) long, is brown above, and white and reddish brown below.

One or two eggs with brown markings are incubated for 36-38 days. Other information about reproductive biology is not available.

Habitat and Current Distribution

The rufous scrub-bird occurs from south of Brisbane into New South Wales, where it inhabits subtropical rain forest with open canopy and a dense scrub layer, and nearby areas of wet *Eucalyptus* forest. The population was estimated in 1983 at 2,500 breeding pairs.

History and Conservation Measures

The rufous scrub-bird is thought to have been much more common at one time. The population may have been as high as 12,000 pairs in the early 1800s, but the species is now greatly reduced in range and number due to habitat destruction and drought. An estimated 90 percent of the remaining population inhabits protected national parks and state forests, among them Mt. Barney National Park, Lamington National Park in Queensland, and the Gibraltar Range, New England, Dorrigo, and Barrington Tops National Parks in New South Wales.

The Forestry Commission of New South Wales has a policy against logging known areas of scrub-bird habitat, but selective logging or burning may be necessary to promote the growth of the dense scrub that is the optimum habitat for the species.

Rufous-winged sunbird

Nectarinia rufipennis

Phylum	Chordata
Class	Aves
Order	Passeriformes
Family	Nectariniidae
Status	Rare, IUCN
Range	Tanzania

Description and Biology

The rufous-winged sunbird is small, with a long, downward curved bill. Like most other sunbirds, it feeds on nectar from flowers and seems to prefer the nectar of *Achryspermum radicans*. This species is particularly aggressive to other sunbirds and chases them away from its feeding area. The male and female of the species feed together and call to each other constantly.

Most sunbirds incubate a clutch of two to three eggs for 13-15 days, but there is no specific information about the breeding behavior of this species.

The male rufous-winged sunbird is quite colorful: the crown, face, nape, and plumage are iridescent violet with a blue gloss. A bronze, triangular patch extends from the lower mandible to the upper chest, and two colored bands extend across the chest. The upper band is violet and 0.16 in (0.4 cm) wide; the lower is brown and 0.39 in (1 cm) wide. It has a yellow greenish belly that turns lime green towards the thighs. The under tail coverts are yellowish green; upper side of the tail is black with a violet tint; and the underside of the tail is gray. True to its common name, this species' secondary feathers are cinnamon-rufous. Its bill and legs are black.

The female of this species is markedly different from the male in appearance. The female's crown, face, and nape are grayish olive, merging to olive-green on the back and upper wing coverts, which have a dappled appearance. There is a slight blue tint to the nape, back, and upper tail coverts. Its throat is olive-yellow, turning to pure yellow on the chest, belly, and under tail coverts. The upperside of the tail is black, and the outer margins of the feathers are brown with a blue gloss and tipped with yellow-green. Secondary wing coverts are black-gray, as are the upperside of the primaries and secondaries. As with the male, the bill and legs are black.

Habitat and Current Distribution

The rufous-winged sunbird is known only from the Mwanihana Forest on the eastern escarpment of the Uzungwa Mountains in eastern Tanzania. It is uncommon below 3,300 ft (1,000 m), but much more numerous above 4,900 ft (1,500 m). There are no estimates of population size.

This sunbird is recorded from forest interior, feeding mainly 6.6-26 ft (2-8 m) above the ground, but it has occasionally been seen up to almost 100 ft (30 m) in the canopy.

History and Conservation Measures

The rufous-winged sunbird was discovered in 1981, when a male and female were collected at around 3,300 ft (1,000 m). Subsequent studies have shown that the bird dwells at altitudes of 1,900-5,600 ft (600-1,700 m) in Mwanihana Forest. It might also inhabit some other rain forests, but searches have been unsuccessful so far, suggesting that its range may prove to be quite limited.

The sunbird is considered to be at risk from habitat destruction because of its limited range. Some logging has taken place in Mwanihana Forest and in other areas on the eastern escarpment of the Uzungwa Mountains. Fortunately, much of the sunbird's likely range occurs within forest reserves, which may provide some measure of protection. The Mwanihana Forest has recently been included within the new Uzungwa National Park; this protection will be important, not only for the rufous-winged sunbird, but also for a number of other threatened bird species known to occur in Mwanihana Forest.

Raso lark

Alauda razae

Phylum	Chordata
Class	Aves
Order	Passeriformes
Family	Alaudidae
Status	Endangered, IUCN
Range	Cape Verde Islands

Description and Biology

A small, brownish bird with short wings, the Raso lark is considered extremely tame. It has a large bill that is thought to be adapted for digging up food, but its diet is not known. It probably digs for grubs but also consumes ants, beetles, seeds, small germinating plants, and other vegetable matter, as well as grit. Kestrels and ravens may be predators.

Breeding has been reported in April and October and probably occurs from September to April, when rainfall is most abundant. Clutch size is thought to be one to three eggs.

Habitat and Current Distribution

This lark only occurs on the uninhabited island of Raso in the windward group of the Cape Verde archipelago. It is found in the southwest area of the island, close to the sea. In the early 1980s, population size was estimated at approximately 20 pairs. In 1985, it was estimated at 150 birds, but the increase may have been a seasonal fluctuation and not an actual long-term increase.

Island habitat includes level plains with mobile volcanic soil and sparse low vegetation. Flocks have been seen feeding among black rocks close to the sea. A frail grass nest is made in a small depression in loose, stony soil in a patch of grass, under a rock, or creeping plant.

History and Conservation Measures

This species was widespread on Raso when it was first described in 1898. It remained fairly abundant until the 1960s, when population was estimated to have dropped below 50 pairs. Despite some population fluctuations attributed to climate, the population may have continued to decline.

Absence or failure of breeding due to drought has been blamed for the bird's decline in numbers, as well as competition from the common rufous-backed sparrow (*Passer iagoensis*). Any collecting, even for scientific purposes, could further imperil the species. Human settlement of Raso could pose new threats to the larks, as would the introduction of rats to the island.

Apparently no conservation measures have been taken on behalf of this lark. In the 1960s, recommendations to establish Raso as a reserve for this species and the giant skink (*Macroscincus coctei*) were ignored. The skink is now thought to be extinct. Habitat protection is still essential, and studies of this species' biology could provide a better understanding of its conservation requirements.

Ash's lark
Mirafra ashi
Degodi lark
Mirafra degodiensis
Somali long-clawed lark
Heteromirafra archeri
Sidamo long-clawed lark
Heteromirafra sidamoensis

Phylum	Chordata
Class	Aves
Order	Passeriformes
Family	Alaudidae
Status	Insufficiently Known, IUCN (*M. ashi; M. degodiensis*)
	Indeterminate, IUCN (*H. archeri; H. sidamoensis*)
Range	Somalia (*M. ashi; H. archeri*)
	Ethiopia (*M. degodiensis; H. sidamoensis*)

Description and Biology

These larks are small birds that usually forage on the ground. The plumage is often brownish, sometimes with lighter or darker markings. The Degodi lark has a noticeably short tail. Ash's lark has a large head, short tail, and a very long hind claw. Information about diet is unavailable except for the Degodi lark, which has been observed to eat small caterpillars and small grasshoppers.

Very little information is available about the reproductive habits or biology of these species. Ash's lark apparently breeds in July at the end of the rains. The Somali long-tailed lark nests in June and has a clutch size of three.

Habitat and Current Distribution

Ash's lark is known only from northeast of Mogadishu, in southern coastal Somalia. The only specimens of the Degodi lark come from the Degodi region of easternmost Sidamo Province in southern Ethiopia. The Somali long-clawed lark is known from the Hargeisa/Buramo area of northwest Somalia along the frontier with Ethiopia. The Sidamo long-clawed lark was collected in Sidamo Province, southern Ethiopia. Population figures are unavailable for any of these lark species.

The habitat of these species is usually known only from few limited observations. Ash's lark is thought to be confined to areas of grazed tufted grass on fixed dunes in grassy, maritime plains. The Degodi lark was found on the ground in very light bush consisting of low bushy acacias on bare soil. The Somali long-clawed lark has been reported to occupy open, fairly short grassland or open rocky country with scattered, sparse bush and limited grass cover; it apparently prefers cover and only flies when flushed. The Sidamo long-clawed lark has been collected in open savanna or grassland, often with scattered acacias.

History and Conservation Measures

Ash's lark is known from only a single site in Somalia, where it was first found in 1981. The apparent restriction of the species' range may be a cause for concern. As this species relies on grazing animals (domestic sheep and goats and wild Speke's gazelle) to keep the grasses low, any loss of domestic stock through drought, combined with over-hunting of the gazelle, could reduce grazing and thus adversely alter habitat. In view of the very limited knowledge of this species, further fieldwork is needed to determine its range and population and to discover the threats it faces and the best means of countering them.

The Degodi lark is only known from two specimens collected together in southern Ethiopia in 1971. The range of the species may prove very restricted, but no other threats have been identified. Further fieldwork in the Degodi region is needed to establish the range and status of this species.

The Somali long-tailed lark has been seen only once in the past 60 years, in 1955, when it was considered very uncommon. Its extremely restricted range is a cause of concern. In addition, a part of its suspected range (Ban Wujaleh) has been under cultivation as a refugee settlement area. If this species still survives, a detailed study of its ecology and behavior is necessary; such a study should also be geared to determining the causes of its restricted range, the impact of cultivation at the Ban Wujaleh, and methods for ensuring its conservation.

The type-specimen for the Sidamo long-clawed lark was collected in 1968, and a second specimen was collected in 1974. Other than the very restricted range of this species, no other threats have been identified. Fieldwork is needed to rediscover this species and to determine its range, population, and any possible threats it may face.

White-eyed river-martin

Pseudochelidon sirintarae

Phylum	Chordata
Class	Aves
Order	Passeriformes
Family	Hirundinidae
Status	Indeterminate, IUCN Appendix I, CITES
Range	Thailand

Description and Biology

The white-eyed river-martin has greenish plumage with a white band at the base of the tail, brownish wings, a blue-black head, and white circles around the eyes. Two elongated inner tail feathers extend from the end of its tail. Its average length is 6 in (15 cm), and its wings are quite long. Little information is available about the species' ecology, social habits, or reproductive biology.

Habitat and Current Distribution

This species is known only from Lake Boraphet in the Nakhon Sawan Province of central Thailand, where a few birds have been found two or three times in winter. Precise breeding locations and summer habitats are unknown, as is population size, although it is undoubtedly small.

In the winter, this martin roosts together with other swallow species at night in beds of reeds. Its daytime habitat is unknown.

History and Conservation Measures

The white-eyed river-martin was first described in 1968 when ten specimens were collected. Two were found in 1972 and six in 1977, but no sighting has been reported since 1980, despite repeated searches. Trappers take large numbers of swallows and other birds in the roosting areas of the martin.

The first step in conserving the remainder of this species is to locate its nesting area and conduct studies to determine its status and ecological needs. Unfortunately, some experts fear that this bird may already be extinct.

Réunion cuckoo-shrike

Coracina newtoni

Phylum	Chordata
Class	Aves
Order	Passeriformes
Family	Campephagidae
Status	Vulnerable, IUCN
	Endangered, USFWS
Range	Réunion (Indian Ocean)

Description and Biology

The Réunion cuckoo-shrike forages for insects and consumes lichens from the leaves, branches, and trunks of tamarins, heath, bois de couleurs, and bamboo. It occupies a territory of 15-20 acres (6-8 ha).

Nest building can begin as early as August and last around a month; the laying season continues until January or February. Clutch size is two and incubation period probably between 14-23 days.

Habitat and Current Distribution

The Réunion cuckoo-shrike is confined to a very small area of forest in the northwest of the French island of Réunion in the Indian Ocean. Population was estimated in the mid-1970s to be around 120 pairs, and it has apparently not changed substantially since then.

Within the present range of this species, at altitudes from 4,200-6,200 ft (1,300-1,900 m), most territories contain elements of three vegetation types: tamarin (*Acacia heterophylla*) forest, mixed evergreen forest, and *Philippia abietina* heath.

History and Conservation Measures

In the 1800s, this species was considered very abundant. It was reported to inhabit remote, impenetrable forests, preferring thick scrub covering steep slopes, and to occur at altitudes as low as 2,600 ft (800 m). Then known to inhabit mixed evergreen forest and to feed on palm beetles, its retreat to a higher level is attributed to the destruction of palm trees by poachers. By the 1940s it was reportedly so rare that it was considered on the verge of extinction. A survey in the mid-1960s led to the conclusion that probably no more than ten pairs survived (though this was almost certainly an underestimate). Its apparent rarity in the 1940s through 1960s was possibly due to the highly destructive cyclones of 1944, 1945, and especially 1948.

Habitat in the range of the Réunion cuckoo-shrike is affected by four human activities: deer hunting, poaching, clearance/reforestation, and tourism. Introduced deer are maintained in high numbers on the Plaine des Chicots and have largely destroyed all undergrowth and prevented any forest regeneration; hunting season for these deer extends into October/November and therefore causes disturbance when birds are breeding. Black rats are common in the trees in this area and may be responsible for nest predation.

Apparently suitable habitat is still extensive on Réunion and the factors restricting it to one particular area in the northwest are unknown. Efforts have been made to stop the cutting of native forest and replanting with exotics in the Plaine des Chicots and Plaine d'Affouches. The increase in population from 1969 to 1974 has been attributed to the presence of a conscientious game-keeper on Plaine des Chicots.

Proposed conservation measures include the establishment of a wardened permanent nature reserve at Plaine des Chicots and Plaine d'Affouches.

The number of deer on the Plaine des Chicots should be drastically reduced or removed entirely to guarantee forest regeneration; meanwhile, deer hunting should be restricted to the period of July through September. Further searches have been recommended in forests that may possibly harbor the species.

Appert's greenbul

Phyllastrephus apperti

Phylum	Chordata
Class	Aves
Order	Passeriformes
Family	Pycnonotidae
Status	Rare, IUCN
Range	Madagascar

Description and Biology

Appert's greenbul is a small, dull-colored songbird averaging 5.9 in (15 cm) in length. It has a dark gray head, white throat, greenish gray upperparts and a yellow underside. It is found in groups of two to eight birds and feeds close to the ground among leaf litter and low-lying branches. Its nesting and breeding habits are unknown.

Habitat and Current Distribution

This species is known with certainty from only two remote localities in southwest Madagascar, where it inhabits dry forest. The population size is unknown, but is probably very small.

History and Conservation Measures

Appert's greenbul was first found in 1962 in a forest 25 mi (40 km) southeast of Ankazoabo in south-west Madagascar, and was described ten years later. Although reported as quite common at the time of its description, it is evident from scattered sightings and unsuccessful searches that it was then, and is now, very local and sparse within its small known range. The corner of the Zombitse forest, where it could always be found between 1976 and 1981, probably supported a population of no more than 20-30 birds.

No conservation efforts are known to have been made on behalf of this species, and its highly restricted range is a continuing source of concern. A cyclone in 1978 or 1979 destroyed some of the forest habitat, and forest burning in this region has also become a serious threat. Fieldwork is necessary to determine the range and status of this species, but the immediate protection of the forests it inhabits is even more urgent to its survival.

Uluguru bushshrike

Malaconotus alius

Phylum	Chordata
Class	Aves
Order	Passeriformes
Family	Laniidae
Status	Rare, IUCN
Range	Tanzania

Description and Biology

The Uluguru bushshrike is a medium-sized bird with a large head and a hooked bill. Its overall color is green; the breast and throat are yellow; its crown is black. This species has a loud, distinctive call.

No information is available about diet, social habits, or reproductive biology.

Habitat and Current Distribution

Sightings of the Uluguru bushshrike have occurred only in the Uluguru Mountain forests in Tanzania at elevations over 4,200 ft (1,300 m), where its total range is probably no larger than 100 sq mi (260 sq km). Population size is unknown.

Primary habitat is the dense canopy of the montane forest, which provides the bird with effective cover and safety from predators.

History and Conservation Measures

This highly elusive species was discovered in 1926, when two specimens were found. Not sighted again until 1948, 15 more specimens were collected in the next 14 years. In 1981 researchers spotted this bird in the Uluguru forest canopy.

The habitat of the Uluguru bushshrike is not immediately threatened, and it currently lies within protected forest reserves. However, given its apparently small population, even a slight alteration of its habitat could have detrimental effects on the remaining populations. Human communities have already begun to encroach upon the lower slopes of the Ulugurus. To ensure greater protection of this species' habitat, the Uluguru forest has been recommended as a national nature reserve. Ecological studies, including an assessment of the species' status, have also been recommended before further conservation measures can be planned.

Mount Kupe bushshrike

Telophorus (Malaconotus) kupeensis

Phylum	Chordata
Class	Aves
Order	Passeriformes
Family	Laniidae
Status	Indeterminate, IUCN
Range	Cameroon

Description and Biology

The Mount Kupe or Serle's bushshrike is a medium-sized bird with a large head and a hooked bill. It is green above and blue-gray below, with a white chin and throat, a blue-gray crown, nape and sides of the neck, and a black stripe extending from the bill back through the eyes. There is a bright yellow area at the base of the belly and the legs and feet are gray. The Mount Kupe bushshrike's call is a distinctive trisyllabic whistle and its diet is primarily insects.

No information is available about social organization or reproductive biology of this species.

Habitat and Current Distribution

This species has been sighted only in the primary rain forest of Mount Kupe in Cameroon, at an altitude of 4,500 ft (1,370 m). Known habitat on Mount Kupe has been estimated to be only 8 sq mi (21 sq km), but it may also inhabit the nearby Bakossi Mountains and Mount Nlonako. No current estimates of population size exist.

History and Conservation Measures

This bushshrike was discovered in 1949 on Mount Kupe and then recorded again in 1951; the distinctive call was heard during an extensive search in 1984, and numerous sightings have been made since 1990. In 1962 population was estimated at around 1,200 birds, but this is clearly much too high. The species survives only in very small numbers.

Since the forest cover on Mount Kupe is so far undisturbed because of local superstitions, it is likely that the species is rare for natural reasons. A new project to conserve the forests on Mount Kupe was initiated in 1990.

Zapata wren

Ferminia cerverai

Phylum	Chordata
Class	Aves
Order	Passeriformes
Family	Troglodytidae
Status	Vulnerable/Rare, IUCN
Range	Cuba

Description and Biology

The Zapata wren is a small, plump bird with short wings. The bird averages about 6-6.5 in (16-16.5 cm) long. Its upperparts are gray-brown with spots on top of the head; black bars line the back, wings, tail, and flanks. The underparts are whitish in color. This bird rarely flies and when it does, its flight is weak. The Zapata wren is considered a superb songster. Diet is composed primarily of insects and possibly small lizards.

This species apparently has a wide breeding season which extends from January to July. Egg laying probably takes place in late April or early May. As many as six eggs can be laid. Nests are built with an entrance at the side.

Habitat and Current Distribution

The Zapata wren is endemic to Cuba and is known only from the Zapata Swamp near Santo Tomas. Recent reports have extended the range to a 12-13 mi (20 km) radius of this area. The population is estimated at fewer than 30 pairs.

Preferred habitat is savanna-like areas, mainly formed of sawgrass, rushes, bayberry, or bog myrtle.

Nests are placed in sawgrass tussocks 20-28 in (50-70 cm) above the ground.

History and Conservation Measures

This species was discovered in Cuba in 1926 and for almost 50 years it was known only to occur in the Zapata Swamp. At one time it was considered quite common, but by the 1970s it could not be located during a search of the swamp. In 1975 it was sighted and heard around 9 mi (15 km) northwest of its usual habitat. In 1988 its known range was again extended by sightings to the north and south-east of Santo Tomas.

Burning of this bird's habitat by local people was apparently the cause of the steep decline of this species. For the most part this practice has been eradicated, but some burning still takes place from year to year. An additional threat to the species is the presence of introduced mongooses and rats. Small portions of the swamp have been drained, but apparently there are no plans for further draining.

A survey of this species is urgently needed, particularly of its range and distribution. Protection of its remaining habitat is also essential, as is the control of dry-season burning of the swamp.

White-breasted thrasher

Ramphocinclus brachyurus

Phylum	Chordata
Class	Aves
Order	Passeriformes
Family	Mimidae
Status	Endangered, IUCN
	Endangered, USFWS
Range	Martinique; St. Lucia (West Indies)

Description and Biology

Two subspecies of the white-breasted thrasher are recognized: *R. brachyurus brachyurus*, found on Martinique, and *R. brachyurus sanctaeluciae*, found on St. Lucia. The white-breasted thrasher is 9-9.5 in (23-24 cm) long, with dark brown upperparts, sides, flanks, and under-tail coverts. The side of the head is black, and the underparts are strikingly white. The St. Lucian thrashers are darker than the Martinique subspecies. Often seen in single pairs or in small flocks of four or five pairs, the white-breasted thrasher is largely terrestrial, foraging on the ground for insects, seeds, berries, and small vertebrates. When threatened, this bird cocks its tail and chatters like a wren.

Breeding season appears to occur between April and July, when a clutch of two greenish blue eggs is laid. Nests are bulky and loose, made of twigs and leaves, and have been found 7-20 ft (2-6 m) above ground in saplings.

Habitat and Current Distribution

The white-breasted thrasher is endemic to the islands of Martinique and St. Lucia. On Martinique, the area between Tartane and Le Phare on the peninsula appears to be the only locality for *R. brachyurus brachyurus*; estimates of population size vary from 15-40 pairs. On St. Lucia, the last stronghold of *R. brachyurus sanctaeluciae* is on the north-east coast in river valleys between Petite Anse and Dennery Knob; population size is estimated to be fewer than 50 pairs.

This species inhabits dense thickets in semi-arid woodland with abundant leaf-litter and riverine forest. On Martinique it has been found in deep woods and along the borders of streams; it has also been reported in the dry zone at the edge of mangroves. On St. Lucia, it has been found in deciduous trees 10-20 ft (3-6 m) tall, and some birds inhabit trees as tall as 60-70 ft (18-21 m). Transitional zones between the dry coastal thickets and the rain forest of the mountains also harbor this bird.

History and Conservation Measures

The white-breasted thrasher is one of the rarest West Indian birds. It was quite common and widespread on Martinique in the nineteenth century but was considered extinct by 1950. That same year, it was rediscovered on the Presqu'île de la Caravelle, a peninsula that juts 5 mi (8 km) into the Atlantic Ocean. The thrasher was considered reasonably common and widespread on St. Lucia in the late 1800s but was extinct in some areas and rare in others by the 1930s.

Habitat destruction is one of the major threats affecting this species, both on St. Lucia and on Mar-

White-breasted thrasher.

tinique. It is also threatened by introduced predators such as mongooses and rats. The white-breasted thrasher is easy prey for these animals because of its terrestrial habits. Nest predators may include the pearly-eyed thrasher (*Margarops fuscatus*) and the trembler (*Cinclocerthia ruficauda*).

On Martinique, the white-breasted thrasher occurs within the Caravelle Natural Reserve; on St. Lucia, part of its present distribution lies within Castries Forest Reserve. On both islands, it is critical to determine whether the present low numbers are the consequence simply of habitat loss or due to other factors, notably predation by introduced mammals. On Martinique, surveys of the Presqu'île de la Caravelle area should be conducted to determine the current status of the species, and investigation of its ecology and population dynamics must begin as soon as possible. Similar research is necessary on St. Lucia. Ravine la Chaloupe has been suggested as a nature reserve, and several other areas merit protection as well.

Nihoa millerbird

Acrocephalus familiaris kingi

Phylum	Chordata
Class	Aves
Order	Passeriformes
Family	Muscicapidae
Status	Vulnerable, IUCN Endangered, USFWS
Range	Hawaii (U.S.A.)

Description and Biology

The Nihoa millerbird is a small dark brown to gray bird with lighter colored underparts. An insect eater, it gets its common name because of a preference for the miller moth.

Nesting probably occurs between January and May, when a clutch of two eggs is laid. Home range is estimated at 0.5-1 acre (0.2-0.4 ha).

Habitat and Current Distribution

This species is endemic to the island of Nihoa in the northwestern Hawaiian Islands. Population has been reported to fluctuate between 200-600 birds, with the latest estimates nearer to 600.

Preferring areas of dense shrub, the millerbird gathers insects from the ground or from leaves, stems, or leaf litter; it also nests in thick shrubbery.

History and Conservation Measures

Since its discovery in 1923, there has apparently been no drastic change in the population of this species; estimates of numbers have varied from around 200-600, either because of fluctuating population or inadequate censusing. A related subspecies, the Laysan millerbird (*Acrocephalus familiaris familiaris*) once occurred on Laysan Island, but became extinct there in the early 1920s, after the introduction of rabbits to the island.

The island of Nihoa is part of the Hawaiian Islands National Wildlife Refuge and can be visited only by special permit. Special precautions are taken to prevent the introduction of exotic organisms; introduced predators such as cats or rats could quickly decimate the bird population, introduced insects could carry avian diseases, and introduced plants can alter habitat and food supplies. Because an island population is always subject to natural disasters that could cause extinction, it has been suggested that a population of Nihoa millerbirds be introduced to suitable neighboring islands.

Nihoa millerbird.

Rodrigues warbler

Acrocephalus (Bebrornis) rodericanus

Phylum	Chordata
Class	Aves
Order	Passeriformes
Family	Muscicapidae
Status	Endangered, IUCN
	Endangered, USFWS
	Appendix III, CITES
Range	Rodrigues (Mauritius)

Description and Biology

The Rodrigues warbler, also known as the Rodrigues brush-warbler, is a medium-sized, dull-colored warbler with a long tail. The bird is quiet and unobtrusive but very inquisitive and will approach an observer to within a few meters. It feeds by gleaning from leaves and small twigs, probably eating insects and larvae.

Breeding has been recorded as beginning in late September and ending in March. The Rodrigues warbler builds a small, cup-shaped nest in the fork of two or more slender branches. Although clutch sizes from 2-5 eggs have been recorded, recent observations have recorded 3 eggs, although one, or at most two, chicks are reared.

Habitat and Current Distribution

This species is confined to a small area on the island of Rodrigues, where it inhabits dense thickets of introduced jamrose (*Syzygium jambos*). The population is estimated at about 60 birds, although, due to the bird's secretive behavior, there may be more. However, there is very little forested area left on Rodrigues, a factor which may limit the bird's numbers.

History and Conservation Measures

In the mid 1800s, this species was apparently quite common and distributed throughout the island of Rodrigues. When most of the indigenous vegetation was cleared from the island early in the 1900s, the warbler survived by adapting to the jamrose which was planted throughout much of the island. Even that habitat was widely cleared, however, in the 1960s, resulting in serious population decline and fragmentation.

Additional threats faced by the species include frequent cyclones and clearing of the forest for firewood; there is also the fear that the black rat is seriously harming the remaining population. Conservation efforts must include control of introduced predators, habitat conservation, and revegetation with native species.

Seychelles warbler

Acrocephalus (Bebrornis) sechellensis

Phylum	Chordata
Class	Aves
Order	Passeriformes
Family	Muscicapidae
Status	Rare, IUCN
	Endangered, USFWS
Range	Seychelles

Description and Biology

A weak flyer, the Seychelles warbler or Seychelles brush-warbler is a small bird with greenish brown plumage above and a lighter underside. It inhabits dense thickets adjoining mangrove swamp, coconut plantations or scrub forest. The warbler eats flying insects and caterpillars, and nests in shrubs, building a cup-like nest composed of grasses and coconut fibers with a lining of fine materials.

Habitat and Current Distribution

Recently confined to the island of Cousin, Seychelles Islands, the Seychelles warbler now inhabits the adjoining island of Aride. Population on Cousin is roughly 400 birds, while Aride currently supports 200 birds.

History and Conservation Measures

In the 1800s this bird also occurred on the island of Marianne, but is now apparently extinct there because of forest clearance. By the 1960s, its population on Cousin had declined to a low of 30 birds, but beginning in 1968 the island has been managed as a nature reserve and the warbler has made a strong recovery.

Efforts on the island of Cousin have included protection of existing habitat and revegetation with native species. Efforts are also made to control the barn owl (*Tyto alba*), which is an introduced predator, and to prevent the introduction of cats or rats. In 1988, 29 warblers were translocated to the island of Aride as a safeguard against extinction on Cousin; today, 200 warblers populate the island. While the species is still considered rare, conservation efforts have apparently assured its survival.

Seychelles warbler.

Thyolo alethe

Alethe choloensis

Phylum	Chordata
Class	Aves
Order	Passeriformes
Family	Muscicapidae
Status	Endangered, IUCN
Range	Malawi; Mozambique

Description and Biology

Occasionally referred to as a forest robin, the Thyolo or Cholo alethe is a small, ground-dwelling bird resembling a thrush. Except during breeding season, members of the species congregate in groups of four to five, often following ant swarms. It feeds mainly on insects flushed by the ants but also forages on its own for other insects such as beetles.

Little is known about this bird's reproductive biology, but breeding is believed to begin in September. Young birds have been observed between December and February.

The general color of this bird is brown-black, including the crown and sides of the face. The area below the chin and throat are white, while the rest of the underparts are grayish white. White marks tip the dark outer tail feathers. Its bill is black, and legs and feet are beige in color. This species measures about 7.8 in (20 cm) with a wing length of 3.9 in (9.9 cm).

Habitat and Current Distribution

The Thyolo alethe has been documented in all areas of suitable habitat in Malawi. However, these locations amount to only 13 sites, all east of the Shire Valley in southern Malawi. Total population is estimated to be approximately 1,500 pairs. The two most significant locales are Mulanje, with a population of 1,000 and Thyolo, with a population of 200. It has also been observed in two areas in northern Mozambique, but no data exists on its status in that country.

Preferred habitat is the open ground area of tall evergreen forest, but the species also inhabits forest with thick, dense undergrowth.

History and Conservation Measures

This species was discovered in 1926 on Thyolo Mountain; various collections and sightings have been made since then in Malawi at altitudes of 3,200-5,900 ft (1,000-1,800 m). It was discovered in Mozambique in 1932 and sighted again in 1950. However, no recent records from Mozambique exist due to lack of fieldwork.

Habitat destruction is probably the major threat to the Thyolo alethe throughout its range. Deforestation and development projects have affected submontane forests on Mulanje and Thyolo, as well as on many of the other mountain forests in Malawi. Outside these two sites, protected populations exist only in Zomba and Malosa.

Most of the known sites of the Thyolo alethe in Malawi are in forest reserves, but these do not generally receive adequate protection. Due to political unrest, no conservation measures have been taken in Mozambique.

São Tomé short-tail

Amaurocichla bocagii

Phylum	Chordata
Class	Aves
Order	Passeriformes
Family	Muscicapidae
Status	Indeterminate, IUCN
Range	São Tomé and Príncipe (Gulf of Guinea)

Description and Biology

The São Tomé short-tail or Bocage's longbill is a small, long-legged forest bird that apparently has both tree-creeping and ground-haunting habits. Its upperparts, wings, and tail are dark chocolate brown, its throat is white, and its underparts are reddish brown, except for a white patch in the middle of its belly which is tinged with reddish buff. It has short, rounded wings, a short tail, a long, straight bill, and is a weak flyer. Living exclusively along rivers with overhanging vegetation in primary forest, the São Tomé short-tail feeds on insects which it finds on mossy boulders and beneath gravel or fallen vegetation along stream banks. Mating season occurs in July-August, at which time males stake out territories and sing during the night from branches adjoining the water.

Habitat and Current Distribution

The São Tomé short-tail is endemic to São Tomé in the Gulf of Guinea, where all records are from forests in the south. Numbers are probably low, the species being confined to the vicinity of forest streams.

Until a study carried out in 1990, only six specimens had been seen. Along the Rio Xutexute and its tributaries, the 1990 expedition recorded 4.1-6.3 pairs of short-tails per km of river, and observed 5.6 pairs per km on the Rio Ana Chaves.

History and Conservation Measures

This species has presumably always been rare and localized. Although the destruction of forest could threaten the species, the inaccessibility of its habitat makes this unlikely in the immediate future.

Seychelles magpie-robin

Copsychus sechellarum

Phylum	Chordata
Class	Aves
Order	Passeriformes
Family	Muscicapidae
Status	Endangered, IUCN
	Endangered, USFWS
Range	Seychelles

Description and Biology

The Seychelles magpie-robin is a thrush-like bird with fairly long legs. Its plumage is glossy black, with large white patches on each wing. Diet includes a variety of invertebrates, small lizards, and a small amount of fruit.

The magpie-robin lays a single egg with an incubation period of 16-20 days. The chick remains in the nest for approximately three weeks and is independent at 6-8 weeks. Juveniles remaining in the parental terrritory often assist in the rearing of subsequent chicks.

Habitat and Current Distribution

This species now survives only on Fregate Island in the Seychelles, where the population in late 1993 was some 40 individuals.

Historic habitat for the magpie-robin was coastal woodland, but that habitat has all been cleared and very few indigenous plants survive on the island. The species' main need is for open substrates on which to forage, and so it has adapted to breadfruit

Seychelles magpie-robin.

groves, plantations that grow cashews, citrus trees, coconut trees, or coffee, and vegetable gardens. It normally nests in tree holes but will also use coconut crowns.

History and Conservation Measures

The magpie-robin was once a very common bird in the Seychelles Island group. It disappeared quite early from Félicité, La Digue, and Praslin, but was present on Marianne and Aride until the 1930s, and on Alphonse until the late 1950s. By 1959, only ten pairs were known to survive on Fregate and the population has not exceeded 41 birds since then.

This species was able to adapt quite well to habitat loss, but it was no match for introduced mammalian predators. A tame, ground-feeding bird, it was particularly susceptible to predation by feral cats. Efforts were made to control cat population in the 1960s and most were finally eradicated by 1982, but there was no resurgence in magpie-robin numbers until the provision of extra food allowed pairs to fledge more young than before. One new difficulty the species faces is competition with the very recently introduced Indian mynah (*Acridotheres tristis*).

The magpie-robin is now one of the rarest birds in the world. To maintain any increase in population, it will be necessary to find another island with suitable habitat (or habitat that can be modified to become suitable), and introduce the bird to that island. In 1978, a few birds were transferred to the island of Aride, a cat-free nature preserve, but the attempt apparently was unsuccessful. Ecological studies to determine habitat requirements and study interactions with other bird species will be necessary to plan further conservation efforts. These are currently being undertaken.

Chuuk monarch

Metabolus rugensis

Phylum	Chordata
Class	Aves
Order	Passeriformes
Family	Muscicapidae
Status	Rare, IUCN
Range	Chuuk (Federated States of Micronesia)

Description and Biology

The Chuuk monarch is a fairly large flycatcher, averaging 7.5-8.5 in (19-21.6 cm) long. Plumage is usually white but can vary from reddish tan to light gray, and it may have a black face and throat. Diet includes a variety of insects.

Little is known of its reproductive biology, but clutch size is usually just one egg.

Habitat and Current Distribution

This species occurs on a number of small islands and islets in the Chuuk group, Federated States of Micronesia. There are no estimates of population size.

Preferred habitat is mangrove forest and primary upland forest, but the species also utilizes some of the cultivated agricultural area on the islands.

History and Conservation Measures

Once common throughout its range, the Chuuk monarch reached its lowest level after World War II, when it became so scarce that it was considered close to extinction. By the late 1950s, it seemed to have made a strong recovery, but by the 1970s, it was again becoming scarce, this time due to deforestation and habitat destruction. Much of the primary forest has now been cleared for agricultural cultivation.

Kamao
Myadestes myadestinus

Puaiohi
Myadestes palmeri

Olomao
Myadestes lanaiensis

Phylum	Chordata
Class	Aves
Order	Passeriformes
Family	Muscicapidae
Status	Endangered, IUCN
	Endangered, USFWS
Range	Hawaii (U.S.A.)

Description and Biology

The Hawaiian thrushes are all somewhat similar in appearance. They have brown upper plumage, with that of the olomao, or Molokai thrush, being slightly darker. All three species have gray underparts, although the puaiohi, or small Kauai thrush, has some white coloring and the Kamao, or large Kauai thrush, has a slightly mottled pattern on the breast. The puaiohi is also distinguished by a white eye-ring or white superciliary line. The puaiohi has flesh-colored legs, in contrast to the dark brown legs of the kamao and the olomao. The olomao averages 7-8 in (17.8-20 cm) in length. The puaiohi averages closer to 7 in (17.8 cm) long and the kamao nearer to 8 in (20 cm). These songbirds feed on fruits and insects; the kamao and the olomao also eat snails.

Little is known about the reproductive biology of these species, but clutch size is probably one or two.

Habitat and Current Distribution

The kamao and the puaiohi are both confined to the wet ohia forests of the Alakai Swamp on the island of Kauai; a 1989 survey found only three kamao and 14 puaiohi. The olomao survives only in wet, montane ohia forest at elevations above 3,000-4,000 ft (900-1,200 m) on the island of Molokai; only one olomao was recorded in a 1988 survey.

History and Conservation Measures

The kamao was once one of the most common thrushes on Kauai, but as forests were cleared for agricultural and industrial development it took shelter in the Alakai Swamp, one of the last refuges on Kauai for a number of threatened birds. The puaiohi was probably always rare and restricted to the swamp. The olomao was not only quite common on Molokai, it also occurred on the islands of Maui and Lanai. It was extirpated from both islands and was long thought to be extinct on Molokai until it was rediscovered in 1963.

Like many other threatened or endangered birds in the Hawaiian islands, these thrushes have been threatened not only with loss of habitat, but with the degradation of their remaining habitat by introduced species. Grazing and browsing animals have eliminated forest understory, allowing the invasion of alien plant species which alter the forest composition and can affect food supply for native species. Nonnative birds compete with native species for food and spread diseases via introduced insects. Finally, introduced predators such as rats, cats, and possibly mongooses prey on the native birds, their nests, and their young.

Efforts are underway to protect primary habitat on Kauai, where the Alakai Wilderness Preserve includes much of the remaining habitat for these birds. The kamao is probably very close to extinction; the puaiohi population appears to be stable but critically low. On Molokai, fencing and control of wild ungulates is underway at the State Natural Area Reserve on the Waikolu Plateau. There are plans to establish a national park at Kalaupapa, and two large reserves have been established at Pelekunu Valley and Kamako. Despite these efforts, the olomao is probably very near extinction. Captive breeding has also been suggested, as there appears to be very little hope of saving them in the wild.

Red-tailed newtonia

Newtonia fanovanae

Phylum	Chordata
Class	Aves
Order	Passeriformes
Family	Muscicapidae
Status	Indeterminate, IUCN
Range	Madagascar

Description and Biology

The single known specimen of this flycatcher was so similar to the red-tailed vanga *(Calicalicus madagascariensis)* that it was not confirmed as a separate species until 1977. The red-tailed newtonia, however, is smaller, has a shorter bill, and lacks the white eye-ring of the red-tailed vanga. The specimen measured 4.7 in (12 cm) in length and was dull brown in color with gray head and neck, light grayish brown chest, and white underparts. It is presumed to feed on insects. Nothing more is known about its ecology or reproductive biology.

Habitat and Current Distribution

The type-specimen of this species was collected in the Fanovana forest in eastern central Madagascar. There is speculation that the species may still inhabit the uppermost levels of the forest canopy at Périnet and in the Sihanaka forest. If the species does survive, its range is certainly limited.

History and Conservation Measures

While the red-tailed newtonia has not been sighted or collected since 1931, it may still inhabit the forest canopy, where it could easily be overlooked. Destruction and disturbance of rain forest is the single most serious threat to this and many other species in Madagascar; the forest at Fanovana, where the type-specimen was found, has been completely cleared.

Because of its sparseness, elusiveness, and inaccessible habitat, the status of the red-tailed newtonia is undetermined. Study is necessary to determine whether the species survives and, if so, to establish its likely requirements.

Long-billed apalis

Orthotomus (Apalis) moreaui

Phylum	Chordata
Class	Aves
Order	Passeriformes
Family	Muscicapidae
Status	Rare, IUCN
Range	Mozambique; Tanzania

Description and Biology

Also known as the long-billed forest warbler or long-billed tailorbird, this species is a slender, gray bird with a long tail and a long bill. It is an inconspicuous species except for its distinctive call, which has been likened to the sound of a mallet hitting an iron peg. Diet consists primarily of insects. It is occasionally found foraging with mixed-species groups. The reproductive biology of this species is unknown.

Habitat and Current Distribution

Two subspecies have been described. *A. m. moreaui* inhabits the forests of the East Usambara Mountains in northeastern Tanzania at altitudes of 2,900-3,400 ft (900-1,050 m). *A. m. sousae* has been sighted on the Njesi Plateau in northern Mozambique, at an altitude of 5,400 ft (1,650 m). No population estimates currently exist for either subspecies.

A. m. moreaui inhabits dense forest undergrowth, clearings, and forest edges. *A. m. sousae* has been seen in forest canopy, but whether this is its natural habitat or an adaptation to diminishing habitat is uncertain.

History and Conservation Measures

Discovered at Amani in 1930, *A. m. moreaui* has since been sighted in several parts of the East Usambara plateau, but only within a narrow altitudinal range. At least seven birds were collected between 1930 and 1932, yet no further documented sightings were made until 1972, when some birds were seen and heard near Amani. In 1945 seven specimens of *A. m. sousae* were collected on the Njesi Plateau in northern Mozambique, but ornithologists have yet to return to the area to conduct further studies.

The most serious threats to *A. m. moreaui* are the rapid deforestation of East Usambara for cardamom plantations and the clearing of undergrowth by local farmers for subsistence agriculture. No recent information exists concerning the state of forest conservation on the Njesi Plateau.

While a number of the forests in the East Usambaras are protected as parts of forest reserves, those areas immediately outside the reserves are being cleared rapidly. However, a major conservation initiative is currently underway in the East Usambaras to resolve the competing demands for forest conservation and rural development. No conservation measures are known for the Njesi Plateau.

Red-lored whistler

Pachycephala rufogularis

Phylum	Chordata
Class	Aves
Order	Passeriformes
Family	Muscicapidae
Status	Insufficiently Known, IUCN
Range	Australia

Description and Biology

This songbird is named for its reddish facial marking that extends from the eye through the upper edge of the bill and down onto the throat. The male is muddy-gray above and lighter gray below; the female has darker gray underparts. Average size is 7.6-8.4 in (19.3-21.3 cm). Diet is comprised primarily of insects taken from the ground or from low bushes or trees.

Breeding follows a courtship display; two to three eggs are laid in a cup-shaped nest made of vegetation.

Habitat and Current Distribution

This species is confined to eastern South Australia and northwestern Victoria, where it inhabits mallee (shrubby *Eucalyptus*) with dense, low ground cover. There are no estimates of population size.

History and Conservation Measures

The red-lored whistler is thought to have declined because of clearing and burning of its habitat. There is no information available about conservation measures.

Chatham Island black robin

Petroica traversi

Phylum	Chordata
Class	Aves
Order	Passeriformes
Family	Muscicapidae
Status	Endangered, IUCN
	Endangered, USFWS
Range	Chatham Islands (New Zealand)

Description and Biology

Named for the color of its plumage, this robin forages in leaf litter to feed on a variety of insects.

Habitat and Current Distribution

Now found on the islands of Mangere and Rangatira in the Chatham Islands, the robin inhabits forest scrublands. By the start of the 1990s over 100 birds were alive.

History and Conservation Measures

Although early population figures are unavailable, this robin was once fairly abundant throughout the Chatham Islands, including Chatham, Pitt, Mangere, and Little Mangere. By the late 1800s it had disappeared, at least partly because of the introduction of cats, from all the islands except Little Mangere. Even on Little Mangere, the population was quite low, estimated until around 1960 at 20-35 pairs. As the scrub habitat on the island began to deteriorate, the population plunged as low as only three pairs and a single bird; at this point the species seemed on the very verge of extinction.

In 1977, the remaining seven birds were translocated to Mangere Island, which had been made a Reserve for the Preservation of Flora and Fauna in 1967. Sheep were removed from the island and efforts were made to return it to a state that would support the bird. The remaining robins were carefully managed and fostering programs resulted in a rapid increase in population and the spread of the bird to the island of Rangatira.

Chatham Island black robin.

White-necked rockfowl

Picathartes gymnocephalus

Phylum	Chordata
Class	Aves
Order	Passeriformes
Family	Muscicapidae
Status	Vulnerable, IUCN
	Endangered, USFWS
	Appendix I, CITES
Range	Côte d'Ivoire; Ghana; Guinea; Liberia; Sierre Leone

Description and Biology

The white-necked picathartes or rockfowl is an unusual ground-hunting bird with a long tail, strong bill and a patch of bare yellow skin on its head. About 15.7 in (40 cm) long, the rockfowl has a brownish gray body, with a white neck and underside. Its food consists of snails, beetles, cockroaches, grasshoppers, earwigs, and other insects taken from the ground; the species is known to join mixed bird parties following ant trails.

This species nests singly or in colonies of two to five pairs, building nests of mud and plant fibers on overhanging cliffs or in caves, usually 6-20 ft (2-6 m) above the ground. Breeding occurs at times of peak rainfall and normal clutch size is two. Incubation takes approximately 24 days and nestling period up to 26 days.

Habitat and Current Distribution

This rockfowl occurs in suitable places throughout the remaining fragments of the rain forest of the Upper Guinea region in Ghana, Côte d'Ivoire; Liberia, Sierra Leone, and Guinea. No estimates of population size are available but the species is clearly very local and uncommon because of its very specialized habitat requirements.

Most records of this species are from rocky ground under a rain forest canopy. It is most numerous in forest in hilly country where there are more suitable breeding sites, but records from riverine forests near Lamto, Côte d'Ivoire, suggest that birds occasionally wander considerable distances from their preferred breeding habitat.

History and Conservation Measures

Earliest records of this species in Ghana are from the late 1800s; it was not again reported until the 1950s, when a number of colonies were discovered. In Guinea, five birds were collected in 1965 and a few nests of the species were found in 1968; a possible sighting was also reported in 1980. In Côte d'Ivoire, a small group was found in 1968, and there are several subsequent records, especially in Taï National Park. Other than an old undated specimen, there were no records of this species in Liberia until several specimens were collected in 1964; it is apparently widely distributed throughout the country. In Sierra Leone there were scattered sightings throughout the early 1900s; in 1950, the species was discovered in several places and by the mid-1960s, it was known to be well distributed in the western, southern, and eastern provinces and suspected to occur in other areas.

White-necked rockfowl.

The chief cause of decline for the white-necked rockfowl is forest clearance; the high rate of forest destruction in Africa west of the Dahomey Gap has put all birds endemic to primary forest at risk. The species is also suffering from losses to hunting.

Only in Ghana is the species fully protected by law; it is to be hoped that Guinea, Côte d'Ivoire, Liberia, Sierra Leone, and Togo will follow Ghana in providing complete legal protection. The survival of the white-necked rockfowl will be insured only by vigorous protection of its habitat and breeding grounds, especially the Kwahu escarpment in Ghana, the Mount Nimba area of Côte d'Ivoire, Liberia, and Guinea, other hilly areas in northern Liberia and southern Guniea, the Loma and Tingi Hills and the area behind Freetown in Sierra Leone, as well as the Taï National Park, Côte d'Ivoire.

Gray-necked rockfowl

Picathartes oreas

Phylum	Chordata
Class	Aves
Order	Passeriformes
Family	Muscicapidae
Status	Rare, IUCN
	Endangered, USFWS
	Appendix I, CITES
Range	Cameroon; Bioko (Equatorial Guinea); Gabon; Nigeria

Description and Biology

The gray-necked rockfowl or gray-necked picathartes is a ground-hunting bird with brownish gray plumage, a gray neck, and a bare head. Its food consists of a variety of insects, tiny snails, and small vertebrates. Pairs or small groups of these rockfowl forage on the forest floor at dawn and in the afternoons, roosting in caves during inactive periods.

This species nests in colonies of as many as ten birds. Nest building and breeding coincides with the wet season and varies with location. The birds build nests with mud and plant fibers within caves or upon overhanging ledges between 4-26 ft (1.2-8 m) above the ground. Normal clutch size is two and it is possible that the whole colony assists in the incubation and rearing of the young; only one bird is normally reared per nest. Although the birds occasionally perch in low vegetation, they are almost always seen less than 6.6 ft (2 m) from the ground, and they usually remain within 320-650 ft (100-200 m) of their roosting caves.

Habitat and Current Distribution

This rockfowl occurs only in southwestern and southern Cameroon, northeastern Gabon, the island of Bioko in Equatorial Guinea, and extreme southeastern Nigeria. Its range covers approximately 15,000 sq mi (40,000 sq km). No estimates of population size are available, but the species is clearly local on account of its highly specialized habitat requirements.

The gray-necked rockfowl inhabits rain forest containing rocky areas and caves. Though most sightings of the bird have occurred in primary forest, they may be able to survive some forest clearance provided it is not complete.

History and Conservation Measures

The type-specimen for the gray-necked rockfowl was collected in Cameroon, near Limbe at the foot of Mount Cameroon. Most reports of the species have been from within 125 mi (200 km) of the coast; it ranges from near the Oban Hills in southeastern Nigeria through Cameroon to the frontier with Equatorial Guinea in the south. The species occurs within Equatorial Guinea in the forest of the southern part of Bioko Island. It might also occur in the mainland area of Equatorial Guinea. In Gabon, six colonies were located in the Belinga area in 1963; it is also known to occur at Oyem near the border with Equatorial Guinea.

Since there is no record of its survival in areas where the forest has been destroyed, the gray-necked rockfowl, like its close relative, the white-necked rockfowl, is probably being jeopardized by the clearance of forest. The unprotected forests of northeastern Gabon, for example, may be subject to further exploitation upon completion of a new railway. The species is also hunted for food on occasion; adults as well as young are sometimes taken by hunters looking for bats in caves.

The gray-necked picathartes is found in the recently established Korup National Park, Cameroon and the Oban Hill National Park in Nigeria; surveys are needed to assess its population there and in southern Cameroon's proposed Dja National Park. The establishment of a national park in northeastern Gabon would be beneficial to this and other species; Cameroon, Gabon, Nigeria, and Equatorial Guinea need to take vigorous action to safeguard the bird from hunting and collecting.

Hinde's pied-babbler

Turdoides hindei

Phylum	Chordata
Class	Aves
Order	Passeriformes
Family	Muscicapidae
Status	Vulnerable, IUCN
Range	Kenya

Description and Biology

Named for the loud babbling noise it makes, Hinde's pied-babbler can also remain silent for long periods of time. It is a sedentary species often found in groups of six to eight. These parties remain within small areas, largely isolated from other groups. Plumage varies widely from individual to individual; mutual preening has been observed. Very little is known about breeding, but it appears to occur in February, April, and September.

Habitat and Current Distribution

Hinde's pied-babbler is endemic to Kenya, where it has been recorded from an area to the south and east of Mount Kenya. No detailed census has been conducted, but the species is known to be relatively common within its very restricted area of distribution. Although uncertain, population size is estimated to be in the thousands.

This species can be found in steep-sided river valleys, particularly along the river systems of the upper Tana. They prefer areas of secondary growth where some trees are left standing, usually valleys that farmers have rejected or left to revert to bushy growth. Hinde's pied-babbler also prefers habitats where the introduced plant *Lantana* is established, a relatively recent adaption which likely occurred after valleys and rocky hillsides were cleared of their original vegetation. The bird has also been sighted less frequently along bushy streams and gullies in drier open woodland. It usually remains in thicket interiors but may perch on exposed riparian trees for several minutes at a time.

History and Conservation Measures

While Hinde's pied-babbler was considered quite common in the 1950s and 1960s, by 1978 it was known from only 23 sites, nearly all consisting of a single party of up to eight birds. A total population of 200 individuals was estimated. However, more birds are thought to exist in hard-to-access locations, especially in the little-known river valleys south of Mount Kenya.

Several factors threaten Hinde's pied-babbler: the most serious is the clearance of *Lantana* habitat for maize cultivation. Secondly, habitat along the Tana River has been destroyed by dam projects and rice irrigation programs. Thirdly, little or no interchange occurs between the isolated populations of Hinde's pied-babbler, resulting in a decrease in genetic diversity. Collecting of specimens by ornithologist may also have contributed to the bird's decline.

No known conservation measures have yet been taken for this species. Further collecting should be prohibited and studies initiated to better assess its range and status. Efforts should also be made to preserve areas of *Lantana* habitat.

Taita thrush

Turdus helleri (T. olivaceus helleri)

Phylum	Chordata
Class	Aves
Order	Passeriformes
Family	Muscicapidae
Status	Endangered, IUCN
Range	Kenya

Description and Biology

The Taita thrush is a ground-dwelling forest bird that forages in leaf litter on the forest floor. Almost nothing is known about the bird's ecology, but specimens collected in November were in breeding condition; the clutch size is thought to be two or three.

Habitat and Current Distribution

This species is confined to natural forest on the Taita Hills in southeast Kenya. The Taita Hills have only three remaining tracts of forest—the Mbololo, Ngangao, and Ronge— covering a total of less than 2 sq mi (5 sq km). Since Mbololo, the largest of these patches of forest, remains moderately intact, it is now probably the main locality for the species in the Taita Hills. The bird's population is thought to be very small.

History and Conservation Measures

Originally undivided forest, the steep slopes of the Taita Hills have now been almost completely cleared for fuel and agriculture. The remaining areas of suitable habitation for this species are very small and are under serious threat of destruction.

A study to gather data about the population, ecology, and conservation needs of the Taita thrush, imperative in view of the small size of its habitat, should be part of a more comprehensive survey of wildlife in the remaining natural forests on the Taita Hills, which hold some remarkable endemic fauna and flora. Since 1985, the National Museums of Kenya have been promoting forest conservation in the Taita Hills.

Algerian nuthatch

Sitta ledanti

Phylum	Chordata
Class	Aves
Order	Passeriformes
Family	Sittidae
Status	Rare, IUCN
Range	Algeria

Description and Biology

The Algerian nuthatch is a small forest species approximately 4.7 in (12 cm) long, with bluish gray coloring and a pale underside. It is an agile climber, able to move nimbly up and down the trunks of trees without the use of stiffened tail feathers as support. The common name of the species comes from its habit of wedging nuts into tree bark and using its strong beak to break into the nut. Insects provide the bulk of its diet in summer and nuts and seeds in the winter. Possible predators of its eggs and nestlings include the Barbary macaque, oak dormouse, North African weasel, great spotted woodpecker, and jay.

This species is apparently sedentary, although it may move to lower altitudes in winter. Breeding season varies with weather conditions. Clutch size is unknown, but the number of young fledged has been reported to be two to four—usually two. Incubation information for this species is unavailable, but for related species the incubation period is 15-19 days and the nestling period 23-30 days.

Habitat and Current Distribution

The Algerian nuthatch was originally believed to be confined to a forest on the peak of Mont Babor, which rises to 6,500 ft (2,000 m) in the Petite Kabylie region of northern Algeria. Population in the Babor Forest is estimated at around 80 pairs. In 1989, a second group was reported in the Taza National Park, and in 1990 the species was discovered in the Tamentout and Djimla forests in the Setif and Jijel regions of Algeria, respectively.

Mont Babor forms a sharp, high ridge; its proximity to the sea gives it a very humid and cold winter climate, including a heavy snow cover from November to April or May, while the period from July or August to October is dry, with a Mediterranean climate. Factors affecting species density include the diversity of tree species, the size and age of trees, and altitude. Forest covers less than 5 sq mi (13 sq km) of Mont Babor, but the optimum habitat for the species, concentrated at upper levels around the peak, consists of less than one sq mi (2.5 sq km). In Setif and Jijel the species inhabits altitudes ranging from 2,950-4,590 ft (900-1,400 m).

History and Conservation Measures

When this species was discovered in 1975, its population was already at a dangerously low level. Although the Babor Forest is contained within a national park, excessive use of the area as grazing and agricultural land has steadily decreased the forested habitat.

Threats to the Algerian nuthatch fall into three categories: reduction of forested area by fire, grazing, and wood-cutting; replacement of mixed forest by cedar in the wake of fire; and decrease in diversity of woody species as a consequence of long-term grazing and agriculture. A major area of concern is Mount Babor's summit forest and adjacent mixed cedar forest, the species' preferred habitats, both of which have been seriously diminished by fire and suffer from chronic lack of regeneration because of high-intensity agriculture. The disappearance of predators such as lions and leopards has resulted in increased summer grazing and browsing by cattle, sheep, and goats and the destruction of much young vegetation by large numbers of wild boars. Construction of tracks into the area has resulted in increased human activity as well. The most serious natural threat to the species is presumed to be the combination of very poor seed production in the autumn and intense snow conditions the following winter.

A series of measures is needed to counter deforestation, to favor the maintenance of old trees and species diversity, and to promote regeneration and soil stability, all without alienating the local community. Proposals include a general policy not to encourage tourism; reduction of agricultural pressures by planting forage outside the forest; negotiation with local people to reduce wood-cutting in exchange for compensation; no further cutting or removal of dead trees by the forest service; establishment of plantations outside the present forest perimeter to alleviate pressure for firewood; no further construction of tracks for access and closure of existing tracks to all but forest service vehicles; and provision of foresters with surveillance, alarm, and fire-fighting equipment and vehicles.

São Tomé sunbird

Nectarinia (Dreptes) thomensis

Phylum	Chordata
Class	Aves
Order	Passeriformes
Family	Nectariniidae
Status	Rare, IUCN
Range	São Tomé and Príncipe (Gulf of Guinea)

Description and Biology

This is the largest of the sunbirds, averaging around 9 in (23 cm) long; the male is larger than the female. Also called the giant sunbird, this species has blue-black plumage and a long, curved bill. While most sunbirds feed only on nectar, this bird also uses its strong bill to probe for insects in tree bark and to pick small insects from the underside of leaves.

Most sunbirds incubate a clutch of two to three eggs for 13-15 days; the bird may be polygynous, as females are seen to congregate during the mating season. The sunbird's nest, built of moss, dead leaves, and roots with a lining of dry grass, is hung from a branch.

Habitat and Current Distribution

This species is restricted to primary forest in the center and west of São Tomé, where it has been sighted along branches and feeding at banana blossoms. There are no estimates of population.

History and Conservation Measures

The São Tomé sunbird has been reported to be reasonably common; a recent study (1990) confirms its abundance in several tracts of primary forest over a wide range of altitudes. Since the bird is almost never seen in secondary forest or other types of habitat, any destruction of primary forest brought on by the encroachment of cultivation and agriculture must be considered a major threat to this species.

Norfolk Island white-eye

Zosterops albogularis

Phylum	Chordata
Class	Aves
Order	Passeriformes
Family	Zosteropidae
Status	Endangered, IUCN
	Endangered, USFWS
	Appendix I, CITES
Range	Norfolk Island (Australia)

Description and Biology

The Norfolk Island white-eye is also known as the white-breasted white-eye or white-chested white-eye and, in Australia, as the white-breasted silver-eye. It is approximately 5.5 in (14 cm) long, with an olive-green back, white underparts, and a white ring of skin around the eye. Its short, thin bill is used to feed on insects and fruits. Potential predators are introduced black rats (*Rattus tattus*) and feral cats (*Felis cattus*).

Little is known about the breeding habits of this species, but it is thought that two eggs are laid from October through December.

Habitat and Current Distribution

This white-eye may now be extinct. If it survives, it is within the remote forests of the Norfolk Island National Park.

Known habitat is indigenous forest, but there are some reports that it may have once frequented cultivated areas.

History and Conservation Measures

This bird has apparently never been common, but was widespread throughout Norfolk Island when the island was covered with rain forest. In 1962, the population was estimated at 50 birds, but later surveys have not resulted in any confirmed sightings since 1980. Unconfirmed sightings since then may have been of the introduced silver-eye (*Zosterops lateralis*).

Loss of habitat was certainly a major factor in the decline of this species. The forest has been cleared for agriculture, but the habitat has also deteriorated as a result of invasion of exotic weeds. The area of weed-free native vegetation has been reduced to less than one percent of its former extent. The species also faced possible competition from the silver-eye, which is now abundant on the island, as well as predation by black rats which first arrived on the island in the 1940s and possibly cats. While there is still hope that a breeding population may be located in the remote forest, it is increasingly likely that the Norfolk Island white-eye no longer survives. The Australian Native Conservation Agency has developed a recovery plan for the species in the event of its rediscovery. This includes the control of rat and cat numbers and the establishment of the species on the nearby rat- and cat-free Phillip Island, if suitable vegetation can be re-established there.

Seychelles white-eye

Zosterops modestus

Phylum	Chordata
Class	Aves
Order	Passeriformes
Family	Zosteropidae
Status	Endangered, IUCN
	Endangered, USFWS
Range	Seychelles

Description and Biology

Named for its white eye-ring, this small perching bird is inconspicuous and difficult to find in its rain forest habitat. The Seychelles white-eye, also known as the Seychelles gray white-eye, has short legs and fairly short, rounded wings. The head, back, and tail are olive-gray; the rump and breast are paler, with a tinge of yellow; the flanks are rusty in color. The throat is white, and the white ring that circles the eye has a small gap in front of the eye. Nomadic feeding parties of four or five birds forage for food, constantly calling out to each other. This bird's brush-tipped tongue is specially adapted for taking insects, including mealy bugs, caterpillars, and possibly ants, but it also feeds on the berries of *Latana camara*.

Breeding season occurs at the start and end of the northwest monsoon, usually in October/November and in February/March. Two eggs are incubated for 10-12 days. Both sexes build the nest, which is made of grass and root fibers, generally 33 ft (10 m) above ground.

Habitat and Current Distribution

This species occurs in mixed secondary forest on one island, Mahé, in the Seychelles, where it is now confined to three tiny areas, each less than two sq mi (5 sq km): La Misère, Mission, and Rochon. In 1979-1980 it was very difficult to find more than one or two birds at the first two localities, while the third was not visited. In 1982 a pair was found at Mission, and it was thought to harbor five or six more pairs in that general region. It is possible that as yet undiscovered populations exist in other localities.

Primary habitat is mixed secondary forest above 1,000 ft (300 m), especially where certain tall trees, including *Albizia falcataria* and *Pterocarpus indica*, have an underlying or adjacent scrub layer partly composed of the same species; most feeding is carried out in this scrub layer, usually below 10 ft (3 m), but foraging has also been seen consistently to occur on tops of *Calophyllum* and other trees. Nests are built in dense foliage of broad-leaved trees.

History and Conservation Measures

Reports from the 1800s and early 1900s classify the Seychelles white-eye as plentiful or at least locally abundant within a fairly restricted range in central Mahé. There were, however, no sightings from around 1940 to 1960, leading to the belief that the species might be extinct. Rediscovered around 1960, it was thought to have declined and then recovered, but surveys in the mid-1970s led to a population estimate of fewer than 100 birds. Since the 1970s, it has undergone a rapid decline in numbers.

The reasons for such a drastic decline in population and range are not fully known, but a number of natural and human-induced factors may be involved. The choice of nest sites in dense foliage of broad-leaved trees, possibly to reduce risk of rain-damage, may contribute to the species' present restricted distribution. Its distribution may also be affected by aggressive interference, shown by Seychelles bulbuls (*Hypsipetes crassirostris*), by introduced Madagascar fodies (*Foudia madagascariensis*), and very probably by introduced Indian mynahs (*Acridotheres tristis*). Shortage of habitat has not been a problem in the past, as there appears to be extensive habitat of the type known to be used on the island of Mahé. Unfortunately, the white-eye occurs in localities that now have considerable human activity. The Mission area is of great importance for both forestry and commercial tea-growing, activities that are really not in keeping with the conservation of endangered species.

The entire Mission population lies within the Morne Seychellois National Park, but this does not protect it from land-use changes; the other two populations are at the periphery of the park and are likely to range outside it. Because the reasons for its decline are unclear, no concrete conservation efforts have been taken on its behalf, and the Seychelles white-eye may soon become extinct. There is an urgent need to determine its status more accurately and to investigate the reasons for its extraordinarily restricted distribution.

Black-eared miner

Manorina flavigula melanotis
(M. melanotis)

Phylum	Chrodata
Class	Aves
Order	Passeriformes
Family	Meliphagidae
Status	Insufficiently Known, IUCN
Range	Australia

Description and Biology

Averaging just under 10 in (25 cm), this honeyeater has dark gray plumage with yellow legs, bill, and a patch behind the eyes. Its common name comes from the black markings on the sides of the face, which give it a masked appearance. The species uses its brush-like tongue to extract nectar from flowering plants or to catch insects.

A shy bird that can be difficult to locate, it is most often found in small groups, perhaps as part of larger colonies. Breeding season ranges from winter to early summer, when three or four pink eggs are laid.

Habitat and Current Distribution

This species occurs in southwestern New South Wales, eastern South Australia, and northwestern Victoria, which may contain the largest population. Total population size is unknown but may be very small.

Preferred habitat is thick mallee shrubland that is formed by thickets of *Eucalyptus* species.

History and Conservation Measures

The initial threat to this species was destruction of its habitat. As the mallee shrublands were cleared to make way for agricultural development and grazing animals, the habitat areas of the black-eared miner became more attractive to the yellow-throated miner (*Manorina flavigula*), which prefers a more open habitat. The mingling of the two miners has led to interbreeding, and hybridization is now the primary threat to the black-eared miner. Studies have been initiated to determine appropriate conservation measures, but no steps have yet been taken to preserve this species.

Bishop's oo

Moho bishopi

Phylum	Chordata
Class	Aves
Order	Passeriformes
Family	Meliphagidae
Status	Endangered, IUCN
Range	Hawaii (U.S.A.)

Description and Biology

Also known as the Molokai oo, this honeycreeper is a relatively large bird, measuring approximately 12 in (30 cm) in length. Although primarily black, the species' plumage is accented by golden yellow feathers covering the ears, at the point where the wings meet the body, and under the tail coverts. The tail itself has a narrow fringe of white. Bishop's oo feeds on nectar from flowering plants, particularly of the lobelia and ohia trees. The species may also occasionally feed on fruit and insects when nectar is scarce.

The species' reproductive biology is unknown.

Habitat and Current Distribution

Bishop's oo has been reported from northeastern slope of the Haleakala volcano, on the island of Maui. If the species is not extinct, the population is likely to be extremely small.

This bird is thought to prefer the canopy of upland rain forest.

History and Conservation Measures

Bishop's oo once occurred not only on Maui but on the island of Molokai as well. However, it has not been seen there since the beginning of this century. On Maui, naturalists had not spotted the bird since 1904 and believed it to be extinct. Then in 1981 it was seen on Haleakala, the last reliable report of its existence.

The earliest cause of the species' decline was hunting, the bird's golden feathers being highly prized. Later, forest destruction and alteration as a result of agricultural development posed a greater threat to Bishop's oo, as it does to other native Hawaiian species. Introduced grazing and browsing animals such as cattle and goats have also destroyed much of the remaining forest's undergrowth, allowing alien plant species to flourish at the expense of native species. Such changes in the forest often affect the food supply of native species.

Surveys of the Haleakala area are needed to determine whether or not Bishop's oo survives. If so, then conservation efforts must be based upon the species' ecological requirements and take into consideration any additional threats it may face.

Kauai oo

Moho braccatus

Phylum	Chordata
Class	Aves
Order	Passeriformes
Family	Meliphagidae
Status	Endangered, IUCN
	Endangered, USFWS
Range	Hawaii (U.S.A.)

Description and Biology

A member of the honeyeater family, the Kauai oo has duller plumage than its relatives, with black upperparts, slightly lighter underparts, and only a small area of yellow on the upper legs. Its average size is 7.6-8.5 in (19-21.6 cm). The oo uses its long, curved bill to drink nectar from flowering plants, as well as to retrieve insects and spiders from cracks in the bark of trees.

Habitat and Current Distribution

This species is endemic to the Hawaiian island of Kauai, where it has been confined to upland rain forest in the Alakai Swamp at altitudes of 3,760-4,500 ft (1,150-1,370 m). A few individual birds may survive, but the species is more than likely extinct.

History and Conservation Measures

The Kauai oo was fairly common in the 1800s, but began a rapid decline in the early 1900s and was considered extinct until it was rediscovered in 1960 in a small patch of swampland. Some estimates placed population at fewer than 100 birds in the 1970s, but sightings in the 1980s were only of one or two birds; a survey in 1989 did not find any birds.

This species remained common for longer than its more brightly colored relatives, who were trapped for their yellow feathers. It could not, however, escape the effects of habitat destruction and degradation. Clearance of montane forests for agricultural development eliminated much suitable habitat, and remaining habitat has been affected by the introduction of alien animals and plants. Feral pigs and goats have been responsible for the clearing of undergrowth, resulting in the invasion of exotic plants that affect food supply for native species. Introduced birds have become competitors and brought avian diseases that were spread to native birds by introduced insects. Predators have also been introduced to the island, primarily the black rat, which preys on bird eggs and young.

Remaining habitat is contained within the Alakai Swamp Wilderness Preserve, where attempts have been made to control exotic species and protect habitat in the hope that the bird still survives.

Black-and-gold tanager

Bangsia (Buthraupis) melanochlamys

Phylum	Chordata
Class	Aves
Order	Passeriformes
Family	Emberizidae
Status	Vulnerable/Rare, IUCN
Range	Colombia

Description and Biology

This tanager has black plumage that shades to blue toward the throat and toward the tail; its underparts are golden yellow. The average length of the bird is 2.6 in (6.6 cm) and it has a strong, fairly short bill. Feeding in pairs or small groups, the tanager eats fruits, berries, and insects.

Breeding appears to peak twice a year in this species, in May-June and September-October, months when rainfall is most abundant. Most tanagers have a clutch size of two and incubate the eggs for 12-18 days.

Habitat and Current Distribution

The black-and-gold tanager is known from two disjunct areas in western Colombia: the north and western slopes of the Central Andes in Antioquia and the western slopes of the West Andes in Chocó. It has not been sighted in the Central Andes since 1948, and it is feared extinct in this area. Population size is not known in the West Andes but appears to be in fair condition since it is reported as not uncommon.

Preferred habitat is subtropical humid forest with heavy undergrowth, at altitudes of 3,300-7,500 ft (1,000-2,285 m). The black-and-gold tanager has also been sighted in disturbed primary and secondary forests; forest patches and borders; and cultivated land surrounded by primary forest.

History and Conservation Measures

The northern population, which may now be extinct, was once considered not uncommon, although its distribution was limited. The southern population has recently been reported as fairly common in the middle elevations of its range but rare to uncommon higher up. The greatest threat to this bird is deforestation. The Tatamá National Park lies within the range of the surviving tanager population, offering it protection from habitat degradation.

The black-and-gold tanager can apparently utilize fragmented, disturbed, or secondary habitat for foraging, but nesting has only been recorded from primary or lightly disturbed forest. It is essential, therefore, to ensure the integrity of Tatamá National Park. In addition, ecological studies of the species need to be conducted, particularly of the habitat requirements as they impact breeding success. A survey of the Central Andes area has also been recommended to assess the possible existence of the black-and gold tanager in this former range.

Gough bunting

Rowettia goughensis

Tristan bunting

Nesospiza acunhae

Grosbeak bunting

Neospiza wilkinsi

Phylum	Chordata
Class	Aves
Order	Passeriformes
Family	Emberizidae
Status	Rare, IUCN
Range	Tristan da Cunha Islands (South Atlantic Ocean)

Description and Biology

Buntings are fairly small birds with conical bills. The Gough bunting is olive-green with a black throat; juveniles are rufous with black streaks. The Tristan bunting and the Grosbeak bunting are olive-green with brownish markings above and yellow below; the Tristan species is reported to occur as brightly colored birds or dull colored birds. These birds are omnivorous, apparently feeding on seeds, berries, flowers, insects, and small invertebrates, in proportions that vary with habitat.

Breeding season varies with species and location and is not well known. Clutch size is one or two, usually two. Incubation period for the Tristan bunting has been reported as 18 days and nestling period as 19 days. The possibility of a second brood in one season has been reported for the Grosbeak bunting.

Habitat and Current Distribution

All three of these buntings are endemic to islands in the Tristan da Cunha group in the South Atlantic. The Gough bunting is restricted to Gough Island, where its population is estimated at approximately 200 pairs. The Tristan bunting occurs on Nightingale and Inaccessible Islands, where population is estimated to be at least several thousand. The Grosbeak bunting is confined to woodland on Nightingale and Inaccessible Islands, where population is estimated to be in the low hundreds.

There are three vegetation types on the island of Gough and the preference of the Gough bunting is uncertain. It is often reported close to or on the seashore, at the edge of sea-cliffs, and along coasts on open upper ground. The preferred habitat of the Tristan bunting on Nightingale Island appears to be tussock-grass (*Spartina arundinacea*); on Inaccessible Island, coastal tussock-grass is replaced on the peaty plateau by fernbush (*Blechnum*) and island-tree (*Phylica arborea*) thickets. The Grosbeak bunting is a woodland species, specializing on the seeds of the island-tree (*Phylica arborea*) which forms groves on both Nightingale and Inaccessible.

History and Conservation Measures

All three of these bunting species are considered to be at risk because of their restricted island distribution. The Gough bunting was long considered to occur in plentiful numbers. In the 1950s population was estimated at 2,000 birds, but by 1974 total population was estimated at only about 200 birds. The Tristan bunting has been abundant on both Nightingale and Inaccessible Islands throughout the 1900s. It was once considered plentiful on Tristan da Cunha, with a population that was probably in the thousands

in 1817, but was uncommon by 1852, and extinct by 1873. The Grosbeak bunting appears to have never been numerous since records are available from the 1950s.

The primary threat to all of these birds is the risk of introduction of mammalian predators to their island habitats. Cats and rats would quickly decimate the bunting populations. Gough, in particular, is considered at risk because of a manned weather station that was established on the island in 1955. Habitat destruction or degradation may also be a long-term threat.

Gough Island was declared a wildlife reserve in 1963, but it has been recommended that permission to man the weather station be rescinded. Efforts were begun in the 1950s to establish management of Inaccessible and its wildlife, but more formal and concrete recognition of its importance to wildlife and science is still desirable.

Narosky's seedeater

Sporophila zelichi

Phylum	Chordata
Class	Aves
Order	Passeriformes
Family	Emberizidae
Status	Endangered, IUCN
Range	Argentina

Description and Biology

Narosky's seedeater, also called the Entre Ríos seedeater, is a small, gregarious finch about 4 in (10 cm) in length. Its crown is gray, its back, rump and underparts are a cinnamon chestnut color, and its tail is blackish. Its wings are also blackish with a white band and whitish edging. This species also has a broad white collar on the nape and sides of its neck, on its throat and on its chest. It has a thick bill and feeds on seeds from a variety of plants and grasses. Narosky's seedeater breeds sometime between November and March; after the nesting season in March adults and juveniles flock with closely related *Sporophila* species.

Habitat and Current Distribution

Known only from a few locations in Entre Ríos Province in northeastern Argentina, Narosky's seedeater lives primarily in marshes or partially open areas near small, clear streams, especially around patchy woodland. Like closely related species, it is believed to migrate, but its winter range, assumed to be north of its breeding range, has not been located. The population of Narosky's seedeater has not been estimated.

History and Conservation Measures

Narosky's seedeater was described as rare when it was first found in 1925. In the 1970s and 1980s, searches for wild birds were unsuccessful and only three captive birds were found, despite the fact that the species was well known to bird-trappers and collectors who reported frequent sightings in marshy areas in central and eastern parts of Entre Ríos Province.

This species is thought to be at serious risk from bird trappers. In Brazil and Argentina such trapping has led to serious declines of several species of seedeaters popular in the caged-bird trade; this species may be especially desired by bird collectors because of its conspicuous plumage. The degradation and burning of this seedeater's summer habitat poses an additional threat; overgrazing and fires in stands of tall native grasses seriously threaten the bird's breeding grounds.

Although this seedeater has been recorded in El Palmar National Park, no conservation efforts have been made on its behalf so far. The prohibition of bird trapping has been urged for this bird and for related species. It is also essential that the locations and sizes of surviving populations be determined; future surveys should include areas where the species has been known previously as well as adjacent areas containing suitable habitat. Preliminary work indicates that Puerto Boca is an important site for the breeding of Narosky's seedeater and of other threatened birds.

Kirtland's warbler

Dendroica kirtlandii

Phylum	Chordata
Class	Aves
Order	Passeriformes
Family	Parulidae
Status	Endangered, IUCN
	Endangered, USFWS
Range	Bahamas; Canada (?); U.S.A.

Description and Biology

The Kirtland's warbler is a songbird averaging 6 in (15 cm) in length. Its blue-gray head and upper body is contrasted with a yellow underside speckled with darker streaks. A spot, black in males and gray in females, can be seen on the bird's cheek and an incomplete ring surrounds its eye. The Kirtland's warbler has a habit of bobbing its tail as it moves along the ground.

Perhaps the warbler's most distinctive characteristic is its set of specialized breeding requirements. Kirtland's warblers select only large stands of young jack pine (*Pinus banksiana*) on relatively level ground within which to breed and nest. These tracts, almost always on a poor soil known as Grayling sand, must contain jack pines between 8 and 22 years in age (6.5-13 ft/2-4 m tall) and must stretch for at least 80 acres (32 hectares) to attract the birds. Such areas develop naturally only as a result of succession after intense forest fires. Kirtland's warblers reject areas with dense underbrush or forest dominated by deciduous trees.

The warbler builds a nest of grass, bark and fibers on the ground beneath a jack pine. The female lays three to five brown-speckled white eggs between mid-May and mid-July, incubating them for 10-14 days. Birds hatched during the summer depart for the wintering grounds around the end of August while the adults remain until late September.

Habitat and Current Distribution

The Kirtland's warbler breeds in only a few counties in north-central lower Michigan where extensive stands of its preferred jack pine are found. Warblers migrate to the Bahamas and the Turks and Caicos Islands near the Dominican Republic, via North and South Carolina. Wintering habitat consists of low scrubland commonly found within its wintering range.

Kirtland's warbler feeding her young.

During the summer, a few individuals are occasionally spotted in Wisconsin and Minnesota and even Ontario or Quebec, Canada, though there is no evidence of nesting in these areas.

A 1951 census of the warbler's population found 432 territorial males; this number increased to 502 males by 1961. An alarming drop to only 167 had taken place by the mid-1970s, but since that time, numbers have increased to a total of 610 singing males in 1994 (implying a total population of 1,200 or more birds), though the bird has suffered significant drops in population during some years.

History and Conservation Measures

The Kirtland's warbler was first discovered in the Bahamas in 1841, but it was 60 years before its nesting grounds were discovered in Michigan. These were found near the Au Sable River in 1903, at the border of Oscoda and Crawford counties. Roughly 90 percent of the warbler's known nesting activity occurs in a three-county vicinity surrounding the site of its discovery.

In 1951, a population census for the Kirtland's warbler was carried out, possibly the first such effort made for a songbird. Within ten years, both the state of Michigan and the United States Forest Service had set aside tracts of forest to serve as management areas for the warbler; within these areas, occasional controlled burns and plantings maintain suitable habitat for nesting.

Though the warbler was probably never abundant due to its very specialized ecological require-ments, a number of factors have impacted it. First, extensive logging in Michigan around the turn of the century completely disrupted the forest ecosystem and its normal succession. In the twentieth century, management policies limiting the occurrence of fire have reduced suitable habitat, as has the replacement of scraggly jack pines with red pines or hardwoods preferred for human use. It is estimated that of 15,000 acres (6,070 hectares) suitable for nesting in the 1950s and 1960s, only about 30 percent, or 4,500 acres (1,820 hectares) is usable today.

Furthermore, the elimination and fragmentation of large tracts of forest accompanying the human presence in the region has reduced habitat as well as encouraging the expansion of the brown-headed cowbird (*Molothrus ater*). This parasitic species, a native of farmland and meadowland, can penetrate all but very large tracts of forest, where it lays its eggs in the nests of other birds including the Kirtland's warbler. From the 1930s to the 1970s, as many as 60 percent of warbler nests were observed to be parasitized; a control program initiated in the early 1970s has reduced this number to 0-9 percent.

The recovery of the warbler will require a continued cowbird management effort, as well as controlled burns, prohibition of human activities in nesting areas, and plantings of jack pine which will at once provide habitat and create expanses of forest too large for cowbirds to invade. Studies of the warbler at its wintering grounds are also needed to determine what steps might be needed for its protection outside of the breeding season.

Bachman's warbler

Vermivora bachmanii

Phylum	Chordata
Class	Aves
Order	Passeriformes
Family	Parulidae
Status	Endangered/Extinct, IUCN
	Endangered, USFWS
Range	Cuba (?); U.S.A.

Description and Biology

If it still exists, the Bachman's warbler is North America's rarest songbird. It has an olive-green back and tail, yellow breast, belly, and face, and a black cap and bib. The female is generally more muted in color and her cap and bib are gray. At 4.75 in (12 cm) long, the warbler is smaller than a sparrow. Its long, pointed bill is used to probe into dense vegetation, dead leaves, and vines to find the insects that form the mainstay of its diet.

The nest is built close to the ground of leaves, grass, and moss; the female incubates three or four eggs for 10-14 days.

Habitat and Current Distribution

The species formerly bred in Missouri, Arkansas, Kentucky, Alabama, and South Carolina, migrating through Florida to winter on Cuba. Present distribution is virtually unknown and the species may already be extinct. Recent sightings have been reported in South Carolina (several records in 1970s), Louisiana (several records in 1970 and one in 1988), and Cuba (eight unconfirmed records between 1978 and 1988). If a breeding ground remains, it may be in inaccessible parts of the I'On Swamp in South Carolina.

Preferred nesting habitat is dense swampy woodland in mature forests. It is suspected that this warbler may inhabit thickets of cane (canebrakes), particularly of the bamboo *Arundinaria gigantea*.

History and Conservation Measures

The Bachman's warbler was first discovered in 1833 by John Bachman, after whom it was named, and was quite common until around 1900. By 1920 the species was rare and very locally distributed. After 1950, sightings became very infrequent, with the last confirmed sighting in Louisiana in 1988. Those species faced habitat destruction, both within breeding grounds in the United States and in the winter range in Cuba. Swampy forests have been drained, cut for lumber, and cleared for agricultural use.

If this warbler is, as suspected, a canebrake specialist, there is even less hope for its survival because, while there remain usable swampy woodlands, canebrakes of sufficient size have been almost completely wiped out for flood control reasons. Because the status of this bird is uncertain, conservation efforts are directed at monitoring last-known habitat for the return of nesting birds. A recent search of the Tensas National Wildlife Refuge was unsuccessful in documenting the presence of Bachman's warbler in the Tensas River basin. Unless and until its continued survival can be confirmed, no other conservation efforts are possible.

Nukupuu

Hemignathus lucidus

Phylum	Chordata
Class	Aves
Order	Passeriformes
Family	Drepanididae
Status	Endangered, IUCN
	Endangered, USFWS
Range	Hawaii (U.S.A.)

Description and Biology

The nukupuu is distinguished by its unique bill—the sickle-shaped upper mandible curves sharply over the lower portion, which is about half as long. Within this particular species of honeycreeper, three subspecies have been recognized: the Maui nukupuu (*H. l. affinis*), the Kauai nukupuu (*H. l. lucidus*), and the Oahu nukupuu (*H. l. hanapepe*). The Maui and Kauai subspecies are similar in appearance: bright yellow plumage adorns the head, throat, and breast of males, and their lores (the space between a bird's eye and the bill) are both connected by a black band. However, the Maui nukupuu has a grayish olive-green back and yellow abdomen, while the Kauai nukupuu has a yellowish olive-green back and white abdomen. Now extinct, the Oahu nukupuu possessed a dark olive-green back and a brighter green head and wings. Adult males average 5.5 in (14 cm), while females are slightly smaller. Female nukupuus are also less brilliantly colored than males. Most are olive-gray on the upper body and dull white to gray on the lower body with only a yellow tinge on the throat. The tail of both sexes is very short.

The nukupuu feeds by hammering on the bark of trees to expose beetles, caterpillars, spiders, and insect larvae. The bird also occasionally takes nectar from flowering plants. No information is currently available about the species' reproductive biology.

Habitat and Current Distribution

The Maui nukupuu occurs on the slopes of the Haleakala volcano on the Hawaiian island of Maui, where the population has been estimated to be fewer than 30 birds. The Kauai nukupuu has been reported from the Alakai Swamp and upper Hanapepe Valley on Kauai island, but no recent sightings have been made, leading conservationists to conclude that either the population is extremely small or that the subspecies is extinct. The Oahu nukupuu originally inhabited the island of Oahu.

The nukupuu prefers undisturbed rain forest habitat. The Kauai nukupuu inhabits swampland, and the Maui nukupuu has been sighted in forests and woodlands.

History and Conservation Measures

Naturalists have always considered the nukupuu to be rare or uncommon. The Maui nukupuu was declared extinct in the late nineteenth century, but was rediscovered on the northwestern slopes of Haleakala in 1967. Since 1899 the Kauai nukupuu has been sighted fewer than ten times, and a survey conducted on Kauai in 1989 failed to locate any individuals.

The decline of the nukupuu and other native Hawaiian species is primarily due to habitat destruction and alteration. Logging and agricultural development have led to the clearing of vast areas of forest. Introduced grazing and browsing animals such as cattle and goats have destroyed much of the remaining forest's undergrowth, allowing alien plant species to flourish at the expense of native species. Such changes in the forest often affect the food supply of native species. In addition, introduced bird species may be competitors or the carriers of avian diseases. Introduced predators such as rats and now perhaps mongooses may pose a further threat to the nukupuu, as they do to other native bird species.

On Maui, Haleakala National Park and the Hanawi Natural Area Reserve encompass the range of the Maui nukupuu. Officials at these two sites have implemented programs to control feral pigs and other ungulates as well as exotic vegetation. The range of the Kauai nukupuu is contained within the island's Alakai Wilderness Preserve, where similar conservation measures are being taken.

Akiapolaau

Hemignathus wilsoni (munroi)

Phylum	Chordata
Class	Aves
Order	Passeriformes
Family	Drepanididae
Status	Endangered, IUCN
	Endangered, USFWS
Range	Hawaii (U.S.A.)

Description and Biology

Actually a finch, the akiapolaau somewhat resembles a tree creeper in its appearance and feeding habits. It has a fairly stout body, a short tail, and a unique deeply curved bill specially adapted for feeding on insects and insect larvae in tree bark; while the short lower mandible is straight, the upper mandible is long and curves sharply downward. Its average length is 5.5 in (14 cm) and it weighs around 1 oz (28 g). Plumage of the male is green above with yellow underparts and head; the female is mostly green, but the underparts are yellow-green.

The akiapolaau has been observed in family groups of male, female, and young. Little is known of reproductive biology.

Habitat and Current Distribution

This species is limited to forest patches in the Kona district of the island of Hawaii. Population is estimated at approximately 1,500 birds, with the largest concentration in or around the Kilauea Forest Reserve.

Primary habitat includes native forest trees such as the koa (*Acacia*), mamane (*Sophora*), naio (*Myoporum*), and ohia (*Metrosideros*) at elevations of 1,600-6,000 ft (500-1,800 m).

History and Conservation Measures

Around 1900, the akiapolaau was considered common throughout the upland forests on Hawaii. It has experienced a very serious decline since that time, primarily due to clearance and degradation of native forest, with the introduction of predators as a further limiting factor.

Destruction of forest for residential and commercial development, logging activity, clearance for agriculture, and conversion for pasturage have left few tracts of forest suitable for the akiapolaau. Nests and juveniles are targets of such introduced predators as rats, cats, and mongoose.

Conservation measures for this species include legal protection and the recent establishment of the Hakalau Forest National Wildlife Refuge. Efforts have been made to improve forest habitat by controlling or eliminating grazing animals, especially sheep, to allow natural regeneration. Reforestation is also in progress, along with control of introduced plants. Surveys and studies are underway to learn more about the life cycle and ecology of the akiapolaau and to better determine factors that are limiting population.

Poo-uli

Melamprosops phaeosoma

Phylum	Chordata
Class	Aves
Order	Passeriformes
Family	Drepanididae
Status	Rare, IUCN
	Endangered, USFWS
Range	Hawaii (U.S.A.)

Description and Biology

The poo-uli is also referred to as the black-faced honeycreeper due to its black, mask-like facial markings. Its upper plumage is brown, with lighter, cinnamon-colored to reddish brown underparts. The throat and upper breast are white. The plump body of the poo-uli averages 5.5 in (14 cm) in length, including its short bill and tail. This honeycreeper primarily feeds on snails and beetles, which it finds by picking through bark and moss.

Habitat and Current Distribution

This species has only been reported from the slopes of the Haleakala volcano on the island of Maui at elevations of 5,000-6,800 ft (1,500-2,100 m). Estimates from the late 1980s place the species' population at 140 birds.

The poo-uli prefers the dense undergrowth of wet, closed canopy ohia forest at high elevations.

History and Conservation Measures

Not discovered until 1973, the poo-uli has probably always existed in small numbers. However, the widespread habitat destruction and alteration which caused the decline of other native Hawaiian bird species has undoubtedly affected the poo-uli as well.

Vast areas of forest have been cleared as a result of logging and agricultural development. Introduced grazing and browsing animals such as cattle and goats have destroyed much of the remaining forest's undergrowth, allowing alien plant species to flourish at the expense of native species. Such changes in the forest's structure often affect the food supply of native species. In addition, introduced bird species may be competitors or the carriers of avian diseases. Introduced predators such as cats, rats and now perhaps mongooses likely pose a further threat to the poo-uli, as they do to other native bird species.

For conservationists, the stabilization and restoration of habitat is fundamental to preserving the poo-uli and other native Hawaiian birds. At the Hanawi Natural Area Reserve, which encompasses most of the known poo-uli habitat, programs to control wild pigs and other feral ungulates have been implemented. Officials at the Haleakala National Park and the Waikamoi Preserve have taken similar measures. Captive breeding has also been suggested; however, such a stopgap measure may only temporarily delay the species' extinction.

Kauai creeper

Oreomystis bairdi

Phylum	Chordata
Class	Aves
Order	Passeriformes
Family	Drepanididae
Status	Rare, IUCN
Range	Hawaii (U.S.A.)

Description and Biology

Also called the akikiki, the Kauai creeper measures approximately 4.5 in (11 cm) in length. The upperparts of adult birds are brownish gray, while the underparts vary from cream to white. The species' song consists of descending trills, and its call is a low "chip" sound. Like other honeycreepers, the Kauai creeper forages in trees for insects and other invertebrates. It is usually observed in family groups, which occasionally join larger flocks of mixed species.

Little is known about the reproductive biology of the Kauai creeper. A few cup-shaped nests have been found in the spring, built approximately 26 ft (8 m) off the ground in ohia trees. Nestlings have brownish green color on the back and wings, white down, and bright yellow beaks.

Habitat and Current Distribution

The Kauai creeper has been reported from mountainous areas on the island of Kauai at altitudes above 3,700 ft (1,100 m). The largest population, estimated at fewer than 7,000 birds, occupies the Alakai Swamp, where the ohia is the dominant tree.

This species prefers the dense understory of montane rain forest.

History and Conservation Measures

Once quite common throughout the native forests of Kauai, the Kauai creeper has since declined in the second half of this century. Surviving individuals are still fairly common within the Alakai Swamp; however, this area represents a fraction of the bird's original range.

The decline of the Kauai creeper and other native Hawaiian species is primarily due to habitat destruction and alteration. Vast areas of forest have been cleared as a result of logging and agricultural development. Introduced grazing and browsing animals such as cattle and goats have destroyed much of the remaining forest's undergrowth, allowing alien plant species to flourish at the expense of native species. Such changes in the forest's structure often affect the food supply of native animals. In addition, the Kauai creeper must compete with introduced species such as the Japanese white-eye (*Zosterops japonica*). Introduced predators, particularly rats, have also adversely affected the Kauai creeper.

The species' range falls with in the Alakai Swamp Wilderness Preserve, and the continued protection of habitat within this area is essential for the survival of the Kauai creeper and other native birds.

Crested honeycreeper

Palmeria dolei

Phylum	Chordata
Class	Aves
Order	Passeriformes
Family	Drepanididae
Status	Vulnerable, IUCN
	Endangered, USFWS
Range	Hawaii (U.S.A.)

Description and Biology

The crested honeycreeper, or akohekohe, is a small songbird with gray and orange flecks in its black plumage, orange bars on the wings, and an orange band on the back of its neck. It has a straight, pointed bill and a gray or white tufted crest on the forehead. Average size is 7 in (17.8 cm). The akohekohe takes nectar from the ohia (*Metrosideros* sp.) and from a number of other flowering plants; it also feeds on insects and fruits.

Little is known about its reproductive biology, but the species is thought to nest in February or March.

Habitat and Current Distribution

This species occurs in high elevation rain forest on the Haleakala Volcano on the island of Maui in the Hawaiian Islands; it is most often found at elevations of 4,000-7,000 ft (1,200-2,100 m). The population has been estimated at 3,800 birds.

History and Conservation Measures

The crested honeycreeper was once at least locally common on the islands of Molokai and Maui but has been extinct on Molokai since 1907 and is now confined to a narrow area of wet upland forest on Maui, where it was once considered extinct.

The decline of this species is attributed to the introduction of alien flora and fauna to the islands and to habitat destruction and degradation. Introduced rats prey on this species, and some introduced birds are competitors. In addition, introduced pigs, goats, and deer have degraded natural vegetation, allowing non-native plants to thrive. Island birds have also been affected by disease from these introduced animals. Finally, large areas of forest have been cleared for human settlements.

Primary conservation efforts are directed at stabilizing and restoring essential habitat. Fencing certain areas and controlling the population of feral animals and exotic vegetation are currently in process, particularly in such protected areas as the Hanawi Natural Area Reserve, Haleakala National Park, and Waikamoi Preserve. Because a species with such limited range and population is subject to sudden catastrophe, a captive-breeding program should be initiated to guard against extinction and to provide birds for possible re-introduction to the wild.

Maui parrotbill

Pseudonestor xanthophrys

Phylum	Chordata
Class	Aves
Order	Passeriformes
Family	Drepanididae
Status	Vulnerable, IUCN
	Endangered, USFWS
Range	Island of Maui, Hawaii (U.S.A.)

Description and Biology

This honeycreeper is named for its thickset, hooked beak that is reminiscent of a parrot's bill. It is a stocky bird averaging 5.5 in (14 cm) in length at physical maturity, and it has a short tail. Its underside is yellow, while its upper body is green with a yellow streak above the eyes. It moves slowly along tree or shrub branches, sometimes hanging upside down, and it feeds on various insects including caterpillars. To reach these larvae, it uses its strong bill to crush or tear away dead wood and reach the larvae below. Predators of this bird include rats, which can climb trees to feast on eggs and young birds. Feral pigs also create problems, not through predation but because they damage undergrowth by rooting and trampling.

Nesting and breeding information for the Maui parrotbill is unknown.

Habitat and Current Distribution

This parrotbill is found on the eastern slopes of Haleakala, an extinct volcano on Maui in the Hawaiian Islands. Population is estimated at approximately 500 birds.

The species' habitat is ohia (*Metrosideros colina*, a Pacific Islands member of the myrtle family) forests above 5,000 ft (1,500 m) elevation. The bird prefers forest with thick undergrowth and open tree canopy.

History and Conservation Measures

This species is considered to have been rare from the time it was discovered by western ornithologists in the 1890s. It was previously found in koa (*Acacia koa*, a Hawaiian timber tree) forests at 5,000 ft (1,500 m) elevation on the northwestern slopes of Haleakala Crater, but it is now found only in ohia forests above that elevation.

The Maui parrotbill, like many other Hawaiian birds, is vulnerable to a number of threats that have been introduced to the islands. Rats are predators; feral pigs destroy undergrowth; introduced plants and insects disrupt habitat; and avian diseases are spread by introduced mosquitoes. To a rare and localized species, these threats can have a devastating impact.

Currently, conservation efforts are being directed to the stabilization and restoration of essential habitat. Specific projects include fencing and controlling feral ungulates at the Hanawi Natural Area Reserve and controlling feral animals and exotic vegetation at both the Haleakala National Park and the Nature Conservancy at Waikamoi Preserve.

Ou

Psittirostra psittacea

Phylum	Chordata
Class	Aves
Order	Passeriformes
Family	Drepanididae
Status	Endangered, IUCN
	Endangered, USFWS
Range	Hawaii (U.S.A.)

Description and Biology

The ou has an olive-green back with underparts that vary in color from olive-green to white on the abdomen. The wings and tail are black-brown and are fringed with olive-green. Males have a bright yellow head. The bill of both sexes resembles that of a parrot. Considered among the larger Hawaiian honeycreepers, adult ous measure approximately 6 in (16 cm) long.

The species feeds primarily on the fruit of the ieie (*Freycinetia*) plant. However, the ou will also consume flowers, nectar, and insects, particularly caterpillars of the family Geometridae. Caterpillars are the primary food source for immature ous. The song of the ou has been described as similar to that of a canary, with three to four distinct whistled notes proceeding the full song. The species' call is a long note which rises in pitch as it ends.

Habitat and Current Distribution

This species occurs on the island of Hawaii in ohia forests at elevations of 2,600-5,000 ft (800-1,500 m) and on the island of Kauai in the Alakai Swamp. In the early to mid-1980s, conservationists estimated the population on Hawaii at 300 to 400 birds and 100 on Kauai. However, only three birds were located on

Kauai during a survey of the island in 1989, and no recent sightings have been made on Hawaii.

The ou prefers the upper canopy of undisturbed wet forest.

History and Conservation Measures

Once relatively common, the ou occurred on several Hawaiian islands in addition to Kauai and Hawaii, mainly Oahu, Molokai, Lanai, and Maui. However, habitat destruction and degradation resulting from European settlement of the islands has led to the species' decline. Logging and agricultural development has resulted in the clearing of vast tracts of forest. In addition, grazing livestock has consumed much of the original undergrowth in these areas, allowing introduced vegetation to quickly spread at the expense of native species such as the ieie. A mysterious dieback of ohia, a tree often used by island birds, has also adversely affected the ou's habitat. Cats, rats and other introduced species have had a detrimental effect on the ou as well as other indigenous animals. In addition to preying on eggs and young, these animals compete with native species for food, and introduced insects can often carry avian diseases.

On the island of Hawaii, the Hakalau Forest National Wildlife Refuge encompasses large areas of habitat suitable for native birds. Programs to control feral animals and exotic vegetation have been put in place at the refuge. Also, population surveys are regularly carried out at the site, and studies have been made to determine how best to counteract the decline of the ou and other endangered bird species. On Kauai, similar measures are being taken; in addition, plans for a captive breeding program are being evaluated. On both islands, habitat conservation and management remains a priority.

Laysan finch

Telespiza (Psittirostra) cantans

Phylum	Chordata
Class	Aves
Order	Passeriformes
Family	Drepanididae
Status	Rare, IUCN
	Endangered, USFWS
Range	Hawaii (U.S.A.)

Description and Biology

The Laysan finch is a songbird with an average size of 6 in (15.2 cm). The upper plumage of the female is a fairly regular pattern of black streaks tinged with yellow-green on a brown background. The underparts are streaked brown and vary from light yellow on the breast to dull white on the abdomen and tail coverts. During the breeding season, the male has bright yellow plumage in its head, throat, and breast. The upper back of the male is yellow-green with broad black streaks, while the lower back is gray. The male's wings are black with yellow-green edging, and its brown tail is also edged with yellow-green. Both sexes have a heavy, gray bill. A widely varied diet includes seeds, shoots, flowers, fruits, insects and their larvae, and seabird eggs.

Breeding season extends from April to June. Laysan finches usually build their nests in clumps of bunchgrass 4 to 17 in (10-43 cm) off the ground. A clutch of three eggs is laid and then incubated for approximately 16 days. The young fledge in just over a month.

Habitat and Current Distribution

This species is endemic to Laysan Island in northwestern Hawaiian Islands and has been introduced to nearby Pearl Island and Hermes Reef as well as other small islands in the vicinity. The population on Laysan is estimated to be at least 10,000 birds, while the introduced populations total 500-1,000 if not more.

Primary habitat on Laysan includes sand dunes

Laysan finch.

around the coastline, with a brackish lagoon in the center of the island. The finch prefers areas of dense scrub or vegetation.

History and Conservation Measures

Early explorers characterized the Laysan finch as a common species with a pleasing song that made it a good cage bird. Near the turn of the century, it was estimated that as many as 4,000 birds may have inhabited Laysan. However, rabbits introduced to the island in 1903 and 1904 decimated the natural vegetation, destroying most of the habitat and food supply for native birds. In 1909 President Theodore Roosevelt designated Laysan and other leeward islands in the Hawaiian chain as part of the Hawaiian Islands Bird Reservation. However, this move had little immediate benefit, and the species' population declined to about 100 birds before the last rabbits were finally removed from Laysan in 1923. Naturalists believe that the finch survived only because it could use a variety of food sources.

Despite a seemingly abundant population today, the Laysan finch is still threatened by introduced animals, including predators such as rats. The species is also susceptible to avian diseases, often borne by introduced birds and insects. An encouraging development, however, is the successful establishment of viable populations on other islands, mitigating the possibility of extinction should a natural or human catastrophe devastate Laysan. Now part of the Hawaiian Islands National Wildlife Refuge, Laysan can be accessed by only a limited number of persons. Annual surveys of the finch and other native species are ongoing, as is a study of the finch's breeding biology.

Nihoa finch

Telespiza (Psittirostra) ultima

Phylum	Chordata
Class	Aves
Order	Passeriformes
Family	Drepanididae
Status	Rare, IUCN Endangered, USFWS
Range	Hawaii (U.S.A.)

Description and Biology

The Nihoa finch is a small songbird averaging 5.4 in (13.7 cm). Plumage of the female is a fairly regular pattern of brownish streaks, with greenish underparts. The male has darker streaks and is easily recognized by its yellow head, throat, and breast. Both sexes have a gray bill. An omnivorous diet includes seeds, flowers, bird eggs, and small invertebrates.

Breeding information is scarce. A clutch of three eggs is laid between February and March, and incubation has been reported in captivity to last 15 days.

Habitat and Current Distribution

This species is endemic to the island of Nihoa in the northwestern Hawaiian Island chain, where it prefers open areas with sparse vegetation. Population was estimated in the late 1980s at over 2,000 individuals.

History and Conservation Measures

The population of the Nihoa finch has fluctuated from a reported low of 500 in the 1960s to a possible high of 5,000 in the 1970s. Like all island populations, it faces the threat of natural disaster, introduced predators, introduced plants that degrade habitat, and introduced disease.

Attempts to introduce the finch to neighboring islands as a safeguard against extinction have thus far been unsuccessful. Nihoa has been managed as a wildlife refuge with restricted access, in an attempt to protect remaining habitat and prevent the introduction of exotic organisms. Annual surveys are ongoing, as is a study of the species' breeding biology.

Black-capped vireo

Vireo atricapillus

Phylum	Chordata
Class	Aves
Order	Passeriformes
Family	Vireonidae
Status	Endangered, IUCN
	Endangered, USFWS
Range	Mexico; Oklahoma, Texas (U.S.A.)

Description and Biology

This small songbird averages about 4.7 in (12 cm) long. Plumage is dull yellowish green above and whitish below; the female is slightly darker, with yellowish underparts. The head is black in the male and gray in the female, with white eye markings in both. The vireo forages in leaves and branches for insects, spiders, fruit, and seeds.

The black-capped vireo lays three to five small eggs in a rounded nest made of vegetation; incubation lasts 14-17 days and is shared by the male and the female. After the young leave the nest, the female may lay eggs again. Snakes and scrub jays sometimes prey on eggs and young.

Habitat and Current Distribution

Today this species breeds only in west-central Oklahoma, Texas, and Coahuila, Mexico; its winter range is poorly surveyed, but records exist from four districts in central and western Mexico: Durango, Sinaloa, Nayarit, and Jalisco. The breeding population is estimated to be approximately 300 birds in Oklahoma and 1,200 in Texas. Estimates of the breeding population in Coahuila vary so drastically as to be quite controversial; recent surveys have located fewer than 30 birds, but other estimates range from several hundred pairs to over 9,000 pairs.

The black-capped vireo requires a very specific nesting habitat; it nests in shrubby growth in the transition zones between forest and grassland, in which vegetation of varying size is distributed irregularly. Moreover, its nesting grounds, usually on rocky slopes or eroded banks, include open spaces between thickets of vegetation, with vegetation extending to ground level. The vireo's winter habitat is poorly understood, but wintering birds have been seen in a variety of habitats.

History and Conservation Measures

At one time, the black-capped vireo bred through much of the south-central United States, including parts of Kansas, Oklahoma, and Texas south to Coahuila, Mexico. Destruction of habitat caused by development, urbanization, agriculture, and livestock overgrazing has fragmented the bird's nesting habitat over the years; other alterations such as ecological succession and the invasion of junipers have also negatively affected this bird's habitat.

A related problem is parasitism by the brown-headed cowbird (*Molothrus ater*). Originally native to grasslands and prairies, the cowbird has spread over a much larger range as woodlands have been fragmented and converted by human activity. The cowbird lays its eggs in songbird nests, including those of the black-capped vireo. Cowbird young then out-compete the host species' chicks for parental food, often killing the host's young. In some areas, cowbird parasitism in vireo nests is estimated to exceed 90 percent.

Conservation measures for the black-capped vireo are focused on cowbird control programs and habitat protection. A National Wildlife Refuge is being established outside of Austin, Texas specifically to maintain habitat for the vireo. In addition, studies of the population, distribution, and habitat requirements of breeding and wintering vireos in Mexico need to be initiated before a recovery program can begin there.

Yellow-shouldered blackbird

Agelaius xanthomus

Phylum	Chordata
Class	Aves
Order	Passeriformes
Family	Icteridae
Status	Endangered, IUCN
	Endangered, USFWS
Range	Puerto Rico (U.S.A.)

Description and Biology

The rare yellow-shouldered blackbird is related and similar to the abundant North American red-winged blackbird (*A. phoeniceus*). Its body is dark gray and 7-9 in (18-23 cm) long with a distinctive yellow patch on the shoulder, from which its name is derived. The female is smaller than the male. Diet consists primarily of arthropods, which the birds forage from plants as well as from the leaves, branches, and bark of trees. Plant material also supplements the species' diet.

Blackbirds nest in colonies and defend the immediate territory around the nests. Mating usually takes place in April or May— though it seems to vary slightly according to the spring rains— between monogamous pairs. The female incubates and broods throughout the incubation period of 12 to 14 days; the male and female share food-gathering duties for the two to three nestlings.

There are two subspecies, both of which are considered endangered: the Puerto Rico yellow-shouldered blackbird (*A. x. xanthomus*) and the Mona yellow-shouldered blackbird (*A. x. monensis*).

Habitat and Current Distribution

The Puerto Rican subspecies nests in coconut palms and mangroves, most often on offshore islets.

Approximately 25 birds can be found on the east side of the island and 350 in the arid scrubland areas of the southwest coast.

The Mona Island subspecies consists of 400-900 birds that nest on ledges or in crevices of the sheer coastal cliffs.

History and Conservation Measures

The Puerto Rico yellow-shouldered blackbird was once abundant throughout the entire coastal plain of Puerto Rico. In the 1970s, population was estimated at 200 birds in eastern Puerto Rico and 2,000 in southwestern Puerto Rico. Its habitat consisted of many different landscapes, including freshwater wetlands, fields, mangroves, and open woodlands. Drainage of almost all of the wetland areas is thought to have been responsible for the species' decline; nest predation by such mammals as mongooses, rats, and cats also continues to contribute to the decline. A more recent threat is the parasitism of nests by the shiny cowbird (*Molothrus bonariensis*), which has been established on Puerto Rico since 1955.

The Mona yellow-shouldered blackbird is found on Mona Island, between Puerto Rico and Hispaniola, West Indies. In addition to historical problems, current threats include the loss of nesting and feeding habitats caused by development on the island, and the introduction of the shiny cowbird.

Steps being taken to assist the recovery of the species include cowbird control, provision of artificial nest structures, official protection of areas like Puerto Rico's Boquerón Commonwealth Forest, where many blackbirds are found, and studies of possible impacts of pesticides. Recovery goals for *A. x. xanthomus,* which has declined drastically in the last 20 years, include maintenance of a minimum of two distinct populations of at least 250 pairs at Roosevelt Roads Naval Station and 1,000 pairs in southwestern Puerto Rico. The previous recovery goal for *A. x. monensis* was the maintenance of a minimum population of at least 250 pairs at Mona Island; that figure has now been exceeded.

Martinique oriole

Icterus bonana

Phylum	Chordata
Class	Aves
Order	Passeriformes
Family	Drepanididae
Status	Endangered, IUCN
Range	Martinique (West Indies)

Description and Biology

The Martinique oriole is a canopy forager, feeding on fruit, berries, and a large variety of insects. This oriole does not appear to form flocks and does not breed communally. Feeding has not been recorded more than 330 ft (100 m) from the nest, and the species apparently defends only a small territory in the immediate vicinity of the nesting site. Breeding has been recorded from December onwards, but the season generally starts in February. Clutch size is three; most young have fledged by mid-July.

Habitat and Current Distribution

This bird is endemic to the French island of Martinique, West Indies. Population size has never been estimated, but it is considered small.

The Martinique oriole apparently inhabits all of the island's forest types; it inhabits dry forest, moist forest, plantations, gardens with trees, and rain forest, with all records coming from below 2,300 ft (700 m). Breeding has been recorded in all habitats except rain forest and wet tropical forest. The nest is built 6.6-13 ft (2-4 m) above the ground and suspended from a large leaf or at the end of a branch.

History and Conservation Measures

This species was originally distributed throughout the forested areas of the island, but its population has declined, especially in coastal mangrove and dry forest areas. At certain census sites, a 75-100 percent decline was recorded in the 1980s. The primary threat to this species is brood-parasitism by the shiny cowbird (*Molothrus bonariensis*), which colonized Martinique during the late 1940s and is increasing in number every year. By some accounts, this bird has taken over 75 percent of the Martinique oriole's nests. The population of the Carib grackle (*Quiscalus lugubris*), which is a natural predator of Martinique oriole eggs and nestlings, is also increasing. Habitat loss and illegal hunting are apparently not threats to this oriole, but deforestation may have played a role in the increase of the predator's population.

Other than legal protection, there have been no conservation measures taken on behalf of this species. Control and elimination of the shiny cowbird have been recommended, along with better monitoring of the oriole's reproductive success. Assessment should also be made of the effect of Carib grackles on the oriole population. Finally, a public awareness campaign should be initiated to focus on the species' plight and its importance as Martinique's only endemic bird.

Pampas meadowlark

Sturnella militaris (defilippi)

Phylum	Chordata
Class	Aves
Order	Passeriformes
Family	Icteridae
Status	Indeterminate, IUCN
Range	Argentina; Brazil (?); Uruguay

Description and Biology

This species is variously known as the Pampas meadowlark, for its grassland habitat, and the lesser red-breasted meadowlark, for its bright red breast and throat. The rest of the plumage is black with whitish underparts. The bird's average size is around 8 in (20 cm). Its diet generally consists of insects, grasses and seeds.

A highly sociable bird that gathers in flocks, the meadowlark breeds in November, when three or four eggs are laid. It builds its nest on the ground, using grass to cover the nest and conceal it from predators.

Habitat and Current Distribution

The Pampas meadowlark occurs in central-eastern Argentina, Uruguay, and southeastern Brazil. The majority of the species' total breeding population occurs in Argentina, where it has declined severely, with almost all recent records being from the Buenos Aires Province, where it is still occasionally reported in flocks of 30-100 birds. In Brazil, where the species is probably a rare winter visitor, flocks of around 35 birds have been reported. The Pampas meadowlark has also been reported as a rare resident of Uruguay. There are no estimates of total population size.

The species' primary habitat includes pampas grasslands, but it can also inhabit short meadows with small shrubs, open bunch-grass, wheat, and mixed grass with arable weeds.

History and Conservation Measures

Although it has always been rare in Brazil and Uruguay, this meadowlark was once common in central-eastern Argentina. However, it has suffered a drastic decline in Argentina in the past century. Population and overall range have been greatly reduced by cultivation and overgrazing. In Buenos Aires, large areas of grassland have been converted to sunflower plantations. Competition with the white-browed blackbird (*Leistes superciliaris*) and the long-tailed meadowlark (*Sturnella loyca*) has been suggested as a possible threat, but investigations are necessary to determine the seriousness of such threats.

The species has legal protection in Brazil but is not known to occur in any protected areas. Surveys are necessary in Argentina to determine the most important breeding grounds and to estimate the populations within them. In Uruguay, where the current status of the species is poorly known, studies should be conducted to determine its distribution, population, possible key sites, and general biology.

Red siskin

Carduelis (Spinus) cucullata

Phylum	Chordata
Class	Aves
Order	Passeriformes
Family	Fringillidae
Status	Endangered, IUCN
	Endangered, USFWS
	Appendix I, CITES
Range	Colombia; Venezuela

Description and Biology

The red siskin is a vibrantly colored finch approximately 4 in (10 cm) long, with a black tail and side patch and a black and white pattern on the end of the wings. The female has red-brown wings with black and white coloration underneath. It feeds on a variety of seeds from wild herbs, grass, and fruits.

In a nest built of grass or moss, the female lays four red-spotted eggs. The male feeds the female while she incubates the eggs for approximately 12 days. Together, they care for the nestlings until they become independent after about six weeks.

Habitat and Current Distribution

This bird has been reduced to a patchy distribution in northern Venezuela. In 1981, population was estimated at 6,000 birds.

Habitats consist of tropical forest, open dry scrub, and pastureland.

History and Conservation Measures

Since about 1835 the red siskin roamed in semi-nomadic flocks over much of northern South America, from northeastern Colombia through northern Venezuela to Trinidad. Early in the 1900s, trappers began to export it to Europe and North America, and it began to disappear from the more accessible areas of Venezuela. This bird is attractive to collectors for a number of reasons. The more brilliantly colored male, because of its beauty, is in great demand as a cage bird. The male is also valuable because it can be crossed with domestic canaries to introduce genes for red plumage. This hybridization produces fertile males which can then be crossed to produce a variety of shades of canaries. The attempt by some aviculturists to breed the red siskin in captivity has created demand for both male and female wild birds. Although the species is legally protected, trapping still continues.

Ankober serin

Serinus ankoberensis

Yellow-throated serin

Serinus flavigula

Phylum	Chordata
Class	Aves
Order	Passeriformes
Family	Fringillidae
Status	Rare, IUCN (*S. ankoberensis*)
	Indeterminate, IUCN (*S. flavigula*)
Range	Ethiopia

Description and Biology

Little is known about these small finches, especially about the yellow-throated serin. The Ankober serin has creamy, streaky plumage which provides camouflage in its rocky habitat. It is a gregarious bird and feeds on grass and seeds.

The nest of an Ankober serin was found in February/March with three eggs; breeding also appeared to have taken place in September/October. Other information about reproductive biology is unknown.

Habitat and Current Distribution

The Ankober serin was found to occur in Shoa Province, Ethiopia, along the top edge of the extreme eastern escarpment of the West Highlands. Specimens of the yellow-throated serin were found at the foot of the eastern escarpment of the West Highlands, east of and below Ankober. There are no estimates of population for either species.

The Ankober serin is known to inhabit broken cliff-tops. It has been observed on sheer cliffs interspersed with areas of steep vegetated slopes and earth banks, where birds spent much time on rock surfaces; they were often seen clinging to vertical stone faces and bare earth banks and did not alight on any vegetation but grass. A nest was found inside a vertical hole on the underside of an overhanging earth bank. Little is known about the yellow-throated serin's habitat, except that it seems to prefer relatively arid locations.

History and Conservation Measures

The Ankober serin was first discovered in 1976 and has been recorded on several occasions since then; flocks of around 15 birds were seen in 1976 and 1977 and two flocks totaling about 50 birds were seen in 1981. The yellow-throated serin is known only from three specimens taken in one relatively small area in 1880, 1885, and 1886, and from sightings of birds in the same area in March 1989.

Although numbers are uncertain, the population of the Ankober serin is thought to be very small; there is no record of the numbers of birds seen at the time specimens of the yellow-throated serin were collected and its status is still uncertain. Other than their very restricted distributions, there are no identified threats to either species. Fieldwork is necessary to determine the range and population of both species and any possible threats they may face.

Mauritius fody

Foudia rubra

Yellow fody

Foudia flavicans

Seychelles fody

Foudia sechellarum

Phylum	Chordata
Class	Aves
Order	Passeriformes
Family	Ploceidae
Status	Endangered, IUCN (*F. rubra; F. flavicans*)
	Rare, IUCN (*F. sechellarum*)
	Endangered, USFWS (*F. sechellarum*)
Range	Mauritius; Seychelles (Indian Ocean)

Description and Biology

These three fodies inhabit islands in the Indian Ocean. The Mauritius fody feeds on insects, nectar, and small fruit. The yellow or Rodrigues fody forages by gleaning on flowers, leaves, and twigs; its diet consists mainly of insects (stick insects, black ants, coccids, planthoppers, leaf-rollers) and spiders but also includes nectar and seeds. The Seychelles fody has a widely varied diet that includes insects and other invertebrates caught on leaves, in cracks in bark, and among flowers; seeds; nectar; fruit; young skinks and geckos or gecko eggs; fish scavenged beneath seabird colonies; and eggs of seabirds.

Breeding for the Mauritius fody extends from October to the end of February, during which time males occupy a territory of 10-20 acres (4-8 ha). These birds tend to remain in pairs throughout the year and produce a clutch of two or three eggs. The yellow fody seems to be an opportunistic breeder, with breeding presumably related to weather. The birds generally remain in pairs throughout the year, and its territories are much smaller than those of the Mauritius fody—only around 0.5 acre (0.2 ha). Clutch size is two or three and two broods per year may be normal. With the Seychelles fody, nesting appears to extend throughout the year, though possibly with greater intensity in the rainy season. Clutch size is generally two. This species appears to be non-territorial and maintains pair bonds for several years, perhaps even for life.

Habitat and Current Distribution

The Mauritius fody is confined to upland areas of southwest Mauritius, an island in the Indian Ocean. In the mid-1970s, the breeding population of the species was estimated to be around 250 pairs. The yellow fody is confined to a small area on the northern slopes of the island of Rodrigues (part of Mauritius); its

Mauritius fody.

population was estimated in 1983 at around 100 birds. The Seychelles fody occurs on the small islands of Cousin, Cousine, and Frégate in the Seychelles archipelago. The population on Cousin was estimated in 1981 to be around 1,000 birds, while estimates in the mid-1960s placed the population on Frégate at 400-600 birds and on Cousine at 100-150 birds.

The preferred habitat of the Mauritius fody includes native scrub vegetation with a few scattered taller trees, but the species also inhabits low native scrub and native forest. In contrast, the yellow fody inhabits tall mixed evergreen forest. The Seychelles fody was probably originally a forest species, but it has adapted to other vegetative habitats as the native forests of the islands have disappeared.

History and Conservation Measures

The Mauritius fody was already becoming farily rare at the turn of the twentieth century, although it was still not considered uncommon as late as the 1950s. Between 1971-1974, the clearing of an upland forest at Les Mares on Plaine Champagne had a devastating effect on the species, decreasing its population by more than 50 percent. Since then, its habitat has been better protected, as remaining native forest habitat received almost complete protection with the

creation of the Macabé/Bel Ombre Nature Reserve in 1974. However, introduced animals—including crab-eating macaques and mongooses—have preyed heavily on Mauritius fody nests, and it is possible that the introduced Madagascar fody has displaced it from some of its habitat. An attempt was made to introduce the species to the island of Réunion, but it was unsuccessful; it is uncertain whether further attempts will be made. The introduction and establishment of two species of nectar-producing shrubs on the high plateau has been suggested.

The yellow fody was numerous in the mid-1800s and remained fairly common until it began to decline at the start of the 1960s. Although the species has been impacted several times by cyclones that have wiped out nests, eggs, and young, two other factors in combination have been determined to be the chief cause of the bird's decline: the clearance of the wooded regions that form the bird's habitat and the introduction of the Madagascar fody, which competes with the yellow fody for food and nests. The introduction of the house sparrow, which may usurp nests, is beginning to be a concern, and there have been reports that black rats—notorious nest predators—now inhabit the island. Human persecution, especially by children, has been a problem, and an education campaign has been proposed as a preventa-

Seychelles fody.

tive. A captive breeding program has been initiated and may eventually lead to reintroductions. Protection of native forests and vegetation at Cascade St. Louis, Anse Quitor, and Grande Montagne is an important goal, as these areas could eventually be restocked with birds from captive breeding programs.

The Seychelles fody once occurred on several islands in the Seychelles archipelago, but it is now restricted to Frégate, Cousin, and Cousine islands. Its extinction on the other islands can been attributed to destruction of the forest habitat and the introduction of various rodents and cats. Cats have now been eradicated from Frégate, which should help the populations there, and Cousin Island, where the species is most plentiful, has been managed as a nature reserve since 1968. On all three islands, the main goal should be to eliminate the introduced rats and mice that plague the species.

Ibadan malimbe

Malimbus ibadanensis

Phylum	Chordata
Class	Aves
Order	Passeriformes
Family	Ploceidae
Status	Endangered, IUCN
Range	Nigeria

Description and Biology

The Ibadan malimbe is a small weaver bird with a short tail. It is usually seen in pairs but is sometimes solitary or found in groups of up to five birds. The breeding season is not well defined, and nesting has been recorded in February, May, June, July, September, October, and December.

Habitat and Current Distribution

The Ibadan malimbe is endemic to Nigeria, where it is only known from a restricted area in southwestern Nigeria. There are no estimates of population size, but it has been reported as locally common around Ibadan and the Gambari Forest, as occasional at Ilaro, and as a resident in very small numbers at Ife.

This species is sometimes seen in farmland and gardens but is usually described as a bird of forest edges and secondary growth. Most birds have been observed at 16-50 ft (5-15 m) up in trees, especially in oil palms.

History and Conservation Measures

This species was discovered at Ibadan University in 1951, and subsequent records from the 1960s come from Ilaro, Iperu, Ife, Olokemeji, and Gambari Forest. Numbers appear to have declined drastically and by the late 1970s it was difficult to locate in the wild. In ten days of searching secondary woodland in Ibadan in 1987, only four birds were sighted.

Massive habitat destruction is considered the primary factor in the Ibadan malimbe's decline. It appears to be tolerant of a certain amount of disturbance to its forest environment, adapting to gardens and nearby farmland, but forest clearance is now so intense in southwestern Nigeria that the survival prospects of this species must now be very poor. No conservation measures have yet been taken. A new survey is urgently needed to determine the status of this species and to establish reserves for its conservation.

Rothchild's starling

Leucopsar rothschildi

Phylum	Chordata
Class	Aves
Order	Passeriformes
Family	Sturnidae
Status	Endangered, IUCN
	Endangered, USFWS
	Appendix I, CITES
Range	Bali (Indonesia)

Description and Biology

The Rothschild's starling or the Bali mynah has mostly white plumage, with bluish markings through the eyes, black tips on the wings and tail, and an erectable crest on the head. Its average length is 8.7 in (22 cm). The mynah's diet includes insects, fruits, and small reptiles.

Rothschild's starling usually breeds in colonies and nests in holes. Two to seven eggs are incubated for 11-18 days; chicks leave the nest within a month.

Habitat and Current Distribution

This species is endemic to Bali, Indonesia, where it is restricted to the remaining savanna woodland in the northwestern coastal area. The Bali-Barat National Park contains all of the starling's range. Population is estimated to be roughly 40-50 birds.

History and Conservation Measures

A number of factors have combined to play a role in the scarcity of this species. Forest clearance has reduced suitable woodland habitat to make way for human settlement and agriculture, causing a reduction in range. Because Rothschild's starling has always been popular as a cage-bird, trapping has caused a dramatic reduction in numbers.

Rothchild's starling.

This species has legal protection in Indonesia, but some problems remain including poaching, human settlement, wood-cutting, and grazing of animals. Rothschild's starling breeds well in captivity.

Success in captive breeding could take some of the trapping pressure from the wild population and is currently providing birds for reintroduction into the wild.

Goldie's bird-of-paradise

Paradisaea decora

Phylum	Chordata
Class	Aves
Order	Passeriformes
Family	Paradisaeidae
Status	Rare, IUCN Appendix II, CITES
Range	Papua New Guinea

Description and Biology

Averaging around 12.6 in (32 cm), the female of this species is rather nondescript, but the male is easily recognizable by the brilliant red plumes that it uses in elaborate courtship display. The male's flamboyant colors and exaggerated mating dance are used to attract possible suitors. Females, in contrast, are colored to blend in with their background, an important strategy for an incubating bird. The bird-of-paradise has strong legs, feet, and bill. Diet includes fruit and arthropods, and most foraging is done on the ground or in the lower branches of trees.

Birds-of-paradise usually incubate a clutch of one or two eggs for 17-21 days.

Habitat and Current Distribution

This species is restricted to the eastern Papuan islands of Fergusson and Normanby in Papua New Guinea, where it inhabits forest and forest edge at altitudes of 1,000-2,300 ft (300-700 m). There are no estimates of population size.

History and Conservation Measures

There is little information on conservation measures for this species, but the preservation of the primary forest it inhabits is essential to its long-term survival.

Hawaiian crow

Corvus hawaiiensis (tropicus)

Phylum	Chordata
Class	Aves
Order	Passeriformes
Family	Corvidae
Status	Endangered, IUCN
	Endangered, USFWS
Range	Hawaii (U.S.A.)

Description and Biology

The Hawaiian crow, also called the alala, is a large, dark brown bird with a thick, strong beak. Its average length at physical maturity is 19 in (48 cm). Its diet consists mainly of fruit but also includes insects, rodents, and small lizards. It also sometimes eats immature small birds. Rats and mongooses are known predators.

Sexual maturity is reached in two to three years. Nests are built high in ohia trees and are reused year after year. Nesting between March and July results in from one to five eggs.

Habitat and Current Distribution

The Hawaiian crow is restricted to the Kona district on the western side of the island of Hawaii at elevations of 3,400-5,000 ft (1,035-1,525 m). In 1992, there were only 11 birds remaining in the wild and only 10 in captivity. The captive population is part of the Olinda Endangered Species Breeding Facility on the island of Maui.

The bird's habitat includes wet and dry forest at high elevations. The birds prefer open forests with an understory of fruit-producing plants and shrubs or groves next to pasture.

History and Conservation Measures

Although always confined to the island of Hawaii, this crow was relatively common until the 1930s. It once nested at higher and lower elevations than it currently does and was found in both the Kau and Kona districts on Hawaii. However, its range has gradually been restricted, and its numbers have declined significantly.

The reasons for the decline are unclear, but a number of factors may have impacted the species. Hunting was once common, but it was outlawed in 1931—to no effect on the bird's shrinking population. A more important factor is habitat loss: habitat has been decreased by development and disrupted by the introduction of feral pigs, goats, and cattle, and this disruption has decreased the food supply provided by some fruit-bearing plant species. Predation by mongooses and rats, as well as disease, has also contributed to a reduction in population.

Perhaps the most critical factor in the species' decline is poor breeding success: survival of young in the wild has dropped to one fledgling per nest or less. This problem affects not only the wild population but the captive breeding program as well, resulting in a limited gene pool and a lack of functional breeding birds. At the Olinda facility, only one chick was produced in 1989 and one in 1990. Researchers will continue to try to add genetic material from the wild flock to the captive flock, but the species' survival prospects at this point are considered critically low.

Recovery goals include a wild population of at least 400 birds and adequate optimum natural habitat within its range.

Reptiles

Central American river turtle

Dermatemys mawii

Phylum	Chordata
Class	Reptilia
Order	Testudines
Family	Dermatemydidae
Status	Vulnerable, IUCN
	Endangered, USFWS
	Appendix II, CITES
Range	Belize; Guatemala; Honduras; Mexico

Description and Biology

The Central American river turtle reaches a length of more than 24 in (60 cm) and a weight of almost 50 lb (22 kg), making it the largest freshwater turtle in its range. Its webbed feet allow only awkward movement on land; as a result, these turtles do not bask upon logs or river banks like other freshwater turtles, but do occasionally float on the water's surface. The turtle is able to remain underwater for long periods without surfacing for air. This species is primarily nocturnal, hiding below the surface or being relatively inactive until twilight. Diet consists of aquatic vegetation and fallen leaves and fruit. Otters are regular predators.

Nesting occurs in April and December along shallow side channels that are easier for turtles to access after the rainy season, when water levels become higher. Eggs are hard-shelled and vary from 6-16 per clutch.

Habitat and Current Distribution

The Central American river turtle is restricted to coastal lowlands of the western Caribbean, from central Veracruz in Mexico southeast through northern Guatemala and Belize. It is not found on the Yucatan Peninsula, but may extend into Honduras. There are no estimates of the population size.

Preferred habitat includes large, open rivers and permanent lakes. The species seems to prefer clear water, which is not typically found in seasonal or temporary ponds, but also tolerates brackish water and is sometimes found in tidal reaches. Nests are dug in sand, clay, or mud within a few feet of the water's edge.

History and Conservation Measures

This species is rapidly declining over much of its primary range in Mexico as a result of exploitation as a food source. The turtle is very easy to catch, and both its meat and eggs are valued. There is no information on its status in Guatemala. In Belize, significant populations remain, but they too are heavily harvested for food. In northern Chiapas, new roads have left previously inaccessible turtle populations vulnerable to exploitation.

With adequate conservation and proper management programs, the species could become a sustained-yield food resource with considerable economic value. Further study is needed to assess this potential and to develop a pilot management program. Existing restrictions on hunting need to be fully enforced and possibly extended or realigned to guarantee that the species is protected during its nesting periods.

River terrapin

Batagur baska

Phylum	Chordata
Class	Reptilia
Order	Testudines
Family	Emydidae
Status	Endangered, IUCN
	Endangered, USFWS
	Appendix I, CITES
Range	Bangladesh; India; Sumatra (Indonesia); Kampuchea; Malaysia; Myanmar (ex?); Singapore (?); Thailand; Vietnam (?)

Description and Biology

Also known as the tuntong, the river terrapin is a moderately large, web-footed aquatic turtle with a shell length that may exceed 24 in (61 cm). It has a strong, high-domed shell that protects it from predators like the saltwater crocodile (*Crocodylus porosus*). The female weighs around 40 lb (18 kg). The terrapin is omnivorous, primarily eating stems, leaves, and fruits of riverside plants as well as molluscs, crustaceans, and fish. Apart from man, this species has few natural predators, and most deaths seem to occur during early egg and juvenile stages. Otters and dogs may consume eggs during nesting, and monitor lizards are able to locate and excavate completed nests. Juveniles are probably eaten by aquatic predators, including fish and crocodiles.

The river terrapin mates between September and November. During this breeding season, males assume a certain color: the skin of the head, neck, and legs turns black, and the iris turns from a yellow-cream color to white. When monsoon flooding subsides in November, the female moves upstream to nest where, along the sand banks of large rivers, she digs a pit about 6-12 in (15-30 cm) deep using her fore and hindlimbs. She lays her eggs—which are about 2.7 in (70 mm) long—in this cavity and then covers it by raising and dropping her body on the sand. The drumming sound caused by this action sounds somewhat like "tuntong," thus the species' alternate common name. Hatchlings emerge in 70-80 days.

Habitat and Current Distribution

There are no current estimates of population size for the river terrapin, which inhabits a wide but increasingly fragmented range in Asia. In Bangladesh, a significant breeding population was discovered in 1982; the species may be extinct in Myanmar; it is probably severely depleted in India; and it is reported as rare and nearly extinct in Sumatra. The only remaining large nesting aggregation is the Perak River population in West Malaysia, where 1,000 nesting females may exist; in Thailand, it occurs in two restricted areas in the Peninsula and is in immediate danger of extinction.

During the nesting season, large sand banks and islands are essential, and high, sloping banks are preferred. Outside the nesting season, this species is typically found in brackish water at the mouth of large rivers or further upstream away from tidal influence.

History and Conservation Measures

The primary threats to the river terrapin are over-exploitation for food, habitat destruction, and pollution. It is uncertain to what extent adults are intentionally captured for food, but eggs are widely prized as a delicacy. Habitat destruction is becoming an increasingly serious threat; in some areas, clearing of forests and tin mining have created large loads of silt which, when deposited on sand nesting areas, promote the growth of grass and sedges that inhibit nesting. Sand mining also directly destroys nesting beach habitats. Clearing of riverside vegetation is a problem in foraging areas, removing the species' food sources and exposing the banks to erosion. In addition, construction of dams and barrages has blocked movement to nesting sites and blocked access to food-rich tributaries. Some mortality is due to collisions with motor boats or to deliberate killing by fishermen. Various toxins in the water have also claimed several turtle deaths.

Conservation efforts thus far have concentrated in three main areas: studies have been initiated to assess the status of populations in the Sunderbans of India and Bangladesh, the Irrawaddy River delta in Burma, and the Indragiri River in Sumatra. The establishment of a hatchery and improved nest site protection in Peninsular Thailand have been priorities and should be complemented by legal protection and educational programs for local inhabitants. Monitoring programs, as well as the expansion and improvement of existing hatcheries in Malaysia, Perak, Kedah, and Terengganu states, are currently in progress. In addition to these steps, further actions are planned to create a sanctuary on the Perak River at Bota and to restore nesting habitat at the Kedah sites. Throughout the river terrapin's range, habitat destruction and water pollution must be curtailed. If managed properly, this species could provide a valuable renewable source of food for human populations in southeast Asia.

Painted terrapin

Callagur borneoensis

Phylum	Chordata
Class	Reptilia
Order	Testudines
Family	Emydidae
Status	Endangered, IUCN
Range	Brunei (?); Kalimantan, Sumatra (Indonesia); Peninsular Malaysia, Sarawak (Malaysia); Thailand

Description and Biology

A rather large aquatic turtle averaging about 19.7 in (50 cm) in length, the painted terrapin is so named because of its beautiful colors. Breeding males have a white head with a broad red stripe down the center, a bluish tip on the snout, and a light gray to cream–colored carapace. Non-breeding males have a dark gray head with a dull orange stripe and a dull brown to gray carapace. Somewhat omnivorous, the terrapin mainly feeds on mangrove fruits and vegetation from riverside plants. It also feeds on a variety of village refuse, especially fruit scraps, discarded into the water.

Reproduction is seasonal, and nesting period varies geographically. Females migrate downstream to nest on ocean beaches near the mouth of the home river; males are not seen near the nesting beaches, and mating probably occurs prior to migration. A clutch of 10-12 large eggs, 2.75 in (70 mm) long, is laid twice a year in a shallow, poorly concealed nest. Hatchlings emerge from the nest in approximately 70 days and move into less saline waters.

Habitat and Current Distribution

This species occurs in the Sundaland region, from the southernmost provinces of Thailand in the north, southward through West Malaysia, and to the islands of Sumatra and Borneo. Although population estimates are unavailable, it is considered one of the most seriously threatened river turtles in Southeast Asia. It is reported to be very rare in Thailand; there are no population estimates for Sumatra or Kalimantan. It is widely distributed in Malaysia, but with few large populations remaining. The largest known breeding population is located on the east coast of Peninsular Malaysia, on the Setiu-Chalok river system, comprising approximately 200 adult females.

The painted terrapin inhabits areas of tidal influence of medium to large rivers. In Sarawak, it was often found in mangrove swamps, resting on submerged snags with just the head exposed above water. In Peninsular Malaysia, individuals are reported to frequently crawl out on logs or mats of vegetation to bask in the sun.

History and Conservation Measures

The primary threat to this species appears to be over-exploitation of its eggs for food. Most of the east coast nesting areas of Peninsular Malaysia are licensed to egg collectors, who gather nearly all the eggs that are laid. The eggs of the painted terrapin are collected along with the eggs of sea turtles who nest on the same beaches, but the eggs of the terrapin are preferred because of the large size and reputed better taste. Adults do not appear to be regularly exploited.

Four states in West Malaysia prohibit the killing of turtles and the leasing of nesting areas to egg collectors. A hatchery program in Trengganu purchases eggs from collectors; additional hatcheries are needed near the major nesting sites in West Malaysia and possibly throughout the range. The nesting site at Kuala Baharu has been proposed as a sanctuary by the State Fisheries Department, which will also help protect the endangered olive ridley turtle (*Lepidochelys olivacea*), green sea turtle (*Chelonia mydas*), and leatherback turtle (*Dermochelys coriacea*). In Malaysia, turtle sanctuaries are off-limits to tourists, but some egg collecting is permitted.

Spotted pond turtle

Geoclemys (Damonia) hamiltonii

Phylum	Chordata
Class	Reptilia
Order	Testudines
Family	Emydidae
Status	Indeterminate, IUCN
	Endangered, USFWS
	Appendix I, CITES
Range	Bangladesh; India; Nepal (?); Pakistan

Description and Biology

Also known as the black pond turtle, the spotted pond turtle has a long, fairly high carapace (upper shell) that measures up to 14 in (36 cm). The carapace is black with yellow markings, and the plastron (lower part of the shell) is light yellow with dark markings. Its large head is black with yellow spots, the neck is gray with light spots, and the forelimbs are black with white spots. Its soft skin is pink or white. The species is thought to feed primarily on snails and is not a powerful swimmer.

Habitat and Current Distribution

The range of the spotted pond turtle extends from Pakistan across India and throughout Bangladesh, except in the hills. It may even reach Nepal. The species inhabits shallow, clear water in vegetated lakes or marshes. No estimates of population currently exist.

History and Conservation Measures

The spotted turtle appears to be common in some localities of its range (for example, it is apparently the most abundant turtle species in the Kaziranga National Park) and rare in others (for example, in the Keoladeo National Park).

The exploitation of turtles in the Ganges Delta is believed to be extremely heavy because the wide variety of turtle species serves as a major food source for the human population. The spotted pond turtle is occasionally eaten in both Bangladesh and India, being seen from time to time in the wholesale markets of Calcutta. A management plan for the sustainable harvesting of this and other turtle species should be put into place following detailed population surveys of key species. Studies should also be conducted of what effect pesticides have upon this and other freshwater turtle species, as these chemicals are likely to have a strong effect upon population dynamics.

The creation of wildlife sanctuaries in the species' range will be vital to future conservation efforts; such reserves along the Ganges and Brahmaputra rivers have already benefitted the spotted pond turtle.

Yellow-blotched map turtle

Graptemys flavimaculata

Phylum	Chordata
Class	Reptilia
Order	Testudines
Family	Emydidae
Status	Indeterminate, IUCN
	Threatened, USFWS
Range	Mississippi (U.S.A.)

Description and Biology

The yellow-blotched map turtle is a medium-sized aquatic species. Its olive to light brown shell has riblike plates with bright yellow or orange blotches. Shell length is 4.75-8 in (12-20 cm), with females being larger than males. Diet includes snails and insects; larger adults also eat small molluscs.

Little is known of the ecology or reproduction biology of this species.

Habitat and Current Distribution

This species has one of the most restricted ranges of any sawback turtle, being found in southeast Mississippi in the Pascagoula River drainage system, including the Pascagoula, Leaf, and Chickasawhay rivers and possibly their larger tributaries. Its few remaining populations are isolated and scattered. Population surveys are underway, but estimates are not yet available.

The yellow-blotched map turtle inhabits marshes with brackish water or rivers that receive several hours of sun each day and have a moderate current, with logs for basking. It nests on sand or gravel bars.

History and Conservation Measures

Habitat degradation has contributed to the decline in this species' population. Flood control programs have resulted in an increased amount of sediment in the water, causing a decrease in the turtle's food supply, and basking and nesting sites have been lost due to altered water flows. Shooting or collecting of basking turtles is also a problem; while collecting for scientific and educational reasons has declined, collecting for commercial purposes continues to be a threat.

Protection of remaining populations and habitat is essential for the recovery of the species. Any future flood-control modifications should be designed to minimize their impact on the turtle's habitat and food supply. Shooting of basking turtles must also be stopped through educational programs and greater enforcement of legal protection. In addition, research is needed to identify the source of pollutants in the rivers and to determine their effect on breeding rates.

Ringed sawback turtle

Graptemys oculifera

Phylum	Chordata
Class	Reptilia
Order	Testudines
Family	Emydidae
Status	Insufficiently Known, IUCN
	Threatened, USFWS
Range	Louisiana, Mississippi (U.S.A.)

Description and Biology

The ringed sawback or ringed map turtle is a small freshwater turtle with an average shell length of 4-7 in (10-18 cm); females are larger than males. It has a greenish brown shell with a spiny central ridge. Its head and forelimbs are striped with yellow, and it has a yellow spot behind each eye. When not basking in the sun on floating debris or vegetation, this turtle feeds on molluscs.

Nesting takes place between mid-May and early August, when a clutch of 4-8 eggs is laid in a nest dug in a sandy beach or gravel bar. Little more is known of the ecology of this species.

Habitat and Current Distribution

Ringed sawback turtles are found only in the Pearl and Bogue Chitto Rivers in Mississippi and Louisiana. These rivers have moderate currents and clear water with large numbers of molluscs, the main food of ringed sawbacks. There are no estimates of total population size.

History and Conservation Measures

While the population of ringed sawbacks remains strong in some areas, it is seriously depleted in regions where declining water quality has threatened its food supply. Pollution and habitat alteration are considered the principal threats to the survival of this species.

An effort is underway to establish a current population estimate through a mark-and-recapture program along the Pearl River. Additional research has been proposed to determine the life history and habitat requirements of the species. Long-range conservation goals include the establishment of 150 river miles (240 km) of secure habitat along two stretches of the Pearl River near the Ross Barnett Reservoir.

Tricarinate Hill turtle

Melanochelys (Geoemyda, Nicoria) tricarinata

Phylum	Chordata
Class	Reptilia
Order	Testudines
Family	Emydidae
Status	Indeterminate, IUCN
	Endangered, USFWS
	Appendix I, CITES
Range	Bangladesh; India; Nepal (?)

Description and Biology

The Tricarinate Hill turtle, also known as the three-keeled Asian turtle or the three-keeled land tortoise, has a long, arched carapace (shell) that is dark reddish purple and has three dark brown keels; it averages around 6 in (15 cm) long. The plastron (lower part of the shell) is yellow-brown. The head and limbs are also dark reddish purple, but the female has a red stripe on each side of the head and under the jaw. Scales are present on the front limbs, which may also have yellow spots. This is a terrestrial species.

Habitat and Current Distribution

The range of the Tricarinate Hill turtle is moderately wide, extending from the northern Indian states of Uttar Pradesh and Arunachal Pradesh to the Teknaf region of southern Bangladesh and southeastern Bihar in India. In India it is mainly reported from grassland in the Himalaya foothill country, but in Bangladesh it may occur in either deciduous or wet evergreen forest. It is generally difficult to find as it is commonly only active at twilight. Its absolute rarity is unknown, and no population estimates currently exist.

History and Conservation Measures

The status of this species is not well known. Individuals are doubtlessly eaten by humans who encounter it by chance, such as the Chakma people of southeastern Bangladesh. While some scientists believe that the Tricarinate Hill turtle is in need of conservation action, definitive surveys must be completed before assumptions can be made concerning the species' status.

Burmese eyed turtle

Morenia ocellata

Phylum	Chordata
Class	Reptilia
Order	Testudines
Family	Emydidae
Status	Insufficiently Known, IUCN
	Endangered, USFWS
	Appendix I, CITES
Range	Myanmar

Description and Biology

The Burmese eyed turtle has a domed carapace (shell) that reaches a length of around 9 in (23 cm). It ranges from light to dark greenish brown, and is darker in the center and along the margin. The underside is yellow, and pale yellow, eye-like circles appear on each scute (bony sections covering the carapace). Two yellow streaks are found on each side of the head.

Habitat and Current Distribution

This species is known from the lower reaches of the Ayeyarwady (Irrawaddy) River in southern Myanmar and may occur as far north as Mandalay and in the Doke-tha-wady at Shwe sar yan. No estimates of population currently exist.

The Burmese eyed turtle is believed to be entirely aquatic, living in rivers, streams, swamps, and ponds. However, the species can be stranded on land during the dry season when water recedes from seasonally inundated plains.

History and Conservation Measures

Because little is known about the Burmese eyed turtle, questions have arisen as to whether or not the species is indeed endangered. Great numbers have been seen in Yangon temple ponds and are also found at the Yangon Zoo, and the species is also widely available in local markets. Thus no evidence has yet been uncovered to suggest that the turtle has declined significantly since it was described as abundant in 1867-68.

However, definitive population surveys must be completed before assumptions can be made concerning the species' status. If the burmese eyed turtle is indeed endangered, suitable reserve and sanctuary areas should be identified and the potential for establishing hatcheries or a sustainable yield harvesting system evaluated. Additionally, the direction and emphasis of any future conservation programs will undoubtedly depend on the attitudes of local people who depend on this and other turtle species for food and trade.

Alabama red-bellied turtle

Pseudemys alabamensis

Phylum	Chordata
Class	Reptilia
Order	Testudines
Family	Emydidae
Status	Rare, IUCN
	Endangered, USFWS
Range	Alabama (U.S.A.)

Description and Biology

The Alabama red-bellied turtle is a large, predominately freshwater turtle that reaches a maximum shell (carapace) length of 13 in (33.5 cm). The color of the carapace is brown to greenish brown with bright yellow-orange to red markings. Skin color is greenish black with facial stripes of yellow or orange. Diet is apparently strictly herbivorous, consisting of aquatic vegetation.

Very little is known about the natural history or biology of this species. Breeding apparently takes place in late spring or early summer. A clutch of three to six eggs is laid in a nest with a depth of 3-6 in (8-16 cm). Several clutches are probably laid per year and incubation takes from 70-80 days. Nests are preyed upon by fish crows (*Corvus ossifragus*), and alligators prey upon young and small adults.

Habitat and Current Distribution

This turtle's distribution is limited to quiet backwaters in Mobile Bay and tributary streams in Baldwin and Mobile counties, Alabama. There is no estimate of current population.

Preferred habitat includes streams, ponds, rivers, and wetlands with an abundance of submerged vegetation. The turtle basks on weed beds and builds nests in fine, moist sand at the base of vegetation and near water. The major known nesting area is along the stretch of the Tensaw River adjacent to Gravine Island.

History and Conservation Measures

The range of the Alabama red-bellied turtle may once have been more extensive, but records of sightings in Texas, Tennessee, and Florida are undocumented; it may still exist in a lake in Little River State Park in southern Monroe County, Alabama, or be found occasionally on Dauphin Island in Mobile County. Today its range is very restricted, and it is not abundant anywhere within that range.

This turtle was once hunted for food and is still often caught inadvertently by fishermen. Natural predators such as crows and alligators have taken their toll, as have introduced predators, especially domestic pigs that eat the species' eggs. River traffic has disturbed habitat, and campers have disrupted nesting areas. These factors become an increased threat when combined with such a limited distribution and low population.

There is a need to protect principal habitats (weed beds) and nesting and hibernation sites. Conservation priority at this point is the protection of critical habitats from south of Gravine Island to the beds of submerged aquatic vegetation south of the I-

10 Causeway across Mobile Bay. This area needs regular wardening, enforceable seasonal access restrictions to limit accidental take by fishermen, and ideally, some small land purchases. Long-term plans include studies to determine the turtle's population, biology, and ecology; location of major nesting habitats; and location of basking and wintering habitats.

Aquatic box turtle

Terrapene coahuila

Phylum	Chordata
Class	Reptilia
Order	Testudines
Family	Emydidae
Status	Vulnerable, IUCN
	Endangered, USFWS
	Appendix I, CITES
Range	Mexico

Description and Biology

The aquatic box turtle is also known as the coahuilan box turtle and belongs to the genus of box turtles (*Terrapene*) that is primarily terrestrial; it may have adopted its aquatic habits to adapt to and survive arid periods. Foraging in shallow water, it follows an erratic course, keeping the head under water while the carapace (shell) remains above the surface; it uses its forelimbs to expose feeding sites. Omnivorous and opportunistic, it feeds on aquatic plants and invertebrates, notably fly larvae, beetles, and nymphs.

This turtle is active throughout the year except for short periods of extreme cold or heat. Mating usually occurs between September and June, most commonly in March and April. Egg laying occurs between May and September, typically with two or three eggs per clutch.

Habitat and Current Distribution

This aquatic box turtle is restricted to the specialized marshy habitats of the intermontane desert basin of Cuatro Cienegas, Coahuila State, northern Mexico. No estimates of population are available.

Preferred habitat is small spring-fed marshes with shallow water, a mud bottom, and dense aquatic vegetation, including sedges, rushes, and willows.

History and Conservation Measures

This species is at risk by virtue of its very small range and its localized distribution within that range. There is also restricted movement of individuals across the inhospitable terrain separating each marsh population. It is threatened primarily by habitat destruction due to the demand for water for irrigation and industry. Canals have been dug or deepened to provide water flow to steel mills and to provide irrigation water. Marshy areas have been drained by culverts placed during highway construction.

In addition to studies to determine status, conservation priorities are to secure protection for the turtle's remaining natural habitat and to devise a long-term management strategy to prevent inappropriate drainage projects. Protection of the habitat in the Cuatro Cienegas basin will also protect at least three other freshwater turtles and several endemic invertebrates and fish.

Captive breeding of this species has been very successful at the Jersey Wildlife Trust and New York Zoological Society, but re-release protocols still need to be developed.

Chaco tortoise

Geochelone chilensis

Phylum	Chordata
Class	Reptilia
Order	Testudines
Family	Testudinidae
Status	Vulnerable, IUCN
	Appendix II, CITES
Range	Argentina; Paraguay

Description and Biology

The Chaco or Argentine tortoise is a small species with a carapace length of around 8 in (20 cm). Carapace coloration varies from ochre-yellow to clay-brown, with specimens from drier areas being lighter in color than those from wetter regions. The scute edges are darker in color. The head and limbs are usually light ochre-yellow. Diet includes fruits of various trees, shrubs, and cacti, as well as cacti pads and grasses. In captivity the Chaco tortoise eats meat and may therefore consume carrion in the wild.

This tortoise digs shallow holes in which it spends the night and much of the day. A deeper hole is used during cold months, when the tortoises emerge only on the warmest days. Courtship and mating take place in November and December, and eggs are laid from January to March. Clutch size is one to six; eggs are round, white, and 1.8 in (4.5 cm) in diameter. Incubation may last more than a year; the eggs of captive specimens in Cordoba Province, Argentina, hatched 14-15 months after they were laid.

Habitat and Current Distribution

G. chilensis is widespread in the dry lowlands from the Gran Chaco region of Paraguay (and possibly adjacent Bolivia) southward through the Chaco region of north and central Argentina. One subspecies, *G. c. donosbarrosi*, is reported from the southern portion of the range, from Mendoza to Rio Negro in Argentina. There are no estimates of population size, but it is considered to have undergone severe decline in the main part of the Argentinean Chaco. It is relatively secure in Paraguay. Its occurrence in Bolivia has not been confirmed.

The arid habitat of this species typically consists of desert scrub and dry deciduous woodland, where seasonal fluctuations in temperature and rainfall are considerable.

Chaco tortoise.

History and Conservation Measures

The Chaco tortoise is under considerable pressure from habitat destruction and the domestic and international pet trade. This tortoise is a popular pet in Argentina, where an estimated 75,000 specimens are sold each year. As many as 32 percent of these animals may die within one year; an additional 3,000 tortoises may be exported annually. In the wild, the burning of chaco vegetation to create pasture land and cropland is diminishing the species' habitat as well as exposing the tortoises to capture. To a lesser extent, the Chaco tortoise is also hunted for food by pioneering farmers who are developing the Chaco region. Direct competition for food is reported between tortoises and goats. Several actions are necessary to conserve the Chaco tortoise in the wild: the internal and international pet trade must be curtailed, and the rapid agricultural expansion currently taking place in this species' Argentinean range must also be regulated.

Galápagos tortoise

Geochelone nigra

Phylum	Chordata
Class	Reptilia
Order	Chelonia
Family	Testudinidae
Status	Vulnerable, IUCN
	Endangered, USFWS
	Appendix I, CITES
Range	Galápagos Islands (Ecuador)

Description and Biology

This gigantic tortoise can weigh up to 580 lbs (263 kg). The shell is high and domed in certain subspecies; in others it is saddlebacked and high only in front, or low overall. Adult length ranges from about 24 in (61 cm) in saddleback females to 50 in (127 cm) in male dome-shelled forms. Mating and nesting are strongly seasonal: mating generally occurs during the rainy season (January to April) and nesting from June to December. Eggs hatch from December to April. Clutch size may be as low as two or as high as 16. In the wild, one to four nests may be made in a season and as many as five in captivity. Diet includes a variety of plants.

This species has a potential longevity of 100 years. Sexual maturity is reached at 20 years of age. Mortality rate among young tortoises is thought to be high but variable, depending on the particular island, the degree of threat from introduced predators and competitors, and year (wet years promote better feeding and cover). Natural predators of young are hawks and the short-eared owl, but the lowland environment is harsh in the Galápagos, and hatchlings can be killed by insolation and entrapment in crevice and fissures.

Habitat and Current Distribution

Unique to the Galápagos Islands, this tortoise is found in various areas, from sea-level to the highest points of the islands. During the dry season the tortoise migrates to higher altitudes in search of food and moisture. The females lay their eggs in the lowlands. Larger animals are found in higher altitudes.

This species is still found on Isabela (five populations), Pinzon, Hood, Santa Cruz, Santiago, and San Cristobal. Formerly found on Abingdon, the only survivor from this island is now in captivity in Santa Cruz. The Floreana population disappeared around 1835. This tortoise was once found on Jervis, Barrington, and Narborough, but no longer occurs on these islands.

History and Conservation Measures

Humans have been a major threat to this tortoise. Thousands of tortoises were killed during the nineteenth century by explorers and whalers who valued these animals as a source of food, oil, and fat. They were sometimes kept alive aboard ship and slaughtered to provide fresh meat.

Galápagos tortoise.

Today, the major threat to this species is predation of eggs, hatchlings, and even juveniles by introduced species, mainly dogs and pigs. Goats compete with tortoises for food, and donkeys have been known to trample or roll in nesting areas, damaging eggs and young. Poaching is reported occasionally. Current conservation measures include egg and hatchling rescue and captive breeding programs. The Charles Darwin Research Station on Santa Cruz Island has long attempted to control the predator population and reduce dependence on captive rearing. Despite the program's successes, some subspecies are still in jeopardy. There are 10 or more surviving subspecies of Galápagos tortoise, and the outlook of individual subspecies ranges from safe to doomed. For example, there are several thousand *G. n. poteri*, but only one male *G. n. abingdoni*. Unless swift actions are taken on behalf of certain subspecies, they may soon become extinct.

Angonoka

Geochelone yniphora

Phylum	Chordata
Class	Reptilia
Order	Testudines
Family	Testudinidae
Status	Endangered, IUCN
	Appendix I, CITES
Range	Madagascar

Description and Biology

The angonoka, sometimes called the Madagascar tortoise or the angulated tortoise, is seriously threatened with extinction, in view of a very limited population (about 400) that is unprotected by legislation. It is a large animal, with a carapace (shell) length of around 18 in (45 cm). Its light brown shell has darker wedge-shaped markings. The species' characteristic feature is a horn-like protuberance on its plastron, or ventral shell. A herbivore in its natural habitat, it feeds on leaves, grass, and shoots.

There is no information on the wild population's reproductive physiology, but breeding in captivity by artificial insemination has been reported at the Honolulu Zoo. Courtship and mating behavior have been observed at the Ampijora Forestry Station, northwest Madagascar, between October and early February, when males engage in duels, apparently vying for the females. Since conservation efforts began in the late 1980s, there have been many successful hatchings of captive-bred angonoka.

Habitat and Current Distribution

Endemic to Madagascar, the angonoka is found in a limited area around Baly Bay, in the northwest part of the island. Its optimal habitat is a mixture of tropical deciduous forests and grasslands.

History and Conservation Measures

Although commercial exploitation of the species, including use as a food source, was apparently

Angonoka.

considerable during the period between the seventeenth century and the latter part of the nineteenth, it is limited now, and therefore not considered instrumental in the population's decline. However, predators, such as wild pigs, which destroy the tortoises' nests, and deforestation caused by agricultural development, are serious threats. The species is protected by Malgasy law and by local food taboos. However, preservation of the natural habitat is crucial for the species' survival. A comprehensive preservation program was launched in 1986 by the IUCN Tortoise Specialist Group, with the participation of WWF International and the Jersey Wildlife Preservation Trust. The program combines captive breeding, captive colony relocation, reserve management, as well as a variety of local educational initiatives.

Desert tortoise

Gopherus agassizii

Phylum	Chordata
Class	Reptilia
Order	Chelonia
Family	Testudinidae
Status	Vulnerable, IUCN
	Threatened, USFWS
	Appendix II, CITES
Range	Arizona, California, Nevada, Utah (U.S.A.); Mexico

Description and Biology

The desert tortoise has an oblong, domed, brown carapace that averages 7.5-15 in (19-38 cm) long; the male is larger than the female. The head is narrow and scaly, and the tail is short. The front legs are armored for digging, and the rear legs are very large. Diet consists primarily of green annual vegetation that is high in water content. In the Mojave Desert, the tortoise has been observed drinking from depressions either scraped out directly by the tortoise or enlarged from natural depressions acting as catchment basins for water. The tortoise is primarily active in spring, although summer activity is prevalent when rains provide moisture and food.

During courtship, males hiss and butt females. A clutch of two to seven hard-shelled eggs is laid in early summer, usually hatching three to four months later. The eggs are covered with only a thin layer of sand, allowing the heat of the sun to incubate them. The immature tortoise has a soft shell which begins to harden after about five years.

This long-lived species does not reach sexual maturity until 15-20 years of age and can live up to 100 years.

Habitat and Current Distribution

The desert tortoise occurs in the Mojave and Sonoran Deserts of the southwestern United States and Mexico. Although occurring over a wide range, distribution is not continuous and populations are scattered and isolated. The total population is thought to be around 100,000 individuals.

Habitat and corresponding behavior vary substantially from one part of its geographic range to another. To the north and west of the Colorado River/ Grand Canyon, tortoises occur in valleys and on alluvial fans in creosote bush and yucca plant communities, where soils are suitable for digging and where annual plants and perennial grass offer adequate forage. Burrows are constructed on open ground, under shrubs, and in wash banks.

To the south and east of the Colorado River/ Grand Canyon in the U.S.A., small, island-like populations occur on the steep, rocky slopes of mountain ranges in paloverde-cactus communities. Little is known about the habitat and ecological preferences of this species in Mexico. They are known to occur in thornscrub and oak woodland communities.

Desert tortoise.

History and Conservation Measures

Until recent decades, the desert tortoise was widespread at lower elevations throughout the Mojave and Sonoran Deserts. In the northern and western parts of its range, large and relatively homogeneous populations extended throughout parts of California and probably into Nevada and Utah. Today, its numbers have declined in most areas. Most populations are now isolated and support much fewer animals.

This species is threatened by a wide variety of factors that vary according to the region and particular site. Population losses occur through poaching for the pet trade and food, vandalism, disease, vehicle kills, trampling by livestock, and excessive predation of juvenile tortoises by an expanding population of common ravens. Habitat has also deteriorated or has been lost through urban and agricultural development, highway and road construction, military and industrial development, livestock grazing, energy development, mineral exploration and development, harvest of vegetation, and disposal of toxic and radioactive wastes. All of these problems continue to occur in the U.S.A., and at least some of them occur in Mexico. Most sites experience more than one type of impact, contributing to serious population and habitat fragmentation. In the late 1980s, a respiratory infection, probably introduced by released pets, reached epidemic levels and prompted quarantine controls over large areas of the Mojave Desert.

In the U.S.A., the future of the desert tortoise is dependent on government agencies at federal, state, county, and local levels taking rapid and coordinated action to set aside and preserve representative populations of sufficient size for long-term viability. At present there are two reserves in California: the Desert Tortoise Research Natural Area and the Chuckwalla Bench Area of Critical Environmental Concern. A small reserve in Utah also contains a few tortoises. Recent research has indicated that there may be three or more distinct subspecies or species, which would alter conservation perspectives for each population and further justify the establishment of more reserves.

Bolson tortoise

Gopherus flavomarginatus

Phylum	Chordata
Class	Reptilia
Order	Testudines
Family	Testudinidae
Status	Endangered, IUCN
	Endangered, USFWS
	Appendix I, CITES
Range	Mexico

Description and Biology

The largest terrestrial reptile in North America, the Bolson tortoise has a carapace (shell) length of at least 15.7 in (40 cm). Males and females are similar in outward appearance. To protect itself from predators and extreme temperatures, this species digs burrows up to 26 ft (8 m) long and 6.6 ft (2 m) deep. Diet includes grasses and forbs.

Reproduction is not well known, and its success seems to depend largely on adequate rainfall; reproduction probably ceases altogether during extremely dry years. The Bolson tortoise mates during the dry season, from April to June; eggs are laid from April to September, hatching from July to October. Captive females have been known to produce three clutches in a year; in the wild, however, each clutch usually consists of a single egg.

Habitat and Current Distribution

Endemic to Mexico, the Bolson tortoise lives in the Bolson de Mapimi area in the north-central plateau of the Chihuahuan desert. The population is estimated at 7,000-10,000 adults.

Preferred habitat is the sloping Toboso (*Hilaria mutica*) grassland.

History and Conservation Measures

Fossil records indicate that the range of the Bolson tortoise once extended from Oklahoma to southern Mexico. The principal cause of this species' decline has been and continues to be over-exploitation for food; desert inhabitants have long depended on tortoises and their eggs as a nutritious source of food. The Bolson tortoise is also threatened by habitat destruction as the result of agricultural development. Protected by Mexican law, the species is safe within the Mapimi Biosphere Reserve, but protective legislation is not properly enforced throughout the species' habitat. Since 1978, Mexico and the United States have been conducting studies on this species, and captive-breeding programs exist in both countries. Hatcheries have also been established at Cerros Emilio, near Rancho Sombreritillo, in Chihuahua, which contains the largest northern population outside the Mapimi Reserve. There are plans to reintroduce the species to the Big Bend National Park in Texas.

Geometric tortoise

Psammobates geometricus

Phylum	Chordata
Class	Reptilia
Order	Testudines
Family	Testudinidae
Status	Vulnerable, IUCN
	Endangered, USFWS
	Appendix I, CITES
Range	South Africa

Description and Biology

The geometric tortoise is a small species, with the male averaging around 4 in (10 cm) in length and weighing 7 oz (200 g) and the female averaging 5 in (12.5 cm) and weighing 15 oz (430 g). The carapace (shell) is highly domed, with that of the male sloping more gradually than that of the female. A brilliant, starred pattern on the carapace greatly contributes to the beauty of this species. Consisting of striking yellow rays against the dark background of the carapace, the pattern is often symmetrical. The animal's head, neck, extremities, and tail are also yellow; there are small black patches on the head and the tail. Diet includes sedges and several varieties of grass.

This tortoise breeds from spring to early summer (between September and November), the female laying a single clutch of two to eight eggs. The eggs hatch six to eight months later (between March and May), after the onset of the winter rains.

Habitat and Current Distribution

Endemic to South Africa, the geometric tortoise is restricted to the extreme southwest of Cape Province, where it occurs in a strip of coastal lowland

Geometric tortoise.

between the mountains and the sea and in two isolated populations east of the mountains. There are probably 10-15 isolated populations remaining, with three–quarters of the total population protected in nature reserves.

It inhabits low-lying areas in vegetation associated with the mild climate of the southwestern tip of Africa. The species favors open spaces, moving to higher elevations during the winter rains in order to escape the waterlogged flatlands.

History and Conservation Measures

The main threat to the survival of the species is habitat destruction, primarily by overgrazing and erosion. The spread of introduced vegetation is another potential threat to this species. The impact of an introduced predator, the yellow mongoose, may be significant. The geometric tortoise is protected in one private and four provincial nature reserves: the private Elandsberg Reserve (4,000-6,000 tortoises), the Eenzaamheid Reserve (170), the Romans River Reserve (41), the Hartebeest Reserve (19), and the Harmony Flats Reserve, (42). The principal conservation strategy which has been adopted is the acquisition of natural habitats to complement the existing reserves. The species is protected by local and international legislation. Extensive research on the species' distribution, as well as its ecological and conservation status is currently underway.

Madagascar flat-tailed tortoise

Pyxis (Acinixys, Testudo) planicauda

Phylum	Chordata
Class	Reptilia
Order	Testudines
Family	Testudinidae
Status	Indeterminate, IUCN Appendix II, CITES
Range	Madagascar

Description and Biology

The Madagascar flat-tailed tortoise is small, its carapace normally not exceeding the length of 5.4 in (13.7 cm). Juveniles are characterized by a black and chestnut carapace with a wide yellow band across each scute (bony sections covering the carapace), while most adults have gray coloration. Diet is unknown.

Biological information about the species is extremely scant. Breeding is thought to occur during the wet season; the clutch usually consists of a single large egg, but there is no data on the number of clutches per season. The flat-tailed tortoise may spend the dry summer season underground, in a state of estivation.

Habitat and Current Distribution

Endemic to Madagascar, the species has been recorded only from an area between the Andranomena and Amborompotsy forests, northeast of Morondava, on the west coast. It has also been seen further north, around Maintirano. There are no reliable population estimates.

This species inhabits dry lowland deciduous forest and bush, in a relatively temperate region.

History and Conservation Measures

The population has diminished as a result of habitat destruction. In particular, timber exploitation and agricultural development have affected the Andranomena forest. Another threat is the growing bush pig population, as these omnivorous animals occasionally prey on tortoise eggs and young. Habitat preservation is considered the paramount conservation measure for the flat-tailed tortoise.

Egyptian tortoise

Testudo kleinmanni

Phylum	Chordata
Class	Reptilia
Order	Testudines
Family	Testudinidae
Status	Vulnerable, IUCN
	Appendix II, CITES
Range	Egypt; Israel; Libya

Description and Biology

One of the world's smallest tortoises, this species measures 4-5 in (10-13 cm) and weighs around 7 oz (200 g). The carapace (shell) is oval, moderately domed, and pale yellow to greenish yellow, with black markings; its plastron (the ventral part of the shell) may have a dark patch. This tortoise is also characterized by exceedingly large scales on its forelimbs. Diet consists primarily of green annual vegetation but may also include leaves of perennial bushes and shrubs, although most parts of these plants are out of the animal's reach. Mating takes place in March, and the female lays two to three clutches of one to three eggs. The incubation period is believed to last 70-90 days.

Among the main predators of this species are ravens and domestic and feral dogs. Other potential natural predators—including the monitor lizard, wolf, hyena, and desert fox—are either nocturnal, very rare, or prey only on juveniles.

The home range of this species varies considerably between individuals and sexes; the average range for males is 0.07 sq mi (0.19 sq km) and 0.03 sq mi (0.07 sq km) for females, with many home ranges overlapping. Movement is limited during summer, but the Egyptian tortoise is most active in winter and spring. Deserted rodent burrows are the first choice for shelter when they are available, but active burrows are also used. The tortoise may dig its own burrow as well.

Habitat and Current Distribution

The Egyptian tortoise inhabits areas of sandy soils, dunes (where they have a fair amount of plant cover of bushes and small shrubs), and hard sands with a denser plant cover.

Found principally in Egypt, this species also occurs in Israel and Libya, in the region of Cyrenaica. In Egypt it is confined to the northern part of the country, in the low-lying areas of Alexandria, Port Said, Damietta, and along Sinai's Mediterranean coastline. In Israel, it is found in the western Negev, as well as in Mishor Yamin and Mishor Rotem. Population is estimated at less than 10,000 individuals.

History and Conservation Measures

Habitat destruction, mostly from agricultural activities and excessive grazing, is the primary threat to the species. Increased human presence has attracted brown-necked ravens (*Corvus ruficollis*) and dogs that prey on the Egyptian tortoise. Hunting has also been reported in parts of this species' range; in Egypt, commercial exploitation is considerable. Unfortunately, protective regulations, in effect since 1982, apparently have not been enforced.

Several conservation priorities have been identified: in Israel, the establishment of protected reserves is essential. An area between the Agur and Halutza sands has been proposed as a major reserve; as it is a border area, it has the advantages of restricted access and little military activity. The vegetation is recovering, and there is already a healthy population of Egyptian tortoises in the proposed reserve area. A nature reserve of this size (15-19 sq mi/40-50 sq km) could sustain a population of 500-1,000 individuals. Other reserve areas are needed and should become an integral part of development planning for the Negev region. In Egypt, habitat protection is also necessary but should take place in conjunction with strict legal enforcement of laws protecting the tortoises. An education program is also necessary to inform local people of the need for tortoise conservation.

Loggerhead sea turtle

Caretta caretta

Phylum	Chordata
Class	Reptilia
Order	Testudines
Family	Cheloniidae
Status	Vulnerable, IUCN
	Threatened, USFWS
	Appendix I, CITES
Range	Oceanic

Description and Biology

The loggerhead is a large sea turtle with a long, reddish brown carapace. The head is yellowish or greenish brown and large in relation to body size. Average shell length is 35-40 in (90-100 cm) and body weight 200-400 lb (90-180 kg). A carnivorous species, it feeds mainly on bottom-dwelling invertebrates, especially molluscs, crustaceans, and sponges. The loggerhead's strong jaws allow it to crunch the shells of clams and crabs.

The nesting of the loggerhead is seasonal and generally takes place from late spring to summer—for instance, from May to August in Florida and South Carolina in the United States, and from November to January in Tongaland, South Africa. After mating offshore, the female emerges from the water at night and makes her way up the sand to dig a pit for the eggs. Once the eggs are laid and covered, she returns to the sea. Clutch size ranges from 100-126 eggs; incubation takes from 55-66 days. Raccoons, lizards and dogs prey on the eggs, while many species of birds feed on hatchlings as they make their way to the sea.

Habitat and Current Distribution

A circumglobal species, the loggerhead is found in temperate and subtropical waters worldwide. Almost all nesting areas except the Western Carib-

bean are either north of the Tropic of Cancer or south of the Tropic of Capricorn. There is no estimate of world population. Year to year, the nesting population varies a great deal, though the cause for this is not understood. The largest known nesting population occurs on Masirah Island, Oman, where an estimated 30,000 females nest each year. In the United States, the Florida population is second in size only to that of Masirah Island, with probably 90 percent of the U.S. population of 6,000-15,000 turtles nesting there.

Long-distance movements of this species appear to take place along coastlines and not over open sea. Like most sea turtles, the loggerhead prefers nesting beaches that are undisturbed and that have clean sand backed by vegetation.

History and Conservation Measures

Loggerhead populations are still widespread, although some are known or suspected to have declined. They are under pressure from local exploitation, accidental capture in shrimp trawls, and beach development throughout the world. Turtle excluder devices (TEDs) have been developed to save turtles from shrimp nets, but their use is controversial because some fishermen claim that they reduce shrimp catches. The loss of nesting habitat to coastal development has been particularly significant in the United States and the Mediterranean. Artificial lights

Loggerhead sea turtle.

can cause the disorientation of nesting females and hatchlings, who may head inland instead of toward the water and be killed on roads or die of desiccation. Waste, including tar balls, carried by ocean currents also presents a hazard to hatchlings and adults.

The loggerhead is totally or partially protected by law over much of its range, but in some areas legislation cannot be adequately enforced. Where possible, existing laws should be enforced and national parks and reserves adequately protected. Protective legislation and adequate enforcement is particularly important for major nesting concentrations. All states having populations of sea turtles, whether nesting, feeding, or migratory, should be encouraged to enter into international regional agreements to develop and coordinate conservation programs.

Green sea turtle

Chelonia mydas (includes *C. agassizii*)

Phylum	Chordata
Class	Reptilia
Order	Testudines
Family	Cheloniidae
Status	Endangered, IUCN
	Threatened, USFWS (Endangered, selected areas)
	Appendix I, CITES
Range	Oceanic; Australia; Indonesia; Costa Rica

Description and Biology

The green sea turtle is the largest of the hard-shelled sea turtles, although size, weight, and carapace shape can vary markedly between different populations. A typical mature green turtle has a carapace length of around 40 in (1 m) and weighs 300-350 lb (136-158 kg). The large, heart-shaped shell varies in color from dark greenish brown to olive brown. The head is small, and the front legs are large and flipper-shaped. Sea turtles are mainly herbivorous, feeding on sea grasses and algae, but hatchlings are at least partly carnivorous, and male turtles have been observed preying on an assortment of invertebrates. Hatchlings are eaten by birds on the beaches and by fish when they reach the water, but adults have few natural enemies in the wild.

Nesting occurs throughout the year at some sites, but is strongly seasonal at others. The female returns to the beach where she was born to lay her eggs. Mating takes place within a half mile (1 km) of the nest beach; the male does not come ashore. Because her limbs are more suited to swimming rather than to crawling, the female's progress on the sand is slow and difficult. She comes ashore at night and is extremely sensitive to disturbances caused by light, sounds, or vibrations. Using her rear flippers to dig a hole, she lays the eggs and buries them with sand, then returns to the water. The average clutch size is 110, and the turtle may lay between three and seven clutches a season, at 10-15 day intervals. Incubation varies with geographic location, lasting from 52-61 days.

Habitat and Current Distribution

The green sea turtle population is regarded as a series of distinct groups, either largely or entirely genetically separate from each other. Some populations, which are specific to certain geographical areas, may be regarded as full species; for example, *C. m. agassizii*, which nests in the Galapagos and east Pacific, is sometimes referred to as a separate species—the black or east Pacific turtle.

The green sea turtle is a pantropical species, nesting mainly in tropical and subtropical regions. Observations have been recorded as far south as Polla Island, Chile, and as far north as the English Channel. About 150 separate nesting areas are known worldwide, but only between 10 and 15 populations of significant size (around 2,000 or more nesting females per year) are known. These large populations occur on Ascension Island, Australia, Western Australia, Costa Rica (Tortuguero), Europa and Tromelin Islands (in Mozambique Channel), Mexico (Pacific coast), Oman (Ras al Had), and Pakistan (Hawkes Bay/Sandspit). In

Green sea turtle.

the United States, the nesting population in Florida is estimated at 300-400 adult females.

Accurate counts of sea turtle populations are difficult to obtain since hatchlings, after reaching the sea, face high mortality rates, and males do not leave the water. Nesting females comprise the only group that can be counted adequately. There are no estimates of total population size.

History and Conservation Measures

Sea turtles have always been exploited for food; the decline in their population has been obvious for hundreds of years. Local subsistence and local commercial exploitation appear to be having an increased impact on sea turtle populations, as tribal cultures decline, modern technology spreads, and human population in the tropics increases. Adults and eggs are used for food, juveniles stuffed as souvenirs, and adults exploited for hide and oil. Large-scale commercial exploitation has played a role, pushing the species to extinction in some areas. Although many nesting locations are known worldwide, most populations are depleted, many are declining, and some have already been extirpated.

In addition to intentional catching, sea turtles are threatened by incidental catching and drowning in shrimp trawls. Devices have been developed to keep turtles out of shrimp nets (TEDs or turtle excluder devices), but their use is controversial because fishermen complain that they decrease shrimp harvests.

In regions with high numbers of turtles—particularly areas near nesting beaches—restricted fishing zones should be instituted, and fishing methods and equipment that prevent or at least reduce the incidental trapping of marine turtles should be investigated. When possible, feeding grounds, offshore mating grounds, and nesting beaches should be protected. In addition, since the sea turtles are migratory and traverse across the boundaries of many countries, regional cooperation regarding its preservation is needed.

Controversy among sea turtle biologists has arisen over the feasibility of turtle farming and the effect of the farming on wild populations of the species. Some experts feel that conservation of sea turtle populations may be achieved most effectively if the demand for sea turtle products is met by the sale of goods from farmed or ranched animals. Others argue that there can be no adequate control over the demand for and use of wild turtles as long as turtle farms/ranches—whose very existence requires the promotion of turtle products—continue to operate. At present, authorities do not appear to share a universally accepted opinion on the subject.

Hawksbill sea turtle

Eretmochelys imbricata

Phylum	Chordata
Class	Reptilia
Order	Testudines
Family	Cheloniidae
Status	Endangered, IUCN
	Endangered, USFWS
	Appendix I, CITES
Range	Tropical and subtropical seas

Description and Biology

The hawksbill sea turtle varies in size throughout its range. Carapace (shell) length measures from 25-35 in (63.5-88.9 cm) and weight varies from 78-110 lb (35.5 -50 kg), with Atlantic and Caribbean specimens often larger than those of the Indian and Pacific Oceans. Shell color is brown with intricate patterning. The head is relatively narrow with the snout forming a tapered, bird-like beak. Although omnivorous, the hawksbill feeds mostly on ocean-bottom invertebrates; individuals are reported to scrape and chew at reef faces, apparently feeding on encrusting organisms, and the beak-like snout is well suited to probing in rock or coral crevices. Once an adequate feeding area is located, turtles appear to be relatively sedentary, and, unlike highly migratory species such as the green or leatherback turtles, often collect numbers of large barnacles on their carapace. The species is usually reported as non-migratory, occupying a small home range, but it has been suggested that many populations may include a proportion of long-distance migrants.

Nesting is usually seasonal, but may occur throughout the year in some areas, with seasonal peaks. Unlike other sea turtle species, the hawksbill female emerges from the water to nest individually. She comes onto the beach at night and is extremely wary and highly susceptible to any disturbance. She chooses a nesting spot carefully, often moving into trees or shrubs backing the beach, where she digs a flask-shaped nest cavity up to 18-20 in (45-50 cm) in depth. Clutch size varies between populations and is strongly correlated with carapace length. Two to four clutches of 73-182 eggs are laid at intervals of 15-19 days. Incubation period ranges from 58-64 days. Most hatchlings emerge at night to make their way to the sea, so predation by birds is minor compared with predation by the ghost crab (*Ocypode ceratopthalmus*), a nocturnal scavenger. Dogs, pigs, and lizards are among the known nest predators.

Habitat and Current Distribution

The hawksbill is a circumtropical species, nesting on beaches of tropical or sub-tropical seas in the Pacific, Atlantic, and Indian Oceans. There are no estimates of total population. Population estimates can only be based on the estimate of the total number of nesting females, as males do not leave the water and hatchlings are thought to be subject to extremely high mortality rates after entering the sea. Even a reliable estimate of nesting female numbers is rarely possible for hawksbills, since nesting is often diffuse.

Hawksbill sea turtle.

The species is still widespread but exists only in low density almost throughout the extensive range. Most populations are known or thought to be severely depleted. Hawksbill nesting is extremely rare in the United States, confined to southern Florida beaches.

Preferred habitat includes shallow tropical waters over rock or coral substrates, especially coral reefs. Typically, nesting occurs on short, isolated, and sheltered sand beaches, on mainland shores, or on continental or oceanic islands; more rarely, nesting may take place on long exposed mainland beaches.

History and Conservation Measures

Trade in tortoiseshell has gone on throughout most of recorded history. The strikingly patterned carapace is worked and polished, then used to make ornaments of all sorts, including jewelry, combs, and fans. The advent of cheap plastic substitutes led to a brief recession in the luxury market trade in the 1950s, but more recently, demand for shells has once again increased. The commercial demand for tortoiseshell has been, and continues to be, the main cause of the widely depleted status of the hawksbill.

A second major threat is posed by the collection of immature specimens to be stuffed, lacquered, and sold in the tourist trade. Polished shells are also marketed in the Caribbean and elsewhere. The main producers are tropical countries with a substantial tourist trade. Japan is a major consumer of tortoiseshell and stuffed turtles. The turtle is a symbol of longevity in Japan, and so it is common for households and restaurants to feature a lacquered turtle as a wall decoration.

Other threats include the harvesting of turtles and eggs for food; habitat destruction, notably loss of nesting beaches; and the use of improved hunting methods to supplant traditional net fisheries. Relatively few nesting beaches are protected or lie within protected areas.

Despite the listing of this species on Appendix I of the CITES treaty, exports contrary to the provisions of this listing continue. Some nations have exempted themselves, or taken reservations, for the hawksbill and other reptile and mammal species. States party to CITES that have taken reservations for this species should be encouraged to withdraw those reservations and to cease providing a major market for hawksbill products. Japan has recently undertaken to phase out tortoiseshell imports and to withdraw its CITES reservation in 1994.

Existing legislation, including that relating to protected areas, should be rigorously enforced and measures should be taken to protect a larger number of known nesting beaches. Unfortunately, the ecological characteristics of the hawskbill are such that protection of nesting beaches may not be sufficient to save the species, because nesting is so diffuse and the turtle is so susceptible to disturbance at the nest site. The primary action required to save the hawksbill is seen to be the rapid termination of trade in its shell and in stuffed juveniles; this can only be accomplished with international cooperation.

Kemp's ridley sea turtle

Lepidochelys kempii

Phylum	Chordata
Class	Reptilia
Order	Testudines
Family	Cheloniidae
Status	Endangered, IUCN
	Endangered, USFWS
	Appendix I, CITES
Range	Atlantic Basin; nesting occurs at Rancho Nuevo (Mexico) on the Gulf of Mexico

Description and Biology

Kemp's ridley is a small sea turtle with an average weight of approximately 90 lb (41 kg). The 26-35 in (66-89 cm) carapace (shell) is broad and flat with a dark mottled-green color. Forelimbs are broad and flipper-like. A carnivorous, bottom-feeding species, it eats fish, jellyfish, echinoderms, crustaceans, and molluscs, but crabs are its favorite food.

Nesting occurs between April and July, peaking in May and June. At the start of the nesting season, mating occurs at sea in the vicinity of the nesting beach. Females emerge from the water to nest in synchronized groups called *arribadas*, which is Spanish for arrival. Each female uses its hind limbs to dig an egg cavity to a depth of 16 in (40 cm) and lays a clutch of approximately 110 round white eggs, which it then covers with sand. Incubation period is 45-60 days, after which the hatchlings make their way to the water as a group. Coyotes prey on eggs, and crabs, vultures, and fish prey on hatchlings. Females can lay from 1-3 clutches each nesting season, at 20-28 day intervals.

Habitat and Current Distribution

Population estimates for this species are limited to mature nesting females, since males do not come ashore and hatchling mortality is assumed to be substantial. The nesting ground for this species is limited to a 12 mile (20 km) stretch of sandy beach backed by dunes and salt marshes on the Gulf Coast near Rancho Nuevo in Tamaulipas, northeast Mexico. Approximately 400-600 females are estimated to nest at this site annually. A few have nested sporadically to the north and south of this primary nesting site, on Padre Island (Texas), and in Veracruz and Tabasco (Mexico). The species feeds in the Gulf of Mexico, particularly in the shallow waters off the coast of Louisiana, in the Mississippi delta area, and in the Tabasco-Campeche area of Mexico. Young turtles are also regularly found off the northern Atlantic coast of North America.

History and Conservation Measures

In 1947, approximately 40,000 of these sea turtles were counted in a single *arribada*. Since that time, the size of *arribadas* has declined steadily, to 5,000 in the mid-1960s, 2,000-2,500 in 1970 and 1971, 1,000 in 1973, and 500 in 1975. Despite subsequent conservation measures, there has been no substantial recovery. Current indications are that the 835 nests recorded in 1989 were made by approximately 365 turtles.

Kemp's ridley sea turtle.

A number of factors have contributed to the decline in this species' population. Eggs have been preyed upon extensively by coyotes, and local people eat both the turtle and its eggs. Exploitation for eggs and meat has continued until recently, although it is now illegal. Turtles are also regularly caught and killed by trawlers as they drag shallow waters for shrimp. This is now the most significant threat to the species, since these sea turtles feed in the crab-rich shallows that are swept by shrimp trawlers. Turtle excluder devices (TEDs) have been developed to keep turtles out of shrimp nets, but their use is controversial; some fishermen complain that they decrease shrimp harvests. The use of these devices could protect the species in its primary ocean habitat.

Unlike most other sea turtles that migrate to many nesting beaches, this species nests almost exclusively on one beach. This has allowed the government of Mexico to protect the area with armed patrols and to conduct a tagging program to learn more about the species. The United States and Mexico have cooperated in protecting the beach and in translocating eggs to Padre Island National Seashore in an attempt to establish a second breeding site. Captive breeding programs have also been proposed, since it is uncertain whether the remaining Kemp's ridley population is capable of recovery to previous numbers without human assistance.

Olive ridley sea turtle

Lepidochelys olivacea

Phylum	Chordata
Class	Reptilia
Order	Testudines
Family	Cheloniidae
Status	Endangered, IUCN
	Threatened, USFWS (Endangered, selected areas)
	Appendix I, CITES
Range	Oceanic; major mass nesting occurs in India, Costa Rica, and Mexico

Description and Biology

The olive ridley is a rather small sea turtle, reaching a carapace length of 23-32 in (58-81 cm) and a weight of around 90 lb (41 kg). Its light green shell is mottled, and its forelimbs are broad. Individuals may dive deeply to feed on bottom-dwelling crustaceans or float over deep water to feed on crustaceans such as the red lobsterette (*Pleuroncode* sp.) that rise to the surface at night. The main food items recorded are crabs and shrimps, supplemented by jellyfish, small invertebrates, and even fish eggs.

Nesting can occur at any time during the year, but seasonal peaks vary with the location of the nesting beach. Females tend to emerge from the water to nest in synchronized groups called *arribadas,* which is Spanish for arrival. They make their way along the sand, dig a shallow nest with the rear limbs, lay a clutch of 74-166 eggs, cover the eggs with sand, then return to the water. Two to three clutches are probably laid each season; incubation takes around 55 days. The hatchlings emerge together and head for the sea as a group. Egg and hatchling predators include a very wide variety of birds and mammals, including

Olive ridley sea turtle.

hawks, vultures, caracaras, opossums, raccoons, and coyotes. Many nesting females show evidence of shark attack.

Habitat and Current Distribution

This circumglobal species is found in tropical regions of the Pacific, Atlantic, and Indian Oceans. Most nesting seems to occur along mainland beaches, seldom on islands. The largest *arribadas*, estimated at up to 500,000 females in the late 1970s, use two nesting beaches in Costa Rica; India and Mexico each attract up to 300,000 individuals per year. There are no estimates of total population.

The olive ridley forages in open water and nests along undisturbed, sandy, mainland beaches.

History and Conservation Measures

In tropical waters, the olive ridley remains fairly numerous and widespread; however, most nesting locales sustain only small or moderate-scale nesting—up to approximately 1,000 females per year. The majority of populations are either known or thought to be depleted, many times to a severe extent; some populations are nearly extinct. It has been suggested that all populations, except for those using major nesting sites, are in danger and may not be self-sustaining in the long term.

Three major threats to olive ridley populations have been identified: commercial harvest of adults, harvest of eggs from nest beaches, and incidental catch in shrimp trawls. These factors are of differing significance in different areas, although some populations are affected by all three. In the 1960s, the skin of the neck, shoulder, and limbs of the turtle were used for the hide trade, while the remainder of the body was discarded. As part of an attempt to put exploitation on a more rational basis, the process was industrialized, and only processing plants able to use the whole animal were legalized. In addition to collection by legal, industrialized fisheries, millions of eggs and many thousands of turtles are taken illegally by poachers each year. Turtles caught in fishing nets are sometimes released, but they often drown after being snared by the nets.

Nancite, which is located inside Santa Rosa National Park, marks one major Costa Rica *arribada* site; Ostional, a second major site, was pronounced a sanctuary for marine turtles in 1982. A significant Orissa site is found within Bhitar Kanika Sanctuary, at Gahirmatha beach. These sanctuaries provide effective protection to the species while it nests, yet when the olive ridley populations move to the sea, they become susceptible to exploitation. To stop the olive ridley fishery, Ecuador has instituted a major preservation plan. In many other areas, protective legislation exists, but is not enforced.

National parks and reserves should be adequately protected, and existing laws should be enforced. Areas containing a large number of the species—especially those areas near nesting beaches—should institute restricted fishing zones. High priority should also be given to the development of fishing equipment which prevents the incidental take of sea turtles; the use of these turtle excluder devices (TEDs) should be encouraged or legislated. Because of the nature of this turtle's distribution, regional agreements on conservation are essential.

Leatherback sea turtle

Dermochelys coriacea

Phylum	Chordata
Class	Reptilia
Order	Testudines
Family	Dermochelyidae
Status	Endangered, IUCN
	Endangered, USFWS
	Appendix I, CITES
Range	Oceanic

Description and Biology

The largest living sea turtle, the leatherback can reach a carapace (shell) length of 4.3-4.9 ft (1.3-1.5 m) and a weight of 800-1,000 lb (365-480 kg). Unlike the bony-plated shells of other turtles, the brown to black carapace of the leatherback has seven raised ridges and the texture of hard rubber. Its front flippers are exceptionally long and powerful and may span over 8 ft (2 m) when extended. The head and neck are black or dark brown with white or yellowish blotches, and its short neck is not completely retractable. Diet consists almost entirely of jellyfish (best suited for its comparatively weak jaws); however, leatherbacks may also consume some squid, fish, blue-green algae, and crustaceans.

Nesting is seasonal, occurring between April and July at most North Atlantic sites and between November and January in the East Pacific. After mating offshore, the nesting female emerges from the sea at night and crosses the beach, heaving herself forward with powerful fore flippers. She first digs a shallow body-pit with all four limbs, then excavates a nest cavity about 39 in (100 cm) deep with her hind limbs. She lays a clutch of about 85 round, white-shelled eggs and toward the end may also deposit a number of small, yolkless eggs. She then covers the eggs with sand and returns to the ocean. After an incubation period of 56-65 days, hatchlings measuring 2.1-2.5 in (55-63 mm) in length emerge from the nest to crawl across the beach to the ocean. Leatherbacks are noted for producing fewer but larger eggs and hatchlings in comparison with other sea turtles. Pigs, ghost crabs, and monitor lizards often eat hatchlings and eggs. Birds, small mammals, and sharks may also occasionally prey on hatchlings. In the water, adults may be eaten by sharks; while nesting, females may be attacked by large cats.

Habitat and Current Distribution

Leatherback turtles range throughout the tropical, temperate, and subpolar seas; the species also migrates great distances to and from nesting sites, which are usually situated on tropical beaches in the Atlantic, Indian, and Pacific oceans, and occasionally in the subtropics and Mediterranean. The species has also been known to move into temperate waters to feed on more abundant concentrations of jellyfish. As with other sea turtles, population estimates are based only on mature, nesting females since males do not venture out of the water and hatchlings are likely to suffer extremely high mortality rates upon entering the sea. The total world population today is thought to

Leatherback sea turtle.

be in excess of 100,000 nesting females, and numbers have certainly increased at some sites.

This powerful swimmer is primarily pelagic (living in the open ocean). When nesting, females prefer relatively undisturbed beaches with a heavy surf and ready access to deep water. Leatherbacks rarely nest on beaches with a fringing reef. The presence of deep water close inshore may ease the female's approach to the beach and return to the sea.

History and Conservation Measures

In the 1960s scientists widely considered the leatherback turtle to be on the verge of extinction. However, more extensive surveys in 1971 established a population of 29,000 to 40,000 breeding females, and current numbers probably reach to well over 100,000. While total population is significantly larger than was once thought, and no evidence now exists for an overall decline in the species, it is nevertheless true that breeding populations are relatively small in size and widely scattered throughout the tropics. Certain populations are thought to have declined, while some have increased.

In comparison to most other sea turtles, the leatherback appears to have a better chance at continued survival. The leatherback and its eggs are heavily exploited as food, but not to the degree that such

other turtles as the green turtle, Olive Ridley, or hawksbill are exploited. The oily meat of adult leatherbacks is generally considered unpalatable and therefore unsuitable for commercial sale, but it still constitutes part of a subsistence diet. The meat is also used as bait. Harvesting of leatherback eggs takes place in most known nesting areas and probably constitutes the most significant threat to the species. Encouragingly, virtually no international trade in leatherback parts or their derivatives currently exists. Marine erosion has resulted in the severe loss of nests in some areas, and incidental catching in shrimp trawls and other nets and lines is increasing markedly. The development of beaches for tourism is also considered a threat. Plastic trash in the ocean is a major hazard as well because leatherbacks cannot distinguish between jellyfish, its major food source, and plastic items that are indigestible and possibly fatal.

In most countries of the species' breeding range, legislation provides limited protection for the leatherback and the beaches where it nests. However, conservationists must consider the fact that leatherback meat and especially eggs are an important source of nutrients or income to local subsistence peoples. In such cases, laws are recommended that restrict harvesting to only a proportion of eggs. However, unregulated killing of adults—particularly females—capable of reproducing is counterproductive and unacceptable. A harvesting and hatchery program has been attempted in Trengganu State (Malaysia) and may serve as a model for later programs. However, problems concerning the incubation of leatherbacks still exist, particularly in regulating the temperature of the nest which determines the sex of the hatchlings. Captive breeding is probably not possible with this species. Restricted fishing zones should also be established in areas of high leatherback concentrations, and the use of turtle excluder devices (TEDs) for trawl nets should be encouraged.

Pig-nosed turtle

Carettochelys insculpta

Phylum	Chordata
Class	Reptilia
Order	Testudines
Family	Carettochelyidae
Status	Insufficiently Known, IUCN
Range	Australia; Irian Jaya (Indonesia); Papua New Guinea

Description and Biology

The pig-nosed turtle, or New Guinea plateless turtle, is a large freshwater or estuarine species, with a shell length reaching approximately 18 in (46 cm) and a body weight of more than 33 lb (15 kg). Diet is primarily vegetarian but includes molluscs and insects such as water beetles. Adults probably have few natural predators other than man, as their large resilient shell offers protection from sharks and from fresh-water crocodiles that prey on juveniles. Eggs and juveniles are vulnerable to predators, particularly monitor lizards.

Little information is available regarding mating habits; according to local people, the turtles mate on muddy riverbanks. Nesting season in Australia is mid-August to early October in the Daly River, with a slightly earlier start and later finish in the Alligator River. In the Gulf Province of Papua New Guinea, nesting occurs during the dry season, from mid-October to mid-February. When nesting begins, female turtles migrate upriver, coming ashore at night or in the early morning to lay their eggs in nests dug in the sand. These nesting cavities have an average depth of 11 in (27 cm). Clutch size ranges from 15-34, and it is probable that females produce at least two clutches each season. Hatchlings usually emerge in 114-118 days.

Habitat and Current Distribution

This species is found in the southern lowlands of New Guinea and the Northern Territory of Australia. Population estimates are not available.

Preferred habitat includes rivers and estuaries, grassy lagoons, swamps, lakes, and water holes. In the Kikori River District, adult pig-nosed turtles are typically found at the mouths of rivers in delta areas, while juveniles are found farther inland where they are frequently caught in small creeks by shrimp fishermen. Nesting takes place on large sandbanks, at the mouths of rivers, on sandy shores of islands in the Fly River delta, and on coastal beaches in the Western Province of Papua New Guinea.

History and Conservation Measures

The primary threat to this species is hunting. The Australian populations are heavily hunted by aboriginals, for whom the pig-headed turtle and its eggs are a favorite food source. Nesting sites have been destroyed by increased river traffic, the con-

Pig-nosed turtle.

struction of dams and other industrial projects, and the clearing of land around rivers. Water buffalo also destroy nesting grounds, but a buffalo-management program is now under way.

Additional research is needed to determine the pig-nosed turtle's habitat requirements and to assess the impact of the current level of exploitation. With careful management, the species can remain a valuable and sustainable food source for local peoples.

Black soft-shell turtle

Aspideretes (Trionyx) nigricans

Phylum	Chordata
Class	Reptilia
Order	Testudines
Family	Trionychidae
Status	Rare, IUCN Endangered, USFWS Appendix I, CITES
Range	Bangladesh

Description and Biology

The black soft-shell turtle has a shell length of 25.2-30.7 in (64-78 cm) for males and 15.4-20.9 in (39-53 cm) for females. The biology of this species has not yet been described in any detail.

Habitat and Current Distribution

Approximately 320 semi-captive black soft-shell turtles inhabit a 263 x 328 ft (80 x 100 m) artificial pond at the shrine of the Islamic Saint Byazid Bostami at Nasirabad, near Chittagong, Bangladesh. Roughly 60 percent of this population is male. Sixteen additional turtles have been found in a nearby ditch, but this may have been the result of overflow from an instance of flooding or females that wandered after nesting. No other populations of this species have ever been recorded.

History and Conservation Measures

Some confusion and uncertainty surrounds the validity of this species: it is possible that it is based upon a long-term captive population of *Aspideretes hurum* that includes some larger and older specimens than those that exist in the wild.

The Chittagong population of black soft-shell turtles is strictly protected. Nevertheless, the species is considered threatened because of its extremely limited range; disease, for example, could eliminate the entire population. The water in the temple pond is very dirty, and many of the older turtles appear to suffer from skin infections. One of the main threats to the semi-captive population is the continuing construction of new walls, temples, and other obstructions, such that adults may soon be unable to reach places where they can nest. The species is being studied at the University of Chittagong, where its eggs have been hatched under laboratory conditions. Other populations should be established in suitable habitats at other sites to preserve the species in the event that the Chittagong population does not survive.

South American river turtle

Podocnemis expansa

Phylum	Chordata
Class	Reptilia
Order	Testudines
Family	Pelomedusidae
Status	Endangered, IUCN
	Appendix II, CITES
Range	Bolivia; Brazil; Colombia; Ecuador; Guyana; Peru; Trinidad and Tobago; Venezuela

Description and Biology

The South American river turtle is a large freshwater species that weighs approximately 110 lb (50 kg). Females reach a maximum shell length of 31.5-35 in (80-89 cm); males are much smaller. The species is omnivorous, with a diet that includes dead fish and other animal matter but consists primarily of aquatic vegetation and fallen fruit.

The nesting season varies in different regions. Basking behavior begins 15 days before egg-laying and continues throughout the season. When nesting begins, female turtles leave the water to occupy sandy beaches, where each lays a clutch of 50-150 eggs in a nesting pit. Once it has finished laying its eggs, the turtle fills the nest with sand, which it compacts by raising and rapidly lowering its shell onto the nest, before returning to the water. It is probable that only a single clutch is laid each season. Incubation takes approximately 48 days. Group nesting occurs in some limited areas, including several sandbanks in the middle reaches of the Orinoco River, Venezuela, two or three smaller sites in Guyana's Rewa River, and the Rio Trombetas in Brazil. More frequently, however, nesting is dispersed over wide areas, with only small numbers using a given sandbank, as is common in Peru and much of the Amazon River basin.

Habitat and Current Distribution

Widespread in the Amazon basin and in the Orinoco River drainage, the South American river turtle is found in Bolivia, Brazil, Colombia, Peru, Venezuela, and probably Ecuador. It also inhabits Guyana's Essequibo River system and may extend into Surinam and French Guiana. Total population of the species is unknown.

Preferred habitat includes large or flooded rivers, oxbow lakes, and flooded forest areas. Nesting is restricted to relatively low, sandy beaches or sandbars.

History and Conservation Measures

Indigenous peoples of the Amazon have historically relied upon the South American river turtle as a food source. Following European colonization, however, traders and missionaries also exploited the species as a source of oil for lamps and cooking, and its population drastically declined in the 18th century. Survival of the species is attributed in part to the introduction of kerosene and vegetable oils in the late 19th century, which reduced the demand for turtle oil.

Habitat alteration is a current threat to the species, especially the clearance of forested areas of floodplains which provide food for the turtle. The construction of dams for hydroelectric plants has also caused loss of habitat. The turtle is still hunted for its eggs and meat despite legal protection of some of its nesting sites. If its depleted population is to recover, more comprehensive protection of nesting areas is necessary in addition to greater enforcement of restrictions on hunting. With proper management programs in place to protect against over–exploitation, the species could be valuable as a cost-effective, manageable, and renewable food resource in northern South America.

Yellow-spotted sideneck turtle

Podocnemis unifilis

Phylum	Chordata
Class	Reptilia
Order	Testudines
Family	Pelomedusidae
Status	Vulnerable, IUCN
	Endangered, USFWS
	Appendix II, CITES
Range	Bolivia; Brazil; Colombia; Ecuador; French Guiana; Guyana; Peru; Suriname; Venezuela

Description and Biology

The yellow-spotted sideneck turtle, also called the yellow-headed sideneck turtle or the tracaja, is a medium–sized freshwater species reaching a maximum carapace (shell) length of 17.4 in (44.3 cm) and weight of 26.5 lb (12 kg); the male is smaller than the female. It is omnivorous but predominantly vegetarian, feeding during the day on aquatic plants and fruits that fall into the water but also scavenging dead fish and other animals. The jaguar may be the major predator of adults, while raptors, caiman, and fish prey on young turtles. The common caracara has also been observed feeding on hatchlings.

Breeding season is well-defined but variable between localities and, to some extent, with the nesting season of related species. Females congregate on or near the beaches during the nesting season, basking on the sands or lying half-submerged in the warm water along the shoreline. This behavior, which precedes egg-laying, may last several days and apparently plays a significant role in egg maturation. Females typically nest alone, but groups of up to 20 females have been observed. Favoring dark nights, this turtle nests even in the rain. The female lays a clutch of 14-49 hard-shelled eggs, leaving them in the sand for an incubation period of about 64 days. The young remain in the shell for two to five more days while the yolk sac is completely absorbed. After leaving the shell, the young gather at the top of the nest chamber and emerge from the nest two to five weeks later, always at night and typically after a rain.

Habitat and Current Distribution

This species is widespread in the Amazon and Orinoco River systems and occurs in several rivers in the Guianas. It is present in Amazonian Brazil, extending into Bolivia, Peru, Ecuador, Colombia, Venezuela, Guyana, French Guiana, and marginally in Suriname. There are no estimates of the population size.

The species uses various habitats, including large rivers, backwaters, oxbow lakes, ponds, lagoons, and seasonally flooded forests. Characteristically, this turtle inhabits rivers only during the nesting season.

History and Conservation Measures

Adult turtles, notably nesting females, and eggs are subject to heavy exploitation by humans throughout the habitat. Consumers prefer this species' meat and eggs to those of other turtles. In the 1960s hatchlings were heavily exploited by the live animal trade in the United States and Europe, but this trade has largely ceased following widespread implementation of the CITES treaty. The species is nominally protected in most countries, but enforcement is generally lacking. For example, floodplain forest, an important feeding area for the species, is rapidly being cleared for agricultural cultivation. It is believed that the species has resisted habitat encroachments by successfully adapting to various localities.

The yellow-spotted sideneck turtle is a potentially cost-effective, easily managed, renewable source of nutrition. It converts otherwise unused vegetable material into animal protein and fat of great nutritive value to the human population in northern South America. Its potential can only be realized if current short-term exploitation is immediately curtailed and rational management plans devised to allow adequate recovery of depleted populations.

Yellow-spotted sideneck turtle.

Dahl's toad-headed turtle

Phrynops dahli

Phylum	Chordata
Class	Reptilia
Order	Testudines
Family	Chelidae
Status	Indeterminate, IUCN
Range	Colombia

Description and Biology

Very little is known about this extremely rare turtle, even by local people who live near its habitat. It probably represents the northwestern limit of distribution of the family Chelidae. It often travels great distances by land and may remain dormant for several weeks under forest leaves. Feeding at the bottom of ponds and streams, Dahl's toad-headed turtle is primarily carnivorous, but it also consumes vegetation from time to time.

Mating takes place from June until July, and approximately six eggs are laid in September or October.

Habitat and Current Distribution

The very limited range of Dahl's toad-headed turtle is centered around Sincelejo in Bolivar State, Colombia, possibly including the middle and upper Rio Sinu drainage. No population estimates currently exist, but conservationists consider the species to be extremely rare.

Preferred habitat includes ponds and small brooks within the forest.

History and Conservation Measures

Severe habitat destruction is the primary threat to Dahl's toad-headed turtle—nearly all of its habitat has been converted into pastureland, particularly around Sincelejo. If destruction continues at its current pace, the species will almost certainly face extinction, given its rarity and extremely restricted range.

Surveys of status and studies of ecology in the wild are necessary to form the basis of effective conservation efforts. Meanwhile, voluntary restraints should be negotiated with major land owners to protect key habitats. Dahl's toad-headed turtles have been kept in captivity at the Instituto Roberto Franco in Villavicencio, Colombia, and though captive breeding has thus far been unsuccessful, such a program may be essential to prevent extinction. It is also important ascertain whether or not this species can persist in local ponds and ditches, such as cattle watering ponds. An encouraging sign is that while most virgin habitat around Sincelejo has been destroyed, a fair number of ponds remain, and some local people have recognized the species in the area.

Western swamp turtle

Pseudemydura umbrina

Phylum	Chordata
Class	Reptilia
Order	Testudines
Family	Chelidae
Status	Endangered, IUCN
	Endangered, USFWS
	Appendix I, CITES
Range	Australia

Description and Biology

The western swamp turtle or short-necked turtle has a flat shell that ranges in color from brown to black. Its neck is short, and the head is usually held sideways under the shell. It is Australia's smallest turtle, and unlike other turtles in the region, males of the species are slightly larger than females. Maximum shell length is 5.5 in (14 cm) for males; females typically have a shell length of 4.4-4.6 in (11.2-11.6 cm) and never exceed 5.3 in (13.5 cm). Semi-aquatic and carnivorous in the wild, the western swamp turtle feeds upon live crustaceans, small tadpoles, and earthworms.

From June to October or early November, water levels are high in the swamps it inhabits, and the turtle has a plentiful supply of food. Shallower pools in the swamps usually begin to dry up in October, and turtles then move into deeper pools or other refuges; most turtles are in such refuges by mid-November or December. Mating takes place in winter and spring, and nesting in early summer (November or early December). Apparently only one clutch of three to five hard-shelled eggs is laid per season, after which the turtle buries itself in the soil. It remains there until the following winter, when rains replenish the swamps. Hatchlings emerge in May or June following a gestation period of approximately 180 days.

Habitat and Current Distribution

The western swamp turtle is now restricted to the Ellen Brook Nature Reserve near the city of Perth, Western Australia, where at least four adult females survive in the wild. The total population is unknown.

The preferred habitat is swamp that is dry in summer and autumn and wet in the winter.

History and Conservation Measures

After a single specimen of the western swamp turtle was discovered in 1839, the species was not sighted again for more than a century. It was rediscovered in 1953, and its two remaining breeding sites at Ellen Brook and Twin Swamps were declared nature reserves by the Western Australian government in 1962. Since that time, however, the Twin Swamps population has become extinct. The species is now protected by legislation, and population monitoring and predator control programs are in place.

A captive breeding program at the Conservation

Western swamp turtle.

and Land Management Centre in Perth is thought to offer the only prospect for the long-term survival of the species. Difficulties were encountered in the early stages of this effort, and it was thought that the turtles required long periods of drought, as in the wild, to trigger their breeding periods. Improved research has helped this program to become more effective through improved husbandry techniques; as a result, the hatchling survival rate is now very high. Since the long-range goal of the captive breeding program is to release captive-bred turtles into the wild, it is important that the remaining natural habitat of the species be protected and maintained. Additional research on the breeding cycle of the species is also needed.

Chinese alligator

Alligator sinensis

Phylum	Chordata
Class	Reptilia
Order	Crocodylia
Family	Alligatoridae
Status	Endangered, IUCN
	Endangered, USFWS
	Appendix I, CITES
Range	China

Description and Biology

Smaller than the American alligator, the Chinese alligator averages 6-6.5 ft (1.8-2 m) long. It is dark olive in color with yellowish spots and has a large head with a short, broad snout that turns up slightly. Semi-aquatic, it feeds on snails, freshwater mussels, fish, insects, and small mammals.

Much of the life cycle is spent in burrows excavated into the banks of rivers, streams, and ponds. The period from late October to late March or mid-April is spent hibernating in the burrows. Daytime activity in May after emergence from hibernation shifts toward nocturnal activity in June, coincident with the mating period. A mound-nesting species, the female lays 10-40 eggs between July and August in a nest made from dry leaves and grasses. As the vegetation rots, the temperature inside the nest rises to a temperature which incubates the eggs in around 70 days. Hatchlings average just over 8 in (21 cm) long and weigh around an ounce (30 g); growth is rapid for the first five years and sexual maturity is reached in four to five years.

Habitat and Current Distribution

This species is endemic to the People's Republic of China, where it is now restricted to the lower Yangzi (Yangtze or Chang Jiang) valley in Anhui (Anhwei), Zhejiang (Chekiang), and Jiangsu (Kiangsu) Provinces. Total population in the wild is estimated at 500 individuals, with over 300 of them in Anhui Province. An additional 4,000 individuals are held at a large captive breeding facility in Anhui and commercial development, with proceeds supporting alligator conservation, are planned.

Primary habitat is the lower Yangzi and adjacent lakes and ponds, where the Chinese alligator inhabits low beaches and dense stands of cane and excavates burrows in the banks of rivers and ponds. Following the disturbance of wetlands in the Jiangnan plain, alligators have apparently moved into pools in lightly wooded hill country in the upper reaches of the Quingyi and Zhanghe Rivers, and significant numbers are now established there.

History and Conservation Measures

The range of the Chinese alligator once extended more widely along the lower and middle Yangzi River basin west to the ancient Yunmeng swamp in Hubei Province, the Dongting Hu in Hunan Province, and north to the Huang Ho (Yellow River). The major portion of the population existed in the area now comprising Anhui, Jiangsu, Zhejiang, and

Chinese alligator.

Jiangxi Provinces. There are no estimates of initial population, but the species has declined and is now considered in danger of extinction.

Many of the threats to this species are caused by humans: expanding population, usurpation of habitat, and intentional killing by local inhabitants. In addition, this alligator is endangered by environmental factors. Animals residing in grassy bank areas are subject to flooding, and many drown in their caves if they are unable to reach an air pocket or the water's surface. In times of drought, available habitat is further reduced and animals leave their drying ponds in search of water and suitable reproduction sites. Drought could severely affect the remaining populations since most individuals live in wetlands and ponds that are frequently distantly scattered.

In addition to governmental protection in China, several conservation areas have been set aside for this species, including the Wuhu Alligator Sanctuary and an alligator rearing station at the Xiadu Commune Tree Farm in Xuancheng County, Anhui Province. Studies of breeding behavior and population surveys have been undertaken to form the basis of further conservation measures.

Black caiman

Melanosuchus niger

Phylum	Chordata
Class	Reptilia
Order	Crocodylia
Family	Alligatoridae
Status	Endangered, IUCN
	Endangered, USFWS
	Appendix I, CITES
Range	Bolivia; Brazil; Colombia; Ecuador; French Guiana; Guyana; Paraguay; Peru; Venezuela

Description and Biology

The largest species of crocodile in the New World, the black caiman averages 13-15 ft (4-4.5 m) in length, and has been known to exceed 19-20 ft (6 m). Adults are black, with lighter brown blotches on the head; young have spots of yellow, green, or white on the head, with a pale underside. Juveniles, up to 3.3 ft (1 m) in length, are known to feed upon fish, amphibians, insects, crustaceans, and snails. Adults prey upon a variety of small animals (especially capybara and other rodents), small deer, cattle, other caiman, and particularly fish, such as catfish and piranha.

Many aspects of the reproductive ecology of this species are unknown. The black caiman lays its eggs in a nest measuring 5 ft (1.5 m) wide and 2.6 ft (0.8 m) high and consisting of a mound built from vegetable debris. Clutch size is typically 30-60 hard-shelled eggs, which are usually incubated for 5-6 weeks. Breeding season depends upon geographic location, varying from September to January, with hatching taking place from November to March.

Habitat and Current Distribution

The black caiman is widely distributed throughout the Amazon Basin. Until recently the largest known population was found at Kaw (French Guiana), where as many as 1,000 individuals survived, but uncontrolled hunting has resulted in a major decline of the species at that location. There are no estimates of total population size.

This species inhabits a freshwater ecosystem, seeking out undisturbed backwaters or bends in lagoons and large rivers, or flooded areas of forests or grasslands.

History and Conservation Measures

The black caiman was once widely distributed throughout the Amazonian region, being extremely abundant in some areas. Its decline is attributed to excessive hunting for its hide; its large size made it sought after by hunters, who killed millions of black caiman for the leather industry. Serious hunting first began in the 1940s, as stocks of the previously abundant South American crocodiles *Crocodylus acutus* and *C. intermedius* were depleted, and continued until the early 1970s, when the black caiman became scarce enough that commercial hunting was no longer economically feasible. Poaching continues in some areas, however. The species is also threatened by loss of habitat to logging and agriculture, including cattle ranching. Considered a threat to livestock, the black caiman is often killed as a pest.

The widespread decline of this species has had a noticeable impact on the ecology of the region. Capybara populations have dramatically increased and have caused damage to crops in certain areas of Bolivia and Brazil. Piranha populations have also increased, and cattle have been attacked as they cross flooded grasslands. Black caiman excrement is also an important part of the food chain, providing nutrients for zooplankton and phytoplankton which in turn are consumed by fish hatchlings. Consequently, the decreasing numbers of black caimans has had a negative effect on the populations of some species of fish.

The black caiman is legally protected in most of the countries in which it is found, but protection is poorly enforced. One of the most important populations within a protected area is that of the Manu National Park, Peru; small numbers also inhabit the Parque Nacional de Amazonia on the Rio Tapajos in Brazil. A program to release captive black caimans into the wild has begun in Bolivia, where 25 were released at the Beni Biological Station in July 1990.

Black caimans.

American crocodile

Crocodylus acutus

Phylum	Chordata
Class	Reptilia
Order	Crocodylia
Family	Crocodylidae
Status	Vulnerable, IUCN
	Endangered, USFWS
	Appendix I, CITES
Range	Belize (?); Colombia; Costa Rica; Cuba; Dominican Republic; Ecuador; El Salvador; Guatemala; Haiti; Honduras; Jamaica; Mexico; Nicaragua; Panama; Peru; Florida (U.S.A.); Venezuela

Description and Biology

The American crocodile reaches an average length of 11-12 ft (3.4-3.6 m); its maximum length is 15-20 ft (4.5-6 m). It has a slender snout and a hump on the forehead between the eyes. Adults are dark brown to dark greenish brown, while juveniles are light greenish brown with dark markings on the body and tail and a pale underside. The species feeds primarily on fish, although juveniles are also known to consume aquatic invertebrates.

Eggs are laid in nests excavated in a beach, usually in late April or early May; if suitable beach space is limited, females will build a mound nest instead. These mounds vary in size, often reaching diameters of up to 15 ft (4.6 m) and heights of up to 2 ft (0.65 m). The same nesting site may be used in subsequent years. Average clutch size is 40, with eggs hatching between late July and early August.

Habitat and Current Distribution

This species is found in Central America, northern South America, southern Florida, the southern coasts of Mexico, and on the Caribbean islands of Cuba, Jamaica, and Hispaniola. One of the largest known populations is found in the Dominican Repub-lic, where 175-250 American crocodiles inhabit Lago Enriquillo. In the United States the species is restricted to the Florida Keys, where its population is estimated at between 100-400 animals. There are no estimates of total population size.

Preferred habitat consists primarily of coastal waters, including brackish areas of rivers and lagoons, but some inland populations inhabit freshwater areas, including reservoirs.

History and Conservation Measures

While at one time the American crocodile was abundant, hunting for its valuable hide and loss of habitat have caused a severe reduction in its numbers. Development has occurred throughout its range in recent decades, and hunting continues in some areas. The species is protected in eight of the 17 countries in which it exists, but enforcement is lacking.

The hide of the species remains commercially valuable, and crocodile ranches or farms with sustainable-use programs have been started in five countries. It has been suggested that these and similar programs be carefully monitored and regulated, as the collection of adults for breeding could further jeopardize the health of wild populations.

American crocodile.

African slender-snouted crocodile

Crocodylus cataphractus

Phylum	Chordata
Class	Reptilia
Order	Crocodylia
Family	Crocodylidae
Status	Vulnerable, IUCN
	Endangered, USFWS
	Appendix I, CITES (Appendix II, Congo pop)
Range	Angola; Benin; Burkina Faso; Cameroon; Central African Republic; Chad; Congo; Côte d'Ivoire; Equatorial Guinea; Gabon; Gambia (ex?); Ghana; Guinea; Guinea-Bissau (ex?); Liberia; Mali; Mauritania; Nigeria; Senegal (ex?); Sierra Leone; Tanzania; Togo; Zaire; Zambia

Description and Biology

The African slender-snouted crocodile is a medium-sized crocodile with a maximum length of 13 ft (4 m); the average adult size is 6.6-8.2 ft (2-2.5 m). It is greenish brown, with dark blotches on the jaw and a striped tail. Although the slender snout seems to indicate that the reptile is a fish–eater, it also appears to consume a variety of other aquatic or waterside vertebrates and crustaceans. Juveniles feed on shrimp, crabs, water snakes, frogs, toads, and grasshoppers.

At the start of the wet season, this species uses organic materials to build mound nests, which most often are located along the banks of rivers. The eggs laid by the female are fairly large, in relation to the female's size, and up to 16 eggs are laid during the nesting period. Little other ecological information is available about this species.

Habitat and Current Distribution

This crocodile has a fairly widespread distribution in West and Central Africa, from Senegal in the west to Tanzania in the east. The heaviest concentration of the species seems to be located in Gabon's Ogoue River, on Africa's western coast. Survey data also indicates that the species survives—although the population is partially depleted—in Côte d'Ivoire, Congo, and the Central African Republic. Data regarding the species' existence in five other countries is not complete; however, it appears that the population is somewhat depleted in Liberia and significantly depleted in Angola, Gambia, Senegal, and Chad.

Habitat is primarily in tropical rain forests, where the slender-snouted crocodile inhabits rivers and larger bodies of water, but also extends into rivers in light savanna woodlands, and in the brackish water of coastal lagoons. It appears to prefer to leave the water at sheltered and inaccessible places.

African slender-snouted crocodile.

History and Conservation Measures

Although it has a widespread distribution, this species apparently has not been common at least since the beginning of twentieth century. The status of the species is very poorly known, but it appears to have declined generally and is regarded as threatened to some degree in many countries in the range, even though adequate populations still exist in some remote localities.

The primary reason for the decline of the African slender-snouted crocodile is hunting for its hide. Though its hide is commercially inferior to that of the Nile crocodile (*C. niloticus*), the slender-snouted crocodile has been increasingly hunted since the decline of the Nile crocodile. It also is used locally in the preparation of leather goods and is widely hunted for food. Loss of habitat is also implicated in the decline, but the extent of this has not been determined.

The slender-snouted crocodile is nominally protected within national parks or reserve areas in Cameroon, Chad, Congo, Gabon, Côte d'Ivoire, Mali, Senegal, Burkina Faso, Zaire, and Zambia. Since very little is known about the status of this species in the wild, surveys are necessary throughout its range. These surveys, measuring the species' population in each individual country, would serve as components of a larger plan for management and preservation.

Orinoco crocodile

Crocodylus intermedius

Phylum	Chordata
Class	Reptilia
Order	Crocodylia
Family	Crocodylidae
Status	Endangered, IUCN
	Endangered, USFWS
	Appendix I, CITES
Range	Orinoco River basin (Colombia; Venezuela)

Description and Biology

The Orinoco is a very large crocodile averaging between 11-17 ft (3-5 m); some males have been reported to be as long as 23 ft (7 m). Coloration is dark green to tan with dark markings and a light underside. It has a long nose and narrow snout. Diet is primarily fish, small mammals, and birds; young animals feed mainly on beetles and other insects, snails, crabs, and other invertebrates.

This is a hole-nesting species, laying its eggs in seasonally exposed sandbars early in the annual dry season (January-February). Clutch size is typically in the 40-70 range, and the young hatch during the seasonal rise in river levels associated with the wet season (February to late March). The female protects the hatchlings for a variable period.

Habitat and Current Distribution

This species occurs in the Orinoco River Basin in eastern Colombia and Venezuela. It is considered extremely depleted and almost extinct in Colombia and very rare and heavily depleted in Venezuela; possibly only 1,500 non-hatchlings survive in the wild.

The Orinoco crocodile prefers wide and very deep parts of large rivers during the rainy season but wanders over great distances in the wet season, when individuals may occupy lakes and pools to avoid the strong river currents. Juveniles seek shelter in quiet waters with abundant aquatic vegetation.

History and Conservation Measures

This species was considered very common up to the mid-1930s but is now one of the most critically endangered New World crocodilians. Its large, high-quality hide makes it the target of hunters; commercial over-exploitation from the 1930s through the 1950s decimated wild populations and little recovery has been evident since that time. Because the last surveys in Colombia were done in the early 1970s, the status of the species there is very poorly known. In Venezuela, recent survey work has found that remaining populations are in isolated areas where human impact has been minimal; however, even these remaining populations are being threatened today by a combination of factors, including habitat destruction, egg collecting, intentional and incidental killing, and the collection of animals for sale. The potential for population recovery may also be inhibited by a large increase in populations of the common caiman. Legal protections are not well enforced in Colombia or in Venezuela.

Orinoco crocodile.

In Venezuela, crocodile habitat has been protected in a newly declared national park (Parque Nacional Santos Luzardo) along the Capanaparo and Cinaruco Rivers, but no management plan has yet been implemented. A recently declared wildlife refuge has been established along the Guaritico River, and this area has been the site of the first release of captive-reared young. Plans for restocking the Capanaparo River are also being developed. Urgent action needs to be taken in both countries, but especially in Colombia, to locate surviving populations and initiate recovery programs.

Philippine crocodile

Crocodylus mindorensis

Phylum	Chordata
Class	Reptilia
Order	Crocodylia
Family	Crocodylidae
Status	Endangered, IUCN
	Endangered, USFWS
	Appendix I, CITES
Range	Philippines

Description and Biology

The Philippine or Mindoro crocodile is a rather small species of crocodile that averages around 8-9 ft (2.4-2.7 m) long, with a maximum length of less than 10 ft (3 m). Its body color is yellowish brown, accented by dark spots and dark stripes on the tail. The crocodile's neck is heavy, and its snout is broad. The species' diet is unknown.

Little information is known on the ecology of the wild population of the Philippine crocodile. In captivity, females build mound nests between April and July, lay 10-20 eggs, and defend the nest vigorously.

Habitat and Current Distribution

This crocodile is endemic to the Philippines and has been recorded on the islands of Busuanga, Luzon, Samar, Masbate, Mindanao, Negros, and Mindoro. It is considered critically endangered with a reported population in 1983 of 500-1,000 individuals.

The habitat of the Philippine crocodile includes freshwater marshes, ponds, small lakes, and tributaries of large rivers.

History and Conservation Measures

Philippine crocodiles were at one time widely distributed throughout the archipelago, but are now restricted to a few islands. Initial population decline was associated with commercial over–exploitation, but trade is minimal now, probably because of the scarcity of the species. At present, the Philippine crocodile is primarily threatened in two ways: loss of habitat and killing by local inhabitants. Loss of habitat is due to the spread of agriculture and aquaculture projects, including fish ponds, rice paddies, and coconut and sugar cane plantations. Killing of the species continues because crocodiles are disliked and feared by local residents.

The main conservation effort for this species has been an attempt at captive breeding for eventual reintroduction to the wild. If captive breeding were to increase the numbers of Philippine crocodiles, a major priority would become the establishment of suitable reserve areas. Unfortunately, future efforts at extensive captive breeding could be hampered by the fact that only a small number of the crocodiles are currently in captivity.

The only officially protected area in which Philippine crocodiles are presently found is the Lake Naujan National Park, but protection in the park is not adequate and needs to be improved. Plans need to be made for the management and conservation of the crocodile nationwide, and suitable areas should be set aside as crocodile reserves. Efforts—perhaps through educational campaigns—also should be made toward securing public and political support for crocodile conservation, since the issue is neither a significant popular nor governmental concern.

Mugger crocodile

Crocodylus palustris

Phylum	Chordata
Class	Reptilia
Order	Crocodylia
Family	Crocodylidae
Status	Vulnerable, IUCN
	Endangered, USFWS
	Appendix I, CITES
Range	Bangladesh (ex?); India; Iran; Nepal; Pakistan; Sri Lanka

Description and Biology

The mugger crocodile has the broadest snout of any living member of the genus *Crocodylus*. It averages 10-13 ft (3-4 m) and can grow to over 16 ft (5 m). Adults are grayish brown in color, and juveniles are light brown with darker brown bands. Hatchlings feed on water insects and young fish; as they increase in size, they shift to larger prey, including frogs, small mammals, and birds. Very large individuals sometimes take big game, including buffalo, wild cattle, and deer.

During courtship season (from November to February in India), males establish a dominance hierarchy and dominant males mate with several females; mating takes place in open water. Females start digging trial nest pits at least two weeks before actual egg–laying. Eggs are laid in a nest chamber 14-20 in (35-50 cm) deep, usually the shape of a wide-mouthed pitcher, dug well away from the water's edge, often in a sloping bank 16-50 ft (5-15 m) high. Clutch size ranges from 10-46 eggs; incubation period varies from 55-75 days. Hatchlings that are ready to emerge make grunting noises from within the nest, stimulating the nest-guarding female to excavate the nest and release the hatchlings to the water. There are many egg predators in the wild, including mongoose, jackal, monitor lizard, and the sloth bear. Hatchling predators include birds such as herons and storks. Natural calamities like flooding and desiccation also take a heavy toll.

Habitat and Current Distribution

The range of the mugger crocodile is centered on the Indian subcontinent, extending into Pakistan, Iran, Nepal, Sri Lanka, and a few in Bangladesh. Sri Lanka has the largest remaining populations, concentrated in two national parks, Wilpattu and Yala. Wild populations are thought to number 3,000-5000. About 1200 muggers were re-introduced to the wild. In recent years, however, it has been difficult locating suitable habitat for additional restocking. As a result over 12,000 captive-bred muggers have accumulated in the breeding facilities and the program is foundering for lack of resources to support these animals.

The mugger crocodile occurs in any kind of freshwater habitat and is occasionally reported in brackish waters well within tidal limits. It may be present in rivers, streams, jungle pools, and man-made lakes ranging in size from village ponds to large irrigation reservoirs. This adaptability to man-made

Mugger crocodile.

water bodies appears to be a significant factor in the widespread persistence of mugger populations. It often basks on rocks in mid-river or along muddy banks. In the drier months, crocodiles living in rivers occupy the deepest pools and are known to wander away from dry rivers in search of water and food. It prefers still waters with a depth of 10-16 ft (3-5 m) and avoids fast-flowing rivers during monsoon periods.

History and Conservation Measures

This crocodile was heavily hunted during the 1950s and 1960s but now faces new threats. The primary threat today is entrapment of these animals in fish nets that are set across rivers or standing bodies of water. It is also subject to egg predation by humans, and crocodile parts are desired by humans for their supposed medicinal properties. Habitat destruction is also a common problem in many areas.

Conservation management of mugger crocodiles is based principally on the legal protection of wild populations; it is therefore important to locate wild breeding populations in suitable habitats so that those areas may be declared as sanctuaries. In India, a large-scale captive rearing program was initiated in 1975. The project has been successful in collecting eggs from the wild as well as producing young in captivity from captive adult breeding stock. The resulting juveniles have been used to restock natural populations in 28 national parks, wildlife reserves, and crocodile sanctuaries throughout the country. Pakistan is planning a similar restocking program.

Another conservation measure under consideration is the development of a sustainable use program for the mugger in India for local consumption of meat and export of skins to benefit poor tribal groups.

Estuarine crocodile

Crocodylus porosus

Phylum . . . . Chordata
Class . . . . Reptilia
Order . . . . Crocodylia
Family . . . . Crocodylidae
Status . . . . Vulnerable, IUCN
Endangered, USFWS
Appendix I, CITES
Appendix II, CITES (Australia; Indonesia; Papua New Guinea)
Range . . . . Australia; Bangladesh; Brunei; China; Kampuchea; India; Indonesia;
Peninsular Malaysia, Sabah, Sarawak (Malaysia); Myanmar; Papua New
Guinea; Philippines; Solomon Islands; Sri Lanka; Thailand; Vanuatu; Vietnam

Description and Biology

One of the largest living crocodiles, the estuarine or saltwater crocodile (sometimes called the Indopacific crocodile) averages 9-23 ft (2.7-7 m) in length and weighs over 2,000 lb (900 kg). It has a large head, a long snout, and webbed hind feet. Adults, after losing their dark, immature markings, are dark green to black with a yellow or cream colored belly. Diet varies with age and size: the young mainly eat crustaceans, insects, and small fish, and as they mature include larger prey in their diet, including snakes, birds, turtles, cattle, and horses. Adult crocodiles are also known to eat humans. Like the Nile crocodile, the estuarine crocodile sometimes drags its prey under the water to consume later.

Males reach sexual maturity at around 16 years, when they measure about 10.5 ft (3.2 m); females reach maturity at 10 years, when they are about 7 ft (2.2 m). The breeding season varies with locality, but nesting often coincides with the wet season. Mound nests are built of leaf litter, grass, reeds, and mud. The female lays 40-60 eggs, which are incubated for 80-90 days. The eggs are vulnerable to collection by humans and predation by monitor lizards. The nestlings are guarded from other crocodiles, which may by cannibalistic. Young are vulnerable to sharks and other aquatic predators.

Habitat and Current Distribution

This is the most widespread species of crocodile, occurring in Southeast Asia, Indonesia, the Philippines, New Guinea, and northern Australia. It is severely depleted and at risk throughout almost all of its range. The estuarine crocodile, as its name suggests, is found in coastal brackish water habitats and the tidal section of rivers. However, it is also well known from the freshwater sections of rivers and frequents inland swamps and marshes.

History and Conservation Measures

The severe depletion of the estuarine crocodile is attributed to hunting for its hide and, secondarily, to habitat loss. The hide of this crocodile yields a large quantity of valued leather. During the 1950s and 1960s, it is estimated that hundreds of thousands of

Estuarine or saltwater crocodile.

estuarine crocodiles were killed every year to satisfy market demands. Selective hunting for large, adult crocodiles resulted in a severe reduction in the breeding population. The CITES treaty now regulates the trade of this species, but illegal trade still continues and is very difficult to control over such a large area.

Habitat loss appears to reduce the recovery prospects of populations already depleted by hunting. Coastal mangrove habitat, in particular, has been subject to clearing and draining for agricultural use.

Basic survey data are available for only eight of the 18 countries in which this species is found (it is now extinct in Singapore), and there is no information on wild populations throughout large parts of the species' range. Population surveys are a high priority, particularly in Thailand, Burma, Malaysia, Indonesia, Vietnam, Brunei, Sri Lanka, and the Philippines.

In Papua New Guinea, a controversial program removes hatchlings from the wild and rears them in commercial establishments to be killed for their skins in about three years. The program assumes a high mortality rate among young crocodiles in the wild and considers the captured hatchlings a harvestable surplus, whose capture would not affect the status of the wild population. This program is an attempt to meet the commercial demand for hides without damaging the species in the wild.

A restocking program in Bhitarkanika National Park (India) has been quite successful, and some of the initial releases have begun to breed. Additional release sites need to be identified for animals still held in captivity.

Cuban crocodile

Crocodylus rhombifer

Phylum	Chordata
Class	Reptilia
Order	Crocodylia
Family	Crocodylidae
Status	Endangered, IUCN
	Endangered, USFWS
	Appendix I, CITES
Range	Cuba

Description and Biology

The Cuban crocodile is a small to medium-sized species that averages 6.6-8.2 ft (2-2.5 m) in length, occasionally reaching 11.5 ft (3.5 m) with a maximum reported length of 16 ft (4.9 m). It has a dark green body with yellow-green spots, and a short snout with teeth that tilt outward. The species is aggressive and can jump well. Its diet includes fish, birds, and small mammals.

Its nesting habits are uncertain: in the wild, females are known to nest in holes dug into peat or soil, but in captivity this species has built mound nests. Clutch size ranges from 30-40 eggs, and the nest is guarded by the female.

Habitat and Current Distribution

The distribution of the Cuban crocodile is more limited than that of similar species, being primarily restricted to the Zapata Swamp in southwestern Cuba, where its population is thought to be several hundred. A small remnant population may also inhabit the Lanier Swamp on the Isla de Juventud.

The Zapata Swamp is a large freshwater marsh, but the species is also known to tolerate saltwater.

History and Conservation Measures

At one time the Cuban crocodile was more widespread on the main island of Cuba and was also found in the Cayman Islands. Its population and distribution were drastically reduced by hunting, and the reduced population has been jeopardized by habitat destruction as a result of development. Proposals to drain the Zapata Swamp for agricultural use led to a translocation effort that further endangered the species. Most of the remaining Cuban crocodiles were captured and placed in pens, where they were able to interbreed with American crocodiles (*Crocodylus acutus*). This hybridization is now the main threat to the genetic integrity of the species.

While most of the remaining pure Cuban crocodiles have been transferred to a separate pen at Tasajera, southwest of Zapata in Habana Province, this new site is insufficiently managed and monitored. One obstacle has been the lack of communication between the scientists and wildlife personnel of Cuba and those of other countries. A large-scale captive breeding program has been established, largely for commercial use of skins and meat. Surveys and long-term ecological study of the species are necessary to plan management programs, including the possible

Cuban crocodile.

introduction of captive-bred Cuban crocodiles to the Zapata Swamp and other suitable habitats.

If a remnant population still exists in the Lanier Swamp, its survival is threatened by the spread of the common caiman *(Caiman crocodilus)*, an introduced species which preys on juvenile crocodiles. The Cuban crocodile is considered the most threatened of any New World crocodilian.

Siamese crocodile

Crocodylus siamensis

Phylum	Chordata
Class	Reptilia
Order.	Crocodylia
Family	Crocodylidae
Status	Endangered, IUCN
	Endangered, USFWS
	Appendix I, CITES
Range	Brunei (?); Kalimantan, Sulawesi, Sumatra (Indonesia); Kampuchea; Laos (?); Peninsular Malaysia, Sabah (?), Sarawak (?) (Malaysia); Myanmar (?); Thailand (ex?); Vietnam

Description and Biology

The Siamese is one of the world's most endangered crocodiles. Coloration is light brown with black stripes; throat is scaled and the snout is broad. Length averages around 10 ft (3 m); maximum size has been reported as 13 ft (4 m). Diet probably consists primarily of fish.

The ecology of the Siamese crocodile in the wild is virtually unknown. Information about reproduction is known only from captive populations. In captivity, mating occurs between December and March, and most females lay their eggs in April or May. A mound nest is formed from vegetable debris for a clutch of 20-48 eggs, which hatch in 67-68 days. The female guards the nest during incubation and excavates the eggs when the young vocalize, which occurs immediately prior to hatching.

Habitat and Current Distribution

This species may be extinct in the wild. The only known population was located in the Bung Boraphet Reservoir in Thailand; however, no recent sightings of crocodiles have been made at this site.

No adequate survey data are available from any part of the Siamese crocodile's range.

Preferred habitat is freshwater swamps and slow-moving sections of streams and rivers, but it has also been found in lakes and rivers.

History and Conservation Measures

The range of the Siamese crocodile formerly extended from Vietnam, Kampuchea (Cambodia), Thailand, possibly southern Laos, and southward through parts of the Malay Peninsula; it was also recorded in Indonesia, Java, and Kalimantan. It now appears to be extinct in the wild almost throughout its range. Survey data for this species is particularly incomplete, due in part to the civil unrest that has been experienced throughout much of southeast Asia.

The decline of this crocodile is attributed to unrestricted hide-hunting and to the loss of suitable habitat. It has always been rare in the Indonesian portion of the range. The populations in Thailand were depleted by hunting in the 1940s, and wetlands at the last known locality (Bung Boraphet) have been reduced by encroachment of rice cultivation. The genetic integrity of the species is also threatened. The

Siamese crocodile.

bulk of the captive population is maintained in the Samutprakan farm, where extensive interbreeding with the saltwater crocodile (*Crocodylus porosus*) has taken place because of the superior commercial qualities of the hybrids.

In the last two years a rejuvenated effort to preserve this species has been initiated by the Royal Thai Forest Service and commercial crocodile farmers. A survey is underway that has located a few wild specimens, and plans for the control and management of the captive population, which numbers many thousands, have been developed. Contact has also been established with Kampuchea, where a large captive population exists, and wild populations are reported in the Tongle Sap. Recent observations of

Siamese crocodiles on crocodile farms in Borneo indicate the species may still occur in the wild in Indonesia but field confirmation is required. Because of the extremely poor status of wild populations, captive breeding groups are of great importance. Efforts need to be made to separate a pure stock of Siamese crocodiles which could be used for future conservation activities. Since the last known wild population was located in Thailand, habitat surveys should be conducted there to determine the feasibility of creating protected areas. Once protected habitats are established, planning for crocodile release programs can begin. The other conservation priority involves surveys to clarify the status of wild populations in southeast Asia and in the Greater Sunda Islands.

False gharial

Tomistoma schlegelii

Phylum	Chordata
Class	Reptilia
Order	Crocodylia
Family	Crocodylidae
Status	Endangered, IUCN
	Endangered, USFWS
	Appendix I, CITES
Range	Kalimantan, Sumatra (Indonesia); Peninsular Malaysia, Sarawak (Malaysia); Myanmar (?); Thailand (ex?)

Description and Biology

The false gharial, or tomistoma, is one of the most unusual and little-known of the crocodilians. It is a large species, averaging 10-13 ft (3-4 m); maximum length for males is reported at 16.5 ft (5 m). Its dark color is accented by black bands and blotches along the sides, on the tail, and on its distinctive, narrow snout. Diet includes fish and a variety of small vertebrates.

This is a mound-nesting species, with nests typically located in the shade of large trees, close to a river. Eggs are laid in the dry season to hatch during the rainy season. Clutch size is 20-60 eggs, which incubate for about 3 months, if not preyed upon by civets, lizards, and wild pigs. The hatchlings emerge by themselves, apparently without parental assistance as in many other crocodilians, and immediately make their way to the water. Mortality rate among hatchlings is thought to be extremely high.

Habitat and Current Distribution

The current range of the false gharial includes the Malay Peninsula (southern Thailand and Malaysia), Sumatra, and Borneo (Indonesia, Malaysia). Some recent reports indicate that it may also be found in Sulawesi (Indonesia). There are no estimates of population size, and very little information is available concerning the status of wild populations.

The false gharial inhabits freshwater swamps, rivers, and lakes and is said to use burrows.

History and Conservation Measures

The former range of this species extended from extreme southern Thailand, through Peninsular Malaysia, to the islands of Borneo (Sabah and Sarawak in East Malaysia, Kalimantan in Indonesia), and Sumatra. Although there is no precise status data available, it is now apparently severely depleted in much of its range. It has been threatened primarily by over-exploitation for hides and by habitat modification. Capture of young for commercial rearing, increased motorized water traffic, timber extraction, and extension of rice cultivation have further contributed to its decline.

Since virtually nothing is known about the status of the false gharial in the wild, population surveys are essential, especially in Sumatra and Borneo. Following initial survey work, conservation plans should be devised, particularly in Indonesia and Malaysia, where it is most widely distributed. If viable populations are located, habitat protection measures should be undertaken and ecological investigations and population monitoring programs initiated.

False gharial.

Gharial

Gavialis gangeticus

Phylum	Chordata
Class	Reptilia
Order	Crocodylia
Family	Gavialidae
Status	Endangered, IUCN
	Endangered, USFWS
	Appendix I, CITES
Range	Bangladesh; Bhutan (?); India; Nepal; Pakistan

Description and Biology

The gharial, sometimes known as the gavial, is a particularly large member of the crocodile family: average length is 13-20 ft (4-6 m). Its long, slender snout has parallel sides and narrow, sharp teeth. In appearance, this species is olive green to brown-gray with a light underside. Sexually mature males have a growth of tissue adjacent to the nostrils. This tissue is shaped like an earthen pot, known as a "ghara" in north India; this is reputed to be the origin of the common name of the species. It feeds primarily on small fish, only occasionally supplemented by birds, dogs, or goats. This species rarely attacks humans.

Sexual maturity is reached at 8-12 years. Elliptical eggs are laid in late March to mid-April in nests excavated in sandbanks. Clutch size is typically 30-50, and eggs are attended by the female for 83-94 days. Eggs and hatchlings are threatened by a variety of predators, so the female guards the nest and tends the hatchlings for a period of several months.

Habitat and Current Distribution

The gharial is found in Bangladesh, India, Nepal, and Pakistan. The species is almost extinct in Bangladesh and Pakistan, where fewer than 40 animals survive; it is thought to be extinct in Bhutan and Myanmar; and it is critically endangered in India and Nepal.

The preferred habitat of the gharial is high-banked rivers with clear, fast-flowing water and deep pools.

History and Conservation Measures

While the gharial was common in many areas in the 19th and early 20th centuries, its numbers have since been severely reduced. The decline is attributed primarily to loss of habitat, hunting for its skin, and accidental killing in the course of fishing operations. An additional concern is the practice of egg collecting by tribal groups, but this would probably not constitute a threat if populations were at higher levels.

The fast-flowing rivers favored by the gharial are prime sites for the construction of dams and reservoirs used by hydroelectric facilities or irrigation projects. Construction of a dam typically eliminates sandbanks and deep pools both upstream and downstream of the site, thus destroying the gharial's preferred habitat. This, in conjunction with commercial hunting of the species for hides, has decimated its population. Hunting has declined following legislative

Gharial.

protection; in addition, the scarcity of the species has made large-scale hunting economically unfeasible.

Programs to collect eggs from the wild and release captive-bred young into protected habitat have been successful in aiding in the recovery of the species, but its numbers remain dangerously low. Gharial inhabit several protected areas in India, in the Royal Chitwan National Park of Nepal, and in a reserve in Pakistan.

Cook Strait tuatara

Sphenodon punctatus

Phylum	Chordata
Class	Reptilia
Order	Rhynchocephalia
Family	Sphenodontidae
Status	Rare, IUCN
	Endangered, USFWS
	Appendix I, CITES
Range	New Zealand

Description and Biology

The Cook Strait tuatara is a lizard-like reptile with a medium-sized head, strong tail, and five-clawed hands and feet. It is olive green, brown, or gray with yellow spots. The female is 20 in (51 cm) long, weighing up to one lb (500 g), and the male averages 24 in (60 cm) and weighs about 2.6 lbs (1.2 kg). A crest of soft spines stretches along the back to the base of the tail. It is active at night, feeding on worms, snails, beetles, and crickets, as well as birds' eggs, lizards, and frogs. It frequently spends the day basking in dappled sunlight or in burrows built by shearwaters or petrels for nesting. Unlike most other reptiles, it is active even in cold weather.

The Cook Strait tuatara reaches sexual maturity between 11-13 years of age. Mating has been observed from January through March and egg laying from October through December. A clutch of 6-10 eggs is laid in a burrow or tunnel, covered with soil, and then abandoned to hatch in 13-15 months.

Habitat and Current Distribution

This species of tuatara occurs on 29 small islands off the coast of New Zealand. The population is estimated at 60,000 animals with over half of this number on Stephens Island, off the northern tip of South Island.

The habitat of this species is offshore, rocky islands, forested or with dense scrub and vegetation, from 1-1,000 ft (0-300 m) above sea level. Breeding populations of petrels and shearwaters are also present on all of tuatara's range.

History and Conservation Measures

Although it resembles a lizard, the Cook Strait tuatara is actually the sole survivor of the order Sphenodontida, a widespread and archaic group that thrived 200 million years ago and which has declined in diversity since the later Mesozoic period. Because it has changed so little from its ancestors, it is sometimes called a living fossil, although some scientists believe it has indeed evolved from its earlier ancestors.

Studies are underway to determine the relationship between the tuatara and the Polynesian rat (*Rattus exulans*), which appears to threaten the survival prospects of the tuatara. All islands on which this species occurs are designated either Wildlife Sanctuaries or Flora and Fauna Reserves, which limit access to visitors.

Cook Strait tuatara.

Leaf-tailed day gecko

Phelsuma serraticauda

Yellow-throated day gecko

Phelsuma flavigularis

Standing's day gecko

Phelsuma standingi

Phylum	Chordata
Class	Reptilia
Order	Sauria
Family	Gekkonidae
Status	Indeterminate, IUCN
	Appendix II, CITES
Range	Madagascar

Description and Biology

There are 63 described species of geckoes in Madagascar, 53 of which are endemic to the island. In contrast to most species within this family, Gekkonidae, which are typically cryptically colored, species of the genus *Phelsuma* are strikingly colored. Diminutive in size, their basic color is emerald green, occasionally marked with red dots or longitudinal lines of various colors.

The leaf-tailed day gecko, also called the flat-tailed day gecko or the fan-tailed day gecko, is light green to yellowish green in color. Three tear-shaped, prominent red markings are present on the back of the tail. The flattened tail, with tiny serrated edges, differentiates this day gecko from other species and greatly enhances its appeal to collectors. Males average 5 in (13 cm) in length, while females are slightly smaller.

The yellow-throated day gecko is light green on the back with reddish markings on the head and red spotting on the dorsal area. As its name suggests, it has a yellow throat. It also has a gray-black lateral stripe with a milky white border. Average lengths are 4.75-5.25 in (12.1-13.3 cm) with males being larger than females.

Standing's day gecko is emerald green with numerous transverse, irregular stripes. The ventral side is whitish and the tail bluish. This is one of the largest of the Malagasy geckoes, and males and females are similar in size (8.25-10 in [21-24.5 cm] in length). Exceptional specimens have been known to exceed 11 in (27.9 cm).

Although most members of the family Gekkonidae are nocturnal, all species in the genus *Phelsuma* have a diurnal activity pattern; hence, they are called day geckoes. They are arboreal and largely insectivorous, consuming only moving and fairly conspicuous prey.

Little is known of the breeding biology of the Malagasy geckoes. A typical clutch size is two and the eggs are small, round, and white in color with a hard shell like a bird's egg. Eggs are often laid in a protected place such as the leaf joints of plants or under tree bark. In common with some other day geckoes, the yellow-throated day gecko is known to "glue" its eggs to the selected laying surface.

The geckoes are particularly adept at escaping from predators and shed their tails if seized from behind. A new tail grows in its place but differs slightly in appearance from the old one. This reaction to danger is not without consequences, however, since the tail is known to store fat.

Habitat and Current Distribution

The leaf-tailed day gecko is known only from the Tomatave region on the east coast of the island, although its range may be larger than currently known. It occurs in degraded forest areas and has been recorded on coconut palms.

The yellow-throated day gecko is found in the eastern rain forests of Madagascar, where it is known only from the areas of Analamazaorta, Réserve Spéciale at Manombo, and Tolagnaro. It has also been found in reasonably high numbers in degraded forest areas around Tolagnaro.

Of the three species, Standing's day gecko is the most severely restricted in distribution. It is found only in the semi-desert regions of southwest Madagascar (with its unique thorn forest vegetation), between Onilahy and Fiherenana, and also in the dry forest of Zombitse.

History and Conservation Measures

No detailed information on the population status, past or present, is available for these three species. Unfortunately, day geckoes are typically brightly colored and, given the right conditions, can be readily kept in captivity. This has made them prime targets for collectors. A recent study (1993) on trade in reptiles from Madagascar showed that all three species figured regularly in trade statistics and both the leaf-tailed and Standing's day geckoes were considered to be in great demand internationally. Since population figures are not available, it is difficult to accurately assess the impact of trade on these species at the present time. However, it is felt that given the restricted distribution of Standing's day gecko, the present levels of trade may lead to population declines in the wild. In recognition of the threats posed by collecting, trade in all three species has been banned by the European Union since 1989.

Mallee worm-lizard

Aprasia aurita

Phylum	Chordata
Class	Reptilia
Order	Sauria
Family	Pygopodidae
Status	Endangered, IUCN
Range	Australia

Description and Biology

The mallee worm-lizard is so named because it lacks forelimbs and has only scaly flaps where the hind limbs would be. It has a slim body and, unlike similar Australian species, a tail shorter than its body length. Its tail can be detached to escape a predator and later regrown. It is believed that this lizard, like related species, feeds only on the eggs of certain types of ants.

Habitat and Current Distribution

This species is found in the Wathe Wildlife Reserve in northwestern Victoria, Australia, where its population size or status is not known. It is apparently active during the day, burrowing into sandy soils of mallee (*Eucalyptus*) vegetation.

History and Conservation Measures

Since it was first described in the early 1900s, this species was not seen for many years, leading to the belief that it had become extinct. It has only recently been rediscovered in the Wathe Wildlife Reserve.

In an effort to preserve the habitat of mallee fowl after several fires occurred in the area around the reserve, a fire prevention strategy was implemented by the Victoria Department of Conservation and Natural Resources. This may inadvertently have preserved the habitat conditions required by the worm-lizard as well, since it is believed that the lizard is dependent on species of ants that thrive only in long-unburnt vegetation. Further studies may provide more specific information about the species' requirements.

Globed chameleon

Calumma (Chamaeleo) globifer

Tsaratanana's chameleon

Calumma (Chamaeleo) tsaratananensis

Fort Carnot's chameleon

Furcifer (Chamaeleo) balteatus

Milvart's chameleon

Furcifer (Chamaeleo) labordi

Phylum	Chordata
Class	Reptilia
Order	Sauria
Family	Chamaeleonidae
Status	Indeterminate, IUCN Appendix II, CITES
Range	Madagascar

Description and Biology

Chameleons are highly adapted for life on branches and tall plants. They are laterally flattened, which helps them balance on narrow branches, and they have a pincer-like grip as a result of the modification of the feet into two pincers, with two toes opposing three toes, the latter being fused together. The soles of the feet are ridged, ensuring a non-slip grip. Together, these features allow chameleons to move effortlessly along narrow branches, with their characteristic swaying gait, as they stalk their prey. Chameleons also have a prehensile tail which is strong enough to hold the weight of the animal. When not in use it remains coiled up.

Modifications of the conical eyes allow them to move independently of each other almost through 180° in the vertical and longitudinal planes. This permits chameleons to survey their surroundings almost completely without moving the head. They are superbly adapted for catching prey—the long, flexible tongue can strike accurately and instantaneously at an insect more than a body's length away, capturing the hapless prey with its swollen, slightly flattened, sticky tongue tip. The unleashing, capturing, and retraction of the prey takes only 40 milliseconds. To accomplish this, however, the chameleon must use both eyes together for binocular vision.

The chameleon's ability to change color is well known. What is not always understood is that this is used as a form of communication between individuals rather than for camouflage. A color change may express aggression, for example, when two males meet (chameleons are essentially solitary). A color change may also signal attraction, such as when a male intensifies his color to impress or reject a female, or when a female changes color to discourage an unwelcome male.

Coloration can vary between individuals, and between males and females as well as between species. Chameleon species differ also in the presence of nasal horns (present only in males), crests and horns on the top of the head, and the occipital lobes which cover the neck in a frill or cape. These protuberances, perhaps, account for the fear and revulsion which most Malagasy tribes express toward these animals.

The globed chameleon is large with a deep green coloration. It owes its common name to the short, paired, nasal appendages in the male which form two globular tubes in front of the nostrils. The longest total length recorded for this species is 15.4 in (39 cm) for males and 12.4 in (31.5 cm) for females.

Tsaratanana's chameleon is known only from the holotype (the originally described specimen). No other descriptive data are available for this species.

Fort Carnot's chameleon, also called the two-banded chameleon, is a large chameleon often with white markings or blackish transversal stripes. It has a characteristic white band which extends from the occipital to the hollow of the groin. The male has short, paired, nasal appendages which are bony, pointed, and triangular. Males as long as 17.3 in (44 cm) have been recorded for this species.

The male of Milvart's chameleon has a single, prominent, nasal appendage. Both the male and female are lime green in color. While males have a distinctive white lateral stripe, females are very variable but always extremely colorful. Females develop a large, bright red spot behind the ear during the breeding season and may also have large orange spots extending down the back and a large number of blue spots on the sides. When rejecting advances by an unwanted male, females of this species go through a startling color change from bright green to cobalt blue.

Details of the ecology and biology of these species range from being barely documented to not known.

Habitat and Current Distribution

Madagascar is home to two-thirds of the world's chameleon species. A recent classification identifies three genera, with 57 species, but their taxonomy is still being studied and these numbers may change. All described species are endemic to Madagascar.

The globed chameleon inhabits humid forests in the eastern slopes and residual forests in the highlands. Tsaratanana's chameleon is known only from the Tsaratanana massif from the type specimen described in 1968. Fort Carnot's chameleon is thought to be restricted to localized sites in the eastern forest region between Ifanadiana and Ikong, while Milvart's chameleon inhabits the forest regions of the west of Madagascar.

None of these species is well studied and there are no population estimates available at the present time.

History and Conservation Measures

These four species are remarkably poorly known and it is not possible to determine the present or past status of each species. Of the four species, Milvart's chameleon is probably the most widespread, although none of them are thought to be common.

With the exception of Tsaratanana's chameleon, all of these species appeared in trade statistics compiled in 1993. A particular problem with trade in chameleons is that they suffer a very high mortality rate during transportation, and many species are difficult to maintain in captivity. Since so little is known of the population status and range of these species, it has proved difficult to assess the impact of trade on wild populations. However, the present crude assessment concludes that the current level of trade is not considered a threat to these species at the present time.

Two of these species, Fort Carnot's and Milvart's chameleons, are thought to be most at risk from habitat degradation. The former occurs in an area where slash-and-burn agriculture is practiced, an activity which degrades forest habitat for chameleons as well as other species, while bush fires are reducing suitable habitat for the latter.

To properly assess the impact of trade and habitat degradation on wild populations of these other chameleons, it is essential that efforts are made to clearly define each species' range and population status. There is also a need to extend the very limited knowledge of the biology and ecology of these fascinating animals.

Culebra Island giant anole

Anolis roosevelti

Phylum	Chordata
Class	Reptilia
Order	Sauria
Family	Iguanidae
Status	Endangered, IUCN
	Endangered, USFWS
Range	Culebra Island (Puerto Rico)

Description and Biology

The Culebra Island giant anole is a member of a group of large tree canopy-dwelling lizards collectively termed "giant anoles" to distinguish them from their smaller relatives, also in the genus *Anolis*. The lizard is brownish gray with two lines on each side of the body. It has a gray throat fan that is bordered on the lower rear quarter by light yellow. The tail is yellowish brown and the belly is whitish in color. Adult males have a deeply scalloped fin along most of the tail. The body measures about 6.5 in (16.5 cm) and the tail adds another 6-7 in (15-18 cm). Weights are unrecorded.

Nothing is known concerning the anole's biology and life history. The original collector of the type series on Isla Culebra stated that the lizards were collected high in trees where they were seen on branches. He saw them most commonly when fruits, particularly figs, were ripe. Observations on the related *A. cuvieri* of Puerto Rico suggest that most activity occurs in the tree canopy at heights of 49-82 ft (15-25 m), that home range may exceed 355 sq ft (33 sq m), and that the lizard probably has a varied diet consisting of many types of invertebrates, small vertebrates, and fruit.

Habitat and Current Distribution

The Culebra Island giant anole is known to have occurred on Islas Culebra and Vieques (Puerto Rico), Tortola (British Virgin Islands), and St. John (U.S. Virgin Islands). These islands are located east of mainland Puerto Rico on the Puerto Rico bank.

The habitat of the anole is unknown for certain except on Isla Culebra. The collector of the type specimens stated that they occurred in the tall gumbo limbo (*Bursera*) and fig (*Ficus*) forest on the north coast.

History and Conservation Measures

Until recently, the Culebra Island giant anole was known from only two specimens collected on Isla Culebra in the early 1930s. Examination of specimens of *A. cuvieri* from several European museums revealed incorrectly identified Culebra Island giant anole collected in the nineteenth century from Isla Vieques, St. John, and Tortola. Less than ten specimens, including only one female, are known. The species has not been collected since 1932. Casual searches of northern Isla Culebra have been made as recently as 1991 without success.

Exactly why the anole is so rare, or if it is now extinct, is unknown. Although the Flamenco Peninsula, where the type specimens were collected on Isla Culebra, was deforested, patches of canopy forest remained until at least 1989 when Hurricane Hugo destroyed much remaining forest habitat. Suitable canopy forest no longer remains on St. John. However, canopy forest remains on Tortola above 1500 ft (460 m) and probably on Isla Vieques. The anole may have been rare naturally, but human-caused deforestation, introduced predators, and natural phenomena such as hurricanes also may have affected its survival.

The U.S. Fish and Wildlife Service approved a recovery plan for the Culebra Island giant anole in 1982. The plan called for the protection of remaining habitat on Isla Culebra and systematic searches of the island to locate remaining populations. The plan did not address the other islands because the historic presence of the lizard on these islands was unknown when the plan was approved. Parts of the potential habitat of this species on Isla Culebra were included within the Culebra National Wildlife Refuge. Much of the island of St. John is located within the Virgin Islands National Park. To date, systematic searches have not been conducted to confirm the lizard's survival or extinction. However, there is reason to believe that it survives in remnant canopy forest on at least one of the islands from which it was historically known. The lizard's survival and status remain somewhat speculative until inventories are completed.

Fiji banded iguana

Brachylophus fasciatus

Phylum	Chordata
Class	Reptilia
Order	Sauria
Family	Iguanidae
Status	Vulnerable, IUCN
	Endangered, USFWS
	Appendix I, CITES
Range	Fiji; Tonga

Description and Biology

The female banded iguana is usually entirely green, but the male has pale, bluish green bands from birth. Skin coloration changes in response to light and shade and can also vary with temperature and temperament. The male's banding becomes most obvious during courtship or in aggressive encounters with other males. Adult iguanas reach a body length of around 7.5 in (19 cm) and have a tail two to three times that length; males are generally longer than females. This species has salt glands in the nasal area that expel excess salt by sneezing; the purpose of these glands is not yet fully understood. The iguanas are primarily vegetarian, feeding on leaves, fruit, flowers, and occasionally insects.

The male banded iguana is territorial and aggressive. Only the dominant male mates with available females. A male's courtship behavior involves head bobbing and a display of his banding and bright coloration. The female digs a burrow for her three or four eggs and then refills the hole with earth.

Habitat and Current Distribution

The species has been recorded from Tonga, from Kadavu and other Fijian islands, and is reportedly an introduced species on Vanuatu (New Hebrides). On Kadavu it is considered abundant but is seldom seen. There are no other estimates of population size.

The iguana's preferred habitat is dense, undisturbed forest.

History and Conservation Measures

The species has declined or disappeared from many islands due to forest clearance. The iguana's secretive nature and superb camouflaging make it difficult to fully assess its status in the wild. The species breeds readily in captivity, and numerous zoos currently have breeding programs. Consequently, there is a captive population available for reintroduction should this conservation action be necessary.

Banded iguana.

Fiji crested iguana

Brachylophus vitiensis

Phylum	Chordata
Class	Reptilia
Order	Sauria
Family	Iguanidae
Status	Vulnerable, IUCN
	Endangered, USFWS
	Appendix I, CITES
Range	Fiji

Description and Biology

The Fiji crested iguana is considered to be one of the world's most endangered lizards. The male of the species is larger and heavier than the female. The male averages 7.9 in (20 cm) in body length and weighs 9.7 oz (276 g); the female averages 7.4 in (19 cm) and 7.9 oz (225 g). The tail is two to three times the body length. The species is often difficult to see in the forest because its subtle colors provide effective camouflage. Feeding habits are not well known, but diet is thought to include leaves, seeds, and bark. Possible predators include the swamp harrier and the barn owl; reef herons may also feed on iguana hatchlings.

Habitat and Current Distribution

This species is known only from several islands of northwestern Fiji, where it occurs in closed forests. Male iguanas are usually found in low vegetation, while females and juveniles inhabit the forest canopy. Total population figures are unavailable, but the popu-

Crested iguana.

lation on the island of Yaduataba is estimated to number 3,000-6,000 individuals.

History and Conservation Measures

While the present population of this species on Yaduataba appears to be healthy and reproductively active, the populations on the islands in the Yasawa Group appear to be fragmented and declining. The primary threat to the iguana is a very restricted range that leaves it vulnerable to natural or human-induced disasters, disease, and destruction or degradation of its habitat. The introduction of competitors or predators further compounds the problem.

Yaduataba, an uninhabited island of 3,360 acres (1,360 ha), was established in 1980 as a wildlife reserve for its population of crested iguanas. The remaining beach forest, which has been replaced by coconut plantations on neighboring islands, is protected in this reserve. Efforts are made to guard against introduced predators, to control fires, and to eliminate goats, which prevent forest regeneration. It is also important to protect the island from the adverse effects of tourism.

Galápagos land iguana

Conolophus subcristatus

Phylum	Chordata
Class	Reptilia
Order	Sauria
Family	Iguanidae
Status	Vulnerable, IUCN
	Appendix II, CITES
Range	Galápagos Islands

Description and Biology

The Galápagos land iguana is superficially similar to other large iguanas, such as those of the genus *Cyclura* in the Caribbean; it is stout-bodied, with well-developed limbs, and has a moderately long tail, a large head with prominent jaw muscles, and a serrated dorsal crest. The largest individuals reach 3.9 ft. (1.2 m) in total length, and large males are always at least twice as heavy as females. The various island populations vary in size and color. Males average about 247 oz. (7 kg). The body is mainly brown, with the head, legs, and belly yellow.

The species is primarily vegetarian, as are other large iguanas, but it does consume animals and animal remains from time to time. Favorite foods include leaves, buds, fruit, and cactus pads. Eggs are laid in July, a few weeks after mating. The eggs weigh about 1.75 oz. (50 g) each and are around 2.4 in. (6 cm) long; a clutch of between seven and more than 20 eggs is laid in a nest excavated where the ground temperature is high and even. The young hatch some 14 weeks later. Iguanas that are heavily infested with ticks have been seen to adopt a special posture which attracts small birds and allows them easy access so they can remove the ticks. As a result, the lizard is cleaned and the birds obtain food.

Habitat and Current Distribution

Restricted to the Galápagos Islands of Ecuador, land iguanas are known on Fernandina, Isabela, Santa Cruz, tiny South Plaza, Santa Fe, and Seymour (where the iguanas were introduced from Baltra, which now has no land iguanas). Santiago also now has no land iguanas, although their burrows were once numerous. The population on Santa Fe is sometimes regarded as a second species of Galápagos land iguana (*Conolophus pallidus*).

The land iguana prefer dry areas whenever the island offers a range of habitats, and individuals occupy quite a large territory around their burrows during the breeding period. Males patrol the boundaries of their territories and deter intruders through vigorous threat displays; each female associates with the male of her choice, and some males may be attended by several females.

History and Conservation Measures

Although the Galápagos land iguana has survived centuries of hunting for food by buccaneers, whalers, and others, and seems able to withstand the threat of the two native predators (snakes and hawks), the introduction of cats, pigs, and dogs has

Galápagos land iguana.

proved a significant threat. All uninhabited areas in the Galpágos were declared a national park by Ecuador as long ago as 1959, and land iguanas are one of the many species that must not be hunted, captured, or disturbed. The Charles Darwin Foundation came into being that same year and, with the cooperation of the government of Ecuador, has planned and undertaken key conservation work in the islands ever since. The species is listed on Appendix II of the Convention of International Trade in Endangered Species.

Anegada rock iguana

Cyclura (Iguana) pinguis

Phylum	Chordata
Class	Reptilia
Order	Sauria
Family	Iguanidae
Status	Endangered, IUCN
	Endangered, USFWS
	Appendix I, CITES
Range	British Virgin Islands

Description and Biology

The Anegada rock iguana, more aptly called the Puerto Rico Bank iguana, is a relatively large and stout member of its genus. Males have been recorded with snout-vent lengths of 1.8 ft (56 cm) and may grow larger. Juveniles are faintly or boldly patterned with wide gray to moss–green bands interspersed with wide gray to black anteriorly-pointing chevrons. The bands fade and are generally lost as the animals mature. Adults are a somber grayish or brownish black dorsally with varying amounts of turquoise blue on the dorsal spines, tail base, and fore and hind legs. Occasionally the bluish color will extend up on to the sides of individuals, particularly males. Females tend to be relatively dull in color, exhibiting less brilliant blue, if any. Ventral coloration of juveniles and adults varies from a solid buffy white to light gray. Sclera of eyes dull yellow when animals are calm but flush pink to blood red with increasing levels of agitation.

Though largely facultative herbivores, all age groups of these iguanas are opportunistic carnivores. Invertebrates (beetles, caterpillars, centipedes, roaches) form only a small portion of the natural diet, however, which may be due to availability. The bulk of their diet consists of leaves and fruit. Over the past 20 years, grazing pressure by goats, sheep, and cattle has radically changed the vegetational composition of Anegada. Not surprisingly, the diet of the rock iguana is now comprised of plant species the feral stock-animals reject. Almost 30 percent of the diet consists of a plant containing secondary compounds apparently toxic to ungulates. Over 55 percent of the diet is composed of fruits the stock ignore.

Estimates in the late 1960s, made before the release of stock animals, showed small home ranges for both sexes (less than 0.25 acre/0.1 ha); studies also showed that each animal had one principal burrow and habits that indicated monogamy (apparent pairs inhabited separate but proximate burrows in a joint home range isolated from other pairs). The current population structure is quite different. Though previous studies may not have been sensitive to long-range movements, it now appears that home ranges are quite large on Anegada: males average 16 acres (6.6 ha), females average 10 acres (4.2 ha). Home ranges broadly overlap but have one or two centers of activity. For males, activity centers may be associated with home ranges of females; one male may have two centers almost a kilometer apart. In 1991 the sex ratio had dropped to one female per three males, which may explain the degree of home range overlap: male competition for mates. Female centers of activity are usually associated with one or several principal burrows. While the degraded vegetation may provide for male subsistence, it may not provide females with sufficient energy to allow them to both produce clutches of eggs and compete with other animals for food to support their own growth and metabolism. Reproducing females may have low survivorship resulting in the present skewed sex ratio. Healthy females lay one clutch of about 12-16 eggs per year in late spring or early summer.

Burrows of both sexes may be located on the old limestone reef-tract or in sandy areas adjacent to it. If available, iguanas will use numbers of additional solution holes or crevices as emergency retreats.

Habitat and Current Distribution

The common name of the Anegada rock iguana is misleading. The animal was once distributed over the entire Puerto Rico Bank. Fossils are known from St. Thomas and Puerto Rico. The animal was likely extirpated when localities became densely settled. Vulnerability to predation by humans as well as dogs and cats may have caused the retreat of the distribution to the only limestone island on the Puerto Rico Bank, Anegada. The numerous solution-holes facilitating escape coupled with the large expanse of undeveloped land supporting few non-native predators may have allowed the iguana populations to persist there. Distribution on Anegada is closely tied to more porous limestone habitats.

In the 1980s, eight iguanas were moved from Anegada to Guana Island (British Virgin Islands) to start a second population. This is not limestone island and does not provide as many natural retreats as Anegada. In the absence of introduced predators, however, the iguanas appear to do well and reproduce in areas that are free of sheep (the only feral grazing competitor present). Approximately 20 adult iguanas are estimated to inhabit Guana Island. Offspring have been seen each year since 1987, but recruitment is very low over much of the island. Guana Island Wildlife Sanctuary has instituted a program to rid the island of sheep, which may improve the habitat for iguanas.

History and Conservation Measures

Areas on Anegada that once contained dense populations of iguanas now support few or none. Research indicates this is due to three major causes: 1) competitive grazing pressure from free-ranging livestock; 2) predation of adults by dogs; 3) predation of young by cats.

This iguana's endangerment may be eased in the future by the creation of a national park designed to protect the iguanas on Anegada. The reservoir of breeding animals on Guana may also be used to restock depleted areas on Anegada. A national park was recently proposed and approved in concept by the Anegada Lands Committee in March 1993; decisions regarding land allocations will follow.

Blunt-nosed leopard lizard

Gambelia (Crotaphytus) silus

Phylum	Chordata
Class	Reptilia
Order	Sauria
Family	Iguanidae
Status	Endangered, IUCN
	Endangered, USFWS
Range	California (U.S.A.)

Description and Biology

As its common name indicates, this lizard has a blunt snout and a leopard-like pattern on the surface of its body. The pattern and color change throughout the day to help regulate the lizard's body temperature: in the morning, dark spots and bars appear on the surface, and as the temperature rises, the pattern fades to a lighter shade. This species also changes color during the mating season: the sides of males turn light pink and the sides of females turn rusty-orange to red. These lizards average 3.5-5 in (9-13 cm) in length, not including the tail, which can be shed–and regrown–if caught by a potential predator. Diet includes grasshoppers, caterpillars, flies, bees, and occasionally young lizards. This species may also eat its own young. Predators include ground squirrels, skunks, shrikes, and snakes.

Winter is spent hibernating in deep burrows made by rodents or other small mammals. Emerging from hibernation in late March or early April, lizards are active during the coolest hours of the day. During mating season in May and June, the male defends a territory which may include a number of females. In

Blunt-nosed leopard lizard.

June or July, the female enters a burrow to lay a clutch of two or three eggs which hatch in August.

Habitat and Current Distribution

Sometimes called the San Joaquin leopard lizard, this species is found in the San Joaquin Valley in California. There are no estimates of its population size.

Known habitats include uncultivated grassland, scrub, and plains areas of central California. This lizard cannot survive in cultivated areas.

History and Conservation Measures

This lizard once ranged throughout the San Joaquin Valley; although its range has not substantially diminished, its numbers have declined drastically, and remaining populations have a much patchier and isolated distribution than in previous times. It was first identified in 1890 from a specimen collected near the city of Fresno. Some habitat areas have been used for residential development, but, for the most part, suitable habitat has been replaced by agricultural cultivation throughout most of the valley.

Since the lizard cannot survive in cultivated areas, the only hope of preserving this species is to acquire and protect its remaining habitat. Conservation goals include the designation of at least nine reserves with a minimum of 6,000 contiguous acres (2,400 ha) each, totaling at least 55,000 acres (22,000 ha). To accomplish this end, land has been acquired in the southern part of the range, and surveys are in progress in the northern region. In the meantime, such measures as local zoning restrictions and protective fencing are being implemented for interim protection.

Hierro giant lizard

Gallotia simonyi

Phylum	Chordata
Class	Reptilia
Order	Sauria
Family	Lacertidae
Status	Endangered, IUCN
	Endangered, USFWS
	Appendix I, CITES
Range	Hierro Island (Spain)

Description and Biology

The Hierro giant lizard is, in general form, a rather typical member of the Lacertidae, an Old World group that includes the familiar and common lizards in Europe. As with several other island lizard species (including the closely related *Gallotia stehlini* on nearby Gran Canaria), it has a large body size. Total length can exceed 20 in (51 cm)—body length alone is up to 7.5 in (19 cm)—and the body is correspondingly stout. Most lacertids are about one-third this size. The body is greenish brown with a few large, pale yellow-tinged spots on the flanks; the head is yellowish brown on top, with irregular black marks; the large scales along and under the jaws have large pale spots surrounded by black.

These lizards have only been observed feeding on plant material, and analysis of droppings shows that the Hierro giant lizard is indeed primarily vegetarian, favoring legumes and succulents, but also takes a significant proportion of insects. (including bumblebees, grasshoppers, and ants). The clutch of up to eight eggs is laid around September, probably in small pockets of soil; it has been speculated that an early clutch might be laid in April, and that the species may breed only in alternate years. As early morning sunrays strike the cliff on which they live, the lizards emerge from hiding in rock crevices and remain active through the day, except for a period around midday.

Habitat and Current Distribution

The entire, very small population of this species, approximately 100 lizards, is restricted to a small area halfway up a precipitous cliff face on El Hierro in the Canary Islands, Spain. The cliff, known locally as the Fuga de Gorreta, is an unstable mass of lavas and basalts cut by numerous volcanic dykes, providing virtually unlimited boulders and crevices for shelter. Vegetation is generally stunted and sparse. The lizards are restricted to a band between 1,150 and 1,640 ft. (350 and 500 m) in altitude. Another large lacertid lizard, generally believed to represent this species, but regarded by some as significantly different, inhabited at least the outer (smaller) of the two offshore islets called the Roques de Salmor until the 1930s. The entire species group was assumed to be extinct until the population on Fuga de Gorreta was discovered in the 1970s (although it had previously been known to local inhabitants).

History and Conservation Measures

The first scientific specimens of Hierro giant lizard from the Roques de Salmor were collected by the traveller Oscar Simonyi in 1889; this population had disappeared (apparently largely due to over-collection) by the late 1930s or thereabouts. The species is thought to have been eradicated from most of Hierro—except for the almost inaccessible cliff it inhabits today—by cats and dogs introduced by humans, and possibly by the general impact of humans and their flocks on the environment.

The Spanish conservation agency ICONA has invested considerable time in studying the Hierro giant lizard as well as preparing a recovery plan involving habitat protection and captive breeding. This is now being implemented by the regional authority and offers considerable promise for the future security of the species.

St. Croix ground lizard

Ameiva polops

Phylum	Chordata
Class	Reptilia
Order	Sauria
Family	Teiidae
Status	Endangered, IUCN
	Endangered, USFWS
Range	U.S. Virgin Islands

Description and Biology

The St. Croix ground lizard is a member of a genus that is widespread on the neotropical mainland and in the West Indies. This species is a diurnal, ground-dwelling reptile. This lizard has a snout-vent length of about 3 in (8 cm). Ventral scales are in 10-12 longitudinal rows and 32-34 transverse rows. The dorsal caudal scales are smooth and straight. The dorsum is tan, brown, or olive, being darker brown on the head and neck. There is a distinctive mid-dorsal zone of light brown, followed laterally on each side by a series of longitudinal stripes of wide dark brown (almost black); narrow brown; black; white; and dark brown mottled with white bordering ventral scales. The lateral-most ventral scale rows are bluish; the midventer is white to gray. The chin, throat, and pectoral region are orange. The tail is dorsally blue to gray with black markings; the underside is buff or white to faintly orange (anteriorly), greenish distally in some individuals.

Habitat and Current Distribution

The St. Croix ground lizard once occurred on St. Croix (U.S. Virgin Islands), but that population has been extirpated by introduced mongooses. This lizard was last seen on this island in 1968. It still occurs on the mongoose-free St. Croix satellites of Green Cay (14 acres/5.7 ha) and Protestant Cay (3 acres/1.2 ha); an attempt to introduce it on mongoose-infested Buck Island (another satellite of St. Croix) was unsuccessful.

This lizard prefers habitats that include coastal forest with adjacent beach areas. They forage actively in forest leaf litter and in beach litter, probably feeding on a variety of invertebrates, including true flies (dipterans), earwigs (dermapterans), ants, bees, wasps (hymenopterans), ringed worms (annelids), and amphipods.

History and Conservation Measures

Like many other reptiles on small islands, the St. Croix ground lizard has been adversely affected by the introduction of alien predators. Around 1884, the small Indian mongoose (*Herpestes auropunctatus*) was introduced to St. Croix to control the damage done to sugar cane by the introduced rat (*Rattus rattus*). As elsewhere, the introduction of the mongoose had a catastrophic impact on native, ground-dwelling wildlife. By 1910, the range of the ground lizard on St. Croix had noticeably shrunk, with lizards most apparent around towns (Frederiksted and Christiansted). The St. Croix ground lizard was last observed on St. Croix in or about 1968 on the beach near Frederiksted.

In 1989, before the devastation of Hurricane Hugo, the population estimate of the St. Croix ground lizard on Green Cay was approximately 530 and on Protestant Cay it was about 60. The single greatest threat to either of these populations would be the introduction of an alien predator, chiefly mongooses or domestic cats. In the absence of alien predators and with minimal habitat modification (either by humans or natural catastrophe), populations of ground lizards on Green and Protestant cays should be relatively secure.

Chinese crocodilian lizard

Shinisaurus crocodilurus

Phylum	Chordata
Class	Reptilia
Order	Sauria
Family	Shinisauridae
Status	Endangered, IUCN
	Appendix II, CITES
Range	China

Description and Biology

The Chinese crocodilian lizard is a medium-sized lizard, averaging 13.6 in (35 cm) long. Its common name comes from its rough scaly skin and its compressed tail with keels that resembles a crocodile's tail. The upper side of this lizard is dark brown, and the sides of the head and the flanks are light brown with a scattering of black bands. Eight black stripes radiate from each eye, its underside is light yellow with short black stripes, and the sides of its tail are marked with alternate black and greenish brown bands. Newborns have a triangular yellow patch on the top of the head. The sides of the head and neck are brilliant red in breeding males. The Chinese crocodilian lizard is carnivorous, feeding on insects, worms, tadpoles, frogs, and small fish. It is preyed upon by snakes; adult lizards are also known to kill young lizards.

This species reproduces annually and the breeding season extends from June to August. Mating takes place in mountain streams. *S. crocodilurus* is ovoviviparous; 2-8 (usually 4-6) young develop within the mother's body, but are retained within the oviduct and are born in April or May of the following year. The newborn lizards are 4.3-5.1 in (11-13 cm) long and weigh 0.11-0.16 oz (3-4.5 g).

Habitat and Current Distribution

This species was previously thought to occur only in the valleys of Mt. Yao in Jinxiu County, Guangxi Zhuang Autonomous Region of China. Recently, it was also found in the mountains of Zhaoping, Mengshan and He counties, in the same region of China. Approximately 2,500 individuals are thought to occur in the wild.

S. crocodilurus inhabits areas of mixed coniferous and broadleaf forest at elevations under 2,625 ft (800 m), where the plant cover is well developed with dense canopy and weak illumination. It prefers areas where the climate is warm and moist—annual average temperatures of 64.5°-68°F (18°-20°C) and annual rainfall of 62.5-100 in (1,600-2,570 mm). The Chinese crocodilian lizard is active both in the morning and at night and is frequently found resting on twigs or vines beside mountain streams.

History and Conservation Measures

S. crocodilurus is a rare and valuable animal; the primary threat to this species appears to be capture for export. The capture of hundreds of these lizards at one time has been reported. Since the species inhabits a fairly restricted range, it is also vulnerable to habitat destruction. In some places the forests it inhabits are being burned to clear the land for cultivation.

The Chinese crocodilian lizard is listed as a first–grade protected animal on the *List of Major* *Protective Wildlife of the State* issued jointly by the Chinese Ministry of Forestry and the Chinese Ministry of Agriculture in 1989. The development of nature reserves to protect populations of this lizard is also a conservation priority.

Lord Howe Island skink

Pseudemoia (Cyclodina) lichenigera

Phylum	Chordata
Class	Reptilia
Order	Sauria
Family	Scincidae
Status	Vulnerable, IUCN
Range	Lord Howe Island, Norfolk Island (Australia)

Description and Biology

The Lord Howe Island skink, in common with other skinks, is a rich metallic-bronze or olive color. It has a pale golden lateral stripe bordered beneath by a darker brown band, and has darker or lighter flecks or indistinct stripes on the neck. The snout to vent length and tail length each average 3.1 in (8 cm).

Feeding on amphipods, insects, and other small invertebrates, the Lord Howe Island Skink sometimes collects these in the littoral zone. This species has also been seen rolling birds' eggs over rocks until they break, and then feeding on the contents.

Habitat and Current Distribution

On Lord Howe Island, this skink may now be confined to a single small area. It still occurs on Phillip Island, the largest of the offshore islands, and on several smaller islands in the complex, but may now be extinct on Norfolk Island. No population estimates have been made, but a survey in the early 1980s concluded that, while numbers were not large anywhere in its range, the total population was probably substantial and not in any danger of extinction.

This skink is found in a wide range of habitats, from closed forest to low open woodland, tussock grassland, the littoral complex, and rocky outcrops.

History and Conservation Measures

The decline in the distribution of this species on Lord Howe Island and its disappearance from the mainland of Norfolk Island have been primarily due to the introduction of predators. A shipwreck brought the black rat (*Rattus rattus*) to Lord Howe Island in 1918, and the Pacific rat (*Rattus exulans*) was introduced to Norfolk Island by Polynesians who are thought to have visited the islands between 1100 and 250 BP. The introduction of pigs, rabbits, and goats in the late 1700s to Phillip Island caused massive habitat destruction and is thought to have brought about a dramatic decline in the skink population. Although the pigs and goats died out quickly, the rabbits were only eradicated in 1986.

Fortunately the entire Lord Howe Island area is listed as a World Heritage site and most skink populations are contained within protected conservation areas. Management activities so far have been directed towards controlling predators and eradicating rabbits. Future activities will include surveying known and potential habitat in the reserves and determining the species' current conservation status; rehabilitating the vegetation on Phillip Island; and obtaining sufficient information on the biology and ecology of the species to enable appropriate management strategies to be formed to safeguard the species.

Komodo dragon

Varanus komodoensis

Phylum	Chordata
Class	Reptilia
Order	Sauria
Family	Varanidae
Status	Rare, IUCN
	Endangered, USFWS
	Appendix I, CITES
Range	Komodo and adjacent islands (Indonesia)

Description and Biology

The Komodo dragon, also called the Komodo Island monitor, is the largest living lizard. The adult dragon can exceed 10 ft (3 m) in length and 300 lbs (135 kg) in weight. It has a dark gray, stocky body and stout, powerful legs with sharply clawed feet. It has a large head and long, forked tongue with which it "tastes" the air. This lizard can move quickly on the ground and is an agile swimmer and climber. It feeds primarily on birds, deer, or wild pigs and scavenges carrion. It will also eat humans if given the opportunity. If prey is not killed instantly but is bitten by the dragon, it will usually die from the bacteria transferred from the mouth of the dragon. The yellow tongue and unpleasant mouth odor may have inspired legends of fire-breathing dragons.

Females lay clutches of 15-30 eggs several times a year in a hole. Eggs with smooth, leather-like shells are usually laid between July and early September and hatch in about 8 1/2 months.

Habitat and Current Distribution

The Komodo Island monitor is found only on the Indonesian islands of Komodo, Rintja, and western Flores. Population estimates vary from 1,000-5,000.

The preferred habitat of this species is dry savanna, woodland thickets, and forest fringes and clearings. Burrows are dug into open hillsides or the banks of dry creek beds.

History and Conservation Measures

The Komodo dragon once occupied many of the islands of Indonesia, but its numbers have been reduced by several factors, most of them human-related. Hunting for collecting, sport, or hides has directly affected the dragon population. Legal protection has reduced commercial hunting, but the dragon is sometimes poisoned by villagers to protect children and domestic animals. Over-hunting of the deer population by humans reduces available prey, as does burning and clearing of woodland.

Komodo dragon feeding on a goat carcass.

Mona blind snake

Typhlops monensis

Phylum	Chordata
Class	Reptilia
Order	Serpentes
Family	Typhlopidae
Status	Rare, IUCN
Range	Mona Island (Puerto Rico)

Description and Biology

This snake belongs to the blind snake family. It is a very small earthworm-sized glossy blind snake with a dorsal coloration, which may range from nearly white with dusky brown markings on the terminus of each scale to brownish with coloration limited to the posterior two-thirds of each scale. The venter is white. This blind snake is distinguished by its relatively depressed head coupled with a pointed, projecting snout. Like other blind snakes, it has a short tail spine which is harmless. The adult snout-vent length of this species is approximately 7 in (18 cm).

Blind snakes are completely fossorial, meaning they spend nearly all of their time underground. They are usually discovered when they are accidentally dug up by human activity. Occasionally they may be found beneath rocks, tree stumps, or in termite nests. They feed primarily on ants and termites. Nothing is known of their reproductive habits, although all blind snakes lay eggs.

Habitat and Current Distribution

This snake is known only from Mona Island. As there is very little soil on Mona, this snake has been captured only in the wetter areas of the coastal terrace where most of the soil exists. It is also thought to be present in some of the larger soil-filled sinkholes and bajuras (depressions) of the plateau.

History and Conservation Measures

The concern expressed for the survival of this species reflects a very typical dilemma biologists face when dealing with secretive species: is the animal really rare, or merely difficult to find? This snake was proposed for U.S. Fish and Wildlife Service (USFWS) threatened status when plans were being made to develop Mona Island into a deep-water oil port. These plans would have resulted in considerable paving of the coastal terrace, which would have seriously threatened the existence of this species. These plans were later abandoned and Mona was protected as a forest reserve by the Department of Natural Resources of Puerto Rico. Subsequently, in the final ruling of March 6, 1978, the USFWS determined that because plans for paving parts of the island had been abandoned, the Mona blind snake was not considered threatened. There appear to be no threats to the survival of this species at the present time.

Madagascar ground boa

Acrantophis madagascariensis

Phylum	Chordata
Class	Reptilia
Order	Serpentes
Family	Boidae
Status	Insufficiently Known, IUCN Appendix I, CITES
Range	Madagascar

Description and Biology

This medium-sized and seemingly placid boa grows to an average length of 4.9-5.9 ft (1.5-1.8 m), although specimens of more than 9.8 ft (3 m) have been recorded. It is generally brown in color, often strongly red-tinged, with black diamond markings. It feeds on small mammals, such as rodents and insectivores, and water birds. Many aspects of the biology of this species are poorly known. After a gestation period of up to nine months, between two and six live young are born; although few in number, the young are very large in relation to those of other boas, up to 25 in (640 mm) in length and 7.4 oz (212 g) in weight.

Habitat and Current Distribution

There are two "ground boas" in Madagascar; this species is much larger than the second (*Acrantophis dumerili*). Although distribution is not known in detail, *A. madagascariensis* appears to occur mostly in the center, north, and northwest, and *A. dumerili* in the south and southwest. Although *A. madagascariensis* is seen most frequently along streams and lake margins, and certainly feeds on ducks, it is not strictly aquatic. In recent surveys in rainforest areas in eastern Madagascar, neither of these species was found, but the third species of boa present was found quite commonly; perhaps these species prefer less humid forest.

It has long been clear that the boas on Madagascar are closely related to the more numerous boas in Central and South America (and similar relationships hold for the iguanid lizards and pelomedusid turtles in Madagascar and in South America). Recent studies of the anatomy and systematics of boas even suggest that the Madagascar boas should be placed in the same genus (*Boa*) as the familiar boa constrictor of Central and South America.

History and Conservation Measures

This species is hunted for the skin trade, and products made from boa skin are common in souvenir shops in Madagascar. It is nominally protected by national law and is listed on the Appendices to the Convention on International Trade in Endangered Species, with the intention of controlling international trade.

Puerto Rican boa

Epicrates inornatus

Phylum	Chordata
Class	Reptilia
Order	Serpentes
Family	Boidae
Status	Insufficiently Known, IUCN
	Endangered, USFWS
	Appendix I, CITES
Range	Puerto Rico (U.S.A.)

Description and Biology

This snake is a member of the boa family. Like other members of this genus, the color and pattern are variable, but ground color of adults is usually a dark or mahogany brown. The dorsal surface usually has a series of narrow angulate blotches with very dark brown to black edges. Most of the larger, older individuals are virtually patternless. The venter is very dark brown to gray, heavily stippled with dark brown. The interior of the mouth is black. Most adults have a body length of 5-6.5 ft (1.5-2 m) and a mass of 4.4-6.6 lb (2-3 kg), but exceptionally large individuals may reach 8.2 ft (2.5 m).

This snake is a nocturnal species and may be found both on the ground and in trees, where it hunts a variety of small vertebrate prey including bats, introduced rodents, and small birds. Small Puerto Rican boas feed almost exclusively on *Anolis* lizards and coquis (Puerto Rican frogs of the genus *Eleutherodactylus*).

Mating occurs in the beginning of the wet season (April-May) in Puerto Rico. Males attempt to mate every year. Females give birth to 10-32 young in late summer-early fall (August-October) every other year. Body masses of the newborns range from 0.4-0.6 oz (12-16 grams) with snout-vent lengths of 13-14 in (33-36 cm).

Habitat and Current Distribution

This species is widespread in Puerto Rico, with the possible exception of the arid southwest, from sea level to about 1,300 ft (400 m). It is most abundant in the Caribbean National Forest and within the Arecibo-San Sebastian-Aguadilla triangle in the northwest and is also reported from Culebra, Icacos, and Vieques islands. Commonly found in karst forest, rain forest, and plantations, it also occurs in subtropical dry forest or even urban areas.

History and Conservation Measures

This snake was one of the first species protected by the U.S. Endangered Species Act. In recent years populations seem to have recovered dramatically as large segments of the Puerto Rican rural population moved to the cities and agricultural lands reverted to secondary forest. It is locally protected under the Regulation to Govern the Management of Threatened and Endangered Species in the Commonwealth of Puerto Rico. Little international trade exists for this species. It faces a limited local threat, as some rural Puerto Ricans ascribe medicinal qualities to the fat of this snake and kill the snakes so that this fat can be extracted.

Puerto Rican boa.

Jamaican boa

Epicrates subflavus

Phylum	Chordata
Class	Reptilia
Order	Serpentes
Family	Boidae
Status	Vulnerable, IUCN
	Endangered, USFWS
	Appendix I, CITES
Range	Jamaica

Description and Biology

The Jamaican boa is a member of the boa family. Coloration may be quite variable. The dorsal ground color is usually a deep tan, pale reddish brown, or olive, but certain individuals are quite yellow. Many of the individual dorsal scales are black or even red, but in most snakes the pigmented scales form an irregular black banding around the midbody. The bands become more pronounced toward the posterior and eventually fuse to form a solid black mantle over the rear of the body and tail. The venter is orange or creamy yellow with occasional black spots. The head has two narrow black postorbital stripes. Juveniles are orange or pinkish tan with an indistinct tan pattern and a cream venter. This is a moderately-sized snake, with a maximum snout-vent length of approximately 6.5 ft (2 m). Body mass ranges from 4.4-11 lb (2-5 kg).

Like most boas, this is a nocturnal or crepuscular snake which is both ground-dwelling and arboreal. The adult diet consists of introduced rodents, native bats, and birds. Juveniles feed on small lizards and frogs.

Female Jamaican boas reproduce every other year, while males reproduce every year. Courtship occurs in the spring (February-May) with births in the fall (September-October). Litter sizes may vary from three to as many as 39 offspring, depending on the size of the female. Larger females have the most offspring per litter. Newborn body masses range from 0.42-0.66 oz (12-19 grams) with snout-vent lengths of about 12.6-14.6 in (32-37 cm).

Habitat and Current Distribution

The species was once widespread throughout Jamaica, but clearing of forests for agriculture and the introduction of exotic predators such as the Indian mongoose and house cat have limited their distribution to scattered localities in the Cockpit Country, Dolphin Head, the Hellshire Hills, and areas of Portland and St. Thomas Parishes. This boa is usually found in moist limestone forest habitats, but it was once abundant in the subtropical dry forest of the south coast in the vicinity of Portland Point.

History and Conservation Measures

This snake has probably had a long history of decline since the colonization of Jamaica by European settlers. Partially intact natural forest makes up less than seven percent of the total forest area in Jamaica, and as the human population on Jamaica grows, there will be great pressure to convert even more forest to agriculture or bauxite mining—even in the wilder areas such as the Cockpit and the Hellshire Hills. This species has been chosen as a preferred candidate for Species Survival Plan Management by the American Association of Zoological Parks and Aquariums, but the greatest hope for the survival of this snake lies in the creation of large natural reserves on Jamaica.

Jamaican boa.

Indian python

Python molurus

Phylum	Chordata
Class	Reptilia
Order	Serpentes
Family	Boidae
Status	Vulnerable, IUCN
	Endangered, USFWS
	Appendix I, CITES (*P. m. molurus*)
	Appendix II, CITES (*P. m. bivittatus*)
Range	South and Southeast Asia

Description and Biology

This large, heavy-bodied and seemingly lethargic snake routinely reaches 10 ft (3 m) in length, and is said to have the potential to exceed 20 ft (6 m). The rate of growth varies according to food availability, but 10 ft may be attained in three to five years of growth; many individuals will be mature at this size. The basic color ranges from straw yellow to brown, sometimes with a rich reddish tinge, with dark markings that vary in detail geographically. Prey animals include a wide variety of mammals, birds, and reptiles. Among mammals, although species as large as deer or leopards are occasionally taken, smaller prey is more usual, and rats appear to be the most common food item (there is some interest in the possible importance of pythons as rodent control agents in agricultural areas). Indian pythons have been reported to ascend fruiting trees so as to ambush animals attracted by fallen fruits, and to frequent hollow trees used by roosting birds, which can readily be taken unawares.

In India, mating occurs during December-February (the colder season). The eggs are about 2.3 by 4.7 in (6 by 12 cm) in size, and there may be between six and 100 in a single clutch, depending largely on the size of the female; the average clutch comprises some 35 eggs. The eggs are laid in a rock crevice, tree hole, termite nest, or other convenient shelter, and are incubated for a period by the female before hatching after about two months. Hatchlings average around 21 in (55 cm) in length.

Habitat and Current Distribution

The Indian python is widespread in Asia, ranging from Pakistan in the west to China in the east, and

Indian python.

south through the Philippines and mainland Southeast Asia (except Malaysia) to parts of Indonesia (certainly Java and Sulawesi, possibly Sumatra and Kalimantan). The species is divided into two subspecies by most taxonomists: a western form in the South Asian subcontinent (*P. m. molurus*) and an eastern form in China and Southeast Asia (*P. m. bivittatus*). The population on Sri Lanka is usually included in *P. m. molurus* but is sometimes recognized as a third subspecies.

This species is found in a variety of habitats but appears to prefer wooded areas, ranging from evergreen rain forest to open dry scrubland; it is an able swimmer and climber.

History and Conservation Measures

Although the species is still present in most of its known historic range and is reasonably abundant in many areas, populations throughout most of the range appear to be depleted, and the species is gone from some areas. In general, the evidence for this decline is largely or entirely anecdotal, but persuasive overall. Decline is especially well-substantiated in India and Bangladesh, and also reported in Laos, Myanmar, Nepal, Pakistan, Sri Lanka and Thailand. Populations have been affected by excess exploitation for the skin trade and by habitat loss from human intervention. The western population is now listed on Appendix I of CITES in an attempt to control international trade in skins, and the eastern form is on Appendix II, designed to allow trade to be reduced and monitored.

Central Asian cobra

Naja oxiana

Phylum	Chordata
Class	Reptilia
Order	Serpentes
Family	Elapidae
Status	Insufficiently Known, IUCN
Range	Asia

Description and Biology

The Central Asian cobra is similar in form and habits to the several other closely related cobras in Asia and Africa: it has a dark color, moderately large body size, around 5 ft (1.5 m) in length, fixed fangs at the front of the mouth, potent venom, and a neck capable of sideways expansion to form the cobra "hood." As with other cobras, if cornered or threatened it will spread the hood and adopt an alert posture, with the front part of the body raised vertically, ready to strike. It differs from most of its Asian relatives in being a fairly uniform brown color, with very reduced banded markings, and no eye- or spectacle-like marking on the back of the hood.

Central Asian cobras often shelter in mammal burrows or similar holes, and feed on a variety of prey, including small mammals, reptiles, and frogs. The clutch comprises 8-20 eggs, and tends to be laid in May, with young emerging in June-July. Although the venom is potent, cobras tend not to bite except as a last resort, and many bites are not life-threatening; however, when especially agitated the snake is likely to hang on and chew venom into its attacker, and these bites are likely to be rapidly fatal.

Habitat and Current Distribution

Cobras occur throughout South and Southeast Asia, from Iran east to Indonesia. Until recently, these were regarded as a single widespread and variable species, with many separate subspecies. Detailed study of range, morphology, and venom components has shown that at least eight separate species are involved. The Central Asian cobra is thus now treated as a full species. It ranges from Iran and the Central Asian states of the former USSR, through Afghanistan to Pakistan and northwest India.

Although the habitat is generally rather desert-like, the species prefers areas with some vegetation, such as damp grassland, and often occurs around villages or areas with some cultivation.

History and Conservation Measures

Concern for this species has been raised because of its use in the skin trade and because of severe modification of its habitat in some areas, the former USSR in particular. More recent work has shown that populations remain in many parts of the range, and it may be removed from the IUCN list of globally threatened species in the future.

Milos viper

Vipera schweizeri

Phylum	Chordata
Class	Reptilia
Order	Serpentes
Family	Viperidae
Status	Endangered, IUCN
Range	Cyclades Islands (Greece)

Description and Biology

This species, alternatively called the Cyclades blunt-nosed viper, is by far the smallest form in a complex of generally large vipers living in the somewhat arid area between Morocco in the west and Kashmir in the east. It averages about 27 in (70 cm) in body length and has fewer than 25 rows of scales around the body, whereas the related forms can be twice that length, stouter in the body, and have more than 25 scale rows. There are a number of other anatomical and behavioral differences. The other island population in this group of species, present in Cyprus, also tends to be smaller than mainland forms. It is mostly gray, speckled with darker gray, and with a dark zigzag dorsal band. In a rare color variant, much prized by collectors, the snake is dull red in color. Like most other vipers, it has a prominently triangular head housing large venom glands, but is usually mild-mannered and no cases of human poisoning appear to have been recorded (other species in this complex can be extremely irritable and many fatalities are known).

The Milos viper feeds on a wide variety of prey, including rodents, lizards, and migrant birds in late summer. This species is the only one in the complex to lay eggs; others give birth to live young. Mating occurs around May; eggs are laid in rock crevices in July and hatch after about five weeks. Clutch size ranges from 15 to 30.

Habitat and Current Distribution

This viper has been recorded on Milos, Kimoloe, Polyaigos and Siphnos in the Western Cyclades island group in Greece (this group is located south of Athens in the Aegean Sea). The Milos viper is now restricted to sheltered stream valleys, often dry in summer, with rough rocky slopes densely covered with Mediterranean vegetation. There are indications that the species may have occurred in other habitats. One estimate suggests there may be around 9,000 snakes in total, nearly all of them on Milos.

History and Conservation Measures

Until 1977 snakes were killed in very large numbers under a bounty system in which viper heads could be exchanged for money. Records suggest that between 1,500 and 2,000 vipers were killed annually, and there were reportedly 3,000 claims in 1977. Removal of such numbers would certainly have had a serious impact on local populations and is thought to be why very few vipers now occur in the populated eastern half of Milos. The Milos viper is also collected in significant numbers for sale abroad, probably 100-1,500 snakes a year. Formerly collected mainly by shepherds, most collection for trade is now done by outside professional collectors.

Increased opencast mining for minerals is another active threat. This destroys landscape features and extends a road network into previously intact habitat. A 1981 presidential decree nominally forbids the killing of most Greek reptiles, including this viper. There is an urgent need to protect suitable habitat in Cyclades, and a Biogenetic Reserve has been proposed for western Milos. This would include representative vegetation as well as many rare or typical animal species, including the Milos viper.

Wyoming toad

Bufo hemiophrys baxteri

Phylum	Chordata
Class	Amphibia
Order	Anura
Family	Bufonidae
Status	Endangered, USFWS
Range	Wyoming (U.S.A.)

Description and Biology

The Wyoming toad is rather small and dark brown, gray, or greenish in color with dark blotches. Its upper body has numerous rounded warts, and its belly is spotted. Adults average 2.2 in (5.6 cm) from snout to vent; males are smaller than females and have a darker throat. Its diet includes ants, beetles, and a variety of other invertebrates.

In May, males of the species move to breeding sites, where they attract females with their calls. Breeding continues until approximately mid-June. Females deposit from 2,000-5,000 black eggs in gelatinous strings, often tangled in among vegetation. Eggs hatch within a week, and the tadpoles transform into toadlets within 4-6 weeks.

Habitat and Current Distribution

This species is found only at a lake and the surrounding wet meadows at a site approximately 20 mi (32 km) from Laramie, Wyoming, ranging in elevation from 7,000-7,500 ft (2,100-2,300 m). In 1990, it was estimated that no more than 100 adults survived.

The species breeds along the borders of bays, ponds, and irrigated meadows, where the water is shallow and vegetation is abundant. These breeding areas may be wet only during the rainy season, drying out by late summer.

History and Conservation Measures

The Wyoming toad was discovered and described in 1946. Although its range was always limited, the species was considered abundant from the 1940s to the early 1970s. Its numbers declined drastically in the 1970s and, after seeming to level off, began to drop again in 1989.

The reasons for the initial decline in population are not fully understood. A number of possibilities have been suggested, but no single factor can account for the abrupt decline. Long-term harm resulting from the use of pesticides may be involved. While insect predation on eggs and tadpoles does not seem to have increased in the years in question, the population decline has been paralleled by an increase in such predators as California gulls, white pelicans, and raccoons. Although sufficient wetlands remain in the habitat area, water quality may have been affected by pollutants and irrigation techniques. Reproductive failure has also been implicated and linked to changes in weather patterns. Disease is considered the major factor in the more recent decline: a bacterial infection called red leg is believed to have taken a toll on the adult population.

Conservation efforts include protecting and monitoring the known population and its habitat, searching for additional populations, establishing a captive population, and researching the life history and habitat needs of the species. Some habitat areas have been acquired, and reintroduction sites have been identified.

Houston toad

Bufo houstonensis

Phylum	Chordata
Class	Amphibia
Order	Anura
Family	Bufonidae
Status	Endangered, IUCN
	Endangered, USFWS
Range	Texas (U.S.A.)

Description and Biology

The Houston toad is usually light brown in color, sometimes tending toward red, with dark brown to black spots containing one or more warts. It is a small to medium-sized toad: the female averages 2.1-3.1 in (53-80 mm) in length, while the male is slightly smaller, averaging 1.8-2.7 in (45-70 mm) in length. Adults feed primarily on insects such as ants and beetles; tadpoles eat algae and pine pollen. Some snakes and turtles may prey on the toad, and certain fish may prey on its larvae or eggs.

The mating call of this species is a long, high-pitched trill, which some have described as similar to the tinkling of a small bell. Calling can begin as early as late January, and breeding begins when the temperature stabilizes around 57°F (14°C). Egg-laying occurs from mid-February to late June, with the female spawning 500-6,000 eggs.

Habitat and Current Distribution

The Houston toad is thought to survive in Harris, Bastrop, and Burleson counties in Texas. Its largest concentration is in Bastrop County, particularly in Bastrop and Buescher State Parks and in the area north of the parks. The total population there has been estimated at 1,500 individuals. In Burleson County, the Houston toad population is thought to be very small, and it has not been sighted in Harris County since 1976.

The toad uses a variety of aquatic habitats, including lakes, ponds, roadside ditches, flooded fields and pastures, and temporary rain pools, as long as the water remains for at least 60 days. Because the toad is a poor burrower, it tends to be found in areas with sandy soil, such as pine forests. When not breeding, it shelters in the sand, in burrows, under logs, or in leaf litter.

Houston toad.

History and Conservation Measures

First discovered in the late 1940s, the Houston toad was for a time thought to have become extinct as a result of severe droughts in Texas in the 1950s. The species was rediscovered in Bastrop State Park in 1965. In addition to the droughts, clearing or modification of its habitat contributed to the reduction of its population. Residential and agricultural development has resulted in the clearing of large tracts of pine forest, and while this has slowed in recent years, this development has led to the introduction of high volumes of pesticides and herbicides into the environment. Long term climatic changes have also been unfavorable for the species, which cannot adapt to a warmer and drier climate.

Conservation efforts for this species include the protection of known populations, reintroduction of the toad into its former habitat, and surveys for additional suitable habitats. Additional surveys for the species continue: specimens have been collected from Leon County, and calling toads have been reported at sites in Colorado and Burleson counties. A study is under way in Bastrop County to determine population size and biological characteristics of the species. If existing populations are protected and additional viable populations can be established, prospects for recovery are good.

Mount Nimba viviparous toad

Nectophrynoides occidentalis

Phylum	Chordata
Class	Amphibia
Order	Anura
Family	Bufonidae
Status	Vulnerable, IUCN
	Appendix I, CITES
Range	Mount Nimba (West Africa)

Description and Biology

This species is one of the "true toads" in the family Bufonidae; most are slow-moving, with a relatively squat body and short legs, and often lacking vivid coloring.

Around one-third of the approximately 4,000 known species of frogs and toads have a life history different from that of the more common north temperate forms, where eggs laid in water hatch into tadpoles that undergo gradual metamorphosis into adult form. Many species do not produce free-living tadpoles but instead invest in fewer but larger eggs out of which tiny metamorphosed frogs emerge. A very few species, principally the toads of the genus *Nectophrynoides*, give birth to live young (that is, they are viviparous). Fertilization is internal. The eggs develop and larvae metamorphose within the female's oviduct. Giving birth to live young means that these species avoid all the dangers faced by eggs and tadpoles, eagerly sought by many predators and vulnerable to desiccation, but bear the costs of supporting the developing toadlets.

Some biologists now place the nine species of *Nectophrynoides* into three separate genera, in which case this species is identified as *Nimbaphrynoides occidentalis*.

Habitat and Current Distribution

The Mt. Nimba viviparous toad is restricted to montane grassland between 3,900 and 5,250 ft (1,200 and 1,600 m) altitude on the summit of Mt. Nimba, an elongate ridge about 45,000 acres (18,000 ha) in extent, located in West Africa where the national borders of Côte d'Ivoire, Guinea, and Liberia meet. The highest peak, at 5,748 ft (1,752 m), is situated within the Guinea portion of the mountain. Mt. Nimba is rich in minerals, notably iron ore, and the habitat of this species, particularly within Liberia, has been greatly affected by mining activities.

History and Conservation Measures

The Mt. Nimba viviparous toad has been regarded as significantly threatened because its original range has been reduced, and the forests on the lower slopes of the mountain have also been degraded. There are nature reserves in both the Côte d'Ivoire and Guinea portions of Mt. Nimba, and a 42,500-acres (17,000-ha) biosphere reserve exists in Guinea. The species is listed on Appendix I of the Convention on International Trade in Endangered Species of Wild Fauna and Flora (CITES) because of the threat posed by trade to this unique and much-prized species.

Malabar tree toad

Pedostibes tuberculosa

Garo Hills tree toad

Pedostibes kempi

Phylum	Chordata
Class	Amphibia
Order	Anura
Family	Bufonidae
Status	Insufficiently Known, IUCN
Range	India

Description and Biology

These small and slender toads reach up to 1.3 in (3.5 cm) in body length, and the tips of the fingers and toes are expanded into discs to aid in climbing.

Habitat and Current Distribution

Both species occur in evergreen and seasonal wet forest. The Malabar tree toad was originally described more than 100 years ago on the basis of a handful of specimens labelled with the origin "Malabar." The Malabar region was part of the Madras Presidency of nineteenth-century colonial India, and it corresponds approximately to the northern half of the present Kerala state in southwest India. The precise origin within Kerala of the original specimens was unknown until recently. The Garo Hills tree toad is known only from the vicinity of the original collection locality: Tura, at 2,500 ft (762 m) elevation in the Garo Hills in Meghalaya in northeast India.

History and Conservation Measures

No specimens of the Malabar tree toad were recorded for more than a century after its discovery, and in view of the enormous loss and fragmentation of the original wet forests along the hill ranges of southwest India, there was legitimate reason to question the existence of the Malabar tree toad. The Zoological Survey of India listed it in a review of rare and endangered species. One specimen was found in the Silent Valley area of Kerala in 1982, and several more were collected near the Ashambu Hills, many miles to the south, in the following year. Relatively large areas in Kerala are now managed as protected areas, thus enhancing the survival prospects for the Malabar tree toad. There has been much deforestation in the Assam area as land is converted for agricultural use in Meghalaya, and there are concerns for the continued survival of the Garo Hills tree toad.

Mallorcan midwife toad

Alytes (Baleaphryne) muletensis

Phylum	Chordata
Class	Amphibia
Order	Anura
Family	Discoglossidae
Status	Endangered, IUCN
Range	Mallorca (Spain)

Description and Biology

This species, known locally as "ferreret," is creamy white in color, with varying amounts of olive patterning. It is more slender than related species and has strikingly large eyes. The family Discoglossidae is rather primitive in some respects; its few species are all quite distinctive and restricted to Eurasia. The Mallorcan midwife toad shares with other species in the genus *Alytes* a particular breeding trait in which the male carries the developing eggs entwined around his hind legs—hence the common name. The eggs are larger than those of other midwives but fewer in number, around ten on average, compared with often more than 50 in other *Alytes*. The male transports the eggs for several weeks and then deposits them in suitable pools around the end of July. The tadpoles, which emerge promptly, can form dense populations in favorable sites; they metamorphose into adults in August-September. The tadpoles can use their mouthparts to cling to rocks, and are especially efficient at filtering food out of the cold and nutrient-poor waters they inhabit. The adults feed on a variety of insects and other invertebrates.

Habitat and Current Distribution

The Mallorcan midwife toad occurs only in the Serra de Tramuntana, a region of precipitous limestone mountains in the north extremity of the island of Mallorca, Spain. The entire known wild population is restricted to about seven mountain torrents in this area, between 984 and 1,312 ft (300 and 400 m) altitude, and has been estimated to comprise probably 500 breeding pairs. Most individuals occur in four torrent systems; another three torrents have small numbers; populations in another two may be extinct or transitory. These torrents run through a series of narrow vertical gorges, and tend to form small pools at different heights, fed by waterfalls or by seepage from the limestone. Breeding occurs in and around these typical ephemeral pools. Large eggs and early egg transport mean that the emerging tadpoles are given a head start in the struggle to secure enough food and metamorphose before the pools dry up or the water temperature falls too low. Some late tadpoles overwinter. Adult Mallorcan midwife toads are unique among discoglossids in being able to climb almost like a tree frog, clearly an advantage in their precipitous environment. Adults have never been seen outside these narrow and poorly accessible gorges, and never more than about 66 ft (20 m) from water; much of their day is spent under rocks or wedged into limestone crevices in the vicinity of pools.

History and Conservation Measures

The species, originally named *Baleaphryne muletensis*, was first described from fossil material of the Pleistocene age; this, and sub-fossil bones from cave and other deposits, show that the species was widely distributed on Mallorca until about 2,000 year ago. It was thought extinct, until the remarkable discovery of living populations in the Serra de Tramuntana in 1980. The living and the fossil toad are thought to represent the same species, but there is still some discussion about whether it should be grouped with other midwife toads in the genus *Alytes*, or whether its peculiarities merit recognition of the separate genus *Baleaphryne*. Whatever name is applied, the species is certainly in a precarious position: from an island-wide distribution it has retreated to isolated gorges just a few square miles (hectares) in total extent. This decline is attributed to human settle-ment over most of the island, and predation by the frog-eating water snake *Natrix maura*, believed to have been introduced by humans. Present threats are modification to the water regime in the Serra Tramuntana, loss of vegetation above the gorges, and disturbance by rock climbers. In partial fulfillment of obligations under the Convention on the Conserva-tion of European Wildlife and Natural Habitats (Berne Convention), the species is strictly protected by Spanish law. The specialized habitat is not yet sufficiently secure. A number of toads bred at the Jersey Wildlife Preservation Trust and Frankfurt Zoo have now been released with the hope of re-establish-ing populations within the species' former range.

Hamilton's frog

Leiopelma hamiltoni

Phylum	Chordata
Class	Amphibia
Order	Anura
Family	Leiopelmatidae
Status	Vulnerable, IUCN
	Endangered, USFWS
Range	Stephens Island, Maud Island (New Zealand)

Description and Biology

Considered one of the rarest frogs in the world, Hamilton's frog is a small amphibian endemic to Stephens Island in the Cook Strait, New Zealand. A closely related species inhabits nearby Maud Island and, until recently, was thought to be the same species as the Stephens Island frog. The Maud Island frog is darker than the frogs found on Stephens Island, and other differences may become apparent as research is conducted on this yet undescribed species. The tuatara (*Sphenodon punctatus*), a large lizard-like reptile, preys on Hamilton's frog on Stephens Island.

Habitat and Current Distribution

Hamilton's frog has one of the most restricted distributions of any frog species. A small population exists on Stephens Island in a 6,500 sq ft (600 sq m) area of rock-tumble. The Maud Island frog inhabits a 38-acre (15-ha) forest. Both these areas are fenced to exclude domestic stock. During 1975-1978, a population of about 200 frogs existed on Stephens Island; the Maud Island population is larger at around 5,000 individuals.

Preferred habitat appears to be rocky forests. The frogs on Stephens Island are found in a rock bank that provides a sheltered micro-environment very similar to the rocky forests that harbor the species on Maud Island.

History and Conservation Measures

Hamilton's frog was first discovered by R.G. Smith, a resident of Stephens Island, in 1915. He sent the frog specimen to Harold Hamilton of the Dominion Museum who named and described it. Due to a substantial clearing of forest on Stephens Island during the early twentieth century, much of this frog's habitat was destroyed, and it was thought to be extinct until 1950, when it was rediscovered. The Maud Island frogs were found in 1958.

The main threat to Hamilton's frog appears to be the accidental arrival of mammalian predators, such as rats and mustelids. The arrival of stoats on Maud Island (by swimming from the mainland) in 1982 posed a potential threat to the frog population there, since stoats are known to eat geckos and other amphibians. These stoats were exterminated by the Wildlife Service in 1983 before any damage was done, but the possibility of future stoat invasions on both islands remains a potential threat. Another potential threat is the reduced genetic variation frequently seen in remnant populations and its impact on the reproductive success.

Hamilton's frog is protected under the New Zealand Wildlife Act of 1953, which prohibits unauthorized collecting and disturbance of this species, and Stephens Island and Maud Island have both been designated reserve areas. Conservation efforts on Stephens Island are guided by research suggesting that a lack of shelter (diurnal retreat sites) has limited the distribution of the species. Between May and October 1991, a new habitat consisting of a rock-filled pit, protected from predators, was created 131 ft (40 m) away from the existing wild population. Twelve adult frogs were captured and transferred to the new

habitat in May 1992, and seven of them are known to have survived. The New Zealand Department of Conservation is currently developing a recovery plan for all the known species of native frogs. The plan involves locating additional wild frog populations, creating new habitats (already begun on Stephens Island), and working to improve captive husbandry techniques. Hamilton's frog has been bred in captivity, but none of these individuals have been released into the wild.

Southern gastric brooding frog

Rheobatrachus silus

Phylum	Chordata
Class	Amphibia
Order	Anura
Family	Myobatrachidae
Status	Endangered, IUCN Appendix II, CITES
Range	Australia

Description and Biology

This small amphibian, also called the platypus frog, reaches a length of only about 2 in (5 cm). Coloration ranges from greenish brown to black, with a creamy yellow undersurface to the limbs. It feeds at night on insects and may be preyed upon by white-faced herons and eels.

The female gastric-brooding frog reaches breeding age at about two years. The reproductive biology of this species is not yet fully understood, but what little is known is certainly fascinating. During the breeding season the female's physiology changes and her stomach is able to stop all digestive action and act as a uterus; it isn't known whether she takes in fertilized eggs or hatched tadpoles, but she later expels froglets through her mouth.

Habitat and Current Distribution

This species is known only from the Blackall and Conondale Ranges, north of Brisbane in southeastern Queensland. It has been found in perennial rain forest streams, sheltering under stones and among submerged leaf litter. There are no known surviving populations.

History and Conservation Measures

While its known range has always been limited, the gastric-brooding frog was considered quite plentiful when it was first found in 1973. The discovery of its unique reproductive processes attracted a lot of scientific attention and study. A sudden population decline began in 1979, and the species has not been reported in the wild since 1981, despite repeated searches; the only known surviving captive specimen died in 1983. The cause of this frog's abrupt and drastic decline is not known. Populations have disappeared from national parks and state forests, where overcollecting and habitat destruction are probably not factors in its decline. An unproven theory is that the species may experience drastic fluctuations in population and that its absence or scarcity may be natural.

Cape platanna

Xenopus gilli

Phylum	Chordata
Class	Amphibia
Order	Anura
Family	Pipidae
Status	Endangered, IUCN
Range	South Africa

Description and Biology

The Cape platanna is a typical member of the strongly aquatic family Pipidae in lacking a tongue, having smooth skin, and strongly webbed hind feet. It is around 2.3 in (6 cm) in length, with a pointed head. The dorsal surface is predominantly dark in color with a paler stripe down the middle of the back and pale, lateral stripes; the belly is usually mottled black and yellow, but pale overall in some populations. Adults feed mainly on aquatic insects during summer, but favor tadpoles and small frogs at other times of year. They are preyed upon by herons, cormorants, and the water mongoose, while tadpoles are eaten by adults of this and other frog species. Breeding starts in July, and most of the resulting tadpoles metamorphose into adult frogs by February of the next year.

Habitat and Current Distribution

The Cape platanna, as the name suggests, is confined to Cape Province in South Africa. More specifically, it is confined to areas with Mediterranean type climate in the southwest Cape. First described in 1927, the species has always been restricted to relatively few sites.

The frog has very narrow habitat requirements and occurs only in deeply stained, acidic ponds and seepages within the local plant communities known as "fynbos."

History and Conservation Measures

The Cape platanna, already at risk because of its precise habitat preferences, faces a number of threats. Modification of the fynbos vegetation can change the water chemistry of Cape platanna pools and allow the larger related species *Xenopus laevis* to move in. This species, already widespread and abundant in Africa, preys upon Cape platanna tadpoles and destroys its genetic integrity by interbreeding with it. It appears that all known Cape platanna populations are suffering hybridization with *X. laevis*, so that even those seemingly secure within the Cape of Good Hope Nature Reserve are threatened. The three best ponds hold perhaps 300 adults each; all other populations are much smaller.

The species is given maximum legal protection by the Cape Nature Conservation Ordinance of 1974. It is present within two protected areas: the Cape of Good Hope Nature Reserve and the private Rhenosterkop Nature Reserve. Conservationists have been working to remove *X. laevis* from key ponds and prevent their re-invasion. It is important to continue these activities, and to create more protected areas around breeding sites. Another endangered frog, *Microbatrachella capensis*, occurs in some Cape platanna ponds, so further increasing the need for their conservation.

Goliath frog

Conraua goliath

Phylum	Chordata
Class	Amphibia
Order	Anura
Family	Ranidae
Status	Vulnerable, IUCN
Range	Cameroon; Equatorial Guinea

Description and Biology

With a recorded maximum weight of nearly 8 lb (3.6 kg) and length (legs extended) of almost 30 in (76 cm), this species is truly a giant among amphibians and certainly the largest frog in the world. The Goliath frog has very granular greenish brown skin dorsally, and so is effectively camouflaged amid the wet moss-covered rocks on which it sits; the underparts are pale orange or yellow. The eyes can be nearly 1 in (2.5 cm) in diameter. The sexes are similar in appearance.

The eggs are large, up to 0.3 in (8 mm) in diameter (including the jelly-like surrounding), and are attached to grass or other vegetation along streamsides or around the margin of rocky pools among rocks. The tadpoles are not noticeably larger than those of other large frogs, so the enormous size of the adult frog must reflect growth after the tadpole stage, which lasts for around 70 days. The tadpoles graze on aquatic vegetation, and are able to cling on to rocks in fast water by their sucker-like mouthparts. It is suspected that the tadpoles feed exclusively on one particular plant during the first weeks of life, and this may help limit the spread of the species. The adult frogs feed on a variety of prey, including insects, crustaceans, molluscs, and amphibians. Smaller adults spend most of their time in water, with perhaps just the snout emerging. Larger adults frequently come out to bask on rocks, with their backs kept moist by splash from the falls typically nearby. The feet in particular are extensively webbed, reflecting the aquatic habits of the species. The frogs are more active during the night, when they search for food along the river margins.

Habitat and Current Distribution

The Goliath frog has narrow habitat requirements and a small world range. It occurs in Africa, where it is restricted to a strip of dense forest, about 150 mi (241 km) long by 55 mi (88 km) wide, near the coast in Cameroon and Equatorial Guinea (and possibly Gabon). Within this forest strip the species is further restricted to rapids and waterfalls in rivers flowing to the coast through dense rain forest. This adds up to a very small world distribution area. As noted above, the presence of key larval food plants may further limit the species. The rivers so far investigated have had very clean, well-oxygenated and slightly acidic water. Average air temperature in a typical locality is 87°F (29°C), and water temperature around 65°F (17°C).

History and Conservation Measures

Not surprisingly, the Goliath frog is highly valued for food among local communities, and it seems possible that this could adversely affect populations. There has been much concern about specimens appearing in international trade in recent years; "large" specimens have been on sale for $2,000. In addition, the Goliath frog is at risk because of its very precise habitat requirements and would be vulnerable to any modification of the water-courses it inhabits and to clearance of the surrounding forest.

Italian agile frog

Rana latastei

Phylum	Chordata
Class	Amphibia
Order	Anura
Family	Ranidae
Status	Vulnerable, IUCN
Range	Italy; Slovenia; Switzerland

Description and Biology

Superficially quite similar to other frogs in the genus *Rana*, the Italian agile frog is a uniform pale reddish brown dorsally; it has a dark brown throat with a pale line down the middle, a white stripe on the upper jaw between the eye and the corner of the mouth, and a smaller external eardrum and longer legs than other European *Rana*.

Breeding reaches a peak in March, when clumps of eggs are deposited in small ponds, ditches, and stream backwaters; sites with slow-flowing water are preferred. Although rather large numbers of small frogs may be seen in autumn, larger adults are rarely found, and are assumed to suffer heavy mortality during winter hibernation. The population seems to have a rapid turnover and large fluctuations in numbers over the year.

Habitat and Current Distribution

The species is closely associated with semi-moist deciduous oak-hornbeam forest typical of the Po valley plains of north Italy, and most sites consist of remnant patches of such forest, always with a high water table, and lush ground cover in summer. Virtually the entire world population of Italian agile frog occurs in about 35 small sites in the Po valley drainage; a couple of sites are known in wetlands just over the border with Switzerland, and a few sites are known in similar wet wooded areas in Slovenia.

Although frogs are mostly restricted to breeding sites during early spring, they become more widespread as the season progresses and the ground cover becomes more dense and the atmosphere within the forest more humid. Nevertheless, the adults show little tendency to migrate away from their breeding area.

History and Conservation Measures

Mainly because most of its original habitat has been drained and given way to agriculture or plantation woods, the species now has a relict distribution within its historic range. Several populations occur within nature reserves in Italy, but none were designed with the needs of the Italian agile frog in mind or are managed with that purpose. One of the three Swiss sites had been damaged but is now restored and managed suitably.

It is highly desirable for the long term survival of the species to improve management at key sites, in particular the Bosco della Fontana. This area, near Mantova, is one of the last remnants of the primeval riverine forest of the Po valley. It was declared a Natural Forest Reserve in 1910. The state Forest Department has made efforts to remove non-native species from the area. With the exception of Le Bine (also near Mantova), the Bosco della Fontana probably holds more Italian agile frogs, perhaps up to 5,000 during the spring population peak, than all other Italian and Swiss sites combined. There are fears for the future of the reserve because the water table appears to be falling, seemingly as a result of increased abstraction for agricultural, industrial, and domestic use in the Po valley.

The Le Bine area, an old branch of the River Olio between Cremona and Mantova, holds the largest known single population of Italian agile frogs. Parts of the site form a WWF Italia reserve for waterbirds, but other parts are under poplar plantation and so of less ecological value. Nevertheless, this site could become even more important if the drying out of the Bosco della Fontana cannot be reversed.

Santa Cruz long-toed salamander

Ambystoma macrodactylum croceum

Phylum	Chordata
Class	Amphibia
Order	Caudata
Family	Ambystomatidae
Status	Endangered, IUCN
	Endangered, USFWS
Range	California (U.S.A.)

Description and Biology

This subspecies of the long-toed salamander is thick-bodied and just over 3 in (8 cm) long, with a broad head that ends in a blunt snout. Light-colored spots highlight its glossy dark brown to black coloration. The species' common name is taken from its long, slim toes. Diet includes insects, eggs, vegetation, insect larvae, and, in times of food shortages, other salamanders. Garter snakes prey upon young and adult salamanders, and aquatic insects eat its eggs and larvae. Other possible predators, including herons, kingfishers, owls, blackbirds, and grebes, rarely get the opportunity to feed on this secretive, primarily nocturnal salamander.

Salamanders arrive at their breeding ponds in November, and breeding peaks during January and February, when rain has replenished the ponds. Eggs are typically laid singly on stalks of spike rush (*Eleocharis* sp.) or other vegetation below the water's surface, although some free-floating, unattached, and clustered eggs have been reported. Each female lays approximately 200 eggs, which hatch in about one week. Metamorphosis of the larvae occurs after 90-140 days, from early May to mid-August.

Habitat and Current Distribution

The Santa Cruz long-toed salamander is known only from Monterey and Santa Cruz counties in California, where it is found in several distinct populations. At Valencia Lagoon the population was estimated in the mid-1970s at approximately 1,000 individuals; another population at Ellicott was estimated in the late 1970s to number 5,000-8,000 adults. Four additional breeding populations have been discovered, but the size of these populations is not known.

Santa Cruz long-toed salamander.

Each population of long-toed salamanders requires two distinct habitats: a pond with an adequate amount of aquatic plant life for breeding, egg laying, hatching, and metamorphosis; and an area of dense vegetation, relatively close to the pond, for the remainder of the year. The species tends to inhabit areas with animals that tunnel underground, such as mice, gophers, and moles, and is known to spend much of its life in the burrows of these animals.

History and Conservation Measures

Discovered in 1954, the Santa Cruz long-toed salamander is related to a prehistoric species that was once widespread but became isolated in several populations after the last Pleistocene ice advance. The limited number and size of the populations of the present-day species is believed to be the result of destruction of its habitat.

The first population was discovered at Valencia Lagoon, which has since been reduced in size and ultimately drained. An artificial pond was constructed at the site to allow the population to survive, although in substantially reduced numbers. The Valencia Lagoon population remains threatened by residential development in the surrounding area, although the pond area itself is now publicly owned and protected. Similarly, the pond site and adjacent areas in the Ellicott habitat have been secured, but nearby development and improper land use threaten the species. In other population areas as well, the habitat is vulnerable to agricultural and residential development.

Efforts are underway to establish a management program that will acquire, protect, and maintain sufficient habitat for the Santa Cruz salamander. Its survival can only be ensured by the preservation of the complete ecosystem upon which it depends.

Chinese giant salamander

Andrias davidianus

Phylum	Chordata
Class	Amphibia
Order	Caudata
Family	Cryptobranchidae
Status	Indeterminate, IUCN
	Endangered, USFWS
	Appendix I, CITES
Range	China

Description and Biology

The Chinese giant salamander is one of the world's largest salamanders with an average length of 3.3 ft (1 m). Its head is broad and flattened with a broad mouth. It has four short limbs and a compressed tail that comprises more than half of its length. This species has smooth skin and paired tubercles (smooth, rounded bumps) on the snout, periphery of the eye, and other parts of the head; thick skin folds with larger tubercles are seen on the sides of its body. *A. davidianus* is dark brown or pale brown above and lighter underneath; irregular black patches are scattered over its upper side.

This salamander is carnivorous and feeds on crabs, fish, frogs, shrimp, molluscs, and aquatic insects. It is especially fond of crabs. It also occasionally feeds on refuse, including putrid meat.

During the breeding season, males move into caves where the females live. A female produces 300 to more than 1,000 eggs depending on her size, but lays about 100 eggs during the breeding season, which peaks in August-September. Each egg is 0.2-0.3 in (6-8 mm) in diameter; its cream color changes to white after it is laid. When the water temperature is 65°-72°F (18°-22°C), fertilized eggs hatch within 45 days. The hatchlings are about 1.2 in (30 mm) long.

These salamanders can live for more than 50 years in captivity.

Habitat and Current Distribution

The Chinese giant salamander ranges widely over north, central, south, and southwest China, apart from the extreme northern and southern regions of the country. There is no estimate of the number of these salamanders in the wild, but the number of wild individuals has decreased. Captured individuals are smaller each year due to over-exploitation.

The Chinese giant salamander inhabits mountain streams at elevations below 3,300 ft (1,000 m) above sea level, where plant cover is well developed, and the water is shallow, cold, clear, and fast-moving with deep pools and abundant caves. This species shelters in caves during the day and emerges to search for food at night.

History and Conservation Measures

The primary threat to the survival of this species is over-exploitation for food and medicine. The meat of this salamander is said to be smooth, white, delicious, and high in nutrients. Since the Chinese giant salamander became a protected animal, dishes containing its meat are not seen in large cities, but live animals or giant salamander meat is still sold in many small cities as well as in the countryside. Habitat destruction and water pollution are other threats to this species.

The Chinese giant salamander is listed as a second grade protected animal on the *List of Major Protective Wildlife of the State* issued by the Chinese Ministry of Forestry and the Chinese Ministry of Agriculture in 1989. Following this listing many Chinese provincial governments also enacted legislation to prohibit the killing of this species. Much remains to be done, however, before effective protection of this species is achieved.

Japanese giant salamander

Andrias japonicus

Phylum	Chordata
Class	Amphibia
Order	Caudata
Family	Cryptobranchidae
Status	Rare, IUCN
	Endangered, USFWS
	Appendix I, CITES
Range	Japan

Description and Biology

One of the largest salamanders, the Japanese giant salamander attains a total length of 4.8 ft (148 cm). Coloration is primarily brown, with many black blotches. The entire body is flat, with a broad, flat head and small eyes. Legs are short, and the tail is about 35 percent of the total length and flattened laterally. The skin folds along the side of the body, giving it a fringed look. Totally aquatic and nocturnal, it eats fish, crustaceans, and occasionally frogs.

Breeding occurs in a cave under the surface of the water in late August or early September. Eggs are laid in a group, consisting of the male nest owner, females, and several other males. Fertilization is external, and rosary-like strings will join into a single egg mass. The owner male guards the egg-mass until larvae hatch two months later, and the young leave the nest in early spring.

Habitat and Current Distribution

This salamander is known only from the Japanese islands of Honshu, Kyushu, and Shikoku, where it lives on the bottom of rivers or streams in mountainous or hilly areas. Population estimates are unavailable.

History and Conservation Measures

This species has been designated a Special Natural Monument, having legal protection since 1952, but due to habitat destruction, the species is still seriously threatened. Captive breeding at the Asa Zoological Park, Hiroshima, Japan, as well as the introduction of artificial nests to selected rivers, has been successful. These experiments are due to be repeated in several other rivers. The Species Survival Commission of the Japanese Association of Zoological Gardens and Aquariums is also making efforts to increase stocks of this animal.

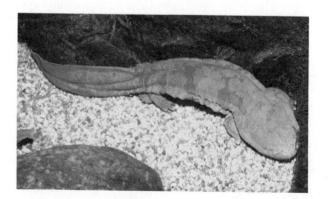

Japanese giant salamander.

Desert slender salamander

Batrachoseps aridus

Phylum	Chordata
Class	Amphibia
Order	Caudata
Family	Plethodontidae
Status	Endangered, IUCN
	Endangered, USFWS
Range	California (U.S.A.)

Description and Biology

Measuring just 4 in (10.2 cm) from its snout to the tip of its tail, this slender salamander is dark brown with grayish spots and gold markings on the surface; the underparts are reddish brown. There are four toes on each foot. Mostly nocturnal, it eats flies, ants, and other small insects.

Eggs are thought to be laid from November to January, depending on the abundance of winter rains. Information on reproductive biology is unavailable.

Habitat and Current Distribution

There are two known populations of this species. The largest is found in Hidden Palms Canyon and is estimated at around 500 animals; the other is found in Guadalupe Canyon, probably numbering fewer than 100 individuals.

The only known habitat is desert canyon and limestone strata, where the salamander takes shelter in loose rocks or soil during the day.

History and Conservation Measures

A recently discovered species, this salamander was described in 1970. The areas it inhabits are well protected from human intrusion, and the only known threat at this time is its very limited distribution. Like all species with a small population and restricted distribution, it is vulnerable to extinction if subjected to natural catastrophes such as extreme drought or heavy rainfall.

Conservation goals include the stabilization of the habitat and existing population in Hidden Palms Canyon and further study of the Guadalupe Canyon population. Surveys are planned to determine if another population exists in a watershed in Hidden Palms Canyon. The population in Guadalupe Canyon has been surveyed regularly and an effort initiated to acquire genetic information on this group.

Jemez Mountains salamander

Plethodon neomexicanus

Phylum	Chordata
Class	Amphibia
Order	Caudata
Family	Plethondontidae
Status	Vulnerable, IUCN
Range	New Mexico (U.S.A.)

Description and Biology

The Jemez Mountains salamander is long and slender, with the female averaging 2.2 in (5.5 cm) long from snout to anal vent, and the male slightly shorter. Coloration is dark brown on top with a very pale to almost transparent underside.

Mating begins in July or August. Eggs are laid from August through the following April, and hatching begins in July. In captivity, the female laid eggs every second year, and two egg clusters averaged seven eggs per clutch.

Habitat and Current Distribution

This species is found in the Jemez Mountains in Los Alamos and Sandoval counties in New Mexico. There are no estimates of population size.

The Jemez Mountains salamander inhabits mixed coniferous forest at altitudes of 7,200-9,200 ft (2,200-2,800 m). It usually shelters under rocks or around rotting logs.

History and Conservation Measures

There is no available information on the history or status of this species.

Jemez Mountains salamander.

Texas blind salamander

Typhlomolge rathbuni

Phylum	Chordata
Class	Amphibia
Order	Caudata
Family	Plethodontidae
Status	Endangered, IUCN
	Endangered, USFWS
Range	Texas (U.S.A.)

Description and Biology

This aquatic, cave-dwelling salamander has whitish to transparent skin; its inner organs are visible through its skin, giving the body a pinkish tinge. It has blood-red external gills, tiny gray dots covering its upper surface, and two dark spots under its skin representing vestigial eyes. Its body is short and slender, with a long tail, a large head with a wide, flattened snout, and long, slender legs resembling toothpicks. This salamander eats invertebrates, including snails, shrimp, and amphipods; juveniles of the species feed primarily on copepods. It is a major predator in its subterranean habitat, but becomes easy prey for a variety of fish if it is brought to the surface through a spring or well.

Very little is known about its reproduction, but it is thought to occur throughout the year.

Habitat and Current Distribution

This species is presently found only in the San Marcos Pool of the Edwards Aquifer in Hays County, Texas. There are no estimates of the population size.

The caverns of the San Marcos Pool have historically had very good water quality and a relatively constant water temperature of just under 70°F (21° C).

History and Conservation Measures

The Texas blind salamander was first described in 1896. The decline in sightings of the species in the 1960s is attributed to overcollecting, since the salamander's adaptation to cave life makes it of special interest to scientists and hobbyists. When the cave was sealed to protect it from human intrusion, a colony of bats was eliminated, thus depriving the ecosystem of important nutrients provided by bat guano. Efforts to reestablish the bat colony have thus far been unsuccessful.

Although the major part of the salamander population is somewhat protected by its inaccessibility,

Texas blind salamander.

the species remains vulnerable to any deterioration in water quality. The water level in the aquifer continues to decrease as an increasing amount of water is used for human consumption and for irrigation. In addition, increased development in the area has raised the threat of urban pollution seeping into the aquifer. Recovery plans for the Texas blind salamander are limited to efforts to protect the Edward's Aquifer from pollution and from further reductions in its water level.

Olm

Proteus anguinus

Phylum . . . . Chordata
Class . . . . Amphibia
Order . . . . Caudata
Family . . . . Proteidae
Status . . . . Vulnerable, IUCN
Range . . . . Coastal mountains along the East Adriatic Sea

Description and Biology

The olm is morphologically and ecologically highly distinct; it is the only European salamander adapted to a totally aquatic existence in underground waters, and one of only a handful of such species in the world (recent evidence suggests that the olm may consist of two species). It is somewhat eel-like in form, with small and slender (but functional) limbs, and vestigial eyes. The skin is not pigmented, so the animal is pinkish white in color. Total length can be up to 11.8 in (30 cm). A group of five species, superficially similar to the olm, occur in North America; there is some dispute whether these six species are related or have evolved separately in similar environments.

The olm is a neotenous form; that is, it retains a larval body form, with red branched external gills, and breeds in this condition. The eggs, typically between 10 and 70, are laid over a period of three or four weeks, and attached in clusters to the rock substrate. The larvae emerge after 13 to 20 weeks. They feed on microscopic bacteria and protozoa during their first year, but, once over 2 or 2.5 in (5 or 6 cm), they switch to oligochaete worms and crustaceans. Most information on breeding has been obtained from captive animals; it seems that reproduction in the wild occurs in remote and inaccessible underground waters, and young are very rarely seen.

Habitat and Current Distribution

This very distinctive species occurs in the waters of certain cave systems in the chain of limestone hills that stretches from the region of Trieste (in northeast Italy) southward parallel to the coast of the former Yugoslavia, to include parts of Bosnia-Herzegovina, Croatia, Montenegro, and Slovenia. Most sites are very difficult of access. Although relatively few caves where the olm can be seen have been documented, the underground waters to some extent interconnect within the limestone hills and so the actual distribution area is larger than is at first apparent. This, however, puts the species at increased risk because pollutants entering the water can be widely disseminated to affect many individuals.

Favored habitat consists of slow-moving, clear, cold and well-oxygenated underground waters in limestone areas. It is impossible to assess the total population of the olm, because so many parts of its probable range are inaccessible.

History and Conservation Measures

Speleologists have indicated that the species is now absent from certain caves and sink holes where it had been occurred in the past, and there is a multitude of threats to the olm and the aquatic systems it inhabits. These threats include over-collection for commercial and scientific purposes and water pollution. The species is listed in the Red Data Book of Slovenia where it is nominally protected by legislation. It is listed on Appendix II of the Convention on the Conservation of European Wildlife and Natural Habitats (Berne Convention); contracting parties to this convention are obliged to take measures for special protection of the species and its habitat.

Great white shark

Carcharodon carcharias

Phylum	Chordata
Class	Chondrichthyes
Order	Lamniformes
Family	Lamnidae
Status	Insufficiently Known, IUCN
Range	Subtropical and warm temperate seas

Description and Biology

Despite its name, this shark is not always white; coloration can range from dull white to blue, brown, gray, or gray-black, while the underside remains light. The tail and dorsal fins are dark to black colored along the margins, and there is often a black spot on the body at the base of the pectoral fins, which are tipped in black. One of the largest species of sharks, it ranges from 11-17 ft (3.4-5.2 m), but specimens of up to 25 ft (7.6 m) have been reported. The great white can swim at high speeds and has been seen to lift its head out of the water. It has excellent senses of sight and smell, usually locating prey by scent. Teeth are serrated and razor sharp, allowing the shark to feed on seals, turtles, fish, and a variety of other prey or carrion. Extremely aggressive, it has been known to attack boats and humans.

The great white is thought to be territorial, with the size of its territory varying with available food. In some regions, it has been reported to group with others of similar size and sex, but mixed groups have also been reported. Sexual maturity is probably reached at 11-14 ft (3.4-4.3 m). Very little is known about the shark's life cycle or reproduction.

Habitat and Current Distribution

The great white shark has been reported in almost every ocean, but usually frequents warm or temperate seas; it is often sighted along shorelines or reefs. There are no estimates of total population size.

History and Conservation Measures

Very little is known about the status of the great white shark. Surveys to determine population and distribution in addition to studies of the species' life cycle and ecological requirements would be necessary to assess its status and conservation needs. The species is protected in South Africa.

Great white shark.

Gray nurse shark

Carcharias taurus
(Odontaspis arenarius)

Phylum	Chordata
Class	Chondrichthyes
Order	Lamniformes
Family	Carcharminidae (Odontaspidae)
Status	Indeterminate, IUCN
Range	Pacific Ocean (off eastern Australia)

Description and Biology

Also known as the sand tiger shark or ragged tooth shark, the gray nurse shark is a ferocious-looking animal with a pointed, upturned snout and fang-like teeth. They are generally grayish brown in color with paler coloring underneath. The upper fork of the tail is nearly three times as long as the lower. Average size ranges from 6-8.5 ft (1.8-2.6 m), with the female larger than the male; maximum reported size is from 10-11 ft (3-3.3 m). Average weight ranges from 200-250 lb (90-115 kg). The gray nurse shark is known to gulp air at the water's surface in order to increase its buoyancy. The species is omnivorous and feeds on smaller fish; sometimes a group of gray nurses will surround and prey upon a school of fish.

In an unusual reproductive process, up to 20 marble- or pea-sized eggs pass into each oviduct, where one embryo hatches and feeds on the other eggs and smaller embryos. In about a year, when the embryo has reached a length of 30-39 in (76-99 cm), it is expelled into the sea where it then develops further.

Habitat and Current Distribution

The gray nurse occurs in tropical and temperate zones in a variety of water depths. Population estimates are unavailable.

History and Conservation Measures

The gray nurse was once abundant, but beginning in 1970 this shark was found less frequently; in one expedition, only two or three gray nurses were sighted. The decrease in population has been attributed in part to fishermen who hunted the fish for sport and for its commercial value. Additionally, large numbers of gray nurse sharks have been caught in beach-protection netting off the coasts of New South Wales and South Africa.

In 1985 the Australian government banned the capture of all sharks, and subsequently a rather dramatic increase in shark population was reported, including the gray nurse population. In 1989, over 80 gray nurses were spotted off the shores of eastern Australia. Today, tourists and divers can swim among the gray nurses, which appear to be accustomed to their presence in the water.

Gray nurse shark.

Hammerhead sharks

Sphyrnidae spp.

Phylum	Chordata
Class	Chondrichthyes
Order	Lamniformes
Family	Sphyrnidae
Range	Oceanic

Description and Biology

Hammerhead sharks are named for their flattened, laterally extended heads, which vary in shape and size with individual species. The reason for the unusually shaped head is not fully understood; theories include increased sensitivity to prey and improved maneuverability. All of the species have gray or greenish coloring and pale underparts. The eyes are located at the tips of the head, as are the nostrils, in most species. The four largest hammerhead species are the great hammerhead (*Sphyrna mokarran*), which is dark yellow-green with a pale underside, and measures 9-15 ft (2.7-4.6 m) long; the common or smooth hammerhead (*S. zygaena*), which is yellow-green with dark tips on the fins and averages 8-12 ft (2.4-3.7 m) long; the scalloped or bronze hammerhead (*S. lewini*), greenish brown with dark tips on the fins and measuring 7-12 ft (2.1-3.7 m) long; and the whitefin hammerhead (*S. couardi*), which is gray to dark gray with white underparts and measures 5.5-8 ft (1.7-2.4 m) long. The winghead shark (*S. blochii*) has the widest head, measuring up to half of its total body length. Its nostrils are placed more toward the middle of the head instead of at the ends near the eyes. It is gray with a pale underside and averages around 5 ft (1.5 m) long. Four somewhat smaller species, all of which are gray with a pale underside, are the small-eye hammerhead (*S. tudes*), measuring

4.2-4.5 ft (1.3-1.4 m); the scoophead (*S. media*), measuring 3.8-4.5 ft (1.2-1.4 m) long; the bonnethead or shovelhead (*S. tiburo*), measuring 3-4 ft (.9-1.2 m) long; and the smallest hammerhead, the scalloped bonnethead (*S. corona*), which averages only around 3 ft (.9 m) in length. Diet includes a variety of fish, rays, skates, and, in some species, other hammerheads.

During reproduction, the egg hatches in the mother's oviduct, after which the embryo remains attached by a placenta to receive nourishment through the mother's bloodstream. The number of young varies with species and seems to correlate to total body length.

Habitat and Current Distribution

Hammerhead sharks occur in many of the oceans of the world, and their choice of water depth and temperature varies with species. There are no estimates of total population. *S. zygaena* and *S. lewini* are known from most oceans of the world, in deep waters and along shorelines, most often in tropical or subtropical waters. *S. mokarran* also has a wide distribution, but tends to frequent shorelines and more modest depths. *S. tiburo* is known from the Atlantic and Pacific Oceans and *S. corona* from the Pacific, where they prefer shallow waters near the North and

Sphyrna tiburo.

South American shorelines or around reefs. *S. blochii* inhabits the Indian and Pacific Oceans, where it inhabits shallow, warm waters. *S. couardi* is found off the western coast of Africa, where it inhabits all water levels. *S. tudes* inhabits inshore waters along the coast of South America and *S. media* the warm, inshore waters along Central and South America.

History and Conservation Measures

There is no information available on the conservation status of these hammerhead species.

Shortnose sturgeon

Acipenser brevirostrum

Phylum	Chordata
Class	Osteichthyes
Order	Acipenseriformes
Family	Acipenseridae
Status	Vulnerable, IUCN
	Endangered, USFWS
	Appendix I, CITES
Range	Atlantic Coast of Canada and U.S.A.

Description and Biology

The shortnose sturgeon is a yellowish brown color, but it may appear to be green or purple in saltwater. It has a black head, back, and sides and white or yellow underparts. Juveniles have dark blotches. The head is short and covered by bony plates; the mouth is wide and the snout short and round. Total length ranges from 2-3 ft (60-90 cm), but individuals longer than 3.3 ft (100 cm) and weighing more than 22 lb (10 kg) are reportedly common in the Saint John River. Females are larger than males, and the northern populations tend to be larger than the southern ones. The sturgeon feeds nocturnally on crustaceans, small molluscs, and aquatic insects. Because of its large size, the species has few predators, although alligators, gars, striped bass, sharks, and seals feed on this fish. Sturgeons in the northern waters have a long life expectancy, with some individuals living up to 60 years.

Spawning takes place upstream and occurs between January and April, peaking between February and May, depending on latitude and water temperature. Little is known about spawning behavior, but it is thought that females spawn once every three years, laying up to 200,000 eggs at a time, many of which do not survive. The males spawn every other year. Eggs are dark brown to black and around 0.1 in (3 mm) in diameter; eggs hatch in about 13 days, and the larvae are dark gray.

Habitat and Current Distribution

The shortnose sturgeon occurs only on the east coast of North America. The largest population re-

Shortnose sturgeon.

sides in the Saint John River in New Brunswick, Canada, but the species' range extends south to the Indian River in Florida, the Hudson River in New York, and the Pee Dee River in South Carolina. There are no estimates of population size.

This sturgeon primarily inhabits rivers and their estuaries; when it occurs at sea, it usually stays fairly close to land. Resting in deep water during the day, it moves along shallow river bottoms at night. Spawning migrations occur in the spring or fall; feeding migrations take place soon after spawning. In autumn, the sturgeon migrates to wintering sites in deep lakes or rivers.

History and Conservation Measures

Although population size is unknown for the shortnose sturgeon, it is believed to be relatively low. A number of factors have led to this status, including water pollution, incidental catching in commercial nets, and the inaccessibility of historical spawning grounds due to the damming of rivers.

The shortnose sturgeon is protected in the United States, and individuals under 4 ft (122 cm) are protected in Canada. Protection of habitat is a conservation priority, and attempts to raise the fish in captivity have been initiated. Additional surveys and studies will be necessary to plan more detailed conservation strategies.

Baltic sturgeon

Acipenser sturio

Phylum	Chordata
Class	Osteichthyes
Order	Acipenseriformes
Family	Acipenseridae
Status	Endangered, IUCN Appendix I, CITES
Range	Northern Atlantic Ocean, Baltic Sea, Mediterranean Sea, Black Sea and rivers of western Europe (Albania; Algeria; Belgium [ex?]; Finland [ex?]; France; Germany [ex?]; Greece; Iceland [ex?]; Ireland [ex?]; Italy; Morocco; Netherlands [ex?]; Norway [ex?]; Poland [ex?]; Portugal; Romania; Russia; Spain [ex?]; Sweden [ex?]; Switzerland [?]; Turkey; Ukraine; United Kingdom; Yugoslavia [ex?])

Description and Biology

Baltic sturgeons are large fish that may grow to over 9.8 ft (3 m) in length and weigh up to 440 lb (200 kg). They are a slow-moving and long-lived species. Baltic sturgeons have shovel-shaped snouts, fleshy barbels between the tip of the snout and the mouth, a ventrally located mouth, and five rows of bony plates along the body. Sturgeons are commercially important as producers of caviar.

Juveniles feed mainly on insect larvae, small crustaceans, molluscs, and small fish, while adults eat small fish, worms, and crustaceans. Sturgeons probe the bottom mud and sand with their snouts, detect food with the sensitive barbels, and pick it up with their protruding lips.

Adult sturgeons spend most of their life at sea, but enter river mouths in the early spring. Spawning takes place in deep (20-26 ft/6-8 m), swiftly flowing rivers with gravel bottoms. After releasing the eggs, adults return immediately to the sea, while the young remain in the river or its estuary for 2-3 years. Males take 7-15 years to reach maturity, while females take

from 8-20 years. This growth rate is more rapid than in other sturgeons.

Habitat and Current Distribution

Baltic sturgeons were formerly widespread in the northeastern Atlantic Ocean, and in the Mediterranean, Baltic and Black Seas. They were occasionally caught around Iceland and North African coasts of the Atlantic and Mediterranean. In the early twentieth century, the catch declined dramatically, and by the 1970s and 1980s only single individuals could be caught or seen in the Rhine, Po, Gironde, Danube, and Douro Rivers. The only remaining population is in the Black Sea, and this was thought to number only 300-1,000 individuals in the 1970s and 1980s.

The species requires deep, fast-flowing rivers for spawning.

History and Conservation Measures

The Baltic sturgeon is threatened mainly through the alteration or degradation of its rivers. In some cases, spawning grounds have been damaged through work designed to make rivers more navigable. In others, weirs, locks, and dams have blocked access to spawning grounds. Pollution and siltation of rivers has also contributed to the decline. The Baltic sturgeon is also vulnerable to overexploitation. It is on the endangered species lists of the former Soviet Union, France, Poland, and Germany, as well as that of the IUCN.

Efforts are being made in France to culture this species for the production of caviar. Captive-bred young may help augment wild stocks, and re-introduction should be encouraged in those rivers in which it formerly spawned and where conditions are still suitable. Strict protection must be given to the species and exploitation must be strictly controlled. Captive breeding using individuals from the Black Sea population may be the only hope for the long-term survival of the species. In addition to captive breeding it will be necessary to create banks of frozen sperm, oocytes (eggs), and embryos. This is particularly important to maintain genetic diversity.

Pallid sturgeon

Scaphirhynchus albus

Phylum	Chordata
Class	Osteichthyes
Order	Acipenseriformes
Family	Acipenseridae
Status	Endangered, IUCN Endangered, USFWS
Range	Arkansas, Iowa, Illinois, Kansas, Kentucky, Louisiana, Missouri, Mississippi, Montana, North Dakota, Nebraska, South Dakota, Tennessee (U.S.A.)

Description and Biology

Also called the white sturgeon, the pallid sturgeon gets its common name from its light coloring. One of the largest fish found in the Missouri-Mississippi River drainage, some specimens have been reported to weigh up to 85 lb (39 kg). The snout is flattened and shovel-shaped, the toothless mouth positioned far under the snout, and the jaw arranged so that the mouth can be extended or withdrawn to facilitate feeding; in front of the mouth is a row of sensory barbels, fleshy protuberances that are used to locate food. Diet includes aquatic invertebrates and fish.

Sexual maturity for males is estimated to occur at 7-9 years of age, females at 15-20 years. Very little is known about the reproductive process. Spawning occurs in June and July in the confluence of the Mississippi and Missouri River.

Habitat and Current Distribution

The pallid sturgeon occurs in the Missouri River and the Mississippi River downstream from the mouth of the Missouri; it also occurs in the lower portion of the Yellowstone River. There are no estimates of population size, but the species is believed to be in decline.

Although habitat preferences are not well known, the pallid sturgeon is usually considered to inhabit the sandy or rocky bottoms of large, turbid, free-flowing rivers. Specimens have been collected from the bottoms of rivers, streams, and lakes and from deep pools, where they are often found in sand flats or gravel bars.

History and Conservation Measures

First described in 1905, the pallid sturgeon was reported in the 1950s to inhabit the middle and lower Mississippi River, the Missouri River, and the lower reaches of the Platte, Kansas, and Yellowstone Rivers, a range of around 3,550 mi (5,700 km). While it was probably never common within that range, it is now considered to be one of the rarest fish of the Missouri and Mississippi River Basins.

The decline of this species is primarily attributed to modification of its riverine habitat. On the Missouri River, more than half of the habitat has been channelized and the rest either impounded (enclosed in reservoirs or dams) or affected by upstream impoundments and altered flow regimes. The Mississippi River has also been modified, primarily by wing dams, dikes, and deepening of the channel. These modifications have blocked the movement of the fish, destroyed or altered spawning areas, and reduced food supplies. When the species was more plentiful, it was subject to commercial harvesting, but population declines eventually made fishing impractical. Pollution is becoming more of a threat to this bottom-feeding species throughout its range; hybridization with the shovelnose sturgeon seems to be increasing, probably as a result of environmental changes and reductions in habitat diversity.

To prevent the extinction of this fish in the wild, several measures have been recommended: protection of the species from overfishing; protection of its habitat; and development of a captive population. Research will be initiated to learn more about the status, distribution, and habitat utilization of this fish. Establishment of a captive population will not only safeguard the species against extinction, it will also supply stock for an eventual re-introduction into historical habitat. The U. S. Fish and Wildlife Service is pursuing captive-breeding programs to that end.

Maluti minnow

Pseudobarbus quathlambae

Phylum	Chordata
Class	Osteichthyes
Order	Cypriniformes
Family	Cyprinidae
Status	Endangered, IUCN
Range	Lesotho

Description and Biology

This is a small fish that reaches a length of 5 in (13 cm). It has a slender body with a single pair of barbels. The Maluti minnow is characterized by extremely small scales. The body is olive or gray-brown to deep blue with silvery white underneath. There is a dark lateral band on the trunk and dark spots or wavy lines on the back. Mature fish have red patches at the base of the fins. It feeds on stream invertebrates, chiefly the aquatic nymphs of ephemeroptera (May flies) and diptera (true flies). In summer, it also preys on the adults of these insects as well as simulid (black fly) larvae.

Spawning occurs during the summer months from November to February, and takes place in and around crevices and boulders. The larval fish undertake a swim-up period during which they are carried by the current from the mid-channel spawning site to quiet backwaters where they begin feeding. Adults occur alone or in small groups.

Habitat and Current Distribution

The Maluti minnow is known only from five high altitude source tributaries of the Orange River system in Lesotho. These include the Tsoelikana River in the Sehlabathebe National Park, the Moremoholo River, the Senqu River, and the Jordane and Bokong tributaries of the Senqunyane River. The first known specimen was found in the Umkomazana River in Natal, but the species has not been recorded there since the 1930s.

This species' habitat is pools and sheltered parts of rocky rivers in clear, low or moderate gradient mountain streams. Suitable substratum is mainly bedrock, boulders, and rocks of basaltic origin.

History and Conservation Measures

The Maluti minnow is threatened by environmental degradation through overgrazing, road and dam construction, and cultivation of steep gradient slopes that leads to soil erosion. The planned Mohale Dam will flood a large proportion of the minnow's Jordane River and Bokong River habitats. It is expected that the development of this scheme will increase human access to the area and rivers and lead to increased pressures from associated sources, such as stocking with trout. At present trout are only a threat to the Tsoelikana population.

Surveys and research into the biology and ecology of the Maluti minnow were undertaken in the mid-1970s. This work is now being extended and has led to the discovery of previously unknown populations in the Jordane and Bokong rivers. The Maluti minnow has been successfully translocated to a previously unpopulated stretch of river in the

Sehlabathebe National Park. In the winter of 1986, 135 fish were translocated to an uninhabited section of the Bokong River. It is planned that additional sanctuary streams be located and stocked, if necessary. The ecology and biology of the Maluti minnow should be further investigated and a captive breeding program established if necessary. All trout stocking should be prohibited. A suitable conservation strategy for the Maluti minnow should be incorporated into the planning, construction, and management programs for the Mohale Dam.

Modoc sucker

Catostomus microps

Phylum	Chordata
Class	Osteichthyes
Order	Cypriniformes
Family	Catostomidae
Status	Endangered, IUCN
	Endangered, USFWS
Range	California (U.S.A.)

Description and Biology

The Modoc sucker is a muddy greenish brown color above, fading to a lighter shade on the sides, and to white or yellow underneath. The fins are pale yellow-orange, and during spawning season a brighter orange band appears on the sides. It is a dwarf species, averaging approximately 4 in (10-11 cm) in length. The species has a sucker-mouth. It feeds on invertebrates and algae from the stream bottom, but other vegetable matter or mud is often ingested with its food. Spawning takes place in the spring.

Habitat and Current Distribution

This species is now restricted to two small creeks in the Pit River system in California's Modoc County. Its population is estimated at approximately 1,300 fish.

Preferred habitat for the Modoc is shallow pools in clear streams; spawning takes place in creeks or tributaries.

History and Conservation Measures

In 1978, the Modoc sucker was known to inhabit at least eight creeks in the Pit River system. The decline in the species is primarily attributed to the degradation of its habitat. Erosion, brought about by livestock overgrazing, has degraded water quality by increasing siltation in the creeks. The artificial redirection of larger creeks in the Pit River system has resulted in the introduction of the Sacramento sucker *(Catostomus occidentalis)* into the historic range of the Modoc sucker, and hybridization threatens to eliminate the Modoc as a distinct species. Competitors and predators such as the brown trout have also had an impact on the population.

Efforts have been made to reintroduce the Modoc sucker into creeks it formerly inhabited in the Pit River system, and plans have been made to restore parts of its habitat. Genetic analysis is necessary to identify pure strains for reintroduction. Conservation efforts have also been directed toward saving fish stranded in streams which have dried up because of drought.

Shortnose sucker

Chasmistes brevirostris

Phylum	Chordata
Class	Osteichthyes
Order	Cypriniformes
Family	Catostomidae
Status	Endangered, IUCN
	Endangered, USFWS
Range	California, Oregon (U.S.A.)

Description and Biology

The shortnose sucker differs in appearance from other suckers by the oblique positioning of its mouth at the end of its head. Its length can reach as much as 25 in (64 cm). Like related species, it feeds by siphoning food from the bottom of the lake. Spawning occurs in the spring. Individuals of the species have been known to live for 40 years or more.

Habitat and Current Distribution

Distribution is primarily limited to Upper Klamath Lake in south-central Oregon, with smaller populations in the Copco and J.C. Boyle reservoirs in Oregon and in the Clear Lake and Iron Gate reservoirs in north-central California. In 1984, it was estimated that 2,650 shortnose suckers left Upper Klamath Lake to spawn; a marked reduction in numbers was noted in subsequent years.

Preferred habitat is freshwater lakes or reservoirs.

History and Conservation Measures

Once common in the Klamath Basin, the shortnose sucker has experienced a dramatic decline in population. Alteration of habitat caused by the construction of dams is primarily responsible; while the resulting reservoirs provide a suitable habitat, they prevent the species from spawning. The existing population consists almost exclusively of older fish. In addition, the reservoir habitats have allowed the hybridization of the species with Klamath largescale and smallscale suckers.

Attempts to facilitate spawning by installing fish ladders have been ineffective because the shortnose sucker is unable to leap over the rungs. Unless a successful effort is made to reestablish a spawning area for the species, its survival is considered unlikely.

Cui-ui

Chasmistes cujus

Phylum	Chordata
Class	Osteichthyes
Order	Cypriniformes
Family	Catostomidae
Status	Endangered, IUCN
	Endangered, USFWS
	Appendix I, CITES
Range	Nevada (U.S.A.)

Description and Biology

The cui-ui is a medium-sized sucker, reaching up to 27 in (70 cm) in length and weighing up to 5.3 lb (2.4 kg). Like other suckers, it has a large head and thin lips, although they are slanted rather than round. Light yellow-green to dark muddy-brown scales cover the plump body. The sides of breeding males are reddish in color.

The cui-ui spawns on gravel at depths of 8.3-43 in (21-110 cm), with the water temperature between 48°-63°F (9°-17°C). It feeds on small crustaceans and fly larvae. The cui-ui can live up to 45 years.

Habitat and Current Distribution

The cui-ui is endemic to Pyramid Lake in Nevada. It spawns in the Truckee River but swims upstream in the spring. In 1986, 36,000 spawning fish were estimated in the Truckee River.

History and Conservation Measures

The cui-ui has disappeared from much of its former range due to habitat degradation and alteration from damming and channeling activities. The changes in water flow have not only prevented the cui-ui from reaching its spawning grounds, but have also resulted in increased siltation and pollution in the water. The Pyramid River population has survived only because a facility constructed in 1987 has allowed cui-ui and other fish to swim upstream to spawning grounds by bypassing the Truckee River Dam. In the first year the facility was open, 4,000 cui-ui were counted passing through.

Conservation efforts for this fish are directed at rehabilitating essential habitat, protecting and managing the remaining cui-ui population, and creating programs to inform the public about the restoration effort. A research study has recently been completed about the species' life history and requirements.

June sucker

Chasmistes liorus

Phylum	Chordata
Class	Osteichthyes
Order	Cypriniformes
Family	Catostomidae
Status	Endangered, IUCN
	Endangered, USFWS
Range	Utah (U.S.A.)

Description and Biology

The June sucker is similar in appearance to the Utah sucker, but its mouth is located on the underside of its wide head. It seldom exceeds 1.3 in (3 cm) in length. The common name of the species comes from the month in which spawning takes place; little else is known of its biology.

Habitat and Current Distribution

This species is found in Utah Lake, a large, shallow, salty body of water in Utah. Spawning occurs primarily in the Provo River. Population is estimated at less than 1,000 fish.

History and Conservation Measures

Utah Lake reportedly held millions of June suckers in the early 1900s. The population was seriously reduced by drainage of much of the lake for irrigation purposes in the 1930s. Since that time, many non-native species of fish, such as walleyes and white bass, have been introduced into Utah Lake, and competition and predation have further reduced the population of June suckers. A diversion barrier on the Provo River some 5 mi (8 km) upstream from the lake has restricted the spawning range of the species as well. This is a particular cause of concern, since the entire adult population of June suckers seems to be at least 15 years old, and there is speculation that no replacement is taking place.

Efforts have been made to avoid the further reduction of spawning habitat that could be caused by the construction of proposed additional dikes and reservoirs. A management plan is also being implemented to counter the effects of predation.

Thailand giant catfish

Pangasianodon gigas

Phylum	Chordata
Class	Osteichthyes
Order	Siluriformes
Family	Pangasiidae
Status	Vulnerable, IUCN
	Endangered, USFWS
	Appendix I, CITES
Range	Mekong Basin (China; Kampuchea; Laos; Myanmar; Thailand); Vietnam

Description and Biology

This is one of the largest catfish species in the world. It can reach a maximum length of 9.8 ft (3 m) and a weight of up to 660 lb (300 kg). The fish has smooth skin and a single pair of short barbels. The food habits of subadults and juveniles are not known. Adults are toothless and thought to feed on algae grazed from stones in the river bed. Fishermen report a greenish paste-like substance in the stomach of this species.

The location of spawning grounds is poorly known. There is a suggestion of spawning grounds in the Mekong Delta and, perhaps, in adjacent brackish coastal waters at least as far west as Bac Lieu, and possibly in the Tonle Sap in Kampuchea. A second area is located in the mainstream Mekong near Chieng Rai, northern Thailand. Adults are known to migrate upstream in north Thailand in April and May. The Thailand giant catfish has the most rapid growth rate of any catfish and one of the most rapid of any freshwater fish species. Artificially reared fry introduced into a large pond connected to the Chao Phraya in Thailand were observed to reach a weight of 220 lb (100 kg) in just three years. The growth rate in the Mekong River may be even higher.

Habitat and Current Distribution

The Thailand giant catfish is found in the Mekong River and its tributaries. Its range in the Mekong extends from the Vietnam-Kampuchea border through Kampuchea, along the borders of Thailand and Myanmar and into Yunnan Province, China. Occupied tributaries include the Tonle River and Tonle Sap in Kampuchea; the Mun, Songkhram, and Kok rivers in Thailand; and the Yangpi River in China. It was reported to occur in Lake Erh Hai in Yunnan Province, but this seems unlikely as there are rapids on the Yangpi River that would bar movement of fish from the Mekong. Artificially reared fry have also been introduced into Thailand's Chao Phraya river system.

The adults can be found in the mainstream water of large rivers, especially in basins and deep depressions. Some spawning seems to occur in mangrove swamps.

History and Conservation Measures

This species is highly vulnerable to the construction of dams that would prevent upstream migration to spawning areas. The Thailand giant catfish has also probably been the object of traditional fisheries for many centuries. By 1950 the catch had already declined from several hundred to just a few dozen. Fishing is now concentrated at Chieng Kong in Thailand and, since 1984, the catch has increased steadily. The fishing season begins in late March and lasts for one month. In 1967 the Fisheries Department in Thailand launched a study that led to an artificial breeding program. In 1984, 80,000 artificially reared fry were released in the Mekong, Chao Phraya, and other natural waters in Thailand. In 1986 this figure had increased to 300,000. The Department is continuing research to improve breeding techniques, to increase survival rates of fry, and to accelerate the growth rate of fry in captivity. At present it is not clear if the increased catch at Chieng Kong is the result of improved fishing methods or evidence of the success of the reintroduction program.

Swan galaxias

Galaxias fontanus

Phylum	Chordata
Class	Osteichthyes
Order	Salmoniformes
Family	Galaxiidae
Status	Endangered, IUCN
Range	Tasmania (Australia)

Description and Biology

Averaging only about 2.3 in (6.5 cm) long, the Swan galaxias is a tiny freshwater fish with a slender, almost tubular, body. It has a flattened snout, a slightly forked tail fin, and—like other members of the family—lacks scales. Very little information is available about the life cycle or reproductive biology of this species, although it is known to spawn in spring.

Habitat and Current Distribution

This galaxias occurs in eastern Tasmania in the Swan River, from which it gets its common name, and the Macquarie River. It occurs in clear, shallow, slow-to-moderately fast flowing tributaries of these rivers, some of which are spring fed. There are no estimates of population size.

History and Conservation Measures

Little is known of the natural history of this tiny fish or of its historical distribution or population size. Its status is precarious because of its limited distribution, the presence of introduced brown trout, and nearby forestry and logging operations. Conservation actions include the creation of protected reserves, including headwater and catchment areas; increasing the effectiveness of natural barriers to upstream movement of trout; and translocation of breeding populations.

Danube salmon

Hucho hucho

Phylum . . . . Chordata
Class . . . . Osteichthyes
Order . . . . Salmoniformes
Family . . . . Salmonidae
Status . . . . Endangered, IUCN
Range . . . . Danube catchment area (Austria; Czech Republic; France; Germany; Italy; Moldavia (?); Poland; Romania; Slovakia; Switzerland; Ukraine; Yugoslavia)

Description and Biology

The Danube salmon has a slender cigar-shaped body with a broad mouth and dense arrangement of teeth. Males are slightly more vivid in color than females, and have an area of dark pink on the rear of the belly during spawning. Females have silvery bellies. This is a large fish that can reach a length of over 5.9 ft (1.8 m) and a weight of 154 lb (70 kg). It is the largest of all salmonids. Adults are highly predatory, consuming fish, amphibians, reptiles, waterfowl, and small mammals.

Spawning takes place on the gravel bottoms of mountain torrents in spring. The first spawning occurs at 3-4 years of age in males and 4-5 years in females. The growth rate of young is very fast, with individuals reaching a length of about 51 in (13 cm) at the end of their first year and 11.8 in (30 cm) at the end of their second. At five years they can measure 21.7 in (55 cm) in length. Juveniles live in small tributaries and, as they grow, move to larger ones.

Habitat and Current Distribution

Historically the Danube salmon was rather common in almost all rivers of the Danube watershed, including the Danube, where it occurred as far downstream as the Iron Gate Gorge and even the Danube delta. In recent times, attempts have been made to introduce Danube salmon to rivers to the west of its natural range, such as the Thames, Rhine, Elbe, and tributaries of the Vistula. Most of these attempts seem to have failed. There are now only a few rivers in Austria, the Czech Republic, Slovakia, and Germany where it reproduces naturally. It is thought to be common in less than one-third of its former range. Moreover, in most rivers its present distribution is not continuous but fragmented; populations in some rivers have become isolated. In general, it has disappeared from the lower stretches of all rivers and is now limited to their submountain zones.

The Danube salmon is a cold water, exclusively

Danube salmon.

freshwater salmonid occurring mainly in running waters and rarely in lakes and impoundments. It prefers streams that are rich in oxygen, with alternating rapid sections and deep pools, and where the bed is composed mainly of pebbles. When temperature and oxygen conditions are right, it may also inhabit the river's lowland zone as far down as the estuary.

History and Conservation Measures

The most significant threat to the Danube salmon comes from habitat degradation. This has resulted from canalization of rivers, construction of dams, the release of industrial waste waters and municipal sewage, eutrophication, deforestation, and the expansion of arable land. Overfishing, including poaching, is a secondary factor in the species' decline.

In Slovakia, after World War II, fishing for Danube salmon was forbidden until 1949. Since that time fishing has required a permit. Despite this restriction, and a shortening of the fishing season, numbers have continued to decline. The success of stocking programs has been limited due to the difficulty in rearing the species. In general, no protective measure, except education, has been effective because of the continuous destruction of its habitat. It is recommended that water purification plants be built, the use of pesticides and artificial fertilizers be controlled, stocking rates be increased, and hatcheries be built on each river containing Danube salmon. In Austria, an Alluvial Zone National Park has been planned on the Danube from Vienna to the border with the Czech Republic. This will establish the legal framework for stopping habitat degradation and should provide funding to improve ecological conditions along the river.

Pupfish

Cyprinodon spp.

Phylum	Chordata
Class	Osteichthyes
Order	Cyprinodontiformes
Family	Cyprinodontidae
Status	Endangered, IUCN (*C. bovinus, C. elegans, C. fontinalis, C. meeki, C. pachycephalus, C. macularius* ssp., *C. radiosus*)
	Vulnerable, IUCN (*C. alvarezi, C. beltrani, C. diabolis, C. labiosus, C. macrolepis, C. maya, C. nazas, C. pecosensis, C. simus, C. verecundus, C. nevadensis* ssp.)
	Rare, IUCN (*C. atrorus, C. bifasciatus, C. tularosa, C. salinus* ssp.)
	Endangered, USFWS
Range	Mexico; Nevada, Texas, California, Arizona (U.S.A.)

Description and Biology

There are at least 35 species and subspecies of *Cyprinodon*, most of which are threatened with extinction. These fish range in size from 0.8 in (2 cm) to 3 in (7.5 cm), and coloration varies with species and subspecies. Some are brightly multi-colored like the *C. radiosus* while others are dull gray or brown. Diet is composed mainly of aquatic insects and plant matter. All pupfish are opportunistic feeders and can even feed on blue-green alga (cyanobacterium). *C. diabolis* is thought to feed only on algae, and *C. radiosus* includes crustaceans in its diet. Spawning depends on the temperature of the habitat, but occurs for most species in the spring.

Habitat and Current Distribution

C. nevadensis and *C. diabolis* are endemic to the Ash Meadows Region, a small area of wetlands in the Mojave Desert northwest of Las Vegas, Nevada. *C. nevadensis mionectes* occurs in 10 spring areas within Ash Meadows. *C. nevadensis pectoralis* occurs in six small springs west of Devil's Hole, where all of its habitats are isolated from other aquatic environments. *C. diabolis* is restricted to a limestone cave on the east-central border of Ash Meadows. The two *C. nevadensis* subspecies inhabit warm springs, while *C. diabolis* spends most of its time on a narrow shelf of rocks in Devil's Hole.

C. elegans and *C. bovinus* both occur in Texas. *C. elegans* is restricted to Giffin and San Solomon

Cyprinodon macularius.

Springs in Reeves County, while *C. bovinus* is known only from Diamond Y Spring and Leon Creek in Pecos County. There are no estimates of population size for either species. Both of these pupfish inhabit shallow regions, but *C. elegans* occurs in freshwater and *C. bovinus* in salt water.

C. radiosus occurs in four springs in Fish Slough, Mono County, California, where it is found along the edges of pools or marshes with clear water and abundant vegetation. It may also occur in Mexico. There are no estimates of population size.

C. macularius occurs in California, where it is found in irrigation ditches, creeks such as San Felipe Creek in Imperial County and Salt Creek in Riverside County, and marshes such as San Sebastian Marsh in Imperial County; in Arizona it is found in Quitobaquito Spring in the Organ Pipe Cactus National Monument; and in Mexico it probably survives in the Colorado River, the drainage area of the Rio Sonoyta, and the Santa Clara Slough. This pupfish can survive in very warm and very salty waters. There are no estimates of population size.

History and Conservation Measures

All *Cyprinodon* species, to some extent, are threatened by habitat alteration, competition from introduced species, and predation. The Ash Meadows species and subspecies have primarily been affected by changes in the water level due to increased human demand for water from the aquifer. Other species are threatened by drying and/or flooding of their habitat from irrigation and damming activities. Introduced predators and competitors such as mosquito fish, crayfish, bullfrogs, large-mouth bass, and snails further threaten the pupfish population. In some cases, extensive hybridization with introduced minnows has occurred.

Conservation priorities for these fish include the eradication of all non-native plants and animals, restoration of former water levels and spring flows, and protection of essential habitat from human disturbances. A research program has been initiated to determine the life history patterns of endemic fish and aquatic invertebrates and to determine the impact of exotic species on their survival rate. Captive-breeding for certain species has also been implemented.

Pygmy sculpin

Cottus pygmaeus

Phylum	Chordata
Class	Osteichthyes
Order	Scorpaeniformes
Family	Cottidae
Status	Endangered, IUCN
	Threatened, USFWS
Range	Alabama (U.S.A.)

Description and Biology

The pygmy sculpin is a small, freshwater fish with a large head. Average length is around 1.8 in (45 mm). While all pygmy sculpins generally have two or three dorsal saddles and mottled or spotted fins, coloration varies with sex, age, and breeding condition. Juveniles have a black head, a grayish black body, and three light colored saddles; mature fish have white heads with scant dark spotting, a lighter body, and two grayish black saddles. Breeding males become almost black and have a reddish orange edge along the dorsal fin; females become darker while breeding. Diet includes isopods or other small aquatic crustaceans, snails, and a variety of insects.

Although spawning peaks in the spring and summer months, it is possible at any time during the year. A type of communal nest is formed when one or more females deposit their eggs on the underside of a rock. The nest is thought to be guarded by a male.

Habitat and Current Distribution

This species only occurs in Coldwater Spring, including the spring run and pool formed by dams, in Calhoun County, Alabama. Population is estimated at 720-1,555 individuals in the spring run and 7,600-8,125 individuals in the spring pool.

There are large mats of vegetation in the spring pool and along the edges of the run, and both have sand and gravel bottoms. Water temperature is constant at 61°-64°F (16°-18°C).

History and Conservation Measures

This sculpin, which was discovered in 1968, is especially vulnerable because of its very restricted range. Because the only known population is at one location, the species could become extinct if a natural or human-induced disaster occurs at the site. Aside from the possibility of a cataclysmic episode, there is a more long-term hazard threatening the species: there is now evidence that the subsurface aquifer for Coldwater Spring is becoming contaminated.

The first conservation priority for the pygmy sculpin is the protection of its habitat and of the surface and subsurface drainage systems that support it. The establishment of additional populations in other suitable habitat would be an important safeguard against extinction of the species.

Eastern freshwater cod

Maccullochella ikei

Phylum	Chordata
Class	Osteichthyes
Order	Perciformes
Family	Percichthyidae
Status	Endangered, IUCN
Range	Northeast New South Wales (Australia)

Description and Biology

This large freshwater cod averages around 2.2 lb (1 kg), although it once averaged almost 50 lb (22 kg). Very little information is available about the life cycle of this fish in the wild. Spawning has been established in captivity, and a large number of fingerlings have been produced.

Habitat and Current Distribution

The eastern freshwater cod is mostly restricted to the tributaries of the Clarence River, including the Nymboida and Mann Rivers. It is found where boulders or fallen timbers provide cover. There are no estimates of population size.

History and Conservation Measures

Once also known from the Richmond River, this fish has experienced a massive decline in range and population. Its decline and extinction from much of its range is attributed to pollution of the rivers as a result of mining operations and to the destruction of natural habitat through clearing of riparian vegetation. There is a total ban on fishing of this species. Fingerlings have been stocked into several areas in the Clarence and Richmond Rivers.

Fountain darter

Etheostoma fonticola

Phylum	Chordata
Class	Osteichthyes
Order	Perciformes
Family	Percidae
Status	Endangered, IUCN
	Endangered, USFWS
Range	Texas (U.S.A.)

Description and Biology

This small darter usually does not exceed 1.5 in (23 mm) in length. Its reddish brown coloration is accented by darker margins along the scales on its sides; its back is covered with fine specks and dark blotches. There are also dark lines along the middle of the sides, three small dark spots on the base of the tail, and dark bars in front of, below, and behind the eye. The black dorsal fin has a broad, red band. True to its name, the darter stays very still until prey has moved within an inch (2.5 cm) and then moves quickly to capture it. It feeds during the day on aquatic vertebrates, taking only live, moving prey. Nematodes and leeches are common parasites.

Although spawning takes place throughout the year, it peaks in late winter to early spring and then again in August. Eggs are deposited on vegetation such as moss or algae and abandoned by the parents.

Habitat and Current Distribution

The largest population of fountain darters occurs in a 2-mi (3-km) area of the San Marcos River in Hays County, Texas, below the confluence with the Blanco River. A smaller, reintroduced population occurs in the upper Comal River in Comal County, Texas. The population in the San Marcos River was estimated in 1976 at 103,000; more recent estimates range from about 1,000 to over 10,000. The population in the Comal River is smaller than that in the San Marcos River.

Preferred habitat for the fountain darter is clear, clean water with a constant water temperature of 70°-73°F (21°-23°C) and abundant vegetation along the stream bed.

History and Conservation Measures

The first known specimen was collected in the San Marcos River in 1884; the first collection in the Comal River was in 1891. The species has been reported from other localities in Texas and from Arkansas, but these reports are believed to be misidentifications. The last collection from the Comal River was in 1954, apparently because the Comal Springs ceased flowing for five months in 1956. A captive stock was maintained in New Mexico for a time, but that operation ceased after the darter was successfully reintroduced into the Comal River in 1975 and 1976.

Dams built in the early 1900s and effluent discharged from a sewage treatment plant have affected this fish's habitat. The primary threat to the species, however, is the increasing demand from local people for water, which is depleting the underground aquifer. Conservation measures for this darter and for other endangered or threatened species in the area are aimed at preserving the ecosystem. Studies of the effects of introduced species have been initiated, and groups of aquifer water users have formed to work on developing water-use plans that will maintain critical spring flows.

Totoaba seatrout

Totoaba macdonaldi

Phylum	Chordata
Class	Osteichthyes
Order	Perciformes
Family	Sciaenidae
Status	Endangered, IUCN
	Endangered, USFWS
	Appendix I, CITES
Range	Gulf of California (Mexico)

Description and Biology

This large fish has a long, compressed body. It can reach a length of almost 6.5 ft (2 m) and a weight of up to 220 lb (100 kg). Adults are silvery blue on the upper half of the body and dusky silver below. The totoaba is a carnivorous fish that feeds on a wide variety of prey including fish, crabs, shrimps, and other crustaceans.

This species spends much of its life in the deeper waters of the Gulf of California, spawning in the areas around the mouth of the Colorado River. Totoaba usually arrive at the spawning grounds in mid-February and spawning may take place from then until June. Young fish remain near the Colorado River mouth for up to two years until they begin a southward migration to join the parent population. The fish may reach about 50 lb (23 kg) in weight by the age of six years. Their lifespan may be more than 35 years.

Habitat and Current Distribution

This species is endemic to the Mexican waters of the Gulf of California. It was formerly found throughout most of the Gulf, but is now confined to the extreme northern end. Each year adults migrate northward along the eastern coast of the Gulf of California to spawn in the shallower, brackish waters around the mouth of the Colorado River. After spawning the adults move southward along the western coast of the Gulf, moving into the deeper waters in the warmer months.

The totoaba requires a variety of habitats including the colder, deeper waters of the Gulf and areas of reduced salinity around the mouth of the Colorado. The fish congregate in submarine tidal channels that lead south from the delta. Juveniles appear to prefer silty substrate with little sand.

History and Conservation Measures

The factors responsible for the decline of this species appear to be a combination of overfishing and habitat alteration. The totoaba formerly supported an important commercial and sport fishing industry. Annual yield peaked at over 2,200 tons (2,000 tonnes) in 1942, but had fallen to just under 66 tons (60 tonnes) by 1975. A total ban on fishing was declared by the Mexican Government in 1975 and in 1976 the species was placed on Appendix I of the Convention on International Trade in Endangered Species of Wild Fauna and Flora (CITES). In 1979 the totoaba was listed as endangered under the U.S. Endangered Species Act. Overfishing of adults occurred during their annual migrations and young fish were being decimated by shrimp trawls in the northern Gulf. In addition, damming of the Colorado River and increased water extraction from its lower reaches resulted in little, if any, flow reaching the Gulf of California. As a result, the only spawning ground for the totoaba became increasingly saline. The decreased flow also reduced the available nursery grounds as the marshes were no longer flooded. In 1989 the totoaba was still thought to be threatened by illegal fishing and accidental catches.

In 1985 a conservation program, Operation Totoaba, was initiated to examine the species' ecology and its potential for captive breeding. Research has shown that apparently over 90 percent of juveniles die in the trawl nets of shrimp vessels operating in the northern area of the Gulf of California. The long-term preservation and enhancement of the totoaba gene pool depends on whether the species can be bred in captivity. If successful, fry could be released to breed among wild stocks and help restore a once viable commercial fishery.

Lake Victoria cichlids

Haplochromine spp.
(250-300 species)

Phylum	Chordata
Class	Osteichthyes
Order	Perciformes
Family	Cichlidae
Status	Indeterminate, IUCN
Range	Lake Victoria (Kenya; Tanzania; Uganda)

Description and Biology

The distinguishing features of cichlids include scales on the head and body and a single nostril on each side. Most species do not exceed 12 in (30 cm) in length. Adults usually have a series of clear spots called "egg spots" or "egg dummies" on the anal fin. These spots assist in the fertilization of the eggs. Courting males generally become darker with the chest and pelvic fins often becoming black.

Haplocromines have developed a wide range of feeding habits. Sources of food include fish, crustaceans, molluscs, insects, algae, zooplankton, and phytoplankton.

The breeding style of cichlids usually involves pair-formation, nest building and the guarding of eggs and young. The female picks up the eggs and broods them in her mouth for a period of 10-14 days. After hatching, young are allowed to forage outside of the female's mouth, returning at any sign of danger. When not courting, haplocromines stay in loose-knit groups and spend most of their time grazing and foraging.

Habitat and Current Distribution

With a surface area of around 26,635 sq mi (69,000 sq km), Lake Victoria is the world's largest tropical lake. It is relatively shallow with a maximum depth of around 260 ft (80 m). Coastal habitats are characterized by rock, cobble, sand, detrital mud, and submerged or partially submerged vegetation. Habitats deeper in the lake are dominated by soft organic mud. Over much of the lake, water below the level of 65-100 ft (20-30 m) is de-oxygenated and uninhabitable by fish. Prior to the 1980s, around 300 species of endemic haplocromine cichlids were thought to inhabit Lake Victoria. Different habitats within Lake Victoria contain their own communities of cichlids.

History and Conservation Measures

Lake Victoria cichlids have been and are being threatened by overfishing, the introduction of exotic species, deleterious land-use practices, and pollution. The lake itself has suffered from oxygen depletion. Overfishing in the early 1900s led to the rapid depletion of some fish. Beginning in the 1950s, Nile perch (*Lates niloticus*) were introduced into the lake. This species remained a minor component of the fauna until there was a rapid population explosion in the 1980s. It is thought that Nile perch consumed many native fish species. In 1978, haplocromines constituted about 80 percent of the biomass in Lake Victoria, while Nile perch constituted about 2 percent. By 1986, Nile perch constituted more than 80 percent of the biomass in the Tanzanian area of the lake with the native fishes forming a small part of the remaining 20 percent. An estimated 200 haplocromine species have disappeared, probably as a result of a major alteration that took place in the physical environment of the lake. From being relatively homogenous, the lake has become almost permanently stratified, with local upwellings of anoxic water that cause extensive fish kills. Pollution has included sedimentation from clearance of forested slopes and riverine vegetation as well as eutrophication from agricultural runoff.

At present, over 30 species of haplocromines are being held in captivity. A Species Survival Plan has been initiated as part of a larger conservation effort for local fauna; the program will eventually include lakeside propagation of endangered native fish species, re-introduction to peripheral lakes within the Lake Victoria basin and, ultimately, re-introduction into Lake Victoria. An agreement has been signed by Kenya, Tanzania, and Uganda to establish a Lake Victoria commission to coordinate lake management and conservation.

Coelacanth

Latimeria chalumnae

Phylum	Chordata
Class	Osteichthyes
Order	Coelacanthiformes
Family	Latimeriidae
Status	Vulnerable, IUCN
	Appendix I, CITES
Range	Comoro Islands; Mozambique; South Africa

Description and Biology

The only living member of an order that was abundant 80-370 million years ago, the coelacanth is a stocky fish with large, rough scales and muscular lobes at the base of its fins (except for the first dorsal fin). Up to 6.5 ft (1.9 m) in length and 22 lb (9.8 kg) in weight, the coelacanth lives on steep, rocky drop-offs and feeds on lantern fish, cuttlefish, and other reef fish. Like its relatives, the lungfishes, the coelacanth can sense electric fields using an electroreceptive organ in its snout. When presented with an electric field, it assumes an unusual "headstanding" posture, possibly a technique by which to detect prey hiding in the sea bed.

Coelacanths are ovoviviparous, giving birth to fully-formed young after a gestation period of over 12 months. Between 5 and 26 offspring are born at a time, averaging 15 in (37 cm) at birth. Juvenile coelacanths probably live in caves and hunt at night and are, therefore, rarely seen or caught. Coelacanths can live up to 80 years, reaching sexual maturity at about 12-15 years.

Because it so closely resembles an ancestor that has been extinct for 80 million years, the coelacanth has been described as a "living fossil." It has a number of unique features that set it apart from most living fish; some of these features have prompted scientists to postulate that the fish was a "missing link" between a group of fossil fish called rhipidistians and the hypothetical tetrapod which gave rise to land-dwelling vertebrates. For example, the coelacanth's fleshy fins can be rotated very widely and can be moved about with a high degree of independence; this would be expected from a tetrapod progenitor. Moreover, when the coelacanth swims, its pelvic and pectoral fins provide stabilization by moving in tandem as crossed pairs: the left pelvic moves with the right pectoral and vice-versa. This pattern is the same as that seen in a moving tetrapod.

However, the idea that the coelacanth was the closest evolutionary precursor to tetrapods was ultimately dismissed because the fish does not possess a number of characteristics that would be expected from such a creature. For instance, it does not have a stocky vertebral column and strong ribs, and it lacks internal nostrils. It has a very primitive heart, resembling that hypothesized for early fish, which lacks any adaptations that would be needed to circulate blood to a primitive lung. The lungfishes, close kin of the coelacanth, are now thought to probably be more closely related to the tetrapods.

Habitat and Current Distribution

Although the first coelacanth was captured near the mouth of the Chalumna River, South Africa, most subsequent records of this species are from the

Coelacanth.

Comoro Islands, an archipelago along the east African coast between Mozambique and Madagascar. Most recent specimens have been captured off Grand Comoro and Anjouan Islands; the vast majority of these have been found near the western coast of Grand Comoro Island. A study conducted in 1989 using a submersible craft estimated the total population at about 210. In August 1991 a large female coelacanth was caught off the coast of central Mozambique by a Japanese trawler. This specimen contained 26 near-term yolksac juveniles, five times more young than previously recorded.

Coelacanths inhabit caves and steep, rocky volcanic drop-offs at depths of 400-1,000 ft (120-300 m), although some have been recorded at depths of 2,297 ft (700 m). The fish congregate in caves during the day and emerge at night, hunting for food individually over stretches of coastline up to 5 miles (8 km) in length; coelacanth distribution appears to be related to the presence of these "roosting" caves.

History and Conservation Measures

In 1938, an extremely unusual fish caught in the nets of a fisherman trawling on the eastern Cape of South Africa was identified by ichthyologist J. L. B. Smith as a coelacanth, previously thought extinct for 80 million years. As it turned out, fishermen 1,000 mi

(1600 km) away in the Comoro Islands, while fishing for other species, had been catching small numbers of coelacanths for years without drawing the attention of the scientific community.

Because of their rarity and value as "living fossils," museums, aquariums, and private collectors prize coelacanths. When discoveries were made, high prices were paid for the catch. The number of coelacanths caught per year increased from 1.9 in the 1950s to 4.9 in the 1960s, 4.8 in the 1970s and 4.0 in the 1980s, and averaged 4.39 for the period between 1952 and 1990. The years in which most coelacanth catches were recorded were 1986 (11 specimens), 1965 (10) and 1973 and 1974 (8 each). The catch rate in the 1990s has been 3.5 per year, a decline from previous decades perhaps due to the protection it was afforded by CITES. (In 1989, a team from Japan's largest aquarium attempted to capture a pair of coelacanths; though they failed, the alarm raised by their attempt prompted the CITES to grant the fish Appendix I status, banning its trade between member nations.)

The development of an effective conservation program for the coelacanth has begun with studies on its distribution, abundance, feeding behavior, and community structure. These field studies have been complemented by internationally coordinated laboratory studies on morphology, physiology, fetal anatomy, growth rates, and sensory efficiency. A demographic model has also been proposed in an attempt to determine breeding rates, age-profile, mortality rates, and longevity. In addition, a search has been initiated on the South African coast to determine whether there are coelacanths living in the region.

In recent years, a coelacanth black market to the Orient has arisen based on the notion that fluid from the fish's notochord promotes longevity; this dangerous development must be met with vigilant enforcement of provisions banning the trade of the coelacanth. The Coelacanth Conservation Council, established in Moroni, Grand Comoro in 1987, with the Secretariat at the JLB Smith Institute of Ichthyology in South Africa, serves as a focal organization for coelacanth protection efforts, coordinating research, maintaining an inventory of catches and bibliography, publishing a newsletter, and promoting public education programs throughout the world.

Molluscs

Tulotoma snail

Tulotoma magnifica

Phylum	Mollusca
Class	Gastropoda
Order	Mesogastropoda
Family	Viviparidae
Status	Endangered, IUCN
	Endangered, USFWS
Range	Alabama (U.S.A.)

Description and Biology

Also known as the Alabama live-bearing snail, the Tulotoma snail possesses a round, brownish black shell somewhat larger than a golf ball with knobby outgrowths that run along spiral lines. The species can be distinguished from other freshwater snails not only by its size and embellishments, but by its diagonal opening and concave edges as well.

Little is known about the life cycle and habits of the Tulotoma snail.

Habitat and Current Distribution

The Tulotoma snail occurs in a small stretch of the Coosa River in Elmore County, Alabama, that runs from the Jordan Dam to the small town of Wetumpka. It has also been recorded from four tributaries of the Coosa River: Kelly Creek in St. Clair County and Shelby County, Ohatchee Creek in Calhoun County, and Weogufka Creek and Hatchet Creek in Coosa County. No population estimates currently exist.

This species usually clings to the bottom of large rocks and boulders in cool, well-oxygenated waters that flow freely.

History and Conservation Measures

The Tulotoma snail was first described in 1834, when it was identified as *Paludina magnifica*. In 1840, naturalists reclassified it as a member of the subgenus *Tulotoma*, along with three other species found in the Alabama-Coosa River system. However, scientists have since determined that these four species of *Tulotoma* are in fact one species, *T. magnifica*.

Originally, this snail inhabited the Alabama River and the Coosa River as well as several of its tributaries. It was known from a stretch of the Alabama River near the town of Clairborne and from one of its tributaries, Chilachee Creek in Dallas County. In the Coosa River system, the species' range encompassed almost 100 miles (160 km) of the river, extending from St. Clair County to the confluence of the Tallapoosa River. Today, the species remains in only 2 percent of its original range on the main rivers and in only 50 percent of their tributaries.

The decline of the Tulotoma snail is primarily due to habitat loss resulting from the dredging and damming of the Alabama and Coosa Rivers. Dredging of the Alabama began in the nineteenth century and continues today; also, numerous dams completed in the 1960s now control water flow on the river. On the

Coosa River, six dams constructed between 1914 and 1966 have destroyed almost all suitable habitat on the main channel and significantly altered the habitat of many of its tributaries.

No specific conservation measures regarding the Tulotoma snail have been implemented.

Socorro springsnail

Pyrgulopsis neomexicana

Phylum	Mollusca
Class	Gastropoda
Order	Mesogastropoda
Family	Hydrobiidae
Status	Endangered, IUCN
	Endangered, USFWS
Range	New Mexico (U.S.A.)

Description and Biology

The minuscule Socorro springsnail measures only 0.1 in (2.5 mm) in length. Its elongated, spiral shell is light tan, and its body and head are black to dark gray. The tentacles are also dark at their base, though they become pale gray at the tips. An operculum, or a flap-like structure that closes the shell when the snail is retracted, is present on the posterior of the foot. Like other members of the species *Pyrgulopsis*, the male Socorro springsnail is distinguished by structural aspects of its sexual organ.

Little is known about the life cycle and habits of the Socorro springsnail. However, scientists do know that it uses gills to breath and that females lay their eggs during the spring and early summer. The species feeds on algae and organic debris on the water surface.

Habitat and Current Distribution

The Socorro springsnail is known from a single natural spring in Socorro County, New Mexico. However, the main source of the spring has been diverted for human use, and only one free-flowing source re-mains, where the species now survives. This source pool measures less than 3 ft (1 m), and its outflow stream runs approximately 8 ft (2.5 m) towards an irrigation ditch.

The Socorro springsnail prefers slow-flowing waters located near thermal springs. They occur on stones, in the top layer of organic mud at the bottom of the stream or pool, or in aquatic vegetation. The total population is estimated to be about 5,000 individuals.

History and Conservation Measures

Naturalists first described the Socorro springsnail in 1916 when it was discovered in several natural springs west of Socorro, New Mexico.

Today, the species is in great danger of becoming extinct due to its extremely limited distribution. Any changes to the source pool and stream, such as pumping, contamination, or vandalism, could result in the extinction of the species. No specific conservation measures have yet been taken. The snail occurs on private property; however, the owners did not protest the species listing as Endangered.

Oahu tree snails

Achatinella spp.

Phylum	Mollusca
Class	Gastropoda
Order	Stylommatophora
Family	Achatinellidae
Status	Endangered, IUCN (24 species)
	Extinct, IUCN (17 species)
	Endangered, USFWS
	Appendix I, CITES
Range	Hawaii (U.S.A.)

Description and Biology

Shells of the adult snails of this genus average in size from 0.5 in (1.25 cm) to just over 1 in (2.7 cm) in length. These shells typically have smooth, glossy surfaces, but some are slightly sculpted. They are variously patterned in shades of orange, yellow, brown, green, gray, black, and white, and vary immensely in size and shape. The number of shell whorls can also vary, ranging from five to seven. The genus is characterized by a small tooth (lamella) which protrudes from the central column (columella) of the shell.

Tree snails are arboreal and mostly nocturnal, although they may become active in the daytime during and after heavy rains. They graze at night on leaf surfaces for microscopic algae and fungi. The radula of *Achatinella* spp. has a vast number of very tiny teeth which overlap closely and are used for scraping algae and fungi from leaf surfaces. This action does not cause any damage to the leaves. Each snail has both male and female sexual organs, but they cannot fertilize themselves. They breed throughout the year, and can bear up to four young each year.

Habitat and Current Distribution

These snails are found in native and introduced forests of the Koolau and Waianae mountain ranges in Oahu, Hawaii. They occur from elevations of about 980 ft (300 m) in the Koolau range to just over 3,600 ft (1,100 m) in the Waianae range. No figures are available for surviving populations, as there have been few recent comprehensive surveys of most of these species.

Native shrubs and trees are among the preferred habitats of these snails. During the day they usually rest on branches, trunks, or undersides of leaves. They are relatively sedentary, with some individuals spending their entire life in a single tree. While some species prefer certain types of trees, they will not necessarily be found in every tree of that species.

History and Conservation Measures

Snails of this genus were once found in lowland valleys, coastal plains, and near the sea at Kahuku. Habitat destruction and the introduction of exotic species of plants and animals have drastically reduced most populations and many have become extinct. In 1970, 14 of the 41 recognized species were declared extinct and another 25 were declared rare and endangered. In 1993, 17 species were presumed extinct and 24 species endangered.

Some destruction or alteration of forest is presumed to have been the result of the activities of the first Polynesian settlers who probably arrived between 500-600 A.D. Later visitors and settlers introduced cattle, goats, sheep, horses, and many other animals to the island after its rediscovery in 1778. By 1850, some tree snail species at lower elevations were already threatened with extinction due to trampling by cattle and destruction of forested areas. As much as 85 percent of the original forest had been cleared for agriculture or radically altered by 1978, especially at altitudes below 1,300 ft (400 m). Native forest is now primarily limited to higher altitudes.

Overcollecting has also contributed to the decline of these species. Many local populations of snails were eliminated between 1850-1900, a period known as "land shell fever," when collectors harvested hundreds of thousands of shells. Some accessible populations, near hiking trails, are still susceptible to collecting, because of increasing pressure to use remaining native forest for recreational purposes.

Before humans inhabited the island, tree snails probably had no significant predators. Several introduced species, particularly flatworms and rats, now prey heavily on the snails, posing a significant threat to the genus because of its low rate of reproduction. The most serious potential predator is the carnivorous snail (*Euglandina rosea*), introduced from Florida to Hawaii between 1955 and 1956 in an attempt to control populations of the African snail (*Achatina fulica*), which was considered a plant pest. The carnivorous snail has proven to be a voracious predator on other species of snails.

A number of conservation measures have been recommended, including the establishment of snail sanctuaries, elimination of predators, and development of propagation programs. Surveys to determine population and distribution are necessary, as are studies of life history and ecological requirements. Three reserves have been established in the Waianae Mountains that include *Achatinella* populations, but protection of further habitat areas is essential. Efforts have begun to establish a captive breeding program, with plans to expand the program to include all species that can be located in the wild.

Madeiran endemic snails

Phylum	Mollusca
Class	Gastropoda
Order	Stylommatophora
Family	Pupillidae, Helicidae
Status	Endangered, IUCN (15 species)
	Vulnerable, IUCN (18 species)
	Rare, IUCN (22 species)
	Indeterminate, IUCN (2 species)
Range	Madeira (Portugal)

Description and Biology

The Madeiran archipelago has one of the richest endemic land-snail faunas in Europe and in the world. A high proportion of these taxa are considered to be under threat (48 of 198 taxa). Like many island faunas the current species diversity has apparently resulted from radiation of a few colonizing taxa. This means that the majority of the endemic species fall in two families, the Pupillidae (15 percent) and the Helicidae, subfamily Geomitrinae (40 percent).

The Pupillidae is a family of small land snails (smaller than 0.2 in [5 mm] in size) which are found throughout the world. It contains the genus *Leiostyla* which has two principal centers of endemism, Madeira and the Caucasus Mountains. The endemic species found on the Madeiran islands have colonized a wide variety of different habitats and show ornate shell sculpture.

The subfamily Geomitrinae (Family Helicidae) comprises the highest proportion of endemic land snails on the islands. These species are strikingly beautiful with very ornate shell sculpture and a wide variety of color patterns, far more than the majority of their European relatives. These species range in size from 0.2 in (5 mm) to 1.2 in (30 mm). They too occupy distinctive habitats and often have small geographical ranges.

Habitat and Current Distribution

The Madeiran archipelago consists of three island groups, all within 25 mi (40 km) of each other. The largest, most mountainous island, Madeira, rises abruptly from the sea to heights of 6,100 ft (1,860 m). This high central area has a distinctive temperate rain forest. The south side of Madeira is in the rain shadow and has a drier climate reaching extremes on the peninsula to the east where there is no forest cover. The southern side is now the region with the most cultivation, and natural vegetation survives only on steep slopes which are unsuitable for farming. The islands of the Desertas and Porto Santo are less mountainous, and today have dry grassland habitats.

Many of the endemic snail species which are considered threatened have small geographical ranges. Each island has a distinct and different fauna, with little overlap between them. The island of Porto Santo has the highest number of endemic taxa in relation to its area due to the number of geographical subspecies on the offshore islets. At present there is concern that some 16 species are extinct, since they have not been recorded since the last century. These were only recorded a few times in the last century and include species from sites on the south coast of Madeira where there has been much development in the last century.

The land snails are most threatened on the south coast of Madeira, the main island of Porto Santo, and the Desertas Islands (Deserte Grande, Bugio, Cima) and the islets off the Pta de Saô Lourenço. On the Desertas much damage has been done to the low scrub cover by introduced goats and rabbits. The goats have been removed from the Ilheu dos Desmbarcourdes and control is being implemented on Deserte Grande where the vegetation has been completely degraded leading to soil erosion.

On Porto Santo many of the endemic species have adapted to living in grassland and on rocky slopes, but some of these now have very restricted distributions. These include *Discula testudinalis*, a large species with only one population on the main island. Other spectacular species of *Discula*, such as *D. turricula*, are restricted to the offshore islets. Some populations of land snails like *D. rotula* appear to have suffered from rodent predation and these populations require monitoring to determine the long-term effects of predation. Fossil evidence suggests that threatened species such as *Idiomela* (*Helix*) *subplicata* formerly had more extensive ranges over Porto Santo, but now are restricted to the southwest islet of Ilheu de Baixo.

History and Conservation Measures

These islands, when first colonized by the Portuguese in the fifteenth century, were reported to be covered with forest. The dry islands of Porto Santo and the Desertas had endemic vegetation composed of dry temperate rain forest and scrubby bush.

Endemic snails living on these islands have very restricted distributions and are vulnerable to alteration of their habitats. Such disturbance has arisen historically through forest clearance and overgrazing by domestic animals and rabbits; more recent threats include development related to tourism.

The recent efforts to formulate conservation plans for the Madeiran Islands have concentrated on the establishment of national parks in the temperate rain forest regions of north and central Madeira and the protection of the Desertas Islands. These regions include habitats for some of the threatened land snails. The area of greatest concern is the dry regions of southern Madeira, such as Ponta de Garajau and Cabo Girao, which are under pressure from development. Endemic threatened land snails such as *Discula tabellata* are found there.

Quarrying of one of the more important fossil sites for land molluscs on the Pta de Saô Lourenço has been halted with the involvement of local people and especially local schools, and it is hoped that these efforts will be extended to other regions. In addition to the species listed as endangered, vulnerable, or rare by the IUCN, 22 species of Madeiran land snails are listed in the Bern Convention and in the European Union Habitats Directive.

Marsh snails

Vertigo angustior

Vertigo genesii

Vertigo geyerii

Phylum	Mollusca
Class	Gastropoda
Order	Stylommatophora
Family	Vertiginidae
Status	Vulnerable, IUCN (*V. genesii*; *V. geyerii*)
	Insufficiently Known, IUCN (*V. angustior*)
Range	Armenia; Austria; Azerbaijan; Belarus; Belgium; Czech Republic; Denmark; Estonia; Finland; France; Georgia; Germany; Hungary; Ireland; Italy; Latvia; Liechtenstein; Lithuania; Netherlands; Norway; Poland; Romania; Russia; Slovakia; Sweden; Switzerland; Ukraine; United Kingdom

Description and Biology

Vertigo snails, sometimes referred to as marsh snails, are found throughout north and central Europe. Three of the four members of the genus are in serious danger of extinction: *V. angustior*, *V. genesii*, and *V. geyerii*. The fourth snail, *V. moulinsiana*, also known as *V. desmoulinsi*, does not appear to be endangered at the present time. Descriptions are not available for these species, but the common names of the snails indicate a differentiation in the shape of the snails' mouths. *V. angustior* is referred to as the narrow-mouthed whorl snail; *V. genesii*—once thought to be the same species as *V. geyerii*—is called the round-mouthed whorl snail; and *V. geyerii* is simply called the whorl snail.

Habitat and Current Distribution

V. angustior is found in open habitat such as wet, grassy meadows, moist dunes, or marshy ground with low vegetation cover. The population

figures for this snail vary according to country; in Austria *V. angustior* is widespread but in Belgium it may be extinct, as there has been only two sightings since 1950. In addition to Austria and Belgium, this species also occurs in Armenia, Azerbaijan, Belarus, the Czech Republic, Denmark, Estonia, Finland, France, Georgia, Germany, Hungary, Ireland, Italy, Liechtenstein, Lithuania, the Netherlands, Norway, Poland, Romania, Russia, Slovakia, Sweden, Switzerland, Ukraine, and the United Kingdom.

V. genesii has been found mainly in the Alps (Switzerland) and the mountains of central Scandinavia (Norway, Sweden, and Finland). This snail prefers wetlands, sloping fens, and marshy ground surrounded by moss and sedge. In the United Kingdom it has been found at an elevation of 1,624 ft (495 m) among Arctic-Alpine plants. In the Alps it is found at elevations of up to 6,562 ft (2,000 m). This snail has an uneven distribution throughout its range (which includes Germany, Poland, Romania, and Russia in addition to the countries mentioned above). In the

United Kingdom it is found in only one locality, and other populations are considered extremely small.

V. geyerii is found mainly in the mountains of Scandinavia (Norway, Sweden, and Finland), Swiss and Austrian Alps, and in Ireland. The habitat of this snail includes marshy areas, wetlands, and fens. In the United Kingdom this animal prefers open fens free of moss but containing *Eleocharis quinqueflora*, *Schoenus nigricans*, and *Carex* species. Although population figures are unavailable for this species, it is unevenly distributed throughout its range (which includes the Czech Republic, Denmark, Germany, Latvia, Lithuania, Poland, and Slovakia in addition to the countries previously mentioned).

History and Conservation Measures

All three *Vertigo* snails face extinction due to habitat loss and degradation. Hydroelectric projects, drainage and water extraction, agricultural runoff and pollution, and even litter threaten the remaining habitat of these animals. Although listed as endangered or threatened in various listings, specific conservation measures for these snails are still lacking.

Moorean snails

Partula spp.

Phylum	Mollusca
Class	Gastropoda
Order	Stylommatophora
Family	Partulidae
Status	Extinct, IUCN
Range	Moorea (French Polynesia)

Description and Biology

Partula snails were once the most common and varied land snails of the Pacific islands. It is thought that there were about 100 species of *Partula* at one time, but only a fraction of that number now survive in the wild. Some species, like the Moorean snails, exist only in zoos and universities.

Partula species are quite diverse in shape and color, ranging from pale to dark brown, with a variable number of bands on their shell. Individuals of the same species also differ in size, striping (spiral lines), and striations (fine vertical lines). They feed on dead cell layers of plants, particularly succulent herbs, ferns, arums, and *Pandanus*. Some species are also carnivorous, feeding on very small snails of other families. Elaborate courtship behavior has been reported. These snails are hermaphroditic and ovoviviparous, producing eggs that hatch within the body of the snail.

Habitat and Current Distribution

Until recently, seven species of *Partula* were found on Moorea in the Society Islands of French Polynesia, living on bushes and trees in the mountains and valleys. They were known to occur in the ridge crest of four valleys: Paparoa, Faamaariri, Uufau, and Maramu. Extensive searches of these areas in 1987 proved futile, and no *Partula* species is known to exist there today.

P. suturalis.

History and Conservation Measures

Partula became extinct on Moorea because *Euglandina rosea*, a carnivorous snail, was introduced to the island to control the giant African snail (*Achatina fulica*), which was considered an agricultural pest on Moorea as well as on other islands of the Society group. *Euglandina* was ineffective in controlling *Achatina* but eradicated all species of *Partula* on Moorea. Nearly all *Partula* habitat is now occupied by *Euglandina*. Other species of *Partula* occur on nearby Tahiti, Raiatea, and Huahine; unfortunately, *Euglandina* has been reported on two of these islands. Unless swift action is taken, scientists fear that these islands may face a similar eradication of these species.

Six of the seven Moorean species are currently flourishing in captive-breeding programs. The seventh, *P. exigua*, is extinct. The Partula Propagation Group, in association with IUCN, has been instrumental in maintaining a captive *Partula* population, with hopes of reintroducing them into the wild.

Iowa Pleistocene snail

Discus macclintocki

Phylum	Mollusca
Class	Gastropoda
Order	Stylommatophora
Family	Discidae
Status	Endangered, IUCN
	Endangered, USFWS
Range	Iowa, Illinois (U.S.A.)

Description and Biology

Adults of this average-sized species of forest snail are 0.3 in (8 mm) wide. The domed shell is brown or off-white with a greenish cast. The whorls of the shell are tightly coiled, and six whorls are typically present. Iowa Pleistocene snails eat tree leaves including the leaves of hard maple, white and yellow birch, willow, and dogwood. These snails burrow in the soil and hibernate after the first hard freeze. They are active during spring and summer, but as their habitat dries out in late summer they become sluggish.

The Iowa Pleistocene snail is hermaphroditic—each snail has both male and female reproductive organs. These snails are not self-fertilizing; apparently each snail can lay eggs as well as fertilize the eggs of other snails. Breeding takes place from late March to August, and two to six eggs are laid under logs or bark, in the soil, or in moist rock crevices. The incubation period is about 28 days. Iowa Pleistocene snails live about five years.

Habitat and Current Distribution

The Iowa Pleistocene snail is now known to survive in only 18 locations in two counties in Iowa (Dubuque and Clayton counties) and one in Illinois (Jo Davies County) in a region called the Driftless Area. These populations are thought to total about 60,000 snails.

This snail has very specific habitat requirements and is found only in a microhabitat described as an *algific talus slope*. This cool, moist microenvironment is found around cave or fissure entrances where nearly permanent underground ice is created by circulating air and percolating water. The underground ice cools the surface where Iowa Pleistocene snails live in deep, moist, deciduous leaf litter. The algific talus slope microhabitat recreates the conditions that were widespread in the Midwest during previous glacial epochs.

History and Conservation Measures

During cooler glacial periods, the Iowa Pleistocene snail was found throughout much of the midwestern United States. Its maximum range included Iowa, Nebraska, Missouri, Illinois, Indiana, and Ohio. This species has been found in the geologic record over a period of 300,000 years and it has survived several cycles of climate change during that time. If glacial conditions were to return to the Midwest, it is likely that populations of Iowa Pleistocene snails would rebound and their range would expand.

Human disturbance poses the most immediate threat to the survival of this species. Over the last 150 years about 75 percent of the habitat suitable for this snail has been destroyed by human activities including quarrying and agriculture. Since the Iowa Pleistocene snail has such specialized habitat requirements, any loss of remaining habitat must be avoided. An important step to conserve remaining snail habitat was taken in 1986, when the Driftless Area Project was instituted by the Nature Conservancy, the Iowa Conservation Commission, and the U.S. Fish and Wildlife Service in northeast Iowa. Designed to protect remaining algific talus slope habitat, this voluntary project contacted private landowners and asked them to make a commitment to conserve this habitat on their land. More than two-thirds of the landowners contacted agreed. While this interim solution is in place, concerned agencies and organizations are attempting to acquire land so that it can be permanently protected.

Virginia fringed mountain snail

Polygyriscus virginianus

Phylum	Mollusca
Class	Gastropoda
Order	Stylommatophora
Family	Polygyridae
Status	Endangered, IUCN
	Endangered, USFWS
Range	Virginia (U.S.A.)

Description and Biology

Due to its rare occurrence and extremely localized distribution, not much is known about the Virginia fringed mountain snail. This snail is the only member of its genus and considered one of the rarest and smallest land snails in North America. The Virginia fringed mountain snail has four to five flat whorls that become thicker as they circle outwards. The greenish brown shell measures 0.18 in (4.5 mm) in diameter, and comb-like fringes line the grooves of the shell surface, hence its common name. The animal's body is white and the snail is considered blind, although it does have eyestalks.

This snail is a burrower and tends to stay underground except during very wet conditions. The diet of this species is not known. It lays two eggs per season.

Habitat and Current Distribution

The Virginia fringed mountain snail has only been found in a 1.5-mi (2.5-km) site along New River in Pulaski County, Virginia. This snail inhabits damp, clay soils along steep river banks. The ground is usually bare and surrounded by pine and oak scrub and honeysuckle.

Only 30 individuals have been found, although there may be more. Conservationists are reluctant to conduct additional surveys for fear of disturbing this animal's already limited habitat.

History and Conservation Measures

The shells of these snails were first discovered in 1947 but a living specimen was not found until 1971; in that year 14 live adults and several juveniles were discovered by Leslie Hubricht. Despite its very limited range and numbers, the Virginia fringed mountain snail population is believed to be in fair condition. There are potential dangers from the use of herbicide in surrounding areas, but currently there are no plans to do so near the New River. Conservation measures for this species include possibly conducting additional searches; research into the snail's biology and ecology; and protection of the river bank from pollution and other environmental changes.

Flat-spired three-toothed snail

Triodopsis (Polygra) platysayoides

Phylum	Mollusca
Class	Gastropoda
Order	Stylommatophora
Family	Polygyridae
Status	Endangered, IUCN
	Threatened, USFWS
Range	West Virginia (U.S.A.)

Description and Biology

A very rare species, the flat-spired three-toothed snail is amply described by its common name. This snail has a thin, flat shell with five whorls and a thick, conical tooth in the inner wall of its shell. The color of the shell ranges from light brown to reddish brown with oblique banding. The snail averages 1.2 in (3 cm) in diameter and 0.4 in (1.1 cm) thick. It has a narrow, white lip at the oblique opening.

The flat-spired three-toothed snail feeds on lichens on rock surfaces and in leaf litter; it is also known to eat other snails. This snail prefers damp, cool weather and has been known to breed in temperatures of 41-59°F (5-15°C). Known predators are shrews and beetles.

Habitat and Current Distribution

There are 28 species in the genus *Triodopsis*, most of which are quite widespread throughout eastern United States. The flat-spired three-toothed snail, however, is very rare and is found in only one location: below the summit of Cooper's Rock next to Cheat River Canyon in Monongalia County, West Virginia. In this habitat, the snail burrows in damp leaf litter among sandstone boulders and cobbles with pine and deciduous forest. In hot, dry weather, this animal retreats to the cool crevices of the boulders. The snail has been found at elevations of 1,800-2,000 ft (540-600 m).

In 1970 population of this species was estimated at between 300-500 individuals, but a more recent census indicated closer to 1,000 animals.

History and Conservation Measures

Currently the habitat of the flat-spired three-toothed snail is a part of the Cooper's Rock Recreational Area and Cooper's Rock State Forest, which affords the snail some protection. Nonetheless, the forest attracts nearly half a million visitors each year, some of whom do not keep to established trails and who unknowingly trample over the snail's leaf litter habitat. As an effort to protect the habitat from further disturbance, park officials have rerouted and fenced hiking trails. If the habitat area is left in its present condition, the population of the flat-spired three-toothed snail is likely to remain stable.

Bonin Islands endemic snails

Mandarina spp.

Phylum	Mollusca
Class	Gastropoda
Order	Stylommatophora
Family	Camaenidae
Status	Endangered, IUCN (5 species)
	Vulnerable, IUCN (4 species)
Range	Bonin Islands (Japan)

Description and Biology

The land snail genus *Mandarina* encompasses 14 species that exhibit a wide variety of shell sizes, forms, and coloration. Species may possess domed, conical, flat, or spired shells that vary in size from approximately 2.8 in (72 mm) in diameter (*M. titan*) to 0.82 in (21 mm) in diameter (*M. nola*).

Shell shape and color pattern may also vary according to the stages of growth.

No information is currently available concerning the life cycles of species in the genus.

Habitat and Current Distribution

The genus *Mandarina* is endemic to the Bonin Islands (also known as the Ogasawara Islands), which are located about 600 miles (965 km) southeast of Japan in the Pacific Ocean.

The macrohabitat of the genus includes fissure deposits as well as the leaves and trunks of the islands' mesic forest and dry scrub vegetation.

History and Conservation Measures

Like the Hawaiian Islands, the Bonin Islands support a highly diverse group of endemic species which have been decimated by habitat destruction and introduced species. First settled in 1830, the islands were extensively exploited by logging and agriculture operations. During World War II, residents were evacuated to Japan, and heavy fighting devastated one of the islands, Iwo Jima. Following the war, the Bonin Islands were placed under the administration of the U.S. government, and from that time until their return to Japan in 1968, the endemic species on the largely abandoned islands were able to recover. However, since the return of the original settlers in 1968, the Bonin Islands have been the site of increasing development.

The Japanese government has listed most of the islands as a national park and has designated the *Mandarina* snails as Japanese Natural Monuments, citing their importance in the country's scientific and natural heritage. However, the government has also supported several development programs on the Bonin Islands which have been criticized as environmentally unsound. Currently, plans are underway to build an airport and marine resort on Anijima Island, one of the last major islands in the group to be exploited and the only home of ten *Mandarina* species. Conservationists are concerned that such development will result in the extinction of these species and have voiced their concerns to the Japanese government.

Manus Island tree snail

Papustyla pulcherrima

Phylum	Mollusca
Class	Gastropoda
Order	Stylommatophora
Family	Camaenidae
Status	Rare, IUCN
	Endangered, USFWS
	Appendix II, CITES
Range	Manus Island (Papua New Guinea)

Description and Biology

The Manus Island tree snail is easily recognized by its brilliant green color. Its shell is approximately 1.6 in (4 cm) long, and is an intense pea-green color with a yellow band along the suture. The color is contained in the hardened protein known as the periostracum, which is found on the outer surface of the shell; this wears off with age to reveal a yellow layer underneath. Within the shell, the animal is tan with a lateral brown stripe on either side.

Very little is known about the ecology or reproductive habits of this species.

Habitat and Current Distribution

This species inhabits the rain forest of Manus Island, northern Papua New Guinea, but its exact distribution is not well known. There are no estimates of population size.

Its primary habitat is the high canopy of the rain forest. The snail is inactive during the day. It can be found attached to the underside of leaves approximately 16 ft (5 m) above ground, primarily in Dillenia

Manus Island tree snail.

(Dillenaceae) and Astronia (Melastomaceae) trees, although it may also be found in several other trees and on large climbing plants of the arum family.

History and Conservation Measures

The intense green coloration of the Manus Island tree snail makes it unique among land molluscs and highly prized by shell collectors. It has traditionally been used by Manus Islanders for decorative purposes, and is currently used in modern jewelry. In the past, large numbers were bought by tourists and exported by dealers. In 1977, it was thought that the snail population was restricted to the wilder central forests of the island and that it had been reduced or eliminated by collecting and agriculture within a several mile radius of the city of Lorengau. In 1981, however, the snail could be found relatively easily, and there was no evidence that particularly heavy collecting had taken place. The primary threat to the species is thought to be logging, as the trees that the snail inhabits have timber potential. The island is still largely covered in natural forest, much of it inaccessible; approximately 11 percent is under a logging concession.

The Manus Island tree snail is only one of a number of snails being collected for export in Papua New Guinea. Since most of these are barely known to science, live specimens should be obtained for anatomical studies, and surveys and ecological studies should be carried out to determine more precisely their distribution patterns and population biology. As long as the current trade continues to be monitored, it is unlikely to have any noticeable effect on populations. Logging could pose a significant threat, however, and if it does, reserve populations will be required in appropriate sites.

Caracol

Hemicycla plicaria

Phylum	Mollusca
Class	Gastropoda
Order	Stylommatophora
Family	Helicidae
Status	Endangered, IUCN
Range	Canary Islands (Spain)

Description and Biology

The land snails of the Canary Islands show a very high degree of diversity with more than 200 endemic species (nearly 84 percent of the total) belonging to 27 genera (8 of these are also endemic). This diversity is even more remarkable when the small surface area of the archipelago (2,924 sq mi/7,574 sq km irregularly distributed on seven islands) and its relatively young age (from 20 million years to less than 800,000 years ago) are taken into consideration. Normally each species is endemic to only one island and is usually restricted to a small area of that island. Because of this, many Canary Island land snails are threatened by human actions.

Hemicycla plicaria is one of the more threatened species of Canary Island endemic land snails and is also one of the most beautiful and elegant members of its genus. The species was first described in 1816 by Jean-Baptiste Lamarck. The snail's body is soft and gray with a wet, wrinkled skin coated by mucus. At the snail's front end is the head, armed with two pairs of tentacles; the upper are longer than the lower and possess eye-spots at the tips. The mouth has a jaw on the upper lip that can be seen when the snail is feeding. Just behind the tentacles on the right side is the genital opening, visible only during courtship and mating. The anus and the respiratory orifice (pneumostome) share a common opening on the right side of the mantle edge. The foot sole is yellowish or whitish and smooth.

The shell of *H. plicaria* is spirally coiled, solid and opaque; it has a depressed conical form with four dextral (right) whorls. The last whorl is large with a weak keel which sometimes disappears before reaching the aperture. The apex of the shell is slightly wrinkled and of a slightly more reddish tone than the adjacent light brown whorl. The suture between the whorls is deep and strongly marked. The diameter of the shell varies from 0.7-0.9 in (17.7-23.3 mm) and the height is 0.4-0.5 in (10.8-13.5 mm).

The aperture of the shell is wide and oval, and the margins have the tendency to converge toward the center of the shell. The mouth-edge (peristome) is very wide and flattened with a 0.08-in (2-mm) lip. It is grayish and the margin nearest to the shell axis is slightly thickened, forming a small fold toward the interior.

H. plicaria is a hermaphrodite, and it mates during the winter (the wet season). It eats plants and lives 1-2 years. Although this species lives in a dry habitat, it is not particularly well adapted to dry conditions and must avoid dessication. For this reason, *H. plicaria* is active at night or in wet weather. During the day it shelters under rocks (with a wetter microhabitat), retreats inside its shell, and secretes a film of mucus which dries to form a hardened layer that adheres to the stone.

Habitat and Current Distribution

This species lives in a very small, dry coastal zone (3.9 sq mi/10 sq km, 16.5-820 ft/5-250 m altitude), 7.5 mi (12 km) south of the provincial capital of Tenerife Island. The higher plant vegetation is sparse, dominated by drought-resistant shrubs (*Euphorbia balsamifera* and *E. canariensis*).

History and Conservation Measures

H. plicaria is severely threatened with extinction due to extensive development and the construction of tourist complexes in the littoral zone of its restricted habitat.

Kerry slug

Geomalacus maculosus

Phylum	Mollusca
Class	Gastropoda
Order	Stylommatophora
Family	Arionidae
Status	Vulnerable, IUCN
Range	Ireland; Portugal; Spain

Description and Biology

The Kerry slug, also known as the spotted Irish slug, has a large, pliable body that can be elongated and flattened at will or rolled up into a ball. The body surface and mantle are patterned in white or yellowish spots and blotches on a gray, charcoal, chocolate-brown or yellowish brown background. In captivity the body ground color often changes to reddish or greenish according to the food given (e.g. carrots), but in nature these extremes are seldom seen. Dark lateral stripes along the length of the body are sometimes present, especially in juveniles. Diet includes fungi, algae, mosses and liverworts, and a wide variety of lichens.

This species is capable of self-fertilization. Between July and October, individuals deposit several batches of 18-30 oval eggs, which hatch approximately six to eight weeks later. The slug is active throughout the winter, but aestivates (becomes inactive) during part of the summer.

Habitat and Current Distribution

This species is known from southwest Ireland and northern Spain. It has been found in northern Portugal, but has since disappeared from many localities in that country. No population estimates are currently available.

The Kerry slug appears to use two separate habitats. It is found either on lichen-covered sandstone boulders and bluffs in open countryside, or in old deciduous forest on lichen- or moss-covered tree trunks or under the bark of logs or fallen branches. Most of the areas where the species occurs have been subject to intense deforestation; therefore, scientists are uncertain whether wooded or open areas are the species' preferred habitat.

History and Conservation Measures

This species was discovered in 1843 in Ireland, then later collected in Spain in 1868 and in Portugal in 1873. Destruction and alteration of habitat probably pose the most significant threat to the species in all three countries. However, the slug is at greatest risk in Portugal where forestry operations and other land-use changes, particularly the conversion of large tracts of sessile oak and cork oak forest to eucalyptus forest, has led to the species' decline.

In Ireland, the Kerry slug occurs in such protected areas as Glengarriff Forest, Uragh Wood Nature Reserve, and the Killarney National Park. Captive breeding and reintroduction programs may be used to re-establish populations in other areas. Unfortunately, little is known about the requirements of the species and further research is necessary to plan for such programs and to manage existing reserves to the benefit of this species.

Louisiana pearlshell

Margaritifera hembeli

Phylum	Mollusca
Class	Pelecypoda (Bivalvia)
Order	Unionoida
Family	Margaritiferidae
Status	Endangered, IUCN
	Endangered, USFWS
Range	Louisiana (U.S.A.)

Description and Biology

One of the rarest members of its family, the Louisiana pearlshell is oval shaped, measuring up to 4 in (10 cm) long and 2 in (5 cm) wide. Its outer shell is dark brown or black, and the inner surface is white.

Like other freshwater mussels, the Louisiana pearlshell breeds in the spring. Males release sperm, which are carried by currents downstream to females. As they feed, the females take in the sperm, which fertilizes the eggs stored in their gills. Glochidia (larvae) hatch soon after and develop in the female's gills, now modified as brood pouches. After a certain period, the glochidia are released and attach themselves to the gill filaments of host fish. When they have grown and developed a shell, the now juvenile mussels detach from the fish and sink to the riverbed where they bury themselves in shoals and riffles, leaving only their shell margins and siphons exposed. Through their siphons, Louisiana pearlshells feed on plankton and other plant matter and expel indigestible particles.

Habitat and Current Distribution

The Louisiana pearlshell is currently found in 11 streams in the headwaters of Bayou Beouf in Rapides Parish, Louisiana. Ninety percent of the species occurs in four of these streams: Long Branch, Bayou Clear, Loving Creek, and Little Loving Creek.

This species prefers shallow streams ranging in depth from 12-20 in (30-60 cm), with clear water and a substrate which has both sand and gravel. The total population of Louisiana pearlshells is estimated to be about 10,000.

History and Conservation Measures

Biologists believe that the Louisiana pearlshell once occurred throughout the Bayou Beouf headwaters. However, dam construction, water diversion, and polluted runoff has led to the decline of the species. Also, tons of silt—eroded from the surrounding watershed as a result of logging along the headwaters—have been deposited in the streams. This silt blankets mussels and clogs their siphons, effectively suffocating them. Due to its rarity, the Louisiana pearlshell is highly coveted by amateur and scientific collectors; yet collection of even limited numbers poses a significant threat to this already depleted species.

The Louisiana pearlshell's range is primarily bounded by the Kisatchie National Forest. The species also occurs on property owned by the U.S. Air Force. Therefore, the U.S. Forest Service or the Air Force must present any land use proposals that may affect the species to the U.S. Fish and Wildlife Service for their review.

Freshwater pearl mussel

Margaritifera margaritifera

Phylum	Mollusca
Class	Pelecypoda (Bivalvia)
Order	Unionoida
Family	Margaritiferidae
Status	Vulnerable, IUCN
Range	Austria; Belgium; Canada; Czech Republic; Denmark; Finland; France; Germany; Iceland; Ireland; Luxembourg; Norway; Poland; Portugal; Russia; Spain; Sweden; United Kingdom; U.S.A.

Description and Biology

Freshwater pearl mussels vary in size but are usually about 4 in (10 cm) long and 2 in (5 cm) high. The shell is thick and elongate. Umbones (the dorsal part of the shell) are low and often unevenly eroded by the high levels of carbonic acid in the soft waters where it lives. The periostracum (the hardened protein on outer surface of shell) is brown to black; the inner surface is iridescent or lustrous. Young shells are light yellowish brown streaked with green rays.

Young mussels mature at 15-20 years of age and continue to reproduce throughout a life span that can extend to over 100 years. Fertilized eggs incubate in the marsupium, a structure formed by the mussel's gills or demibranchs. After the glochidia (larvae) are released in late summer to autumn, they move passively through water currents until they reach a host fish, where they spend the parasitic larval stage. Host fish in central Europe are the stream or brown trout (*Salmo trutta fario*) and the salmon (*Salmo salar*); in the United States the brook (*Salvelinus fontinalis*), brown (*Salmo trutta*), and rainbow (*Salmo gairdneri*) trout are common hosts. Two types of life cycles have

been identified: one in which the glochidia attach to

Freshwater pearl mussel.

the gills of the host fish between July and September and fall off between May and July the following year, and a second in which the glochidia fall off in October of the same year of attachment. Young mussels probably spend their early years deep in the river bed.

Habitat and Current Distribution

This species is found in eastern North America, northern Europe (including Scandinavia), and Eurasia. Populations in North America are the most stable, although they are thought to be in decline. In Austria, the mussel is extinct in all but a few unpolluted tributaries in western Waldviertel, Lower Austria; the total population is estimated at 9,000-10,000. In Belgium, the population is seriously declining and only locally common. In the Czech Republic, only a small number of populations still survives, mainly in south Bohemia. Denmark has only one population, in the River Varde Aa, west Jutland, but it has not been recorded there since 1930 and may be extinct. The population in Finland is described as declining catastrophically and is currently estimated at 1.5 million. In France populations are strongly declining. In Germany, southern populations are thought to have declined by 90 percent and most now lack young mussels. It is very local in north and west Britain (mainly Scotland) and in Ireland it is absent from many suitable sites and declining in many rivers. In Luxembourg, only one population of approximately 3,000 individuals survives. In Norway, the population is widespread, but is mainly coastal and declining. It may be extinct in Poland and in Portugal, and is in decline in Spain and Sweden.

The freshwater mussel is usually restricted to waters which are relatively poor in lime, although it may occur in hard water with not too slow a current and not too high a temperature, such as forest or mountain regions, or in areas with crystalline rock. Its upper limit of distribution is 1,640-1,970 ft (500-600 m). It generally is not found in rivers on plains, but watercourses on sandy heaths satisfy its ecological requirements. It also may flourish in clear river lakes, if suitable rivers flow through them. Unable to withstand drought, it is found only in permanent rivers. It is typically found in water 1.6-4.9 ft (0.5-1.5 m) deep in a mixture of boulders, stones, and sand, half buried in the substrate. It cannot survive in sediment or silt. It tends to be sedentary as an adult but may move short distances, leaving tracks in substrate.

History and Conservation Measures

The freshwater pearl mussel once had a wide distribution throughout northern Europe, eastern North America, and Eurasia. While it is thought to be declining throughout its range, it is especially vulnerable in Europe, where it has been extensively exploited for its highly valued pearls since pre-Roman times. Later industrialization brought pollution, and increased agriculture resulted in the channelization of rivers and streams. The decline in Central Europe is thought to be 95 percent since the beginning of this century. The causes of decline often differ based on locale: in northern countries pearl fishing has been the major problem, whereas in Central Europe pollution is more important. The main threat in continental Europe is eutrophication—nutrient enrichment of an aquatic ecosystem that results in excessive growth of algae and aquatic plants and the eventual depletion of oxygen; young mussels can develop only in sediment with low organic content, and even slight eutrophication increases juvenile mortality. Many of the remaining populations in Europe are no longer reproducing. In addition, any adverse effects on the fish hosts will also affect the mussel.

The plight of the pearl mussel emphasizes the need for much stricter pollution control measures throughout Europe and North America, and for greater control of channelization and alteration of watercourses. The most important requirement for the long-term survival of the species is reduction of eutrophication and pollution through strict control measures and monitoring of water quality. Reserves also should be created in unpolluted areas wherever possible, and management plans should be initiated for rivers. Illegal pearl fishing should be prevented and strict control implemented on licensed fishing. Additional conservation recommendations include control of engineering activities that alter river banks, water flow, and sedimentation; restocking of rivers with brown trout and protection where appropriate; reintroduction of mussels by introducing fish infected with glochidia to appropriate rivers; prevention of the reintroduction of foreign salmonids which may compete with the native host fish; further surveys; improved national protective legislation where necessary; and coordination of research projects currently underway.

Dwarf wedge mussel

Alasmidonta heterodon

Phylum	Mollusca
Class	Pelecypoda (Bivalvia)
Order	Unionoida
Family	Unionidae
Status	Endangered, IUCN
	Endangered, USFWS
Range	Maryland, New Hampshire, North Carolina, Vermont (U.S.A.)

Description and Biology

This small mussel is unique among all North American freshwater mussels, having two lateral teeth on its right valve but only one tooth on its left. The species usually does not grow any longer than 1.5 in (3.8 cm).

Like other freshwater mussels, the dwarf wedge mussel breeds in the spring. Males release sperm, which are carried by currents downstream to females. As they feed, the females take in the sperm, which fertilizes the eggs stored in their gills. Glochidia (larvae) hatch soon after and develop in the female's gills, now modified as brood pouches. After a certain time, the glochidia are released and attach themselves to the gill filaments of host fish (glochidia that do not find host fish sink to the river bottom and die). When they have grown and developed a shell, the now juvenile mussels detach from the fish and sink to the riverbed. Here, they bury themselves in shoals and riffles, leaving only their shell margins and siphons exposed. Through their siphons, the mussels feed on plankton and other plant matter and expel indigestible particles.

Dwarf wedge mussel.

Habitat and Current Distribution

The dwarf wedge mussel inhabits sandy and muddy river bottoms where there is not much current and very little silt. Currently, the species occurs in four states: Maryland (McIntosh Run and Tuckahoe Creek), New Hampshire (Ashuelot and Connecticut rivers), North Carolina (Little and Tar rivers), and Vermont (Connecticut River). Estimates of total population are unavailable.

History and Conservation Measures

Although population estimates—both initial and current—are unavailable, the dwarf wedge mussel is obviously in decline. Previously, it was found as far north as New Brunswick, Canada, and its range extended down through North Carolina. As with other North American freshwater mussels, water pollution and damming have played havoc with this species' habitat. Where dams are constructed, areas upstream display increased siltation while areas downstream show an increased variability of temperatures and water levels.

Ouachita rock-pocketbook

Arkansia (Arcidens) wheeleri

Phylum	Mollusca
Class	Pelecypoda (Bivalvia)
Order	Unionoida
Family	Unionidae
Status	Endangered, IUCN
Range	Arkansas, Oklahoma (U.S.A.)

Description and Biology

This freshwater mussel, also known as Wheeler's pearly mussel, inhabits backwater areas containing muddy bottoms and minimal current. It has a silken, brown to black shell and can grow to 4 in (10 cm) in length.

Like other freshwater mussels, the Ouachita rock-pocketbook breeds in the spring. Males release sperm, which are carried by currents downstream to females. As they feed, the females take in the sperm, which fertilizes the eggs stored in their gills. Glochidia (larvae) hatch soon after and develop in the female's gills, now modified as brood pouches. After a certain time, the glochidia are released and attach themselves to the gill filaments of host fish (glochidia that do not find host fish sink to the river's bottom and die). When they have grown and developed a shell, the now juvenile mussels detach from the fish and sink to the riverbed. Here, they bury themselves in shoals and riffles, leaving only their shell margins and siphons exposed. Through their siphons, the mussels feed on plankton and other plant matter and expel indigestible particles.

Habitat and Current Distribution

The Ouachita rock-pocketbook lives in rocky or muddy bottoms in lakes and rivers where there is very little current. Currently, the only two rivers in which this mussel is found are the Kiamichi River in southeastern Oklahoma and the Little River, which stretches across the southern Oklahoma-Arkansas border. Its distribution in the Little River is limited to

Ouachita rock-pocketbook.

a 5-mi (8-km) band between Sevier and Little River counties in extreme southwestern Arkansas; less than 100 snails are thought to survive there. In the Kiamichi River, its numbers are somewhat higher— about 1,000—but its distribution is still very limited, with the species found only in a small stretch of the river between LeFlore and Pushmataha counties.

History and Conservation Measures

Initial population figures for the Ouachita rock-pocketbook are unavailable, but the species is undeniably in decline. In addition to its current distribution, this mussel also used to be found in a series of oxbow lakes and the Ouachita River near Arkadelphia, Arkansas.

Water pollution and the construction of dams are the major threats to the animal's existence, although the presence of the introduced Asiatic clam (*Corbicula fluminae*) also poses a danger. In the Little River, pollution keeps this mussel confined to a 5-mi stretch of the river; the discharges from the Pine Creek Dam do not help matters. In the Kiamichi River, a planned reservoir in Pushmataha County could have a devastating impact on the species. With the demand for water resources in the Ouachita rock-pocketbook's range unlikely to abate, this species faces a difficult and uncertain future.

Pale lilliput pearly mussel

Carunculina (Toxolasma) cylindrellus

Phylum	Mollusca
Class	Pelecypoda (Bivalvia)
Order	Unionoida
Family	Unionidae
Status	Endangered, IUCN
	Endangered, USFWS
	Appendix I, CITES
Range	Alabama (U.S.A.)

Description and Biology

This small freshwater mussel has a smooth yellowish green shell. This shell is nearly cylindrical in shape and measures 1.8 in (4.5 cm) long, 0.64 in (1.6 cm) wide, and 1 in (2.5 cm) high. The color of the inner surface of the shell varies from white to light yellow highlighted with metallic blue and purple.

Like other North American freshwater mussels, *Toxolasma cylindrellus* must have a stable habitat (mainly clean water and an undisturbed stream bottom) and access to suitable host fish (for larval development) in order to reproduce successfully. The complex life cycle of these mussels begins in the spring with a male releasing sperm for dispersal by stream currents. These sperm, taken in by a female while she is feeding, fertilize eggs stored in her gills. The eggs hatch and larvae develop in the female's gills. After a time the larvae are released into the stream where they attach themselves to the gills of host fish. Any larva not fortunate enough to come into contact with a host fish after release by the female mussel sinks to the bottom of the stream and dies.

Pale lilliput pearly mussel.

Larvae can only develop into juveniles while attached to the gills of a host fish.

The larvae remain attached to the host fish until they become juveniles, by which time they have developed a shell and are large enough to survive on their own. The juveniles then detach from the host fish and fall to the stream bottom, where they bury themselves in riffles or shoals with only their shell margins and feeding siphons exposed. Freshwater mussels feed by siphoning plant material from the water. Any silt or sediment in the water can pose a serious threat to them, since it can clog their feeding siphons and ultimately kill them.

Habitat and Current Distribution

This extremely rare freshwater mussel is currently found only in a 10-mi (16-km) stretch of the Paint Rock River and its tributaries, Estill Fork and Hurricane Creek, in northern Alabama (U.S.A.). It prefers shallow streams with clean, fast-moving water and firm, silt-free, gravel or sand bottoms. Population figures are unknown.

History and Conservation Measures

Although it seems to have been rare since its discovery, the pale lilliput pearly mussel was once found throughout the narrower tributaries of the Tennessee River (Tennessee and Alabama), including the Flint, Elk, Sequatchie, Little Sequatchie, Buffalo, and Duck rivers. Dam construction, stream siltation, and pollution have caused the species to disappear from most of its former range. Siltation caused by strip mining, clear-cutting, dredging, and unsound agricultural practices has buried many of the mussel beds in the Tennessee River system, smothering the inhabitants. Pesticide runoff has polluted streams, and these pollutants are taken in by the mussels as they feed. The construction of dams has restricted the flow in many of the water courses in the Tennessee River system, further degrading mussel habitat.

The best hope for the survival and eventual recovery of this species lies in rehabilitation of its habitat. A comprehensive water management plan under development by the Tennessee Valley Authority (TVA) would mandate minimum, year-round flows in all rivers within the Tennessee River system. Carefully orchestrated water releases by the TVA dams would establish these new conditions. The Paint Creek River may also be eligible to receive additional protection as a scenic river under the National Wild and Scenic Rivers Act. In addition, reseach is underway to determine the feasibility of reintroducing *T. cylindrellus* to suitable habitat within its former range.

Birdwing pearly mussel

Conradilla caelata

Phylum	Mollusca
Class	Pelecypoda (Bivalvia)
Order	Unionoida
Family	Unionidae
Status	Endangered, IUCN
	Endangered, USFWS
	Appendix I, CITES
Range	Tennessee, Virginia (U.S.A.)

Description and Biology

This small mussel is generally only 2 in (5 cm) in width. Its shell is dark green on the outside and white on the inside; the shell surface is distinguished by irregular growth lines. The valves of the birdwing pearly mussel are solid and inflated, particularly in females, and are triangular or oval.

Like other freshwater mussels, the birdwing pearly mussel breeds in the spring. Males release sperm, which are carried by currents downstream to females. As they feed, the females take in the sperm, which fertilizes the eggs stored in their gills. Glochidia (larvae) hatch soon after and develop in the female's gills, now modified as brood pouches. After a certain time, the glochidia are released and attach themselves to the gill filaments of host fish (glochidia that do not find host fish sink to the river's bottom and die). Researchers believe that one such host fish for the birdwing pearly mussel is a shiner, *Notropis galacturus*. When they have grown and have developed a shell, the now juvenile mussels detach from the fish and sink to the riverbed. Here, they bury themselves in shoals and riffles, leaving only their shell margins and siphons exposed. Through their siphons, the mussels feed on plankton and other plant matter and expel indigestible particles.

Habitat and Current Distribution

This species inhabits the sandy bottoms of clean, silt-free streams and rivers. Unlike many other North American freshwater mussels, the birdwing

Birdwing pearly mussel.

pearly mussel prefers fast-moving streams with strong currents.

Currently, this species is found only in a few large tributaries of the Tennessee River, including the Clinch, Duck, Elk, and Powell rivers of Tennessee and Virginia. Although total population figures are unavailable, this mussel is still fairly numerous in the Duck River, which contains between 20,000-30,000 individuals.

History and Conservation Measures

The birdwing pearly mussel apparently has always been confined to the Tennessee River and its tributaries, and it has always been considered rare. These two features have made it vulnerable to habitat alteration and water pollution.

Because a large number of the species inhabit the Duck River, the planned Columbia Dam project of the Tennessee Valley Authority (TVA) caused great concern among environmentalists. This project would have flooded this mussel's habitat and wiped out the entire birdwing pearly mussel population in the river. The dam was begun and partially constructed during the 1980s, but work was halted due to the threat the dam posed to the birdwing pearly mussel and other endangered species that inhabit the Duck River. Currently, it is unlikely that the dam will be completed, and any future work on the river—including removal of the partial dam structure—will proceed only if the status of the river's endangered species can be assured. At present, the main threat to the birdwing pearly mussel is probably water pollution.

Fanshell

Cyprogenia stegaria (irrorata)

Phylum	Mollusca
Class	Pelecypoda (Bivalvia)
Order	Unionoida
Family	Unionidae
Status	Endangered, IUCN
	Endangered, USFWS
Range	Illinois, Indiana, Ohio, Kentucky, Tennessee, Virginia, West Virginia (U.S.A.)

Description and Biology

The fanshell is a medium-sized freshwater mussel about 3.2 in (8 cm) long. Its shell is yellowish-green with fine, green lines across the surface. Interior of the shell is grey-white. Muskrats are known predators.

Like other North American freshwater mussels, the fanshell must have a stable habitat (mainly clean water and an undisturbed stream bottom) and access to suitable host fish (for larval development) in order to reproduce successfully. The complex life cycle of these mussels begins in the spring with a male releasing sperm for dispersal by stream currents. These sperm, taken in by a female while she is feeding, fertilize eggs stored in her gills. The eggs hatch and larvae develop in the female's gills. After a time the larvae are released into the stream where they attach themselves to the gills of host fish. Any larva not fortunate enough to come into contact with a host fish after release by the female mussel sinks to the bottom of the stream and dies. Larvae can only develop into juveniles while attached to the gills of a host fish.

The larvae remain attached to the host fish until they become juveniles, by which time they have developed a shell and are large enough to survive on their own. The juveniles then detach from the host fish and fall to the stream bottom, where they bury themselves in riffles or shoals with only their shell margins and feeding siphons exposed. Freshwater mussels feed by siphoning plant material from the

Fanshell.

water. Any silt or sediment in the water can pose a serious threat to them, since it can clog their feeding siphons and ultimately kill them.

Habitat and Current Distribution

The fanshell was once found in 26 rivers, but viable populations are now found in only three locations: in Clinch River in Tennessee and Virginia; in Kentucky's Green River, which contains the healthiest population; and in Licking River, also in Kentucky. Other populations are scattered throughout eight other rivers, but fanshells in those populations are beyond the sexually reproductive age.

The fanshell prefers gravel riffles in streams.

History and Conservation Measures

Damming, sand and gravel mining, and water pollution currently threaten the survival of this species. As with other freshwater mussels, the fanshell has experienced major, detrimental changes to its habitat. Even in Green River, which partly flows through Mammoth Cave National Park, pollution has affected various species of fauna and flora. In Clinch River, coal mining activities and toxic spills from a power plant have killed a substantial number of fish and molluscs. If the fanshell is to survive into the near future, the protection of its habitat is essential.

Dromedary pearly mussel

Dromus dromas

Phylum	Mollusca
Class	Pelecypoda (Bivalvia)
Order	Unionoida
Family	Unionidae
Status	Endangered, IUCN
	Endangered, USFWS
	Appendix I, CITES
Range	Tennessee, Virginia (U.S.A.)

Description and Biology

There are two types of dromedary pearly mussel: the big river mussel *Dromus dromas* and the headwater mussel *D. d. caperatus*. On the surface they appear similar; they both have an elliptical to triangular yellow-green shell with broken green lines across the surface. The valves are solid and slightly inflated with a row of small knobs at the center of the shell. It is the color of the inner shell that distinguishes the two animals: in *Dromus dromas*, the color is white or pink, while in *D. d. caperatus* it is pinkish, salmon, or reddish in color.

Like other freshwater mussels, the dromedary pearly mussel breeds in the spring. Males release sperm, which are carried by currents downstream to females. As they feed, the females take in the sperm, which fertilizes the eggs stored in their gills. Glochidia (larvae) hatch soon after and develop in the female's gills, now modified as brood pouches. After a certain time, the glochidia are released and attach themselves to the gill filaments of host fish (glochidia that do not find host fish sink to the river's bottom and die). When they have grown and have developed a shell, the now juvenile mussels detach from the fish and sink to the riverbed. Here, they bury themselves in shoals and riffles, leaving only their shell margins and siphons exposed. Through their siphons, the mussels feed on plankton and other plant matter and expel indigestible particles.

Habitat and Current Distribution

The dromedary pearly mussel is found in shallow riffle and shoal areas. They prefer firm rubble and gravel substrates with fast-flowing current.

This mussel is endemic to the southern Appalachian Mountains and the Cumberland Plateau region. It occurs in sections of the Tennessee, Cumberland, Clinch, and Powell Rivers. Only three live specimens have been seen in the Tennessee River since 1918; five mussels were reported from the Cumberland River in 1981; 16 from Clinch River; and six from Powell River. Total population size is unknown.

History and Conservation Measures

Dromus dromas was first discovered in the Harpeth and Cumberland rivers in Tennessee, while *D. d. caperatus* was found in Clinch River in Virginia and Tennessee. It was reportedly widely distributed throughout the Tennessee and Cumberland river systems. Since their initial discovery, the numbers of dromedary pearly mussels have diminished greatly, largely due to the degradation of their habitat from the construction of dams and channels. Siltation and water pollution have compounded the problem, stressing the mussels and their food supply.

The first conservation priority for this pearly mussel is the protection of the remaining populations, particularly in Clinch and Powell rivers where they are most abundant. Once these populations are stable, some mussels may be transported from these rivers to other suitable areas in order to distribute the species. In addition, Clinch and Powell rivers have been proposed as scenic rivers under the Wild and Scenic Rivers Act (1968) which affords protection of the waters from environmental changes. It is hoped that by protecting the dromedary pearly mussel's remaining habitat, this animal can survive in the wild for at least the immediate future.

Dromedary pearly mussel.

Penitent mussel

Dysnomia (Epioblasma) penita

Phylum	Mollusca
Class	Pelecypoda (Bivalvia)
Order	Unionoida
Family	Unionidae
Status	Endangered, IUCN
	Endangered, USFWS
Range	Alabama, Georgia, Mississippi (U.S.A.)

Description and Biology

The penitent mussel, formerly classified as *Unio penitus*, has a 2.1-in (5.5-cm) yellowish rhomboid shell that is sometimes marked with dark spots. The surface of the shell is also etched with irregular growth lines. The inside of the shell is white or beige. Both sexes have sculptured posteriors, and the female has a large, grooved swelling at the rear of the shell.

Like other North American freshwater mussels, the penitent mussel must have a stable habitat (mainly clean water and an undisturbed stream bottom) and access to suitable host fish (for larval development) in order to reproduce successfully. The complex life cycle of these mussels begins in the spring with a male releasing sperm for dispersal by stream currents. These sperm, taken in by a female while she is feeding, fertilize eggs stored in her gills. The eggs hatch and larvae develop in the female's gills. After a time the larvae are released into the stream where they attach themselves to the gills of host fish. Any larva not fortunate enough to come into contact with a host fish after release by the female mussel sinks to the bottom of the stream and dies. Larvae can only develop into juveniles while attached to the gills of a host fish.

The larvae remain attached to the host fish until they become juveniles, by which time they have de-veloped a shell and are large enough to survive on their own. The juveniles then detach from the host fish and fall to the stream bottom, where they bury

Penitent mussel.

themselves in riffles or shoals with only their shell margins and feeding siphons exposed. Freshwater mussels feed by siphoning plant material from the water. Any silt or sediment in the water can pose a serious threat to them, since it can clog their feeding siphons and ultimately kill them.

Habitat and Current Distribution

The penitent mussel is found in sandy gravel river bottoms with moderately strong currents. This mussel prefers riffles and is found at depths below 2.3 ft (70 cm).

The penitent mussel is currently found in three locations: in the Gainesville Bendway of Tombigbee River in Alabama, where siltation, reduced water flow, and poor water quality threaten the species; in East Fork Tombigbee River; and in Buttahatchie River.

History and Conservation Measures

First discovered in 1834, the penitent mussel was once found in Tombigbee, Alabama, Buttahatchie, Cahaba, and Coosa rivers in Alabama, Georgia, and Mississippi. It has since disappeared from Alabama and Cahaba rivers. It was last collected from the mainstream Tombigbee River in 1972; likewise no penitent mussels have been found in Coosa River since 1974, when a dam was built. Loss of habitat is the chief reason for this mussel's endangered status.

Today, dams, dredging, and siltation threaten the remaining population of the penitent mussel. Canal construction has drastically affected the habitat by altering water flow and temperature. The change in water current, for example, has disturbed the mussel's reproductive cycle, and larvae are unable to develop. Furthermore, mussels prefer cool water temperatures, but human activities, especially on the East Fork Tombigbee River, have caused water temperatures to increase, resulting in additional stress and less food for these mussels. In addition, agricultural runoff and pesticides also threaten the species. Any further alterations to this mussel's habitat—including several proposed channel improvement projects—will surely hasten this animal's extinction. Conservation measures for this species should include the protection of its habitat from any changes in water flow or quality.

Turgid-blossom pearly mussel

Dysnomia (Epioblasma) turgidula

Phylum	Mollusca
Class	Pelecypoda (Bivalvia)
Order	Unionoida
Family	Unionidae
Status	Endangered, IUCN
	Endangered, USFWS
	Appendix I, CITES
Range	Alabama, Tennessee (U.S.A.)

Description and Biology

Mollusc experts consider the turgid-blossom pearly mussel extinct, but some scientists hold out hope that this animal still exists in the wild. This pearly mussel is highly dimorphic; in fact, the female and male of the species were once considered separate species due to their differences in shape and structure. The male turgid-blossom pearly mussel has an elliptical or oval shell; the female has a more rounded shell with strong, irregular growth lines. In both sexes, the shell is about 1.6 in (4 cm) long and is yellowish green in color with fine green lines across the surface. Inside, the shell is bluish white. The valves are inequilateral and slightly bumpy.

Like other freshwater mussels, the turgid-blossom pearly mussel breeds in the spring. Males release sperm, which are carried by currents downstream to females. As they feed, the females take in the sperm, which fertilizes the eggs stored in their gills. Glochidia (larvae) hatch soon after and develop in the female's gills, now modified as brood pouches. After a certain time, the glochidia are released and attach themselves to the gill filaments of host fish (glochidia that do not find host fish sink to the river's bottom and die). When they have grown and developed a shell, the now juvenile mussels detach from the fish and sink to the riverbed. Here, they bury themselves in shoals and riffles, leaving only their shell margins and siphons exposed. Through

Turgid-blossom pearly mussel.

their siphons, the mussels feed on plankton and other plant matter and expel indigestible particles.

Habitat and Current Distribution

The turgid-blossom pearly mussel is considered a Cumberlandian species because it is endemic to the southern Appalachian Mountains and the Cumberland Plateau. It has been found in sandy and gravel substrates in shallow, fast-flowing waters of the Tennessee and Cumberland rivers and their tributaries. Sightings have also been reported in Spring Creek, Black River, and White River in the Ozark Mountains.

History and Conservation Measures

This pearly mussel was last seen in the mid-1960s in Duck River, a tributary of Tennessee River. Due to its rare occurrence, the General Accounting Office in 1988 declared that this species may well be extinct. The causes of this animal's demise are habitat loss, pollution, and siltation due to the construction of dams and reservoirs. The increased turbidity and siltation have clogged this mussel's siphon and smothered the mussel beds. Water pollution from mining, farming, and logging activities has also killed many fish in the rivers, including the host fish species that are vital to this mussel's reproduction. A survey has been recommended to determine if any viable population of the turgid-blossom pearly mussel still exists.

Tar River spinymussel

Elliptio (Canthyria) steinstansana

Phylum	Mollusca
Class	Pelecypoda (Bivalvia)
Order	Unionoida
Family	Unionidae
Status	Endangered, IUCN
	Endangered, USFWS
Range	North Carolina (U.S.A.)

Description and Biology

The Tar River spinymussel is one of three freshwater spiny mussels in the world—the James River spinymussel (*Fusconaia collina*) and the larger *Elliptio spinosa* are the other two. The Tar River spinymussel has a 2.4-in (6-cm) rhomboidal shell with several short spines on each valve, which are used to keep the mussel upright as it feeds on muddy bottoms. Apart from the knobby spines, the shell is smooth with clear, concentric rings. The interior of the shell is yellowish or pinkish; juveniles have orange-brown outer shells with fine green lines across the surface.

Like other North American freshwater mussels, the Tar River spinymussel must have a stable habitat (mainly clean water and an undisturbed stream bottom) and access to suitable host fish (for larval development) in order to reproduce successfully. The complex life cycle of these mussels begins in the spring with a male releasing sperm for dispersal by stream currents. These sperm, taken in by a female while she is feeding, fertilize eggs stored in her gills. The eggs hatch and larvae develop in the female's gills. After a time the larvae are released into the stream where they attach themselves to the gills of host fish. Any larva not fortunate enough to come into contact with a host fish after release by the female mussel sinks to the bottom of the stream and dies.

Larvae can only develop into juveniles while attached to the gills of a host fish.

The larvae remain attached to the host fish until

Tar River spinymussel.

they become juveniles, by which time they have developed a shell and are large enough to survive on their own. The juveniles then detach from the host fish and fall to the stream bottom, where they bury themselves in riffles or shoals with only their shell margins and feeding siphons exposed. Freshwater mussels feed by siphoning plant material from the water. Any silt or sediment in the water can pose a serious threat to them, since it can clog their feeding siphons and ultimately kill them.

Habitat and Current Distribution

The Tar River spinymussel is found in sandy or muddy bottoms of clean streams. This mussel is found only along a 12-mi (19-km) area of the Tar River in North Carolina. A major interstate highway bridge passes over this mussel's habitat, often transporting trucks that carry toxic chemicals and other hazardous substances. Between 100-500 individuals are believed to exist.

History and Conservation Measures

First discovered in the Tar River in 1966, this spinymussel has always been considered rare. Because of its low numbers, one catastrophic event could destroy the entire species. Today, its small population is threatened by habitat degradation, particularly by water pollution from excessive nutrients and pesticides in the river. Because this mussel is considered unique and rare, collectors also value its shell.

The Tar River spinymussel is further threatened by the Asiatic clam (*Corbicula fluminae*), an introduced species that competes for the mussel's habitat and food, mainly phytoplankton. Hydroelectric and flood control projects have also been proposed along the Tar River, but alternatives may be necessary to help ensure the survival of the remaining population of the Tar River spinymussel.

Fine-rayed pigtoe pearly mussel

Fusconaia cuneolus

Phylum	Mollusca
Class	Pelecypoda (Bivalvia)
Order	Unionoida
Family	Unionidae
Status	Endangered, IUCN
	Endangered, USFWS
Range	Alabama, Tennessee, Virginia (U.S.A.)

Description and Biology

The shell of the fine-rayed pigtoe pearly mussel measures 2.5 in (6 cm). Its smooth outer surface is yellowish green to light brown, and its inner surface is white. Fine green rays also radiate over the exterior, giving the species its common name. While basically oval, the shell possesses a straight edge on its outside margin opposite the hinge.

Like other freshwater mussels, the fine-rayed pigtoe pearly mussel breeds in the spring. Males release sperm, which are carried by currents downstream to females. As they feed, the females take in the sperm, which fertilizes the eggs stored in their gills. Glochidia (larvae) hatch soon after and develop in the female's gills, now modified as brood pouches. After a certain period, the glochidia are released and attach themselves to the gill filaments of host fish. When they have grown and developed a shell, the now juvenile mussels detach from the fish and sink to the riverbed where they bury themselves in shoals and riffles, leaving only their shell margins and siphons exposed. Through their siphons, fine-rayed

Fine-rayed pigtoe pearly mussel.

pigtoe pearly mussels feed on plankton and other plant matter and expel indigestible particles.

Habitat and Current Distribution

This species was found as late as 1981 in the Powell River at Buchanan Ford and McDowell Shoal in Tennessee and Fletcher Ford in Virginia. It has also been reported from over 30 sites in the Clinch River and several of its tributaries, ranging from Cedar Bluff, Virginia, to Kelly Branch, Tennessee. Specimens have been found as well in the Elk River and the Paint Rock River, two tributaries of the Tennessee River.

Fine-rayed pigtoe pearly mussels prefer shallow riffles and shoals in rivers and streams where the riverbed consists of gravel or compacted sand.

History and Conservation Measures

First described in 1840, the fine-rayed pigtoe pearly mussel originally ranged throughout the southern Appalachian Mountains. However, the construction of dams and reservoirs on the region's rivers have significantly altered the habitat. The resulting siltation, lowered oxygen content, and fluctuations in water temperature and acidity have rendered many streams and rivers inhospitable to this and other mussel species. Suspended solids from industrial pollution, strip mining, and soil erosion also pose a threat to fine-rayed pigtoe pearly mussels, in effect suffocating them by clogging their syphons.

Due to its relatively widespread distribution, this species does not appear to be in immediate danger of extinction as are several other mussel species in the Appalachian region. However, movement on the local, state, and federal level are needed to ensure its survival. Stricter enforcement of existing water quality regulations, additional surveys to locate new populations, and the creation of mussel sanctuaries in Virginia similar to those in Tennessee are recommended as primary action steps.

Cracking pearly mussel

Hemistena (Lastena) lata

Phylum	Mollusca
Class	Pelecypoda (Bivalvia)
Order	Unionoida
Family	Unionidae
Status	Endangered, IUCN
	Endangered, USFWS
Range	Kentucky, Tennessee, Virginia (U.S.A.)

Description and Biology

The shell of the medium-sized cracking pearly mussel is oval and thin. Its greenish brown or brown exterior features discontinuous rays that are dark green in color. The inner surface of the shell is light blue to purple.

Like other freshwater mussels, the cracking pearly mussel breeds in the spring. Males release sperm, which are carried by currents downstream to females. As they feed, the females take in the sperm, which fertilizes the eggs stored in their gills. Glochidia (larvae) hatch soon after and develop in the female's gills, now modified as brood pouches. After a certain period, the glochidia are released and attach themselves to the gill filaments of host fish. When they have grown and developed a shell, the now juvenile mussels detach from the fish and sink to the riverbed where they bury themselves in shoals and riffles, leaving only their shell margins and siphons exposed. Through their siphons, cracking pearly mussels feed on plankton and other plant matter and expel indigestible particles.

Habitat and Current Distribution

Only three populations of cracking pearly mussels currently exist: in the Elk River in Lincoln County, Tennessee; in the Clinch River in Scott County, Virginia, and Hancock County, Tennessee; and in the Powell River in Hancock County, Tennessee, and Lee County, Virginia. The species may per-

Cracking pearly mussel.

sist in the Green River and the Tennessee River where suitable habitat remains; however, no live specimens have been found at these sites in recent years.

Cracking pearly mussels prefer medium-sized streams with gravel riffles.

History and Conservation Measures

Originally, this species ranged throughout the Tennessee, Ohio, and Cumberland river systems. However, pollution and habitat destruction have led to its decline. The extensive network of dams constructed by the Tennessee Valley Authority (TVA) during the past century have significantly altered the species' environment, as have such accompanying activities as gravel dredging and cold water discharges from reservoirs. Both the Powell River and the Clinch River have been polluted by run-off resulting from coal mining; the Clinch River has also been adversely affected by toxic discharges from a local power plant. Specific conservation measures for the cracking pearly mussel have yet to be implemented.

Higgins' eye pearly mussel

Lampsilis higginsi

Phylum	Mollusca
Class	Pelecypoda (Bivalvia)
Order	Unionoida
Family	Unionidae
Status	Endangered, IUCN Endangered, USFWS
Range	Illinois, Iowa, Minnesota, Wisconsin (U.S.A.)

Description and Biology

The shell of Higgins' eye pearly mussel is tan or brown with narrow black rays along the growth lines. Males are approximately 2.4 in (6 cm) in length, while females are slightly smaller.

Like other freshwater mussels, the Higgins' eye pearly mussel breeds in the spring. Males release sperm, which are carried by currents downstream to females. As they feed, the females take in the sperm, which fertilizes the eggs stored in their gills. Glochidia (larvae) hatch soon after and develop in the female's gills, now modified as brood pouches. The female carries the larvae through the winter until the next spring when the glochidia are released and attach themselves to the gill filaments of host fish. Sauger or freshwater drum usually serve as the host fish for Higgins' eye pearly mussels. When they have grown and developed a shell, the now juvenile mussels detach from the fish and sink to the riverbed where they bury themselves in shoals and riffles, leaving only their shell margins and siphons exposed. Through their siphons, pearly mussels feed on plank-

Higgins' eye pearly mussel.

ton and other plant matter and expel indigestible particles.

Habitat and Current Distribution

Higgins' eye pearly mussels occur in the upper Mississippi River and the St. Croix River. A survey of the Mississippi in the late 1970s and early 1980s located populations in isolated stretches of the river near La Crosse, Wisconsin; from the Minnesota state line to Praire du Chein, Wisconsin; from Clayton in northern Iowa to Dubuque, Iowa; and from Clinton, Iowa, to West Burlington, Iowa. In the St. Croix River, the species has been reported from areas north of Hudson, Wisconsin.

No population estimates currently exist.

History and Conservation Measures

Although no original population statistics exist for the Higgins' eye pearly mussel, the species was never considered abundant. Major populations occurred near Prescott, Minnesota, Muscatine and Dav-

enport, Iowa, as well as Praire du Chien and La Crosse, Wisconsin. The species also inhabited several Mississippi River tributaries, including the St. Croix River, the Illinois River, and Sangamon River in Illinois, and the Iowa River, Cedar River, and Wapsipinicon River in Iowa. Experts believe that the species now occupies only 45 percent of its original range and has been largely eliminated from areas south of West Davenport.

Damming of the Mississippi River and its tributaries—resulting in erratic waterflow, increased siltation, and altered water temperatures—has degraded much of the mussel's habitat. Also contributing to the species' decline are effluents from industrial and municipal sources as well as agricultural run-off. Currently, conservationists have designated six sites along the Mississippi in Wisconsin, Iowa, and Illinois as well as one along the St. Croix River in Wisconsin as integral to the species' survival. Experts have also recommended that the Higgins' eye pearly mussel be relocated from threatened habitats to more stable sites; however, more research is needed before such a program could be undertaken.

Ring pink mussel

Obovaria retusa

Phylum	Mollusca
Class	Pelecypoda (Bivalvia)
Order	Unionoida
Family	Unionidae
Status	Endangered, IUCN
	Endangered, USFWS
Range	Kentucky, Tennessee (U.S.A.)

Description and Biology

This medium-sized mussel, also known as the golf stick pearly mussel, is one of the most endangered of all North American freshwater mussels. Its shell is yellow-green to brown on the outside and dark purple with a white border on the inside.

Like other freshwater mussels, the ring pink mussel breeds in the spring. Males release sperm, which are carried by currents downstream to females. As they feed, the females take in the sperm, which fertilizes the eggs stored in their gills. Glochidia (larvae) hatch soon after and develop in the female's gills, now modified as brood pouches. After a certain time, the glochidia are released and attach themselves to the gill filaments of host fish (glochidia that do not find host fish sink to the river's bottom and die). When they have grown and developed a shell, the now juvenile mussels detach from the fish and sink to the riverbed. Here, they bury themselves in shoals and riffles, leaving only their shell margins and siphons exposed. Through their siphons, the mussels feed on plankton and other plant matter and expel indigestible particles.

Ring pink mussel.

Habitat and Current Distribution

This mussel inhabits the sandy but silt-free bottoms of large rivers. Its current distribution includes stretches of three rivers in Tennessee and Kentucky: the Tennessee, Cumberland, and Green rivers. Total population figures are unavailable.

History and Conservation Measures

The ring pink mussel is in grave danger of extinction, because all of the known populations of the species are apparently too old to reproduce. This mussel was once found in several major tributaries of the Ohio River, including those that stretched into Alabama, Illinois, Indiana, Ohio, Pennsylvania, and West Virginia, so its current limited range signals a major decline in the species. As with many other freshwater mussels, the ring pink mussel's decline can be blamed on human manipulation of its habitat. Damming has historically been the most significant factor, but now the main threats to the surviving populations are water pollution, dredging, and channel maintenance. Unless undiscovered, viable populations of the ring pink mussel exist, the future of this species in the wild is uncertain.

Little-wing pearly mussel

Pegias fabula

Phylum	Mollusca
Class	Pelecypoda (Bivalvia)
Order	Unionoida
Family	Unionidae
Status	Endangered, IUCN
	Endangered, USFWS
Range	Kentucky, Tennessee, Virginia (U.S.A.)

Description and Biology

The little-wing pearly mussel has a light green or yellow-brown outer shell that measures up to 1.5 in (3.8 cm) in length and 0.5 in (1.3) in width. Dark rays run along the shell's front edge, and a white, chalky film often flakes off its surface.

Like other freshwater mussels, the little-wing pearly mussel breeds in the spring. Males release sperm, which are carried by currents downstream to females. As they feed, the females take in the sperm, which fertilizes the eggs stored in their gills. Glochidia (larvae) hatch soon after and develop in the female's gills, now modified as brood pouches. After a certain period, the glochidia are released and attach themselves to the gill filaments of host fish. When they have grown and developed a shell, the now juvenile mussels detach from the fish and sink to the riverbed where they bury themselves in shoals and riffles, leaving only their shell margins and siphons exposed. Through their siphons, the mussels feed on plankton and other plant matter and expel indigestible particles.

Habitat and Current Distribution

A 1986 study reported this very rare species from five locations: Horse Lick Creek, the Big South Fork Cumberland River, and the Little South Fork Cumberland River in Kentucky; Great Falls Lake in Tennessee; and the North Fork Holston River in Virginia. A total of 17 live specimens were located during this study.

The little-wing pearly mussel requires cool wa-

Little-wing pearly mussel.

ters and moderately to steeply inclined streambeds where they are usually found in the transitional zones between riffles and pools.

History and Conservation Measures

While always considered rare due to its specialized habitat, the little-wing pearly mussel did exist in at least 27 cool water tributaries of the Tennessee and Cumberland rivers. The species has since become extinct in North Carolina and Alabama, and a total of 18 populations have been lost in Kentucky, Tennessee, and Virginia.

Water pollution has been the major factor in the decline of the little-wing pearly mussel. Toxic runoff resulting from strip mining, agriculture, and industry has clouded water that was once clear, and increased amounts of sediment have settled on mussel beds, suffocating them.

In Kentucky, Tennessee, and Virginia, laws have been passed prohibiting the harvesting of freshwater mussels without a permit. In Kentucky, part of the mussel's remaining habitat is bounded by the Daniel Boone National Forest, and the state has designated Horse Lick Creek as one of its Outstanding Resource Waters. A joint federal-state conservation effort aimed at increasing populations at these sites are underway. However, continuing exploration for coal threatens to pollute habitat falling outside these protected areas.

James River spinymussel

Pleurobema collina

Phylum	Mollusca
Class	Pelecypoda (Bivalvia)
Order	Unionoida
Family	Unionidae
Status	Endangered, IUCN
	Endangered, USFWS
Range	Virginia, West Virginia (U.S.A.)

Description and Biology

One of only three recognized freshwater spinymussels, this species is also known as the Virginia spinymussel or the James spineymussel. Its adult shell size ranges from 2-3.5 in (5-9 cm); juveniles normally possess one to three spines on each valve, but these spines are usually lost by adulthood. The foot and mantle are bright orange, while a thin, darker band surrounds the edges of the mantle's branchial and anal openings.

Like other freshwater mussels, the James River spinymussel breeds in the spring. Males release sperm, which are carried by currents downstream to females. As they feed, the females take in the sperm, which fertilizes the eggs stored in their gills. Glochidia (larvae) hatch soon after and develop in the female's gills, now modified as brood pouches. After a certain time, the glochidia are released and attach themselves to the gill fillaments of host fish (glochidia that do not find host fish sink to the river's bottom and die). When they have grown large enough and developed a shell, the now juvenile mussels detach from the fish and sink to the riverbed where they bury themselves in shoals and riffles, leaving only their shell margins and siphons exposed. Through their siphons, spinymussels feed on plank-ton and other plant matter and expel indigestible particles.

Habitat and Current Distribution

This species is currently found in four headwater streams of the James River. In Virginia, it inhabits Craig Creek, Catawba Creek, and Johns Creek, which are in Craig and Botetourt counties. In West Virginia, it has been recorded from Potts Creek in Monroe County.

The James River spinymussel prefers slow-flowing freshwater streams with high water quality and a high mineral content. They generally bury themselves in gravel or sand substrates.

History and Conservation Measures

The James River spinymussel was discovered in 1836 in the Calfpasture River in Rockbridge County, Virginia. The species originally occured throughout the James River drainage; however, its range has since been reduced by over 90 percent. A primary factor contributing to the species' decline is habitat destruction due to land development and agricultural run-off, which includes pesticides, herbicides, and silt. Indeed, agricultural run-off currently threatens remaining spinymussel populations. Conservationists see federal regulations retricting development as a means of stemming further disturbance in and around the headwaters where the species is still found.

The James River spinymussel is further threatened by the Asiatic clam (*Corbicula fluminae*), an introduced species that has overtaken much of the mussel's former habitat. The Asiatic clam siphons off the majority of phytophankton in the water, depriving the spinymussel and other native mussels of sufficient nutrients. A program to control the Asiatic clam must be a vital component of any conservation plan for the James River spinymussel.

Rough pigtoe pearly mussel

Pleurobema plenum

Phylum	Mollusca
Class	Pelecypoda (Bivalvia)
Order	Unionoida
Family	Unionidae
Status	Endangered, IUCN
	Endangered, USFWS
	Appendix I, CITES
Range	Alabama, Kentucky, Tennessee (U.S.A.)

Description and Biology

The rough pigtoe pearly mussel has a solid, heavy, triangular shell that is a glossy yellowish to reddish brown. The color of the inner surface of the shell varies from white to pinkish to orange. In mature individuals, the shell measures 2.5 in (6.5 cm) long, 2.8 in (7.1 cm) high, and 1.7 in (4.3 cm) wide. The rough surface of the shell is marked by irregular, concentric growth rings.

Like other North American freshwater mussels, *Pleurobema plenum* must have a stable habitat (mainly clean water and an undisturbed stream bottom) and access to suitable host fish (for larval development) in order to reproduce successfully. The complex life cycle of these mussels begins in the spring with a male releasing sperm for dispersal by stream currents. These sperm, taken in by a female while she is feeding, fertilize eggs stored in her gills. The eggs hatch and larvae develop in the female's gills. In the late summer the larvae are released into the stream where they attach themselves to the gills of host fish. For this mussel host fish include the rosefin shiner and possibly the bluegill. Any larva not fortunate enough to come into contact with a host fish after release by the female mussel sinks to the bottom of the stream and dies. Larvae can only develop into juveniles while attached to the gills of a host fish.

The larvae remain attached to the host fish until they become juveniles, by which time they have developed a shell and are large enough to survive on their own. The juveniles then detach from the host fish and fall to the stream bottom, where they bury themselves in riffles or shoals with only their shell margins and feeding siphons exposed. Freshwater mussels feed by siphoning plant material from the water. Any silt or sediment in the water can pose a serious threat to them, since it can clog their feeding siphons and ultimately kill them. *P. plenum* can live up to 50 years in the wild.

Habitat and Current Distribution

The rough pigtoe pearly mussel is now found in the Tennessee River below Pickwick Dam (Tennessee), Wilson Dam (Alabama), and Guntersville Dam (Alabama); in the Clinch River near Evansville, Indiana; and around the confluence of the Green River and the Barren River in southwestern Kentucky. There are no estimates of the sizes of these populations.

P. plenum inhabits shoals in large rivers and

streams more than 65 ft (20 m) wide. It is found in deeper waters, buried in the sand or gravel of the river bottom.

History and Conservation Measures

This species was formerly widespread through four major regions—the Mississippi River in Arkansas; the Ozarks in Kansas, Missouri, and Arkansas; the Ohio River basin in Ohio, Indiana, and Illinois; and the Cumberland and Tennessee river basins in Virginia, Kentucky, Tennessee, and Alabama. This species has disappeared from many areas of its former range, but the reasons for its decline are not completely understood. As with other species of North American freshwater molluscs, habitat alteration, habitat destruction, and water pollution have certainly had an impact. More than 50 dams have been constructed in the watersheds of the Tennessee

and Cumberland rivers since the 1940s. These dams, along with siltation, dredging, and pollution by agricultural chemicals have permanently altered or destroyed mussel habitat. Sanctuaries for freshwater mussels have been established by the states of Tennessee and Alabama in portions of the Tennessee and Cumberland rivers, but pollutants (from strip mining and coal washing) introduced into these rivers at their headwaters in Virginia threaten the success of these efforts. Unless regional water pollution control programs can be implemented, the recovery of this species remains uncertain. The Tennessee Valley Authority (the administrative agency for the dams on the Tennessee and Cumberland rivers) is also developing a comprehensive water management plan that would establish minimum flows in these rivers. If such a plan is implemented, the negative impacts of these dams on mussel habitats could be reversed or improved.

Fat pocketbook pearly mussel

Potamilus (Proptera) capax

Phylum	Mollusca
Class	Pelecypoda (Bivalvia)
Order	Unionoida
Family	Unionidae
Status	Endangered, IUCN
	Endangered, USFWS
	Appendix I, CITES
Range	Arkansas, Indiana (U.S.A.)

Description and Biology

This rather large freshwater mussel has a spherical shell about 4 in (10 cm) long. This shiny, yellow to brown shell is smooth and lacks distinctive markings. The inside of the shell is an iridescent bluish white. This species is distinguished from similar mussels by the strong S-curve of its shell hinge.

Like other North American freshwater mussels, *Potamilus capax* must have a stable habitat (mainly clean water and an undisturbed stream bottom) and access to suitable host fish (for larval development) in order to reproduce successfully. The complex life cycle of these mussels begins in the spring with a male releasing sperm for dispersal by stream currents. These sperm, taken in by a female while she is feeding, fertilize eggs stored in her gills. The eggs hatch and larvae develop in the female's gills. After a time the larvae are released into the stream where they attach themselves to the gills of host fish. Any larva not fortunate enough to come into contact with a host fish after release by the female mussel sinks to the bottom of the stream and dies. Larvae can only

Fat pocketbook pearly mussel.

develop into juveniles while attached to the gills of a host fish.

The larvae remain attached to the host fish until they become juveniles, by which time they have developed a shell and are large enough to survive on their own. The juveniles then detach from the host fish and fall to the stream bottom, where they bury themselves in riffles or shoals with only their shell margins and feeding siphons exposed. Freshwater mussels feed by siphoning plant material from the water. Any silt or sediment in the water can pose a serious threat to them, since it can clog their feeding siphons and ultimately kill them.

Habitat and Current Distribution

This species is found in the St. Francis River, near Madison, Arkansas; in the Wabash River, near New Harmony, Indiana; and in the White River near Bowman, Indiana. In the St. Francis River, the mussel is only found in the section of the river that has not been dredged. More than 11,000 post-juveniles of this species were found during a 1986 survey, making it the most common mussel in the St. Francis River. The status of the other two populations is less certain. Each population is known from only a few individuals, and it is not known if the species survives in either river as a reproducing population.

The fat pocketbook pearly mussel inhabits rivers and streams with sand, mud, or gravel bottoms. It prefers stretches of these watercourses where the depths are less than 8 ft (2.5 m).

History and Conservation Measures

Although this species was formerly found over a much wider area, it does not seem to have ever occurred in large concentrations. *P. capax* was previously documented in the Wabash River (Indiana), the Ohio River (Illinois), the Illinois River (Illinois), and the Mississippi River between Wabasha, Minnesota, and Grafton, Illinois. Most, if not all, of these populations have been extirpated by habitat destruction or alterations caused by dredging, dam and artificial channel construction, siltation, and pollution from agricultural runoff.

The St. Francis River, which supports a vigorous population of this species, is prone to seasonal flooding, and local residents continue to apply pressure for ongoing dredging of the river for flood control. Under the provisions of the U.S. Fish and Wildlife Service (USFWS) Recovery Plan for *P. capax*, dredging is currently prohibited in the stretch of river above Madison, Arkansas. The USFWS also hopes to establish two additional populations of this species elsewhere in the St. Francis watershed. Introduction of this species to the White River (Indiana), the upper Mississippi River, or the Hatchie River (Tennessee) has been proposed by the U.S. Army Corps of Engineers. Although the Hatchie River is outside the original range of this species, it does support populations of similar mussels and it is protected under the Wild and Scenic Rivers Act. Such an introduction outside the original range of a species requires special permission under the U.S. Endangered Species Act, but is seen as a potentially useful conservation strategy.

Winged mapleleaf

Quadrula fragosa

Phylum	Mollusca
Class	Pelecypoda (Bivalvia)
Order	Unionoida
Family	Unionidae
Status	Endangered, IUCN
	Endangered, USFWS
Range	Wisconsin (U.S.A.)

Description and Biology

This mussel, a close relative of the more common mapleleaf species, has a more inflated shell than its relative. In addition, it differs from the common mapleleaf in the position of its beaks—the upper portion of the hinge between valves.

Like other freshwater mussels, the winged mapleleaf breeds in the spring. Males release sperm, which are carried by currents downstream to females. As they feed, the females take in the sperm, which fertilizes the eggs stored in their gills. Glochidia (larvae) hatch soon after and develop in the female's gills, now modified as brood pouches. After a certain time, the glochidia are released and attach themselves to the gill filaments of host fish (glochidia that do not find host fish sink to the river's bottom and die). When they have grown and developed a shell, the now juvenile mussels detach from the fish and sink to the riverbed. Here, they bury themselves in shoals and riffles, leaving only their shell margins and siphons exposed. Through their siphons, the mussels feed on plankton and other plant matter and expel indigestible particles.

Winged mapleleaf.

Habitat and Current Distribution

The winged mapleleaf inhabits sandy areas of shallow, silt-free rivers. Its current distribution is confined to a 5-mi (8 km) stretch of the St. Croix River, in Wisconsin near the Minnesota border. Total population is unknown, but its density is very low—one individual per 560 sq ft (52 sq m).

History and Conservation Measures

This mussel used to be found in four large river systems—the Mississippi, the Tennessee, the Ohio, and the Cumberland—in 11 different states stretching from Wisconsin to Tennessee. Its steep decline can be attributed to alteration and destruction of its habitat through impoundment and sedimentation.

The only remaining population of the winged mapleleaf occurs in a national scenic river, so impoundment is probably not a threat. Rather, the chief threat to this species is internal: all individuals in the surviving population appear to be past reproductive age. If this is indeed the case, extinction of the winged mapleleaf is probably inevitable.

Stirrup shell

Quadrula stapes

Phylum	Mollusca
Class	Pelecypoda (Bivalvia)
Order	Unionoida
Family	Unionidae
Status	Endangered, IUCN
	Endangered, USFWS
Range	Alabama (U.S.A.)

Description and Biology

The stirrup shell is a small freshwater mussel with a yellowish green, quadrangular shell. This shell is 2.2 in (5.5 cm) long and is marked with a pattern of zig-zag lines. These lines are light green on young individuals and dark brown on older individuals. The inner surface of the shell is silvery white.

Like other North American freshwater mussels, *Quadrula stapes* must have a stable habitat (mainly clean water and an undisturbed stream bottom) and access to suitable host fish (for larval development) in order to reproduce successfully. The complex life cycle of these mussels begins in the spring with a male releasing sperm for dispersal by stream currents. These sperm, taken in by a female while she is feeding, fertilize eggs stored in her gills. The eggs hatch and larvae develop in the female's gills. After a time the larvae are released into the stream where they attach themselves to the gills of host fish. Any larva not fortunate enough to come into contact with a host fish after release by the female mussel sinks to the bottom of the stream and dies. Larvae can only develop into juveniles while attached to the gills of a host fish.

The larvae remain attached to the host fish until they become juveniles, by which time they have developed a shell and are large enough to survive on

their own. The juveniles then detach from the host fish and fall to the stream bottom, where they bury themselves in riffles or shoals with only their shell

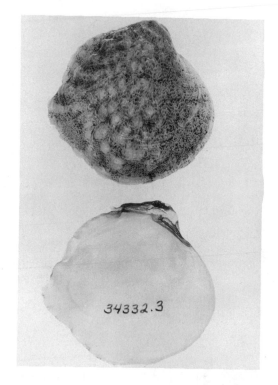

Stirrup shell.

margins and feeding siphons exposed. Freshwater mussels feed by siphoning plant material from the water. Any silt or sediment in the water can pose a serious threat to them, since it can clog their feeding siphons and ultimately kill them.

Habitat and Current Distribution

The stirrup shell is found in the Sipsey River and the Gainesville Bendway (a meander of the East Fork Tombigbee River severed by the construction of the Tennessee-Tombigbee Waterway). Both sites are in Alabama. This species inhabits shoals and riffles in fast-flowing waters. Current population figures are not known.

History and Conservation Measures

This species once occurred in the Tombigbee River from Columbus, Mississippi, to Epes, Alabama, and in the Alabama, Black Warrior, and Sipsey rivers. In recent decades it has not been found in the Alabama River or the Black Warrior River. Much of the decline of this species can be attributed to the construction of the Tennessee-Tombigbee Waterway, a series of channels, locks, and impoundments built to provide a link for barge traffic between these two rivers. Dredging to create channels destroyed many mussel beds, and this dredging continues periodically to maintain these channels. The construction of dams and locks for this waterway caused mussel beds to be flooded; water flow was also slowed, resulting in increased siltation and the smothering of mussel beds.

Ongoing flood control and channel improvement activities pose a threat to the mussel beds in the Tombigbee and Sipsey rivers. Dredging and siltation could destroy or degrade mussel habitat. U.S. federal agencies, including the Army Corps of Engineers and the Soil Conservation Service, are required by the Endangered Species Act to consult with the U.S. Fish and Wildlife Service before undertaking projects or activities that could jeopardize endangered populations, such as the populations of *Q. stapes* in these rivers. In some cases, projects are redesigned following such consultations to protect habitat for vulnerable species.

Cumberland bean pearly mussel

Villosa (Micromya) trabalis

Phylum	Mollusca
Class	Pelecypoda (Bivalvia)
Order	Unionoida
Family	Unionidae
Status	Endangered, IUCN
	Endangered, USFWS
Range	Kentucky, Tennessee (U.S.A.)

Description and Biology

A small- to medium-sized mussel, the Cumberland bean pearly mussel has an oval shell that is a semi-glossy olive green, yellowish brown or black on its outer surface. Concentric growth ridges and wavy, green to black rays adorn the shell's surface; ridges are also found on the beak, or the upper portion of the hinge between valves. The shell's inner surface is pearly white with iridescent blue-green coloring at its posterior.

Like other freshwater mussels, the Cumberland bean pearly mussel breeds in the spring. Males release sperm, which are carried by currents downstream to females. As they feed, the females take in the sperm, which fertilizes the eggs stored in their gills. Glochidia (larvae) hatch soon after and develop in the female's gills, now modified as brood pouches. After a certain period, the glochidia are released and attach themselves to the gill filaments of host fish. When they have grown and developed a shell, the now juvenile mussels detach from the fish and sink to the riverbed where they bury themselves in shoals and riffles, leaving only their shell margins and si-

Cumberland bean pearly mussel.

phons exposed. Through their siphons, pearly mussels feed on plankton and other plant matter and expel indigestible particles.

Habitat and Current Distribution

The largest population of the Cumberland bean pearly mussel now in existence has been recorded from a 20-mi (32-km) stretch of the Little South Fork Cumberland River in McCreary County, Kentucky. Smaller populations have been found in Camp Creek in the Tennessee headwaters of the Big South Fork Cumberland River and in the Rockcastle River and its tributaries, including Horse Lick Creek, Middle Fork Creek, and Roundstone Creek in Laurel County, Kentucky, and Buck Creek in Pulaski County, Kentucky.

Cumberland bean pearly mussels prefer gravel or sand shoals in clean, rapidly flowing waters that keep silt from settling on the shoal. No population estimates currently exist.

History and Conservation Measures

In the past, Cumberland bean pearly mussels were spread throughout many of the tributary streams feeding into the upper Cumberland River. In the 1920s it also was reported from the Tennessee River and its tributaries, its range reaching as far south as northern Georgia and Alabama.

The construction of 36 dams by the Tennessee Valley Authority in the Tennessee River basin since the 1930s has had a tremendous impact on this species. Biologists believe that such projects are responsible for the elimination of the species from the Tennessee River watershed. On the Cumberland River, five major dams have been erected, and six have been completed on its tributaries, further endangering the species, which often cannot survive in the cold tailwaters extending above a dam.

A further threat to the species is the silt generated by agriculture, strip mining, and logging, which often suffocates mussel beds after settling to the river bottom. Increased water pollution, including pesticides and fertilizers from agricultural run-off, has also contributed to the decline of the Cumberland bean pearly mussel.

Two rivers in the species range—Buck Creek and Little South Fork Cumberland River—are eligible for protection as Scenic Rivers under the National Wild and Scenic Rivers Act. Also, about 10 mi (16 km) of the Little South Fork River has been designated by Kentucky as a State Wild River, providing protection for endangered species in that area. Unfortuately the Cumberland bean pearly mussel has yet to be found in that part of the river, which has been severely affected by acid mine drainage. The Tennessee Valley Authority is also in the midst of developing a water management plan that would ensure year-round minimum water flows in all rivers by precisely timing water discharges from its dams.

Danube endemic molluscs

Theodoxus transversalis

Viviparus acerosus

Fagotia esperi

Phylum	Mollusca
Class	Gastropoda
Order	Archaeogastropoda; Mesogastropoda
Family	Neritidae (*T. transversalis*); Viviparidae (*V. acerosus*); Melanopsidae (*F. esperi*)
Status	Vulnerable, IUCN
Range	Austria; Belarus; Bulgaria; Germany; Hungary; Moldova; Romania; Slovakia; Ukraine; Yugoslavia (?)

Description and Biology

Three species of snails endemic to the Danube River system are seriously threatened with extinction: *Theodoxus transversalis*, *Viviparus acerosus*, and *Fagotia esperi*. Information on these and other non-marine European molluscs is scant; even as scientists are studying these molluscs, they are quickly disappearing in the wild due to habitat loss and degradation. The habitat of these snails, the Danube River located in central Europe, is Europe's second largest river (the Volga is the largest). Formed by two mountain streams, the Breg and Brigach rivers, in the Black Forest, western Germany, the Danube flows southeast across Austria and Hungary and empties out into the Black Sea. It is 1,770 mi (2,850 km) long and has about 300 tributaries.

Habitat and Current Distribution

T. transversalis is found on hard surfaces in slow-moving waters mainly in the Middle Danube in the countries of Austria, Bulgaria, Germany, Hungary, Moldova, Romania, Slovakia, Ukraine, and possibly Yugoslavia. *V. acerosus* is endemic to the Danube Basin from Vienna to its mouth and prefers muddy, stagnant, or sluggish water. It is currently found in Austria, Bulgaria, Germany, Hungary, Romania, and Slovakia. *F. esperi* is found at several locations along the Danube River system in the countries of Austria, Belarus, Hungary, Moldova, Slovakia, and Ukraine. No information is available about this species' habitat preference.

History and Conservation Measures

The Danube River has historically been an important trade route in Europe. Several large cities are located on the banks of this river, including Vienna and Budapest, and about 70 million people live in the Danube Basin. These factors have combined to place a great deal of stress on the river system; both domestic and industrial pollution, eutrophication, and agricultural run-off threaten the flora and fauna in and around the river. Additionally, hydropower stations and other hydroelectric projects impact water courses, affecting the flow of water currents and thereby altering the snails' habitat. Aside from the three known species, other unindentified molluscs are believed to be endemic to the Danube River, but due to the speed of habitat degradation, research on these species has been difficult.

Currently only *T. transversalis* is protected in a national park; the Kiskunsag National Park in Hungary harbors a certain number of this species. In an effort to protect this and other species along the Danube River, eight countries signed the "Danube Declaration" as a promise to monitor pollution affecting the river and assess any environmental impact.

Queen conch

Strombus gigas

Phylum	Mollusca
Class	Gastropoda
Order	Archaeogastropoda
Family	Strombidae
Status	Commercially Threatened, IUCN
Range	Caribbean Sea

Description and Biology

The queen conch or pink conch has a heavy, solid shell which reaches a maximum length of approximately 8 in (20.5 cm) at maturity. The exterior of the shell is light pink to white, and the interior of the aperture is a rich pink, yellow, or peach; the shell also has a row of blunt spines on the whorls below the suture. The conch has a foot with a large, horny plate, known as an operculum, which it uses to close the aperture of its shell when its foot is retracted. The operculum is also used in a clawlike fashion to pull its body rapidly forward and to right itself. Adults may weigh more than 5.5 lb (2.5 kg), with males being smaller than females. The conch consumes a variety of species of algae. Its food preferences seem to change seasonally and vary according to geographic location. Very occasionally a queen conch will produce a pink pearl of moderate value. Juveniles of the species are heavily preyed upon, particularly by tulip murex (*Fasciolaria tulipa*), apple murex (*Murex pomum*), octopi, hermit crabs, loggerhead turtles, and fish. Adults are probably only preyed upon by loggerheads, the Florida horse-conch (*Pleuroploca gigantea*), octopi, and rays.

Queen conchs breed in shallow waters during the summer months. In Florida, the spawning season is late May to September; in the Bahamas, Turks, and Caicos it is March to October; and in Venezuela it is July to November. Each season a female can lay eight or more spawn masses, each of which typically contain 400,000 eggs but can contain as many as 750,000. This egg mass consists of a single continuous tube which is sticky when extruded so that sand grains

Queen conch.

adhere to it; this may camouflage the eggs and deter predators. The shelled larvae hatch approximately four to five days later. After metamorphosis, which can occur approximately 28 days after hatching, juveniles bury themselves in the substrate, where they remain for the following year.

Habitat and Current Distribution

The queen conch is found in Bermuda, southeast Florida, and throughout the Caribbean and Southern Gulf of Mexico, down to Belize, Panama, Colombia, and Venezuela. Actual population numbers are unknown; the queen conch has declined near areas of high human population density but may still be common in more remote areas.

This species is found near islands and coral reefs on sandflats, gravel, coral rubble, and hard coral rock bottoms or in sea grass, generally in shallow water where enough light penetrates to allow the growth of large quantities of algae. Juveniles are found on shallow sandflats and grass beds where the vegetation is not too thick. While conchs have been recorded at depths up to 400 ft (120 m), they are rarely found deeper than 100 ft (30 m), possibly because of the lack of food at greater depths. The species is primarily nocturnal.

Conchs are migratory, moving in groups from deeper to shallower water to spawn. They also seem to migrate in winter to deeper offshore waters with sparse algae and sand, with adult conchs migrating farther than juveniles. Adults as well as juveniles may remain partially or completely buried for several weeks in the winter, when they probably become dormant.

History and Conservation Measures

In all Caribbean countries, heavy fishing has severely depleted conch populations in areas close to island population centers and fishing villages, such that catches have decreased and contain smaller specimens. Deeper areas, which in the past may have provided a refuge for the species, are being exploited by scuba divers. In some regions, conch populations may be incapable of recovering naturally even if fishing is completely curtailed. While the status of the species itself remains unclear, international concern has been raised regarding the future viability of conch fishing; the queen conch is a major food resource in the Caribbean and brings high prices on the export market. Many small scale fishermen in the Caribbean depend upon it for their livelihood.

With increasing evidence of the overexploitation of the species, efforts have been made to put legal restrictions in place, including catch limits and the prohibition of the use of scuba gear for conch fishing; however, greater enforcement of these restrictions is necessary. Healthy conch populations remain in some remote areas, but effective management programs are needed if these stocks are to provide a sustainable yield. Additional research is needed on the biology and habitat requirements of the species. Intensive research into conch mariculture is underway in several countries. Successful hatchery techniques have been developed, but captive-bred juveniles have a poor survival rate when released. Until the variables that affect this survival rate are better understood, there is little hope of using captive-bred specimens to restock depleted areas.

Lake Baikal endemic molluscs

Phylum	Mollusca
Class	Gastropoda; Bivalvia
Order.	Mesogastropoda; Basommatophora; Veneroida
Family	Valvatidae (4 species); Hydrobiidae (7 species); Baicaliidae (32 species); Planorbidae (7 species); Ancylidae (3 species); Sphaeriidae (3 species)
Status	Threatened, IUCN
Range	Lake Baikal (Russia)

Description and Biology

There are over 150,000 species of molluscs, making this the second most diverse animal group after the arthropods. Molluscs play an important role in the food chain, breaking down organic material and providing food for a variety of animals. They are also sensitive to environmental changes and conditions and serve as indicators of environmental stress for other fauna as well as flora.

Fifty-six of the 84 mollusc species found in Lake Baikal, in eastern Siberia, are endemic. Varying in size, shape, color, knobs, and striation, Lake Baikal endemic molluscs are found throughout the main body of the lake.

Habitat and Current Distribution

Molluscs in Lake Baikal are found at depths greater than 1.6 ft (0.5 m), most often at depths between 49-66 ft (15-20 m). A few species such as *Benedicta fragilis*, *B. maxima*, and *Valvata bathybia* prefer deeper areas and are found in waters as deep as 820 ft (250 m). Lake Baikal molluscs prefer colder waters and tend to have thin shells. Depending on the species, molluscs are found on sandy bottoms, on sand and silt, on stony bottoms, or on rocks with sponges and algae. Population estimates are unavailable.

History and Conservation Measures

Lake Baikal—also called the "Pearl of Siberia" and the "Sacred Sea"—is the deepest lake in the world, and its ecosystem includes many species found nowhere else on earth. Although the lake is cleaner than most other large lakes, Lake Baikal and its inhabitants, including the molluscs, are threatened by pollution. Effluents from nearby pulp and paper mills, a power plant, sewage treatment centers, and a fish cannery have contaminated the lake. Pesticide runoff has also polluted the lake. These factors have combined to alter the chemical composition of the lake water and the lake's microbial flora. As a result, large numbers of the small crayfish that filter and purify the lake water are dying. Fish populations have also suffered. By January 1989, the omul, an endemic fish, had stopped spawning naturally and the fertility and growth rates of other fish species had also declined. All but one species of fish tested to monitor pollution levels contained traces of DDT, PCBs, and hexachlorocyclohexane. Since 1987 large numbers of nerpa, Lake Baikal's endemic seal, have died from consuming the toxic pollutants that accumulate in the fish they eat. The pollution may also have affected the seals' immune systems, making them more vulnerable to epidemics of disease. Although the specific effects of these pollutants and ecosystem alterations on Lake Baikal's endemic molluscs are not known, these molluscs must be considered threatened since their ecosystem remains at risk of permanent degradation.

A number of research projects currently are underway to study the ecosystem of the Lake Baikal region. While some efforts are directed toward saving specific species, most conservationists agree that efforts should focus on protecting the entire Lake Baikal region. Two national parks and three reserves are already established near the lake, and the area has been proposed as a World Heritage Site. A delegation from UNESCO (the agency responsible for designating World Heritage Sites) visited Lake Baikal in 1990, but recommended postponing Baikal's designation until its environmental problems are solved.

Giant clams

Tridacnidae spp.

Phylum	Mollusca
Class	Pelecypoda (Bivalvia)
Order	Veneroida
Family	Tridacnidae
Status	Indeterminate, IUCN (*Hippopus hippopus, H. porcellanus, Tridacna squamosa*)
	Insufficiently Known, IUCN (*Tridacna crocea, T. maxima, T. tevoroa*)
	Vulnerable, IUCN (*Tridacna derasa, T. gigas*)
	Appendix II, CITES
Range	Indo-Pacific Ocean

Description and Biology

The Tridacnidae family contains nine species, and they are all of conservation concern. In most species, the size and appearance of the mantle (the fold of skin that lines the shell and bears shell-secreting glands) varies geographically and ranges through brilliant blue, green, purple, and brown, depending on incident light. The vivid pigmentation is caused by iridophores and may help to protect the tissues against the effects of the intense light to which they are continually exposed. It also may serve to confuse potential predators or to warn them of potential danger. Giant clams feed by filtering plankton from the sea with their gills. *Hippopus hippopus* reaches 15.6 in (39.7 cm) in length. The shell is elongate to ovate, triangular, or sub-rhombical in shape and the valves are heavy and thick, usually colored with strawberry blotches and often obscured by encrusting organisms. The mantle is irregularly mottled along the edges and in the center with deep yellowish green. *Hippopus porcellanus* has a thinner and smoother shell than *H. hippopus*, usually lacking the strawberry coloration, and more semi-circular in outline. The mantle is a somber olive green color. *Tridacna crocea*

is the smallest giant clam, reaching only 5.9 in (15 cm) in length. The valves are grayish white, often tinged with pinkish orange or yellow both inside and out, and are usually quite smooth. They are triangularly ovate in shape. *Tridacna derasa*, the second largest tridacnid, is distinguished by its low primary and radial sculpture, variable shape, lack of spiny projections, and white shell. It reaches 20.2 in (51.4 cm) or more in length. *Tridacna gigas* is the largest living shelled mollusc and may weigh over 440 lb (200 kg), of which the living tissue may account for 121-143 lb (55-65 kg). The shell may grow to 53.9 in (137 cm) in length, is sub-oval to fan-shaped and white, and bears a number of radiating ribs. *Tridacna maxima*, probably the most widespread species, reaches 13.8-15.7 in (35-40 cm) in length, and has the brightest mantle coloring of all the giant clams. Its shell shape and mantle color vary widely. *Tridacna squamosa* has an elongate shell with about five strong, low, rounded radial ridges, each carrying fluted scales growing large toward the edge of the valve. The valves are white, tinged with lemon yellow toward the margin, and may reach 13.8-15.7 in (35-40 cm) in length. In the southern Philippines and Indonesia some individuals are found with deep orange and yellow shells. Recently, two additional molluscs—*T. tevoroa* and *T. rosewateri*—were identified; little information is available on their descriptions.

Giant clams may live for up to 100 years. They are protandrous hermaphrodites, meaning that the male gonad matures before the female gonad, and sperm are released before the eggs. Unlike most hermaphrodite bivavles, giant clams rarely self-fertilize. Reproductive success may be largely a function of the population density of breeding adults, and the probability of fertilization will decrease rapidly as the distance between the spawning adults increases. Seasonality is the only strong influence on gonad development and initiation of spawning behavior, but different species seem to have different breeding seasons, and different cues may act as triggers. The pelagic (open water) life of the veliger (shelled larvae) is much shorter than that reported for most tropical molluscs. It has been calculated from laboratory experiments at 12 days for *T. crocea*, 11-12 days for *T. maxima*, 10 days for *T. squamosa,* and 9 days for *H. hippopus*, although under natural conditions it could be even shorter. After settlement and metamorphosis, juveniles seek a suitable permanent settling spot that will give them maximum protection.

Habitat and Current Distribution

Giant clams are restricted to limited areas of the Indo-Pacific region. They may be confined to their present ranges by their need for shallow waters of coral reefs and their short larval life that prevents long range dispersal. In many areas populations are now much reduced, but the smaller species are still abundant in many areas. *H. hippopus* occurs from the Malay Peninsula to eastern Melanesia, and is found on sandy substrates on coral reefs down to almost 20 ft (6 m) in depth and on sea grass beds near the reef. *H. porcellanus* appears to have a more restricted range than *H. hippopus* but the ranges do overlap. *T. crocea* ranges from the western coast of the Malay Peninsula east to Micronesia and north to the Ryukyu Islands, Japan, including Thailand, Singapore, the Philippines, Indonesia, North Borneo, Papua New Guinea, New Caledonia, and the Caroline Islands. It burrows by mechanical, and possibly chemical, means into the coral reef and lives with only the valve margins visible; it is found most often on top of small, detached coral boulders on the interior reef flat. *T. derasa* is known from the Philippines, Indonesia, Guam, the Cocos-Keeling Islands, Australia, Papua New Guinea, New Caledonia, and the Caroline Islands. It generally occurs on the outer edges of reefs at about 13-33 ft (4-10 m); it appears to be restricted to oceanic environments and is not found on reefs adja-

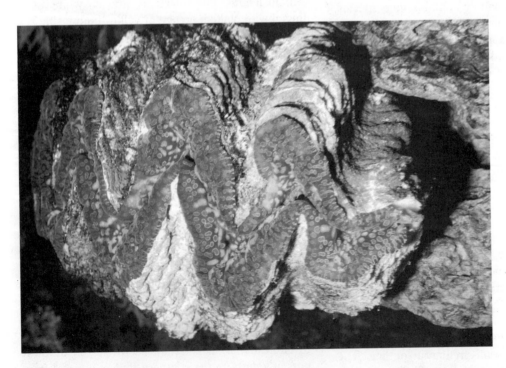

Tridacna gigas.

cent to large land masses. *T. gigas* occurs from the Philippines to Micronesia. It is found on sand and among corals on reefs from about 4-66 ft (1-20 m) in depth; some or all of the shell may be exposed at low tides. *T. maxima* and *T. squamosa* are the most widespread, extending from the Red Sea and the East African coast to the Tuamotu Archipelago and Pitcairn Island, and from southern Japan to the coast of New South Wales, Australia. *T. maxima* is essentially a reef-top inhabitant living on the surfaces of the reef or sand, or partly embedded in coral. *T. squamosa* usually occurs on coral reef surfaces in depths less than 49 ft (15 m), most often in protected environments such as reef canyons and fissures and sheltered lagoons. It is uncommon in atoll environments. Both *T. tevoroa* and *T. rosewateri* have limited ranges. The former has been identified in the northern portion of Tonga and in the waters surrounding Fiji. The species appears to occupy the deepest waters: it has been located at depths of up to approximately 131 ft (40 m). The latter has been found on the Saya de Malha Bank in the Indian Ocean.

History and Conservation Measures

Giant clams, in particular the larger species, are very vulnerable to over-exploitation. These species, which are in demand for their adductor muscles, were depleted in large amounts by commercial fisheries, particularly long-range Taiwanese fishing craft. Around the mid-1970s, activity on the part of the Taiwanese decreased because of depleted supply and international pressures; however, as a result of continued demand, Fiji, the Maldives, and Papua New Guinea developed their own fisheries. These were subsequently closed after the depletion of local stocks. In nine years, for instance, the Fijian fishing industry harvested almost 50 tons of clams, virtually eliminating the supply. The populations of large species have also declined because of the shell and meat trade and due to the demand from the aquarium industry.

Methods for managing the species include the placement of restrictions on the size of harvested clams, as well as the imposition of annual quotas on yields. Other methods of management include restocking current supplies and establishing giant clam refuges. Some authorities advocate restocking tridacnid species with juveniles raised in hatcheries. Recent research, however, seems to indicate that this might not be economically beneficial, as unprotected juveniles released onto reef systems face high mortality rates. Protected areas for giant clams should be instituted, especially in areas where stocks are depleted.

Arachnids, Crustaceans, Insects

Tooth Cave spider

Leptoneta (Neoleptoneta) myopica

Phylum	Arthropoda
Class	Arachnida
Order	Araneae
Family	Leptonetidae
Status	Endangered, IUCN
	Endangered, USFWS
Range	Texas (U.S.A.)

Description and Biology

A very small, slender species with long legs, the Tooth Cave spider is 0.06 in (1.6 mm) long. The front legs are six times the length of the carapace. Coloration is pale to white, and the spider has reduced eyes. It preys on very small arthropods.

Habitat and Current Distribution

This species is only found in the caves of the Jollyville Plateau karst fauna region in Travis County, Texas. It is known to occur in Tooth Cave and in New Comanche Trail Cave and has been tentatively identified in Gallifer Cave and Stovepipe Caves. There are no estimates of population size.

Usually found hanging from a web, the Tooth Cave spider inhabits karst terrain, which is formed by the gradual dissolution of calcium carbonate from limestone bedrock, creating many caves, fractures, or sinkholes. The species requires stable temperatures, high humidity, and a constant supply of small invertebrates.

History and Conservation Measures

There is no early information about this spider's range or distribution because surveys and studies of the region were not initiated until the early 1960s.

The primary threat to this species and to a number of other residents of the karst region is loss or degradation of habitat. Rapid residential and urban develop-

Tooth Cave spider.

ment continues and can lead to the destruction or drastic alteration of unprotected habitat areas. Diversion or increase of water flows can dry out or flood the caves, and alteration of vegetation above the caves can diminish supplies of nutrients and introduce exotic species into the ecosystem; in particular, fire ant infestations are becoming increasingly common and harmful. Because the caves are formed by seeping water, they are especially vulnerable to contamination and pollution.

Conservation efforts are underway to protect the habitat of this and other endangered species. Approximately 7,000 acres (2,800 ha) is proposed for protection, and efforts are ongoing with private landholders to protect the caves and restrict human access. A small, isolated population is always at particular risk of extinction, so surveys will be conducted in hopes of locating additional populations.

No-eyed big-eyed wolf spider

Adelocosa anops

Phylum	Arthropoda
Class	Arachnida
Order	Araneae
Family	Lycosidae
Status	Endangered, IUCN
Range	Hawaii (U.S.A.)

Description and Biology

Known in Hawaii as *pe'e pe'e maka'ole*, this cave-dwelling blind spider has a body length of 0.39-0.78 in (10-20 mm). The cephalothorax (fused head and thorax) is light brown or orange, with no eyes and long, translucent, orange bristly legs; the abdomen is dull white. All other members of this family have large, well-developed eyes, thus their common name. The no-eyed big-eyed wolf spider does not spin webs but actively stalks and overwhelms other invertebrates.

The species has a low reproductive capacity, laying only 15-30 eggs per clutch. The adult lifespan is at least six months.

Habitat and Current Distribution

The no-eyed big-eyed wolf spider is known only from the deep zone of Koloa Cave, from where the type specimen was described, and from smaller populations in nearby segments of the same cave some 1.5 mi (2.4 km) away on the southeast coast of Kauai Island, in the Hawaiian group. These caves are lava tubes resulting from a single eruption of the Koloa volcanic series. This spider inhabits small cavities impenetrable to humans, as well as the caves themselves, but its distribution is limited to a single series of lava flows.

In its extremely limited cave ecosystem, the spider requires a permanent moisture source, con-stant 100 percent relative humidity, and stagnant air; temperatures between 75°-80°F (24°-27°C) are its preferred conditions.

History and Conservation Measures

The greatest threats to this species are the withdrawal and pollution of groundwater and alterations on the surface for tourist facilities and urbanization. Water is already scarce, and natural water sources have been disrupted; some moisture in the caves now comes from surface irrigation of sugar cane. The spider and other cave invertebrates are extremely sensitive to desiccation, and a failure in water supply could be disastrous. Runoff from developments and urban areas can pollute the groundwater with pesticides and toxic chemicals. Agriculture has already ruined the largest lava cave in the area: it became covered with waste residue from sugar cane production. The introduction and spread of invertebrate disease organisms for biological control of soil pests may decimate the endemic cave fauna. The elimination of plant roots by destruction of the surface vegetation removes an important food source from the habitat. Human visitors may affect cave habitats by trampling, littering, smoking, vandalizing, destroying tree roots, or altering the microclimate. Until recently, the two Koloa caves were Civil Defense shelters and are well known to local people. Although the spiders would probably survive in remote crevices, human interference could destroy those spiders accessible to scientists and the public.

Some beneficial cooperation has been obtained from landowners in the area, and limited funds have been acquired, which have permitted intermittent surveys and research. Of the many small caves in the area, only four segments in two areas have suitable moisture and microclimates and harbor small populations of the spider. Plans have been initiated to establish reserves for these caves; two are slated for protection within a golf course development, and the Koloa caves are to be protected within a new housing development. Another cave segment has been protected and efforts made to attract the spider.

The largest and most stable populations of the spider occur in Koloa Cave No. 2, and formal reserve status for all of this cave should be established. Long-term monitoring of the populations within the two reserve caves on resort property is necessary to ensure that the size of these reserves is adequate for the survival of the species. Management regulations need to be developed and should include provisions for limiting access to the caves and restrictions on the type of modifications allowed on the surface near and above the caves.

Doryonychus raptor

Phylum	Arthropoda
Class	Arachnida
Order	Araneae
Family	Tetragnathidae
Status	Indeterminate, IUCN
Range	Hawaii (U.S.A.)

Description and Biology

Doryonychus raptor is the only species in the genus *Doryonychus*. The placement of the species in its own genus reflects its unique and extraordinary morphology: the robust, elongate, bright green spider is characterized by a remarkable elongation of the prolateral tarsal claws on the first two pairs of legs and the development of a thick "pretarsus" lined with stout macrotricheae. Approximate body measurements are: cephalothorax and abdomen 0.39 in (1 cm) in length; and total length 1.4 in (3.5 cm) when outstretched.

The most extraordinary and unique aspect of this species is the foraging mode associated with this morphology. *D. raptor* has completely abandoned the web-building behavior characteristic of the genus. Prey are captured, either in flight or from the substrate, by impalement with the claws, which occurs through a very rapid movement of one or more of the first two pairs of legs. The number of tarsal claws used to impale the prey varies according to the size of the prey, a single claw being used for very small flies (the most common prey item), all four claws being used for larger insects.

D. raptor is strictly nocturnal. During daylight the spider lies flat against a vertical substrate in a characteristic posture, with legs splayed out to the side. Spiders hunt actively at night and spend most of their time hanging upside down from silk threads, using the third and fourth pairs of legs.

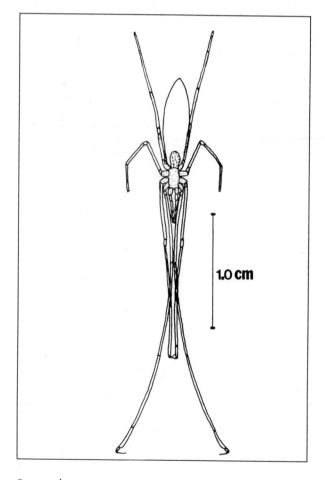

Doryonychus raptor.

1.0 cm

The life history of the species is known only from a few observations in the laboratory on field-collected individuals. Mating occurs in a manner characteristic of the genus *Tetragnatha*: a male and female approach each other in a combative manner, chelicerae and fangs outstretched. The male then locks the fangs of the female against a spur on the dorsal surface of his chelicerae, thus securing the female in position for mating. In one instance three egg sacs from a single female were observed; a total of 32 young spiders were hatched from the egg sacs. Young spiders possess the greatly elongated prolateral claws on the first two pairs of legs even at the first instar. In addition, they do not build webs and adopt a resting position similar to that of the adult.

The phylogenetic placement of *Doryonychus* relative to the genus *Tetragnatha* has generated considerable interest among arachnologists, as well as those interested in evolution. The genus *Tetragnatha* has undergone a spectacular, explosive adaptive radiation within the Hawaiian Islands, and studies are underway to determine whether *D. raptor* is a deviant representative of the primary radiation of Hawaiian *Tetragnatha*.

Habitat and Current Distribution

D. raptor is confined to the Hawaiian Island of Kauai. It was initially discovered by R.C.L. Perkins in the 1890s and described in 1900. Since Perkins's initial collection of the holotype, *D. raptor* was not seen again until it was discovered in low elevation forest on Kauai in 1990. Except for a single immature specimen collected at slightly higher elevation, specimens have been found only in low elevation native (or mixed native) forest directly below high waterfalls along the steep cliffs coming off the Alakai plateau of windward Kauai.

History and Conservation Measures

The lowland areas of Kauai, in common with those on all the Hawaiian Islands, are the most severely impacted, and most have surrendered to the enormous pressure of alien intrusion. *D. raptor* is confined to native, or native-dominated, vegetation; only isolated pockets of such vegetation remain on lowland Kauai. The species is found associated primarily with *Pipturus* species. However, where native forests have been invaded by guava (*Psidium*), spiders have been collected from guava leaves, although this appears to be the only plant invasion to which the species has at least some degree of tolerance. Also, the persistence of the species in these currently disturbed, yet native-dominated, forests may be transitory. It is highly improbable that the species can continue to exist in the face of the onslaught of alien species that colonize lowland forests on the Hawaiian Islands in ever-increasing numbers. In addition to invasion by alien plants, observations on the fauna indicate that goats and ants may play a large part in the restricted range and possible demise of the species.

Bee Creek Cave harvestman

Texella reddelli

Phylum	Arthropoda
Class	Arachnida
Order	Opiliones
Family	Phalangodidae
Status	Endangered, IUCN
	Endangered, USFWS
Range	Texas (U.S.A.)

Description and Biology

A small, orange spider averaging only 0.07-0.09 in (1.9-2.2 mm in size), the Bee Creek Cave harvestman is a slow-moving, predatory species. It uses its long legs, particularly the pedipalps (second of the six pair of appendages), to grasp and consume small invertebrates. Its eye mound is broadly conical, and the eyes are well developed. Juveniles are white to yellowish white in color.

Habitat and Current Distribution

This species is thought to occur in Kretschmarr Double Pit and Jester Estates Cave, north of the Colorado River on the Jollyville Plateau, and in three caves in the Rollingwood karst fauna region in Travis County, Texas. The occurrence of this species on both sides of the Colorado River indicates that the populations are probably genetically distinct. There are no estimates of population size.

Usually found under rocks in darkness or in dim twilight, the harvestman inhabits karst terrain, which is formed by the gradual dissolution of calcium carbonate from limestone bedrock, creating many caves, fractures, and sinkholes. The species requires stable temperatures, high humidity, and a supply of small invertebrates that feed on nutrients which seep into the cave system.

History and Conservation Measures

The Bee Creek Cave harvestman was originally reported from a number of other caves, but recent research has shown that these sightings were of different species. The primary threat to this spider and to a number of other residents of the karst region is loss or degradation of habitat. Rapid residential and urban development continues and can lead to the destruction or drastic alteration of unprotected habitat areas. Diversion or increase of water flows can dry out or flood the caves, and alteration of vegetation above the caves can diminish supplies of nutrients and introduce exotic species into the ecosystem; in particular, fire ant infestations are becoming increasingly common and harmful. Because the caves are formed by seeping water, they are especially vulnerable to contamination and pollution.

Conservation efforts are underway to protect the habitat of this and other endangered species. Approximately 7,000 acres (2,800 ha) are proposed for protection, and efforts are ongoing with private landholders to protect the caves and restrict human access. A small, isolated population is always at particular risk of extinction, so surveys will be conducted in hopes of locating additional populations.

Madison Cave isopod

Antrolana lira

Phylum	Arthropoda
Class	Crustacea
Order	Isopoda
Family	Cirolanidae
Status	Vulnerable, IUCN
	Threatened, USFWS
Range	Virginia (U.S.A.)

Description and Biology

The only freshwater member of its family, the Madison Cave isopod is a tiny, shrimp-like crustacean that averages 0.47 in (12 mm) long and 0.16 in (4 mm) wide. It has no eyes and is unpigmented. Reproduction has never been observed, but is known to take place in the wild. Diet consists of decaying organic matter including leaf litter, small twigs or wood particles, and insect remains.

Habitat and Current Distribution

This species is restricted to caves or fissures in the Shenandoah Valley of northwestern Virginia. It has long been known to inhabit two deep subterranean pools in Madison Cave and one in nearby Stegers Fissure, and has recently been discovered in four new locations. The discovery of these additional populations extends the range of the species almost 60 mi (96 km) north-northeast of Cave Hill. There are no estimates of total population size.

The Madison Cave isopod inhabits freshwater pools with clay banks. The pools seep into the South River, a tributary of the South Fork Shenandoah River, and their water levels vary.

History and Conservation Measures

Madison Cave has historical value as it was mapped by Thomas Jefferson (the first instance of cave-mapping in the United States), and George Washington's signature is found on a wall of the cave. The Madison Cave isopod was first collected in 1958 and described and named in 1964. It is the only species of its kind occurring in North America north of Texas, and is unusual in that it is derived from marine ancestors but is found far inland.

Because a single groundwater system feeds the caves and connects them to the South River, the cave pools are subject to pollution from chemicals that seep in from surrounding areas and from those dumped into the river. Madison Cave has also been subject to damage from humans entering the cave for recreational purposes and to mine bat guano. Traffic along the banks has knocked clay into the pools, increasing siltation, and garbage has also accumu-

Madison Cave isopod.

lated in the cave. In 1981 Madison Cave was gated, and access is now allowed only for scientific and educational purposes. Since groundwater contamination could pose a serious threat to the species, it is important to restrict the use of herbicides and pesticides in the vicinity of the caves and to monitor the pools for the presence of mercury, which has been discovered in South River. Limiting development around the caves is essential, as is the maintenance of a suitable groundwater table.

Socorro isopod

Thermosphaeroma thermophilum

Phylum	Arthropoda
Class	Crustacea
Order	Isopoda
Family	Sphaeromatidae
Status	Endangered, IUCN
	Endangered, USFWS
Range	New Mexico (U.S.A.)

Description and Biology

The Socorro isopod has a flattened body with seven pairs of legs, two pairs of antennae on its head, and oarlike extensions (uropods) on its last body segment. Both sexes are grayish brown with small black spots and lines which run together to form a broad black band in the center of each segment of the middle region of its body. Exposed edges of the body are tinged with bright orange. Average length ranges from 0.18-0.23 in (4.5-6.0 mm) in the female, and from 0.16-0.51 in (4-13 mm) in the male. Its primary food source is blue-green bacteria, but detritus and dragonfly nymphs are also eaten, as are other isopods on occasion. Predation pressure is very low, since there are no fish in the isopod's habitat and it is unlikely to be accessible to birds.

The reproductive cycle is not fully known. Reproduction occurs at two-month intervals throughout the year, with a peak of activity in the spring; 3-57 eggs are laid, following a gestation period of approximately 30 days.

Habitat and Current Distribution

The wild population of the species is restricted to a thermal outflow from Sedillo Spring in the water system of an abandoned bath house in the Socorro Mountains in south-central Socorro County, New Mexico. This consists of a small, cement-lined animal watering tank, a smaller pool, and approximately 130 ft (40 m) of open irrigation pipe. Water temperature ranges from 81°-93°F (27°-34°C). Much of the population is confined to the pool, where the flat bottom is covered with 0.4-1.6 in (1-4 cm) of finely divided substrate into which the animals burrow during the day, emerging at dusk.

Population was estimated in the late 1970s at just under 2,500 individuals. Additional populations exist in captivity.

Socorro isopod.

History and Conservation Measures

The natural habitat of the Socorro isopod was completely eliminated by the capping and diversion of naturally occurring warm springs to meet the needs of municipal and private developments. The isopod remains at risk because of its very limited habitat and because the minimal amount of water in its present habitat could easily be stopped or interrupted. In 1987, the species became extinct in the wild when a pipe breakage stopped the flow of water into the system. Captive breeding programs had pre-

served the species, and it was reintroduced into the pool.

Sedillo Spring should be fully protected to ensure that the site is not altered through contamination, erosion, or the introduction of predatory or competitive species, and to maintain a permanent flow of water into the system. Plans have been made to construct a larger, more stable habitat as well. The captive population is being maintained as a safeguard against any further disasters which could result in another extinction in the wild.

Hay's Spring amphipod

Stygobromus hayi

Phylum	Arthropoda
Class	Crustacea
Order	Amphipoda
Family	Crangonyctidae
Status	Endangered, IUCN
	Endangered, USFWS
Range	District of Columbia (U.S.A.)

Description and Biology

Hay's Spring amphipod is a tiny, shrimp-like crustacean that averages 0.47 in (12 mm) in length. It lacks eyes and is whitish in color. Diet includes such decaying organic material as insect parts and leaf litter. Its life span ranges between 5-10 years.

Habitat and Current Distribution

This species has only been found in Hay's Spring, located within the National Zoological Park in Washington, D.C. There are no estimates of total population size, but fewer than 10 individuals have ever been observed at one time.

History and Conservation Measures

This amphipod was discovered in 1940, and has not been found anywhere but in Hay's Spring since that time. This extremely limited distribution places the small population at risk of extinction, particularly since the water quality of its habitat can be negatively affected by floodwaters from Rock Creek, into which Hay's Spring flows. The site has been fenced to protect it from the many visitors to the National Zoological Park. Efforts to preserve the species have focused on monitoring and protecting its habitat.

Alabama cave shrimp

Palaemonias alabamae

Phylum	Arthropoda
Class	Crustacea
Order	Decapoda
Family	Atyidae
Status	Endangered, IUCN
	Endangered, USFWS
Range	Alabama (U.S.A.)

Description and Biology

The Alabama cave shrimp is a colorless, nearly transparent decapod that grows to a length of only 0.8 in (20 mm). The female is slightly longer than the male and her rostrum is slightly shorter. The first and second legs are almost equal in length, and it has a spiny exoskeleton and unpigmented eyes. Although it resembles the Kentucky cave shrimp (*Palaemonias ganteri*), this species is smaller and has a shorter rostrum and fewer scales. It feeds indiscriminately on detritus and other organics in shallow pools.

Habitat and Current Distribution

The species is restricted to two caves in Madison County, Alabama: Shelta Cave, which is in Huntsville, and Bobcat Cave, southwest of Shelta Cave. The population in Bobcat Cave is thought to be quite small, and the shrimp has not been found in Shelta Cave in recent surveys.

Silt-bottom pools in the caves provide a habitat for the shrimp, but the water level fluctuates dramatically between the wet spring and winter months and the drier fall and summer months, during which some of the pools dry out completely.

History and Conservation Measures

The Alabama cave shrimp was first sighted in Bobcat Cave in 1975, and a 1990 survey indicated that the population might be increasing. There is uncertainty about the shrimp's continued presence in Shelta Cave; it was not sighted in surveys in 1987 and 1990, but its transparent body makes it difficult to spot.

Degradation of habitat has been the primary threat to this species, as pesticides and other contaminants have seeped into the subsurface aquifers of the caves, and increased demands for water have lowered aquifer levels. The decline of the gray bat (*Myotis grisescens*) and its disappearance from the caves has eliminated the supply of bat guano which supplied nutrients to the cave's aquatic species. Predation by the southern cavefish, cave salamanders, and cave crayfish would not normally present a problem but may take a toll on the species when combined with habitat contamination and a low reproductive rate.

The cave entrances are protected and public access to the caves is restricted. A study of water quality has also been initiated. Further conservation efforts will be directed toward protecting and monitoring existing populations; determining potential sources of contamination for the caves and taking corrective action; initiating additional research; and searching for new populations and for potential introduction sites.

Kentucky cave shrimp

Palaemonias ganteri

Phylum	Arthropoda
Class	Crustacea
Order	Decapoda
Family	Atyidae
Status	Endangered, IUCN
	Endangered, USFWS
Range	Kentucky (U.S.A.)

Description and Biology

The Kentucky cave shrimp is a small decapod that reaches a length of up to 1.2 in (30 mm). It lacks pigmentation, making it almost transparent, and has only rudimentary eyestalks. Diet includes organic detritus and probably insects, protozoans, algae, and fungi.

Habitat and Current Distribution

This species is prevalent in the Mammoth Cave National Park region of central Kentucky, inhabiting freshwater streams and pools in the deeper, more remote areas of the Flint-Mammoth Cave System. It has been found in five localities in the Mammoth Cave system; in most of the base level passages in the Echo River Spring Groundwater Basin; in five localities in the Pike Spring Groundwater Basin; one each in the Mile 205.7 Spring, Suds Spring, and McCoy Blue Spring Groundwater Basins; in Sandhouse Cave in the Double Sink Groundwater Basin; in Ganter Cave and Lee Cave in the Turnhole Spring Groundwater Basin; and in Running Branch Cave. The population was estimated in the early 1980s at

500 individuals, but some additional sites were discovered subsequent to that estimate.

History and Conservation Measures

The cave shrimp depends on a food supply that is provided by nutrients washed into the caves by an elaborate system of sinkholes and streams. It is affected by pollution that seeps into the water system from fertilizers, pesticides, and herbicides used on the surface near the caves, and from inadequate sewage treatment. Increased siltation has been observed in the caves, but a direct connection to agricultural development has not been proven.

The small population of Kentucky cave shrimp leaves the species very vulnerable. Conservation measures necessary for its preservation and recovery include surveys to determine the location and extent of the areas that support this shrimp; research on life history to determine what constitutes a viable population; research to determine factors adversely impacting the species; monitoring of population status; maintenance of adequate water quality; protection from introduced predators; and education programs about the shrimp, its status, and required conservation efforts.

California freshwater shrimp

Syncaris pacifica

Phylum	Arthropoda
Class	Crustacea
Order	Decapoda
Family	Atyidae
Status	Endangered, IUCN
	Endangered, USFWS
Range	California (U.S.A.)

Description and Biology

Similar in appearance to the common ocean shrimp, the California freshwater shrimp has a greenish gray body with light blue tail fins but looks transparent when seen in the water. Its length can reach up to 2-2.5 in (5-6.3 cm).

Eggs are carried on the female's body during the winter and grow very slowly for approximately eight to nine months. The number of eggs laid is relatively low, estimated at 50-120, with up to half of those lost before producing embryos.

Habitat and Current Distribution

This species is presently found in Napa County, where it inhabits the Napa River near Calistoga, and in Marin and Sonoma counties in Big Austin, East Austin, Blucher, Green Valley, Huichica, Jonive, Lagunitas, Salmon, Walker, and Yulupa creeks. There are no estimates of population size.

Quiet, clear freshwater streams provide habitat for this species. It is found in fairly slow-moving water at elevations below 300 ft (91 m), where it moves along the streambed among aquatic vegetation. Suit-able streams are usually tree-lined and have underwater vegetation and exposed tree roots.

California freshwater shrimp.

History and Conservation Measures

The range of the California freshwater shrimp has not changed, but its distribution within that range has diminished; it has disappeared from a number of streams where it was previously found. The primary threat to the species is the loss or degradation of its freshwater habitat as streams are diverted or dammed for irrigation purposes and other uses. Water quality has also been degraded as grazing and construction have increased siltation. Runoff from fields has introduced agricultural chemicals to the water, and the number of introduced fish species has increased. The low reproductive potential of the species, its slow maturity, and its limited distribution combine to make the shrimp extremely vulnerable to changes in its habitat.

Studies have been initiated to assess distribution, gather information about ecological requirements, and determine the effects of water diversion. Some dams have been removed in an attempt to restore habitat, and the effects of future dams or construction will be examined before they are approved.

Squirrel Chimney cave shrimp

Palaemonetes cummingi

Phylum	Arthropoda
Class	Crustacea
Order	Decapoda
Family	Palaemonidae
Status	Vulnerable, IUCN
	Threatened, USFWS
Range	Florida (U.S.A.)

Description and Biology

Also called the Florida cave shrimp, the Squirrel Chimney cave shrimp reaches a length of approximately 1.2 in (30 mm). The body is unpigmented and transparent; the eyes are also unpigmented and smaller than those of related surface-dwelling species. The diet of this species is not known, but it is assumed to consist of insects, tiny protozoans, algae, and fungi.

Habitat and Current Distribution

This cave shrimp is presently known to exist in only one location: a sinkhole called Squirrel Chimney near the city of Gainesville in Alachua County, Florida. The small, deep sinkhole leads to a flooded cave system of unknown size; together they provide the habitat for this species and for a variety of other cave invertebrates. Surrounding the sinkhole is an area of dense, tangled ground cover and a canopy of second-growth live oak trees. Fewer than 12 individuals have been seen near the surface of the water table in the sinkhole, and the number inhabiting deeper waters is unknown.

History and Conservation Measures

First described in 1954, the Squirrel Chimney cave shrimp survives precariously because of its very limited distribution; any alteration to its habitat could result in extinction of the species. The sinkhole has been proposed as a National Natural Landmark, but is currently privately owned. Although the owners have cooperated in restricting access to the site, its long-term protection is not guaranteed. If the surrounding area is opened to residential development, water pollution from septic tanks could be extremely hazardous to the aquifer throughout the cave system. In addition, erosion and the use of pesticides or herbicides could negatively affect water quality.

Because it is considered adequately protected by a single landholder, no conservation measures have been planned for this species. If the surrounding area is developed, steps should be taken to prevent damage to the aquifer and to limit human traffic near the sinkhole. A buffer zone around the site would be a positive step to protecting the habitat of the Squirrel Chimney cave shrimp.

Hell Creek Cave crayfish

Cambarus zophonastes

Phylum	Arthropoda
Class	Crustacea
Order	Decapoda
Family	Cambaridae
Status	Endangered, IUCN
	Endangered, USFWS
Range	Arkansas (U.S.A.)

Description and Biology

The Hell Creek Cave crayfish is a colorless decapod with small, unpigmented eyes and a spined rostrum (snout). Total body length reaches approximately 2.6 in (6.6 cm). Like other crayfish, it feeds on both plant and animal matter. Its metabolism and reproductive rate are relatively low; females are thought to lay eggs on an average of once every five years.

Habitat and Current Distribution

This species is found only in a deep pool in Hell Creek Cave, located in Stone County, Arkansas, in the Ozark Mountains. The population was estimated to be less than 50 individuals in 1984.

Hell Creek Cave is a solution channel, which is mostly wet and muddy throughout the year. Many of its passages are flooded during rainy seasons and after storms. A narrow, shallow stream leads into the pool, which is approximately 150 ft (46 m) inside the cave. When the stream becomes turbid, the crayfish seem to seek clear water.

History and Conservation Measures

This species faces a number of threats to its survival. Water is supplied to the cave by a sinking stream, a surface water course that leaks water into the subsurface and can easily introduce pollutants into the pool; the quality of the water is affected by industrial operations and developments in the area. The low reproductive rate of the species is thought to be due in part to the cave's shortage of organic material for the crayfish to use for energy. Historically, most of the nourishment available to the cave crayfish was provided by guano from gray bats (*Myotis grisescens*) which used the cave as a maternity roosting site. However, the gray bat is now an endangered species and has disappeared from Hell Creek Cave as it has from many others. The low reproductive rate in

Hell Creek Cave crayfish.

such a small population of crayfish leads to a loss of genetic variability, which further complicates the problems for conserving this species. In addition, the crayfish is threatened by collection; the removal of any adult, especially a reproducing female, could have a dramatic effect on the species' population.

A tract of land that includes the cave's entrance has recently been acquired and protected; this should limit collecting and lead to a reduction in human disturbance, which may allow the return of the gray bat to the site. Searches should be continued in the hope of finding additional populations, because a population so small and restricted could easily be lost. Population surveys and monitoring of water quality in the cave should also be continued.

Nashville crayfish

Orconectes shoupi

Phylum	Arthropoda
Class	Crustacea
Order	Decapoda
Family	Cambaridae
Status	Endangered, IUCN
	Endangered, USFWS
Range	Tennessee (U.S.A.)

Description and Biology

The Nashville crayfish, or Shoup's crayfish, is a freshwater decapod with a carapace (shell) length measuring up to 1.8 in (4.5 cm). It has thickened ridges on the rostrum, four pairs of walking legs, and two long-fingered chelae (claws or pincers). An omnivorous and opportunistic feeder, it probably consumes small invertebrates, fish eggs, and plant and animal matter. Raccoons (*Procyon lotor*), fish, reptiles, and amphibians are presumed to be the major predators of the Nashville crayfish.

With the exception of the mating season, most adults are solitary creatures. Very little is known about reproductive biology in this species. Mating can take place from late summer to early spring, depending on winter and early spring temperatures; egg laying seems to occur in early spring, and is thought to be related to water temperature and day length.

Habitat and Current Distribution

This crayfish is restricted to the Mill and Sevenmile creeks, tributaries of the Cumberland River in the vicinity of Nashville in Davidson and Williamson counties, Tennessee. The size of these populations is unknown. Like other species, the Nashville crayfish requires adequate cover in its streambed habitat: specimens from Mill Creek have typically been found in pool areas under flat slabs of limestone and other rocks.

History and Conservation Measures

Records show that in the past this species was found in three additional localities in Tennessee: Big Creek in the Elk River system in Giles County; South Harpeth River in the Harpeth River system in Davidson County; and Richland Creek in the Cumberland River system in Davidson County. The disappearance of the Nashville crayfish from these locations may have been the result of displacement by a more aggressive species, or may represent failed attempts to introduce the species into these areas.

Since the main distribution of the species is limited to Nashville and its suburbs, continued development of the area, including the possibility of a wastewater management facility and a reservoir, threatens to further deteriorate the habitat and could result in the elimination of the species. The construction of a modern airport, presently underway, could also have a negative impact.

The Nashville crayfish is unable to tolerate pollution and siltation; much of its habitat has been destroyed or degraded by contamination or increased siltation of the water resulting from residential, urban, and agricultural development. It is therefore necessary for conservation efforts to focus on protecting the Mill Creek watershed from siltation and further contamination. Research is also needed on the bio-logy and habitat requirements of this species. It has been proposed that efforts be made to establish a second population in another location to increase the chances of species survival.

Shasta crayfish

Pacifastacus fortis

Phylum	Arthropoda
Class	Crustacea
Order	Decapoda
Family	Astacidae
Status	Endangered, IUCN
	Vulnerable, USFWS
Range	California (U.S.A.)

Description and Biology

The Shasta or placid crayfish is a small- to medium-sized species that reaches 1-2 in (25-50 mm) adult carapace (shell) length. It has the darkest overall coloring of any North American crayfish, generally appearing to be black to dark green or brown, depending upon light conditions; ventral coloration is bright orange. In some individuals, coloration varies from blue to blue-green with a light orange to yellow underside.

Although little is known of the diet of the Shasta crayfish, it has been suggested that the species feeds on encrusting organisms, or detritus. While it has no known specific predators, a number of vertebrates could be expected to feed upon this species.

The Shasta crayfish is usually solitary, but occasionally a dozen or more individuals are found together under a large rock. It reaches sexual maturity after five years, mating in late September and October after the final molt of the season; females lay relatively few eggs, usually 10-70, which hatch the following spring.

Habitat and Current Distribution

This species inhabits the Pit River in Shasta County in northeastern California, and the watersheds of two of its tributary systems, Fall River and Hat Creek. The Fall River system supports a larger population than the Hat Creek system, although the crayfish has recently disappeared from springs in both systems. Total population was estimated at 6,000 in 1980 and at 3,000 in 1988.

Primary habitat consists of cool, clear, spring-fed lakes and streams, usually at or near the spring source, in waters which show relatively little annual fluctuation in temperature. The species prefers standing waters or those with slow to moderate flow. It is found only under rocks larger than 3 in (7.5 cm) in diameter, usually on clear, firm sand or gravel substrate. It is most abundant where plants are absent

Shasta crayfish.

and in deep water in wide streams. The most important habitat requirement appears to be the presence of adequate rock rubble for cover. All known populations occur below 3,400 ft (1,036 m) elevation.

History and Conservation Measures

The habitats of this species at Fall River Mills and other sections of the Pit River basin have been drastically changed by diking and diversion of water for agricultural purposes. Streams that were once free-flowing have been impounded and channeled as a result of the construction of several power plants and reservoirs, further reducing suitable habitat. Increasing demand for water has lowered the water table, and remaining streams are becoming polluted by fertilizers and other chemicals from agricultural run-off. In addition to habitat loss, exotic crayfish species that reproduce more quickly have been introduced into its habitats; these more aggressive species have significantly displaced the Shasta crayfish. Finally, the crayfish is also captured for human consumption.

Some of the questions concerning the survival potential of this species could be answered by a study of its ecology, life history, and behavior; knowledge of its interaction with introduced exotic species could establish whether or not the exotic species should be removed from its habitat. Additionally, studies to identify the components of the species' diet need to be initiated, since knowledge of food habits will be important in developing a viable management plan. Attempts should be made to transplant the Shasta crayfish into isolated waters, and legal protection is required to prevent over-exploitation by collectors.

Hemiphlebia damselfly

Hemiphlebia mirabilis

Phylum	Arthropoda
Class	Insecta
Order	Odonata
Family	Hemiphlebiidae
Status	Rare, IUCN
Range	Australia

Description and Biology

This minute, extremely primitive damselfly has a wingspan of only 0.8-1.0 in (20-25 mm). It has bright metallic green coloring with white anal appendages. Its feeding habits and reproductive behavior are not well known.

Habitat and Current Distribution

The *Hemiphlebia* damselfly was originally known to inhabit three locations in Victoria, Australia: the floodplain lagoons of the Goulburn River at Alexandra, the middle to upper course of the Yarra River, and Wilsons Promontory in southern Victoria. Populations of the species have now been confirmed at other sites in Victoria, in Tasmania, and on the islands of Bass Strait, which separates Victoria from Tasmania.

The species is reported to frequent reedy lagoons on floodplains and appears to depend on the seasonal flooding of those lagoons. At Wilsons Promontory the damselfly was found in a vegetated dune lake or swamp, which may have some features in common with floodplain lagoons.

History and Conservation Measures

Although the first report of the *Hemiphlebia* damselfly was from northern Queensland, Australia, that is now thought to be an error, and it is believed that the species was first discovered in Victoria. In the early 1980s, the damselfly seemed to have disappeared from known sites in Victoria, and it was feared that the species had become extinct. The decline in its numbers was attributed to habitat alteration caused by the construction of a dam on the Goulburn River, which altered the floodplain lagoons inhabited by the species. The floodplains had also been affected by agriculture and cattle raising. Since then, however, a population was discovered at the national park in Wilsons Promontory. Additional populations have also been discovered at Alexandra; at Yea, near the Goulburn River; near Mt. William and other sites in northeastern Tasmania; and at two sites on Flinders Island in Bass Strait. At least three of these populations—Wilsons Promontory, Flinders Island, and Mt. William—are within national parks or nature reserves. At these protected sites the *Hemiphlebia* damselfly is locally abundant, and the species is now regarded as rare rather than endangered.

Pacific damselfly

Megalagrion pacificum

Phylum	Arthropoda
Class	Insecta
Order	Odonata
Family	Coenagrionidae
Status	Endangered, IUCN
Range	Hawaii (U.S.A.)

Description and Biology

The Pacific damselfly is a small black insect with limited dark red markings on the head, thorax, and distal abdomen. The damselfly is apparently territorial, with each male requiring approximately 20 ft (6 m) of the edge of a body of water.

Habitat and Current Distribution

The Pacific damselfly is apparently restricted to Maui and Molokai in the Hawaiian Islands. There are no estimates of population size, but it appears that this species is not as rare on these two islands as was previously reported. The species appears to have been extirpated from Kauai, Oahu, and Lanai.

The only known habitat of the species consists of pools or lowland stream systems of various sizes.

History and Conservation Measures

This damselfly was once found on most of the Hawaiian Islands and was considered widespread in the late 1940s. Since that time, however, it has declined due to habitat disturbance. In many lowland areas throughout the Hawaiian Islands water has been diverted from natural water systems to agricultural uses. This habitat alteration has had a negative impact on damselfly populations. The disappearance of the species from some large ponds and stream systems in the lowlands is also attributed to the introduction of mosquito fish (*Gambusia* spp.) to these waters to control mosquito larvae. The Pacific damselfly no longer survives in areas where these species occur.

Searches of some of the islands in 1982 resulted in the collection of specimens from two locations. Fortunately, these sites lie within a nature reserve, where the species can be protected from the introduction of mosquito fish. The Pacific damselfly is also known to occur in the Palikea Stream within Haleakala National Park. Further surveys should be initiated on all of the Hawaiian Islands, particularly at sites that do not contain mosquito fish.

Ohio emerald dragonfly

Somatochlora hineana

Phylum	Arthropoda
Class	Insecta
Order	Odonata
Family	Corduliidae
Status	Endangered, IUCN
Range	Indiana, Ohio (U.S.A.)

Description and Biology

This is a fairly large dragonfly with a yellow labrum (upper part of the mouth), metallic green frons (front of the head capsule), and black leg segments. On its dark thorax (body segment between head and abdomen) are two yellow stripes, the second slightly wider and shorter than the first. Information regarding the diet and reproductive biology of this species is unavailable.

Habitat and Current Distribution

The Ohio emerald dragonfly has been found primarily in Logan, Lucas, and Williams Counties in northwest Ohio and in northwest Indiana's Lake County. Specimens have not been collected at those locations since 1953, however, and the species was thought to be extinct until recently, when a population was discovered at a site in Wisconsin.

Most of the known specimens were found in bogs, but some were found along a dredged channel of a small stream flowing through heavy swamp woods. Breeding places were in wilder districts where original conditions had not been disturbed.

History and Conservation Measures

The largest number of specimens were collected from Oak Openings State Park at the western end of Lake Erie in Lucas County, near the urban and heavily industrialized Toledo area. Because of the habitat requirements of this species, its survival in that area is questionable. It has not been found in Logan County since 1930, in spite of intensive collecting of similar species. A single, probably stray, male was recorded from Gary, Indiana, but it is doubtful if a viable population was ever present there, since the area is heavily polluted from steel mills and associated industries.

Habitat destruction is the principal cause of the decline in this species' population. An intensive search should be made for any remaining populations in Ohio and Indiana, especially in Lucas County, where the creation of Oak Openings State Park has provided incidental habitat protection. If a population is found there, efforts could be made to maintain the relatively undisturbed conditions in the park. The Wisconsin population is jeopardized by the proposed construction of a garbage compacting and hauling facility near its habitat. Efforts should be made to ensure that the habitat of this and any other surviving populations be protected.

Weta species

Deinacrida spp.

Phylum	Arthropoda
Class	Insecta
Order	Orthoptera
Family	Stenopelmatidae
Status	Vulnerable, IUCN
Range	New Zealand

Description and Biology

The giant wetas are among the largest insects in the world, and the wetapunga (*D. heteracantha*), the heaviest of the giant weta species, weighs up to 2.5 oz (72 g), making it the heaviest insect in the world. An adult female may measure 4 in (100 mm) long, spreading to 7 in (178 mm) with their armored and spiny legs. The adults of all species are various shades of brown and wingless with rounded bodies. They have a broad protective shield behind the head; this detail, reminiscent of some dinosaurs, attests to their primitive origin.

The 11 species of giant wetas are nocturnal, and their life cycle takes a little over two years. Young wetas are solitary until they reach maturity, when males seek out females and mate with them over several days in the safety of the female's retreat. While the female lays her eggs, the smaller male often waits nearby, and mating and egg-laying are usually repeated several times. Giant wetas mate and lay eggs during all but the winter months. The female lays 4-6 eggs each time she pushes her ovipositor into the shaded soil beneath a shrub, and may lay up to 400 eggs in total. The male dies soon after the final mating, and the female also dies after all her eggs are laid. The eggs are approximately 0.27 in (7 mm) long and 0.08 in (2 mm) wide, and are laid vertically at a depth of up to 0.78 in (20 mm) below the soil surface.

During midsummer some eggs hatch within three weeks, but most stay in the ground through the winter and hatch nine or ten months later. The newly hatched nymphs, which are pale, mottled miniatures of the adults, moult their skins about 10 times during the two years it takes them to reach adulthood. The nymphs usually move away from their hatching site and hide in the tops of shrubs during the day, seldom venturing to the ground with the adults.

All giant wetas are primarily vegetarians, and emerge soon after dusk to feed on the leaves of a wide variety of trees, shrubs, herbs, and grasses. They occasionally also eat dead invertebrates. They are active throughout the winter, feeding even at tempera-

Stephens Island weta.

tures as low as 40°F (3°C). By day they hide close to the ground in dry sites among tangles of vegetation and dead leaves that accumulate at the bases of plants. Female wetas often occupy the same nest site throughout their adult lives. Many vertebrates, including cats, rats, possums, pigs, hedgehogs, several native birds, the tuatara, and lizards, prey upon wetas.

Habitat and Current Distribution

The three largest species of giant weta are now confined to islands without populations of ship rats (*Rattus rattus*) or Norway rats (*Rattus norvegicus*). Wetapunga, once found on the mainland, are found only on Little Barrier Island, where they share their home with kiore, a small Polynesian rat (*Rattus exulans*). They are arboreal, spending most of their time in kauri, pohutukawa, kanuka, and other broadleaf trees, seldom venturing down to the ground. The Poor Knights weta (*D. fallai*) is found commonly in two of the Poor Knights islands, and like wetapunga, lives in the forest. The Stephens Island giant wetas are now confined to four rat-free islands in the Cook Strait region. This weta, unlike its northern forest-dwelling relatives, prefers low-growing shrub in clearings and forest margins. On the Cook Strait islands they are found in tauhinu scrub (*Cassinia leptophylla*) and low windswept and tangled shrubs.

Several other species of giant weta (*D. tibiospina, D. parva,* and three recently discovered species) are confined to mountainous sub-alpine grassland and herbfields above the treeline. The alpine scree weta (*D. connectens*) is the only giant weta that is widespread in the South Island but restricted to rocky screes on mountains above 4,500 ft (1,380 m). This weta is found near the glaciers of Mt. Cook at altitudes of more than 10,000 ft (3,075 m), where most plant and animal life cannot survive. With its adaptability to extremes of temperature and diet in such hostile conditions, it is little wonder that this weta has survived a multitude of past ice ages and local extinctions.

History and Conservation Measures

Before human settlement, bats were the only warm-blooded mammals in the New Zealand ecosys-

tem, and the wetas thrived in safety. A devastating blow to the weta populations was the arrival of kiore rats with the Maori people, joined soon after by an enormous array of other animals brought by later settlers. Soon, the whole shape of the landscape had changed due to the felling of forests for timber and farmland. In the 200 years since the arrival of European settlers, over 80 percent of New Zealand's natural vegetation has disappeared. Even those lands not immediately felled or burned were quickly overrun with rodents, deer, goats, pigs, and possums.

All 11 species are protected by law and occur in reserves, but not all the island reserves are predator-free. Since the domestic cats that were living in the wild on Little Barrier Island were exterminated, the kiore rats have probably benefited and increased in numbers. It is not known whether there has been any increase in attacks on wetapunga from increased numbers of kiore since cats were removed. Saddleback wattlebirds (*Philesturnus carunculatus*) also prey on the wetas. Monitoring of wetapunga on Little Barrier Island should be conducted regularly and consideration given to establishing additional colonies on suitable islands.

In 1976, 43 Stephens Island giant wetas from Mana Island were released on Maud Island, where there are no predators. This transfer of an insect species to a new home to ensure its survival was a first for New Zealand. A recent survey of Maud Island found many thousands of wetas thriving in their new predator-free home. The most southern giant weta, *D. carinata,* has been discovered on a small island in Foveaux Strait, where the weka (a native rail) is the sole predator. The population of sixteen weka are to be relocated. A specific weta reserve had been established in gorse-covered farmland for a remnant population of Mahoenui giant wetas. Management of this reserve requires some goat husbandry to keep the gorse plants thick and stunted as refuge for the wetas.

Six of the giant weta species have been established in captive breeding colonies, which should be maintained in order to provide basic research for effective management plans.

Rocky Mountain grasshopper

Melanoplus spretus

Phylum	Anthropoda
Class	Insecta
Order	Orthoptera
Family	Acrididae
Status	Extinct, IUCN
Range	Rocky Mountains (U.S.A.; Canada)

Description and Biology

During the nineteenth century, the Rocky Mountain grasshopper was considered the most serious crop pest in the United States. This insect has since disappeared, and the last living specimen was collected in 1902. Scientists today are not entirely sure why this grasshopper became extinct. During the 1800s, these insects numbered in the billions and created massive swarms in the air as they migrated. It is reported that one swarm size was almost as large as the state of Colorado.

The female Rocky Mountain grasshopper laid one to four egg pods in her lifetime. Each pod contained about 25 eggs and was buried underground during late summer months. It generally took between 40 and 60 days for this insect to reach adulthood. Diet included a variety of crops, among them barley, wheat, oat, corn, potato, radish, cabbage, melon, strawberry, tobacco, and tomato. It also ate bark and leaves of trees, plants, and shrubs. Some also reported that it ate clothing, fence posts, leather, dead animals, and wool.

Natural predators included badgers, birds, chipmunks, fish, lizards, skunks, snakes, parasites, and mites. Because of the tremendous damage they caused to valuable crops, humans tried to control this species. During the 1800s, people were offered one to five dollars for a bushel of dead grasshoppers. Concentrated efforts were also made to destroy this insect by flooding its egg beds and by setting fires to grasslands.

Habitat and Current Distribution

The Rocky Mountain grasshopper occurred throughout the Great Plains region of North America. It preferred barren plains with bunch grasses and sagebrush, although it laid its eggs near rivers and streams.

History and Conservation Measures

This insect has not been seen since the last living specimen was collected in 1902. Scientists have proposed several reasons for their extinction; some suggest that environmental factors and human activity affected the range of the Rocky Mountain grasshopper. Climate change, population reduction of the bison, and the introduction of birds and cattle may have affected the grasshopper population. Some also believe that habitat destruction and alteration—flooding, irrigation, and hydrologic developments, for example—further contributed to the extinction of this species.

St. Helena giant earwig

Labidura herculeana

Phylum	Arthropoda
Class	Insecta
Order	Dermaptera
Family	Labiduridae
Status	Endangered, IUCN
Range	St. Helena (South Atlantic Ocean)

Description and Biology

This is the largest earwig in the world, with a body length of 1.4-2.1 in (36-54 mm) and additional forceps of 0.6-0.9 in (15-24 mm). Females tend to be smaller, with relatively shorter forceps. The largest entire specimen recorded, which is preserved in a museum in Belgium, is a male with a total length of more than 3 in (78 mm). However, a pair of male forceps were once found which measured 1.3 in (34 mm), suggesting an overall length for that specimen of 3.6 in (90 mm). This species is wingless and is distinguished by its entirely black body and reddish legs. The male has very long, smooth, cylindrical forceps. The St. Helena earwig is active at night.

Mating seems to occur between December and February, and females with eggs have been observed in March.

Habitat and Current Distribution

This species is found only on the mid-Atlantic island of St. Helena, where it is restricted to Horse Point Plain in the extreme northeast portion of the island. Any surviving population is certain to be very small.

Horse Point Plain is dry and barren; its vegetation consists of small bushes and tufts of grass. Most living specimens of the species were found under stones or in the soil near burrows which the earwig

uses as escape routes. The earwig is active during the summer rains and seeks shelter underground when the dry season begins.

St. Helena giant earwig.

History and Conservation Measures

The St. Helena earwig was originally described in 1798, after which it was not rediscovered until 1965, when it was reportedly common. At that time its limited distribution was cause for concern about its future status. Recent searches have failed to find the earwig. Field work by the London Zoo's Invertebrate Conservation Centre suggests that the giant earwig has suffered from a number of alterations to its habitat, including the loss of original endemic plant cover, resulting in soil erosion, and surface rock removal for building needs. In addition to the loss of its original micro-habitat, the giant earwig is directly threatened by predation by a number of introduced alien animal species, particularly mice and centipedes.

Since it is possible that a small population of the St. Helena giant earwig still survives, it is essential that the many threats facing the species be removed as soon as possible if extinction is to be avoided. Conservation measures should include the eradication of introduced predators, the establishment of a captive breeding population, the restoration of the species' micro-habitat, and conferring legal protection to the site. In addition, further field research is needed to clarify the environmental and ecological dynamics of the area.

Otway stonefly

Eusthenia nothofagi

Phylum	Arthropoda
Class	Insecta
Order	Plecoptera
Family	Eustheniidae
Status	Endangered, IUCN
Range	Australia

Description and Biology

Measuring approximately 1.5 in (38 mm) in length, the primitive Otway stonefly is a relatively large species of the stonefly family. It is brachypterous, meaning that its wings, which are reddish purple, are abnormally small. The species is distinguished from the related *E. venosa* by the male genitalia. Details concerning the Otway stonefly's life cycle are unknown.

Habitat and Current Distribution

This species is known only from the Otway Ranges in Victoria, Australia. No estimates of population size currently exist.

Little information about the habitat of the Otway stonefly is available. Scientists believe that the nymphs are stream dwellers and the adults, being flightless or virtually so, should therefore be found near streams.

History and Conservation Measures

Until recently, the only known specimens of this species were those taken in 1932, and the stonefly was not definitely identified again until 1992 when individuals were rediscovered by the Museum of Victoria in the Otway Ranges. It is considered to be the most archaic and least evolved member of its order.

Streams in the Otway range where this stonefly is found have been adversely affected by the loss of native forests in favor of farms and plantations of exotic trees (mostly *Pinus radiata*). Plans to establish a wood chip industry in a significant section of the remaining native forest poses a further hazard to the species.

Mount Stirling stonefly

Thaumatoperla flaveola

Phylum	Arthropoda
Class	Insecta
Order	Plecoptera
Family	Eustheniidae
Status	Indeterminate, IUCN
Range	Australia

Description and Biology

The Mount Stirling stonefly is one of several unusual primitive endemic stoneflies of conservation concern in alpine regions of southeastern Australia. One of four species of *Thaumatoperla*, all highly localized, the Mount Stirling stonefly is predominantly yellowish to dark brown in color, whereas other species in this genus are sometimes dark purplish black or red. The stonefly is flightless, and the wings are short and rounded. Body length is around 1.5 in (4 cm), or up to 3 in (8 cm) if antennae and cerci (jointed appendages at the end of the abdomen) are also measured. The aquatic larvae occur in small alpine streams, above about 3,600 ft (1,100 m).

Adults are found in late March-early April. They rest on low vegetable in early morning and move to undergrowth later in the day. They live for little more than a month, at most. By contrast, larvae take three to four years to develop and may descend deeper into the stream substrate during summer, when the streams may contain little or no conspicuous water; in some streams, water is permanently subterranean. Larvae are usually found among stones on the stream bottoms. *Thaumatoperla* shows many features of ancient stoneflies and has high evolutionary interest. It is also a "flagship" for benthic communities in the alpine region.

Habitat and Current Distribution

The stonefly is known only from a small area of the Victorian alps and has probably never been more widespread. It occurs on Mt. Stirling and the adjacent Mt. Buller, about 150 mi (240 km) northeast of Melbourne, Australia. Recent surveys suggest that it is reasonably widely distributed there at high altitudes.

History and Conservation Measures

Concerns expressed over the survival of this species have related to the use of Mt. Buller as a major winter sports center (Victoria's largest downhill ski resort) with clearing of vegetation to establish ski runs. Selective logging and cutting of native trees have also occurred in the area. Increased resort size has been associated with nutrient enrichment of streams from sewage effluent, and increased sedimentation of stream beds was feared to destroy the larval habitat. Indeed, it was suspected formerly that this had resulted in the stonefly's extinction. Possible future developments include damming of streams for production of artificial snow. The stonefly was described initially from a single male in 1957, and the female was described (together with the larva) only two years later.

The stonefly is listed under the Victorian Flora

and Fauna Guarantee Act of 1988, and a study of its status was funded by the Endangered Species Program of the Australian National Parks and Wildlife Service in early 1990. The impetus for this study was a major development proposal to integrate Mt. Stirling and Mt. Buller into a single resort complex. This proposal involved "upgrading" Buller's ski-fields, development of new fields on Stirling, an alpine village to accommodate 5,500 people, a new nordic center, and sealed access roads. Concern for the Mt. Stirling stonefly was raised because of perceived threats from these activities. The survey revealed larvae at 13 (of 58) sites, mainly in very small numbers, implying a "patchy" distribution in the region. A climatic modeling analysis implied that this stonefly was unlikely to occur outside the area surveyed. The overall effects of current and past intrusion on the stonefly are by no means clear. Warming of streams by the long-term greenhouse effect was viewed as a serious threat, with any human activity which could increase exposure and degradation of stream waters likely to enhance this in the shorter term. Rigorous protection of selected catchments to prevent further damage appears to be warranted.

How this might occur, and if it is possible in the face of strong pressure from the winter sports industry and users, is currently the subject of energetic debate in Victoria. Listing of the stonefly under Schedule 2 of the Flora and Fauna Guarantee Act demands production of an Action Statement evaluating the species' needs, and this document is currently being prepared.

There seems little chance of establishing captive stocks of the stonefly, and protection of adequate field habitat in the small area where it occurs is the only major conservation option.

Mount Donna Buang wingless stonefly

Riekoperla darlingtoni

Phylum	Arthropoda
Class	Insecta
Order	Plecoptera
Family	Gripopterygidae
Status	Rare, IUCN
Range	Australia

Description and Biology

The Mount Donna Buang wingless stonefly is a small, brown, wingless species with a body length ranging from 0.23-0.47 in (6-12 mm). The male is generally twice as long as the female. Both sexes have conspicuous antennae up to 0.47 in (12 mm) in length.

Hatching occurs in the autumn from February to May, and emergence occurs in the spring around September, two years later.

Habitat and Current Distribution

This species has only been collected within 0.4 mi (1 km) of the summit of Mt. Donna Buang in Victoria, Australia, despite surveys outside this locality. The size of its population is not known.

Mt. Donna Buang is covered by a forest of eucalyptus trees and dense underlying vegetation. Adults of the species are commonly found in rolled pieces of bark near small temporary streams close to the mountain's summit. Nymphs are found under stones and in the silty gravel of tiny streams; they survive dry periods by burrowing into the gravel of the stream bed.

History and Conservation Measures

The extent of the threats to this species is not clear. Mt. Donna Buang is a popular tourist attraction for the people of Melbourne, particularly in winter, and several large parking areas and various other facilities have been constructed to serve visitors. The stream where stonefly nymphs are most abundant is close to these parking areas, and any extension of the facilities would pose a threat to the species.

The summit of Mt. Donna Buang is a scenic reserve, but this does not provide any direct protection to the species, nor have any specific conservation measures been undertaken on its behalf. Regular population surveys are needed to monitor the status of the species. Additional construction of visitor facilities on the summit should be discouraged, not only for the sake of the stonefly, but for the continued viability of the unique ecosystem. Finally, the cooperation of the management authorities of the Mt. Donna Buang Scenic Reserve should be sought in implementing preservation measures.

Pygmy hog sucking louse

Haematopinus oliveri

Phylum	Arthropoda
Class	Insecta
Order	Anoplura
Family	Haematopinidae
Status	Endangered, IUCN
Range	India

Description and Biology

The pygmy hog sucking louse is a parasite that is known to live only upon the pygmy hog (*Sus salvanius*). It is wingless and has a flat, leathery body. Its head is relatively short, its eyes are reduced or absent, and its mouth parts are highly modified for piercing and sucking blood. Its legs are strongly developed and have powerful claws for clinging to hairs on the pygmy hog's body. The female louse is 0.15-0.16 in (3.9-4.2 mm) in length; the male has not been described. This species feeds solely on blood and cannot survive independently of the pygmy hog.

Details of the biology of the louse are not known. Mating presumably occurs on the host; eggs are cemented to hairs on the host's body and are thought to hatch within two weeks.

Habitat and Current Distribution

The host species of this louse, the pygmy hog, is restricted to two small wildlife sanctuaries, Manas and Barnadi, in northwestern Assam, India. The number of surviving pygmy hogs is unknown, but is unlikely to number more than a few hundred individuals.

The primary habitat of the host is unburnt thatch-scrub savanna, consisting of mixed scrub and tall grasses.

History and Conservation Measures

The only known specimens of this species include three females and one nymph, which were collected in 1977 from a pygmy hog killed by local hunters in what was then the Barnadi Reserve Forest. The pygmy hog was once thought to be extinct, but was rediscovered in 1971 near Barnadi. Very little of that population survives, and the only remaining known population that is potentially viable is in Manas National Park and surrounding forests.

The pygmy hog louse is threatened by the loss of its host. Hunting has substantially reduced pygmy hog populations, and the species is also jeopardized by the destruction of its savanna habitat. The upland savannas of northern India are fertile and ideal for conversion to agriculture. The remaining habitat is subjected to reforestation and thatch-grass harvesting, both of which entail annual fires. The area is also threatened by local insurgency problems.

No specific measures have been taken to protect the louse; its host has legal protection, but this has been ineffective due to the destruction of the pygmy hog's habitat. The conservation needs of the pygmy hog and its louse pose difficult questions. While the louse might transmit a disease that could threaten the survival of the pygmy hog, most diseases would probably only affect feeble hogs. Bacteria which live symbiotically with the louse are known to produce B vitamins and therefore could be of value in the rapidly evolving disciplines of genetic engineering and biotechnology.

Habitat protection with full legal backing is re-quired, particularly in the Manas National Park and its buffer forests. The louse is likely to survive if the pygmy hog does, but unless the hog and its habitat are more effectively protected, both species will probably become extinct.

Ash Meadows bug

Ambrysus amargosus

Phylum	Arthropoda
Class	Insecta
Order	Hemiptera
Family	Naucoridae
Status	Endangered, IUCN
	Threatened, USFWS
Range	Nevada (U.S.A.)

Description and Biology

The Ash Meadows bug is a small, brown, aquatic insect with a body length averaging 0.23 in (6 mm). Although little is known of its natural history, study of related naucorids suggests that it feeds on aquatic insect larvae. In the early spring and summer, the female deposits eggs that cling to the rock or pebble substrate during incubation.

Habitat and Current Distribution

This species is known only to occur at and around Point of Rocks Springs, Ash Meadows, which is situated at an elevation of approximately 2,200 ft (670 m) in the Mojave Desert northwest of Las Vegas, Nevada. There are no estimates of population size.

Ash Meadows is an isolated island or oasis of wetlands in the surrounding desert; it is fed by springs from an underground aquifer. The Ash Meadows bug is restricted to these warm springs where the water moves over rock and gravel substrate.

History and Conservation Measures

The unique and restricted habitat of Ash Meadows remained virtually unexploited until the 1960s. At that time some of the marshland was further destroyed by mining activities; in the 1970s it ther destroyed by mining activities; in the 1970s it was degraded by cattle grazing, and some of the spring outflows were channeled for agriculture; in the early 1980s the habitat was further disturbed by development. Further demands for water could result in depletion of the underground aquifer (water-bearing stratum of rock, sand, or gravel) that supplies the area with water. The Ash Meadows ecosystem is a fragile one that harbors a number of threatened or endangered species; the habitat of this naucorid is only a small part of that ecosystem, leaving the naucorid very vulnerable to extirpation.

In the 1980s the Ash Meadows Wildlife Refuge was created; an area of approximately 10 acres (4 ha) within that reserve has been designated critical habitat for the naucorid. Conservation efforts in the Ash Meadows area are directed toward eradicating non-native species; securing the aquifer to restore the spring flows and maintain adequate water levels; and securing habitat from human disturbance. Specific actions on behalf of the naucorid include frequent monitoring of the population and its distribution and attempts to determine what factors control population size. As a result of efforts to provide suitable habitat for the endangered Ash Meadows Amargosa pupfish (*Cyprinodon nevadensis mionectes*), the Ash Meadows naucorid population is still declining. However, there is now enough knowledge of the naucorid to formulate a recovery plan which could prevent further decline in the population of this insect.

Columbia River tiger beetle

Cicindela columbica

Phylum	Arthropoda
Class	Insecta
Order	Coleoptera
Family	Cicindelidae
Status	Endangered, IUCN
Range	Idaho (U.S.A.)

Description and Biology

The Columbia River tiger beetle is typical in size and appearance to most other *Cicindela* species. The dorsal surface is brown to gray-brown with the anterior wings (elytron) having cream-colored markings. There are three bands on each elytron: the humeral lunule, the middle band, and the apical lunule. Total body length averages less than an inch (9-12 mm).

Very little is known about this tiger beetle, but much of its biology is probably quite similar to related species which have been studied. Adult tiger beetles are active surface predators that feed on small arthropods which they attack with short runs. They use their large mandibles to capture and process prey. Larvae are sedentary predators that live in burrows in the ground. They capture prey which pass near their burrow opening. Adult Columbia tiger beetles have a spring-fall activity pattern. New adults emerge in late summer (late July to early August) and forage actively until early October, when they dig burrows deep into the sand to spend the winter. These fall adults are sexually immature and exhibit no reproductive activity. Adults re-emerge from their burrows about mid-April and are active through June. Mating and oviposition (egg-laying) occur during this period. As with many other tiger beetle species development through the three larval instars probably requires one or two years.

Habitat and Current Distribution

This species occurs along open sand dunes and sand bars along rivers. It shares this habitat with two other common species, *Cicindela repanda* and *C. hirticollis*. Historically, it occurred along the Columbia, Snake, and Salmon rivers in rather large, gregarious populations. The most recent systematic survey in 1977 indicated the species is now found at only 14 sites along a 40-mile (64-km) section of the lower Salmon River canyon, in mostly small populations totalling less than 1000 individuals. The largest populations had approximately 200 and 400 individuals. Most occurrences were on older, well-established sand bars that extended back from the river where there was less chance of inundation during spring floods.

History and Conservation Measures

The Columbia River tiger beetle was reported to be extirpated from some or all of its former range along the Columbia and Snake rivers in the early 1970s as a result of dam construction on these rivers. Because of the significant range decline and apparent reduction of populations, the U.S. Fish and Wildlife Service (USFWS) was petitioned to list the Columbia River tiger beetle as a rare or endangered species. A 1985 survey indicated that remaining populations were stable, but it was still determined by the Service that the species warranted listing. However, in April 1990, after a call for comment, the USFWS decided that listing was no longer necessary because the remaining habitat of this species would be adequately protected as a scenic river and because no additional dams were proposed for this section of the Salmon River.

American burying beetle

Nicrophorus americanus

Phylum	Arthropoda
Class	Insecta
Order	Coleoptera
Family	Silphidae
Status	Endangered, IUCN
	Endangered, USFWS
Range	Canada; U.S.A.

Description and Biology

This shiny black beetle, also known as the giant carrion beetle, is the largest of the North American carrion beetles, reaching a length of 0.98-1.4 in (25-36 mm). It is easily distinguished not only by its large size, but also by the red frons (front part of the head capsule) and the red pronotal disc (segment behind the head). The antennal club is orange, and the black elytra (hard forewing coverings) have two pairs of scalloped red spots.

A pair of adult beetles buries small vertebrate carcasses in the soil. The male and female work together, lying on their backs beneath the carcass and using their legs to lever the body to soft ground up to 3.3 ft (1 m) away. The body is interred in a chamber probably 8 in (20 cm) deep within the soil, thus preventing other scavengers, particularly flies, from finding the booty. The beetles prepare the carcass by trimming it of fur and feathers, shaping it into a ball and coating it with anal and oral secretions that retard decomposition. As the corpse slowly decomposes, it is fed upon by the adults and the larvae. The female lays her eggs in the walls of a passage directly above the carcass, and the hatched larvae are fed on the liquids. Parental care usually continues through to pupation. This genus is unique among beetles in the extent of parental cooperation and care of the young.

The adults can produce a clearly audible buzzing sound by rubbing the elytra across the abdomen; this mechanism is used when the beetles are alarmed and also in communicating with the larvae.

Habitat and Current Distribution

This beetle is now known from only four locations: one on Block Island in Rhode Island, a 14-county area of Oklahoma and adjacent Arkansas, two counties in Nebraska, and a small island in Massachusetts with a reintroduced population. Fewer than a thousand beetles are estimated to occur in the Rhode Island and Massachusetts populations, and no estimates are available for the other areas.

Mature, undisturbed, moist forest may have historically been the preferred habitat of this species, but it has recently been collected in lightly grazed pastures, maritime grasslands, and shrub thickets in the east and in oak-hickory mixed forest, pasture, and grassland in the west. Most specimens are encountered in baited pitfall traps or in light traps, rather than on carrion.

History and Conservation Measures

The American burying beetle was formerly widespread across eastern temperate North America.

American burying beetle.

The causes for its decline are not clearly defined. Available evidence suggests that widespread habitat alteration and fragmentation have changed the vertebrate fauna in two critical ways—there are fewer small animals of the size preferred by the American burying beetle for food and reproduction, and there are now more scavenging animals such as foxes, skunks, and racoons with which the beetle must compete for this limited resource. Insecticides may also have played a role in this species' decline, but the extent is unknown. Other factors in the decline and current limiting factors are yet to be determined.

Studies of ecology and reproduction have been initiated, as have surveys in the western portion of the range. Efforts have begun to reintroduce the beetle into suitable habitat. As research better determines ecological and habitat requirements, conservation efforts will continue and improve.

Giant torrent midge

Edwardsina gigantea

Phylum	Arthropoda
Class	Insecta
Order	Diptera
Family	Blepharoceridae
Status	Endangered, IUCN
Range	Australia

Description and Biology

This species is one of the largest members of the family of Australian torrent or net-veined midges, with a wingspan of up to 1 in (25 mm). It is an elongated, long-legged fly with a fine network of lines on its wings, having the general appearance of a very large mosquito. Both its larvae and pupae are aquatic. The pupae are dark colored and egg-shaped; its larvae have not been described.

Little is known of the biology of this species. In similar species, larvae usually feed upon algae; adults fly weakly along the borders of streams, where the females prey on small two-winged flies and the males eat nectar.

Habitat and Current Distribution

The giant torrent midge now inhabits just two streams in the Snowy Mountains region of Australia: Spencer's Creek and the Thredbo River below the village of Thredbo in New South Wales. There are no estimates of population size.

The species is confined to hilly and mountain-ous districts. Its larvae are found in rapidly flowing streams, where they cling to stones using their ventral suckers.

History and Conservation Measures

This midge was once widespread, but has been eliminated from many of its former sites as a result of changes in river flow during and after dam construction. Australian midges are unable to tolerate pollution, siltation, and changes in stream level. Sewage is discharged into both of the streams known to harbor the giant torrent midge, and any further decrease in water quality would constitute a serious threat to its survival.

Both of the known habitats of this species lie within Kosciusko National Park. Studies have been begun on the Thredbo River with the aim of improving or at least stabilizing water quality. Monitoring of water quality should also continue at Spencer's Creek. Surveys of the other streams in Kosciusko National Park would be useful to better assess the status of the species.

Belkin's Dune tabanid fly

Brennania belkini

Phylum	Arthropoda
Class	Insecta
Order	Diptera
Family	Tabanidae
Status	Endangered, IUCN
Range	Mexico; U.S.A.

Description and Biology

Belkin's Dune tabanid is a stoutly built fly that resembles a bee. It has large iridescent eyes that are laterally extended, and a proboscis which, in females of the species, is adapted for piercing. In many related species, females feed upon blood, but this is apparently not true of the Belkin's Dune tabanid. Its feeding requirements are not fully understood, but male tabanids are known to feed on honeydew, nectar, and plant juices.

Little ecological or biological information is available about this species. Its larvae remain undescribed. Adults are on the wing in late May to early July.

Habitat and Current Distribution

This extremely rare fly is restricted to coastal sand dunes from Playa del Rey in California's Los Angeles County south to Ensenada in Baja California Norte, Mexico. The only known breeding colony is at Ballona Creek in California. There are no estimates of population size; any surviving populations in the United States are thought to be very small, and there is no information about the status of the species in Mexico.

Very little is known about its habitat require-

ments. It breeds only on coastal sand dunes, and a single larva has been found at a depth of 20 in (50 cm) in the soil at Ballona Creek.

History and Conservation Measures

Only seven adult specimens of this species, three males and four females, are known from collections. Six of these were collected from California and one from Mexico; five were collected before 1960. Habitat destruction is thought to be responsible for its rarity. The California coastal sand dunes are rapidly being destroyed by the introduction of exotic plants, off-road vehicle use, and increased urban development.

No specific conservation measures have been taken for this species, but it is thought to occur in the El Segundo Blue Butterfly Preserve in Los Angeles County. Careful regulation of coastal development may indirectly provide protection to any remaining populations. The few remaining intact sand dune habitats in southern California should be surveyed for the species, and incompatible activities should be banned from its current habitats. The species' biology and ecology should be studied in order to develop management plans. Surveys are also necessary in Mexico to determine the status of the insect in that country.

Queen Alexandra's birdwing butterfly

Ornithoptera (Troides) alexandrae

Phylum	Arthropoda
Class	Insecta
Order	Lepidoptera
Family	Papilionidae
Status	Endangered, IUCN
	Endangered, USFWS
	Appendix I, CITES
Range	Papua New Guinea

Description and Biology

Believed to be the world's largest butterfly, Queen Alexandra's birdwing averages 3 in (7.5 cm) in head and body length. Females may have a wingspan of more than 10 in (25 cm), while males possess a smaller wingspan of 7 in (18 cm). Markings and coloration also vary according to sex—brighter males have iridescent yellow, pale blue, and pale green markings on a black background, while females are distinguished by cream markings on a dark, chocolate-brown background. The abdomen of both sexes, however, is bright yellow and the ventral (lower) wingbases are bright red.

The lifespan of Queen Alexandra's birdwing is approximately seven months. Females lay extremely large eggs, about 0.16 in (4 mm) in diameter, on the leaves of the vine *Aristolochia schlecteri*, which later serve as the exclusive food source for larvae. After about four months, the larvae metamorphose into adults, which may live for three months. Although this butterfly is a strong flier, it usually remains within a limited home range. Adults are rarely eaten by predators; however, eggs are eaten by ants, and lar-vae are preyed upon by snakes, lizards, and toads, as well as by such birds as drongos, cuckoos, and crow pheasants.

Habitat and Current Distribution

This species has been recorded from a small area on the Popondetta Plain in Northern Province, Papua New Guinea, and is known as well from a few other sites in this country. The species is not as restricted as previously thought, though it is still very rare. Population figures are difficult to determine for this butterfly, because it flies high and is rarely seen. In addition, the leaves of *A. schlecteri* are frequently as high as 130 ft (40 m) in the forest's canopy, making observation of larvae difficult, if not impossible.

Primary habitat is primary and secondary lowland rain forest at elevations up to 1,300 ft (400 m) on the volcanic ash soils of the Popondetta Plain. In the second locality, habitat is secondary hill forest on clay soils at elevations of 1,800-2,600 ft (550-800 m). It has been reported that male butterflies swarm around Kwila trees, a large timber species, when they are in flower. Observers indicate that females will not accept males unless they have visited these flowers. If so, the Kwila's distribution may explain the butterfly's absence from areas where apparently suitable habitat exists.

History and Conservation Measures

The first specimen of Queen Alexandra's birdwing to be collected was a female found in 1906 on the upper reaches of the Mambare River, well outside its present range. Scientists believe that the species' distribution, already fragmented by agriculture and logging, was further disrupted by the eruption in 1951 of Mt. Lamington, which destroyed 100 sq mi (250 sq km) of prime habitat.

While cocoa and rubber plantations have already claimed large tracts of suitable habitat in the Popondetta region, the area's expanding oil palm industry currently poses the most significant threat to the species. Human population growth has also resulted in localized extinctions, communities and individuals having cleared the forest for gardens. In addition, the species fetches a high price on the black market given its attractiveness, rarity, and status as the largest butterfly in the world.

The Papua New Guinea government has passed and strictly enforces legislation protecting Queen Alexandra's birdwing and other butterfly species. A Wildlife Management Area, comprising approximately 27,000 acres (11,000 ha) of grassland and forest, has been established north of Popondetta, and negotiations are in progress to establish more reserves. Status evaluation is continuing and the key to successful conservation may lie with butterfly ranching operations in secondary habitats (through habitat enrichment) to provide an alternative source of income for local people. This possibility is being actively explored, and educational programs have been initiated to explain the need for conservation to local communities.

An area of primary forest on government land has been set aside as a future reserve and study area for the species. In addition a study of *A. schlecteri* has been undertaken at the Popondetta Agricultural Training Institute to see if the vines can be grown in an artificial habitat and whether or not the butterfly will eventually use them. Breeding the butterfly in captivity would provide the opportunity to study the species' biology, particularly its dependency on a single food plant. However, the costs of such a program are currently prohibitive.

Luzon peacock

Papilio chikae

Phylum	Arthropoda
Class	Insecta
Order	Lepidoptera
Family	Papilionidae
Status	Endangered, IUCN Appendix I, CITES
Range	Philippines

Description and Biology

Highly prized by collectors for its beauty and rarity, the Luzon peacock is a glossy, relatively large swallowtail butterfly, with each forewing measuring over 2 in (55 mm). The male's forewings are black; scattered across the upper (left) forewing are golden-green scales; a pale gray band tapers toward the bottom of the lower (right) forewing, where it becomes light blue. The male's black hindwings have crescent-shaped, pale purple and reddish orange markings on their lower edges. Its tail is relatively long, tapering toward the inner hindwing. The female's appearance is very similar, the only differences being that the hindwing markings are more pronounced and the tail is longer. The size and markings of the species vary slightly according to season; the spring form is more brightly colored, while the summer form is somewhat larger.

The reproductive biology and developmental stages of this species are unknown, as is its diet.

Habitat and Current Distribution

The Luzon peacock is found on Luzon, the northernmost island of the Philippines. It is confined to the Cordillera Central mountain range at altitudes above 4,900 ft (1,500 m) in the northern regions of Baguio and Bontoc. It can be seen from February through October. There are currently no population estimates, but the species is considered rare.

The habitat of the Luzon peacock is subtropical montane countryside characterized by grassy meadows, scattered bushes, and groves of small trees growing in rifts and ravines. The most common tree appearing in the habitat is the Benguet pine.

History and Conservation Measures

The species was discovered in 1965 on Mt. Santo-Tomas in the Cordilleras. Scientists have since speculated that it is a relict species which migrated to Luzon from China and Taiwan during the last ice age when sea levels were extremely low. The species would have become isolated in the Cordilleras when the polar ice caps melted and sea levels returned to normal.

Currently, the primary threat to this species is over-collection. The Luzon peacock is coveted by foreign collectors, some of whom have offered 35mm cameras to Filipinos in exchange for a specimen. Collectors can easily access its habitat by road, and because the species flies slowly and is readily attracted to decoys, it is easily captured, even by amateurs. Although demand for the species has greatly declined in recent years, over-collection is still a significant problem.

Habitat destruction also threatens the Luzon peacock. The Baguio area is a popular tourist destination in the summer; recreational activities and the construction of roads to accommodate tourists and growing local populations have both contributed to the destruction of this species' habitat. Fortunately, the ravines and gullies preferred by the butterfly remain undeveloped at the present time because they are considered "unusable."

Detailed studies to determine the species' exact distribution and biology are needed before specific conservation measures can be taken. Once the studies are completed, it may be that commercial demand for the swallowtail can be met by controlled ranching. Such a program may also encourage local communities to conserve wild populations of the butterfly.

Protected areas do not exist within the range of the Luzon peacock, although the Philippine government is currently reviewing the national park system. Conservation of butterfly habitat is essential and may be promoted within the context of preserving the Baguio region so as to sustain the tourist trade.

Homerus swallowtail

Papilio homerus

Phylum	Arthropoda
Class	Insecta
Order	Lepidoptera
Family	Papilionidae
Status	Endangered, IUCN Appendix I, CITES
Range	Jamaica

Description and Biology

Slow-flying and powerful, with a forewing size of almost 3 in (75 mm), the Homerus swallowtail is the largest species in its genus. It is primarily black, or very dark brown, with broad yellow bands across the wings. The forewings also have four or five yellow spots on the upper side, near the edge, and usually no more than one on the bottom; the hindwings have powder-blue spots or circular markings and pronounced tails. The male differs from the female in having hair scales on its hindwings alongside the abdomen. The full-grown caterpillar is dark green with a brown underbody; it has a white band, an eye spot, and brown markings on each side of its body.

Adult *P. homerus* feed on nectar from a variety of sources. The species is seen flying during the day-time from February to April and September to October.

Habitat and Current Distribution

The Homerus swallowtail butterfly is endemic to the island of Jamaica and only lives in two small areas of less than one sq mi (2 sq km) each. The eastern population is found in the Blue Mountains of St. Thomas and Portland, and the western population occurs in the Cockpit Country of Trelawny Parish. Despite reports that the butterfly is quite common in its few favored localities, the total population of the species is small.

This swallowtail frequents mountain slopes and gullies at fairly low elevations of 500-2,000 ft (150-600 m) but is occasionally seen at higher altitudes.

History and Conservation Measures

This species has been recorded from seven of the 13 parishes on Jamaica, but its distribution is now much reduced; sightings are less common, and the once continuous eastern and western populations are now apparently disjunct. The IUCN listed *P. homerus* on its "Top 12 Endangered Species List" in 1988. Habitat destruction from the timber and coffee industries is the main threat to this butterfly. Although the rate of destruction in the east has slowed since the early 1950s, that population is still on the decline. The western population is also suffering a reduction in range. Collecting is very difficult in such mountainous country, but, because of the aesthetic value of the butterfly, commercial collecting still continues.

Some conservation projects are underway: there are efforts to create a Jamaican Mountain National Park, which would help protect this species, and there are plans to declare *P. homerus* the Jamaican national butterfly. Captive breeding of the species could reduce collection of wild specimens and per-haps support a viable, local commercial venture. Collecting in the wild should be restricted to scientific purposes only.

Corsican swallowtail

Papilio hospiton

Phylum	Arthropoda
Class	Insecta
Order	Lepidoptera
Family	Papilionidae
Status	Endangered, IUCN Appendix I, CITES
Range	Corsica (France); Sardinia (Italy)

Description and Biology

Primarily black and yellow, this butterfly has a wingspan of just under 3 in (72-76 mm). Its hind wings are each marked with a small red "eye spot" near the back and highlighted with a row of small blue spots. The tails are small and tapered.

Adult butterflies emerge from pupae between May and June and remain active until early August. Numerous new adults and even caterpillars have been found on Corsica in early August, suggesting that the species may produce two broods each year. Caterpillars eat various plants of the Umbelliferae family, which includes fennel, giant fennel, and carrots. Young caterpillars are subject to attack by the parasitic wasp *Trogus violaceus*.

Habitat and Current Distribution

These butterflies can be found in open mountainous country at altitudes of 2,000-4,900 ft (600-1500 m) on the islands of Corsica and Sardinia in the Mediterranean Sea. Breeding areas are very localized on Corsica; breeding sites on Sardinia have not been identified but are also presumed to be local.

History and Conservation Measures

Currently, the chief threat to the Corsican swallowtail is habitat destruction; the plant species consumed by larval *P. hospiton* are burned by local sheepherders, who claim the vegetation is poisonous to their livestock. Development for skiing resorts and other projects has also caused profound damage to this species' habitat.

For the Corsican swallowtail and many other butterfly species worldwide, amateur and commercial butterfly collectors pose another major threat. Adults as well as immature swallowtails are illegally captured by local and foreign collectors because some specimens can secure huge prices on the world market.

Full protection by French law on Corsica has failed to provide any practical help to the species, and there are no laws protecting *P. hospiton* on Sardinia. The most important step needed to preserve the swallowtail is to determine with greater precision its population, feeding habits, and breeding areas; once this is done, critical habitat areas need to be designated as nature reserves. Additional legal protection could be helpful if mechanisms for enforcement are also implemented.

Large blue butterflies

Maculinea spp.

Phylum	Arthropoda
Class	Insecta
Order	Lepidoptera
Family	Lycaenidae
Status	Vulnerable, IUCN (*M. arionides*)
	Endangered, IUCN (*M. alcon, M. arion, M. nausithous, M. teleius*)
Range	Palearctic region

Description and Biology

As their common name indicates, these blue butterflies are fairly large, with wingspans ranging from 1.2-1.8 in (30-45 mm). Most species and subspecies are heavily marked with black spots and borders. However, *M. alcon* and *M. teleius* males may be entirely blue and free from spotting, while *M. nausithous* may be almost wholly covered with dusky brown scales, showing little blue. The underside of all species is a shade of brownish gray, crossed by arcs of white-circled black dots. Markings vary greatly within and between colonies. *Maculinea* are unique among western Palearctic butterflies in feeding on plants for part of their lives and on animals for the rest; they first feed on their host plants and then, later, on ant eggs, grubs, and prepupae.

All species have a single brood per year and generally fly for three to four weeks between late May and August, depending on the locality. Eggs are laid—singly by some species and in groups by others—on flower buds of plants that vary by species, including thyme, oregano, and gentians. Young caterpillars burrow into the flowerhead of the host plant and feed on the developing structure. After molting, they fall to the ground and wait to be found by a passing ant of the genus *Myrmica*. The ant is attracted to the larva because of the honeydew it secretes from a posterior gland; after being "milked," the larva is carried off to the ant nest and placed among the brood. Large blue larvae spend the next nine months living among the ants, spending the winter in their nests. Pupation occurs about four weeks prior to emergence. Pupae, also attractive to the ants, are enclosed in cells. The adult butterfly emerges at dawn, crawls out, and expands its wings once it reaches the surface.

Habitat and Current Distribution

The genus is restricted to the Palearctic region. *M. arion* has been found from western Europe to southern Siberia, Armenia, Mongolia, and China, but has recently gone extinct from much of northern Europe, including the U.K., Netherlands, Belgium, and northern France. *M. alcon* is found from northern Spain and France through central Europe to central Asia, but is extinct in many former European localities. *M. teleius* extends from Spain through central and eastern Europe to China, Korea, and Hokkaido, Honshu, and Kyushu, Japan; it is very rare and local, and is apparently in decline throughout its range. *M. teleius* is extinct in Belgium and the Netherlands, as is *M. nausithous*. The latter occurs sparingly in northern Spain and central Europe but local extinctions are occurring. *M. arionides* is found in Amurland and the alpine forests of Hokkaido and Honshu, Japan, and is the only large blue absent from Europe. Populations and abundance of colonies of large blues are not well known. Nearly all species and races form small, isolated colonies whose populations fluctuate annually. Individual colonies are estimated to range in population from less than 50 up to 500, but, in rare cases, can number several thousand.

Large blues require a habitat with a high density of their host ants as well as their host plants, fairly close to each other, if not together. Habitat conditions vary with species and with location, and include dry grasslands, meadows, wetlands, and alpine forest.

History and Conservation Measures

Large blue butterflies occur only in small colonies in special habitats, and have always been uncommon; today, however, destruction and modification of these habitats make the large blues some of the most threatened species of butterflies in Europe, and, probably, Asia. Most *Maculinea* populations breed on commercially managed private land and are being eliminated by intensive land-use practices. All large blues require unimproved land which has not been treated with fertilizer or herbicide, although some management may be necessary in the form of grazing or scrub removal. Wetland species are declining very rapidly through the development and drainage of wetlands. Drastic changes such as conversion to arable fields or improvement of pastures by ploughing, seeding, drilling, or application of fertilizers or herbicides are obvious, but more subtle changes in habitat, such as changes in burning or grazing practices, may also have negative effects that render the habitat unusable for these species.

The earliest efforts at conservation for these butterflies were made for *M. arion* in the U.K.: surveys were organized, sites were patrolled to deter collectors, and other sites were obtained as nature reserves. All of these actions eventually failed, because nothing was known about the ecology of the butterfly other than its basic life cycle. Full-time ecological research was begun in 1972, when the species had been reduced to about 250 individuals on two sites in England. The studies soon revealed the need for high densities of the ant species *Myrmica sabuleti* and that these had largely disappeared, even from nature reserves, because heavy grazing had been abandoned. It was not difficult to recreate suitable conditions, but *M. arion* had declined to the point where it could not be saved from extinction.

Recovery recommendations include surveys to discover surviving colonies, the establishment of nature reserves where suitable, and further ecological research to discover how these may be appropriately managed. Captive breeding does not offer a viable means of perpetuating any species of *Maculinea* in the foreseeable future. The broad ranges of the large blues means that it is still possible to prevent their overall extinction. In the long term, however, there is no suitable alternative to maintaining wild habitats in the appropriate condition, with both the food plants and the host ants upon which the butterflies depend.

False ringlet butterfly

Coenonympha oedippus

Phylum	Arthropoda
Class	Insecta
Order	Lepidoptera
Family	Nymphalidae (Satyridae)
Status	Endangered, IUCN
Range	Austria; Belgium; France; Germany; Hungary; Italy; Japan; Kazakhstan (?); Liechtenstein; Mongolia (?); Poland; Portugal; Russia; Slovakia; Spain; Switzerland; Ukraine

Description and Biology

Although the false ringlet butterfly is a member of the Heath group of satyrine butterflies (*Coenonympha* spp.), it is darker than most other species and more closely resembles small specimens of the ringlet (*Aphantopus hyperanthus*). Apart from the dark upperside, it can be distinguished from other *Coenonympha* species by the position of the large ocellus (eye-like marking) on the costa (anterior vein or margin) of the underside of the hindwing, which is closer to the base of the wing than in other species, and the metallic antemarginal line on the same wing surface. The length of the forewing of the male ranges from 0.7-0.8 in (17-21 mm); the female is slightly larger on average.

The butterfly is single-brooded, adults flying from the end of June until August. The larvae feed on a variety of monocotyledonous plants. Recorded hosts include species of *Molinia*, *Eriophorum*, and possibly *Lolium*, and *Carex panicea*, *Poa palustris*, *P. pratensis*, and *Iris pseudacorus*.

Habitat and Current Distribution

Subspecies *C. o. oedippus* has a scattered distribution, occurring as isolated colonies in parts of western France and northern Italy, central Europe and formerly at least, in other parts of western Europe, including Germany. Subspecies *hungarica* occurs in Austria, Hungary, and eastwards through Russia to China and Japan. The distribution of the species in the eastern Palaeractic part of its range is not known exactly. *C. oedippus* inhabits wetlands, wet meadows in forest clearings (often in *Fagus* or *Quercus-Betula* woodland), forests in stream valleys, and meadowland generally. The habitats are infrequently, if ever, mown, and tall, dense vegetation is essential for the survival of the species. In some of its dryer sites the butterfly is associated with south-facing, warm slopes.

History and Conservation Measures

This species has become extinct in many of its former sites in western Europe and has declined markedly during the last 50 years. It may be extinct in Slovakia, Germany, and Spain, and it is classified as endangered, and in some cases protected, in Austria, Switzerland, France, Hungary, Italy, and Portugal.

The reason for its decline is almost certainly the intensification of agriculture, including drainage, use of fertilizers, more intensive mowing and grazing regimes, and the use of heavy farm machinery. Changes in forest management may also have had an adverse effect. Damage to populations from collectors is less easy to assess.

Now that conservation concern has been focused on the species, the outlook is reasonably good. The key feature of the conservation of the false ringlet butterfly is sensitive and knowledgeable management of its habitats. Drainage, fertilizer use and the impact of heavy machinery must be avoided. Rotational mowing of meadows should be introduced, with only small areas of each site being mowed in any one year.

Bay checkerspot butterfly

Euphydryas editha bayensis

Phylum	Arthropoda
Class	Insecta
Order	Lepidoptera
Family	Nymphalidae
Status	Endangered, IUCN
	Threatened, USFWS
Range	California (U.S.A.)

Description and Biology

This medium-sized butterfly has a maximum wing span of 2.25 in (5.6 cm), with the female slightly larger than the male. The predominant color on the upper surface is black, checkered with bright red and yellow markings. The underside is predominantly yellow with sharp patterns in black and red. The male and female are very similar in appearance.

Adults emerge in early spring, and females may lay eggs in batches of 20 to 95 on the larval host plants. Some females lay as many as 1,200 eggs, but the maximum is normally 600-700 eggs. The larvae enter diapause (period of dormancy) by early summer and remain inactive until the autumn rains, when they begin to feed on new plant growth. Post-diapause larvae appear simultaneously with the new annual plants in early spring, when they feed for several months before pupating. Adult emergence occurs about two weeks later. The adults feed on the nectar of several plants.

Habitat and Current Distribution

The bay checkerspot butterfly is thought to occur in about eight separate populations in California. The largest is near Morgan Hill in Santa Clara County; another is in San Mateo County and includes a small population at the Jasper Ridge Preserve at Stanford University. Dramatic annual fluctuations in populations with frequent local extinctions are particularly characteristic of the bay checkerspot, and the total population size has never been estimated.

The bay checkerspot is patchily distributed, occurring only on isolated areas of grassland on serpentine outcrops that support high densities of the larval host plants *Plantago erecta*, *Castilleja densiflora*, and *C. exserta*.

History and Conservation Measures

The range of this subspecies has always been small, but it is now extremely restricted. Three populations once existed at Jasper Ridge, two of which were extinct by 1992, and the remaining population had fewer than 50 adult butterflies in 1993. Although decimated by drought, grazing, and pesticides, the Jasper Ridge colony is presently safe from immediate habitat destruction; it is too small, however, to ensure perpetuation of the species, especially given its characteristic population fluctuations. The colony in San Mateo County is threatened by plans for the creation of a golf course. The Morgan Hill population (around 100,000 individuals) is partially protected in a butterfly preserve, but parts of the grassland, although managed for the butterfly, are still threatened by residential and commercial encroachment. Overall, the habitat is also threatened by invasive, non-native grasses.

It is essential to preserve and manage the remaining habitat of the bay checkerspot butterfly, or the species will not survive. Efforts are underway to secure cooperation from landowners in preservation of areas of suitable habitat.

Australian ant

Nothomyrmecia macrops

Phylum	Arthropoda
Class	Insecta
Order	Hymenoptera
Family	Formicidae
Status	Insufficiently Known, IUCN
Range	Australia

Description and Biology

The Australian ant, or dinosaur ant, is considered to be the most primitive living ant. Workers measure approximately 0.4 in (1 cm) long and are golden yellow. Their jaws are long, and they possess a single waist node. The species' sting is strong and effective. The stridulatory (sound-producing) organ, which produces a barely audible chirp, is located on the abdomen instead of on the back, as it is in most related species. The queens, while somewhat larger, generally resemble the workers in appearance. The species' wings, which are very short and unusually clipped, are incapable of maintaining flight.

Individuals emerge from the nest shortly after nightfall to forage for insects. They remain aboveground until just before dawn when they return to the nest. Australian ants, unlike other ant species which use scent markers or trails to navigate, are believed to use the silhouette of the forest canopy as a map when traveling above ground. Individuals collected by researchers are able to return to their nest from the point of capture for up to three days afterwards.

In the late spring and early autumn, winged virgin queens and males are produced in colonies, from which they then depart in late summer. Mating activity has not yet been observed. Founding queens forage with workers while rearing their first brood, and several may co-found a colony.

Habitat and Current Distribution

This species is only known from several sites within an area of South Australia amounting to less than 0.4 sq mi (1 sq km). No population estimates exist.

Documented sites occur in tall eucalyptus woodland, where the tree canopy is virtually uninterrupted and few herbs or grasses grow amid the layer of leaf litter that thinly blankets the forest floor. Nests are underground and have concealed entrances.

History and Conservation Measures

Until the 1970s, the only known specimens of this species were those taken in 1934 from Western Australia. It was not definitely identified again until 1977 when it was rediscovered in South Australia. This site has since been destroyed following the laying of an underground telephone line, decimating much of the resident population. However, three other nearby sites have since been identified, two of them larger and more populous than the original.

Habitat destruction has undoubtedly fragmented local distribution. Clearance of vegetation is a major threat, due to the species' dependency on the overhead canopy for navigation. Fire is also a concern—nighttime bush fires could wipe out colonies by killing large numbers of foraging workers.

The local human population has cooperated in protection of the species. However, given the fact that the area is heavily settled, formal measures to preserve the species' presently known habitat are apparently impractical. Targeted conservation plans may prove successful if other populations are found in less developed areas.

Aurantioporus croceus

Family	Coriolaceae
Status	Endangered (?), IUCN
Range	North temperate zone

Description and Biology

Aurantioporus croceus is a mushroom with pores rather than gills (a polypore); it has an annual, saffron-yellow to orange-yellow cap, and fleshy fruiting body. The brackets are up to 7.8 in (20 cm) wide, 3.9 in (10 cm) deep, and 2.3 in (6 cm) thick. Young fruiting bodies have a hairy surface, while older ones are smooth. The pores are angular, and the tubes are up to 0.6 in (15 mm) long. This species grows at the base of tree trunks, within cavities of living oak (*Quercus* spp.) or, more rarely, on dead wood. It has also been recorded from sweet chestnut (*Castanea sativa*), poplars (*Populus* spp.) and *Robinia* spp. The spores measure approximately 6×4 μm and are wind dispersed.

Habitat and Current Distribution

A. croceus was formerly widespread in the North temperate zone, but in Europe it is now restricted to a few isolated sites where mature trees still occur, as well as in protected areas. Its status in North America is less certain; it may not be threatened at present, but modern forestry practices pose a threat throughout its range.

History and Conservation Measures

Within Europe, the species is considered extinct in Norway and Denmark and endangered in Germany. In Sweden, it is listed as vulnerable. It does not occur in Great Britain, probably reflecting a continental distribution rather than a previous extinction. The habitat favored by this species is also extremely important for many other fungi (including lichens), mosses, and invertebrates. Protection of the preferred habitat of this species could therefore have multiple benefits.

Sarcosoma globosum

Family	Sarcosomataceae
Status	Endangered (?), IUCN
Range	North temperate zone

Description and Biology

This remarkable cup fungus has black, liquid-storing fruiting bodies, 2-3.5 in (5-9 cm) in diameter, about the size of a fist. The fruiting bodies appear following snow melt, but the species may occasionally fruit in late autumn. The wind-dispersed, ellipsoid spores develop when the storage tissue has virtually disappeared. The process is very slow, and many fruiting bodies fail to develop mature spores.

Habitat and Current Distribution

Sarcosoma globosum occurs in scattered localities in Scandinavia (where a drastic decline has been recorded), in the Central European mountains, and in northern North America. It is saprophytic (lives on dead or decaying organic matter) and restricted to ancient spruce (*Picea abies*) woodland on well-drained soils (mainly calcareous sand), often with a thick moss cover. In North America it may occur with *Pinus* spp.

History and Conservation Measures

Modern forestry practices pose a severe threat to this unique species. Most countries where it occurs, or was known to occur, list it on their national list of threatened species. The species does not tolerate clear-cutting. Traditional management of woodland pasture is required to ensure survival of its habitat.

Mixed Northern Atlantic hepatic mat

Family	Adelanthaceae (*Adelanthus*); Herbertaceae (*Herbertus*); Lepicoleaceae (*Mastigophora*); Lepidoziaceae (*Bazzania*); Lophoziaceae (*Anastrepta, Anastrophyllum*); Plagiochilaceae (*Plagiochila*); Pleuroziaceae (*Pleurozia*); Scapaniaceae (*Scapania*)
Status	Endangered, IUCN
Range	Ireland; Norway; Scotland (United Kingdom)

Description and Biology

This is a characteristic community of large leafy liverworts with very specific habitat and climatic requirements. The species typically found in this community include *Adelanthus lindenbergianus, Anastrepta orcadensis, Anastrophyllum donnianum, A. joergensenii, Bazzania pearsonii, B. tricrenata, Herbertus aduncus* ssp. *hutchinsiae, H. borealis, Mastigophora woodsii, Plagiochila carringtonii, Pleurozia purpurea, Scapania nimbosa*, and *S. ornithopodioides*. These species sometimes replace the more usual moss layer in heaths dominated by dwarf ericaceous shrubs in oceanic parts of western Europe. The community usually consists of not less than six of the 13 species listed above. The overall appearance of the community varies according to the luxuriance it develops, but, at its best, the species form conspicuous low hummocks beneath more or less aging *Calluna, Vaccinium*, and *Empetrum*. The individual species are readily recognizable and are often highly pigmented. These are mostly relict species, often with extremely disjunct world distributions, which are not well equipped to survive any change in environment. Most of them do not produce spores or vegetative propagules (only male plants are known of *Plagiochila carringtonii*), so they are very inefficient at dispersing, and are unable to recolonize areas once they have disappeared from these loca-

tions. Therefore, they are very vulnerable to catastrophic events such as fires.

Habitat and Current Distribution

The individual species tend to have a wider distribution than the community as a whole, which is confined to the western coastal fringes of northern Scotland and Ireland, with an underdeveloped selection occurring at isolated sites on the west coast of Norway. Some of the species show wide dispersion patterns, with *Plagiochila carringtonii*, for example, occurring only in Scotland, Ireland, the Faeroes, and Japan (with a different subspecies occurring in Nepal). Several of the species are, however, rare themselves. For example, *Herbertus borealis* is known only from one site in Scotland and three in Norway. *Anastrophyllum joergensenii* is also known only from Scotland and Norway.

The habitat of the mixed hepatic mat is characteristically well-drained soil in dwarf shrub heaths, scree slopes, and on cliff ledges on north or northeast facing upland slopes, where there is a constant high atmospheric humidity. In the British Isles, the community is almost restricted to those small areas in the west where there are more than 220 wet days (a "wet day" is defined as a period of 24 hours in which 1 mm of rain is recorded) in a year.

History and Conservation Measures

This community and its habitat requirements were first recognized in the late 1960s, although most of the individual species have been known for some time. The community has already disappeared from some parts of its range through habitat destruction by burning and grazing. It is very susceptible to pro- longed drought and excessive exposure to direct sun- light, which may be a major threat if global warming proves to be a genuine phenomenon. A program of monitoring is required at selected populations to de- termine the possible effects of climate change. Collecting by botanists may be a threat to some of the rarer species at some sites.

Marsupella profunda

Family	Gymnomitriaceae
Status	Endangered, IUCN
Range	Canary Islands (Spain); Madeira Island (Portugal); Portugal; United Kingdom

Description and Biology

Marsupella profunda is a delicate plant that forms a dark chestnut-brown tuft about 0.2 in (5 mm) tall. The leaves of this plant are divided by a sharp-pointed space into two lobes for one-third to one-half of their length; overall they have a rounded shape with rounded tips and inflexed (bent abruptly inward) margins, and they overlap on the stem. This species is similar to *Marsupella ustulata*, but in this latter species the upper leaves on female plants are deeply bilobate (two-lobed) and incurved at the apex, larger than vegetative leaves. *M. profunda* is frequently fertile and possesses neither vegetative propagules nor gemmae (specialized groups of asexual reproductive cells).

Habitat and Current Distribution

Marsupella profunda is a European species which has been recorded from a few sites in Britain, Portugal, and Macaronesia (Madeira and the Canary Islands). It is found at fairly low altitudes, unlike most of its nearest relatives. *M. profunda* is a euoceanic species, which grows in pioneer communities on open acidic soils. In Britain it grows in kaolin quarries on clay soil or on more or less exposed rocks.

History and Conservation Measures

Marsupella profunda was first recorded in 1887 in Portugal. The first samples were gathered from micaceous rock in an Atlantic area of the Iberian Peninsula. Due to its small size as well as its rarity, it was not found again in Portugal until 1970. Two new Portuguese sites have subsequently been identified. Since 1950 the species has been located at three sites in the British Isles (all in Cornwall), two on Madeira Island, and one in the Canary Islands. It has not been seen in Britain since 1971. Major threats to the species include changes in humidity, fires, forest management practices, and tourist pressure, particularly in the Atlantic islands. Conservation measures for this species should emphasize habitat protection and management plans.

Taxitheliella richardsii

Family	Hypnaceae
Status	Endangered, IUCN
Range	Sarawak (Malaysia)

Description and Biology

Taxitheliella richardsii is a moss with creeping, slender, and highly branched stems. The leaves are flattened, broadly ovate, acute (sharp-pointed), without a costa (midrib of the leaf), and with little cellular differentiation at the leaf basal corners. The leaf margins are weakly toothed. The seta (the stalk that supports the capsule) is about 0.15 in (4 mm) long, and the capsules (spore-producing structures) are erect and funnel-shaped.

Habitat and Current Distribution

Taxitheliella is a monotypic genus endemic to the lowland rain forest of Gunong Dulit in Sarawak, north Borneo. It is known only from the type collection made by P. W. Richards. According to H. N. Dixon who described the genus in 1935, the plants grow on rotten logs and lianas in forest undergrowth, forming vivid green patches. The habitat of *Taxitheliella richardsii*, the lowland rain forests of Malaysian Borneo, is very rich in plant species and includes several rare Malesian mosses such as *Fissidens beccarii* and *Chionoloma longifolium*. The latter two are also known from the single type collection.

History and Conservation Measures

The lowland rain forests in tropical Southeast Asia, including the portion in Malaysian Borneo, are highly threatened by excessive logging and slash-and-burn shifting agriculture practiced by an increasing human population. The current economic and social conflicts reported between the logging companies and tribal inhabitants in the Sarawak rain forest highlight the urgency for the conservation of rain forests to prevent the mass extinction of indigenous flora and fauna, including *Taxitheliella richardsii*.

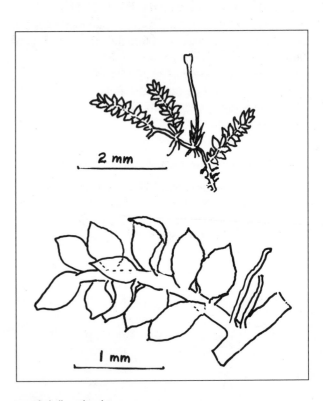

Taxitheliella richardsii.

Ochyraea tatrensis

Family	Hypnobartlettiaceae
Status	Endangered, IUCN
Range	Slovakia

Description and Biology

A medium-sized moss, 1-1.5 in (3-4 cm) long, this species forms dark green to olive-green mats. The leaves of *O. tatrensis* have a curious form—they are sickle-shaped, their cells are arranged in two or three layers, and they lack a discrete midrib. The leaf tips are blunt or rounded, and the leaf margins are flat and more or less smooth. This species is dioecious (the male and female organs are found on separate plants) and has only once been found with sporophytes (two capsules).

Habitat and Current Distribution

Ochyraea tatrensis is known only from two localities in the Nízké Tatry National Park in Central Slovakia. Both localities are near each other and are at an altitude of 5,250 ft (1,600 m). One site is just below a road, the other in a closed valley further away from civilization. Neither site is longer than 164 ft (50 m). This moss grows on granite or on submerged rocks in streams and below small waterfalls.

History and Conservation Measures

Ochyraea tatrensis was first recorded in 1985 in a stream in Slovakia and was later found at another site along the same water system. The moss still occurs at both of these sites. However, mosses are very sensitive to pollution, and any decline in the air or water quality of this catchment area could threaten the species with extinction. If these sites can be protected from pollution and the effects of the construction of additional roads and bridges, the species may survive at the original sites. Additional surveys should, however, be conducted to determine whether populations of this species occur elsewhere.

Jamesoniella undulifolia

Family	Jungermanniaceae
Status	Vulnerable, IUCN
Range	Europe; Greenland; Russia

Description and Biology

Jamesoniella undulifolia is a medium-sized leafy liverwort that is reddish brown in appearance. It has rounded leaves with smooth margins that are obliquely attached to the stem. *J. undulifolia* is likely to be confused with *J. autumnalis*, but it occupies a distinct habitat, has larger undulate leaves with larger cells, and has smaller teeth at the perianth mouth. This plant is rarely fertile.

Habitat and Current Distribution

This liverwort has a temperate and boreal distribution and is confined to Europe, Greenland, and the Russian part of Asia. In Europe it has an apparent western distribution but is absent from the Mediterranean region. It reaches east to northern Bohemia, south to France, and north to Scandinavia. *J. undulifolia* grows among and over *Sphagnum* spp. in mires, where it seems to prefer more or less level ground. Most sites are in wet mires supplied with ground water, but the species may also occur in bogs that receive water from precipitation rather than from the ground.

History and Conservation Measures

J. undulifolia has decreased dramatically in many countries. For example in Britain, it was once recorded from 10 sites, but now remains in only four. In Bohemia (Czech Republic) it was known to occur in four localities, but has not been found since 1907 and is probably extinct in that country. In Sweden, it had been recorded from eight sites but no longer exists at any of these. Similar situations exist in Finland and Denmark. The main threats to this species are drainage and other forms of habitat destruction, including burning. One of the British sites was lost due to the creation of a reservoir, and two other sites have been lost due to the planting of conifers and habitat deterioration, including eutrophication. Conservation measures should include protection of the remaining habitat from further destruction.

Spruceanthus theobromae

Family	Lejeuneaceae
Status	Endangered, IUCN
Range	Ecuador

Description and Biology

Spruceanthus theobromae is a rather robust, leafy liverwort that forms loose, upright, or hanging tufts on bark of rain forest trees. The stems are up to 2 in (5 cm) long and have forked branching. The leaves are made up of narrowly elongated cells and have very tiny water sacs. There are also tiny, ovate (egg-shaped) underleaves. The plants are usually fertile, and sporophytes arise from perianths with many (5-8) folds.

Habitat and Current Distribution

This species is known only from coastal Ecuador, where it has been collected three times in the Los Rios Province, between Quevedo and Guayaquil. The species has been found growing on bark of trees along running water in virgin semi-deciduous rain forest at the foot of the Andes about 500-1,000 ft (150-300 m) above sea level. The other species of this genus occurs in Southeast Asia and Australia.

History and Conservation Measures

Spruceanthus theobromae has only been collected in the mid-nineteenth century and in 1947 in the province of Los Rios, Ecuador. Since the 1960s most of the region has been deforested, but the forest in the area of Hacienda Clementina, where it was collected in 1947, is still largely intact. It is not known whether *S. theobromae* continues to exist in the area. Its conservation is of considerable importance as the species is the only representative of *Spruceanthus* in the New World.

Orthotrichum truncato-dentatum

Family	Orthotrichaceae
Status	Insufficiently known, IUCN
Range	Argentina; Uruguay

Description and Biology

Most *Orthotrichum* species are small mosses known by their large bell-like hoods covering the young capsules (spore-producing structures) and their dry, erect leaves. Only three species of *Orthotrichum* have been reported from the area concerned: *O. truncato-dentatum*; *O. araucarieti*; and *O. diaphanum* var. *podocarpi*. *O. truncato-dentatum* grows in loose, olive-green tufts up to 0.8 in (2 cm) tall. This moss differs from *O. araucarieti* in its shorter, less sharply pointed leaves, and from *O. diaphanum* var. *podocarpi* in having all leaf tips green, never yellow, brown, or hyaline (thin and translucent or transparent). Additional characteristics that differentiate the three species can be seen under a microscope.

Habitat and Current Distribution

Orthotrichum truncato-dentatum has a very restricted distribution and has only been found in southern Uruguay and the neighboring areas of Argentina. It grows only on tree trunks.

History and Conservation Measures

This species was described from a collection made on Isla Recreo, Argentina, in 1880. Recently two "new" specimens were located in the herbarium of the New York Botanical Garden. Both originated from Montevideo and were collected before 1880. No additional specimens of this species seem to have been collected in the past 100 years. Both known localities of this species are now heavily urbanized. Since the previous habitats for *O. truncato-dentatum* have, as far as is known, been destroyed, some scientists believe that this moss may already be extinct. Further investigations in southern Uruguay and the neighboring areas of Argentina are necessary to determine whether or not this species still exists.

Takakia ceratophyllum

Family . . . . Takakiaceae
Status . . . . Vulnerable, IUCN
Range . . . . India; Aleutian Islands (U.S.A.)

Description and Biology

Takakia ceratophyllum is a tiny, mat-forming plant with underground stems and numerous, simple, erect shoots measuring about 0.2 in (5 mm) long and covered with three- or four-lobed, cylindrical, leafy appendages. Rhizoids (roothair-like structures) are completely absent. Glandular hairs are abundant on the underground stems and the lower portion of the erect stems. The sporophyte consists of a well-developed seta (stalk that supports the capsule) and capsule (spore-producing structure). At maturity, it splits along a single, spiral line around the capsule. The genus also includes a second species, *T. lepidozioides*, which differs from *T. ceratophyllum* in having the leafy appendages two-forked to the base and in possessing thin glandular hairs. *T. lepidozioides* is presently known only from female plants.

Habitat and Current Distribution

Takakia ceratophyllum is known at present from two widely disjunctive places in the world: the eastern Himalayas and the Aleutian Islands. *T. lepidozioides* has a much wider, but narrowly scattered, range from northern Japan, Nepal, Tibet (China), and Sabah (Malaysian Borneo) to Alaska and Queen Charlotte Island in Canada. Both species of *Takakia* grow primarily on misty cliffs near waterfalls; on damp, sheltered rock faces and crevices; and on very wet ground or banks with late snow cover in subalpine elevations or at high altitudes. Locally, populations can form luxuriant greenish cover in suitable habitat.

History and Conservation Measures

Takakia ceratophyllum was first described as a liverwort in 1861 based on a collection from Sikkim (India). It wasn't until 1967 that a second site on Amchitka Island was discovered. In recent years, a few more localities in east Nepal and Tibet were disclosed. In 1990, D. K. Smith for the first time collected specimens with male plants and sporophytes from the central Aleutian Islands. Before the discovery of the male plant and the sporophyte, *Takakia* was accepted as a primitive liverwort related to *Haplomitrium*. Its systematic position as a moss taxon in the division Bryophyta has become controversial in light of this new finding. The genus, as represented by *T. ceratophyllum*, appears to possess an unique combination of characteristics of moss and liverwort. It probably represents an early offshoot of evolution before the common ancestor of bryophytes diverged into mosses and liverworts. Although the present habitats of *Takakia* are far from human settlements, threats from the expansion of human activities, especially detrimental land use practices, pose a serious threat to the survival of *Takakia*. Several areas in the Aleutian Islands have already been closed off to the public for military use. *Takakia ceratophyllum* needs full protection and aggressive conservation efforts not only because of its patchy distribution in the world, but also because of its intriguing, systematic position in the evolution of bryophytes.

Fineleaf pteridophyte

Cystoathyrium chinense

Family	Athyriaceae
Status	Rare, IUCN
Range	China

Description and Biology

This perennial grows to a height of almost 16 in (40 cm). Its creeping stem is short and stout with one or two small, brown, lance-shaped scales at the tip and base of the supporting stalk. Fronds are dense with up to 30 pairs of leaflets; the bottom leaflets are the smallest, at 0.23-0.47 in (6-12 mm), and the middle ones are the largest, ranging in size from 1-1.6 in (2.54-4 cm) in length and 0.3-0.4 in (8-10 mm) in width. Leaves unfold in late spring; spores appear in July and August and ripen in September.

Habitat and Current Distribution

This species is found only between Yuanyangyan and Tuanniuping in the Erlang Mountains of Tianquan County, Sichuan Province, at an altitude of about 4,760 ft (1,450 m). The species grows in evergreen and deciduous, mixed broad-leaved forests and is distributed on the west boundary of the Sichuan Basin, where foggy and rainy days are frequent all year round. The yellow or yellow-brown soil is derived from limestone, sandstone, or shale. There are no estimates of population size.

History and Conservation Measures

C. chinense was found in 1963 in Tuanniuping in the Erlang Mountains, but when the locality was explored again a year later, very few plants were found. The decline of this species is due to habitat destruction resulting from deforestation. Consideration should be given to immediate cessation of destruction of the native habitat of this species, and artificial propagation and cultivation programs should be undertaken.

Sphaeropteris crinita

Family	Cyatheaceae
Status	Endangered, IUCN
Range	India; Sri Lanka

Description and Biology

This tree fern has a terminal cluster of divided feather-shaped fronds with stalks that are 16 in (40 cm) long, dark purple at the base, and covered with scales. The primary segments of the fronds reach up to 24 in (60 cm) in length and have fringed scales on the lower surface; the end segments are sickle-shaped with finely-toothed margins.

The reproductive biology of this species is not known.

Habitat and Current Distribution

This species has been found in Sri Lanka and the Western Ghats of Tamil Nadu and Kerala, India, where it was confined to moist, cool habitats of evergreen forests between 4,900-6,900 ft (1,500-2,100 m) above sea level. There are no known surviving populations, and the species may be extinct.

History and Conservation Measures

Little is known of this tree fern. It was last collected from southern India in 1910, and it has not been collected from Sri Lanka in this century. If it is not extinct, it is thought to be confined to a few sheltered forest pockets which are inaccessible to humans. The reason for the decline of this species is thought to be habitat loss.

The most urgent conservation measure to be taken on behalf of this species would be intensive field exploration in areas of historical distribution. If the tree fern could be located in the wild, studies of its reproductive biology and ecology could be instituted and efforts could be made to bring it into cultivation in botanic gardens.

Bristle fern

Trichomanes speciosum

Family	Hymenophyllaceae
Status	Endangered, IUCN
Range	Western Europe; Azores; Canary Islands; Madeira

Description and Biology

This fern has thin, membranous, highly dissected (incised nearly to the midrib), ovate to triangular leaves about 3.9-15.8 in (10-40 cm) long. These leaves arise from a creeping, almost wiry stem. The sporangia (spore cases) are located in flask-shaped pockets on the margins of the leaves, attached to a cylindrical receptacle which protrudes beyond the mouth of the flask as it matures; the sporangia open and the receptacle hardens to form the bristle that gives the plant its common name. The spores are green and are probably dispersed by water rather than wind. They cannot undergo a dormant period but germinate directly into a filamentous gametophyte which bears the sex organs, undergoes fertilization, and produces the next spore-bearing generation.

Over the past five years gametophytes have been found over a much wider geographic area than the sporophyte stage (the diploid, spore-producing generation in the life cycle of plants which have an alternation of generations), partly due to vegetative spread by means of gemmae; disjunct occurrences may also be relict members from former, now extinct, populations of the sporophyte.

Habitat and Current Distribution

The bristle fern is dependent on a constant source of flowing water. Because of its very thin leaf texture, this species is confined to moist, often dark crevices and gullies in deep, narrow, wooded valleys in areas of high rainfall. For this reason it has become established in isolated man-made wells or mine shafts in France and Ireland. In more natural situations it is usually found growing in sandstone or similar porous rock fissures close to streams and waterfalls. Otherwise, its natural distribution is indicative of enclaves of an ancient Tertiary flora in the Apuane Alps (Italy), from the western Pyrenees to northern Spain and Cádiz, Brittany (France), Ireland, and on the western seaboard of Britain. The single recorded site in mainland Portugal may be extinct. It is common throughout the Macaronesian archipelagoes—the Azores, Madeira, and the Canary Islands. Only the gametophyte has been found in Belgium, the Czech Republic, and Germany.

History and Conservation Measures

Throughout its range this species is threatened by deforestation. In a number of localities in northern Spain, it is particularly threatened by *Eucalyptus* plantations. The drying out of smaller water courses is detrimental, although in areas of high rainfall, such as the Azores, it colonizes terrace walls in open areas. The gametophyte can withstand much drier conditions and is less at risk. It is also more difficult to identify and may be much more widespread than is presently known.

In the past, this species was highly sought after to adorn the sitting rooms of Victorian England and elsewhere in Europe. Because of its popularity, the plant is commonly grown in botanical gardens, although the source of the original specimens is unfortunately obscure and of little scientific value. The bristle fern is protected under the Bern Convention and the European Union Habitats Directive.

Tirupati cycad

Cycas beddonei

Family	Cycadaceae
Status	Vulnerable, IUCN
Range	India

Description and Biology

A palm-like plant, this shrub has a 4-6 in (10-15 cm) stem and a terminal cluster of feather-shaped leaves up to 3.3 ft (1 m) long. The leaflets are long and narrow, with downward-rolled margins. Two to four stems usually form a single clump, and the new foliage sprouts in March or April. The plants are dioecious (having male and female organs on different plants), and the cones appear along with new foliage. Male cones are rusty brown and measure about 8 in long and 3 in wide (20 cm by 8 cm). Seeds are spherical or rounded and measure around 1.6 in (4 cm) across.

The species reproduces through seed and is probably also propagated by vegetative means, as in other cycads.

Habitat and Current Distribution

Endemic to the Cuddapah-Tirupati range of the southern Eastern Ghats of Andhra Pradesh, India, the species is now restricted to Tirupati Hills only. It is found on exposed, rocky slopes at elevations of 1,000-3,000 ft (300-900 m) on the Tirupati Hills, which harbor a dry, deciduous forest. The species prefers rock-strewn streams and thrives on soils of lateritic, gneissic, and quartzitic origin; it is also quite drought-tolerant. Estimates of population are unavailable, but the shrub is considered to be near extinction.

History and Conservation Measures

Several factors have contributed to the decline of this species in the wild. This plant is highly prized for its ornamental value and is a popular item in private gardens. The male cones are used for medical purposes. Most seriously, however, urbanization and deforestation have destroyed much of this species' habitat.

Conservation measures should include studies of this plant's biology and ecology; protection of existing habitat and establishment of a national park; introduction and multiplication of the species in botanic gardens; and reintroductions in native habitats after their rehabilitation.

Natal grass cycad

Stangeria eriopus

Family	Stangeriaceae
Status	Endangered, IUCN
	Appendix I, CITES
Range	South Africa

Description and Biology

The Natal grass cycad is a low growing plant with a completely subterranean stem which may branch into several heads. Up to four leaves grow from each growing point; these are variable in size and shape, depending on the habitat. Plants from open grassland have erect, compact leaves with short, leathery, entire (smooth-margined) leaflets. The leaves of those from forested habitats are taller and have serrated (saw-toothed) to deeply fringed leaflets. The leaflets are 4-16 in (10-40 cm) in length and 0.8-2.4 in (2-6 cm) broad, with a prominent midvein. While the leaves differ morphologically according to the habitat, there are no differences in the cones.

Plants are dioecious (male and female reproductive organs are on separate plants) and reach maturity after 7-8 years. Each stem, or growing point, produces a solitary cone. Both male and female cones are silvery pubescent (covered with soft hair or down) at first, becoming brownish with age. Male cones are 4-6 in (10-15 cm) in length and 1.2-2 in (3-5 cm) in diameter; female cones are 7-8 in (18-20 cm) in length and 3.2-4 in (8-10 cm) in diameter, with closely overlapping cone scales. Female cones bear 80-100 seeds.

Habitat and Current Distribution

This species is endemic to the eastern coastal areas of South Africa and is restricted to a relatively narrow area between latitudes 27°S and 33°S from as far south as the districts of Bathurst in the Eastern Cape Province northwards to Ingwavuma in Natal, on the Mozambique border. *S. eriopus* occurs both in coastal grassland in full sun and in semi to dense shade in inland evergreen forests within 31 mi (50 km) from the sea. Soils range from sands derived from sandstone and granite to heavy black clay. The annual rainfall ranges from 29.25 in (750 mm) in the south to over 39-48.75 in (1000-1250 mm) in the north. Frosts are rare. Plants in full sun produce cones more regularly than those in dense shade. Those growing in open grassland are subject to regular fires; this is thought to contribute to the development of multi-headed plants after the growing point has been destroyed.

History and Conservation Measures

S. eriopus has been known since 1853, when it was mistakenly identified as a fern (genus *Lomaria*). Since then it has been popular with collectors and botanic gardens worldwide because of its unique status. Today the primary threat to this monotypic (having only one species) genus is overcollecting from the wild for magical and medicinal purposes.

Ethnobotanists estimate that more than 50,000 plants are gathered annually for the herbal trade in Natal. Phytochemical studies show that, despite the claims of herbalists as to its efficacy, its main usage is magical rather than medicinal. An infusion known as *intelezi* is scattered around the home to ward off lightning and evil spirits. It is also taken orally and as a snuff to relieve congestion in infants. Pharmacological studies have not substantiated these claims.

S. eriopus is protected by legislation as a Specially Protected Plant in all South African provinces. It is regarded as rare and endangered and, under its CITES Appendix I listing, the international trade in this species is limited to artificially propagated plants.

In order to cater to the increasing demand for indigenous plants by the herbal trade, an attempt is being made to artificially propagate these plants on a large scale. Commercial growers as well as the Durban Municipality's Silverglen Nature Reserve are at present actively propagating this endangered species. The distribution and status of this plant throughout its range also requires study to determine further conservation efforts.

Cuban tree cycad

Microcycas calocoma

> **Family** . . . . Zamiaceae
> **Status** . . . . Endangered, IUCN
> **Range** . . . . Cuba

Description and Biology

The Cuban tree cycad, also known as *palma corcho*, has a stout woody stem that can be branched or unbranched and grows to 10-39 ft (3-12 m) in height. Younger plants are marked with conspicuous rings. The stem carries a crown of 6-40 feather-shaped leaves 24-47 in (60-120 cm) long. Leaf stalks have shieldlike bases and grow to 4 in (10 cm) in length. Fifty to 80 pairs of bright green, pointed leaflets grow in an opposite or alternate pattern; they are covered with long, soft, fine hairs when young, but are hairless and glistening when mature. Male cones are cylindrical and measure 10-12 in (25-30 cm) by 2-3 in (5-8 cm); female cones are also cylindrical, but taper slightly from the base to the tip, and measure 20-28 in (50-70 cm) by 5-6 in (13-16 cm).

Cones are produced in April or May. It has been suggested that pollen is transported from the male to the female tree by weevils. Pollination is not very effective; often cones are found which contain just one or two fertile seeds.

Habitat and Current Distribution

This species is found in Cuba in the southern range of the Organas Mountains between Santo Tomas and San Diego de los Banos in the Pinar del Rio Province. In the late 1970s, the number of existing trees was estimated at approximately 600. Two areas where the species occurred were in the triangle between Pinar del Rio, Santo Tomas, and Vinales; at one of these localities there were almost 200 individuals. Six or seven other small, dispersed populations were found east of Vinales, between Consolación del Sur and San Andrés.

The known habitat of this species is in the hill region between 160-650 ft (50-200 m) on a wide range of geological substrata. On lower hills, it grows in tropical forests on semi-arid, bare rocks of hard Jurassic limestone or in the soil developed from them. More frequently it grows on yellow siliceous clays developed from sandstones and shales; on siliceous soils it is found primarily in evergreen oak forests and oak-pine woodland. It has a wide tolerance of soil pH, growing in both calcareous and acid soils; it does, however, prefer habitats where competition is low.

History and Conservation Measures

Four locations were known for this cycad in 1907; at three of these the plants were few and distinctly local, but at the fourth, they occurred in clusters of one, two, or even six, spread at infrequent intervals over a distance of 1.2-1.9 mi (2-3 km).

Although it is protected in all of its habitats, the small remaining populations remain especially vulnerable because the number of individuals of each sex is very unbalanced, and the pollinating species may also be threatened or extinct. Three of the most important areas for the species have been proposed as Natural Conservation Areas. This cycad is highly valued for its ornamental value and, despite the difficulties of cultivation, is grown in private gardens in Cuba and in botanic gardens throughout the world.

Saharan cypress

Cupressus dupreziana

Family	Cupressaceae
Status	Endangered, IUCN
Range	Algeria

Description and Biology

The Saharan cypress has a reddish brown bark containing many deep cracks. It can live for more than 1,000 years and has been recorded to grow to a height of 66 ft (20 m) and a diameter of 13 ft (4 m). It has upward curving branches and flattened branchlets that grow in two opposite rows. Its dense foliage consists of small green leaves measuring 0.04-0.06 in (1-1.5 mm) in length. Its cones are small and yellow or gray-brown in color.

Habitat and Current Distribution

This species is found in Algeria in the Tassili Plateau of the central Sahara. In the late 1970s, its population size was estimated at approximately 150 adult trees.

Its known habitat is sandstone or gravel in an area with an average annual rainfall of just 0.7 in (18 mm). The species grows in the bottom of usually dry stream beds or valleys where water sometimes collects, allowing it to take full advantage of the small amount of moisture that is available.

History and Conservation Measures

Most of the surviving trees of this species are more than 100 years old. They are endangered because of a lack of natural regeneration, probably resulting from the amount of grazing and cutting that has taken place over thousands of years.

There is hope that the cypress will survive in the wild if its remaining habitats can be managed and protected to allow its natural regeneration without interference. The Saharan cypress has successfully been brought into cultivation and could be important for reforestation projects.

Bigcone pinyon pine

Pinus maximartinezii

Family	Pinaceae
Status	Endangered, IUCN
Range	Mexico

Description and Biology

Pinus maximartinezii forms a small, bushy tree with a short, often contorted, trunk and long, irregularly spaced, widely spreading branches, forming a rather open, rounded crown. It usually reaches only 16.4-32.8 ft (5-10 m), occasionally 49 ft (15 m), in height and the short trunk may be up to 19.7 in (50 cm) in diameter. The bark is dark brown and tesselated into square plates about 3.9 in (10 cm) in diameter. Most trees of this species have distinctly glaucous (covered with a removable waxy coating which gives the surface a whitish or bluish cast) foliage, but greener individuals do occur. The needles are in close clusters or bundles of five, are slender and flexible, and measure 3.2-3.9 in (8-10 cm) long. In these characters *P. maximartinezii* is similar to several other, closely related, pinyons or "nut pines."

The most remarkable feature of this species is its huge cone; it ranks among the largest and heaviest cones of the more than 100 species in the entire genus, including the Coulter (*P. coulteri*) and Digger (*P. sabiniana*) pines, both from California. The cones of *P. maximartinezii* vary from 5.9-9.9 in (15-25 cm) in length and 3.9-5.9 in (10-15 cm) in width, with thick woody scales that vary in shape but are often strongly curved down or backward. The wingless seeds are similarly among the largest in the genus—0.8-1 in (20-25 mm) long and 0.4-0.5 in (10-12 mm) wide. They are 3-4 times the weight of the seeds of the common Mexican pinyon pine (*P. cembroides*).

The cones take 2-2.5 years to ripen and hang like woody pineapples (local people call them *piñas*) from pendulous branches up to one year after seed dispersal. Its nearest relatives appear to be *Pinus nelsonii* and *P. pinceana*, both Mexican pinyons with restricted ranges.

Habitat and Current Distribution

This pine grows on dry, rocky sites on volcanic lavas and tuffs; the annual precipitation in this area is 19.7-31.5 in (50-80 cm) virtually restricted to June-August. There are occasional winter frosts.

Pinus maximartinezii occurs in just one locality in Mexico, near the village of Pueblo Viejo in southern Zacatecas, about 62 mi (100 km) north-northeast of Guadalajara and 6.2 mi (10 km) southwest of the town of Juchipila. The trees occupy a range of 1.9-3.9 sq mi (5-10 sq km) on the eastern flanks of the Sierra de Morone in an area aptly named Cerro de Piñones. Local people are well informed about this distribution due to their interest in harvesting the edible seeds. As a result, the stands are now degraded, reduced to scattered trees and small denser stands in gullies or other inaccessible areas. The total population is somewhere between a few thousand and 10,000 trees. Due to limited botanical exploration of this part of Mexico and the likelihood that similar ecological conditions occur on other "mesas" in the region, future finds of other populations cannot be ruled out.

History and Conservation Measures

This extraordinary species was only discovered in 1964, by J. Rzedowski. It appears that Dr. Rzedowski's attention was first drawn to the huge pine seeds offered for sale in a local market which he recognized to be very different from the commonly displayed pinyon nuts. Villagers led him to the trees, about two hours walk from the nearest road. Exploitation of the seeds as a minor food source appears to make a heavy impact on the total seed crop, but collection (by knocking down and breaking up ripe cones) is not excessive and many cones remain on the trees. However, regeneration is very poor. Fires are frequent and prevalent across most of the area and appear to be the main constraint on regeneration; in 1986 an extensive fire devastated a large area, burning mature trees, seedlings and saplings. Additional pressure is imposed by grazing, mainly by cattle. Land tenure is complex due to the number of small, private land owners; at present no part of the range is under protective management.

This unusual pine is now well known among Mexican botanists and foresters, and there is considerable awareness of its endangered status. The 1986 fire was fought by army personnel. Proposals for funding for *in situ* conservation measures have recently been made. Researchers from the Department of Forestry, North Carolina State University, have recently re-investigated the distribution and ecology of the species and collected seeds from 80 trees for the purposes of *ex situ* conservation. Support and interest from, and direct benefits to, the local population are deemed essential for success, since the area is privately owned and the trees are heavily used. The local interest in seed production needs to be coupled with effective land management and prevention of fires. Subsidized restraint on seed harvesting, in conjunction with fencing of remaining stands, could encourage regeneration at selected sites. Increased seed production for use and sale by local people could provide the framework for their cooperation and active protection of remaining trees.

Given the difficulties of *in situ* protection in this area, the establishment of *ex situ* stands in protected areas in Mexico, as well as propagation programs in Mexico and abroad are also recommended. Research is urgently needed and should focus on inventories of the species' range, genetic variation, fire-related ecology, and population dynamics.

Chinese conifers

Abies beshanzuensis

Cathaya argyrophylla

Metasequoia glyptostroboides

Family	Pinaceae (*A. beshanzuensis, C. argyrophylla*)
	Taxodiaceae (*M. glyptostroboides*)
Status	Endangered, IUCN (*A. beshanzuensis*)
	Vulnerable, IUCN (*M. glyptostroboides; C. argyrophylla*)
Range	China

Description and Biology

Abies beshanzuensis, or the Baishan fir, is an evergreen tree with spreading, whorled branches and grayish yellow bark; it grows to a height of 56 ft (17 m) and a chest-height diameter of 31.5 in (80 cm). Annual shoots are pale yellow or gray-yellow and smooth; winter buds are pale yellow-brown and ovoid. Leaves are spirally arranged and measure 0.4-1.7 in (1-4.2 cm) long and 0.10-0.14 in (2.5-3.5 mm) wide. Cones are pale brown or brownish yellow when mature; they are erect, cylindrical, short-stalked, measuring 2.8-4.7 in (7-12 cm) long and 1.4-1.6 in (3.5-4 cm) wide. The tree is monoecious (has separate male and female reproductive structures on the same plant) and sets seeds every four to six years. It flowers in May, and cones ripen in November.

Cathaya argyrophylla, or Cathaya silver fir, has horizontal branches, a straight trunk, and dark gray bark that peels off irregularly. It grows up to 80 ft (24 m) tall and is usually around 16 in (40 cm) in diameter at chest-height, although the diameter can, rarely, be as large as 33 in (85 cm). Dark green rounded or bluntly pointed leaves are spirally arranged and radially scattered, usually measuring 1.2-2 in (3-5 cm) long and 0.10-0.12 in (2.5-3 mm) wide. Cones are pale brown or chestnut at maturity and measure 1.2- 2.0 in

(3-5 cm) long and 0.6-1.2 in (1.5-3 cm) in diameter. The tree is monoecious; flowering and pollination take place in May, but fertilization does not occur until June the following year. Cones ripen in October of the next year. *Metasequoia glyptostroboides*, or dawn redwood, is a deciduous tree that grows up to 115-140 ft (35-42 m) tall and 5.3-5.9 ft (1.6-2.4 m) in chest-height diameter. The bark is gray-brown or dark gray and peels off in long, flaky strips. Soft leaves grow in pairs at right angles to those above and below, and measure 0.5-0.8 in (1.3-2 cm) long and 0.06-0.08 in (1.5-2 mm) wide. Cones are dark brown at maturity and measure 0.7-1.0 in (1.8-2.5 cm) long. The tree is monoecious; it flowers in late February, and its cones ripen that year from late October to November.

Habitat and Current Distribution

A. beshanzuensis occurs in East China, where it is found at an elevation of 5,570 ft (1,700 m) on sunny forest slopes of Baishanzu Mountain, Qingyuan County, southern Zhejiang. It grows in the subtropical zone, where the climate is characterized by warm summers and cool, moist winters. It is a component of the deciduous broad-leaved forest, and is a heliophyte (a plant which grows in sunlight), although seedlings will tolerate shade. At present only five living specimens are known in its range, and two of them are in poor conditions.

C. argyrophylla grows in mountainous regions at altitudes of 3,000-6,100 ft (940-1,870 m). It occurs disjunctly in Huaping in Longsheng County of northern Guangxi; in Luohandong on the boundary between Xinning and Chengbu counties, Hunan Province; in Jinfo, Baizhi, and Quingzhu Mountains in Nanchuan County and Mt. Baima in Wulong County of Sichuan; and in Dashahe in Daozhen County and Mt. Baizang in Tongzi County of Guizhou. The species is distributed in middle elevation mountains in the mid-subtropical region, where the climate is cool in summer and cold in winter, where rainfall is abundant, and the atmosphere is moist, cloudy, and foggy. The soil is yellow or yellow-brown earth developed from limestones, shales, and sandstones, and is slightly acidic. The tree likes light, moistness, and fog; is tolerant of cold, drought, and barren conditions; and is resistant to the wind, always growing on narrow mountain ridges with shallow soil and ex-

posed rocks, on top of isolated cap-like rocky mountains, or in crevices of sheer precipices and overhanging rocks. Its occurrence is very scattered, and colonies consist of one or a few individuals or, at the most, several dozen, except at Laotizi in Jinfo Mountain, where the density is higher.

M. glyptostroboides is confined to local areas of Lichuan, Shizhu, and Longshan counties on the boundary of Hubei, Sichuan, and Hunan provinces. It grows at altitudes of 3,280-3,940 ft (1,000-1,200 m), in an area that is warm and humid in summer and mild winter. The soil is acidic mountain yellow earth or purple soil. The species mostly grows in flat, humid, and slightly water-logged places in mountain valleys with deep soil. In poorly drained and long-term water-logged places, it grows slowly and its trunks become swollen at the base, with vertical ridges. There are no estimates of population size.

History and Conservation Measures

A. beshanzuensis is a recently discovered species in an area where the natural vegetation has been greatly degraded due to constant slash-and-burn cultivation by local inhabitants. Most of its population has been eliminated by fire, but poor regeneration has posed an additional threat to its survival. The local forestry department has given a degree of protection to the species, and efforts are underway to propagate the tree by using graft techniques on stems of a related species, *A. firma*, from Japan.

C. argyrophylla was discovered in the 1950s in the eastern Dalou Mountains and in the Yuecheng Range. It was first seen in Huaping, Longsheng County, Guangxi, and in Jinfo Mountain, Nanchuan County, Sichuan, but more populations have been found in adjacent mountainous regions in recent years. It may be at risk of being replaced by fast-growing broad-leaved trees. Whenever new populations of this species are found, they have been placed under efficient protection by local governments. At present, nature reserves in Jinfo Mountain, Sichuan, and in Huaping, Guangxi, have been established, with an emphasis on protection of this species. Within the reserves, experiments on propagation and cultivation are underway. In order to promote regeneration and make the species naturally widespread, it has been recommended that some fast-growing canopy trees of other species be removed in stands with higher canopy density, where a single adult and some young trees of this species exist. It is also necessary to remove some trees on both sides of the mountain

Dawn redwood.

ridges where the species occurs so as to stimulate the growth of seedlings and young trees.

M. glyptostroboides was widely distributed in the Northern Hemisphere during the Tertiary period, but is now almost extinct as a result of the action of the Pleistocene glaciers. Its fossils have been found in strata from the late Cretaceous period up to the Pliocene epoch in Europe, North America, and East Asia. In the 1940s, Chinese botanists discovered thriving trees in Modaoxi on the border of Hubei and Sichuan; those trees were huge and over 400 years old. Not long after, some of its survivors were found in Shuishanba and Xiaohe in Lichuan County, Hubei; in

addition, a large number of living trunks and stumps were found in the gullies and farming land. Still later, some 200-300 year old individuals were seen in succession in Lingshui, Shizhu County, Sichuan, and in Luota and Tani, Longshan County, Hunan. In addition to being considered a "living fossil," the species has strong economic and aesthetic appeal; it is fast growing and has a tall and straight trunk, making it an ideal timber tree and a good ornamental for plains, especially in subtropical regions. An inventory of seed trees has been undertaken for preservation of the species, and these trees have been given protection. The dawn redwood is now widely grown both inside and outside China.

Florida torreya

Torreya taxifolia

Family	Taxaceae
Status	Endangered, IUCN
	Endangered, USFWS
Range	Florida, Georgia (U.S.A.)

Description and Biology

The Florida torreya is an evergreen tree that usually grows to an average height of 30 ft (9 m) but can reach as high as 59 ft (18 m). Stiff, sharp needles grow along each side of the branches, giving a flattened appearance; when the needles are crushed, they give off a strongly pungent, resinous odor. Pollen or male cones grow on separate trees from ovulate or female cones; pollen is exchanged in March and April. The female cone develops into a single, dark green seed that is oval in shape and 1-1.5 in (2.5-4 cm) long; the seed has a fleshy covering and is coated with a whitish bloom. Sexual maturity is reached in 16-20 years.

Habitat and Current Distribution

Endemic to an area along the Apalachicola River, the species occurs in Gadsden, Liberty, and Jackson counties in Florida, and in Decatur County, Georgia. It grows along the steep sides of ravines and on bluffs in the moist shade of associated pine and hardwood trees. Scattered immature trees occur within the range, but population estimates are unavailable.

History and Conservation Measures

The range of the Florida torreya has apparently not changed substantially in recent history, but the population has declined within that range. Habitat clearance for residential development was once a problem, but the remaining habitat is in areas that are not accessible to developers. The primary threat to the species is now disease. Beginning in the 1950s, a fungal disease attacked and killed most of the mature trees in the area. Under normal circumstances, when a tree died the root sprouts would begin to grow again, but the disease killed many of the trees before they had reached sexual maturity.

The Georgia population of this species occurs on protected land, but the Florida populations, other than those in a city park and in Torreya State Park, are largely on private land. Research has been initiated to try to combat the disease that is responsible for the loss of these trees from the wild. The Florida torreya has been brought into cultivation in an attempt to preserve a representative gene pool and to provide stock for eventual reintroduction into its former habitat. Unless a solution can be found for the disease problems of this species, it may soon become extinct in the wild.

Crinum mauritanum

Family	Amaryllidaceae
Status	Endangered, IUCN
Range	Mauritius (Indian Ocean)

Description and Biology

A large, spectacular bulbous plant, this species has attractive, whitish, delicate flowers with prominent stamens. The bulb has a long neck, producing large clasping leaves whose bases form a stout, false stem. The yellow-green, strap-shaped leaves extend to 39-51 in (100-130 cm) long and up to 3 in (8 cm) wide. The shoots can grow as tall as 3.3 ft (1 m) and bear 4-12 large flowers. The fruits, which turn yellow and are mostly smooth, are spherical and measure 2-2.4 in (4-6 cm) long. Its seeds are large, soft, polygonal, and greenish in color. The flowers have been observed to open just before dusk, and may be pollinated by hawk moths.

Habitat and Current Distribution

The only known locality for this species is on the island of Mauritius, in the Indian Ocean. The population is estimated at about 150 individuals, which has remained stable since 1973.

This plant occurs in shallow, still water, or in muddy soil along the water's edge. Larger plants have their bases up to 8-10 in (20-25 cm) deep in mud. The only known site for this species is the edge of a reservoir at around 1,600 ft (500 m), created presumably from an existing stream which was apparently the natural habitat.

History and Conservation Measures

Rediscovered in 1973 after an absence of over 150 years, the remaining colony of this plant was apparently spared from extinction by geological faults that caused leaking in the reservoir that would have otherwise flooded this last remaining population. Most of the island of Mauritius is now under cultivation, and the indigenous vegetation has been irretrievably degraded, with only small fragments surviving; even these fragments are threatened by illegal woodcutting and invasion by vigorous introduced species. Nature reserves have been established, but the reserves are also usually invaded by introduced plant species that are easily spread by alien animals such as pigs, bulbuls, and monkeys.

Crinum mauritianum is easy to propagate, and numerous seeds have been distributed throughout the island and to botanic gardens abroad. It has also been re-introduced to two managed nature reserves which are fenced to keep out deer and pigs and regularly weeded of invasive introduced plants that compete with the native species. Unfortunately, with the rapid development of Mauritius, increased water supplies are urgently needed. In 1993 it was decided to repair the dam since this reservoir is now of vital importance to the country. Therefore the entire wild population of *Crinum mauritianum* will soon be under water, and a concentrated effort to propagate this species, retaining as much genetic diversity as possible, is urgently required. Although this species is now fairly common in gardens both in Mauritius and elsewhere, most specimens probably come from one or a few parent plants. Therefore if the last wild habitat of this species is to disappear, then a scientific, controlled program to re-introduce this species to other suitable reserves must be a priority.

Sternbergia candida

Family	Amaryllidaceae
Status	Vulnerable, IUCN
	Appendix II, CITES
Range	Turkey

Description and Biology

Sternbergia candida is a white, spring-flowering bulbous plant. Flowers grow to a height of 4.7-7.8 in (12-20 cm), with six white, finely veined petals (1.75-2 in/4.5-5 cm in length) and six orange anthers. All other species of this genus have yellow flowers and the majority flower in the autumn.

Habitat and Current Distribution

S. candida is found in southwest Turkey, near Fethiye. It grows in clumps among limestone rocks at the edge of cedar forests. Current population figures are unknown.

History and Conservation Measures

This attractive species was discovered about 15 years ago. Its discovery caused great excitement in the horticultural world and, almost immediately, this naturally rare species was threatened. Thousands of wild bulbs were collected from the type location: within two years, bulbs were available in German and British nurseries.

Four more common species of *Sternbergia* occur in Turkey and, until recently, up to 560,000 wild bulbs of the genus were exported each year. In 1986, the export of wild *Sternbergia* bulbs was banned by the Turkish government, but the trade continued in wild bulbs temporarily transplanted into "nurseries." Unfortunately, wild bulbs of *S. candida* have been mixed with trade consignments of more common species making it difficult to detect the rarer ones. In 1990, for example, a tonne (2,200 lb) of *S. candida* bulbs (about 250,000 bulbs) was discovered in the warehouse of a major bulb exporter. These bulbs had apparently been accidentally collected by hired village laborers. Even today, this rare species continues to show up in garden centers and supermarkets in Britain, France, Germany, and the United States.

Some specialist nurseries in the United Kingdom and elsewhere in Europe are now propagating *S. candida*; this helps to take the pressure off wild populations. Research into propagation of the genus is also being carried out in Turkey as part of a joint bulb conservation project undertaken by the Turkish Society for the Protection of Nature and the UK-based Flora and Fauna Preservation Society. This project aims to provide an income for villagers and bulb traders through the sale of nursery-raised bulbs, a system which would pose no threat to wild bulb populations.

Carossier palm

Attalea crassispatha

Family	Arecaceae (Palmae)
Status	Endangered, IUCN
Range	Haiti

Description and Biology

The carossier or *petit coco* (little coconut) is a tall, solitary palm that grows up to 65 ft (20 m) in height with a smooth gray trunk measuring up to 13.8 in (35 cm) in diameter. It has an open crown of 15-19 arching pinnate leaves which are, including the sheath and petiole, up to 17.5 ft (5.35 m) in length. Leaflets are smooth, regularly spaced, and spread on one plane. Inflorescences are borne among the leaves and are either male, or male and female, and occur on the same tree; flowers of both sexes are small, male flowers are creamy white. Fruits are ovoid, 1.25-1.75 in (3.2-4.4 cm) long, tapering to a sharp point and have a reddish color when mature.

The fruit consists of a fibrous husk, hard shell, and a small, white, hollow kernel that is edible; it resembles a tiny coconut, a palm to which it is closely related. In the wild, natural regeneration is significantly reduced by children who gather the fallen fruit and eat the kernels.

Habitat and Current Distribution

Attalea crassispatha is known to occur only in Haiti's southwestern peninsula, an area of natural tropical scrub vegetation that is now highly degraded. In the late 1980s, field excursions located 26 palms of all ages remaining in the wild, in five small populations. The palm grows in full sun, at or near sea level, on sites not associated with streams. All surviving wild palms occur on private lands.

History and Conservation Measures

The carossier was first described in 1689 by a French priest and naturalist who stated that the palm was abundant in southwestern Haiti. The subsequent history of this palm is unknown until the 1920s and 1930s when botanists collected it again from the same area, but already its numbers were small and it was considered to be a rarity. Scientific interest in *A. crassispatha* is strong because it represents the only species of *Attalea* occurring in the Caribbean; the other 28 species are found in Panama and South America.

Because of extreme human pressure on natural resources in Haiti, and the absence of any protected areas where the remaining wild populations occur, the prognosis for survival of this species is not good. This palm was brought into cultivation in the early 1940s at Fairchild Tropical Garden in Miami, Florida. At that location, palms have grown to 26 ft (8 m) in height, but despite their size and age, none has ever flowered. Seed collected in the late 1980s were distributed to botanical gardens in Haiti and other countries and have germinated successfully. The potential for *ex situ* conservation, however, remains uncertain until cultivated plants produce viable seed.

Nicobar palm

Bentinckia nicobarica

Family	Arecaceae (Palmae)
Status	Endangered, IUCN
Range	Nicobar Islands (India)

Description and Biology

The Nicobar palm grows to a height of 40-50 ft (12-15 m) and has a diameter of 10-12 in (25-30 cm) at the swollen, ringed base of its solitary stem. Its leaves arch gracefully and measure approximately 10-13 ft (3-4 m) long. The palm is monoecious: it has separate male and female reproductive structures occurring on the same plant. The floral clusters which grow beneath the leaves are pitted with male and female flowers. The fruit is one-seeded and roughly ovoid in shape.

Reproductive biology of this fast-growing palm is not known.

Habitat and Current Distribution

This species is found in the tropical evergreen forests of the Nicobar group of islands. It is restricted to a few reserves, and estimates of its population size are unavailable.

History and Conservation Measures

When the Nicobar palm was first described in 1875, it was characterized as dominating the landscape. Its drastic decline is attributed to the loss of habitat that resulted from deforestation for human settlements. Even the reserves in which it still occurs may be vulnerable to developmental activities such as the cultivation of the African oil palm.

A few individuals of this species, which is considered of ornamental value, survive in cultivation in the Indian Botanical Garden in Calcutta, India, and in the Fairchild Tropical Garden in Miami, Florida. As yet, no measures have been taken to protect this species in the wild. Recommended conservation measures include the establishment of protected areas; further cultivation in botanic gardens; reintroduction of the species into restored areas of its historical habitat; multiplication through seed and in vitro methods; and the initiation of studies on the biology and ecology of the species.

Argun palm

Medemia argun

Family	Arecaceae (Palmae)
Status	Endangered, IUCN
Range	Egypt; Sudan

Description and Biology

The Argun palm can grow to a height of almost 33 ft (10 m). It has a bare, unbranched trunk carrying a crown of fan-shaped leaves up to approximately 4.4 ft (1.35 m) long on equally long stalks. The leaflets are stiff, sword-shaped, and 0.4-1.6 in (1-4 cm) wide, those on the side being considerably shorter than those toward the center. The palm is dioecious: male and female flowers are on separate trees. Male flowers are small, with three spreading petals based by felted bracts on dense spikes approximately 6-11 in (15-28 cm) long and 0.4 in (1 cm) thick. Females flowers are approximately 0.2 in (5 mm) across and rounded; they are on stout stalks 0.4 in (1 cm) long which protrude from the spike. Fruits are ellipsoid, around 0.8-2 in (2-5 cm) long, and have a shiny, brown-violet surface.

Habitat and Current Distribution

This species has been found in only three localities in Egypt and one in Sudan. In Egypt in 1963, one tree and a few small seedlings were found in an uninhabited oasis 140 mi (220 km) southwest of Aswan; one tree was found in a similar site about 125 mi (200 km) west of Aswan; and the species was also found on the east side of the Nile in the south. It may survive at one location in the Sudan approximately 125 mi (200 km) southeast of Wadi Halfa. A similar species, *M. abiadensis*, has also been described in the Sudan, and this may be a synonym of *M. argun*. A live Argun palm has not been found since 1964, however, and the species may now be extinct.

Presumably at one time forming groves, this species was found on river banks or in oases or wadis (stream beds or valleys that are usually dry except during the rainy season).

History and Conservation Measures

This palm is thought to have been widespread in Ancient Egypt, where it was called *Mama enxanine* and was placed as an offering in tombs.

This species is the most threatened of any palm. Its decline to near extinction is attributed to two causes: the tree has been exploited for its leaves, which are used to make mats; and its natural habitat has been destroyed by irrigation projects along the banks of the Nile. It is not known to be in cultivation anywhere, and there have apparently been no steps taken to preserve it in the wild. If any Argun palms survive, they should be given full protection.

Glomeropitcairnia erectiflora

Family	Bromeliaceae
Status	Vulnerable, IUCN
Range	Trinidad and Tobago; Venezuela

Description and Biology

A giant rosette herb, this species blooms only once and then dies. It has a basal cluster of numerous, erect-to-arching leaves that measure 28 in (70 cm) long, with strap-shaped blades 3 in (8 cm) wide, pointed at first but soon rounded by withering. The feather-shaped floral cluster is slender and grows to a length of 6.6 ft (2 m) on an unbranched stem which emerges from the leaves and is sheathed by tight red bracts. Flowers are stalkless, erect, and grow in compact clusters; floral bracts are elliptical, rounded, and shorter than the sepals, which are 0.8-1 in (21-28 mm) long and lance-shaped. Petals grow to around 1 in (25 mm) and are yellow-to-white in color.

This species grows both as an epiphyte (nonparasitic plant growing on another plant) and on the ground. In Venezuela, this plant is mainly terrestrial and is one of the main floristic components of montane scrub.

Habitat and Current Distribution

Generally found at 2,300 ft (700 m) above sea level, this plant is found in Trinidad, where it is confined to the country's three tallest mountains of Trinidad: El Tucuche, Cerro del Aripo, and Mt. Chaguaramal. It is also found in the extreme east of the Paria Peninsula in the State of Sucre, Venezuela, and on Mt. Copey (Isla Margarita) in the State of Nueva Esparta, just to the north of the Paria Peninsula. About 25-30 percent of the original population on Mt. Copey has recently been destroyed by the construction of several new television antennas, and there are plans to build a larger system of military radar antennas, which may reduce the population of this plant even further. There is no estimate of the population size of this species in the wild.

History and Conservation Measures

All known populations of this species are very low; that on Mt. Tucuche is threatened from habitat disturbance by an increasing number of visitors climbing to the summit. Protection of this area would be beneficial to this plant as well as to a number of other rare species.

This plant is valued for its spectacular appearance and large size. It is grown in a few botanical gardens, where it can be easily propagated by seed and by removal of the sucker shoots which develop once the parent plant has flowered.

Perennial teosinte

Euchlaena perennis

Family	Gramineae (Poaceae)
Status	Extinct, IUCN
Range	Mexico

Description and Biology

Teosinte is a perennial grass with strong scaly rhizomes (underground stems) and erect stems 3.3-6.6 ft (1-2 m) high. The leaf blade is linear or slightly lance-shaped, up to 16 in (40 cm) long and 1.2 in (3 cm) wide, with a prominent white vein on the underside. There is a terminal cluster of male florets; female floral clusters occur in the leaf axils, partly protruding from the sheaths, with each wrapped in one or more sheathing bracts.

This species is self-fertilizing and is easy to propagate vegetatively, by division and at some times of the year by rooting at the nodes.

Habitat and Current Distribution

The perennial teosinte is only known from one locality in Mexico, near Ciudad Guzman in Jalisco. It is now extinct in the wild.

History and Conservation Measures

This species was last found in the wild in 1910 and 1921. It now survives in cultivation from just a single plant gathered in 1910, which has since been widely distributed to botanic gardens. One of the few wild relatives of maize (corn), this species once grew at the edges of fields of cultivated maize in Mexico; through hybridization it has given the maize crop added variability and vigor. Once considered a vital part of the genetic underpinnings of the world corn crop, hybridization has been declining as annual teosinte has rapidly declined in the wild, primarily due to grazing and changes in agricultural techniques.

Many of the variable and genetically diverse races of cultivated maize have been replaced by new and uniform cultivated varieties based only on a very small fraction of the gene pool. The uniformity of these modern crops greatly increases their vulnerability to pests and diseases. It is therefore essential that both the wild relatives and the range of variation within the crop itself are preserved as a genetic base for future breeding.

Texas wild rice

Zizania texana

Family	Gramineae (Poaceae)
Status	Vulnerable, IUCN
	Endangered, USFWS
Range	Texas (U.S.A.)

Description and Biology

Texas wild rice is a coarse, perennial, aquatic grass with long, underwater stems that root at the nodes. Averaging 3.3-5 ft (1-1.5 m) long, the lower part of the grass, with leaves, often floats on the water, and the upper part is erect. Leaf blades are long, flat, and hairless; the lower part forming underwater streamers averages 5-43 in (12-110 cm) long, and the aerial part measures 6-8 in (15-20 cm) long. The flower stalk is erect, 8-12 in (20-30 cm) long, and extends 12-35 in (30-90 cm) above the water; the upper or female branches lie close to the stem, while the lower or male branches ascend and spread. Flowering occurs from April to November.

For a number of years, reproduction has been primarily vegetative, rather than sexual.

Habitat and Current Distribution

This species is restricted to a 1.5 mi (2.4 km) length of the headwaters of the San Marcos River in Texas. There are no estimates of population size.

Texas wild rice is adapted to clear, relatively constant, cool, fast-flowing spring water. It forms large clumps which are firmly rooted in the gravel bottom of the river, both in swift currents and in deep water.

History and Conservation Measures

When this species was described in 1933 it was abundant in the headwaters of the San Marcos River, in irrigation ditches, and for around 1,000 ft (300 m)

Texas wild rice.

behind the Spring Lake Dam. Within about 30 years, the species was almost completely absent from Spring Lake and its overall abundance has been drastically reduced. Today, flowering plants are rarely seen, and they seldom extend very far above the surface.

The primary cause of the decline of this species has been habitat degradation. Floating debris, bottom ploughing, sewage and chemical pollution, swimming, boating, siltation, and the introduction of exotic species have all played a role in damaging the habitat. Many of the damaging physical factors have now abated, and the species has been declining at a slower rate, but sexual reproduction has not yet been restored. The location of the surviving population within the city limits of San Marcos complicates conservation efforts.

The most important factor in the recovery of this species is the conservation and recovery of its habitat. Increased use of groundwater in the region, primarily because of human population growth, has reduced the flow of water from the San Marcos Springs; it has been predicted that the flow will cease around the year 2000. Increased urbanization is responsible for increased flooding and erosion, pollution, and siltation, all of which adversely affect the aquatic environment.

Efforts have been made to transplant Texas wild rice, but these efforts have largely been unsuccessful. Continued research into factors that affect the survival of the species is necessary, but immediate efforts must be made to educate the public about the plight of the species and to save it in its native habitat.

Golden gladiolus

Gladiolus aureus

Family	Iridaceae
Status	Endangered, IUCN
Range	South Africa

Description and Biology

This slender geophytic herb has delicate stems that are 6-33.5 in (15-85 cm) tall. The leaves are erect, very finely haired, and up to 17.7 in (45 cm) long. Up to six uniformly golden yellow flowers grow on a spike; the perianth tube is funnel-shaped, slightly curved, slender at the base, and 0.7-0.8 in (1.8-2 cm) long. The golden gladiolus regularly sets seed in the wild and is probably pollinated by bees; it flowers between July and September. The unscented flowers remain partially closed in cool weather, opening fully only on warm days.

Habitat and Current Distribution

This species is endemic to the Cape Peninsula in the southwestern Cape Province, South Africa. The species was recorded from damp, sandy places on the flats or lower hill slopes. The remaining population is on a patch of poorly drained sandy soil underlain by gravel and clay. The area becomes waterlogged during the winter rainy season. Mature plants require a moist soil before they start flowering.

History and Conservation Measures

The golden gladiolus was once known from several localities along a 3 mi (5 km) stretch of the coast near Kommetjie on the western side of the Cape Peninsula. All of the known populations, except for one, have been destroyed by changes in land use that took place mainly in the mid- to late 1970s. The number of plants in the remaining population fluctuates considerably from year-to-year. In the early 1970s there were between 50 and 70 plants, and in 1977 only 18 were counted. In 1982 there were over 100 but by 1991 they had dwindled again to just 20. The remaining site is invaded by a dense infestation of alien woody plants from Australia and the Mediterranean. Other threats include foot traffic through the site and picking of flowers for decorative purposes. Bulldozing for gravel above the site may also have had some impact as it has probably modified the drainage system, which appears to be a critical factor for the stimulation of flowers.

Efforts have been initiated to remove the infestations of wattle and pine around the population of gladiolus and to secure nature reserve status for the area. Agreements have been reached to avoid quarrying activities at the site, and seed has been placed in the Bolus Herbarium seed bank. It was also proposed that an alternative site under less pressure be found to which cultivated plants could be taken and established. Two such introductions have since been attempted in the Cape of Good Hope Nature Reserve. These introductions have only been partially successful, mainly because of the depredations of wild animals, and it will no doubt take many years to establish viable populations. These new populations are being monitored regularly, and a large stock of plants is being maintained under cultivation at Kirstenbosch National Botanical Garden as a safeguard against extinction in the wild.

Iris winogradowii

Family	Iridaceae
Status	Endangered, IUCN
Range	Georgia (former U.S.S.R.)

Description and Biology

This bulbous perennial herb can grow as tall as 6 in (15 cm) when in flower. The mature bulb is more or less egg-shaped and measures 0.8-1.2 in (2-3 cm) in diameter, often with one or two smaller, "daughter" bulbs. The bulbs are covered with pale brown tunics which ultimately become reduced to a delicate network of fibers. Each bulb produces two to four erect, very narrow leaves that are quadrangular in cross-section and up to 16 in (40 cm) long, with a tip that narrows abruptly into a whitish point. Flowers are lemon yellow, are borne on a leafless flower stalk, and measure about 1.6-2 in (4-5 cm) across.

Habitat and Current Distribution

This plant is known from the slopes of a single mountain near Bakuriani in the Adzharo-Imeretinskiy Mountain Range, Georgia. Only a few hundred plants were known from the subalpine zone—its seemingly preferred habitat—in the late 1970s.

History and Conservation Measures

The small size of the remaining population of this species may be a result of uprooting and collection by gardeners and amateur botanists. When in flower, it is an attractive species and is becoming widespread in cultivation. There is no information on conservation measures being implemented on behalf of this species in the wild.

Aloe bowiea

Family	Liliaceae (Aloaceae)
Status	Endangered, IUCN
	Appendix II, CITES
Range	South Africa

Description and Biology

Aloe bowiea is a dwarf, succulent-leaved herb that grows up to 11.8 in (30 cm) at the flowering stage. It is stemless (or nearly so), and has fusiform (spindle-shaped) roots. The 18-25 linear-subulate leaves are borne in a basal rosette and have small, white spots scattered mainly on the undersurfaces. The margins of the pale green leaves are armed with soft, white prickles. Twelve to 15 greenish white flowers are borne on a loosely flowered raceme (an unbranched flower stalk in which the individual flowers are borne on pedicels along the main axis). Flowers are produced irregularly throughout the year, but flowering reaches a peak in the summer months between October and March. The plants are pollinated by insects, presumably solitary bees.

Habitat and Current Distribution

Aloe bowiea is known only from three localities near Port Elizabeth in the eastern Cape Province of South Africa. The plants are found growing on level and southwest-facing slopes in rocky soils. The main vegetation pattern is Subtropical Transition Thicket, but the habitat in which this species occurs is not the typically dense, impenetrable thicket, but open, less dense karroid/grass communities. The associated plant community is dominated by succulents which include other species of *Aloe, Bulbine, Euphorbia, Cotyledon, Crassula, Pachypodium*, and various mesembs (Aizoaceae).

History and Conservation Measures

Although first collected in 1822, this species, which has been plagued by taxonomic confusion, remained poorly known until recently. The habitat where this species occurs is currently subjected to a number of threats including agricultural mismanagement, particularly overstocking and overgrazing during times of drought; the clearance of non-arable thicket for crop cultivation; industrial expansion; urban development; road construction; and unauthorized collecting by succulent enthusiasts. These latter threats have already lead to the extinction of one population. In 1983 the Uitenhage population consisted of 141 plants in four separate groups. By 1988 this population was extinct. The Coega population which numbered approximately 250 individuals in 1983, had declined by 1988. The third population at Kariega comprised only a few individuals in 1988. The Coega population occurs on a privately owned game reserve and the population at Kariega is on the land of a conservation-minded farmer.

The acquisition of land is an urgent priority to protect this and other succulent species. The future of remaining populations needs to be secured to ensure the maintenance of genetic diversity. The populations need to be fenced off to prevent grazing by both domestic stock and game animals. This would allow plants to flower and set seed which would hopefully lead to the expansion of existing populations and the establishment of new ones. The education of land owners about the vulnerability of vegetation is also essential, if this species is to be saved from extinction.

Spiral aloe

Aloe polyphylla

Family	Liliaceae (Aloaceae)
Status	Vulnerable, IUCN
	Appendix I, CITES
Range	Lesotho

Description and Biology

The spiral aloe, also known as the kharetsa, is a succulent perennial with a rounded rosette of 75-150 mostly erect leaves measuring up to 31 in (80 cm) across, arranged in five spiral rows, either clockwise or counterclockwise. Individual leaves are egg-shaped and very fleshy, 8-12 in (20-30 cm) long and 2.4-4 in (6-10 cm) broad, nearly flat above and un-evenly ridged below, and with rather soft white teeth on the margin. A flowering shoot extends 20-24 in (50-60 cm) high, branching from near the base, with flowers crowded on the branch tips. Each of its flow-ers have a narrow, triangular bract 0.8-1.2 in (2-3 cm) long, and a cylindrical corolla 1.8-2.1 in (45-55 mm) long; the bloom can be pale red to salmon pink or, very rarely, yellow. Flowering occurs from August through December, peaking in September and Octo-ber.

Pollination by the Malachite sunbird (*Nectarina famosa famosa*) has frequently been observed, but insects may also be involved. The spiral aloe pro-duces a large amount of seed, but only about half is viable and the species mainly seems to reproduce vegetatively.

Habitat and Current Distribution

This species is found in scattered areas throughout Lesotho, with a concentration in the Thaba Putsoa Range and the Maseru area of the Drakensberg Mountains. Population size was esti-mated in 1991 at 12,500-14,000 individuals in about 50 localities, most of which were less than 2.5 acres (1 ha) in size.

The spiral aloe grows at elevations of 7,300-8,900 (2,230-2,720 m) on steep basalt slopes with loose rock. It is usually found on north-facing slopes, but at altitudes above 8,600 ft (2,620 m) it is found on more easterly slopes. It grows in areas where its roots are kept moist in summer by a continual flow of water, where there are mostly low shrubs, and where rainfall is around 43 in (1,100 mm).

History and Conservation Measures

When the spiral aloe was more plentiful, it re-portedly grew in colonies of 12 or more plants. One of the primary reasons that its population has been de-pleted is the uprooting of plants for sale to gardeners and nursery operations—it is valued for the striking spiral arrangements of the leaves. Overgrazing on the surrounding vegetation may also have been a factor, and the construction of roads and an ongoing dam project could further threaten the habitat of the spe-cies. Very few seedlings were seen in the wild, and it has been suggested that its decline may be due in part to biological reasons.

This aloe is the national flower of Lesotho and has been legally protected since 1938. More effective enforcement of this legal protection is needed, how-ever, as is the protection of selected populations in reserves. It has been recommended that a national park be created in which the species would be protected from grazing animals. The spiral aloe is best grown from seed and is in cultivation at the National Botanic Gardens in Pretoria and other locations. England's Royal Botanic Gardens at Kew has successfully micropropagated the species and distributed it to other botanic gardens. A nursery has also been set up to build stocks for commercial sale, thus taking the pressure off wild populations.

Nubian dragon tree

Dracaena ombet

Family . . . . Liliaceae
Status . . . . Vulnerable, possibly Endangered, IUCN
Range . . . . Djibouti; Ethiopia; Somalia; Sudan

Description and Biology

The umbrella-shaped Nubian dragon tree grows to a height of 10-13 ft (3-4 m). Its stout branches regularly fork after flowering and have at their tips dense clusters of thick, sword-shaped leaves measuring 15.7-27.6 in (40-70 cm) long. Its flowers also grow in clusters on short stalks and are white or pale pink, with six perianth segments of 0.24 in (6 mm) and six slightly shorter stamens surrounding an oblong ovary with a simple style of equal length. Its berries are spherical and yellow when ripe.

Habitat and Current Distribution

This species has been found in Djibouti, Ethiopia, and Sudan, and may also occur along the north coast of Somalia. It grows in scrub on arid sandstone hillsides or on quartz outcrops at altitudes of 2,460-3,940 ft (750-1,200 m). It is uncertain whether the species still survives in the wild.

History and Conservation Measures

The Nubian dragon tree was once a subdominant species on the hills where it was found, but by the 1970s only scattered trees remained amid immense areas of bare rock. Its decline is attributed to a number of factors which have eliminated all plant life over vast areas formerly covered by *Dracaena* scrub. Exploitation has been a problem, as the trunk is cut for firewood and the tree's fibrous leaves are used for weaving mats and baskets. Additional factors include overgrazing by domestic livestock and a succession of droughts.

Some areas of this species' habitat were protected in the past, but no conservation efforts were made for some time, and most vegetation in those areas has deteriorated or disappeared. If the species cannot be saved in the wild, efforts should be made to cultivate and maintain it in botanical gardens.

Haworthia marginata

Family	Liliaceae (Aloaceae)
Status	Endangered, IUCN
Range	South Africa

Description and Biology

Haworthia marginata is a stemless, dwarf leaf succulent which reaches 7.9 in (20 cm) high and 5.9 in (15 cm) diameter. The ovate-lanceolate leaves form a dense rosette (with up to 35 leaves) with the young leaves erect and incurved and the older leaves ascending and recurved. The leaves are whitish green, are smooth on both surfaces, and are 3.2 in (8 cm) long, 1.6 in (4 cm) wide, and up to 0.47 in (12 mm) thick, with a central raised keel on the lower surface. About 25 flowers are borne on each branch of a loosely flowered stalk which measures 11.8 in (30 cm). The flowers are pinkish white with green keels and are 0.51 in (13 mm) in length. This species flowers in September and October, with only one or two flowers opening simultaneously. It is thought to be insect pollinated.

Habitat and Current Distribution

This species is found in southwestern Cape Province, South Africa, between Riversdale in the east and Ashton in the west. It occurs at an altitude of 656 ft (200 m) in an area where rainfall is more or less evenly distributed throughout the year. *H. marginata* grows mainly in South Coast Renosterveld vegetation on shales, where plants can be very small and deeply buried, or on sandstone or Witteberg gravels, where they may grow openly on the surface. It usually grows next to, or under, low scrub on slight inclines.

History and Conservation Measures

This is an extremely popular pot plant, especially among amateur succulent enthusiasts. It is not surprising that this species was known by the early 1700s as it was apparently common along the route followed by the early explorers to the Cape. Today only three very small populations are left, each only a few hectares in extent. There is no recent estimate of the total number of plants left in the wild, but numbers in all three populations are declining as a result of over-collecting, road construction, and agricultural development for wheat or other cereal crops. One of the remaining populations is also threatened by an expanding refuse dump. There is also a problem in the maintenance of genetic integrity in the remaining populations, as hybrids with *Haworthia pumila* and *H. minima* have been recorded.

Plants are in cultivation in a number of botanical gardens including the Karoo National Botanical Garden at Worcester. Plants produced in cultivation at these botanical gardens should be used for reintroduction to suitable protected habitat in the wild.

Shirhoy lily

Lilium mackliniae

Family	Liliaceae
Status	Endangered, IUCN
Range	India

Description and Biology

The Shirhoy lily is a herb that grows to around 3.3 ft (1 m) tall. It has an underground stem or rootstalk and leaves with a long, flattened, roughly circular shape. The rootstalk survives the winter period and produces blooms during May and June. One or two pinkish white flowers are borne on leafy shoots. The fruit is an ovoid capsule containing many seeds.

The species reproduces both sexually and asexually, but further details of its reproductive biology and ecology are not known.

Habitat and Current Distribution

Restricted to the Shirhoy Hills in Manipur, India, the species thrives well in open, grassy slopes and among rock crevices. A few scattered populations survive, but population estimates are unavailable.

History and Conservation Measures

Once described as forming a carpet of pink-white blooms, the species is now drastically reduced in range and population. Illegal collection for its ornamental value, heavy tourist traffic, and human interference in its habitat all threaten the survival of this species. Shirhoy Hill has been declared a national park, but poaching continues in the region.

Attempts to cultivate the species have so far been unsuccessful. Conservation measures should include studies on the reproductive biology and ecology; development of protocols for cultivation; reintroductions through seeds and *in vitro* methods; and development of strategies for sustainable use of the species.

Relict trillium

Trillium reliquum

Family	Liliaceae
Status	Endangered, IUCN
	Endangered, USFWS
Range	Alabama, Georgia, South Carolina (U.S.A.)

Description and Biology

This perennial herb differs from other species in its family in the shape of its leaves and anthers and its S-curved stems. Varying in color from pure yellow, to green, to brownish purple, the flowers bloom in early spring. The fruit is an oval-shaped, berry-like capsule that matures in early summer. After the fruit matures, the plant dies back to its underground stem.

Habitat and Current Distribution

This species occurs in the states of Alabama, Georgia, and South Carolina, where there are now 21 known populations. At least 10 of these populations number less than 200 plants, but other sites support several thousand individuals. The largest single site in Aiken and Edgefield counties, South Carolina, is estimated to harbor 50,000-100,000 plants.

Optimal habitat is mature, moist, undisturbed hardwood forest. Soil type can range from alluvial sands to rocky clays, but a high organic content in the upper layer is necessary.

History and Conservation Measures

The historic range of this species is uncertain; at least one population in Georgia is known to have been extirpated and, even if the number of populations has not been drastically reduced, the size of individual populations has probably decreased. A number of factors threaten existing sites, including logging, road construction, quarrying, and clearance for agriculture, industry, and residential development. The introduction of Japanese honeysuckle and kudzu, both weedy vines, has also begun to degrade habitat.

While several of the sites are at least partly on

Relict trillium.

protected land, the majority of the population is on private land. Some landowners have agreed to cooperate in protecting the plant, but some of the colonies are still at risk. A recovery plan for the species is underway and will most likely involve further agree-

ments with private landowners. Preservation and/or acquisition of habitat; plans to introduce the plant into protected areas; and surveys for as yet undiscovered populations are also underway.

Orchidantha

Orchidantha chinensis

Family	Musaceae
Status	Rare, IUCN
Range	China

Description and Biology

This perennial plant has creeping rhizomes and grows approximately 17.7 in (45 cm) tall. Its leaves are arranged in two rows; they are wedge-shaped at the base and taper to a point at the tip, measuring 8.7-11.8 in (22-30 cm) long and 2.8-3.5 in (7-9 cm) wide. Its flowers are purple, with one or two arising from rhizomes. The capsules are oval in outline and the seeds have an outer covering. Flowering occurs in March, and the fruit ripen in July.

Habitat and Current Distribution

This species is now found only in the Yunkai Mountains of Xinyi County in Guangdong and in the Shiwan Mountains in Guangxi, where it grows in forests of ravines at an elevation of approximately 1,200 ft (370 m). There are no estimates of population size.

As a moisture-loving and shade-tolerant plant, this species prefers valley slopes where the soil is fertile, well-drained, and covered with a thick layer of litter.

History and Conservation Measures

This species was first discovered in 1932, and its rhizomes are used in China as a medicine for the treatment of fever. With its very limited distribution area and small population, the plant is considered to be rare. It is in danger of extinction due to excessive deforestation and destruction of its habitat.

A protected area for this species has been established in the Shiwan Mountains; its natural habitat in the Hongqui Forest Farm of Ladang Township should also be protected. It is essential that this species is brought into cultivation in an attempt to safeguard it against further loss in the wild.

Bulbophyllum rothschildianum

Family	Orchidaceae
Status	Endangered, IUCN
	Appendix II, CITES
Range	India

Description and Biology

This beautiful orchid is an epiphyte (an organism that grows on another plant but which is not parasitic) on broad-leaved trees of mixed evergreen forests. A cluster of five florets grow on individual stalks from the end of a single stem. The species can be distinguished by the hood-shaped sepal with a fringed margin, a sensitive plume at the apex, and a tongue-like lip.

The biology and pollination ecology of natural populations of this species are not known.

Habitat and Current Distribution

Restricted to the hills of northeast India, this species is localized in the humid, broad-leaved, mixed evergreen forest patch of Longsa Village in Mokokchung District, Nagaland. The remaining population is very small, and the species is considered very close to extinction.

History and Conservation Measures

First described from a nursery collection, this orchid was long considered to be extinct in the wild. Repeated field explorations failed to locate the species, until a small natural population was located in a patch of the mixed evergreen forest of Longsa Village.

The nursery stock of this orchid has contributed to the genes of outstanding hybrids that have received awards of merit from horticultural and orchid societies. In the wild, however, it is near extinction, and the only way to secure the single rediscovered population is to declare the area a national park. Other conservation measures should include studies on the pollination biology and ecology of this plant; multiplication through seeds and *in vitro* cultures; maintenance of the species in cultivation; reintroduction of the species in habitats similar to its native range; and establishment of orchid gene sanctuaries.

Small whorled pogonia

Isotria medeoloides

Family	Orchidaceae
Status	Vulnerable or Endangered, IUCN
	Endangered, USFWS
	Appendix II, CITES
Range	Ontario (Canada); Connecticut, Georgia, Illinois, Maine, Maryland, Massachusetts, Michigan, New Hampshire, New Jersey, New York, North Carolina, Pennsylvania, Rhode Island, South Carolina, Vermont, Virginia (U.S.A.)

Description and Biology

Considered one of the rarest orchids in eastern North America, the small whorled pogonia is a terrestrial, perennial orchid with a waxy, pale green or purplish stem that grows 3.5-10 in (9-25 cm) high. It is topped by a whorl of five or six drooping, dusty green leaves 0.8-3.3 in (2-8.5 cm) long. Growing above the leaves are one or two yellowish green flowers that bloom and die very quickly. Sepals are green, long, and narrowly oblong, up to 1 in (2.5 cm) in length. Petals are pale green, lance-shaped, and broad at the tip. The lip is almost white but with green veins and a hard protuberance extending from the base; wart-like projections stand erect on the middle veins. Flowering occurs in May and June.

No evidence of insect pollination has been observed, and the species is believed to be self-pollinating. Some colonies of this plant have been reported to lie dormant for as long as 10 or 20 years between periods of flowering, but extended dormancy has not been documented.

Habitat and Current Distribution

In Canada, the species occurs in Ontario; in the United States, the largest populations are in New Hampshire and Maine, but it also occurs in Connecticut, Georgia, Illinois, Maryland, Massachusetts, Michigan, New Jersey, New York, North Carolina,

Small whorled pogonia.

Pennsylvania, Rhode Island, South Carolina, Vermont, and Virginia. It has been extirpated from several states. The population is estimated at approximately 1,500 individuals.

Primary habitat is dry, open deciduous woods, where the species grows in deep leaf litter and favors acidic soil. It occurs sporadically, and colonies typically consist of very few individuals.

History and Conservation Measures

The small whorled pogonia's population has decreased across its vast range because of a number of factors. Destruction of habitat for the expansion of residential, industrial, and commercial development has been responsible for much of the decline in this species, but it has also been subject to overcollecting by scientists and private collectors. Natural factors have also contributed, especially plant succession and genetic deficiencies that can result from isolated populations.

The status of this species seems to be improving. Conservation activities have included surveys and monitoring of existing populations, demographic studies, and habitat protection. Protection of habitat will continue to be a priority, while surveys for additional populations continue.

Paphiopedilum rothschildianum

Family	Orchidaceae
Status	Endangered, IUCN
	Appendix I, CITES
Range	Sabah (Malaysia)

Description and Biology

This plant is often considered the most spectacular species of all the slipper orchids. It is a terrestrial orchid with glossy green leaves, up to 23.5 in (60 cm) long. The large flowers, up to 1 ft (30 cm) in diameter, are borne on purple, slightly hairy stems. Sepals are cordate (shaped like a stylized heart) and creamy-white with broad brown stripes; petals are widespread, narrow and gently tapering, greenish white with brown-purple streaks and spots. The pouch is rose-colored shading to yellow at the aperture with reddish brown veins.

The pollination system of *P. rothschildianum* is unlike that of any other slipper orchid. The pollinator is a fly, *Dideopsis aegrota*, which has a special relationship with the plant. The orchid flowers mimic brood sites for the female flies. Eggs are laid on the staminode (the sterile stamen that does not produce pollen) which resembles an aphid colony on which *D. aegrota* normally deposits its eggs. The insect is then trapped in the flower long enough to deposit pollen on the stigma and to be smeared with pollen before it escapes.

Habitat and Current Distribution

P. rothschildianum grows on rocky surfaces in the forests of Mt. Kinabalu on the island of Borneo. It is now known from only two sites on the lower slopes of Mt. Kinabalu—one discovered in 1959, the other in 1979. The size of these populations are not known.

History and Conservation Measures

P. rothschildianum was first cultivated in 1887. Its origin was claimed to be New Guinea in a deliberate attempt to mislead collecting rivals in the highly lucrative Victorian orchid trade. For around 70 years the species was assumed to be extinct in the wild until its rediscovery in 1959. A second locality was discovered 20 years later. Extensive searching has revealed no further populations. This species is the rarest of all 60 *Paphiopedilum* species. The two sites where *P. rothschildianum* grows are threatened by logging, mining, and shifting agriculture.

The collection of wild plants continues to be a threat, even though the sites where *P. rothschildianum* occurs are within a national park. Illegally collected wild plants have been on sale in Europe and the U.S.A. in recent years. Concern about the impact of this trade and levels of trade in other rare *Paphiopedilum* spp. led to the listing of the entire genus on Appendix I of CITES in 1989. Artificially propagated plants of *P. rothschildianum* are available in the trade so that orchid enthusiasts can enjoy this species without threatening its survival.

Steps have been taken to improve the conservation status of this orchid in its natural habitat. Attempts have been made, for example, to re-introduce seedlings (from wild-collected seed) raised in cultivation in Germany back into the wild. Without constant vigilance, however, the species remains at risk of extinction.

Eastern prairie fringed orchid

Platanthera leucophaea

Family	Orchidaceae
Status	Threatened, USFWS
	Appendix II, CITES
Range	Nova Scotia, Ontario (Canada); Illinois, Iowa, Maine, Michigan, Ohio, Virginia, Wisconsin (U.S.A.)

Description and Biology

One of the loveliest North American plants, the eastern prairie fringed orchid is a winter-dormant perennial which sends up leaves and a flower spike from June to July. The plant has a rather stout appearance, and its height varies from 7.9-39.4 in (20-100 cm) depending on the moisture of the season. The stem is angled and leafy, and the two lowermost leaves are larger than the rest. The silver-green, alternate leaves are 3.2-7.9 in (8-20 cm) long and 0.8-2 in (2-5 cm) wide; they are oblong-elliptic to lanceolate (lance-shaped) and are widest near the base. Ten to 40 showy, white flowers are borne on the stem. These flowers have very long spurs and a three-part lower lip that is deeply fringed, giving the plant its common name. *Platanthera leucophaea* releases a delightful scent after nightfall to attract the nocturnal hawkmoths that pollinate the plant. Unlike other *Platanthera* species, *P. leucophaea* appears to be quite long-lived; individual plants have been known to survive for more than 30 years.

P. leucophaea is closely related to *P. praeclara*, the western prairie fringed orchid, and until the mid-1980s these plants were considered to be a single species. The two species are distinguished by flower size and number, details of the flower structure, and their pollination strategies. In *P. leucophaea*, pollen is deposited on the moths' proboscis, while in *P. praeclara*, with its larger flowers, pollen is deposited on the moths' eyes. *P. praeclara* is also considered threatened by the U.S. Fish and Wildlife Service and is listed in Appendix II of CITES.

Habitat and Current Distribution

The eastern prairie fringed orchid is currently found in the Canadian provinces of Nova Scotia and Ontario and in seven U.S. states: Illinois, Iowa, Maine, Michigan, Ohio, Virginia, and Wisconsin. It is considered rare and local in Nova Scotia and Ontario. Populations of moderate size occur in Wisconsin (nine small populations and one large population of several hundred plants) and Illinois (20 populations only two of which contain more than 100 plants); the species is most numerous in Michigan (18 populations that included more than 1,300 plants in 1984). Very small populations occur in Iowa (one small population of three plants), Maine (one small population of about 20 plants), Ohio (three declining populations ranging in size from 2-60 plants), and Virginia (one small population of three plants, seen only intermittently since 1983).

This species commonly grows on the rich, moist, sandy, calcareous soils of open prairies. It also grows on sedge mats in open bogs and, especially, on the margins of bog lakes. In Michigan it is often found growing on tufts of sedge or grass or on logs out in lake water. *P. leucophaea* requires full sunlight and is vulnerable to natural vegetational succession.

History and Conservation Measures

The eastern prairie fringed orchid was once common in parts of its prairie range, but its preference for the fertile, moist soils prized by farmers and truck-gardeners led to its rapid decline as this land was taken for cultivation. Although most of this conversion of prairie land to agricultural uses has already taken place, this process may still pose a threat to some surviving orchid populations. This species is also threatened by natural succession, particularly from fast-growing species. The size of these orchid populations is likely to decline over time, unless measures are taken to manage the habitat for the benefit of the orchid populations. Some populations of *P. leucophaea* occur on prairie remnants, and the small size of these habitats limits population growth. None of the known populations of eastern prairie fringed orchid occur on federally protected land, but a number of populations occur in areas that receive state protection. The largest population in Wisconsin is protected, as are about half of the populations in Michigan and most of the Illinois populations.

Eastern prairie fringed orchid.

Nanchuan tangtsinica

Tangtsinica nanchuanica

Family	Orchidaceae
Status	Rare, IUCN
Range	China

Description and Biology

Also call *jinlan*, this perennial averages 6-14 in (15-35 cm) in height. The rhizome (an underground or horizontal stem) is short, slightly fleshy, and covered with soft hairs. The stems have four to six leaves above and four sheaths at the base, the lowest sheath being scaly. Leaves are elliptic, but those above are nearly lance-shaped. Flower clusters are 1.2-2.4 in (3-6 cm) long and have three to five yellow flowers with whitish bases. Capsules are erect and oblong; seeds are numerous. The plant flowers in May, and its fruits ripen in September.

Habitat and Current Distribution

Endemic to China, this species is found only in a small area of just under 100 sq mi (250 sq km) on the Jinfo Mountain of Sichuan. It occurs at elevations of 2,300-6,900 ft (700-2,100 m) but is most often found between 3,300-4,900 ft (1,000-1,500 m). The climate in this area is cold in winter, with a long period of frost, cool in summer, and is often foggy and rainy, with high humidity. This species can grow in a variety of soils. It usually grows in forests, on the edges of forests, on barren slopes, and among bushes in open areas with full sunlight. It is a self-fertilizing plant, and its fleshy roots stretch along rocky crevices. Figures are unavailable, but the population is considered small.

History and Conservation Measures

This rare and ancient species is the only member of its genus. The individual plants are isolated from one another in a restricted area where the habitat has been seriously disturbed as a result of forest destruction. No conservation measures are known to have been undertaken on behalf of this species. Jinfo Shan Nature Reserve in Sichuan Province could provide some protection for the species. Ecological and biological studies have also been recommended, in addition to establishing a cultivation program.

Restio acockii

Family	Restionaceae
Status	Endangered, IUCN
Range	South Africa

Description and Biology

An erect reed with numerous, very slender stems that can be simple or sparingly branched, *R. acockii* can grow up to 3.3 ft (1 m). Flower clusters are 0.6-0.8 in (1.5-2 cm) long and about 0.08 in (2 mm) wide, cylindrical, pointed at both ends, and have pale brown bracts. The very compressed stems distinguish this species from others with similar spikelets or flowers.

Habitat and Current Distribution

The only known locality for this species is on the heavily farmed plains about 31 mi (50 km) north of Cape Town, South Africa. Estimates of population size are unavailable.

The species appears to be restricted to low-lying marshy areas on sandy flats with a clay subsoil that impedes drainage and causes a build-up of surface moisture during the wet winter months. During the dry summer, these soils remain moist at the surface.

History and Conservation Measures

The population where this species was first described has been destroyed by urban development. Considered extinct for over 40 years, this species was rediscovered in an isolated patch of natural vegetation in the wheatlands some 28 mi (45 km) north of its original locality. The new population, which consists of several thousand plants, extends over an area of about 15 acres (6 ha). The entire population now falls within the Riverlands Nature Reserve, a Provincial Reserve of 3,000 acres (1,200 ha) established in 1985. A number of other critically rare and endangered species also find refuge within this reserve. Although the species occurs within a conservation area, it is still threatened by occasional accidental fires and, more importantly, by invasions of the introduced *Acacia saligna*. Dense stands of the acacia are now within 656 ft (200 m) of every *Restio* plant in the population. Due to the lack of local funds, funding is being sought overseas to pay for a program to eradicate alien plant species. Another potential threat is increased salinization of the soil as a result of fertilizers used on neighboring croplands. Seeds of this species are kept in the Bolus Herbarium seed bank and at Wakehurst Place, Royal Botanic Garden in the United Kingdom.

Dicliptera dodsonii

Family	Acanthaceae
Status	Endangered, IUCN
Range	Ecuador

Description and Biology

This herb is a climbing vine with large orange flowers. It has hexagonal stems bearing pairs of opposite, lance-shaped leaves measuring 2-2.4 in (5-6.5 cm) by 0.7-0.9 in (1.9-2.2 cm) on short stalks. Its flower clusters are subtended (enclosed in an angle) by straight or lance-shaped bracts 0.4-0.5 in (10-12 mm) long and by uneven egg-shaped bracts 1-1.4 in (2.5-3.5 cm) long; individual flowers are subtended by several pairs of lance-shaped bracts 0.2-0.3 in (5-8.5 mm) long. The calyx is hairy, the corolla orange, and the capsule egg-shaped and flattened.

Habitat and Current Distribution

This plant is found at an elevation of approximately 650 ft (200 m) in the Río Palenque Biological Center, one of the few remaining patches of lowland wet forest along the western base of the Andes in Central Ecuador. Only one plant was located when the species was described in 1977.

History and Conservation Measures

At the time of its discovery, there was apparently only one plant of this species surviving, and its survival was attributed to the fact that it was preserved in the Río Palenque Biological Station. The small patch of forest at Río Palenque is an area of biological richness, with a very high level of plant diversity. This region is conspicuous in a flat landscape otherwise converted to agriculture, and is highly vulnerable both to illegal timber cutting and settlers. Protection of this reserve is essential for this species and for a range of other threatened species.

Quebrachos

Schinopsis balansae

Schinopsis quebracho-colorado

Family . . . . Anacardiaceae
Status . . . . Vulnerable, IUCN
Range . . . . Argentina; Bolivia; Paraguay

Description and Biology

The red quebrachos (*Quebrachos colorados*) are the dominant trees in the dry deciduous or semi-deciduous forest of the Chaco region in South America. Mature specimens may reach 82 ft (25 m) in height and a trunk diameter of 5 ft (1.5 m). These trees have brownish gray, resinous bark and rather loose foliage. The two species, *Schinopsis balansae* and *S. quebracho-colorado* are easy to distinguish because *S. balansae* has entire (smooth-margined) leaves and *S. quebracho-colorado* has compound (a leaf of two or more leaflets) leaves. The flowers are small, greenish, and inconspicuous, and the seeds are contained in a winged dry fruit. This species reproduces by seeds which are abundantly produced by mature trees. The hard wood contains up to 35 percent of the best quality tannins. This heavy timber is very resistant to decay.

Habitat and Current Distribution

Species of the genus *Schinopsis* are the most characteristic trees of the Gran Chaco region (eastern Bolivia, western Paraguay, and northern Argentina). The eastern (humid) portion of the region is dominated by *S. balansae*, while *S. quebracho-colorado* is abundant in the western part. Natural hybrids occur in the areas where the two species overlap. A third species (*S. haenkeana*) has a much more restricted distribution in the mountainous areas of the region.

History and Conservation Measures

The once abundant quebrachos formed forests which covered enormous expanses of the Chaco area. Since the beginning of the twentieth century, the development of the tannin industry led to over-exploitation of *S. balansae* forests and ultimately caused their destruction. *S. quebracho-colorado* was extensively used to make charcoal. It was also a popular building material due to its resistance to water and decay. Most of the Argentinian railroad is built on quebracho sleepers. The slow growth rate of these species makes reforestation options economically unattractive. The immediate and long-term threats to both species have been recognized by several researchers. Further research is needed to determine the most practical means of conserving these species in their natural environment.

Frerea indica

Family	Asclepiadaceae
Status	Endangered, IUCN
	Appendix I, CITES
Range	India

Description and Biology

A perennial herb about 4-6 in (10-15 cm) tall, this species grows in small dense clumps. It is an attractive plant with fleshy leaves about 1.2 in (3 cm) long and purplish starry flowers about 0.8 in (2 cm) across. It is a member of the milkweed family and is characterized by its succulent habit, fringed corolla lobes, and purple corona.

This species reproduces sexually; no information is available on other reproductive strategies. Transplanted plants have survived in an experimental garden. The species produces flowers after periods of heavy rain (September-October); no information is available on seed biology or seedling establishment. This decorative plant has potential horticultural value as an indoor plant.

Habitat and Current Distribution

Frerea indica is endemic to the Purandhar and Junnar Hills of Maharashtra ranges of Western Ghats. It prefers exposed bare rocks of hill slopes and cliffs at an altitude of 3,300 ft (1,000 m). More precise details of its ecology are not known.

History and Conservation Measures

Originally discovered on a hill near Junnar of Pune (Maharashtra, India), the species is now represented by an extremely small population in the Purandhar Hill Fort area. The reduction in the distribution range, as well as in population size, is due to erosion caused by grazing and deforestation. Although the habitat of the species is declared as a prohibited area for civilians, the species may become extinct unless the habitat is rehabilitated. A few transplanted plants are now growing at the Botanic Garden of Botanical Survey of India, Pune.

Conservation efforts for this plant should include research on its reproductive biology and ecology, multiplication of the species through seed and micropropagation, and restoration of the habitat.

Whitesloanea crassa

Family	Asclepiadaceae
Status	Endangered, IUCN
Range	Somalia

Description and Biology

This small succulent plant has an unbranched stem 1.6-2 in (4-5 cm) high and 2-2.2 in (5-5.5 cm) wide, and no leaves. The floral cluster develops from the base of the stem at ground level from a deciduous fleshy stalk around 0.66 in (17 mm) long; several stalked flowers develop in succession. Sepals are lance-shaped and 0.16 in (4 mm) long; the corolla is 1.29 in (33 mm) in diameter, whitish green with purple spots on the outer surface, wrinkled and light yellow with dark red dots on the inner surface. The outer corona arises at the base of the corolla; it has dark purple lobes that are long, broad, pointed, and divided to the middle. The inner corona is inversely cone-shaped, with the point of attachment at the small end, five-lobed and slightly higher than the outer corona lobes; it encloses the staminal column. Fruit has one or two spindle-shaped follicles.

Habitat and Current Distribution

Endemic to Somalia, this species was first found near Odweina, and then further north, just south of the Sheikh Pass in the Golis Mountains between Burao and Berbera. The habitat where the species occurred was stony, very arid semi-desert, where the species grew in bare ground among stones which it superficially resembled. It was found in a rather small area. More recently, this plant has been found growing in another habitat, an area of broken limestone rock.

History and Conservation Measures

First discovered in 1914, this plant was not found again in its original locality, but was discovered in 1957 in a second locality. Suspected to be extinct, it was rediscovered in 1985 in northeastern Somalia, 310 mi (500 km) from the original habitat. Because it is a succulent, but lacks protective spines, it is particularly susceptible to grazing animals in the region. However, cultivation has been successful, and plants are now being artificially propagated.

Puto hornbeam

Carpinus putoensis

Family . . . . Betulaceae
Status . . . . Endangered, IUCN
Range . . . . China

Description and Biology

This deciduous tree grows to a height of around 43 ft (13 m), with a diameter of 27.6 in (70 cm). The bark is gray-white and smooth, and the shoots are gray-brown with long, sparse, soft hairs. Leaves are paper-thin, egg-shaped, and measure 2-4 in (5-10 cm) long and 1.4-2 in (3.5-5 cm) wide; they are rounded or wedge-shaped at the base and tapered at the tip. Flowers are monoecious (male and female flowers on the same plant). Nutlets are egg-shaped and smooth with several ribs and measure 0.20-0.23 in (5-6 mm).

Male flowers blossom in early April before the leaves develop, while females bloom simultaneously with the unfolding of new leaves. Fruits begin to ripen in late September and early October.

Habitat and Current Distribution

Endemic to China, this species is known only from Mt. Foding on Putuo Island in the Zhoushan Archipelago, Zhejiang Province. At present there is only one tree known to survive in the wild.

The region in which this tree is found is warm in winter and cool in summer. The species originally grew in evergreen broad-leaved forests, but this single tree now occurs at the edge of a sparse, mixed forest, at an altitude of 790 ft (240 m) on red, fertile soil.

History and Conservation Measures

The almost complete disappearance of this species in the wild is thought to be the result of vegetation destruction and habitat loss. The very low rate of seed production is due to strong winds at the flowering and seed-setting stages and to typhoons at the seed-ripening stage. Natural regeneration, therefore, is extremely poor, and almost no seedlings are found under the tree.

Putuo Island has been proclaimed a key nature reserve in China, and a special management bureau has been formed to oversee the island. Recently a fence was erected around the tree to keep tourists away. The tree is cultivated in the Hangzhou Botanical Garden, where various propagation experiments are being conducted to provide seedlings for future distribution. Strict protection of the remaining tree is absolutely necessary for the preservation of the germplasm of this species.

Chatham Islands
forget-me-not

Myosotidium hortensia

Family	Boraginaceae
Status	Vulnerable, IUCN
Range	Chatham Islands (New Zealand)

Description and Biology

This succulent perennial has a stout, fleshy, cylindrical underground stem which produces a crowded rosette of large basal leaves 6-17 in (15-45 cm) long. The leaves are more or less broadly heart-shaped, thick, fleshy, and deeply grooved. Flowering branches average 3.3 ft (1 m) high, with oblong, stalkless stem leaves. Floral clusters measure 4-10 in (10-25 cm) across, with the flowers on pedicels around 0.4 in (1 cm) in length. The saucer-shaped corolla is pale to dark blue, 0.5-0.6 in (12-15 mm) across, with a short tube and five rounded lobes. Four flattened, broadly winged nutlets measure 0.6 in (15 mm) in diameter.

Habitat and Current Distribution

This species is known from the Chatham Islands, where it is still locally common on some of the small islets. It also occurs locally in small populations in the main islands of the group. Although numerous populations of the species survive, they are all small, and it is a rare plant in most of its localities.

Always found close to the sea, the Chatham Islands forget-me-not occurs on coastal dunes, sandy beaches, cliff ledges, and peat-covered rocks.

History and Conservation Measures

This species has been recorded from the islands of Chatham, Pitt, South-East, Mangere, Little Mangere, and other islets. It was once reported as plentiful along the seashore, covering many acres of the shoreline just above the high-water mark, spreading further inland over the sand dunes. It has been greatly depleted in the wild as a result of grazing by introduced animals, especially pigs, which feed on the stout fleshy stems, and sheep which graze on the leaves. More recently, introduced goats have added to the grazing pressure.

Mangere and South-East Islands are nature reserves, and the species is slowly re-establishing itself at these locations. The population on Te Whakuru Island (the northeast cape of Chatham Island) has been totally destroyed by grazing animals. Fortunately, this species is easily propagated from seed and offshoots, and is widespread in cultivation.

Onosma tornensis

Family	Boraginaceae
Status	Vulnerable, IUCN
Range	Hungary; Slovakia

Description and Biology

This hairy perennial has brown-red, carmine-staining roots; its several stems are simple or slightly branched and measure 6-12 in (15-30 cm). Its leaves are lance-shaped to narrowly oblong and measure 2 in (50 mm) by 0.08-0.12 in (2-3 mm), with stiff erect hairs 0.08-0.10 in (2-2.5 mm) long arising from nodules ringed by shorter, spreading hairs. Its flowers are on very short stalks with small bracts. The calyx is 0.2-0.4 in (6-10 mm) in flower and up to 0.5 in (12 mm) in fruit, and is divided nearly to the base into long, narrow, feather-shaped lobes. The yellow corolla is tubular and 0.6-0.8 in (15-20 mm) long with barely distinguished lobes. The fruit of four smooth, shining nutlets is 0.10-0.12 in (2.5-3 mm).

This species is pollinated by bees, and seed production is adequate. Effective dispersal may involve epizoochory, a process by which parts of the fruiting floral clusters attach themselves to persons or animals by their stiff, bristly hairs.

Habitat and Current Distribution

Onosma tornensis is found in three or four distinct subpopulations—one in Hungary, the others in Slovakia—within a 6.2 by 12.4 mi (10 by 20 km) range of the Torna Carstic Mountains. The population size in Hungary is approximately 200-250 mature plants; the Slovakian subpopulations are somewhat larger.

The primary habitat of the species in Slovakia is open, sunny grassland. In Hungary it is found in the rocky, grassy patches of bush-forest and grassland mosaic, often in half shade. It grows at elevations of 750-920 ft (230-280 m).

History and Conservation Measures

Known only from a few closely adjacent localities, this species has historically been threatened by intensive grazing of sheep and by trampling and rooting of wild boars. More recently, it has been threatened by quarrying activities, industrial development, and other human activities, including an unsuccessful attempt in the 1950s to establish a forest of black pines in the area. Mass tourism also poses a threat to the largest population in Slovakia. The species and much of its habitat are legally protected. When in flower, this species is considered highly decorative and is easily cultivated in gardens.

Agave living rock

Ariocarpus agavoides

Family	Cactaceae
Status	Endangered, IUCN
	Appendix I, CITES
Range	Mexico

Description and Biology

This small cactus plant measures 2-3 in (5-8 cm) across and consists of a stout, spindle-shaped stem from which arises an erect or spreading rosette of fleshy, rough-skinned, gray-green, leaf-like organs 1.6 in (4 cm) long. These organs produce flowers which bloom in November or December. The flowers are rose-pink to magenta, funnel-shaped, and 1.6-2 in (2-3 cm) long. Fruits are red to brownish and club-shaped, measuring 0.8-1 in (2-2.5 cm) long.

Habitat and Current Distribution

This species is found in the foothills of Sierra Madre Oriental, Tamaulipas State, Mexico, where it occurs in dry, calcareous silt at around 3,900 ft (1,200 m). A survey conducted in 1992 found more than 12,000 individuals.

History and Conservation Measures

The agave living-rock cactus has been heavily depleted in its only known locality because of excessive collecting and illegal exporting of plants for sale to the horticultural trade. It is prized by cactus enthusiasts because of its unusual shape and its status as a collector's item. It can be raised from seed, but is very slow growing. Urban expansion, rubbish dumping, and soil erosion are also contributing factors to this species' decline.

The region in which this plant occurs, between Monterrey and San Luis Potosí, contains a large number of rare cacti which have been over-collected for many years. Export of cacti collected from the wild is prohibited, except under license, and trade in certain plants is prohibited. Legal protection for this species should be enforced, and surveys should be conducted to locate any possible additional populations.

Aztekium ritteri

Family	Cactaceae
Status	Vulnerable, IUCN
	Appendix I, CITES
Range	Mexico

Description and Biology

This small cactus with a short taproot is about 2 in (5 cm) in diameter and 1.2 in (3 cm) high. Offsets (short, lateral shoots or branches which develop at the base of the main stem, providing a means of asexual reproduction) are formed. *Aztekium ritteri* has a distinctive corrugated surface with about nine spineless, wrinkled ribs. Flowers are pink or white and are about 0.6 in (1.5 cm) in diameter.

Habitat and Current Distribution

This species grows only on sheer cliffs, mostly of limestone origin. It is remarkably well adapted to mimic the specialized habitat where it occurs. Large quantities of seed are produced in the wild. These are carried by rain water down the cliff face and germinate among mosses and lichens in rock crevices.

A. ritteri is only found in the Mexican state of Nuevo Leon. Current population figures are not available.

History and Conservation Measures

This species was discovered in 1928. It is now known from five locations within an area of 19 sq mi (50 sq km) in the Valley of Rayones. At the cliff sites where it occurs *A. ritteri* is abundant, and the threat of habitat destruction is limited. Collecting from the wild is the main threat to the survival of this species.

A. ritteri is believed to be the slowest growing of all cacti and is very difficult to maintain in cultivation. It is, however, highly prized by cactus enthusiasts. The international trade in this species has consisted almost entirely of illegally collected wild plants. Its inclusion in Appendix I of CITES has not eliminated the trade; wild specimens have recently been offered for sale by European nurseries.

In 1991, a second species of *Aztekium, Aztekium hintonii*, was discovered. This species grows on gypsum rocks at about 3,300 ft (1,000 m) in the Sierra Madre Oriental. It is abundant in its native habitat, but there is a strong risk of collecting. There have already been rumors that wild plants of this newly described species are available at a European nursery.

Brady pincushion cactus

Pediocactus bradyi

Knowlton cactus

Pediocactus knowltonii

Peebles Navajo cactus

Pediocactus peeblesianus

Family	Cactaceae
Status	Endangered, IUCN
	Endangered, USFWS
	Appendix I, CITES
Range	Arizona (*P. bradyi* and *P. peeblesianus*), Colorado (*P. knowltonii*), New Mexico (*P. knowltonii*) (U.S.A.)

Description and Biology

These pediocacti are small, globe-shaped plants with no central spine. The Brady pincushion cactus grows to around 2.4 in (6 cm) tall and 2 in (5 cm) in diameter and has straw-yellow flowers that average around 1 in (2.5 cm) in diameter. Peebles Navajo cactus grows to around 2.4 in (6 cm) tall and 2 in (5 cm) in diameter. Its yellow to yellow-green flowers average up to 1 in (2.5 cm) in diameter. The Knowlton cactus is 0.3-2.2 in (0.7-5.5 cm) tall and 0.4-1.2 in (1-3 cm) in diameter, and its pink flowers average 0.4-1.2 in (1-3 cm) in diameter. All three species flower in the spring and have small fruit that turns from green to tan or brown at maturity.

Habitat and Current Distribution

The Brady pincushion cactus grows on plateau benches and terraces on each side of the Colorado River in Coconino County, northern Arizona. The main population is found in the Glen Canyon National Recreation Area, while other scattered populations occur on public and private land; the species has also been reported from the Navajo Indian Reservation. It is found at elevations of 3,900-4,500 ft (1,200-1,370 m) on shale or sandstone overlaid by limestone chips, in full sun. The population is estimated at approximately 10,000 plants.

The Peebles Navajo cactus occurs on low hills in Navajo County, Arizona. There are five known populations, with a total population of around 1,000 plants; two populations exist near Joseph City and three near Holbrook. The species is usually found at elevations of 5,575-5,740 ft (1,700-1,750 m) in gravel, usually alkaline, soils with good drainage.

The only viable population of Knowlton cactus occurs in a pinyon-juniper woodland south of La Boca, Colorado, in San Juan County, New Mexico, where it numbers around 7,000 plants. It grows on gravel slopes and on top of a single hill at an elevation

Pediocactus knowltonii.

of 6,800-6,875 ft (2,075-2,095 m). A second population that consists of only two plants is located at an elevation of 7,550 ft (2,300 m) in Reese Canyon in San Juan County, New Mexico.

History and Conservation Measures

All of these species have declined in number, if not also in range, since their discovery. The Knowlton cactus was thought to be extinct, or near extinction, in the 1970s, just 10 years after its population had been estimated to be over 100,000 plants.

The primary reasons for the decline of these species include excessive collecting and habitat degradation or destruction. Because of their rarity and the difficulty of growing pediocacti in cultivation, these plants are often the target of private collectors and commercial suppliers. Most of the populations are easily accessible and could be wiped out by overzealous collectors. A number of factors have affected the habitat of these plants, including road construction, trampling by grazing animals, damage from four-wheel-drive recreational vehicles, and mining activities. An additional problem for the species is their restricted distribution and specialized soil requirements, which apparently limit them to only a portion of possible habitat.

Conservation efforts have been directed toward monitoring and protecting existing populations and preserving habitat. In addition, efforts have been made to reintroduce the Knowlton cactus into parts of its former habitat. If the collection of these plants can be curtailed and natural habitat preserved, these species may be able to replenish themselves naturally in the wild.

Aylacophora deserticola

Family . . . . Compositae (Asteraceae)
Status . . . . Rare, IUCN
Range . . . . Argentina

Description and Biology

Aylacophora deserticola is a very rare, low shrub of about 1.8 ft (0.5 m) with striated stems and deciduous whitish leaves, each about 0.4 in (1 cm) long. Small yellow flowers are grouped in heads about 0.2 in (0.5 cm) in diameter. Almost nothing is known about the biology of this species, except that it is well adapted to extreme environmental conditions of temperature, drought, and wind. The plant produces normally shaped, apparently viable seeds, but there are no estimates of seed germination or successful seedling establishment in the field.

Habitat and Current Distribution

This species has been collected on several occasions, always in a restricted area near Plaza Huincul, Province of Neuquén, southwestern Argentina. Attempts to find it in other nearby areas have proven unsuccessful. It grows in a semi-desert area also populated by shrubby species characteristic of the Monte vegetation type.

History and Conservation Measures

The only known records of *Aylacophora deserticola* were collected by field botanists, and the species has not been given a common name. Although it inhabits an almost unpopulated area in which obvious disturbance forces are absent, the plant has become more rare in recent years. Since there is little economic or tourist interest in the area where it naturally occurs, the implementation of projects to study its biology and to develop conservation measures to ensure its survival seems unlikely.

Bidens hendersonensis

Family . . . . Compositae (Asteraceae)
Status . . . . Rare or Endangered, IUCN
Range . . . . Henderson Island (South Pacific Ocean)

Description and Biology

This species is a shrub which grows to around 13 ft (4 m) high. The stem is approximately one inch (2.5 cm) thick at the base and has pale brown bark. Leaves are long and oval, 2-3 in (5-8 cm) in length, with toothed edges. Flowers are small, 0.4 in (1 cm) across, and numerous on short, slender stalks, each having about five yellow rays. The fruit are dry, black, and single-seeded, measuring 0.27-0.39 in (7-10 mm) long and 0.04 in (1 mm) wide. Pollination is carried out by short-tongued insects.

Habitat and Current Distribution

Restricted to Henderson Island, a raised coral island of about 12 sq mi (30 sq km) in the Pitcairn Island District of the Pacific Ocean, this species occurs in dense forest. Small trees that are about 17-33 ft (5-10 m) high cover the deeply fissured, flat top of the island at about 10 ft (3 m) above sea level. The undergrowth is sparse, and there is no fresh water on the island. There are no estimates of the population size of this species.

History and Conservation Measures

The lack of fresh water on the island makes it unlikely that introduced species will be a threat to *B. hendersonensis,* but the plant is a part of a unique and fragile ecosystem, vulnerable to natural disasters. Protection of Henderson Island will be beneficial to this and other endemic plant species.

Littleflower heteroplexis

Heteroplexis microcephala

Family	Compositae (Asteraceae)
Status	Rare, IUCN
Range	China

Description and Biology

This perennial herb grows to a height of approximately 20-28 in (51-71 cm). Its cylindrical stems are elongated and densely covered with soft, close hairs; its stems and branches are gray-white. The leaves are thick, but papery in texture; they are wedge-shaped or triangular, tapering to a point at the tip and measuring 2-4 in (5-10 cm) long and 0.6-0.8 in (1.5-2 cm) wide. Its flowers—four male and four bisexual—are yellow with small, disk-shaped heads.

Habitat and Current Distribution

This species is found only in Yangshuo County of Guangxi, China. It grows scattered among shrubs or in open places on limestone hills at elevations of 820-1,310 ft (250-400 m). There are no estimates of the population size.

History and Conservation Measures

Heteroplexis microcephala was first discovered in Guangxi's Longzhou County in 1937. The population in that area was lost, however, after being extensively exploited for firewood. In the 1960s, an additional population consisting of more than 10 plants was discovered in the mountains of Yangshuo County.

Because of its low population and highly restricted range, this species is likely to become extinct unless it is protected. As of yet, no conservation measures have been taken on its behalf. Efforts should be made to bring it into cultivation.

Palaeocyanus crassifolius

Family	Compositae (Asteraceae)
Status	Rare, IUCN
Range	Malta

Description and Biology

This hairless evergreen shrub typically grows to a height of approximately 3.3 ft (1 m). Its leaves are somewhat succulent and spoon-shaped, measuring 2-4 in (5-10 cm) by 0.6-0.8 in (1.5-2 cm), growing mostly in rosettes. Flower heads of 0.8-1.2 in (2-3 cm) in diameter develop on the ends of long ridged stems, each with one or more whorls of bracts; florets are tubular and mauve. Its achenes (simple, dried, one-celled, one-seeded fruits that remain closed at maturity) measure 0.2-0.3 in (6-8 mm) and are hairless.

Habitat and Current Distribution

This species is found on vertical maritime cliff faces along the southern and western coasts of the islands of Malta and Gozo. In the late 1970s, it was known from approximately ten localities, the majority of which contained fewer than 500 individuals.

History and Conservation Measures

This species was first described in 1827 as *Centaurea spathulata*. On Gozo, it has apparently become much rarer than it was thought to be in the 1920s. The species is vulnerable to parasites: in the late 1970s, very few young plants were found in the natural habitat because a moth larva had parasitized the plant ovaries. One of the largest and presumably oldest plants was parasitized over a number of years by the dodder plant (*Cuscuta epithymum*), but the dodder subsequently died and the plant, though debilitated, survived the attack. A method of controlling parasites is needed, as are efforts to conserve as much of the natural habitat as possible. The species was declared Malta's National Plant in 1971 and has had legal protection since 1993. It has been introduced in cultivation in Maltese public gardens, since it roots well from cuttings and is decorative.

Button wrinklewort

Rutidosis leptorhynchoides

Family	Compositae (Asteraceae)
Status	Endangered
Range	Australia

Description and Biology

The button wrinklewort is a perennial herb which reaches a height of 10-14 in (25-35 cm). Narrow leaves can be up to 1 in (2.5 cm) long; their edges curl under the leaf, concealing the underside. Yellow, button-shaped flowers bloom from October to April; they grow at the end of an upright stem and average 0.8 in (2 cm) in diameter.

Habitat and Current Distribution

This species is mainly restricted to a number of localities west of Melbourne, Victoria, but there are several other small, scattered populations, including some in the Queanbeyan Nature Reserve, which has been established especially for the protection of this species.

Traditional habitat includes grassy areas of open woodlands or plains.

History and Conservation Measures

Most of the vast areas of habitat which once supported this species have now been cleared for agricultural development and pasture. Remaining habitats are those that could not be exploited, such as railroad rights-of-way, cemeteries, and roadsides; even in these areas, however, the species is subject to competition with aggressive weed species and accidental clearing or destruction by maintenance crews.

Remaining populations should be marked and protected from human interference and from competition with weeds. Re-introduction, which has been attempted without great success, should be enhanced. Finally, research to determine appropriate management and fire regimes should be initiated.

Short's goldenrod

Solidago shortii

Family	Compositae (Asteraceae)
Status	Endangered, USFWS
Range	Kentucky (U.S.A.)

Description and Biology

Short's goldenrod is a perennial herb that grows to around 24-30 in (61-76 cm) in height. It has an underground stem that produces as many as six separate stems during the growing season. Narrow leaves are alternately arranged and measure about 2-4 in (5-10 cm) long by 0.2-0.6 in (0.5-1.5 cm) wide; the leaves are larger near the middle of the stem and decrease in size toward each end. Clusters of 10 or more yellow flowers bloom from mid-August to early November; seeds are released from late September to late November.

The method of pollination is uncertain, but sweat bees have been observed to visit the flowers.

Habitat and Current Distribution

Endemic to Kentucky, this goldenrod is known from five populations, the largest of which lies within Blue Licks Battlefield State Park; the other four are within a 2-mi (3.2-km) radius of the park. Total population is estimated at 3,400-4,000 individuals, more than half of which are found in the state park. Most of the known habitat is in cedar glades, pastures, and open areas in oak and hickory forests.

History and Conservation Measures

The species was originally described in 1842 from a site near the Ohio River in Jefferson County; the site was later flooded as a result of dam construction. Until 1939, numerous populations were said to survive on rocky slopes and in pastures in Nicholas and Fleming counties. Its distribution is thought to

have once been determined by the movement of bison through the area and the resulting clearance caused by their browsing; fire clearance may also

Short's goldenrod.

have played a role in providing open areas for the species.

The primary threat to this species is the modification or loss of its habitat as a result of human activities or fire; while fire may once have been beneficial to an abundant population, it could now destroy the small remaining populations. Overcollecting for scientific purposes is an additional threat.

Part of the Blue Licks Battlefield State Park has been designated a nature reserve to protect Short's goldenrod. Since most of the remaining populations are on private land, it is important to enlist the cooperation of the landowners. Conservation measures include studies of life history and habitat requirements of this plant and studies to determine species management requirements. To ensure the survival of a species with such a restricted distribution and small population, it may become necessary to reintroduce Short's goldenrod into areas of former distribution.

Draba ladina

Family . . . . Cruciferae (Brassicaceae)
Status . . . . Rare, IUCN
Range . . . . Switzerland

Description and Biology

This small, tufted perennial is a characteristic species of the high alpine plant community. It has a thin, branching, underground stem and produces several dense, basal rosettes of lance-shaped leaves. The leaves are up to 0.3 in (3 mm) long, three to five times longer than they are broad, and often somewhat fleshy; on the lower surface and margins of the leaves are numerous, scattered, star-shaped hairs. A flowering stem arises from the rosette; it is unbranched and leafless, up to 2 in (5 cm) high, and bears a terminal cluster of one to four flowers. The flowers have four sepals that are long and hairless, and four petals that are pale yellow. The fruit has a few short hairs.

Habitat and Current Distribution

Endemic to Switzerland, this species occurs in the Engadine chain of the Dolomite mountains, northwest to north of the Pass dal Fuorn (Ofenpass) between Piz Nuna and Piz Tavrü, two of the local peaks. It forms dense tussocks up to 3.1 in (8 cm) across, in clefts of dolomitic rock at altitudes of 8,500-10,000 ft (2,600-3,040 m); it also occasionally occurs on limestone scree. There is no estimate of population size.

History and Conservation Measures

Discovered in 1917 by the noted Swiss botanist Josias Braun-Banquet, this is considered to be the only species of flowering plant endemic to Switzerland. Most of the known localities in which it occurs are in parts of the Swiss National Park, where access is not normally permitted. Although the population is well protected, the species is considered rare because of its very small population size and limited distribution. There is no information on conservation activities in addition to the legal protection accorded to the species in 1963.

Motio-hiran chobbo

Farsetia macrantha

Family	Cruciferae (Brassicaceae)
Status	Endangered, IUCN
Range	India

Description and Biology

This desert undershrub grows to a height of approximately 3.3 ft (1 m). The foliage is covered with short, stiff hairs to protect it from herbivores and to prevent water loss. The leaves are thick, long, and broadly lance-shaped, measuring about 1.6-2.8 by 0.6-0.9 in (4-7 by 1.5-2.2 cm). White or creamy white flowers with spoon-shaped petals are borne in 5-15 clusters. The fruit measures 1.17-1.37 by 0.20-0.23 in (30-35 by 5-6 mm) and is oblong and compressed. Seeds are compressed and winged around a brown or golden yellow nucleus that measures 0.23 by 0.12 in (6 by 3 mm). Flowers and fruits are produced from August to January.

Habitat and Current Distribution

Endemic to northwestern Rajasthan, India, this species is now only known from one site: a rocky area behind Mataji's Temple, Barmer. Exact population figures are unavailable.

History and Conservation Measures

The species was described from its present locality in 1918 and is not known from elsewhere. Its limited distribution is attributed to the loss of habitat due to grazing and to shifting sand dunes. Conservation measures should include studies on reproductive biology and ecology; cultivation in botanic gardens located in deserts; rehabilitation of native habitat; and multiplication through seeds and *in vitro* methods.

Lundy cabbage

Rhynchosinapsis wrightii

Family	Cruciferae (Brassicaceae)
Status	Rare, IUCN
Range	Lundy Island (United Kingdom)

Description and Biology

The Lundy cabbage is a perennial herb with a slender taproot. Initially it bears a rosette of stalked, hairy leaves 6-12 in (15-30 cm) long with feather-shaped lobes and coarsely-toothed segments. Subsequent flowering stems are stout and erect, rising to 3.3 ft (1 m) in height, woody below and branching above, densely covered with downward spreading hairs, and with a few leaves. Flowers cluster in flat-topped groupings of about 20 blossoms, each with four erect sepals and four long, yellow petals. The dry, two-celled seed pod is 2.4-3.1 in (6-8 cm) long and very narrow; it splits open at maturity, releasing spherical, purplish-black seeds that have a fine, net-like pattern.

Habitat and Current Distribution

This species is confined to Lundy Island, off the coast of north Devon in the United Kingdom. The island is about 1.5 sq mi (4 sq km) in size, but the species is restricted to about 0.3 mi (0.5 km) of cliff habitat in the southeast corner and to a few isolated areas along the east coast. Estimates of population size are unavailable.

The cabbage grows on east- and south-facing slopes and sea cliffs of Devonian shales, sandstones, and granite. It does not thrive on soils containing lime. It occurs in the lee of the island, where it is protected from the Atlantic gales, and favors sheltered spots such as gullies, where it is damp in the winter but hot and sunny in the summer.

History and Conservation Measures

The Lundy cabbage population is threatened by the presence of goats and deer on the island; the sheep population does not appear to touch the plant, even though they graze widely on the slopes where it grows. The spreading growth of bracken (*Pteridium*

Lundy cabbage.

aquilinum) and possibly the introduced *Rhododendron ponticum* may also threaten the species. The island is subject to some tourism, but most of the cabbage population is not easily reached.

Lundy Island is owned by the National Trust of the United Kingdom and managed by the Landmark Trust. Its vegetation and flora are protected, and the cabbage population is carefully monitored. The species is important as part of the gene pool available for breeding with other members of the *Brassica* genus (which includes watercress, cabbages, and sweet alyssum). It is also a host for two beetles with very restricted distributions. The English Nature Recovery Programme has collaborated with the Royal Botanic Gardens to store Lundy cabbage seeds and has recommended bracken clearance from parts of the island as a conservation measure.

Shrubby cress-rocket

Vella pseudocytiscus ssp.

Family	Cruciferae (Brassicaceae)
Status	Vulnerable, IUCN
Range	Spain

Description and Biology

The shrubby cress-rocket is a small shrub that grows over 24-28 in (60-70 cm) in height; it has many branches and dense leaves. The stems are covered with short, rigid hairs, and they bear stalkless, somewhat leathery, egg-shaped leaves with broad tips. Rough bristly hairs grow on both sides of the leaf. Flowers grow in loose clusters on short stalks; each flower has a tube of four sepals, from which protrude four yellow petals. Two subspecies have been described from Spain: *V. p. paui (badallii)* is distinguished from *V. p. pseudocytisus* by its smooth leaves.

Habitat and Current Distribution

V. p. pseudocytisus is found in the Aranjuez Province of Madrid, Spain, where it grows on the slope of a river terrace. The population here is estimated at 2,000-3,000 individuals. *V. p. paui* occurs in Villalba Baja in Teruel Province, east of Madrid, on inclined rocks. Only 100-150 individuals survive in this locality.

History and Conservation Measures

This shrub has disappeared from some of its former localities because of habitat destruction. It has been recorded from parts of southern Spain, but a detailed search in 1976 failed to find any plants there. In the past *V. pseudocytisus* has been used for fuel, and goats are known to feed upon it, despite the tough, stiff hairs on its leaves.

Currently the population in Aranjuez is protected and restricted to visitors, but consideration should be given to the creation of a local nature reserve around this area. Viable seed of the species is being stored in a seed bank and re-introduction experiments have been initiated.

Alluaudiopsis marneriana

Family	Didiereaceae
Status	Endangered, IUCN
	Appendix II, CITES
Range	Madagascar

Description and Biology

Alluaudiopsis marneriana is a member of the family Didiereaceae, which contains 11 species endemic to the semi-arid Southern Floristic Domain of Madagascar. Members of this family often occur as co-dominants with various succulent species of *Euphorbia*, and *A. marneriana* is not an exception. Unlike most other Didiereaceae, which are trees, *A. marneriana* and *A. fiherenensis* (the only other known species in this genus) are much-branched shrubs commonly reaching 6.5-13 ft (2-4 m) in height. Several main trunks up to about 4 in (10 cm) in diameter develop from a thick, fleshy, succulent tap-root. The branches of *A. marneriana* are thin, wiry, and have pairs of straight spines up to 0.4 in (10 mm) long at regular intervals. The leaves are succulent, cylindrical, and very narrow in diameter; they are deciduous, falling during the long, dry winter season. On young shoots the leaves are borne singly between the spines and are up to 0.59 in (15 mm) long. Older stems bear short lateral shoots that produce paired leaves. These leaves reach about 0.47 in (12 mm) on male plants and only about 0.2 (5 mm) on females. The flowers are the largest and most brightly colored of all Didiereaceae blossoms. They are commonly borne in pairs and may be very abundant during the short flowering period in spring (October). The pair of sepals are a rich golden color, and the four petals are deep carmine. The female flowers open to a diameter of about 0.8 in (20 mm), while the male flowers are a little smaller. Although individual plants bear only flowers of a single sex (dioecious), male flowers retain vestigial female parts and *vice versa*.

Although *A. marneriana* is placed in the same genus as *A. fiherenensis*, the two species differ in many important features, and it is possible that they should be placed in separate genera. *A. marneriana* is probably the sole surviving relict of an otherwise extinct group of Didiereaceae. However, little is known of the phylogeny of the Didiereaceae, and much of the evidence is confusing, as a result, the evolutionary classifications of the family are somewhat contradictory.

Habitat and Current Distribution

Alluaudiopsis marneriana is only known from a small area in southwest Madagascar. It occurs on the narrow coastal plain near the city of Tuléar, at an altitude of about 164 ft (50 m), growing in red sandy soils. To date it seems to have been recorded from only two localities about 25 mi (40 km) apart. Although additional populations of the species may remain as yet undiscovered, there can be little doubt that the species is very localized and rare. At both localities the populations consist of numerous plants of varying ages, apparently in good health. They appear to be quite abundant at both sites, but are confined to very small patches (within an area under 2.47 acres/1 ha).

At one site, *A. marneriana* occurs in a deciduous thicket dominated by succulent *Euphorbia* spp. and *Didierea madagascariensis*, with numerous other trees including individuals of *Adansonia rubrostipa*, *Colvillea racemosa*, *Delonix floribunda*, and *Givotia madagascariensis*. At the other site, the plants grow in disturbed vegetation near traditional tombs, where much of the natural vegetation has evidently been cleared. The abundance of *Alluaudiopsis* at this site is curious, and it is uncertain whether it has been intentionally left by local inhabitants and has some cultural significance, or whether it is difficult to eradicate and able to regenerate easily after clearance. The natural vegetation at this site would formerly have been similar to that of the other site.

A. marneriana is an attractive plant and may appeal to growers of succulent plants. Attempts to introduce *A. marneriana* into cultivation have not been very successful to date, although it is grown in some specialist collections. Seed is not readily available, and, unlike some other Didiereaceae, cuttings do not seem to root with ease. Grafting *A. marneriana* onto plants of other Didiereaceae is a more effective means of propagation.

History and Conservation Measures

It is not known whether *A. marneriana* was previously more widespread than it is now, or whether some human or biological factor may have reduced its range. Plant communities similar to those in which the known populations of *A. marneriana* occur are found along the coastal plain north of Tuléar, and may harbor additional populations. However, none of these are within Madagascar's network of protected areas. The city of Tuléar is a provincial capital with a developing tourist industry. Accessible areas of deciduous thicket are being destroyed at an alarming rate to provide domestic fuel wood and charcoal. Some charcoal production already takes place in villages near the *A. marneriana* populations, and it is likely to expand. Tuléar's main beach resorts are adjacent to the deciduous thicket in which *A. marneriana* occurs. While the plants are probably far enough from the sea to escape direct threat from the development of these resorts, the development of neighboring villages, associated amenities, and the increase in the number of people in the area does pose a direct threat. Some means of *in situ* conservation in highly desirable.

In order to ensure effective *ex situ* conservation of the species, efforts should be undertaken to make new collections of seeds from the wild populations. These seeds should be placed in seed banks and distributed to appropriate institutions for cultivation.

Dirachma socotrana

Family	Dirachmaceae
Status	Endangered, IUCN
Range	Socotra (Indian Ocean)

Description and Biology

This sweet-smelling shrub or small tree has rigid young shoots that bear toothed, elliptical leaves 0.2-1.2 in (5-30 mm) long; the leaves are usually in clusters, and a mass of blossoms appears after the North East Monsoon. Individual flowers are attractive and decorative, each with an adjacent whorl of four small green leaves; eight reddish sepals that are lance-shaped, downwardly-curved, and 0.4 in (10 mm) long; and eight obovate (inversely egg-shaped) petals that form a bowl about 0.8 in (2 cm) across. Fruits are more or less oval and beaked, consisting of eight single-seeded valves with dense white hair within.

Habitat and Current Distribution

This plant is endemic to Socotra, an island territory of the People's Democratic Republic of Yemen, lying 140 mi (225 km) east of the Horn of Africa.

Known habitat is low open thicket among limestone boulders, on a steep slope at an elevation of about 800 ft (240 m). Rainfall here is the highest on the island for that altitude, and this is reflected in the thickets, which are dense and rich in species.

History and Conservation Measures

In 1967 a grove of 30 mature *Dirachma* trees was all that remained; no seeds or saplings were in evidence. The decline of this plant was probably due to overgrazing by goats and cattle. However, subsequent visits to the area have indicated an improvement in the species' status; in 1992 scientists discovered dozens of trees, including some seedlings, apparently thriving. Unfortunately, there are plans for gas exploration and the creation of a port, new roads, wells, and a hospital on the island; these developments could have a negative impact on this and other species if suitable precautionary measures are not taken.

This species is considered to be of great scientific importance because it is the only member of its family, and its extinction would represent a major loss of diversity in the plant kingdom. It should be brought into cultivation as a matter of extreme urgency, and a reserve created to protect this and other threatened endemic plants growing nearby.

Venus flytrap

Dionaea muscipula

Family	Droseraceae
Status	Vulnerable, IUCN
Range	North Carolina, South Carolina (U.S.A.)

Description and Biology

The Venus flytrap is a perennial with 4-8 leaves, each 0.8-4.7 in (2-12 cm) long, that form a spreading rosette. Each consists of a flat expanded leaf stem ending in a blade of two identical semi-circular halves. The midrib or central vein of the blade can contract to form a hinged trap, with marginal bristles that interlock when the halves close. Insects are trapped when they touch the trigger hairs or bristles and the two hinged lobes of the leaf rapidly close together. Four to 10 flowers in a terminal cluster are white.

Flowering begins near the last week in May and is usually over before the middle of June. New seedlings first appear at the end of July. Cross-pollination is effected by various beetles, small flies, and possibly spiders.

Habitat and Current Distribution

This plant is found on the coastal plain of North and South Carolina in the United States. Its range extends southwest for about 200 mi (320 km), from Beaufort County in North Carolina to Charleston County in South Carolina. There is no estimate of population size.

The primary habitat of the species is the wetland between the wet evergreen-shrub bogs (pocosins) and the dry sandy regions of the surrounding savannas. In the more northern counties, where the transition between pocosin and savanna is abrupt, the species is found in well-defined zones around the edge of pocosins; in the southeastern part of its range, the transition zone is more extensive, and the plant is spread over wider areas. The soil in which it grows is medium to fine sand containing some organic matter, either as humus or as peat, and few mineral nutrients, with a high moisture content.

Venus flytrap.

History and Conservation Measures

Once reported to have extensive populations, this plant could not be located in any large numbers in the 1970s. Its range had apparently been diminished, probably by a number of threats. Fire plays an important role in maintaining its habitat, as frequent fires remove most of the low vegetation and reduce competition. Suppression of fire has resulted in even-aged pine plantations, with the shade created by the pines and increased competition from other plants destroying the flytrap populations. Another severe threat to its habitat is the drainage that accompanies construction projects and agricultural development. Any permanent, significant drop in the water level can destroy the flytrap population at that site. Finally, because the flytrap is of interest as a curiosity, it has been illegally collected in the wild.

A survey of existing sites and populations is necessary to make plans for protected areas. To prevent the further reduction of the wild populations of this species, flytraps for cultivation should be grown from seed division or tissue culture rather than collected from the wild.

Sulawesi ebony

Diospyros celebica

Family	Ebenaceae
Status	Rare, IUCN
Range	Sulawesi (Indonesia)

Description and Biology

Sulawesi ebony, a timber tree endemic to the island of Sulawesi, reaches a height of 115 ft (35 m). The trunk has a diameter of 7.9-39.4 in (20-100 cm).

Habitat and Current Distribution

Diospyros celebica grows in the lowland rain forests of Sulawesi.

History and Conservation Measures

This species of ebony occurs only on Sulawesi, and is found mainly in the central and northern parts of the island. The tree produces an attractive black ebony, streaked with fine brown stripes. This precious wood is used for carving, wood turning, inlaying, fine furniture, and musical instruments. Demand for the timber is a threat to the species in the wild. Fifty years ago, about 1,000 tons were exported each year, mainly to Japan. Very few ebony trees remain in southern Sulawesi because of felling and forest clearance by shifting cultivators.

D. celebica is a protected species in Sulawesi, with some felling allowed under a quota set by the Indonesian government. Japan remains the most important market for ebony, but the wood is also sold in Europe and North America. Illegal logging and export of Sulawesi ebony is a difficult problem to control. Fortunately, *D. celebica* can be grown from seed in nurseries and there is considerable interest in developing commercial plantations. Since the lowland rain forests of Sulawesi are among the most threatened of all Indonesia's rain forests, the need for propagating the species will increase as these forests disappear.

Erica jasminiflora

Family	Ericaceae
Status	Endangered, IUCN
Range	South Africa

Description and Biology

An erect, sparsely branched shrub, *E. jasminiflora* has needle-shaped leaves and grows up to 24 in (60 cm) high. Long, slender flowers grow in clusters of one to three on stalks 0.3 in (8 mm) long and resemble those of a jasmine. The corolla can be white or pale rose with red veins; it forms a slender tube up to 1.3 in (3.2 cm) long and 0.1 in (3 mm) wide and has spreading, star-shaped lobes around 0.4 in (1 cm) long at the tip. Flowers can bloom profusely in exposed hot and dry conditions in the summer months of November and December and again in February and March.

The sticky corolla tube is a deterrent to bees and other insects that may bite into the side of the flower for nectar without pollinating the species. Flies of the Nemestrinidae and Tabanidae families may act as pollinators since they would be able to reach the nectar with their proboscises, using the non-sticky lobes as a landing platform.

Habitat and Current Distribution

The only known locality for this species is in South Africa, near Caledon in southwestern Cape Province. The soil there is hard, rust-colored gravel or sand with subsurface clay derived from shale. The altitude of the site is approximately 650 ft (200 m). An estimated 150 plants survived there in the late 1970s.

History and Conservation Measures

This species was probably at one time fairly common in the area around Caledon, although only two populations have ever been recorded. One of the populations which was recorded in the late 1700s is now extinct as a result of agricultural activities, particularly wheat cultivation. The remaining population is very small and numbers probably less than 100 plants, although the species is very difficult to find when not in flower. The construction of a road destroyed a number of plants, and the use of fire to create grazing lands in adjacent farming areas has resulted in the further decline of the species. The plants were burnt twice in recent years, first by accident and then deliberately. With each fire it was thought that the species had become extinct, but fortunately this species appears to be quite vigorous.

The land on which the population occurs belongs to the Caledon Divisional Council, and for a number of years they have leased the site to the Cape Nature Conservation Department. During this time, a fence was put around the remaining plants, and seeds were sown nearby in a prepared strip in order to extend the population. There were also plans to provide a buffer zone with fire-belts. In 1992, Cape Nature Conservation did not renew their lease of the land, and the area was leased to a local school teacher who plans to develop the area as an outdoor school camp. To date, there have been no further developments, but if action is not taken soon to secure the land for conservation, this species could well become extinct in the wild.

As the population is surrounded by farmland, frequently burnt vegetation and roads may isolate the pollinators and thus negatively affect *E. jasminiflora*.

Studies on the pollination biology of this species are essential if it is to be conserved *in situ*. Fortunately, as it is once again fashionable to grow Erica plants, this species is available from most Erica nurseries in South Africa. Some seed has also been preserved in a seed bank.

Chapman's rhododendron

Rhododendron chapmanii

Family	Ericaceae
Status	Endangered, IUCN
	Endangered, USFWS
	Appendix I, CITES
Range	Florida (U.S.A.)

Description and Biology

An evergreen shrub, Chapman's rhododendron can reach 6.6 ft (2 m) in height. The bark is reddish brown on new shoots but turns gray and starts to peel with age. Leaves have an oval shape, wrinkled surface, and smooth edges, measuring 1.2-2.6 in (3.0-6.5 cm); they are green on top but have flat, reddish scales underneath. A cluster of large flowers blooms in March and April; flowers are often pink, but color can vary in large populations. Fruit is an ovoid capsule measuring around 0.4 in (1 cm).

The scattered distribution of the species suggests that it has reproduced by seed in the past, but little or no reproduction seems to be occurring from seed in the wild. Most reproduction now seems to occur asexually, with the plant resprouting from the roots.

Habitat and Current Distribution

This species is restricted to three populations in Florida. The largest population is found in Gadsden and Liberty counties, where it covers 150-200 acres (60-80 ha) and numbers around 500 individual plants. A population in Gulf County includes several hundred plants, and one in Clay County probably has fewer than 50 plants.

Chapman's rhododendron is typically found in transition zones between dry, pine-turkey oak and moist titi (*Cliftonia*) bogs. It requires light shade, sandy soil with good drainage and abundant organic matter, and a stable, lightly acidic water table near the surface.

Chapman's rhododendron.

History and Conservation Measures

Much of the habitat for this species has been destroyed by logging and by the preparation of sites for pine plantations. A certain amount of disturbance to a site seems beneficial to this rhododendron, which often thrives in areas of periodic burning.

Clearing of the understory reduces competition and allows the species to flourish, but too much disturbance can be destructive. Because much of this population is on private land, efforts are underway to enlist the cooperation of landowners to preserve this plant's habitat. Conservation measures also include regulation of logging and other forestry practices.

Euphorbia handiensis

Family	Euphorbiaceae
Status	Endangered, IUCN Appendix II, CITES
Range	Canary Islands (Spain)

Description and Biology

This plant is a spiny, cactus-like succulent that grows to a height of 20-40 in (50-100 cm) and is often densely branched. Its numerous and crowded erect stems are cylindrical, 2.4-3.1 in (6-8 cm) thick, and fluted with 8-14 ridges. Straight spines, 0.8-1.2 in (2-3 cm) long, grow at regular intervals on the ridges with a tuft of spines at the tip. Its flowers are greenish to red, 0.1 in (3 mm) long, and borne singly or in pairs; each is surrounded by two semi-circular, almost black bracts. The capsule is brown or red.

Habitat and Current Distribution

This plant is found in coastal areas of the Canary Islands in the lower parts of the valleys which lead southward from the ridge of the Jandia Peninsula in the southwest of Fuerteventura. The three main populations, all at altitudes between sea level and 492 ft (150 m), total less than 3,000 individuals.

The primary habitat of the species is sand and rock debris. Jandia is a high volcanic ridge with steep slopes on either side dropping down to the coast. The region is very arid, and its low rainfall results in vegetation that more closely resembles that of North Africa than the vegetation of the western Canaries.

History and Conservation Measures

In 1924 this plant was reported to occur in three small valleys, and in two of these its population size was reported to be in the millions. By the 1970s it was still reported from these three valleys but had become very rare. Its decline is primarily due to the species being parasitized by a stem-boring beetle. Collecting of the plants for horticulture is also likely to have contributed to the depletion of the species.

Many threatened plant species of the Canary Islands are in cultivation under semi-natural conditions at the Jardin Botanico Viera y Clavijo on Gran Canaria. This botanical garden has incorporated *E. handiensis* seed into its regional germplasm bank and has developed tissue culture techniques for the species. In warm, humid nursery conditions plants grown from seed can reach 4 in (10 cm) in less than two years. Further study has been recommended for this succulent. On the Jandia Peninsula, approximately 35,800 acres (14,318 ha) have been declared a Parque Natural, and all of the natural populations of *E. handiensis* are found within its limits. The species also has legal protection.

Euphorbia obesa

Family	Euphorbiaceae
Status	Endangered, IUCN
	Appendix II, CITES
Range	South Africa

Description and Biology

Euphorbia obesa is a unisexual, spineless, dwarf stem succulent plant which grows up to 7.9 in (20 cm) tall and reaches 3.5 in (9 cm) in diameter. The stem is unbranched, sub-globose when young, becoming more or less cylindrical with age; it is gray-green with irregular transverse, dull purple bands, and is generally eight-angled. The apex of the stem has small, tuberlike swellings which are rudimentary deciduous leaves. This species typically flowers from July to September, but flowering has been recorded as early as March. Once the seeds are released from the capsules they are apparently drought resistant and can lie dormant for a number of years.

Habitat and Current Distribution

This species is known only from a few localities between Graaff Reinet and Kendrew in the eastern Cape Province of South Africa. The highly scattered (and now very small) populations occur mainly on the lower southern and southwestern slopes of low hills, often in association with *Rhigozum obovatum*. *Euphorbia obesa* grows in karroid vegetation on stony, loamy, slightly alkaline soils derived from Karoo shales and outcrops of doleritic sandstone.

History and Conservation Measures

Ever since its discovery in 1897, this species has suffered from severe exploitation. It is highly sought after by succulent collectors and is probably one of the best known succulent euphorbias in the world due to its attractive shape and because it is relatively easy to maintain in cultivation. This species was considered to be endangered as early as 1915, when it was said that it would soon become extinct if the rate of collecting for export continued. It was estimated in 1975 that there were at least 10,000 plants in the main population which covered an area of 11.5 sq mi (30 sq km). By 1986 it was concluded that there were not more than 500 plants left in the wild and that all plants close to roads and in easily accessible areas had been removed. It was also reported that a local resident had been responsible for sending thousands of wild-collected plants to succulent collectors overseas. In 1987 a succulent enthusiast reported that only two small populations were known to him and that each one consisted of only about 30 plants. Recent evidence suggests that this was an underestimate. Despite legislation to protect this species, however, and despite the protection provided by some land owners, numbers have continued to decline. The populations have been reduced so much that they may now cover an area of only 49.5 acres (20 ha). Recently, the Cape Nature Conservation Department reintroduced 800 plants into the wild, all of which had been confiscated from a succulent dealer who had collected the plants illegally.

A number of small areas need to be fenced off as sanctuaries for this species. If necessary, ex-nursery stock, preferably not all from the same clone, should be reintroduced to help boost existing wild populations. Strict control of access to fenced-off populations is essential and the sites should be monitored on a regular basis. Education of the land owners and local community is also essential.

Brazilian rosewood

Dalbergia nigra

Family	Fabaceae
Status	Endangered, IUCN
	Appendix I, CITES
Range	Brazil

Description and Biology

Dalbergia nigra is a timber tree that grows to a height of 50-82 ft (15-25 m). The trunk is relatively thin, generally measuring 1-1.3 ft (0.3-0.4 m) in diameter. Trees with thicker trunks are now rarely found because most have been logged. The bark is thin, gray, and rough with irregular parallel fissures. The branches are dark and roundish, and grow in a slightly zig-zag manner. The compound, alternate leaves have 12-18 leaflets, up to 0.6 in (15 mm) long and 0.3 in (8 mm) wide.

Brazilian rosewood flowers in October and November. The pale, violet-scented flowers are about 0.35 in (9 mm) long and are arranged in short axial bunches on leafless shoots.

Habitat and Current Distribution

Brazilian rosewood is found in the Atlantic Coastal Forests of Brazil. It grows under a range of climatic conditions and is most frequently found in rolling or mountainous terrain with relatively fertile soils. Current population figures are not available.

History and Conservation Measures

Indigenous populations of *D. nigra* are scattered in the Atlantic Coastal Forests from southern Bahia to Minas Gerais. These forests, growing in areas first settled by Europeans in 1500, have declined dramatically and are now reduced to less than five percent of their former range. Exploitation for timber, as well as clearance for plantation agriculture and mining have led to the loss of forest cover, with deforestation accelerating rapidly during the present century. Only a tiny proportion of the remaining forests are protected in national parks and reserves.

D. nigra is highly prized for its valuable timber, which has a distinctive appearance, texture, and fragrance. The wood is used for decorative veneers, high quality furniture, musical instruments, and craft products. It has been traded internationally for at least 300 years. No plantations have been developed to supply the market. In recent years, with most natural stands exhausted, timber cruisers (*madereiros*) have searched large areas to find any remaining stands of Brazilian rosewood which they can cut and sell for high prices. The timber is used within Brazil, mainly to produce goods for export.

The export of logs of *D. nigra* has been banned for 30 years. The species was added to Appendix I of CITES in 1992, which means that no international trade in timber taken from the wild is allowed. Exploitation of Brazil's Atlantic Coastal Forest, in general, is now forbidden by national law but, because of its high value, illegal felling of *D. nigra* continues to be a threat.

Small purple-pea

Swainsona recta

Family . . . . Fabaceae
Range . . . . Australia

Description and Biology

This perennial herb can grow to a height of 14 in (35 cm). It has feather-like leaves measuring 1.2-3.5 in (3-9 cm) formed by 5-13 narrow leaflets. Approximately 10-20 small, round, purple flowers bloom on each flower stem from September through December.

Habitat and Current Distribution

The species is restricted to six small local sites in southeastern New South Wales. The largest population, estimated at approximately 800 plants, is found along a railroad easement between Queanbeyan and Williamsdale. Its primary habitat is open woodland or forest with a grassy understory.

History and Conservation Measures

The small purple-pea once had a much wider distribution in New South Wales and northeastern Victoria, but it is no longer found in Victoria and survives only in remnant populations in New South Wales. Most of its former habitat has been cleared for agricultural development and to provide pasture for domestic livestock.

The species has been cultivated, but efforts should be made to preserve it in the wild. One obstacle to doing so is a lack of knowledge about appropriate fire regimes. Reproduction of the plant seems to be negatively affected by a lack of burning, leaving the seeds in dormancy. Research on the nature of this relationship might allow the formulation of a conservation plan for the remaining wild populations.

Old father live-forever

Pelargonium cotyledonis

Family	Geraniaceae
Status	Endangered, IUCN
Range	St. Helena (South Atlantic Ocean)

Description and Biology

For most of the year this perennial herb has a thick and contorted, leafless, woody brown stem that is approximately 1.2-6 in (3-15 cm) wide and up to 12 in (30 cm) high. In May or June the plant produces a loose rosette of wrinkled, more or less circular leaves on 3-in (8-cm) long stalks. Leaf blades are minutely hairy on top, but have paler undersides covered with dense, matted, woolly hairs; the stalk is attached toward the middle of the underside. In the center of the leaves is a slender, leafless flower stalk that supports loose flat clusters of flowers. Each flower has five white, egg-shaped petals that measure 0.5 in (14 mm) across. The fruit are long, narrow, and ribbed, up to 0.8 in (2 cm) long, and emerge from the small cup of the attached sepals.

Habitat and Current Distribution

This species is endemic to the island of St. Helena in the South Atlantic Ocean, where it is confined to the southwest region of the island; there have been no reports of this species in the interior of the island since the 1870s. Population size was estimated at 300 mature plants in 1993.

P. cotyledonis clings to more or less inaccessible, exposed rocky cliffs at altitudes of 500-1,000 ft (150-300 m), which overhang the sea on the windward side of the island. This area has a rainfall of only 6-15 in (15-38 cm) per year. The species' ability to survive for months without either soil or water has earned this plant its common name.

History and Conservation Measures

Although several thriving plants were found in 1970, the species has been very rare since the late 1800s. The species' decline has resulted from the grazing of goats, which were introduced to the island in the early 1500s, and from the spread of invasive weeds.

An effort was begun in the 1950s to remove feral goats from certain areas of the island; they have now been virtually eradicated. Many species, including *P. cotyledonis*, have begun to regenerate on the island since the removal of the goats. This species is well represented in cultivation, but it would still be advantageous to designate a small reserve in the southwest of the island as a safeguard for its long-term survival.

Monarto mintbush

Prostanthera eurybioides

Family	Labiatae (Lamiaceae)
Status	Endangered, IUCN
Range	Australia

Description and Biology

An aromatic perennial shrub, the Monarto mintbush is fairly small, reaching 3.3 ft (1 m) in height. Its hairy branches bear small leaves that grow close together. The double-lipped flowers are a purplish color, with rust-colored spots on the lower lip; they measure 0.2 in (5 mm) long and bloom between August and October.

Habitat and Current Distribution

This species is known from two widely separated areas in Australia. The largest population occurs in Mount Monster Conservation Park and numbers 100-150 plants. The Monarto mintbush also occurs in a number of small populations in southeastern South Australia, where approximately 16 populations of fewer than 20 plants each occur between Monarto and Murray Bridge.

Primary habitat of the species is sandy soil in mallee (*Eucalyptus*) shrub, heath, or woodland.

History and Conservation Measures

A number of threats have combined with a naturally restricted habitat to bring this species to its present endangered status. Habitat destruction for development, building of roads, and quarrying activity has historically been a threat to the Monarto mintbush. The species is considered a tasty treat by grazing cattle and rabbits. It is also vulnerable to competition from fast-growing weeds, especially broombrush. Collecting has further endangered the population. Attempts have been made to cultivate this species and to establish new colonies, but so far with little success.

Lactoris fernandeziana

Family . . . . Lactoridaceae
Status . . . . Endangered, IUCN
Range . . . . Juan Fernández Islands (Chile)

Description and Biology

This densely branched, rounded shrub usually grows no higher than 3.3 ft (1 m) high. It has one main stem and many branches bearing small, egg-shaped leaves which are 0.3-0.8 in (8-20 mm) long and wider at the tip than at the base; the leaves are covered with many small, clear dots. In the leaf axils are small clusters of two or three tiny flowers that are each around 0.1 in (3 mm) across and can be either unisexual or bisexual, with both occurring on the same plant; each flower has three green spreading sepals, no petals, six stamens in two whorls and/or three spreading carpels, which are nearly free from one another and each tipped by a white stigma. Each fruit contains four to six seeds.

Habitat and Current Distribution

This plant is endemic to Isla Robinson Crusoe (formerly Más a Tierra), Juan Fernández Islands, in the South Pacific Ocean. It is found in high altitude forest and has only been recorded from above 1,600 ft (500 m).

History and Conservation Measures

Probably never common, this plant numbered only about ten individuals in five localities in the mid-1950s; the numbers declined to only three in just around ten years. The reason for the decline was the introduction of exotic species to the island, both flora and fauna. Goats, sheep, cattle, horses, rabbits, and rats have been responsible for the destruction of many endemic plants. In addition, introduced plants have displaced many endemic plants; *Rubus* has been reported as an especially aggressive colonizer. In 1965 only three individuals of flowering size were known. According to a 1988 report, however, the species is showing signs of natural regeneration in five localities. In 1992 experts discovered hundreds of plants in remote mountain forests. Sucessful cultivation has been reported outside of Chile, notably in Salt Lake City.

As the only member of its family, this plant is of great scientific importance. It is present in the Parque Nacional Juan Fernández, but grazing animals are a threat, even within the park; they should be eliminated from the island, or at least excluded from selected areas. Introduced plants, also a threat, need to be removed from the island. Cultivation should be enhanced.

Caoba

Persea theobromifolia

Family	Lauraceae
Status	Endangered, IUCN
Range	Colombia; Ecuador

Description and Biology

Sometimes referred to as *aguacatillo* in Latin America, this large canopy tree is usually 100-130 ft (30-40 m) tall. Its paired leaves are elliptical, obtuse at the base and tip, measuring 4-8.7 in (10-22 cm) long and 1.6-4.7 in (4-12 cm) wide. The underside of the leaf is waxy and has minute scales. Flowers are gray-green and grow in clusters; the sepals are about 0.04 in (1 mm) long and the hairy petals measure 0.10 in (2.5 mm) in length. The fruit is large, fleshy, reddish brown, and egg-shaped. It measures 3.3-4 in (8.5-10 cm) long and 2.2 in (5.5 cm) wide, and has a single large seed that measures around 2 in (5 cm).

Habitat and Current Distribution

This species is known from the Río Palenque Biological Center, the only remaining patch of lowland wet forest along the western base of the Andes in Central Ecuador, Los Ríos Province. In Colombia, it has been found in a few places in the southern portion of the Pacific lowland forests, including the Gorgona Island National Park. The total known population in the late 1970s was probably no more than 12 reproducing individuals.

History and Conservation Measures

Although this species was a major source of timber for many years, it was not officially described until 1977. Between 1960 and 1970, its habitat was almost entirely converted to banana and oil palm plantations. Had the caoba not occurred in the Río Palenque Biological Station, the species may have become extinct without ever having been described. Yet in this protected reserve, the species is still vulnerable to illegal cutting. As a fast-growing tree with established commercial value, the caoba could be managed and perhaps redeveloped into a valuable timber product.

Ye'eb nut

Cordeauxia edulis

Family	Leguminosae
Status	Vulnerable, IUCN
Range	Ethiopia; Somalia

Description and Biology

The Ye'eb plant is also referred to as Ye-eb, Yi'ib, or Yi-ib. The edible nut from this plant is highly valued. The Ye'eb bush can grow as tall as 7 ft (2 m) and has many ascending, multi-branched stems. Two to ten pairs of leaflets form a leaf. The leaflets are about 1 in (2.5 cm) long, olive-green in color, and are dotted with numerous, scale-like red glands which stain the hands when touched. Flowers are bright yellow and about 1 in (2.5 cm) across; they grow in terminal clusters. Each seed-pod is a compressed ovoid, curved into a horn that holds one or two nuts.

Habitat and Current Distribution

This bush occurs in Ethiopia and Somalia; in the 1970s it was believed to be restricted to three areas in the arid region known as the Haud, near Bokh and Gerlogubi in the Ogaden Province of Ethiopia and near Adawilif in Somalia. There is no estimate of population available, but it is believed to be at low levels in the wild. It is in cultivation in Somalia and Kenya.

The species is found in open bush savanna on very poor red, sandy soil with an annual rainfall of less than 10 in (25 cm), growing in scattered, isolated clumps surrounded by open tufted grassland. The seeds can probably only develop successfully in exceptionally rainy years when the taproot reaches the water table.

History and Conservation Measures

The decline of this species can be associated with the general deterioration of the vegetation in the Horn of Africa, mainly due to overgrazing by livestock. Regeneration of this bush has been inhibited by human consumption of almost all the nuts and by goats eating any seedlings that may come up.

The Ye'eb nut has potential as a food crop; it contains starch, sugar, protein, and fat and is reported to have a pleasant, sweet flavor. It was once of considerable economic importance within its range and has great potential because the low rainfall in the area makes the cultivation of other crop legumes impossible. It is a deep rooted species which requires deep sand, will not tolerate water-logging, and does not require tending when planted. The bush has been cultivated in Somalia and Kenya for evaluation as a crop plant. Whether its potential for cultivation is realized, it should be established in a National Park or equivalent reserve to ensure the survival of the species.

Chinese manglietiastrum

Manglietiastrum sinicum

Family	Magnoliaceae
Status	Endangered, IUCN
Range	China

Description and Biology

This large evergreen tree grows to a height of 130 ft (40 m) with a diameter of 4 ft (1.2 m). Its bark is gray-white and smooth; annual shoots are green. Leaves are thick and leathery, usually egg-like in shape. They are dark green and measure 6-10 in (15-26 cm) long and 2-3.1 in (5-8 cm) wide. The fragrant whorled flowers are colorful: three of the outer whorls are oblong and dark red, with white insides, and measure 3.1-3.9 in (8-10 cm) long; the inner two whorls are white and narrower in shape. There are one to three red seeds in each follicle.

Manglietiastrum sinicum blossoms once every two or three years; flowers are few and the fecundity low. It blooms in late April, and fruits ripen from September to November.

Habitat and Current Distribution

This tree occurs in only two localities in Fadou, Xichou County, southeastern Yunnan: the Caoguo Mountain and the Nanchang Mountain. It inhabits the upper parts of mountain slopes of sunny, moist valleys at 4,260-5,080 ft (1,300-1,550 m). Total population consists of only seven mature individuals.

M. sinicum is distributed in the monsoon forest where the humidity is consistently high. The soil on which this species is found is derived from sandstone and shale. It is a tree of the upper canopy, with a broad crown, and a strong root system.

History and Conservation Measures

This is a very rare but valuable timber tree in southeastern Yunnan because of its tall, straight trunk and fine-textured wood that is rot- and insect-resistant. At the present time, the range of this species is being altered and destroyed due to forest clearance. Additionally, trees in general bear very few mature seeds because the gynoecia (female parts) of the very fragrant flowers are frequently eaten by insects. Even when a few mature seeds are produced, they rarely germinate because of the high oil content in the seed coat. The combination of these factors threaten the survival prospects of this species. A nature reserve encompassing *M. sinicum* habitat would help protect the species from further cutting and has been recommended. A cultivation program should also be considered.

Hau Kuahiwi

Hibiscadelphus giffardianus

Family	Malvaceae
Status	Endangered, IUCN
Range	Hawaii (U.S.A.)

Description and Biology

The hau kuahiwi is a tree that grows to approximately 23 ft (7 m) and has a multi-branched, rounded crown and smooth, whitish bark. Its leaves are somewhat heart-shaped, being notched at the base and pointed at the tip; they measure 3.5-6 in (9-15 cm) wide and have a thin covering of star-shaped hairs. Its flowers are 2-2.8 in (5-7 cm) long; at the base of each blossom is a ring of 5-7 stiff, spreading, almost thread-like bracts 0.8 in (2 cm) long. The calyx is cup-shaped, yellowish green, and irregularly lobed. Petals are tightly rolled on one another, forming a curving tube which is only open at the tip; inside, they are deep magenta and grayish green on the outside with a dense covering of star-shaped hairs. The capsule is oblong and yellowish-green, 1.6-2 in (4-5 cm) long, and contains kidney-shaped seeds covered by whitish-gray wool.

By failing to open completely, the corolla forms a tube which adapts the flower for pollination by birds, presumably by members of the endemic, nectar-feeding Drepanididae, the Hawaiian honey-creepers, whose bills fit the curvature of the corolla.

Habitat and Current Distribution

The species was originally found at an elevation of approximately 4,000 ft (1,200 m) on the outer, southeastern rim of a collapsed lava tube. The last known hau kuahiwi in the wild died in 1930, but the species has been re-introduced into its original locality in Hawaii's Volcanoes National Park. By 1968 there were 10 healthy, mature trees with a number of seedlings; by 1993, seven of the re-introduced plants survived—six flowering adults and one juvenile.

History and Conservation Measures

The reasons for the disappearance of the original population of this species in the wild are not fully known. It may have been heavily depleted by lava flow, surviving on one or more isolated patches of vegetation surrounded by lava. The decline of the Hawaiian honey-creepers, the likely pollinators of the hau kuahiwi, may also have had an impact on these plants. More recently, the remaining habitat has been depleted by cattle and by land clearance for development.

Since the species was re-introduced into Volcanoes National Park, its habitat is protected, and considerable success has been achieved in removing feral goats from the park. It is fortunate that the species had been brought into cultivation before its extinction in the wild; the re-introduction effort has thus far been successful.

Hibiscus insularis

Family . . . . Malvaceae
Status . . . . Endangered, IUCN
Range . . . . Philip Island (South Pacific Ocean)

Description and Biology

This is a rounded, densely branched shrub 3.3-8.2 ft (1-2.5 m) high, with 1.6-2.4 in (4-6 cm) leaves that are egg-shaped and scalloped. Juvenile leaves are deeply lobed, whereas those of adults are ovate and serrated. Flowers grow singly in the leaf axils, around 3.1 in (8 cm) across, each with three to six egg-shaped bracts around 0.4-0.5 in (10-13 mm) long; a five-lobed, bell-shaped, felted (matted with inter-twined hairs) calyx around 0.9 in (22 mm) long; and five oblong, pale lemon-yellow, partly down-curved petals that are around 2.4 in (6 cm) long and veined with purple. The whole flower becomes purplish with age.

Habitat and Current Distribution

The species is endemic to Philip Island in the South Pacific Ocean, an uninhabited precipitous island of volcanic origin about one square mile (2.6 sq km) in area, around 6 mi (10 km) south of Norfolk Island. The natural habitat on the island is likely to have been scrub on volcanic deposits. Only four bushes were known to survive in the 1960s; experts now believe that there are more on the island.

History and Conservation Measures

When first discovered by Captain Cook in 1774, Philip Island was believed to have carried scrub or dense forest in the valleys and at the lower altitudes. Shortly after the colonization of Norfolk Island in 1788, goats and pigs were placed on Philip Island to provide a reserve of meat. By the 1830s, vegetation was confined to the valleys and erosion had begun. As the vegetation disappeared, the pigs and goats died out, but rabbits were introduced at a later date, and remain a problem.

Necessary conservation measures include preservation and restoration of island habitat, and control of the rabbit population. The species is in cultivation on Norfolk Island, on the mainland of Australia, and in Hawaii.

Jumping-jack wattle

Acacia enterocarpa

Family . . . . Mimosaceae
Range . . . . Australia

Description and Biology

The jumping-jack wattle is a small, spreading shrub that grows to a height and width of around 3.3 ft (1 m). Stiff, sharp leaves—resembling needles—measure 0.8-1.8 in (2-4.5 cm) in length by 0.04 in (1 mm) in diameter. One or two round, orangish yellow flowers grow on short stems and bloom in August and September. The pod-shaped fruits measure 0.8-1.2 in (2-3 cm).

Habitat and Current Distribution

This species occurs at a low density in several locations in southern Australia. In western Victoria, for example, the population is estimated at 600 individuals; in South Australia, approximately 200 plants occur on the Eyre Peninsula, while less than 100 individuals occur on the Yorke Peninsula.

The jumping-jack wattle is apparently adapted to a variety of habitats, including open mallee (*Eucalyptus*) scrub and woodland. It requires fertile soil that is neutral to mildly alkaline.

History and Conservation Measures

This species is still found throughout its historic range, but its numbers have decreased and it is now extinct in some areas. Loss of habitat due to agricultural development is the primary cause of its decline; remaining areas of suitable habitat are vulnerable to grazing by domestic animals. Many of the remaining populations are along roadsides or railroads, where they could easily be destroyed by humans or animals.

Conservation efforts should be directed at preserving and managing the remaining areas of habitat; to this end, studies to determine appropriate management regimes should be initiated. The plant has now been cultivated, and this should safeguard the species against extinction and provide stock for eventual re-introduction into its former habitat. About 100 plants have been set in a small flora reserve in Victoria.

Flat-leaved wattle

Acacia pinguifolia

Family	Mimosaceae
Range	Australia

Description and Biology

This small- to medium-sized shrub grows to a height of 3.3-6.6 ft (1-2 m) and has arching branches that grow from its base. Stiff, fleshy leaves that end in a rigid point measure 0.4-1.4 in (1-3.5 cm) long by 0.08-0.12 in (2-3 mm) in diameter. Round, yellow flowers that bloom from July through October measure around 0.2 in (0.5 cm) in diameter. The pod-like fruits average 2-2.8 in (5-7 cm) long and 0.2 in (0.5 cm) wide.

Habitat and Current Distribution

The flat-leaved wattle is known from two locations in South Australia. A location on the southern end of Eyre Peninsula contains the largest population.

Several smaller populations, estimated at 5-50 plants each, occur near Finniss, southeast of Adelaide.

This species is associated with mallee (*Eucalyptus*) open shrub and grows on alkaline brown or white clay or on neutral gray sand.

History and Conservation Measures

Because much of its habitat has been cleared for agricultural development, flat-leaved wattle is now found primarily along the edges of roads and railway beds, where it suffers from competition with weeds. The most important conservation priority is identifying and marking existing populations so that they can be protected from further damage. Studies are necessary to determine appropriate conservation regimes and methods of regeneration.

Mogumber bell

Darwinia carnea

Family	Myrtaceae
Status	Endangered, IUCN
Range	Australia

Description and Biology

This shrub gets its common name from the area where it was first discovered and from its bell-shaped flowers. It grows to a height of approximately 13 ft (4 m), and its sharply pointed leaves measure 0.6 in (1.5 cm) long by 0.16 in (0.4 cm) wide. Clusters of 8-14 flowers bloom at the tips of its branches from October to December; the 1.2 in (3 cm) bracts have a green or pink coloration.

Habitat and Current Distribution

This species is found near Narrogin in a small population estimated at 25 plants in 1989, and in a larger population near Mogumber, where an esti-

mated 500 plants occur. Both populations grow on hilltops in poor, acidic soil.

History and Conservation Measures

After a population of this plant near Mogumber was eliminated by grazing animals, the species was known to exist only in the small population near Narrogin. The Narrogin population reached a low of approximately six plants in 1978; after it was fenced and protected from animals, it had a limited recovery. The larger population near Mogumber was discovered in 1990, and although it is on private property, it has been fenced by the landowner. Both of these surviving populations require continued and increased protection, and searches should be initiated to determine whether other populations exist.

Morrisby's gum

Eucalyptus morrisbyi

Family . . . . Myrtaceae
Range . . . . Australia

Description and Biology

Morrisby's gum tree grows to around 50 ft (15 m) and has a bark color that varies from light brown or light gray to a pinkish gray. Leaves—measuring 2-4 in (5-10 cm) by 0.5-0.9 in (1.2-2.3 cm)—are circular in shape but become lance-shaped as they mature. Between January and April, white flowers bloom in clusters of three. Its white, woody fruits have a cylindrical shape and a waxy coating.

Habitat and Current Distribution

Only four stands of Morrisby's gum survive, all of them in southern Tasmania. The largest population, at Calverts Hill, is estimated to contain approximately 2,000 trees; another in the East Risdon Nature Reserve has fewer than 20 trees; the remaining stands are small, remnant populations near roads. Primary habitat is sandy soil in open woodland at sea level.

History and Conservation Measures

Once widespread and plentiful, this species has been reduced to its present remnant status by habitat clearance, primarily for agricultural development. Protection of the remaining populations is essential. The majority of these trees are on private land where they could easily be removed for development or destroyed by grazing cattle. Re-introduction attempts have been initiated and more planting should be encouraged.

Mongarlowe mallee

Eucalyptus recurva

Family . . . . Myrtaceae
Range . . . . Australia

Description and Biology

Australia's rarest species of *Eucalyptus*, this shrub reaches a height of around 5.6 ft (1.7 m). Its leaves measure only 1.1 in (2.8 cm) long by 0.3 in (0.7 cm) wide, have downward-curved tips, and are covered with oil glands. White flowers bloom in January in clusters of three; and small, woody fruits measure 0.12 in by 0.20 in (3 mm by 5 mm).

Habitat and Current Distribution

This species is presently known from only two localities near Mongarlowe in New South Wales. At the first of these, five separate plants occur, all of which are thought to be derived from a single ancestor since their genetic composition is similar. A single plant—discovered in 1990—survives at the second location. Both specimens occur in clay soil in low, open, wooded areas.

History and Conservation Measures

The Mongarlowe mallee is indeed a very rare plant. Neither of the remaining plants are on private property, so it is essential that they are protected from collecting and human traffic in the area. Because of the extremely small remaining population, very little genetic variation has been preserved, which makes survival of the species in the wild uncertain. As the shrub has been very difficult to cultivate, research is necessary to facilitate cultivation, with the long-term goal of supplementing the wild population with plants grown under controlled conditions.

Syzygium travancoricum

Family	Myrtaceae
Status	Endangered, IUCN
Range	India

Description and Biology

This medium-sized tree has four angular branches bearing leaves that are egg-shaped, broader at the base and broadly pointed at the tip, and measure 3.1-4.7 long and 2-2.4 in (8-12 by 5-6 cm) wide. Leaves are long-stalked, and the flowers small and white. The species flowers in March; nothing else is known about its reproductive biology.

Habitat and Current Distribution

Restricted to the southern region of Kerala, India, this species is found in swampy wetland areas at an elevation of just over 200 ft (65 m). The four known surviving individuals all occur in a sacred grove of Aickad, Quilon District.

History and Conservation Measures

First described in 1918, this species was twice collected from the sacred groves of Kodumon and was then considered extinct until it was rediscovered in the sacred grove of Aickad. In addition to having religious significance, its bark has also been used in herbal medicine.

The cause of near extinction of this tree has been the draining of its wetland habitat for rice cultivation. While surviving trees are well protected, other steps must be taken for the conservation of the species. Studies of reproductive biology and ecology should be initiated, as well as studies of *in vitro* multiplication. Seedlings should be transplanted to similar habitats and the species should be brought into cultivation. Finally, former habitat should be rehabilitated and other likely swamps or wetlands preserved from conversion into rice paddies.

Basket of the Devil

Nepenthes khasiana

Family	Nepenthaceae
Status	Vulnerable, IUCN
	Appendix II, CITES
Range	India

Description and Biology

A climbing evergreen undershrub, this carnivorous plant can reach up to 13 ft (4 m). Stalkless leaves end in a pitcher measuring 6.3 in (16 cm) long and 1.2-3.9 in (3-10 cm) wide. The plants are dioecious (having male and female organs on different plants) and produce 10-inch (25-cm) floral clusters of copious greenish or brown flowers. Female flowers develop into capsular fruit. The seeds are numerous and spindle-shaped with tailed ends. Flowering and fruiting occur from June to October.

Habitat and Current Distribution

Endemic to Khasi, Jaintia, and Garo Hills of Meghalaya, India, the species grows on open and shady grassy slopes, particularly along the watercourses of streams and springs. Population figures are unavailable, but the species is declining.

History and Conservation Measures

First described in 1886 from Khasi and Jaintia Hills, this species is the most elegant and one of the largest insectivorous plants. It has experienced a serious reduction in range, in the number of surviving populations, and in its population size largely because of loss of forest cover, together with soil erosion and grazing.

In addition to being considered a botanical curiosity, the species is used for medicinal purposes. The fluid in the unopened pitcher is used by the local people as eye drops, to treat diabetes, or for stomach, urinary, and gynecological problems; the pitcher with its contents is also made into a paste to be applied to the affected parts of leprosy patients.

Habitat areas in Jarain and Baghmara are protected, and the species is grown in botanic gardens throughout the world. It has been successfully multiplied *in vitro*, and plants derived from tissue culture have been reintroduced into native habitat. Conservation efforts should include ecological studies of the habitat and rehabilitation of the habitat for successful reintroductions.

Giant Malaysian pitcher plant

Nepenthes rajah

Family	Nepenthaceae
Status	Vulnerable, IUCN
	Appendix I, CITES
Range	Sabah (Malaysia)

Description and Biology

N. rajah is a dioecious (male and female reproductive organs are on different plants), perennial, terrestrial, insectivorous herb with stout, cylindrical stems ranging from 4.9-8.2 ft (1.5-2.5 m) in length. The leaves are lanceolate (lance-shaped) to oblong in shape, measuring 3.3 ft (1 m) long and 7.5 in (19 cm) wide. The tendrils, which are extensions of leaf midribs, are uncoiled and straight (unlike other *Nepenthes* species) and can reach up to 21.3 in (54 cm) long in the wild. This species is best known for its enormous pitchers which are borne on stout tendrils at the ends of leaves. Pitchers can grow up to 13.8 in (35 cm) long and 7 in (18 cm) wide with two wings, measuring 0.2-0.6 in (6-15 mm) across, running along the front of the pitchers. The slanted mouth has a broad slippery collar with an incurved comb-like margin. The large oval lid, domelike in appearance, is scarlet to purple on the outside and yellow-green on the inside.

Habitat and Current Distribution

The giant Malaysian pitcher plant is a non-climbing highland species, colonizing montane rain forest between 5,410 and 8,690 ft (1,650-2,650 m). It often grows in open, sunny, wet places or among *Leptospermum* and *Dacrydium* scrub on serpentine soils. These plants are also known to inhabit mossy forest and damp places in the vicinity of waterfalls. Seedlings favor disturbed semi-bare ground.

N. rajah is restricted to four known localities within the Kinabalu National Park on the island of Borneo—Marai Parai Plateau, east Mesilau Creek, the upper Kolopsis River, and the eastern slope of Mt. Tambuyukon. It is estimated that several thousand plants remain at these four localities.

History and Conservation Measures

Threats to these populations include continued illegal collection for trade and habitat disturbance and destruction, including that from casual visitors and tourists. The smaller populations (such as the one at Mesilau Creek) could easily be eradicated from over-collection. The giant Malaysian pitcher plant is in high demand by plant collectors; pressure on the remaining populations is increased by want-ad listings in various national and international carnivorous plant hobbyist newsletters.

All fauna and flora within Kinabalu National Park are protected by Sabah Parks laws. As such, special permits are required to collect this species: legal collection of seeds and plants has been permitted in the past for scientific research purposes. However, due to the comparatively easy access to these locations and the difficulty of patrolling these areas, individuals and commercial collectors have regularly smuggled plants out of Kinabalu National Park.

Since these laws have offered little protection at the international level, *N. rajah* was listed in Appendix I of CITES (Convention on International Trade in Endangered Species of Wild Fauna and Flora) in 1981. Only six recorded CITES transactions were reported between 1981 and 1988 (two for scientific purposes and four for artificial propagation material for commercial use).

There appears to be a definite specialist market for this rare species with large sums of money being offered for individual plants. Prices can vary from $50 for artificially propagated plants to $1,000 for a wild-collected plant. However, the comparative absence of *N. rajah* in trade as opposed to other *Nepenthes* species appears to be due to propagation difficulties. Among these are the challenge of replicating its natural growing conditions, short seed viability, and the length of time required for plants to reach saleable size.

Olea laperrinei

Family . . . . Oleaceae
Status . . . . Vulnerable, IUCN
Range . . . . Algeria; Morocco(?); Niger; Sudan

Description and Biology

This small tree grows to a height of approximately 40 ft (12 m) and a diameter of more than 6.6 ft (2 m), and is closely related to the cultivated olive tree. Its long, narrow leaves are lance-shaped, having a slender point at the apex; they are silvery on the underside and measure 1.2-2.4 in (3-6 cm) long and 0.16-0.23 in (4-6 mm) wide. Very small flowers grow in loose clusters in the leaf axils. The calyx is short and four-lobed and the corolla is white, with four egg-shaped lobes that are 0.1 in (3 mm) long. Its fruit is dark purple and elliptical, tapering at the tip and resembling a very small olive.

Habitat and Current Distribution

This species is found in Algeria, Niger, Sudan, and possibly Morocco. The trees in Algeria and Niger are apparently not regenerating. The largest surviving population is in Sudan, but current population figures are unavailable.

Olea laperrinei is generally found at altitudes of 3,300-9,900 ft (1,000-3,000 m) on stony ground under cliffs and near water. In Sudan, the species is found throughout the upper slopes of a small hill called Jebel Gurgei, but not in the open grassland on the top of the hill; it is also thinly scattered over the montane grassland on Jebel Marra at altitudes of 7,000-9,700 ft (2,150-2,950 m).

History and Conservation Measures

This species has not thrived in the Central Saharan localities in Algeria and Niger for quite some time. In the 1930s it was reported that young branches of the trees were regularly cut for cattle fodder, and the extent of grazing, browsing, and cutting probably increased greatly during the Sahel drought of the early 1970s. In the Sudanese localities, however, the species has reportedly been more stable, with an estimated 1,000 trees in one population on Jebel Marra in the mid-1950s, and a small but abundant population on Jebel Gurgei.

It has been suggested that some areas on Jebel Marra be designated as nature reserves. The close relationship of this species to the cultivated olive tree is important, because near-relatives of crop plants are often used in efforts to make those crop plants more resistant to disease and drought.

Indotristicha tirunelveliana

Family	Podostemaceae
Status	Endangered, IUCN
Range	India

Description and Biology

These minute, submerged aquatic plants are attached to rocks by horizontal stems 2-10 in (5-25 cm) long. The stems produce densely crowded leafy shoots that bear stalkless, egg- to lance-shaped leaves measuring 0.06 by 0.03 in (1.5 by 0.8 mm); solitary flowers are borne on the leafy shoots. The fruit is an ellipsoid capsule and contains numerous minute seeds.

The species reproduces sexually and probably by vegetative means, but its reproductive biology—particularly pollination mechanisms—and its ecology are not known.

Habitat and Current Distribution

Endemic to the southern portion of Western Ghats (Tirunelveli Hills) in Tamil Nadu, India, at an elevation of 2,800 ft (850 m), this species is found on submerged rocks in turbulent streams and waterfalls. Population estimates are unavailable.

History and Conservation Measures

Populations of this species are dwindling because of habitat loss due to the construction of dams. Conservation of this plant and of other members of its family is especially problematic because the habitat cannot be created and maintained in botanic gardens, and the number of locations having this habitat is extremely low. In addition, there are difficulties in protecting the original habitat because of natural factors such as landslides in the upstream and catchment areas.

Conservation measures should include studies on the reproductive biology and ecology of the species; exploration of the area to locate safe habitats which have not been disturbed; incorporation of present habitat of this species and other members of its family into reserves; and reintroduction of *in vitro* grown plants.

Brown's banksia

Banksia brownii

Family . . . . Proteaceae
Range . . . . Australia

Description and Biology

This shrub can reach up to 20 ft (6 m) in height. Soft, green leaves with white undersides measure 4.7 in (12 cm) long by 0.3 in (0.8 cm) wide. Paired flowers, each measuring 4-8 in (10-20 cm) long and 3.5 in (9 cm) wide, are red to reddish-brown in color and bloom in January and again between April and August. Dead flowers remain on the tree, sheltering long, furry fruit.

Habitat and Current Distribution

Only two remaining populations of this species have been identified, both in southern Western Aus-tralia. In the northern or Stirling Ranges population, the habitat is sandy soil in open mallee (*Eucalyptus*) heath; the more southern population is found north-east of Albany, where it occurs on gravel or sand in woodlands or heath.

History and Conservation Measures

The endangered status of this species is the result of a widespread dieback disease associated with a fungus that causes root rot. Research has been initiated to determine the cause of the disease and to discover some way to control or eliminate it; without a remedy to the disease, the species will most likely become extinct in the wild.

Leucadendron verticillatum

Family	Proteaceae
Status	Endangered, IUCN
Range	South Africa

Description and Biology

Erect and slender, this dioecious shrub develops from a single stem and grows up to 6.6 ft (2 m) tall. Its silvery leaves are lance-shaped, narrowing at the base and measuring up to 1 in (2.54 cm) long and 0.2 in (4.5 mm) wide; leaves of male plants are smaller. Flower heads are small and borne among the leaves at the ends of the branches. Male flower heads are spherical, 0.3 in (7 mm) long and 0.4 in (11 mm) in diameter; they have about six linear basal bracts 0.10-0.16 in (3-4 mm) long and very small floral bracts. Female flower heads are similar but smaller, around 0.3 in (8 mm) across; they have up to 12 florets towards the apex, with about 10 basal bracts approximately 0.2 in (5 mm) long.

Flowering occurs in September and October, and pollination is apparently achieved by insects. Fruits ripen in February, and the relatively few nut-like seeds that are produced soon fall to the ground. Regeneration from seed is most successful if the area is burnt shortly after seed release (in late summer or early autumn). Spring fires, when seeds have not yet formed, can be disastrous; if hot enough, many of the plants could be killed.

Habitat and Current Distribution

This South African endemic was once fairly widespread in an area of approximately 116 sq mi (300 sq km) situated between Cape Town and Paarl in the southwestern Cape Province. Due to habitat destruction caused by agricultural activities and urbanization, this species has been reduced to eight relict populations in an 11 sq mi (30 sq km) area. The species grows on fairly level sandy soils with a clay subsoil, in an area which is seasonally wet in winter. Plants occur at an altitude of 300 ft (100 m), and the associated vegetation is Lowland Fynbos dominated by species of Restionaceae and other vegetation characterized by thick, hard foliage on better-drained areas.

History and Conservation Measures

The only population of *L. verticillatum* to receive conservation management is that on the Eensaamheid Nature Reserve, which is a Provincial Nature Reserve situated on privately owned land. The land was initially set aside as a reserve for the endangered geometric tortoise (*Psammobates geometricus*). It was subsequently extended to include the *L. verticillatum* population, and much of the invasive thickets of the alien *Acacia saligna* has been cleared. In 1986 this population numbered over 200 plants; however, by June 1990 there were less than 100 widely scattered plants. The population nevertheless appears to be vigorous with an equal number of young and old plants.

The remaining populations—with the exception of those at Muldersvlei and Joostenbergkloof—are too small, too seriously invaded by alien plants, or threatened by plowing and industrial development to warrant conservation action. A new population of over 100 plants was discovered in 1990 on Muldersvlei farm which is owned by the Salvation Army. This population needs to be investigated further.

The population at Joostenbergkloof (a privately owned farm) is the most important as it is the largest and probably most viable population of this species. In 1990, over 1,000 plants were counted, of which about 90 percent were seedlings concentrated in a 5,000 sq m (12,944 sq km) area. The site is now being invaded by *Pinus* and *Acacia* species, and an *Acacia* thicket adjoins the area. Urgent attention needs to be given to clearing these alien plants. It is also essential to gain the cooperation of the farm's owner to prevent plowing of the site and to ensure protection of this species. Establishment of the area as a South African Natural Heritage Site is being investigated.

Giant rafflesia

Rafflesia arnoldii

Family	Rafflesiaceae
Status	Vulnerable, possibly Endangered, IUCN
Range	Sumatra (Indonesia)

Description and Biology

The most specialized of all parasitic plants, the striking giant rafflesia produces the largest flower in the world. Having no stem, leaves, or roots, this plant consists of colorless, thread-like structures that exist within the stem and larger roots of its host, a climbing vine of the genus *Tetrastigma*. Flower buds apparently develop within these threads before bursting through the bark of the host, which is stimulated to produce a cup-like swelling on which the flower is borne, usually at ground level, but rarely up to 6.6 ft (2 m) above the ground. About 19-21 months elapse before the buds open as flowers. Surrounded at its base by scales, the open flower measures up to 3.3 ft (1 m) or more in diameter. They are basin-shaped and surrounded by five rounded, overlapping, extremely fleshy perianth lobes, which are dull liver-brown with paler wart-like spots; each lobe has a large diaphragm (dividing membrane or partition) near its base on the inside. The flowers usually bloom for one week, then wither.

Very little is known about the giant rafflesia's biology; even its life cycle has still not been studied in detail. It is apparently dioecious (having male and female organs on different plants). The flowers smell of rotten meat and attract large numbers of flies, which are believed to aid in pollination. Few flowers seem to develop into fruits. The seeds are very small, and their method of transportation to and infestation of other host plants is unknown. Some scientists have suggested that the seed may be distributed by such animals as rats, tree shrews, pigs, and squirrels, which may tread on the fruits and carry away the seeds while foraging for other food. Scientists further postulate that the seed may only be able to penetrate a host when its bark has been damaged, for example, by the trampling of large mammals such as the elephant, tapir, and rhinoceros.

Habitat and Current Distribution

The exact distribution of this species, which is only found in Sumatra, Indonesia, is uncertain, but it is known to occur in several reserves in Bengkulu and West Sumatra. Population estimates are unavailable.

The giant rafflesia is found on *Tetrastigma* vines in tropical forest dominated by the tall hardwoods of the family Dipterocarpaceae on moist valley bottoms or on steep but moist slopes, generally between 1,600-3,300 ft (500-1,000 m). Some botanists suspect that the host vines prefer old clearings such as may be formed by fallen trees or landslides.

History and Conservation Measures

The giant rafflesia is threatened by over-collection as well as by the destruction and disturbance of its rain forest habitat. It is often taken for medicine or as a novelty and has been overcollected by field botanists because of its unusual biology. That it is dependent upon a particular host genus is especially hazardous; changes in the host vine's biology or distribution or the extinction of one of the main agents of seed dispersal such as the Sumatran rhinoc-

eros could significantly affect the giant rafflesia, which is believed to be declining in several areas and extinct in one of the nature reserves created for it.

Before specific conservation measures can be taken, more detailed field studies are needed so as to better understand the giant rafflesia's morphology and its relationship with its host. Studies of this kind would also be of value in evaluating how best to integrate the protection of this and related species into wide-reaching programs of ecosystem conservation.

Robbins' cinquefoil

Potentilla robbinsiana

Family	Rosaceae
Status	Endangered, IUCN
	Endangered, USFWS
Range	New Hampshire, Vermont (U.S.A.)

Description and Biology

A member of the rose family, this almost stemless perennial herb has a deep taproot and a dense rosette. The rosette measures 0.7-1.2 in (18-30 mm) and is made up of compound leaves with leaflets arranged in three parts; the new leaves develop from mid-May to late August. The three-part leaves are deeply toothed and covered with dense, long hairs. Yellow flowers bloom primarily in June, but scattered blooms are sometimes found as late as October; the flower stems are slender and only 0.4-1.4 in (1-3.5 cm) long. The average plant produces five or six flowers, but as many as 50 flowers have been observed on very large plants.

Seeds are dispersed from the seed head on dry, windy days but usually travel no further than 2-2.4 in (5-6 cm) from the adult plant. Seeds are apparently produced asexually and the species requires self-pollination for fruit production.

Habitat and Current Distribution

The largest natural population of Robbins' cinquefoil occurs on the Monroe Flats, southwest of Mt. Washington in the White Mountains of New Hampshire; it is estimated to number approximately 1,550 flowering individuals. The other natural population is located around 20 mi (32 km) southwest of the Monroe Flats, in the Franconia Range; these plants, thought to be a remnant population established from seeds of a larger, extirpated population, numbered three flowering and 12 non-flowering individuals in 1990.

This species is found in a harsh, barren alpine zone at an elevation of 5,000 ft (1,550 m), where it occurs in sandy or rocky soil, usually with a southern exposure.

History and Conservation Measures

Because this species apparently has a naturally restricted distribution and population size, human disturbance within its limited habitat has had a devastating effect. Several of the original populations have been extirpated as a result of specimen collecting and trampling by hikers, and the large remaining colony occurs near a shelter for hikers.

In addition to diverting foot trails from habitat areas, conservation efforts have included campaigns to educate hikers about the species. Monitoring of the main population is ongoing, and two additional colonies have been established. The Monroe Flats area has been designated a critical habitat and will be the focus of reintroduction efforts.

Alectryon ramiflorus

Family . . . . Sapindaceae
Range . . . . Australia

Description and Biology

This medium-sized tree, with variously shaped leaves, has two to nine leaflets on a branch. Each leaflet is divided, feather-shaped, and 0.8-2.8 in (2-7 cm) long. In the spring, clusters of small, light-colored flowers grow on mature branches. The fruit are green and measure 0.20-0.23 in by 0.35 in (5-6 mm by 9 mm); seeds are brown.

Habitat and Current Distribution

The species occurs in the rain forests of the Childers District, coastal southern Queensland. Estimates of population size are unavailable.

History and Conservation Measures

The primary reason for the endangered status of this species has been the clearance of its rain forest habitat. At least one population, estimated at around 20 plants, occurs in a state forest, but other remaining habitat is subject to clearance and destruction. The species has been cultivated, but conservation efforts should be directed at protecting the known population in the state forest. Surveys should be conducted to look for other possible populations.

Common otophora

Otophora unicularis

Family	Sapindaceae
Status	Presumably Extinct, IUCN
Range	China

Description and Biology

This evergreen can grow to a height of just under 10 ft (3 m). Leaves are 8.7-11.8 in (22-30 cm) long and feather-like, with 15-29 leaflets—measuring around 0.6 in (1.5 cm) long—arranged along a common axis. A leaflet is also present at the tip. Fruits are berry-like and red when mature; they average 0.4-0.5 in (10-12 mm) long, are smooth and hairless, and have one seed.

Habitat and Current Distribution

Endemic to Hainan Province, this species has been found only on sands along seashores of Foluo in Ledong County, southwestern Hainan, where the climate is extremely hot and dry. Foluo is on a sandy beach, with the sandy soil containing a large amount of salt and very little organic matter; the main vegetation cover is thorny bush. The otophora plant is now presumed to be extinct or near extinction.

History and Conservation Measures

Because this evergreen has not been seen in Foluo since it was first discovered there in 1935, it is thought to be extinct. Searches of the locality and its vicinity should be conducted to determine whether there are any remaining populations. As an extremely drought-resistant species that tolerates poor soil, and as one of the few tropical tree species that grows on the sandy soil along rivers in Hainan, it would be an ideal plant for afforestation throughout its range. If the species is rediscovered, efforts should be made to protect and cultivate the plant.

Green pitcher plant

Sarracenia oreophila

Family	Sarraceniaceae
Status	Endangered, USFWS
	Appendix I, CITES
Range	Alabama, Georgia (U.S.A.)

Description and Biology

An insectivorous perennial, the green pitcher plant traps insects with bristles located inside its pitcher-shaped leaves. These leaves are green or yellow-green in color, are wider at the top than at the bottom, and reach a height of 7.9-29.5 in (20-75 cm). Leaves exposed to bright sunlight may develop maroon veins and a purple blotch at the mouth of the pitcher. The leaves and flower buds appear in early April, and the leaves mature with the yellow flowers during late April and May. By late summer, the pitcher-shaped leaves have withered and are replaced by flat leaves that persist until the next season.

Habitat and Current Distribution

The green pitcher plant is found in Alabama and Georgia in three geological provinces: the Cumberland Plateau, the Blue Ridge, and the Ridge and Valley. The Cumberland Plateau region in Alabama supports most of the remaining populations. The most recent population data available indicates that about 26 colonies of *Sarracenia oreophila* still exist in the wild; the size of these individual populations varies from a single plant to more than 1,000 plants.

This species is found in a variety of habitats. It requires highly acidic soils and is dependent on wetlands for part of its growing season. The habitats for this species include seepage bogs with high levels

Green pitcher plant.

of organic matter; woodland sites that are poorly drained in winter, but dry in summer; sloping stream banks; and sandy shoals.

History and Conservation Measures

Although it appears never to have been common, the green pitcher plant was formerly found over a wider range than it presently inhabits. In addition to the provinces noted above, the species was formerly also found in the Piedmont and the Coastal Plain. Its range also extended into the state of Tennessee.

Much of the decline of this species can be tied to the loss of the wetlands habitat it requires during part of the growing season. Long-term survival and recovery of the species can only be assured if wetlands are preserved and an adequate water table is maintained. Pitcher plant habitat is also damaged by herbicide and fertilizer run-off from agricultural lands. *S. oreophila* is vulnerable to natural succession, and some colonies may require intensive management (including burning or cutting) to maintain suitable habitat. Collectors also have had a negative impact on green pitcher plant populations, and some sites may require fencing. To further promote recovery of the species, nursery-raised plants may be reintroduced into suitable secure habitat and wild plants might also be transplanted to new colonies.

Alabama canebrake
pitcher-plant

Sarracenia rubra alabamensis

Family	Sarraceniaceae
Status	Vulnerable, IUCN
	Endangered, USFWS
	Appendix I, CITES
Range	Alabama (U.S.A.)

Description and Biology

This carnivorous, perennial plant gets its common name from its tubular-shaped leaves. In the spring, the leaves are curved and 6.7-19.7 in (17-50 cm) long, gradually tapering from a narrow base to a relatively broad mouth 0.28-1.2 in (0.7-3 cm) wide. The leaves are clear to yellow-green and maroon on the inside. In the summer, the leaves are larger and erect, up to 28.8 in (72 cm) high and covered with short, soft hairs. The conspicuously curved hoods are large, and the rim of the pitcher is bright yellow-green. The ripe fruit forms a small capsule, 0.23-0.39 in (6-10 mm) wide. Flowering occurs from late April to early June.

This species attracts insects to the mouth of the pitcher by secreting nectar. Once the prey lands on the plant and proceeds past the mouth, downward-pointing hairs below the lip prevent the escape of the prey, which eventually slides down the smooth, deep throat of the pitcher where it drowns and is eventually digested by special enzymes and bacteria contained at the base of the pitcher.

Habitat and Current Distribution

This subspecies is restricted to central Alabama, U.S.A., where it occurs along the Fall Line Sand Hills of Elmore, Chilton, and Autauga counties.

Four populations have 70-300 plants; two have fewer than 50 plants; and a number of smaller populations do not exceed 20 plants.

The pitcher-plant occurs in waterlogged soils. It occurs in somewhat sandy and gravelly bogs, usually on sloping ground, or in damp peaty or mucky soil around small spring-heads and tiny brooks. Highly acidic sands or clays are usually preferred. Although tolerant of some shade, it requires a habitat kept open by the fires that normally check the growth of grass, shrubs, and trees in the area or, alternatively, by moderate levels of grazing.

History and Conservation Measures

Regarded as a botanical curiosity, the canebrake pitcher-plant has been collected for hobby trading or for commercial sale. In addition to threats posed by collectors, it is declining because of the loss of wetland habitat. Drainage for road building, agricultural development, and pasture land has claimed large areas of former habitat. Gravel mining and herbicide use along railroads have also contributed to the species' decline, as have the introduction of shade plants such as honeysuckle and the suppression of fire which has allowed the growth of other shade plants.

The U. S. Fish and Wildlife Service has recommended several conservation measures for this species: protect existing populations and habitat; survey for additional populations; evaluate habitat needs and implement appropriate management; conduct further studies of the species' biology; preserve genetic stock; establish new populations and/or enhance existing sites; and develop a public awareness program.

Linaria hellenica

Family	Scrophulariaceae
Status	Endangered, IUCN
Range	Greece

Description and Biology

This annual plant has slender, branched stems that can be erect or arching and which may reach up to 24 in (60 cm) high. Leaves can be long and narrow or long and slightly broader; they are succulent, obtuse, and measure 0.16-1.8 in (4-45 mm) by 0.04-0.10 in (1-2.5 mm). From 5-20 flowers bloom along an erect stalk up to 0.6 in (15 mm) long. The corolla tube is cylindrical, and the corolla itself yellow, with a two-lobed upper lip and a three-lobed lower lip. The capsule is spherical or rounded; seeds are kidney-shaped, wrinkled, and black.

Habitat and Current Distribution

Occurring in Greece, by the late 1970s this species was confined to a few maritime sites within an area of less than 8 sq mi (20 sq km). It was found in four localities, with only two to six individuals in three of these and approximately 100 plants in the fourth.

Known habitat of this species includes beaches and other sandy areas near the sea. *Linaria hellenica* is poorly competitive with other species and is more or less restricted to flat, open sites, and never occurs on sand dunes.

History and Conservation Measures

Originally discovered in 1955, this species has been recorded from six localities on the Maléa Peninsula at the southeastern tip of the Pelopónnisos, occurring in the Gulf of Neápolis and on the neighboring island of Elafónisos. It has probably always been rare because of its very restricted coastal habitat, but it has become endangered through loss of habitat as development spread. It occurs in a few cultivated areas, but even there it is threatened by agricultural activity, especially by efforts to control agricultural weeds.

Because the suitable habitat of this species is very rare, steps should be taken to protect certain sandy coastal areas where the species occurs. Consideration could be given to prohibiting its collection or its eradication as a weed. In cultivation, its numbers should be greatly increased and the plant more widely distributed to botanic gardens, and seed deposited in a seed bank.

Hainan sonneratia

Sonneratia hainanensis

Family . . . . Sonneratiaceae
Status . . . . Endangered, IUCN
Range . . . . China

Description and Biology

This evergreen tree grows to a height of around 13-26 ft (4-8 m) and may develop a spreading crown. Shoots are stout, and its thick leaves have a circular to egg-like shape and measure 2.6-3.1 in (6.5-8 cm) long and 2-2.4 in (5-6 cm) wide; they grow in pairs along opposite sides of the stem. Flowers have white petals and usually grow in bunches of three but can also be solitary. Seeds are numerous and minute. The tree flowers and fruits from February to November.

Habitat and Current Distribution

There are only five known specimens of this species, all confined to a mangrove forest on the coast of Wenchang County, Hainan Province. The locality is 260-330 ft (80-100 m) away from the low tide line and, when the tide is out, it is 8-12 in (20-30 cm) above water level. The species is a component of the mangrove forest, growing on tidal flats along the coast, where the ground is covered with salt water for some time each day. It is well adapted to the salty soil and periodic drought and immersion in salt water: the shiny surfaces of the leaves reflect the intense sunlight, and the numerous aerating roots arising from the arching prop roots provide the plant with oxygen.

History and Conservation Measures

This rare tree is commercially valued for its wood and used to make furniture and souvenir items; the palm-shaped roots can be used as corks after being treated. Due to the minute size of the seeds, which are easily washed away by sea water, this tree suffers from poor natural regeneration. The protection of the remaining specimens is essential, and cultivation programs should be initiated to ensure against possible extinction in the wild.

Freziera forerorum

Family	Theaceae
Status	Endangered, IUCN
Range	Colombia; Panama

Description and Biology

This slender tree has strongly angled branches and grows to approximately 26 ft (8 m) in height. Its leaves are stalkless and leathery, tapering and asymmetrical at the base, and broad and pointed at the tip; they measure 3-7 in (8-18 cm) long and 0.7-2 in (1.8-5.2 cm) wide. Its flowers grow in clusters of one to three in the leaf axils or below the leaves. Immature fruit are small and more or less spherical, measuring 0.12-0.16 in (3-4 mm) across, with numerous tiny, kidney-shaped seeds.

Habitat and Current Distribution

The population of this species is confined to the summit of Pico Tacarcuna, the highest point of the Serrania del Darien, on the border of Panama and Colombia. In the late 1970s, there were only three surviving trees.

The summit where these trees survive has an elevation of approximately 6,200 ft (1,900 m); unlike similar species, *Freziera forerorum* does not occur at lower elevations. The summit is flat and covered by open montane thicket.

History and Conservation Measures

By the time this species was discovered in 1976, all of the trees on one side of the summit where it is found were dead or dying, and most of the surviving trees had sparse canopies and many dead branches. The whole montane thicket in which it grew was unstable and undergoing natural elimination.

The cause of the decline of this species seems to be natural and unrelated to human activity. To date, no conservation measures have been taken on behalf of this species, and it is not in cultivation.

Gunn's tetratheca

Tetratheca gunni

Family . . . . Tremandraceae
Range . . . . Australia

Description and Biology

Reaching 12 in (30 cm) in height, this shrub has a single woody stem supporting a number of other stems, which bear slim leaves measuring 0.08-0.20 in (2-5 mm) by 0.02-0.06 in (0.5-1.5 mm). Flower stalks measuring 0.08-0.18 in (2-4.5 mm) bear one or two flowers in various shades of purple; the flowers bloom from September through early December and measure around 0.4 in (1 cm) in diameter.

Habitat and Current Distribution

The only known sites for this species are in the eastern foothills of the Dazzler Range, just west of Beaconsfield, where it occurs on rocky soil in *Eucalyptus* woodland.

History and Conservation Measures

Until recent years, this species was known only from specimens collected in 1843 and was long considered extinct. Scientists from the IUCN rediscovered it in 1985. Grazing by domestic cattle was once considered a threat, but the most serious problem for the species has been a change in the frequency and temperature of fires. Because the plant may only germinate after an intense fire, changes to more frequent, but less intense, fire regimes may be interfering with regeneration.

Conservation efforts must be directed at preserving the remaining habitat and searching for additional populations. Any management program should consider the effect of fire regime on regeneration.

Pucedanum dehradunensis

Family	Umbelliferae (Apiaceae)
Status	Insufficiently known, IUCN
Range	India

Description and Biology

This perennial herb has a rootstock that sends up a rosette of compound leaves 12-18 in (30-45 cm) long and leafy aerial stems that end in a large, compound floral cluster. Within the cluster, 6-10 rays each bear 15-40 white flowers. The fruit is ellipsoid, 0.35-0.39 in by 0.16 in (0.9-1 cm by 0.4 cm), with winged marginal ribs. Flowering occurs from March to May, and fruits ripen during May and June.

Habitat and Current Distribution

This species is restricted to an area on a slope located close to human settlements in Doon Valley, India. It grows amid grasses and sedges, forming a component of the ground flora of open mixed deciduous forests with *Shorea robusta* as a dominant tree. The surviving population of fewer than 150 individuals grows on a sheltered, gentle slope of a low-lying hill range, isolated by deep ravines.

History and Conservation Measures

Once probably widely distributed throughout low-lying hill ranges of Doon Valley, this species has declined in range and population as the result of urban expansion. The area occupied by the lone extant population is protected, but any expansion of human settlement into its habitat could push the species into extinction. In addition to its horticultural value, this species could be of use in developing drugs for medical purposes; a related species has already been useful for its diuretic properties. Recommendations for conservation measures include legislation to protect its habitat; prevention of cattle grazing in remaining habitat; multiplication through seed and *in vitro* methods for introduction into habitats similar to that of its original site; introduction and maintenance of the species in cultivation; and initiation of studies on reproductive biology and ecology to determine factors that regulate population size and limit distribution.

APPENDIX I

Species Watch
(A Selected List)

Extinct since 1900

Mammals:

Thylacine (*Thylacinus cynocephalus*)

Pig-footed bandicoot (*Chaeropus ecaudatus*)

Lesser bilby (*Macrotis leucura*)

Desert bandicoot (*Perameles eremiana*)

Desert rat-kangaroo (*Caloprymnus campestris*)

Central hare-wallaby (*Lagorchestes asomatus*)

Toolache wallaby (*Macropus greyi*)

Crescent nailtail wallaby (*Onychogalea lunata*)

Atalaye nesophontes (*Nesophontes hypomicrus*)

Western Cuban nesophontes (*Nesophontes micrus*)

Saint Michel nesophontes (*Nesophontes paramicrus*)

Haitian nesophontes (*Nesophontes zamicrus*)

Nyctimene sanctarcruis

Pteropus subniger

Puerto Rican flower bat (*Phyllonycteris major*)

Bonin pipistrelle (*Pipistrellus sturdeei*)

Caribbean monk seal (*Monachus tropicalis*)

Mexican grizzly bear (*Ursus arctos nelsoni*)

Syrian wild ass (*Equus hemionus hemippus*)

Hexaprotodon liberiensis heslopi

Egyptian barbary sheep (*Ammotragus lervia ornatus*)

Schomburgk's deer (*Cervus schomburgki*)

Lesser stick-nest rat (*Leporillus apicalis*)

Martinique rice rat (*Megalomys desmarestii*)

Santa Cruz rice rat (*Nesoryzomys darwini*)

Long-tailed hopping-mouse (*Notomys longicaudatus*)

Pemberton's deer mouse (*Peromyscus pembertoni*)

Gould's mouse (*Pseudomys gouldii*)

Maclear's rat (*Rattus macleari*)

Bulldog rat (*Rattus nativitatis*)

Boromys offella

Boromys torrei

Brotomys contractus

Brotomys voratus

Geocapromys columbianus

Isolobodon portoricensis

Plagiodontia velozi

Sardinian pika (*Prolagus sardus*)

Birds:

King Island emu (*Dromaius ater*)

Atitlan grebe (*Podilymbus gigas*)

Black-backed bittern (*Ixobrychus novaezelandiae*)

Auckland Islands merganser (*Mergus australis*)

Pink-headed duck (*Rhodonessa caryophyllacea*)

Guadalupe caracara (*Polyborus lutosus*)

Samoan moorhen (*Gallinula pacifica*)

New Caledonian rail (*Gallirallus lafresnayanus*)

Chatham Islands rail (*Gallirallus modestus*)

Wake Island rail (*Gallirallus wakensis*)

Woodford's rail (*Nesoclopeus woodfordi*)

Laysan crake (*Porzana palmeri*)

Canary Islands oystercatcher (*Haematopus meadewaldoi*)

Ryukyu pigeon (*Columba jouyi*)

Passenger pigeon (*Ectopistes migratorius*)

Choiseul pigeon (*Microgoura meeki*)

Red-moustached fruit-dove (*Ptillinopus mercierii*)

Carolina parakeet (*Conuropsis carolinesis*)

Paradise parrot (*Psephotus pulcherrimus*)

Snail-eating coua (*Coua delalandei*)

Laughing owl (*Sceloglaux albifacies*)

Cerulean paradise-flycatcher (*Eutrichomyias rowleyi*)

Lord Howe gerygone (*Gerygone insularis*)

Piopio (*Turnagra capensis*)

Grand Cayman thrush (*Turdus ravidus*)

Bonin thrush (*Zoothera terrestris*)

Robust white-eye (*Zosterops strenuus*)

Hawaii oo (*Moho nobilis*)

Dusky seaside sparrow (*Ammodramus maritimus mirabilis*)

Black mamo (*Drepanis funerea*)

Molokai creeper (*Paroreomyza flammea*)

Greater amakihi (*Viridonia sagittirostris*)

Slender-billed grackle (*Quiscalus palustris*)

Tasman starling (*Aplonis fusca*)

Pohnpei starling (*Aplonis pelzelni*)

Huia (*Heteralocha acutirostris*)

Reptiles:

Rodrigues day gecko (*Phelsuma gigas*)

Leiocephalus eremitus

Ameiva cineracea

Martinique giant ameiva (*Ameiva major*)

Saint Croix racer (*Alsophis sancticrucis*)

Fish:

Miller Lake lamprey (*Lampetra minima*)

Mexican dace (*Evarra bustamantei; E. eigenmanni; E. tlahuacensis*)

Pahranagat spinedace (*Lepidomeda altivelis*)

Notropis spp. (3 species)

Clear Lake splittail (*Pogonichthys ciscoides*)

Las Vegas dace (*Rhinichthys deaconi*)

Stumptooth minnow (*Stypodon signifer*)

Snake River sucker (*Chasmistes muriei*)

Harelip sucker (*Lagochila lacera*)

Rhizosomichthys totae

New Zealand grayling (*Prototroctes oxyrhynchus*)

Coregonus spp. (2 species)

Silver trout (*Salvelinus agassizi*)

Perrito de Parras (*Cyprinodon latifasciatus*)

Whiteline topminnow (*Fundulus albolineatus*)

Parras characodon (*Characodon garmani*)

Ash Meadows killifish (*Empetrichthys merriami*)

Gambusia spp. (2 species)

Guayacon ojiazul (*Priapella bonita*)

River pipefish (*Syngnathus watermayeri*)

Utah Lake sculpin (*Cottus echinatus*)

Molluscs:

Eelgrass limpet (*Lottia alveus*)

Ogasawarana spp. (6 species)

Cyclosurus mariei

Cyclophorus horridulum

Tropidophora spp. (2 species)

Bythinella intermedia

Bythiospeum pfeifferi

Umbilicate pebblesnail (*Lithoglyphus umbilicata*)

Ohridohauffenia drimica

Conacmella vagans

Omphalotropis plicosa

Anthony's River snail (*Anculopsis anthonyix*)

Anculosa spp. (8 species)

Goniobasis spp. (11 species)

Gyrotoma spp. (6 species)

Achatinella spp. (11 species)

Auriculella spp. (2 species)

Lamellidea spp. (2 species)

Newcombia philippiana

Partulina spp. (2 species)

Perdicella spp. (3 species)

Amastra spp. (9 species)

Carelia spp. (22 species)

Gastrocopta spp. (2 species)

Lyropupa perlonga

Rhachis spp. (2 species)

Partula spp. (47 species)

Samoana abbreviata

Aspastus spp. (2 species)

Edentulina thomasetti

Gibbus lyonetianus

Gonidomus newtoni

Gonospira nevilli

Gulella mayottensis

Hirasea spp. (9 species)

Kondoconcha othnius

Opanara spp. (12 species)

Rhysoconcha spp. (2 species)

Ruatara spp. (2 species)

Succinea guamensis

Erepta nevilli

Harmogenanina spp. (2 species)

Colparion madgei

Vitrinula spp. (3 species)

Mandarina luhuana

Chilostoma ziegleri

Arion simrothi

Cardina elktoe (*Alasmidonta robusta*)

Dysnomia spp. (9 species)

Invertebrates:

Rubious Cave amphipod (*Stygobromus lucifugus*)

Pasadena freshwater shrimp (*Syncaris pasadenas*)

Pecatonica River mayfly (*Acanthometropus pecatonica*)

Robust burrowing mayfly (*Pantagenia robusta*)

Antioch Dune shieldback katydid (*Neduba extincta*)

Robert's stonefly (*Alloperla roberti*)

Clavicoccus erinaceus

Phyllococcus oahuensis

Mecodema punctellum

Xylotoles costatus

Dryophthorus distinguendus

Dryotribus mimeticus

Macrancylus linearis

Oedemasylus laysanensis

Volutine stoneyian tabanid fly (*Stonemyia volutina*)

Campsicnemus mirabilis

Drosophila lanaiensis

Castle Lake caddisfly (*Rhyacophila amabilis*)

Tobias' caddisfly (*Hydropsyche tobiasi*)
Triaenodes spp. (2 species)
Levuana moth (*Levuana irridescens*)
Deloneura immaculata
Glaucopsyche xerces
Lepidochrysops hypopolia
Genophantis leahi
Hedylepta asaphrombra
Oeobia sp.
Agrotis spp. (3 species)
Minute noctuid moth (*Helicoverpa minuta*)
Laysan dropseed noctuid moth (*Hypena laysanensis*)

Plants:

Cuneate bidens (*Bidens cuneata*)
Franklin tree (*Franklinia alatamaha*)
Agalinus caddoensis
Hubbardia heptaneuron
Caladenia pumila
Zanthoxylum leonis
Lysimachia forbesii
Astyria rosea
Hypoestes inconspicua
Rhamphogyne rhynchocarpa
Euphorbia daphnoides
Claoxylon grandiflorum
Nesogenes orerensis

Most Endangered

Mammals:

Philippine tube-nosed fruit bat (*Nyctimene rabori*)
Mariana fruit bat (*Pteropus mariannus*)
Rodrigues flying-fox (*Pteropus rodricensis*)
Comoro black flying-fox (*Pteropus voeltzkowi*)
Seychelles sheath-tailed bat (*Coleura seychellensis*)
Sucker-footed bat (*Myzopoda aurita*)
New Zealand lesser short-tailed bat (*Mystacina robusta*)
Hairy-eared dwarf lemur (*Allocebus trichotis*)

Golden bamboo lemur (*Hapalemur aureus*)
Ruffed lemur (*Varecia variegata*)
Diademed sifaka (*Propithecus diadema*)
Golden-crowned sifaka (*Propithecus tattersalli*)
Aye-aye (*Daubentonia madagascariensis*)
Buffy tufted-ear marmoset (*Callithrix aurita*)
Lion tamarins (*Leontopithecus* spp.)
Muriqui (*Brachyteles arachnoides*)
Javan gibbon (*Hylobates moloch*)
Mountain gorilla (*Gorilla gorilla berengei*)
Red wolf (*Canis rufus*)
Northern white rhinoceros (*Ceratotherium simum cottoni*)
Javan rhinoceros (*Rhinoceros sodaicus*)
Pygmy hog (*Sus salvanius*)
Wild yak (*Bos grunniens*)
Slender-horned gazelle (*Gazella leptoceros*)
Scimitar-horned oryx (*Oryx dammah*)

Birds:

Puna grebe (*Podiceps taezanowskii*)
Short-tailed albatross (*Diomedea albatrus*)
Cahow (*Pterodroma cahow*)
Nothern bald ibis (*Geronticus eremita*)
Crested ibis (*Nipponia nippon*)
Giant ibis (*Pseudibis gigantea*)
California condor (*Gymnogyps californianus*)
Madagascar fish eagle (*Haliaeetus vociferoides*)
Great Philippine eagle (*Pithecophaga jefferyi*)
Mauritius kestrel (*Falco punctatus*)
Maleo (*Macrocephalon maleo*)
Alagoas curassow (*Mitu mitu*)
White-winged guan (*Penelope albipennis*)

Whooping crane (*Grus americana*)
Takahe (*Natornis mantelli*)
Black stilt (*Himantopus novaezealandiae*)
New Zealand shore plover (*Thinornis novaeseelandidae*)
Eskimo curlew (*Numenius borealis*)
Pink pigeon (*Nesoenas mayeri*)
Black-cheeked lovebird (*Agapornis nigrigenis*)
Puerto Rican parrot (*Amazona vittata*)
Lear's macaw (*Anodorhynchus leari*)
Little blue macaw (*Cyanopsitta spixii*)
Mauritius parakeet (*Psittacula echo*)
Kakapo (*Strigops habroptilus*)
Congo Bay owl (*Phodilus prigoginei*)
Black-breasted puffleg (*Eriocnemis nigrivestis*)
Hooked-bill hermit (*Glaucis dohrnii*)
Imperial woodpecker (*Campephilus imperialis*)
Ivory-billed woodpecker (*Campephilus principalis*)
Okinaw woodpecker (*Sapheopipo noguchii*)
Gurney's pitta (*Pitta gurneyi*)
Zapata wren (*Ferminia cerverai*)
White-breasted thrasher (*Ramphocinclus brachyurus*)
Seychelles magpie-robin (*Copsychus sechellarum*)
Olomao (*Myadestes lanaiensis*)
Kamao (*Myadestes myadestinus*)
Puaiohi (*Myadestes palmeri*)
Red-tailed newtonia (*Newtonia fanovanae*)
Norfolk Island white-eye (*Zosterops albogularis*)
Bishop's oo (*Moho bishopi*)
Kauai oo (*Moho braccatus*)
Nukupuu (*Hemignathus lucidus*)
Poo-uli (*Melamprosops phaeosoma*)
Ou (*Psittirostra psittacea*)

Rothchild's starling (*Leucospar rothschildi*)

Reptiles and Amphibians:
Geochelone nigra abingdoni
Black soft-shell turtle (*Aspideretes [Trionyx] nigricans*)
Dahl's toad-headed turtle (*Phrynops dahli*)
Gharial (*Gavialis gangeticus*)
Culebra Island giant anole (*Anolis roosevelti*)
Southern gastric brooding frog (*Rheobatrachus silus*)

Molluscs:
Socorro springsnail (*Pyrgulopsis neomexicana*)
Caracol (*Hemicycla plicaria*)
Turgid-blossom pearly mussel (*Epioblasma [Dysnomia] turgidula*)
Tar River spinymussel (*Elliptio [Canthyria] steinstansana*)
Ring pink mussel (*Obovaria retusa*)
Winged mapleleaf (*Quadrula fragosa*)
Theodoxus transversalis

Viviparus acerosus
Fagotia esperi

Invertebrates:
Hay's Spring amphipod (*Stygobromus hayi*)
Hell Creek Cave crayfish (*Cambarus zophonastes*)
Ohio emerald dragonfly (*Somatochlora hineana*)
St. Helena giant earwig (*Labidura herculeana*)
Pygmy hog sucking louse (*Haematopinus oliveri*)

Plants:
Herbertus borealis
Anastrophyllum joergensenii
Marsupella profunda
Taxitheliella richardsii
Ochyraea tatrensis
Orthotrichum truncato-dentatum
Sphaeropteris crinita
Tirupati cycad (*Cycas beddonei*)
Saharan cypress (*Cupressus dupreziana*)
Abies beshanzuensis
Florida torreya (*Torreya taxifolia*)

Carossier palm (*Attalea crassispatha*)
Argun palm (*Medemia argun*)
Nubian dragon tree (*Dracaena ombet*)
Orchidantha (*Orchidantha chinensis*)
Dicliptera dodsonii
Frerea indica
Littleflower heteroplexis (*Heteroplexis microcephala*)
Motio-hiran chobbo (*Farsetia macrantha*)
Vella pseudocytiscus paui
Erica jasminiflora
Caoba (*Persea theobromifolia*)
Chinese manglietiastrum (*Manglietiastrum sinicum*)
Mongarlowe mallee (*Eucalyptus recurva*)
Syzygium travancoricum
Brown's banksia (*Banksia brownii*)
Common otophora (*Otophora unicularis*)
Hainan sonneratia (*Sonneratia hainanensis*)
Freziera forerorum

APPENDIX II

Wildlife and Conservation Organizations

African Wildlife Foundation
1717 Massachusetts Ave. NW
Washington, DC 20036

American Cetacean Society
PO Box 2639
San Pedro, CA 90731

American Committee for International Conservation
Center for Marine Conservation
1725 De Sales St. NW, Ste. 500
Washington, DC 20036

American Horse Protection Association
1000 29th St. NW, T100
Washington, DC 20007

American Pheasant and Waterfowl Society
RR1, Box 164-A
Granton, WI 54436

American Wilderness Alliance
7600 E. Arapahoe, Ste. 114
Englewood, CO 80112

Animal Welfare Institute
PO Box 3650
Georgetown Station
Washington, DC 20007

Bat Conservation International
PO Box 162603
Austin, TX 78716

Big Island Rainforest Group
PO Box 341
Kurtistown, HI 96760

Birdlife International (ICBP)
c/o World Wildlife Fund
1250 24th St. NW
Washington, DC 20037

Caribbean Conservation Corporation
PO Box 2866
Gainesville, FL 32602

Center for Marine Conservation
1725 De Sales St. NW, Ste. 500
Washington, DC 20036

Center for Plant Conservation
125 Arborway
Jamaica Plain, MA 02130

Cetacean Society International
PO Box 290145
Wethersfield, CT 06109-0145

Charles Darwin Foundation for the Galápagos Isles
National Zoological Park
Washington, DC 20008

Conservation Fund
1800 N. Kent St., Ste. 1120
Arlington, VA 22209

Conservation International
1015 18th Street NW, Ste. 100
Washington, DC 20036

Convention on International Trade in Endangered
    Species of Wild Fauna and Flora (CITES)
6, rue du Maupas
Case Postale 78
CH-1000 9
Lausanne, Switzerland

The Cousteau Society
870 Greenbriar Circle, Ste. 402
Chesapeake, VA 23320

Cycad Society
1161 Phyllis Ct.
Mountain View, CA 94040

Defenders of Wildlife
1244 19th St. NW
Washington, DC 20036

Desert Tortoise Council
PO Box 1738
Palm Desert, CA 92261-1738

Ducks Unlimited
One Waterfowl Way
Long Grove, IL 60047

Earth First!
PO Box 5176
Missoula, MT 59806

Earth Island Institute
300 Broadway, Ste. 28
San Francisco, CA 94133

Elephant Interest Group
106 E. Hickory Grove
Bloomfield Hills, MI 48013

Endangered Species Act Reauthorization
    Coordinating Committee
1725 De Sales St. NW, Ste. 500
Washington, DC 20036

Federation of Western Outdoor Clubs
365 W. 29th St.
Eugene, OR 97405

Foundation for North American Wild Sheep
720 Allen Ave.
Cody, WY 82414-3403

Friends of Africa in America
330 S. Broadway
Tarrytown, NY 10591

Friends of Animals
PO Box 1244
Norwalk, CT 06856

Friends of the Sea Otter
PO Box 221220
Carmel, CA 93922

Fund for Animals
200 West 57th St.
New York, NY 10019

Game Conservation International
PO Box 17444
San Antonio, TX 78217

Great Bear Foundation
PO Box 2699
Missoula, MT 59806

Greenpeace USA
1436 U St. NW
Washington, DC 20009

Hawk Mountain Sanctuary Association
RR 2, Box 191
Kempton, PA 19529

Humane Society of the United States
2100 L St. NW
Washington, DC 20037

International Association for Bears Research and
    Management
c/o ADF & G
333 Rasberry Rd.
Anchorge, AK 99518-1599

International Crane Foundation
E-11376 Shady Lane Rd.
Baraboo, WI 53913-9778

International Ecology Society
1471 Barclay St.
St. Paul, MN 55106-1405

International Oceanographic Foundation
3979 Rickenbacker Causeway, Virginia Key
Miami, FL 33149-9900

The International Osprey Foundation
PO Box 250
Sanibel, FL 33957

International Primate Protection League
PO Box 766
Summerville, SC 29484

International Wild Waterfowl Association
Hidden Lake Waterfowl
5614 River Styx Rd.
Medina, OH 44256

International Wildlife Coalition
634 N. Falmouth Hwy.
PO Box 388
N. Falmouth, MA 02556

IUCN-The World Conservation Union
Rue Mauverney 28
CH-1196
Gland, Switzerland

Izaak Walton League of America
1401 Wilson Blvd., Level B
Arlington, VA 22209

Jane Goodhall Institute for Wildlife Research,
    Education, and Conservation
PO Box 41720
Tucson, AZ 85717

Mountain Gorilla Project
1717 Massachusetts Ave. NW, Ste. 602
Washington, DC 20036

National Arbor Day Foundation
100 Arbor Ave
Nebraska City, NE 68410

National Audubon Society
950 Third Ave.
New York, NY 10022

National Elephant Collectors Society
38 Medford St.
Somerville, MA 02145-3810

National Institute for Urban Wildlife
10921 Trotting Ridge Way
Columbia, MD 21044

National Tree Society
PO Box 10808
Bakersfield, CA 93389

National Wildflower Research Center
2600 F.M. 973 North
Austin, TX 78725

National Wildlife Federation
1400 16th St. NW
Washington, DC 20036-2266

Natural Resources Defense Council
40 West 20th St.
New York, NY 10011

Nature Conservancy
1815 N. Lynn St.
Arlington, VA 22209

New England Wildflower Society
Hemenway Rd.
Framingham, MA 01701

New York Turtle and Tortoise Society
163 Amsterdam Ave., Ste. 365
New York, NY 10023

North American Benthological Society
Savannah River Ecology Laboratory
Drawer E
Aiken, SC 29802

North American Wolf Society
PO Box 82950
Fairbanks, AK 99708

Ocean Society
1536 16th St. NW
Washington, DC 20036

Pacific Seabirds Group
University of California
Dept. of Avian Sciences
Davis, CA 95616

Pacific Whale Foundation
Kealia Beach Plaza, Ste. 25
101 N. Kihei Rd.
Kihei, HI 96753

Peregrine Fund
World Center for Birds of Prey
5666 W. Flying Hawk Lane
Boise, ID 83709

Quail Unlimited
PO Box 10041
Augusta, GA 30903

Rainforest Action Movement
430 E. University
Ann Arbor, MI 48109

Rainforest Action Network
301 Broadway, Ste. A
San Francisco, CA 94133

Rainforest Alliance
270 Lafayette St., Ste. 512
New York, NY 10012

Rainforest Information Centre
PO Box 368
Lismore, NSW 2480
Australia

RARE Center for Tropical Bird Conservation
19th & Parkway
Philadelphia, PA 19103

Save the Manatee Club
500 North Maitland Ave.
Maitland, FL 32751

Save-the-Redwoods League
114 Sansome St., Room 605
San Francisco, CA 94104

Save the Whales
PO Box 3650
Washington, DC 20007

Sea Shepherd Conservation Society
1314 2nd St.
Santa Monica, CA 90401

Sierra Club
PO Box 7959
San Francisco, CA 94120-9943

Society for the Conservation of Bighorn Sheep
3113 Mesaloa Lane
Pasadena, CA 91107

Southern African Wildlife Management Association
PO Box 3051
Pietermaritzburg 3200
Republic of South Africa

Tree People
12601 Mulholland Drive
Beverly Hills, CA 90210

Trout Unlimited
501 Church St. NE
Vienna, VA 22180

The Whale Center
3933 Peidmont Ave., Ste. 2
Oakland, CA 94611

Whooping Crane Conservation Association
3000 Meadowlark Dr.
Sierra Vista, AZ 85635

Wild Canid Survival and Research Center—Wolf
Sanctuary
PO Box 760
Eureka, MO 63025

Wildlife Conservation Fund of America
50 West Broad St., Ste. 1025
Columbus, OH 43215

Wildlife Conservation International
New York Zoological Society
Bronx, NY 10461

Wildlife Information Center
629 Green St.
Allentown, PA 18102

Wildlife Preservation Trust International
34th St. & Girard Ave.
Philadelphia, PA 19104

World Pheasant Association
PO Box 5
Lower Basildon
Berks, Reading RG89PF
England

World Wildlife Fund
1250 24th St. NW
Washington, DC 20031

WHERE TO LEARN MORE

General Reading

Allan, T. and A. Warren, eds. *Deserts: The Encroaching Wilderness.* Gland, Switzerland: IUCN-The World Conservation Union, 1993.

Cadieux, C. L. *Wildlife Extinction.* Washington, DC: Stone Wall Press, 1991.

Caring for the Earth: A Strategy for Survival. Gland, Switzerland: IUCN-The World Conservation Union, 1993.

Caring for the Earth: A Strategy for Sustainable Living. Gland, Switzerland: IUCN-The World Conservation Union, 1991.

Collins, M., ed. *The Last Rain Forests.* Gland, Switzerland: IUCN-The World Conservation Union, 1990.

DiSilvestro, R. L. *The Endangered Kingdom: The Struggle to Save America's Wildlife.* New York: Wiley, 1989.

Dugan, P. J., ed. *Wetlands in Danger.* Gland, Switzerland: IUCN-The World Conservation Union, 1993.

Dunlap, T. R. *Saving America's Wildlife.* Princeton, NJ: Princeton University Press, 1988.

Ehrlich, P. R. *Extinction: The Causes and Consequences of the Disappearance of Species.* New York: Random House, 1981.

Elder, D. and J. Pernetta, eds. *Oceans.* Cary, NC: Oxford University Press, 1991.

Groombridge, B., ed. *Global Biodiversity: Status of the Earth's Living Resources.* Compiled by the World Conservation Monitoring Centre. United Kingdom: Chapman & Hall, 1992.

——. *1994 IUCN Red List of Threatened Animals.* Gland, Switzerland: IUCN-The World Conservation Union, 1993.

Hermes, N. *Australia's Endangered Wildlife.* Frenchs Forest, NSW, Australia: Child & Associates, 1990.

Moseley, C. J. *The Official World Wildlife Guide to Endangered Species of North America.* Vols. 1-3. Washington, DC: Beacham Publishing, 1992.

Stuart, S. N. and R. J. Adams. *Biodiversity in Sub-Saharan Africa and Its Islands: Conservation, Management, and Sustainable Use.* Gland, Switzerland: IUCN-The World Conservation Union, 1990.

Tudge, C. *Last Animals at the Zoo: How Mass Extinction Can Be Stopped.* Washington, DC: Island Press, 1992.

Mammals

Bateman, G., ed. *All the World's Animals: Primates.* New York: Torstar Books Inc., 1984.

Chapman, J. A. *Rabbits, Hares, and Pikas: Status Surveys and Conservation Action Plan.* Gland, Switzerland: IUCN-The World Conservation Union, 1991.

Duncan, P. *Zebras, Horses and Asses: An Action Plan for the Conservation of Wild Equids.* Gland, Switzerland: IUCN-The World Conservation Union, 1992.

East, R. *Antelopes: Global Survey and Regional Action Plans.* Parts 1-3. Gland, Switzerland: IUCN-The World Conservation Union, 1990.

Foster-Turley, P., S. Macdonald, and C. Mason. *Otters: An Action Plan for Their Conservation.* Gland, Switzerland: IUCN-The World Conservation Union, 1991.

Ginsberg, J. R. and D. W. Macdonald. *Foxes, Wolves, Jackals, and Dogs: An Action Plan for the Conservation of Canids.* Gland, Switzerland: IUCN-The World Conservation Union, 1990.

Glatston, A. *The Red Panda, Olingos, Coatis, Raccoons and Their Relatives: An Action Plan for the Conservation of Procyonids and Ailurids.* Gland, Switzerland: IUCN-The World Conservation Union, 1993.

Jackson, P. *Weasels, Badgers, Civets and Mongoose and Their Relatives.* Gland, Switzerland: IUCN-The World Conservation Union, 1990.

Jackson, P. and K. Nowell. *The Wild Cats: A Status Survey and Conservation Action Plan.* Gland, Switzerland: IUCN-The World Conservation Union, 1993.

Jackson, P. and O. Sheean-Stone. *Wild Dogs and Their Relatives.* Gland, Switzerland: IUCN-The World Conservation Union, 1991.

Kennedy, M. *Australasian Marsupials and Monotremes.* Gland, Switzerland: IUCN-The World Conservation Union, 1992.

Klinowska, M. *Dolphins, Porpoises and Whales of the World.* The IUCN Red Data Book. Gland, Switzerland: IUCN-The World Conservation Union, 1991.

Leader-Williams, N. *The World Trade in Rhino Horn: A Review.* Gland, Switzerland: IUCN-The World Conservation Union, 1992.

Lee, P. C., J. Thornback, and E. L. Bennett. *Threatened Primates of Africa.* The IUCN Red Data Book. Gland, Switzerland: IUCN-The World Conservation Union, 1988.

Lemurs of Madagascar and the Comoros. The IUCN Red Data Book. Gland, Switzerland: IUCN-The World Conservation Union, 1990.

Lidicker, W. Z., Jr., ed. *Rodents: A World Survey of Species of Conservation Concern.* Gland, Switzerland: IUCN-The World Conservation Union, 1989.

Mackinnon, J. R. and S. N. Stuart. *The Kouprey: An Action Plan for Its Conservation.* Gland, Switzerland: IUCN-The World Conservation Union, 1989.

Mickleburgh, S. P., P. A. Racey, and A. M. Hutson. *Old World Fruit Bats: An Action Plan for the Conservation of the Family Pteropodidae.* Gland, Switzerland: IUCN-The World Conservation Union, 1992.

Milliken, T., K. Nowell, and J. B. Thomsen. *The Decline of the Black Rhino in Zimbabwe: Implications for Future Rhino Conservation.* Gland, Switzerland: IUCN-The World Conservation Union, 1993.

Mittermeier, R. et. al. *Lemurs of Madagascar: An Action Plan for Their Conservation 1993-1999.* Gland, Switzerland: IUCN-The World Conservation Union, 1992.

Nicholl, M. A. and G. B. Rathbun. *African Insectivora and Elephant-Shrews.* Gland, Switzerland: IUCN-The World Conservation Union, 1991.

Nowak, R. M. *Walker's Mammals of the World.* 5th ed. Baltimore and London: The Johns Hopkins University Press, 1991.

Oliver, W. *Pigs, Peccaries and Hippos: An Action Plan for the Suiformes.* Gland, Switzerland: IUCN-The World Conservation Union, 1993.

Reijnders, J. H. *Seals, Fur Seals, Sea Lions and Walruses: An Action Plan for Their Conservation.* Gland, Switzerland: IUCN-The World Conservation Union, 1993.

Santiapillai, C. and P. Jackson. *The Asian Elephant: An Action Plan for Its Conservation.* Gland, Switzerland: IUCN-The World Conservation Union, 1990.

Stone, D. *The Seals.* Gland, Switzerland: IUCN-The World Conservation Union, 1993.

————. *Wild Cats and Their Relatives.* Gland, Switzerland: IUCN-The World Conservation Union, 1993.

Thornback, J. and M. Jenkins. *The IUCN Mammal Red Data Book.* Gland, Switzerland: IUCN-The World Conservation Union, 1981.

Torres, H., ed. *South American Camelids.* Gland, Switzerland: IUCN-The World Conservation Union, 1992.

Birds

Berger, A. J. *Hawaiian Birdlife.* 2nd ed. Honolulu: The University Press of Hawaii, 1982.

Collar, N. J. and P. A. Andrew. *Birds to Watch: The ICBP World Checklist of Threatened Birds.* Cambridge: ICBP, 1988.

Collar, N. J. and S. N. Stuart. *Threatened Birds of Africa and Related Islands.* The ICBP/IUCN Red Data Book, Part 1. 3rd ed. Gland, Switzerland: IUCN-The World Conservation Union, 1985.

Collar, N. J. et. al. *Threatened Birds of the Americas.* The ICBP/IUCN Red Data Book. Part 2. 3rd ed. Washington, DC: Smithsonian Institution Press, 1992.

De Schauensee, R. *A Guide to the Birds of South America.* Wynnewood, PA: Livingston Pub. Co., 1970.

Ehrlich, P. R. *Birds in Jeopardy: The Imperiled and Extinct Birds of United States and Canada.* Stanford, CA: Stanford University Press, 1992.

Flint, V. E. et. al. *A Field Guide to Birds of the USSR.* Princeton, NJ: Princeton University Press, 1984.

Garnett, ed. *Threatened and Extinct Birds of Australia.* Gland, Switzerland: IUCN-The World Conservation Union, 1992.

Goodwin, D. *Pigeons and Doves of the World.* 3rd ed. Ithaca, NY: Cornell University Press, 1983.

Green, A. J. "Wildfowl at Risk, 1992." *Wildfowl* 43 (1992): 160-84.

Hammond, N. *Birds of Prey.* London: Hamlyn, 1993.

Handbook of the Birds of the World. Barcelona: Lynx Edicions, 1992.

Johnsgard, P. A. *The Plovers, Sandpipers, and Snipes of the World.* Lincoln and London: University of Nebraska Press, 1981.

————. *Cranes of the World.* Bloomington: Indiana University Press, 1983.

Perrins, C., ed. *The Illustrated Encyclopedia of Birds.* New York: Prentice Hall Press, 1990.

Ridgely, R. S. *The Birds of South America.* Austin: University of Texas Press, 1989.

Snyder, N. F. R. *Birds of Prey: Natural History and Conservation of North American Raptors.* Stillwater, MN: Voyageur Press, 1991.

Wallace, I. *Birds of Prey of Britain and Europe.* New York: Oxford University Press, 1983.

Reptiles and Amphibians

Corbett, K., ed. *The Conservation of European Reptiles and Amphibians.* London: C. Helm, 1989.

Groombridge, B. *The IUCN Amphibia-Reptilia Red Data Book.* Gland, Switzerland: IUCN-The World Conservation Union, 1982.

Levy, C. K. *Crocodiles and Alligators.* London: Apple Press, 1991.

Pritchard, P. C. *Encyclopedia of Turtles.* Neptune, NJ: T. F. H. Publications, 1979.

Stubbs, D. *Tortoises and Freshwater Turtles.* Gland, Switzerland: IUCN-The World Conservation Union, 1989. Reprint 1991.

Swingland, I. R. and M. W. Klemens. *The Conservation Biology of Tortoises.* Gland, Switzerland: IUCN-The World Conservation Union, 1989.

Thorbjarnarson, J. *Crocodiles*. Gland, Switzerland: IUCN-The World Conservation Union, 1992.

Fish

Minckley, W. L., and J. E. Deacon, eds. *Battle Against Extinction: Native Fish Management in the American West*. Tucson and London: The University of Arizona Press, 1991.

Invertebrates

Collins, N. M. and M. G. Morris. *Threatened Swallowtail Butterflies of the World*. The IUCN Red Data Book. Gland, Switzerland: IUCN-The World Conservation Union, 1985. Reprint 1988.

Harris, J. L. and M. E. Gordon. *Distribution and Status of Rare and Endangered Mussels in Arkansas*. Little Rock, AR: Arkansas Game and Fish Commission, 1987.

Kay, A. *The Conservation Biology of Molluscs*. Gland, Switzerland: IUCN-The World Conservation Union, 1993.

New, T. R. *The Conservation Biology of Lycaenidae (Butterflies)*. Gland, Switzerland: IUCN-The World Conservation Union, 1993.

New, T. R. and N. M. Collins. *Swallowtail Butterflies*. Gland, Switzerland: IUCN-The World Conservation Union, 1991.

Pfleger, V., and J. Chatfield. *A Guide to Snails of Britain and Europe*. London: Hamlyn, 1988.

Wells, S. M. and J. E. Chatfield. *Threatened Non-Marine Molluscs of Europe*. Council of Europe. Nature and Environment, No. 64, 1992.

Wells, S. M., R. M. Pyle, and N. M. Collins. *The IUCN Invertebrate Red Data Book*. Gland, Switzerland: IUCN-The World Conservation Union, 1983. Reprint 1984.

Plants

Callister, D. J. *Illegal Tropical Timber Trade: Asia Pacific*. Gland, Switzerland: IUCN-The World Conservation Union, 1992.

Case, F. W., Jr. *Orchids of the Western Great Lakes Region*. Bloomfield Hills, MI: Cranbrook Institute of Science, 1987.

Conservation of Medicinal Plants. Gland, Switzerland: IUCN-The World Conservation Union, 1991.

Cuddihy, L. W. and C. P. Stone. *Alteration of Native Hawaiian Vegetation: Effects of Humans, Their Activities and Introduction*. Honolulu: University of Hawaii Press, 1985.

Davis, S. D. *Plants in Danger: What Do We Know?* Gland, Switzerland: IUCN-The World Conservation Union, 1986.

Jenkins, M. and S. Oldfield. *Wild Plants in Trade*. Gland, Switzerland: IUCN-The World Conservation Union, 1992.

Johnson, D. V. *Palms: An Action Plan for Their Conservation*. Gland, Switzerland: IUCN-The World Conservation Union, 1993.

Lewington, A. *Medicinal Plants and Plant Extracts: A Review of Their Importation into Europe*. Gland, Switzerland: IUCN-The World Conservation Union, 1993.

Lucas, G. and H. Synge. *The IUCN Plant Red Data Book*. Gland, Switzerland: IUCN-The World Conservation Union, 1978.

World Plant Conservation Bibliography. Compiled by Royal Botanic Gardens, Kew, Threatened Plants Unit, World Conservation Monitoring Centre. Kew, Surrey, England: The Gardens, 1990.

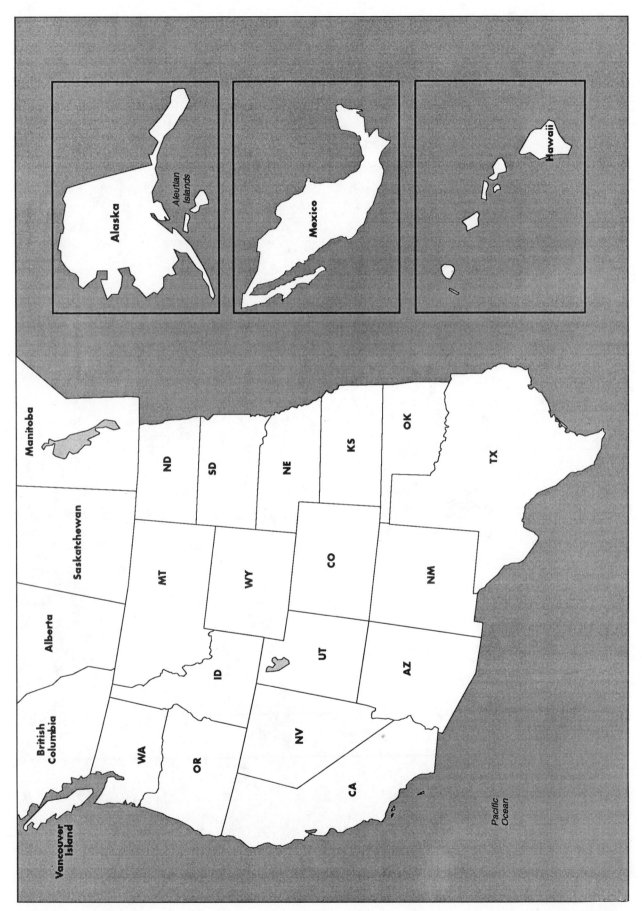

Western United States

Aleutian Islands

Alaska

Mexico

Hawaii

Manitoba

Saskatchewan

Alberta

British Columbia

Vancouver Island

ND

SD

NE

KS

OK

TX

MT

WY

CO

NM

ID

UT

AZ

WA

OR

NV

CA

Pacific Ocean

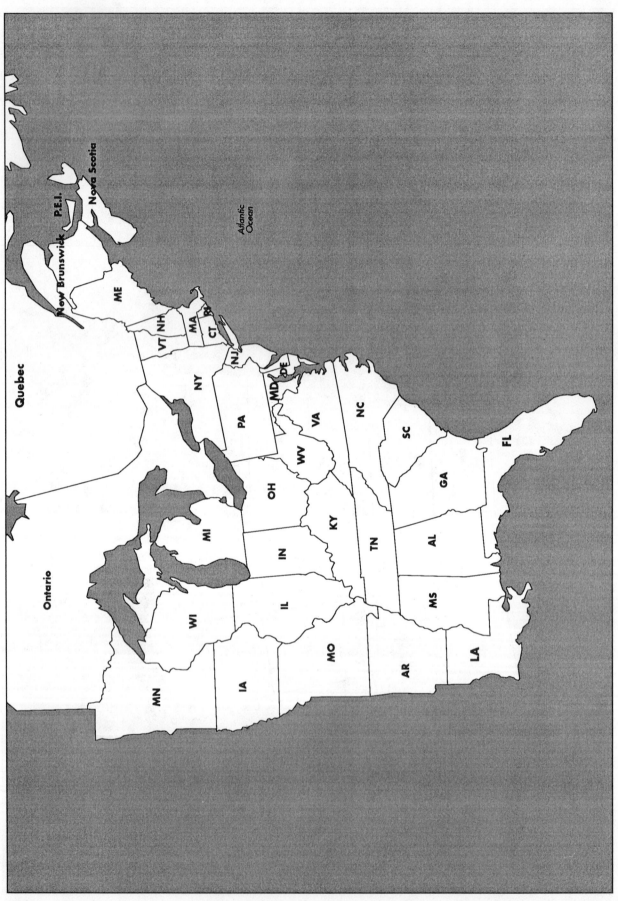

Eastern United States

Central America and the Caribbean

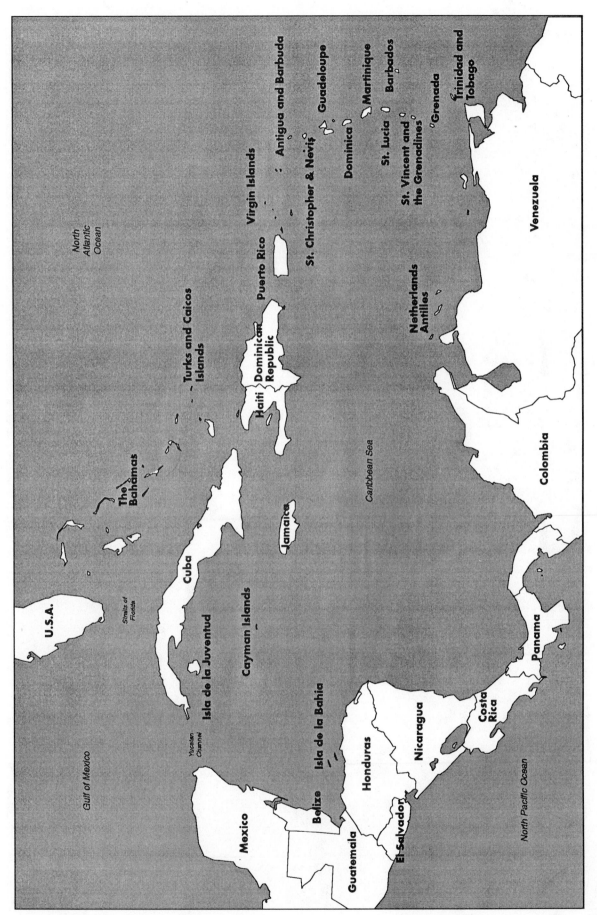

South America

Caribbean Sea

North
Atlantic
Ocean

Venezuela

Guyana

Suriname

French Guiana
(France)

Colombia

Ecuador

Galápagos
Islands

Brazil

Peru

Bolivia

Paraguay

South
Pacific
Ocean

Uruguay

Argentina

Chile

Juan Fernández
Islands

Chiloé
Island

South
Atlantic
Ocean

Falkland Islands

Europe

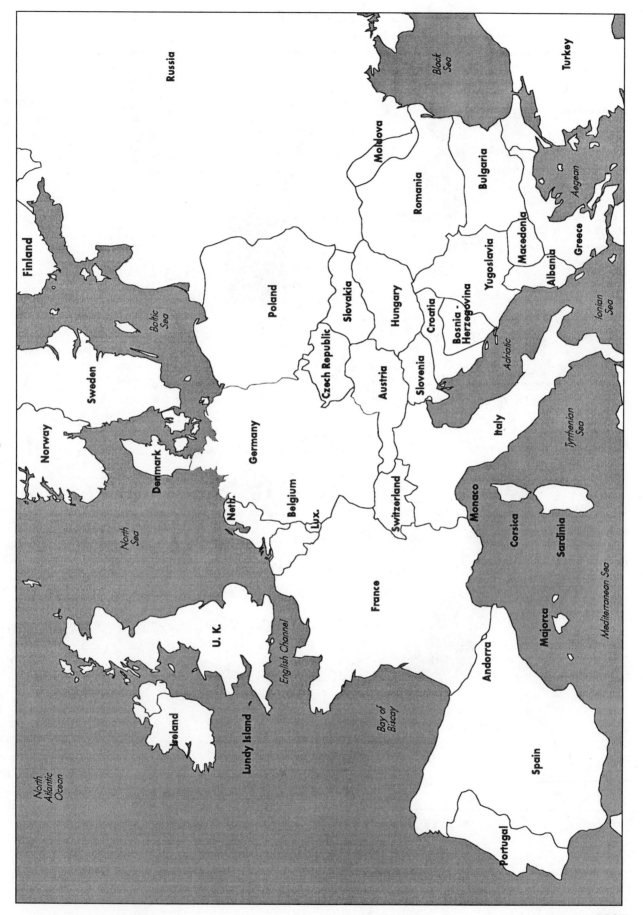

Middle East

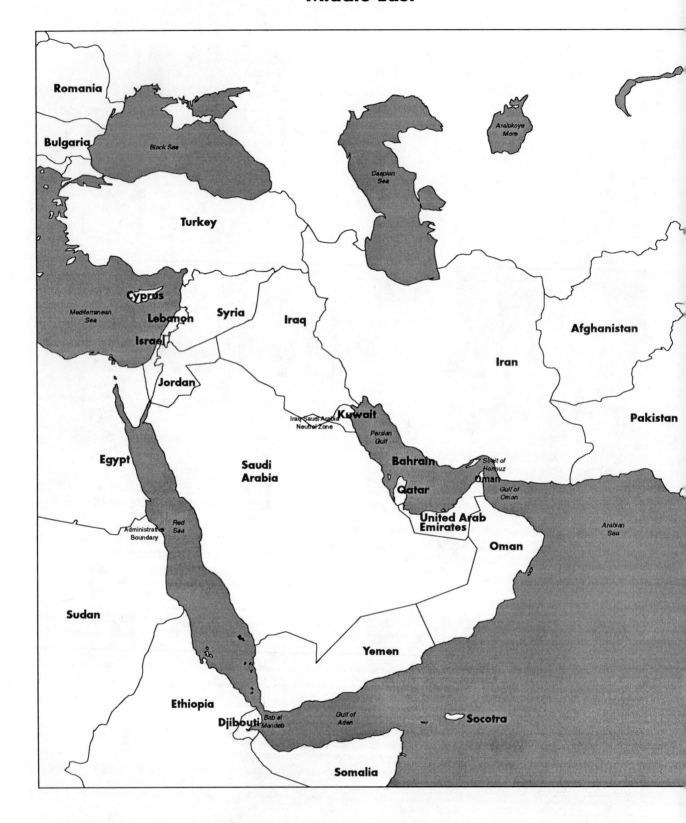

Africa

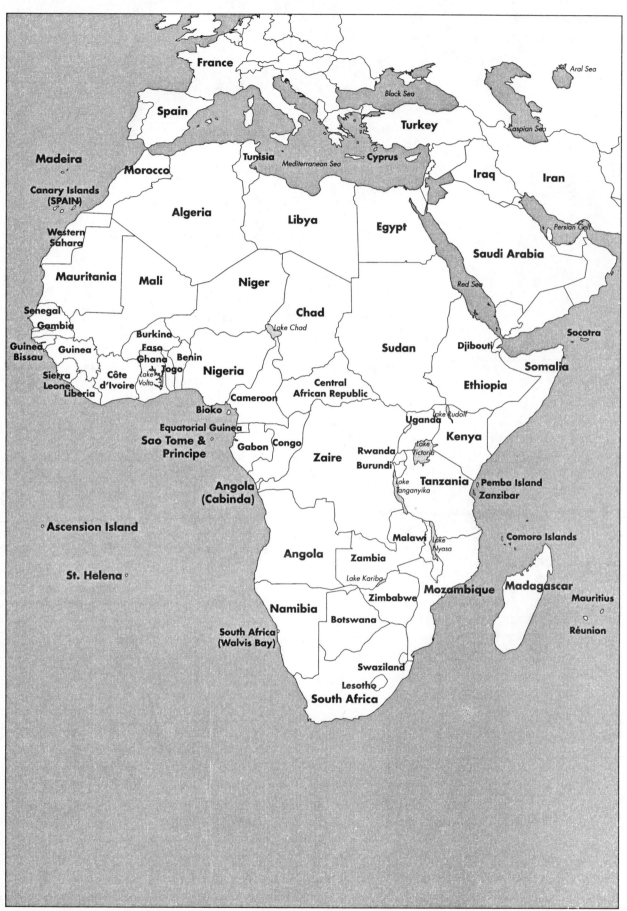

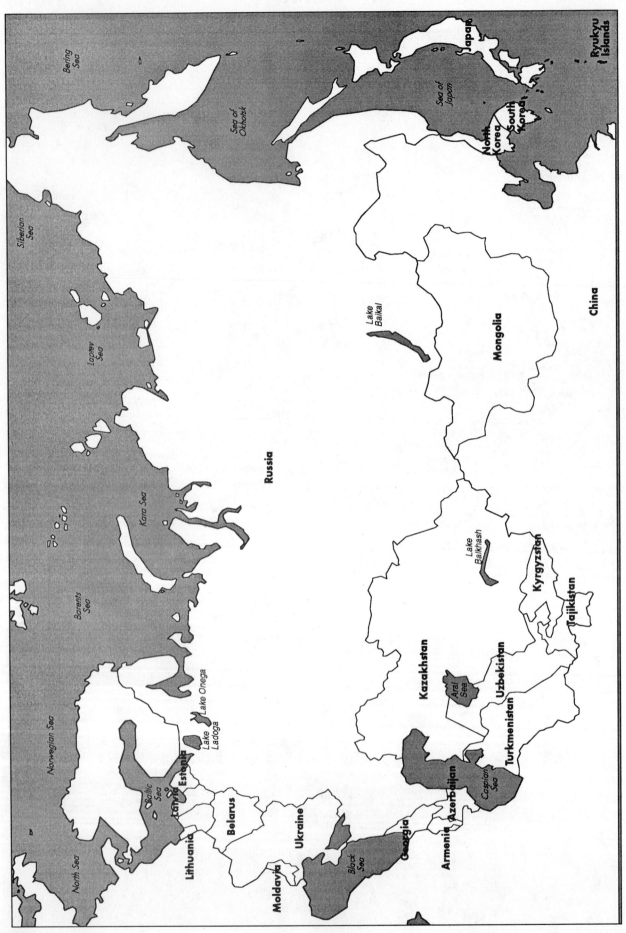

Northern Asia

Southern Asia

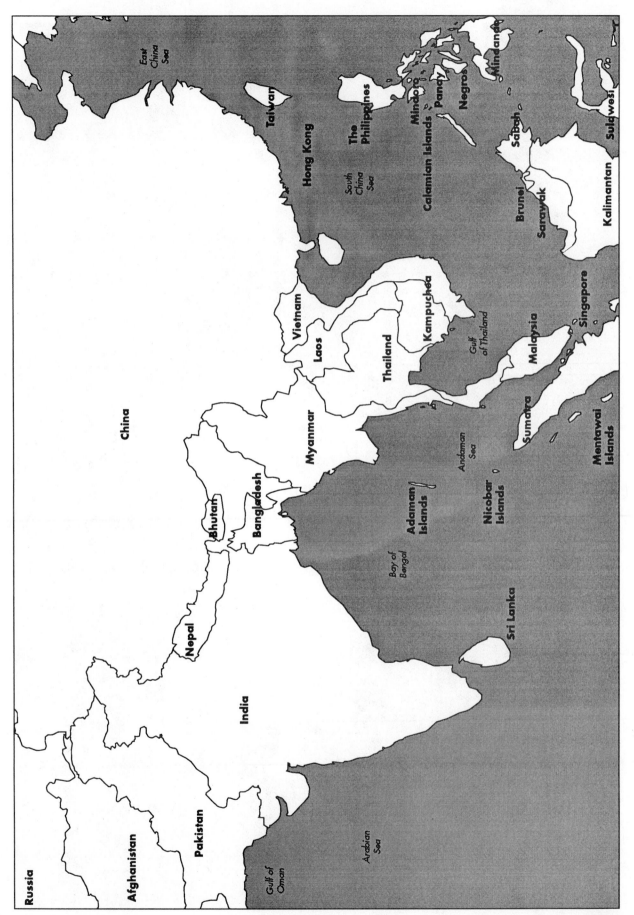

Russia

Afghanistan

Pakistan

Gulf of Oman

Arabian Sea

India

China

Nepal

Bhutan

Bangladesh

Myanmar

East China Sea

Taiwan

Hong Kong

Vietnam

Laos

Thailand

Kampuchea

South China Sea

The Philippines

Mindoro

Calamian Islands

Panay

Negros

Mindanao

Sabah

Brunei

Sarawak

Kalimantan

Sulawesi

Singapore

Malaysia

Gulf of Thailand

Sumatra

Mentawai Islands

Andaman Sea

Adaman Islands

Nicobar Islands

Bay of Bengal

Sri Lanka

Australia

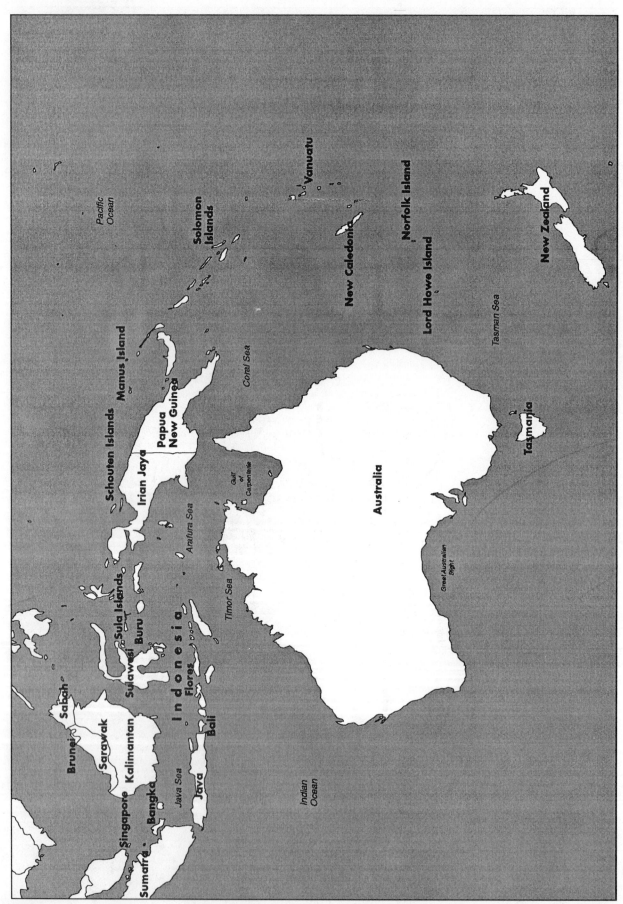

Geographic Index

Afghanistan

Argali 388
Asiatic black bear 241
Central Asian cobra 842
Cheetah 191
Dalmatian pelican 451
Great bustard 534
Markhor 368
Siberian crane 517
Snow leopard 205
Tiger 202
White-headed duck 479
Wild yak 355

Alabama (U.S.A.)

Alabama canebrake
    pitcher-plant 1174
Alabama cave shrimp 1003
Alabama red-bellied
    turtle 741
Fine-rayed pigtoe pearly
    mussel 957
Gray bat 83
Green pitcher plant 1172
Indiana bat 85
Pale lilliput pearly
    mussel 943
Penitent mussel 951
Pygmy sculpin 902
Red-cockaded
    woodpecker 628
Relict trillium 1096
Rough pigtoe pearly
    mussel 969
Stirrup shell 975
Tulotoma snail 915
Turgid-blossom pearly
    mussel 953

Alaska (U.S.A.)

Eskimo curlew 546
Short-tailed albatross 447

Albania

Baltic sturgeon 885

Dalmatian pelican 451
Mediterranean monk
    seal 229
White-headed duck 479

Aleutian Islands

Takakia ceratophyllum 1063

Algeria

African wild dog 185
Algerian nuthatch 683
Audouin's gull 552
Baltic sturgeon 885
Barbary sheep 346
Cheetah 191
Dama gazelle 378
Mediterranean monk
    seal 229
Northern bald ibis 465
Olea laperrinei 1161
Saharan cypress 1071
Slender-horned gazelle 380
Southwest Asian garden
    dormouse 415
White-headed duck 479

American Samoa

Insular flying-fox 71
Samoan flying-fox 69

Andorra

Pyrenean desman 56

Angola

African elephant 282
African slender-snouted
    crocodile 788
African wild dog 185
Black rhinoceros 304
Brown hyena 208
Cheetah 191
Chimpanzee 169
Congo clawless otter 210
Gorilla 163
Mountain zebra 286

West African manatee 278

Argentina

Andean cat 196
Andean flamingo 470
Aylacophora deserticola 1118
Blue-throated macaw 580
Burmeister's armadillo 37
Bush dog 187
Chaco tortoise 744
Chacoan peccary 314
Chilean shrew opossum 32
Colocolo 33
Giant anteater 42
Giant armadillo 39
Giant otter 221
Gray zorro 183
Helmeted woodpecker 627
Jaguar 198
Long-tailed chinchilla 419
Maned wolf 179
Marine otter 212
Marsh deer 327
Narosky's seedeater 695
North Andean huemul 335
Olrog's gull 551
Orthotrichum truncato-
    dentatum 1062
Pampas deer 339
Pampas meadowlark 716
Pink fairy armadillo 37
Puna flamingo 470
Purple-winged ground-
    dove 556
Quebrachos 1108
Short-tailed chinchilla 419
South Andean huemul 335
Southern river otter 214
Spectacled bear 243
Vicuña 320

Arizona (U.S.A.)

Brady pincushion
    cactus 1116
Desert tortoise 750

Peebles Navajo cactus 1116
Pupfish 900
Thick-billed parrot 598

Arkansas (U.S.A.)

Fat pocketbook pearly
    mussel 971
Gray bat 83
Hell Creek Cave
    crayfish 1008
Ouachita rock-
    pocketbook 941
Pallid sturgeon 887
Red-cockaded
    woodpecker 628

Armenia

Dalmatian pelican 451
Large blue butterflies 1042
Marsh snails 922

Ascension Island

Ascension frigatebird 460

Atlantic Ocean

Baltic sturgeon 885
Mediterranean monk
    seal 229
Shortnose sturgeon 883

Australia

Alectryon ramiflorus 1170
Australian ant 1048
Banded hare-wallaby 25
Black-eared miner 689
Bridled nailtail wallaby 26
Brown's banksia 1163
Button wrinklewort 1122
Chuditch 7
Dibbler 8
Dusky hopping-mouse 408
Eastern freshwater cod 903
Estuarine crocodile 796
False water-rat 414
Flat-leaved wattle 1153

Ghost bat 78
Giant torrent midge 1033
Golden bandicoot 13
Golden-shouldered
parakeet 592
Greater stick-nest rat 402
Green sea turtle 760
Ground parrot 591
Gunn's tetratheca 1179
Hemiphlebia damselfly 1014
Hooded parakeet 594
Julia Creek dunnart 12
Jumping-jack wattle 1152
Kowari 5
Leadbeater's possum 31
Long-footed potoroo 22
Lord Howe Island skink 831
Lord Howe rail 524
Mallee worm-lizard 810
Mogumber bell 1154
Monarto mintbush 1145
Mongarlowe mallee 1156
Morrisby's gum 1155
Mount Donna Buang wingless
stonefly 1025
Mount Stirling stonefly 1023
Mountain pygmy-possum 29
Night parrot 590
Noisy scrub-bird 645
Norfolk Island white-eye 686
Northern hairy-nosed
wombat 17
Northern hopping-
mouse 407
Numbat 3
Orange-bellied parakeet 587
Otway stonefly 1022
Pig-nosed turtle 772
Prosperine rock-wallaby 28
Rat-kangaroo species 20
Red-lored whistler 675
Red-tailed phascogale 10
Rufous hare-wallaby 24
Rufous scrub-bird 647
Scarlet-chested parakeet 588
Shark Bay mouse 413
Small purple-pea 1143
Southern gastric brooding
frog 857
Swan galaxias 897
Thornton Peak melomys 406
Western barred bandicoot 14
Western swamp turtle 780

Austria

Bavarian pine vole 411
Danube endemic
molluscs 979
Danube salmon 898
False ringlet butterfly 1044
Freshwater pearl mussel 937
Great bustard 534
Marsh snails 922

Azerbaijan

Dalmatian pelican 451
Great bustard 534
Marsh snails 922

Azores

Bristle fern 1066

Bahamas

Bahamian hutia 425
Caribbean manatee 276
Kirtland's warbler 696
Piping plover 539

Baikal, Lake

Lake Baikal endemic
molluscs 983

Bali

Banteng 353
Rothchild's starling 723

Baltic Sea

Baltic sturgeon 885

Bangka

Hairy-nosed otter 216

Bangladesh

Asian elephant 280
Asiatic black bear 241
Asiatic wild dog 181
Banteng 353
Black soft-shell turtle 774
Dalmatian pelican 451
Estuarine crocodile 796
Ganges River dolphin 270
Gaur 351
Gharial 804
Great Indian rhinoceros 308
Hispid hare 430
Indian python 840
Mugger crocodile 794
Nordmann's greenshank 550
River terrapin 732
Sloth bear 239
Spoon-billed sandpiper 545
Spot-billed pelican 453
Spotted pond turtle 736
Tiger 202
Tricarinate Hill turtle 739
White-winged wood
duck 477

Barbados

Piping plover 539

Bawean Island

Bawean deer 325

Belarus

Danube endemic
molluscs 979

European bison 348
Marsh snails 922
Russian desman 55

Belgium

Baltic sturgeon 885
False ringlet butterfly 1044
Freshwater pearl mussel 937
Marsh snails 922

Belize

American crocodile 786
Caribbean manatee 276
Central American river
turtle 731
Central American tapir 294
Giant anteater 42

Benin

African elephant 282
African slender-snouted
crocodile 788
African wild dog 185
Cheetah 191
Red-bellied guenon 131
West African manatee 278

Bermuda

Bermuda petrel 449
Piping plover 539

Bhutan

Asian elephant 280
Asiatic black bear 241
Asiatic wild dog 181
Bengal florican 533
Black-necked crane 519
Ganges River dolphin 270
Gaur 351
Gharial 804
Great Indian rhinoceros 308
Pygmy hog 312
Red panda 232
Sloth bear 239
Snow leopard 205
Takin 366
Tiger 202
Wild water buffalo 359
Wild yak 355

Bioko

African pygmy squirrel 395
Black colobus 135
Drill 143
Gray-necked rockfowl 679
Preuss's guenon 134
Red-eared nose-spotted
guenon 132

Black Sea

Baltic sturgeon 885
Mediterranean monk
seal 229

Bolivia

Andean cat 196
Andean flamingo 470
Black caiman 784
Blue-throated macaw 580
Burmeister's armadillo 37
Bush dog 187
Chacoan peccary 314
Giant anteater 42
Giant armadillo 39
Giant otter 221
Harpy eagle 489
Jaguar 198
Maned wolf 179
Marsh deer 327
North Andean huemul 335
Pampas deer 339
Puna flamingo 470
Quebrachos 1108
Short-tailed chinchilla 419
South American river
turtle 775
Spectacled bear 243
Vicuña 320
Yellow-spotted sideneck
turtle 777

Bonin Islands

Bonin Islands endemic
snails 930

Borneo

See Brunei, Kalimantan,
Sabah, Sarawak

Bosnia-Herzegovina

Olm 872

Botswana

African elephant 282
African wild dog 185
Black-cheeked lovebird 568
Black rhinoceros 304
Brown hyena 208
Cape vulture 486
Cheetah 191

Brazil

Alagoas curassow 497
Alagoas foliage-gleaner 635
Bare-faced tamarin 117
Black caiman 784
Brazilian rosewood 1142
Brazilian three-banded
armadillo 41
Brazilian three-toed sloth 35
Buffy-headed marmoset 111
Buffy tufted-ear
marmoset 113
Bush dog 187
Caribbean manatee 276
Eskimo curlew 546
Fork-tailed pygmy-tyrant 642
Giant anteater 42

South Korea

Asiatic black bear   241
Asiatic wild dog   181
Chinese egret   462
Large blue butterflies   1042
Nordmann's greenshank   550
Red-crowned crane   515
Spoon-billed sandpiper   545

Spain

Audouin's gull   552
Baltic sturgeon   885
Caracol   933
Euphorbia handiensis   1140
False ringlet butterfly   1044
Freshwater pearl mussel   937
Great bustard   534
Hierro giant lizard   825
Kerry slug   935
Large blue butterflies   1042
Mallorcan midwife toad   853
Marsupella profunda   1057
Mediterranean monk
    seal   229
Pyrenean desman   56
Shrubby cress-rocket   1129
Spanish ibex   370
Spanish lynx   194
White-headed duck   479
White-tailed laurel
    pigeon   559

Sri Lanka

Asian elephant   280
Asiatic wild dog   181
Estuarine crocodile   796
Indian python   840
Mugger crocodile   794
Sloth bear   239
Sphaeropteris crinita   1065
Spot-billed pelican   453

St. Helena

Old father live-forever   1144
St. Helena giant earwig   1020
St. Helena plover   543

St. Lucia

St. Lucia parrot   574
White-breasted thrasher   660

St. Vincent

St. Vincent parrot   570

Stephens Island

Hamilton's frog   855

Sudan

African elephant   282
African gerbils   400
African wild ass   284
African wild dog   185
Argun palm   1083
Barbary sheep   346

Black rhinoceros   304
Cheetah   191
Dama gazelle   378
Nubian dragon tree   1093
Olea laperrinei   1161
Slender-horned gazelle   380

Sula Islands

Babirusa   310

Sulawesi

Babirusa   310
Lowland anoa   361
Mountain anoa   361
Siamese crocodile   800
Sulawesi ebony   1135

Sumatra

Asiatic wild dog   181
False gharial   802
Giant rafflesia   1166
Hairy-nosed otter   216
Helmeted hornbill   623
Malayan tapir   296
Orang-utan   172
Otter civet   246
Painted terrapin   734
River terrapin   732
Siamese crocodile   800
Spot-billed pelican   453
Sumatran rabbit   432
Sumatran rhinoceros   302
Sun bear   237
White-winged wood
    duck   477

Suriname

Bush dog   187
Caribbean manatee   276
Eskimo curlew   546
Giant anteater   42
Giant armadillo   39
Giant otter   221
Harpy eagle   489
Jaguar   198
Yellow-spotted sideneck
    turtle   777

Swaziland

African wild dog   185
Black rhinoceros   304
Cape vulture   486
Cheetah   191

Sweden

Baltic sturgeon   885
Freshwater pearl mussel   937
Marsh snails   922

Switzerland

Baltic sturgeon   885
Danube salmon   898
Draba ladina   1125
False ringlet butterfly   1044

Italian agile frog   861
Marsh snails   922

Syria

Dalmatian pelican   451
Great bustard   534
Mediterranean monk
    seal   229
Southwest Asian garden
    dormouse   415
White-headed duck   479

Taiwan

Asiatic black bear   241
Black-faced spoonbill   468
Chinese egret   462
Short-tailed albatross   447

Tajikistan

Argali   388
Asiatic wild dog   181
Central Asian cobra   842
Great bustard   534
Markhor   368
Snow leopard   205
Tiger   202
White-headed duck   479

Tanzania

African elephant   282
African slender-snouted
    crocodile   788
African wild dog   185
Black rhinoceros   304
Cheetah   191
Chimpanzee   169
Lake Victoria cichlids   908
Long-billed apalis   674
Pemba flying-fox   73
Rufous-winged sunbird   648
Sokoke scops-owl   608
Uluguru bushshrike   657
Usambara eagle owl   606
Usambara squirrel   396
Zanzibar red colobus   139

Tasmania

Swan galaxias   897

Tennessee (U.S.A.)

Birdwing pearly mussel   945
Cracking pearly mussel   959
Cumberland bean pearly
    mussel   977
Dromedary pearly
    mussel   949
Fanshell   947
Fine-rayed pigtoe pearly
    mussel   957
Gray bat   83
Indiana bat   85
Little-wing pearly mussel   965
Nashville crayfish   1010
Pallid sturgeon   887

Ring pink mussel   963
Rough pigtoe pearly
    mussel   969
Turgid-blossom pearly
    mussel   953

Texas (U.S.A.)

Bee Creek Cave
    harvestman   997
Big long-nosed bat   80
Black-capped vireo   711
Fountain darter   904
Houston toad   849
Pupfish   900
Red-cockaded
    woodpecker   628
Texas blind salamander   870
Texas wild rice   1086
Tooth Cave spider   991
Whooping crane   513

Thailand

Asian elephant   280
Asiatic black bear   241
Asiatic wild dog   181
Banteng   353
Bumblebee bat   75
Christmas Island
    frigatebird   458
Eld's deer   332
Estuarine crocodile   796
False gharial   802
Fea's muntjac   337
Gaur   351
Greater adjutant   463
Gurney's pitta   643
Hairy-nosed otter   216
Helmeted hornbill   623
Indian python   840
Javan rhinoceros   306
Kouprey   357
Malayan tapir   296
Nordmann's greenshank   550
Otter civet   246
Painted terrapin   734
River terrapin   732
Siamese crocodile   800
Spot-billed pelican   453
Sumatran rhinoceros   302
Sun bear   237
Thailand giant catfish   895
Tiger   202
White-eyed river-martin   653
White-winged wood
    duck   477
Wild water buffalo   359

Tibet

Gongshan muntjac   337

Togian Islands

Babirusa   310

Togo

African elephant 282
African slender-snouted
    crocodile 788
African wild dog 185
Diana monkey 129
West African manatee 278

Tonga

Fiji banded iguana 815
Insular flying-fox 71
Polynesian megapode 496

Trinidad and Tobago

Caribbean manatee 276
*Glomeropitcairnia
    erectiflora* 1084
South American river
    turtle 775
White-tailed sabrewing 613

Tristan da Cunha Islands

Gough bunting 693
Grosbeak bunting 693
Tristan bunting 693

Tromelin Island

Green sea turtle 760

Tuamotu Archipelago

Polynesian imperial-
    pigeon 563
Tuamotu sandpiper 548

Tubuai Islands

Rapa fruit-dove 565

Tunisia

Audouin's gull 552
Barbary sheep 346
Mediterranean monk
    seal 229
Slender-horned gazelle 380
White-headed duck 479

Turkey

Audouin's gull 552
Baltic sturgeon 885
Dalmatian pelican 451
European souslik 397
Great bustard 534
Mediterranean monk
    seal 229
Southwest Asian garden
    dormouse 415
Sternbergia candida 1080
Turkish dormouse 415
White-headed duck 479

Turkmenistan

Asian wild ass 289
Central Asian cobra 842
Cheetah 191
Dalmatian pelican 451
Great bustard 534
Markhor 368
Russian desman 55
Tiger 202
White-headed duck 479

U.S. Virgin Islands

Piping plover 539
St. Croix ground lizard 827

U.S.A.

Akiapolaau 701
Alabama canebrake
    pitcher-plant 1174
Alabama cave shrimp 1003
Alabama red-bellied
    turtle 741
American bison 348
American burying
    beetle 1031
American crocodile 786
Ash Meadows bug 1028
Bachman's warbler 698
Bay checkerspot
    butterfly 1046
Bee Creek Cave
    harvestman 997
Belkin's Dune tabanid
    fly 1034
Big long-nosed bat 80
Birdwing pearly mussel 945
Bishop's oo 690
Black-capped vireo 711
Black-footed ferret 219
Blunt-nosed leopard
    lizard 823
Brady pincushion
    cactus 1116
California condor 480
California freshwater
    shrimp 1005
California kangaroo rats 398
Caribbean manatee 276
Chapman's
    rhododendron 1138
Columbia River tiger
    beetle 1029
Cracking pearly mussel 959
Crested honeycreeper 704
Cui-ui 893
Cumberland bean pearly
    mussel 977
Desert slender
    salamander 868
Desert tortoise 750
Doryonychus raptor 995
Dromedary pearly
    mussel 949
Dwarf wedge mussel 939

Eastern prairie fringed
    orchid 1103
Eskimo curlew 546
Fanshell 947
Fat pocketbook pearly
    mussel 971
Fine-rayed pigtoe pearly
    mussel 957
Flat-spired three-toothed
    snail 929
Florida torreya 1077
Fountain darter 904
Freshwater pearl mussel 937
Green pitcher plant 1172
Guadalupe fur seal 225
Hau Kuahiwi 1150
Hawaiian crow 726
Hawaiian goose 475
Hawaiian hawk 484
Hawaiian monk seal 229
Hay's Spring amphipod 1002
Hell Creek Cave
    crayfish 1008
Higgins' eye pearly
    mussel 961
Houston toad 849
Iowa Pleistocene snail 926
Island gray fox 189
Ivory-billed woodpecker 625
James River spinymussel 967
Jemez Mountains
    salamander 869
June sucker 894
Kamao 671
Kauai creeper 703
Kauai oo 691
Kentucky cave shrimp 1004
Kirtland's warbler 696
Knowlton cactus 1116
Laysan duck 472
Laysan finch 708
Little long-nosed bat 80
Little-wing pearly mussel 965
Louisiana pearlshell 936
Madison Cave isopod 998
Maui parrotbill 705
Modoc sucker 891
Nashville crayfish 1010
Nihoa finch 710
Nihoa millerbird 662
No-eyed big-eyed wolf
    spider 993
Northern spotted owl 610
Nukupuu 699
Oahu tree snails 918
Ohio emerald dragonfly 1016
Olomao 671
Ou 706
Ouachita rock-
    pocketbook 941
Pacific damselfly 1015
Pale lilliput pearly
    mussel 943
Pallid sturgeon 887
Peebles Navajo cactus 1116

Penitent mussel 951
Piping plover 539
Poo-uli 702
Puaiohi 671
Puerto Rican boa 836
Puerto Rican parrot 576
Pupfish 900
Pygmy sculpin 902
Red-cockaded
    woodpecker 628
Red wolf 175
Relict trillium 1096
Ring pink mussel 963
Ringed sawback turtle 738
Robbins' cinquefoil 1169
Rocky Mountain
    grasshopper 1019
Rough pigtoe pearly
    mussel 969
Santa Cruz long-toed
    salamander 863
Shasta crayfish 1012
Short-tailed albatross 447
Shortnose sturgeon 883
Shortnose sucker 892
Short's goldenrod 1123
Silver rice rat 410
Small whorled pogonia 1100
Socorro isopod 1000
Socorro springsnail 917
Squirrel Chimney cave
    shrimp 1007
Stirrup shell 975
Takakia ceratophyllum 1063
Tar River spinymussel 955
Texas blind salamander 870
Texas wild rice 1086
Thick-billed parrot 598
Tooth Cave spider 991
Townsend's big-eared bat 87
Tulotoma snail 915
Turgid-blossom pearly
    mussel 953
Venus flytrap 1133
Virginia fringed mountain
    snail 928
Whooping crane 513
Winged mapleleaf 973
Wyoming toad 847
Yellow-blotched map
    turtle 737
Yellow-shouldered
    blackbird 713

Uganda

African elephant 282
African green broadbill 631
African wild dog 185
Cheetah 191
Chimpanzee 169
Congo clawless otter 210
Gorilla 163
Lake Victoria cichlids 908
Okapi 341

SPECIES INDEX

Thailand giant catfish 895
Thamin 332
Thaumatoperla flaveola 1023
Theodoxus transversalis 979
Thermosphaeroma thermophilum 1000
Thick-billed parrot 598
Thin-spined porcupine 417
Thomas's shrew-tenrec 50
Thornton Peak melomys 406
Thrasher *See* White-breasted thrasher
Three-keeled Asian turtle 739
Three-keeled land tortoise 739
Thrush *See* Large Kauai thrush,
   Molokai thrush, Small Kauai thrush,
   Taita thrush
Thyolo alethe 666
Tibetan bear 241
Tiger 202
Tipton kangaroo rat 398
Tirupati cycad 1067
Tit-spinetail *See* White-browed tit-
   spinetail
Titi *See* Masked titi
Toad *See* Garo Hills tree toad, Houston
   toad, Malabar tree toad, Mallorcan
   midwife toad, Mount Nimba
   viviparous toad, Wyoming toad
Tolypeutes tricinctus 41
Tomistoma 802
Tomistoma schlegelii 802
Tonga flying-fox 71
Tonkin langur 158
Tonkin leaf monkey 158
Tonkin snub-nosed monkey 152
Tooth Cave spider 991
Torreya taxifolia 1077
Tortoise *See* Angulated tortoise,
   Argentine tortoise, Bolson tortoise,
   Chaco tortoise, Desert tortoise,
   Egyptian tortoise, Galápagos tortoise,
   Geometric tortoise, Madagascar
   tortoise, Madagascar flat-tailed
   tortoise, Three-keeled land tortoise
Totoaba macdonaldi 906
Totoaba seatrout 906
Townsend's big-eared bat 87
Tracaja 777
Trachypithecus francoisi 158
Tragelaphus buxtoni 390
Tragopan melanocephalus 511
Tragopan *See* Western tragopan
Tree-shrew *See* Montane tree-shrew
Tremarctos ornatus 243
Tricarinate Hill turtle 739
Trichechus manatus 276
Trichechus senegalensis 278
Trichomanes speciosum 1066
Tridacnidae spp. 985
Trillium reliquum 1096
Tringa guttifer 550
Triodopsis (Polygra) platysayoides 929
Tristan bunting 693
Tsaratanana's chameleon 811
Tuamotu sandpiper 548
Tuatara *See* Cook Strait tuatara

Tulotoma magnifica 915
Tulotoma snail 915
Tuntong 732
Tupaia montana 57
Turaco *See* Bannerman's turaco
Turdoides hindei 681
Turdus helleri (T. olivaceus helleri) 682
Turgid-blossom pearly mussel 953
Turkish dormouse 415
Turtle *See* Alabama red-bellied turtle,
   Aquatic box turtle, Black pond turtle,
   Black soft-shell turtle, Burmese eyed
   turtle, Central American river turtle,
   Coahuilan box turtle, Dahl's toad-
   headed turtle, Green sea turtle,
   Hawksbill sea turtle, Kemp's ridley
   sea turtle, Leatherback sea turtle,
   Loggerhead sea turtle, New Guinea
   plateless turtle, Olive ridley sea turtle,
   Pig-nosed turtle, Ringed map turtle,
   Ringed sawback turtle, Short-necked
   turtle, South American river turtle,
   Spotted pond turtle, Three-keeled
   Asian turtle, Tricarinate Hill turtle,
   Western swamp turtle, Yellow-
   blotched map turtle, Yellow-headed
   sideneck turtle, Yellow-spotted
   sideneck turtle
Two-humped camel 318
Typhlomolge rathbuni 870
Typhlops monensis 834

U

Uganda red colobus 137
Ultramarine lorikeet 567
Uluguru bushshrike 657
Uncia (Panthera) uncia 205
Urocyon littoralis 189
Usambara eagle owl 606
Usambara squirrel 396

V

Van Zyl's golden mole 52
Vancouver Island marmot 393
Vaquita 266
Varanus komodoensis 832
Varecia variegata 99
Vella pseudocytiscus ssp. 1129
Venus flytrap 1133
Vermivora bachmanii 698
Verreaux's sifaka 107
Vertigo angustior 922
Vertigo genesii 922
Vertigo geyerii 922
Vertigo snails 922
Vicugna vicugna 320
Vicuña 320
Villosa (Micromya) trabalis 977
Vini ultramina 567
Viper *See* Cyclades blunt-nosed viper,
   Milos viper
Vipera schweizeri 843
Vireo atricapillus 711
Vireo *See* Black-capped vireo
Virginia big-eared bat 87

Virginia fringed mountain snail 928
Virginia spinymussel 967
Visagie's golden mole 53
Visayan spotted deer 329
*Viverra megaspila civettina (V.
   civettina)* 248
Viviparus acerosus 979
Vo Quy's pheasant 509
Volcano rabbit 436
Vole *See* Bavarian pine vole
Vulture *See* Cape vulture

W

Waldrapp 465
Walia ibex 372
Wallaby *See* Banded hare-wallaby,
   Bridled nailtail wallaby, Prosperine
   rock-wallaby, Rufous hare-wallaby,
   Western hare-wallaby
Warbler *See* Bachman's warbler,
   Kirtland's warbler, Long-billed forest
   warbler, Rodrigues warbler,
   Rodrigues brush-warbler, Seychelles
   warbler, Seychelles brush-warbler
Weasel *See* Colombian weasel
West African manatee 278
West Indian manatee 276
Western barred bandicoot 14
Western hare-wallaby 24
Western quoll 7
Western short-tailed shrew-tenrec 49
Western swamp turtle 780
Western tragopan 511
Weta species 1017
Whale *See* Blue whale, Bowhead whale,
   Fin whale, Humpback whale,
   Northern right whale, Sei whale,
   Southern right whale
Wheeler's pearly mussel 941
White-breasted guineafowl 504
White-breasted silver-eye 686
White-breasted thrasher 660
White-breasted white-eye 686
White-browed tit-spinetail 633
White-chested white-eye 686
White-eye *See* Norfolk Island white-eye,
   Seychelles white-eye, Seychelles gray
   white-eye, White-breasted white-eye,
   White-chested white-eye
White-eyed river-martin 653
White-footed tamarin 119
White-headed dolphin 264
White-headed duck 479
White-necked picathartes 677
White-necked rockfowl 677
White sturgeon 887
White-tailed hummingbird 617
White-tailed laurel pigeon 559
White-tailed sabrewing 613
White-throated monkey 131
White-winged flufftail 528
White-winged guan 501
White-winged wood duck 477
Whitesloanea crassa 1110
Whooping crane 513